NONCLASSICAL IONS

FRONTIERS IN CHEMISTRY

Ronald Breslow and Martin Karplus, Editors
Columbia University

CONTRIBUTIONS TO THE THEORY
OF CHEMICAL KINETICS

T. A. Bak   *Københavns Universitet*

MOLECULAR ORBITAL THEORY

C. J. Ballhausen   *Københavns Universitet*
H. B. Gray   *Columbia University*

NONCLASSICAL IONS: Reprints and Commentary

P. D. Bartlett   *Harvard University*

OPTICAL PUMPING: An Introduction

R. A. Bernheim   *The Pennsylvania State University*

ELECTRON PARAMAGNETIC RESONANCE

M. Bersohn   *University of Toronto*
J. Baird   *Brown University*

TOPICS IN BIOORGANIC MECHANISMS

T. C. Bruice   *University of California, Santa Barbara*
S. J. Benkovic   *The Pennsylvania State University*

THERMODYNAMICS OF SMALL SYSTEMS: Parts 1 and 2

T. L. Hill   *University of Oregon*

LECTURES ON QUANTUM THEORY OF MOLECULAR
ELECTRONIC STRUCTURE

R. G. Parr   *Johns Hopkins University*

THE BIOSYNTHESIS OF STEROIDS, TERPENES,
AND ACETOGENINS

J. H. Richards   *California Institute of Technology*
J. B. Hendrickson   *Brandeis University*

OXIDATION MECHANISMS: Applications to Organic Chemistry

R. Stewart   *University of British Columbia*

MOLECULAR PHOTOCHEMISTRY

N. J. Turro   *Columbia University*

COMPUTER PROGRAMMING FOR CHEMISTS

K. B. Wiberg   *Yale University*

NONCLASSICAL IONS

Reprints and Commentary

PAUL D. BARTLETT
Harvard University

W. A. BENJAMIN, INC.　　　　1965
New York　　　　　　　　Amsterdam

NONCLASSICAL IONS: Reprints and Commentary

Library of Congress Catalog Card Number 65-21750
Manufactured in the United States of America

*The final manuscript was put into production on April 5, 1965;
this volume was published on November 12, 1965*

W. A. BENJAMIN, INC.
New York, New York 10016

Preface

The transition from the impersonal textbook world to the current research scene places new demands upon the student. He must now, as never before, have in mind how we know what we know, and why we hold our present opinions. In this connection it should be helpful to consider the recent history of a problem in structure and mechanism which is still under development, and in which the original contributors are still very active. This reprint collection is intended for students in second-year organic chemistry and for others whose attention has been attracted by the vigorous current activity in this field. The background needed for reading these papers is contained in such textbooks of organic chemistry as Roberts and Caserio,[1] or Cram and Hammond.[2] There are pertinent reviews by Streitwieser[3] and by Berson.[4]

Formally, nonclassical ions represent a small special field of inquiry. Its importance comes from several circumstances: (1) It has led to an extension of valence theory and has defined the meeting-ground of organic chemistry with the electron-deficient bonding principles as seen in boron compounds; (2) its study has provided new tools and new insight relating to the ionization process in solution; (3) it has evolved some elegant methods of stereochemical study; (4) it has rationalized the unique features of the chemistry of bicyclohexanes, -heptanes, and -octanes.

After protesting for years against the inappropriate name "nonclassical ions," I have been overruled by general usage and am employing the term because of its extreme familiarity.[5] For the present purpose, an ion is nonclassical if its ground state has delocalized bonding σ electrons. By this definition there may not be any-

[1] J. D. Roberts and M. C. Caserio, *Basic Principles of Organic Chemistry* (W. A. Benjamin, New York, 1964).

[2] D. J. Cram and G. S. Hammond, *Organic Chemistry*, 2nd Edition (McGraw-Hill, New York, 1964).

[3] A. Streitwieser, Jr., *Solvolytic Displacement Reactions* [McGraw-Hill, New York, 1962; *Chem. Rev.* **56**, 571 (1956)].

[4] J. A. Berson, "Carbonium Ion Rearrangements in Bridged Bicyclic Systems," Chapter 3 of *Molecular Rearrangements,* ed. P. deMayo (Interscience, New York, 1963).

[5] Familiarity and contempt are still not entirely separable. I quote from *Chemical Abstracts* **59**, 912b (1964): "Only a dark, undistillable resin remained upon removal of the solvent. This suggests that a nonclassical carbonium ion intermediate is involved in the mechanism."

thing nonclassical about the phenonium ion, but it is treated in this collection since many of the methods and problems are alike for it and for the saturated bridged ions. The collection contains 75 reprinted papers going back as far as 1937, but 68 of them are dated 1950 or later, and 34 of them 1960 or later. There is no more exact basis of selection than my feeling that a paper contributes to an understanding of the present position of the field. Obviously many other papers of which this is also true are not included. Except for what was judged a practical limitation of space, I cannot defend the many omissions of this kind. Even a skeleton bibliography of nonclassical ions must include the papers cited in these 75 but not reprinted here.

At two or three points a preliminary Communication to the Editor has had an immediate effect upon the thinking of others, and is included here for its historical significance, even though the full paper which appeared several years later is also included. In other cases only the full paper is given, though there may have been a condensed earlier disclosure.

Each paper is attended by a commentary, long or short. The commentary is written on the assumption that the reader of it will also read the paper, and it commonly contains references to formulas and figures in the paper itself. As will be apparent, these comments have no uniform function. Some of the comments attempt to summarize the paper at hand. More often they concern correlations with facts developed later, or aspects which I consider of special interest.

The author index of about a thousand names and the subject index will serve as a quick-reference guide to the location of specific material. When a topic listed in the subject index is one of the chief concerns of a paper, reference is made only to the first page of that paper; otherwise, reference is to the first page on which the topic is mentioned.

I want to thank the authors for permission to reprint their papers and Professor John D. Roberts for reading all the commentaries and making suggestions. The preparation of this collection was made a greater pleasure by the expert help of Miss Kathleen McCarthy, who did the typing, prepared the figures, and compiled the author index.

PAUL D. BARTLETT

Cambridge, Massachusetts
August 20, 1965

Contents

Preface   v

Before Nonclassical Ions   1

1   The Bromonium Ion   3

   I. Roberts and G. E. Kimball, *J. Am. Chem. Soc.* **59**, 947–48 (1937).
The Halogenation of Ethylenes   4

2, 3   Participation by Neighboring Bromine   6

   S. Winstein and H. J. Lucas, *ibid.,* **61**, 1576–81 (1939). Retention of
Configuration in the Reaction of the 3-Bromo-2-butanols with Hydrogen
Bromide   7

   S. Winstein and H. J. Lucas, *ibid.,* **61**, 2845–48 (1939). The Loss of
Optical Activity in the Reaction of the Optically Active *erythro-* and
threo-3-Bromo-2-butanols with Hydrobromic Acid   12

4   The Double Bond in Cholesterol   16

   C. W. Shoppee, *J. Chem. Soc.* **1946**, 1147–51. Steroids and the Walden
Inversion. Part II. Derivatives of Δ^5-Cholestene and Δ^5-Androstene   17

5, 6   The Double Bond in Cholesterol   22

   S. Winstein and Rowland Adams, *J. Am. Chem. Soc.* **70**, 838–40 (1948).
The Role of Neighboring Groups in Replacement Reactions. XIV. The
5,6-Double Bond in Cholesteryl *p*-Toluenesulfonate as a Neighboring
Group   23

   S. Winstein and A. H. Schlesinger, *ibid.,* **70**, 3528–29 (1948). Exchange
at the 6-Position of *i*-Cholesteryl Methyl Ether   26

7   The Norbornyl Cation   27

   S. Winstein and D. S. Trifan, *ibid.,* **71**, 2953 (1949). The Structure of
the Bicyclo[2,2,1]2-heptyl (Norbornyl) Carbonium Ion   28

8 The Norbornenyl Cation   29

J. D. Roberts, W. Bennett, and R. Armstrong, *ibid.*, **72**, 3329–33 (1950). Solvolytic Reactivities of Nortricyclyl, Dehydronorbornyl and Norbornyl Halides. Possible Steric Requirements for Hyperconjugative Resonance   30

9, 10 Hughes and Winstein at Montpellier   35

E. D. Hughes, *Bull. soc. chim. France* [5] **18**, C39–43 (1951). Anionotropy, and the Wagner Rearrangement   36

S. Winstein, *ibid.*, [5] **18**, C55–61 (1951). Neighboring Groups in Displacements and Rearrangements   41

11 Ingold on Synartetic Ions   48

F. Brown, E. D. Hughes, C. K. Ingold, and J. F. Smith, *Nature* **168**, 65–67 (1951). Wagner Changes, Synartetic Acceleration and Synartetic Ions   49

12 The Cyclobutyl-cyclopropylcarbinyl System   52

J. D. Roberts and R. H. Mazur, *J. Am. Chem. Soc.* **73**, 2509–20 (1951). Small-ring Compounds. IV. Interconversion Reactions of Cyclobutyl, Cyclopropylcarbinyl and Allylcarbinyl Derivatives   53

13 Tracer Experiments on the Norbornyl Cation   65

J. D. Roberts and C. C. Lee, *ibid.*, **73**, 5009 (1951). The Nature of the Intermediate in the Solvolysis of Norbornyl Derivatives   68

14 The Reactivity of Cyclopropylmethyl Benzenesulfonate   69

C. G. Bergstrom and S. Siegel, *ibid.*, **74**, 145–51 (1952). The Effect of a Cyclopropyl Group on a Displacement Reaction at an Adjacent Saturated Carbon Atom. I. The Ethanolysis of Cyclopropylmethyl Benzenesulfonate   70

15 Driving Forces in Neighboring Group Participation   77

S. Winstein, B. K. Morse, E. Grunwald, K. C. Schreiber, and J. Corse, *ibid.*, **74**, 1113–20 (1952). Neighboring Carbon and Hydrogen. V. Driving Forces in the Wagner-Meerwein Rearrangement   78

16, 17 *endo*- and *exo*-Norbornyl Arenesulfonates   86

S. Winstein and D. Trifan, *ibid.*, **74**, 1147–54 (1952). Neighboring Carbon and Hydrogen. X. Solvolysis of *endo*-Norbornyl Arylsulfonates   87

S. Winstein and D. Trifan, *ibid.*, **74**, 1154–60 (1952). Neighboring Carbon and Hydrogen. XI. Solvolysis of *exo*-Norbornyl *p*-Bromobenzenesulfonate   95

18   3-Phenyl-2-butanol; the Phenonium Ion   102

D. J. Cram, *ibid.*, **74**, 2129–37 (1952). Studies in Stereochemistry. V. Phenonium Sulfonate Ion-pairs as Intermediates in the Intramolecular Rearrangements and Solvolysis Reactions that Occur in the 3-Phenyl-2-butanol System   104

19-21   Where Nonclassical Ions Are Absent   113

J. D. Roberts, W. Bennett, R. E. McMahon, and E. W. Holroyd, Jr., *ibid.*, **74**, 4283–86 (1952). Rearrangements in the Solvolysis of 2-Butyl-1-C^{14} *p*-Toluenesulfonate   114

J. D. Roberts and J. A. Yancey, *ibid.*, **74**, 5943–45 (1952). The Reaction of Ethylamine-1-C^{14} with Nitrous Acid   118

J. D. Roberts and M. Halmann, *ibid.*, **75**, 5759–60 (1953). Rearrangement in the Reaction of C^{14}-Labeled *n*-Propylamine (1-Aminopropane-1-C^{14}) with Nitrous Acid   121

22   MO Calculations on Homoallylic Cations   123

M. Simonetta and S. Winstein, *ibid.*, **76**, 18–21 (1954). Neighboring Carbon and Hydrogen. XVI. 1,3-Interactions and Homoallylic Resonance   124

23   Tracer Experiments on the Norbornyl Cation   128

J. D. Roberts, C. C. Lee, and W. H. Saunders, Jr., *ibid.*, **76**, 4501–10 (1954). Rearrangements in Carbonium Ion-Type Reactions of C^{14}-Labeled Norbornyl Derivatives   130

24   The 1,2,2-Triphenylethyl Cation   140

W. A. Bonner and C. J. Collins, *ibid.*, **77**, 99–103 (1955). Molecular Rearrangements. IV. Triple-labeling Experiments on the Isotope Position Isomerization of 1,2,2-Triphenylethyl Acetate   141

25   Tracer Experiments on the 2-Norbornenyl Cation   146

J. D. Roberts, C. C. Lee, and W. H. Saunders, Jr., *ibid.*, **77**, 3034–37 (1955). Rearrangements in Carbonium Ion-Type Reactions of C^{14}-Labeled Dehydronorbornyl Derivatives   147

26   7-Norbornyl and 7-Norbornenyl Tosylates   151

S. Winstein, M. Shatavsky, C. Norton, and R. B. Woodward, *ibid.*, **77**, 4183–84 (1955). 7-Norbornenyl and 7-Norbornyl Cations   153

27   The Classical Pentamethylethyl Cation   154

J. D. Roberts and J. A. Yancey, *ibid.*, **77**, 5558–62 (1955). Rearrangements in Carbonium-ion Type Reactions of C^{14}-Labeled Pentamethylethanol (2,3,3-Trimethyl-2-butanol-1-C^{14})   155

28 *cis*- and *trans*-**2-Phenylcyclohexanols**   160

H. J. Schaeffer and C. J. Collins, *ibid.*, **78**, 124–33 (1956). Molecular
Rearrangements. VI. The Dehydration of *cis*- and of *trans*-2-Phenyl-
cyclohexanol   161

29 **7-*anti*-Norbornenol**   171

S. Winstein and M. Shatavsky, *ibid.*, **78**, 592–97 (1956). Neighboring
Carbon and Hydrogen. XXI. *Anti*-7 Derivatives of Norbornene (Bicyclo-
[2.2.1]heptene) as Homoallylic Systems   172

30 **The Series of Cycloalkyl Tosylates**   178

H. C. Brown and G. Ham, *ibid.*, **78**, 2735–39 (1956). The Effect of Ring
Size on the Rate of Acetolysis of the Cycloalkyl *p*-Toluene and *p*-Bro-
mobenzenesulfonates   179

31 **Correlation of Solvolysis with Model Reactions**   184

H. C. Brown and K. Ichikawa, *Tetrahedron* **1**, 221–30 (1957). Chemical
Effects of Steric Strains. XIV. The Effect of Ring Size on the Rate of
Reaction of the Cyclanones with Sodium Borohydride   186

32 **Transannular Hydride Shifts**   196

V. Prelog, *Record Chem. Progr.* **18**, 247–60 (1957). Investigations on
the Transannular Effects in Elimination and Substitution Reactions by
Tracer Techniques   197

33 **The 7-Oxa-norbornyl Chlorides**   211

J. C. Martin and P. D. Bartlett, *J. Am. Chem. Soc.* **79**, 2533–41 (1957).
The Synthesis and Solvolysis of the 2-Halo-1,4-endoxocyclohexanes   213

34 **The Special Salt Effect**   222

S. Winstein and G. C. Robinson, *ibid.*, **80**, 169–81 (1958). Salt Effects
and Ion Pairs in Solvolysis and Related Reactions. IX. The *threo*-3-
p-Anisyl-2-butyl System   223

35 **The Acetoxonium Ion**   236

R. M. Roberts, J. Corse, R. Boschan, D. Seymour, and S. Winstein, *ibid.*,
80, 1247–54 (1958). The Role of Neighboring Groups in Replacement
Reactions. XXIV. The Acetoxy Group. Preparation and Reactions of
the Ketene Acetal of *cis*-1,2-Cyclohexanediol (2-Methylene-*cis*-4,5-
tetramethylenedioxolane)   237

36 **Tertiary Cyclopropylcarbinols**   245

H. Hart and J. M. Sandri, *ibid.*, **81**, 320–26 (1959). The Solvolysis of
p-Nitrobenzoates of Certain Cyclopropylcarbinols   246

37 The 1,2,2-Triphenylethyl Cation   253

C. J. Collins, W. A. Bonner, and C. T. Lester, *ibid.*, **81**, 466–75 (1959).
Molecular Rearrangements. XV. The Stereochemistry of the Solvolytic
and Deamination Reactions of 1,2,2-Triphenylethyl Derivatives   254

38 Migration Aptitudes   264

M. Stiles and R. P. Mayer, *ibid.*, **81**, 1497–1503 (1959). Rearrangement
of Alkyl Groups. Kinetic and Tracer Studies in the Pinacol Rearrange-
ment   265

39 The Bicyclobutonium Ion   272

R. H. Mazur, W. N. White, D. A. Semenow, C. C. Lee, M. S. Silver, and
J. D. Roberts, *ibid.*, **81**, 4390–98 (1959). Small-ring Compounds.
XXIII. The Nature of the Intermediates in Carbonium Ion-type Interconversion Reactions of Cyclopropylcarbinyl, Cyclobutyl and Allylcar-
binyl Derivatives   276

40 The Reversible Cholesteryl Rearrangement   285

S. Winstein and E. M. Kosower, *ibid.*, **81**, 4399–4408 (1959). Neighboring Carbon and Hydrogen. XXXIII. Reactivities of 3,5-Cyclocholestan-
6-yl Derivatives. Strain and Reactivity in Homoallylic Systems   288

41 3-Bicyclo(3.1.0)hexyl Tosylate   298

S. Winstein, J. Sonnenberg, and L. deVries, *ibid.*, **81**, 6523 (1959). The
Tris-homocyclopropenyl Cation   299

42 Cyclobutyl Solvolysis Reinvestigated   300

M. C. Caserio, W. A. Graham, and J. D. Roberts, *Tetrahedron* **11**, 171–
82 (1960). Small-Ring Compounds. XXIX. A Reinvestigation of the
Solvolysis of Cyclopropylcarbinyl Chloride in Aqueous Ethanol. Isomerization of Cyclopropylcarbinol   302

43 Benzonorbornenyl Sulfonates   314

P. D. Bartlett and W. P. Giddings, *J. Am. Chem. Soc.* **82**, 1240–46
(1960). Some 2- and 7-Derivatives of Benznorbornene   316

44 4-Cycloheptenylmethyl Bromobenzenesulfonate   323

G. Le Ny, *Compt. rend.* **251**, 1526–28 (1960). Chimie Organique. Participation transannulaire de la double liaison lors de l'acétolyse du
p-bromobenzènesulfonate de cycloheptène-4 yle   324

45 7-Norbornadienyl Chloride   327

S. Winstein and C. Ordronneau, *J. Am. Chem. Soc.* **82**, 2084–85 (1960).
The 7-Norbornadienyl Non-Classical Cation   328

46-48   Some Special Transannular Effects   330

P. Bruck, D. Thompson, and S. Winstein, *Chem. Ind.* (*London*) **1960**,
590–91. New Carbonium Routes to the Bird-Cage Hydrocarbon and
Related Compounds   331
S. Winstein and R. L. Hansen, *J. Am. Chem. Soc.* **82**, 6206–07 (1960).
1,5-Hydrogen Shift in a Decahydrodimethanonaphthalene System   333
S. Winstein and R. L. Hansen, *Tetrahedron Letters* **1960**, No. 25, 4–8.
An Octahydrodimethanonaphthyl Non-Classical Homocyclopropenyl
Cation   335

49, 50   Bicyclooctyl Derivatives   340

H. M. Walborsky, M. E. Baum, and A. A. Youssef, *J. Am. Chem. Soc.*
83, 988–93 (1961). Acetolysis of Bicyclo(2.2.2)octyl-2 *p*-Bromoben-
zenesulfonate and the Absolute Configurations of Bicyclo(2.2.2)octanol-
2 and *cis*- and *trans*-Bicyclo(3.2.1)octanol-2   343
H. L. Goering and M. F. Sloan, *ibid.*, **83**, 1397–1401 (1961). Ionic Reactions in Bicyclic Systems. II. Carbonium Ion Reactions in Bicyclo-
(2.2.2)octane and Bicyclo(3.2.1)octane Derivatives   349

51   Stereospecific Participation   354

C. H. DePuy, I. A. Ogawa, and J. C. McDaniel, *ibid.*, **83**, 1668–71
(1961). The Solvolysis of *exo*- and *endo*-7-Isopropylidene-dehydronor-
bornyl Tosylates   355

52   Bicyclooctyl and Bicyclooctenyl Cations   359

H. L. Goering and M. F. Sloan, *ibid.*, **83**, 1992–99 (1961). Ionic Reactions in Bicyclic Systems. III. Solvolysis of Bicycloöctanyl and Bicyclo-
öctenyl *p*-Toluenesulfonates   360

53   Solvolytic Ring Closure to Norbornyl Acetate   368

R. G. Lawton, *ibid.*, **83**, 2399 (1961). 1,5 Participation in the Solvolysis
of β-(Δ³-Cyclopentenyl)ethyl *p*-Nitrobenzenesulfonate   369

54, 55   The Trishomocyclopropenyl and Related Cations   370

S. Winstein and J. Sonnenberg, *ibid.*, **83**, 3235–44 (1961). Homoconjugation and Homoaromaticity. III. The 3-Bicyclo(3.1.0)hexyl System   372
S. Winstein and J. Sonnenberg, *ibid.*, **83**, 3244–51 (1961). Homoconjugation and Homoaromaticity. IV. The Trishomocyclopropenyl Cation.
A Homoaromatic Structure   382

56   Solvolytic Ring Closure to the Decalin System   389

H. L. Goering and W. D. Closson, *ibid.*, **83**, 3511–17 (1961). Transannular Interactions. IV. Products and Rates of Solvolysis of *cis*- and
trans-5-Cyclodecen-1-yl *p*-Nitrobenzoate in Aqueous Acetone   390

57 The π-Route to Bicyclooctyl Cations   397

S. Winstein and P. Carter, *ibid.*, **83**, 4485–86 (1961). The π-Route to a
Bicycloöctyl Non-Classical Cation   398

58 Reactions of the Solvent Separated Ion Pair   400

S. Winstein, P. E. Klinedinst, Jr., and E. Clippinger, *ibid.*, **83**, 4986–89
(1961). Salt Effects and Ion Pairs in Solvolysis and Related Reactions.
XXI. Acetolysis, Bromide Exchange and the Special Salt Effect   401

59 Ring Closure involving Hydroxyphenyl Groups   405

R. Baird and S. Winstein, *ibid.*, **84**, 788–92 (1962). Neighboring Carbon
and Hydrogen. XLVI. Spiro-(4,5)-deca-1,4-diene-3-one from $Ar_1^\ominus$-5
Participation   406

60 1,3-Rearrangement in the *n*-Propyl Cation   411

O. A. Reutov and T. N. Shatkina, *Tetrahedron* **18**, 237–43 (1962). Rearrangement of Alkyl-cations Formed during Reaction between Nitrous
Acid and Alkylamine Perchlorates   412

61 Mechanisms in the Dicyclopentadiene System   419

S. J. Cristol, W. K. Seifert, D. W. Johnson, and J. B. Jurale, *J. Am. Chem.
Soc.* **84**, 3918–25 (1962). Bridged Polycyclic Compounds. XIX. Some
Addition and Solvolysis Reactions in Norbornane Systems   420

62 The Long-lived Norbornadienyl Cation   428

P. R. Story and M. Saunders, *ibid.*, **84**, 4876–82 (1962). Structure of the
7-Norbornadienyl Carbonium Ion   430

63 A Dissenting View   437

H. C. Brown, *Chem. Soc.* (*London*) *Spec. Publ.* **16**, 140–62 (1962).
Strained Transition States   438

64, 68 Deamination of Norbornylamines   463

E. J. Corey, J. Casanova, Jr., P. A. Vatakencherry, and R. Winter, *J. Am.
Chem. Soc.* **85**, 169–73 (1963). On the Norbornyl Cation Problem   465

65 "Puckered" Cyclobutyl Tosylates   470

K. B. Wiberg and R. Fenoglio, *Tetrahedron Letters* **1963**, No. 20, 1273–
75. On the Acetolysis of *exo*- and *endo*-Bicyclo(2.1.1)hexyl-5 Tosylates   471

66 The 1,2-Dianisylnorbornyl Cation   474

P. von R. Schleyer, D. C. Kleinfelter, and H. G. Richey, Jr., *J. Am. Chem.
Soc.* **85**, 479–81 (1963). Nonclassical Carbonium Ions: The Structure
of Stable Aryl Substituted Norbornyl Cations   475

67   The Conjugate Base of the Ethylene *p*-Hydroxyphenonium Ion   478

R. Baird and S. Winstein, *ibid.*, **85**, 567–78 (1963). Neighboring Carbon
and Hydrogen. LI. Dienones from $Ar_1^{\ominus}$-3 Participation. Isolation and
Behavior of Spiro(2,5)octa-1,4-diene-3-one   479

68   Deamination of Norbornylamines (Continued)   491

J. A. Berson and A. Remanick, *ibid.*, **86**, 1749–55 (1964). The Nitrous
Acid Deamination of the Norbornylamines.   Carbon and Nitrogen Rearrangements of Norbornyl Cations   492

69   Bond Angle and Solvolysis Rate   499

C. S. Foote, *ibid.*, **86**, 1853–54 (1964). Correlation of Solvolysis Rates
and Estimation of Rate Enhancements   500

70, 71   Predicting Solvolysis Rate   502

P. von R. Schleyer, *ibid.*, **86**, 1854–56 (1964). Estimation of Nonassisted
Solvolysis Rates   503
P. von R. Schleyer, *ibid.*, **86**, 1856–57 (1964). The Nonclassical Car-
bonium Ion Problem: Reaction Rates   505

72   Substituted Benzonorbornenyl Cations   507

H. Tanida, T. Tsuji, and H. Ishitobi, *ibid.*, **86**, 4904–12 (1964). Substituent Effects and Homobenzylic Conjugation in *anti*-7-Benzonorbor-
nenyl *p*-Bromobenzenesulfonate Solvolyses   509

73   1-Phenyl-1,2-norbornanediol   518

C. J. Collins, Z. K. Cheema, R. G. Werth, and B. M. Benjamin, *ibid.*, **86**,
4913–17 (1964). Molecular Rearrangements. XXI. The Pinacol Rearrangement of 2-Phenylnorbornane-2,3-*cis-exo*-diol   520

74, 75   The Long-lived Norbornyl Cation   525

P. von R. Schleyer, W. E. Watts, R. C. Fort, Jr., M. B. Comisarow, and
G. A. Olah, *ibid.*, **86**, 5679–80 (1964). Stable Carbonium Ions. X.
Direct Nuclear Magnetic Resonance Observation of the 2-Norbornyl
Cation   527
M. Saunders, P. von R. Schleyer, and G. A. Olah, *ibid.*, **86**, 5680–81
(1964). Stable Carbonium Ions. XI. The Rate of Hydride Shifts in the
2-Norbornyl Cation   529

Appendix: Supplementary References   531

Author Index   535

Subject Index   555

Before Nonclassical Ions

The intensive study of the nucleophilic displacement reaction rests on a foundation laid in the thirties by Ingold, Hughes, and their co-workers. In six papers on "Reaction Kinetics and the Walden Inversion," they examined a network of stereochemical and kinetic evidence[1] on the course and mechanism of a number of second-order and first-order displacements. In summarizing their conclusions, they wrote[2]:

. . . Unimolecular substitution in alkyl compounds leads normally to racemization, because the intermediate ion has a plane of symmetry; but if the life of the ion is short, racemization will be incomplete and will accompany a predominating inversion, owing to the circumstance that the separating ions shield each other; and since the life of an ion can be varied by altering the composition of the medium the degree of incompleteness of the racemization should vary in a predictable way with such changes. An unsaturated substituent (e.g., aryl) at the seat of substitution should increase the tendency to racemization, because mesomerism confers additional stability on the planar ion. *A charged substituent of neutralizing sign (e.g., a carboxylate-ion substituent in a cation) may stabilize a pyramidal configuration in the ion, and lead to eventual substitution with retention of form.* (Italics added.)

The early example of participation of a neighboring group in a displacement reaction which led to this statement was the hydrolysis of sodium α-bromopropionate which, in contrast to the neutral acid or its ester, proceeded with predominating retention of configuration:

---

[1] E. D. Hughes, C. K. Ingold, and co-workers, *J. Chem. Soc.* **1937**, 1196–1271.

[2] W. A. Cowdrey, E. D. Hughes, C. K. Ingold, S. Masterman, and A. D. Scott, *ibid.*, **1937**, 1270.

The intermediate B is analogous to a carbonium ion in an S_N1 displacement, but this intermediate is uncharged. It is now regarded as an α-lactone, but the authors of this paper preferred to regard it as a dipolar ion (D). In it the electrostatic force between the carbonium carbon and the carboxylate oxygen was considered sufficiently bonding to preserve the asymmetry of the ion, yet its ionic character was invoked to guarantee that attack of a strong nucleophile would per-

form a new displacement at the original asymmetric atom, with the result of two inversions or net retention.

Today there seems to be no objection to calling the intermediate an α-lactone. Many equally tenuous structures have been postulated in a self-consistent scheme to explain retentions of configuration by means of double inversions. β-Lactones, which can be isolated, provide examples of similar behavior as intermediates in displacement reactions.[3] The α-bromopropionate displacement has been further studied by Grunwald and Winstein.[4] α-Lactones produced by free-radical mechanisms can be intercepted by methanol and shown to react by "alkyl-oxygen cleavage" at the α-carbon atom.[5] This 1937 example of retention by double inversion served as a prototype which influenced much later work.

---

[3] F. A. Long and A. R. Olson, *J. Phys. Chem.* **41**, 267 (1937).
[4] E. Grunwald and S. Winstein, *J. Am. Chem. Soc.* **70**, 841 (1948).
[5] P. D. Bartlett and L. B. Gortler, *ibid.,* **85**, 1864 (1963).

1 | The Bromonium Ion

At about the same time Roberts and Kimball, in an imaginative note, first proposed the stabilization of a carbonium ion both thermodynamically and stereochemically by bridging of a neighboring bromine atom. They expected the ethylene-bromonium ion to be slightly unsymmetrical; the work of Winstein and Lucas (Papers 2, 3) showed that it is either symmetrical or has an extremely low barrier between the two unsymmetrical forms. In connection with some discussions arising later, it is worthwhile to remember that nothing in the original theory of neighboring group participation requires complete momentary equivalence of the two carbon atoms involved. It does require that an energy minimum or minima correspond to some degree of bonding of the cationic center to the neighboring group.

From: *J. Am. Chem. Soc.* **59,** 947–48 (1937)

The Halogenation of Ethylenes

BY IRVING ROBERTS AND GEORGE E. KIMBALL

Recent work by Bartlett and Tarbell[1,2] has shown that the first step in the reaction of halogen molecules with the ethylene linkage leads to the formation of a negative halide ion and a positively charged organic ion. This ion has been postulated by Robinson[3] to have the structure

$$\begin{array}{c} R_1 \\ R_2 \end{array} C \!\!-\!\! C^+ \begin{array}{c} R_3 \\ R_4 \end{array} \qquad (1)$$

Some doubt has been cast on this mechanism[4] because of the presumption that there should be free rotation about the C–C single bond, which would lead to a mixture of equal amounts of the *cis* and *trans* halogenation products. In those cases in which the halogenation is homogeneous and not photochemical it is observed that either the *cis* or *trans* halogenation reaction predominates, forming at least 80% of the product.[5] It

(1) Bartlett and Tarbell, THIS JOURNAL, **58**, 466 (1936).

(2) Tarbell and Bartlett, *ibid.*, **59**, 407 (1937).

(3) Robinson, "Outline of an Electrochemical (Electronic) Theory of the Course of Organic Reactions," Institute of Chemistry of Great Britain and Ireland, London, 1932; Ingold, *Chem. Rev.*, **15**, 225 (1934).

(4) See, *e. g.*, Ogg, THIS JOURNAL, **57**, 2727 (1935).

(5) *Cf.* Freudenberg, "Stereochemie," Verlag Franz Deuticke Vienna, 1933, p. 520. Some of the reactions listed here are photochemical or complicated by side reactions.

has, therefore, been postulated that the second step of the reaction (the addition of halide ion to the positive organic ion) takes place so rapidly that there is not sufficient time for rotation about the single bond to take place.

We would like to point out that free rotation about the C–C bond is *not* to be expected. If this structure is assumed, one of the orbitals of the C^+ must be completely empty. The X atom on the other hand has three orbitals occupied by pairs of electrons. This arrangement is such that a co-ordinate link will almost certainly be formed by the sharing of one of the pairs of electrons of the halogen with the unoccupied orbital of the carbon. Another possible structure of the ion is one in which the positive charge is on the halogen. The X^+, being isoelectronic with a member of the oxygen family, should show a valence of two, *i. e.*, it should form a structure of the ethylene oxide type

$$
\begin{array}{c}
R_1 \\ \diagdown \\ R_2 \diagup
\end{array}
C \!\!-\!\!-\!\!-\!\! C
\begin{array}{c}
\diagup R_3 \\ \diagdown R_4
\end{array}
\qquad (2)
$$
$$ X^+ $$

From an electronic viewpoint structures (1) and (2) are identical. The difference between the ionization potential of carbon (11.22 volts) and that of a halogen (*e. g.*, 11.80 volts for bromine) is so small that the actual structure of the ion is undoubtedly intermediate between (1) and (2). Since the two carbons in either structure are joined by a single bond and by a halogen bridge, free rotation is not to be expected.

If, however, R_1 and R_3 (or R_2 and R_4) are similarly charged groups (*e. g.*, COO^-) there may be sufficient repulsion between them to overcome the restraining force of the double linkage, and rotation to the opposite configuration may take place before the second step of the reaction occurs.

This second step, which may be the addition of either a halogen ion X^- or some other atom or molecule, is probably a simple "three-atom" reaction of the type proposed by London,[6] and developed by Polanyi[7] and Olson.[8] In this case the new atom will approach one of the carbon atoms from the side opposite to the X atom already present. A bond to this carbon will be formed while the bond from the original X to the carbon is broken, with simultaneous neutraliza-

tion of the charge of the ion. This process will always lead to *trans* addition, except in the previously mentioned case in which there are two like charged groups initially in the *cis* position.

With this modification the mechanism suggested by Robinson and by Bartlett and Tarbell explains all the existing data on the reactions of the halogens with ethylene linkages. The additions of bromine and chlorine to maleic and fumaric acids are very largely *trans*,[9] as the theory predicts. The additions of bromine and chlorine to fumarate ion are again predominantly *trans*, but the addition of bromine or chlorine to maleate ion, with its two negatively charged *cis*-carboxylate ions, is almost entirely *cis*.[10]

The difficulty of explaining the maintenance of configuration in the bromination of stilbene and isostilbene, which yield different methoxybromides and different dibromides[1] no longer exists if this structure of the intermediate ion is postulated. This is also true of the formation of the halo-beta-lactones from dimethylmaleic and dimethylfumaric acids.[2]

The authors wish to thank Prof. L. P. Hammett for his helpful discussions of this problem.

(9) McKenzie, *J. Chem. Soc.*, **101**, 1196 (1912).

(10) Terry and Eichelberger, This Journal, **47**, 1067 (1925); Kuhn and Wagner-Jauregg, *Ber.*, **61**, 519 (1928).

Department of Chemistry
Columbia University
New York, N. Y.

Received March 4, 1937

(6) London, *Z. Elektrochem.*, **35**, 552 (1929).

(7) Meer and Polanyi, *Z. physik. Chem.*, **B19**, 164 (1932); Bergmann, Polanyi, and Szabo, *ibid.*, **B20**, 161 (1933).

(8) Olson, *J. Chem. Phys.*, **1**, 418 (1933); Olson and Voge, This Journal, **56**, 1690 (1934).

2, 3 | Participation by Neighboring Bromine

Although we are restricting the papers after 1939 in this collection to those dealing with three-center "nonclassical" carbonium ions where all three centers are carbon atoms, we include two important papers by Winstein and Lucas on the stereochemical role of neighboring bromine in displacement reactions. These papers introduced an elegant proof that bromine on carbon adjacent to the site of displacement causes coupling of the configurations of the two adjacent carbon atoms, while rendering them both equivalent toward an attacking reagent. This argument recurs with ramifications in the work of Winstein on neighboring bromine, iodine, and acetoxyl in cyclohexane rings,[1, 2] of Cram[3] on neighboring phenyl, and of Winstein and Trifan (Papers 7, 16, 17) on the norbornyl bromobenzenesulfonates.

---

[1] S. Winstein and R. E. Buckles, *J. Am. Chem. Soc.* **64**, 2780, 2787 (1942).
[2] S. Winstein, *ibid.*, **64**, 2792 (1942).
[3] D. J. Cram, *ibid.*, **71**, 3836 (1949).

From: *J. Am. Chem. Soc.* **61,** 1576–81 (1939)

[Reprinted from the Journal of the American Chemical Society, 61, 1576 (1939).]

[CONTRIBUTION FROM THE GATES AND CRELLIN LABORATORIES OF CHEMISTRY, CALIFORNIA INSTITUTE OF TECHNOLOGY. No. 701]

Retention of Configuration in the Reaction of the 3-Bromo-2-butanols with Hydrogen Bromide

BY S. WINSTEIN AND H. J. LUCAS

When 2,3-diacetoxybutane is converted into 2,3-dibromobutane by the action of fuming hydrobromic acid, the transformation appears to be accompanied by an odd number of inversions, for the *dl*-diacetate gives rise to the *meso*-dibromide, and the *meso*-diacetate to the *dl*-dibromide.[1] Moreover, the purity of the products shows that the various reaction steps proceed with either 100% inversion, or 100% retention of configura-

tion. One would have expected, on the assumption that the reaction proceeds similarly at each asymmetric carbon atom, an even number of inversions. In order to ascertain the number of inversions and the steps at which they take place, it has been necessary to follow the reaction step by step, through the isolation of intermediate products and to study the behavior of each intermediate with hydrobromic acid.

It has been found that 3-bromo-2-butanol is

(1) Wilson and Lucas, THIS JOURNAL, **58**, 2396 (1936).

TABLE I

PROPERTIES OF 2,3-DIBROMOBUTANES

Source	B. p., °C. (50 mm.)	n^{25}D	K_2	
erythro - 3 - Bromo - 2 - butanol from *trans* oxide	73.2	1.5090	0.0558	
threo - 3 - Bromo - 2 - butanol from *cis* oxide	76.5	1.5125	.0299	
threo - 3 - Bromo - 2 - butanol from *cis* - 2 - butene	76.3	1.5125		5.771
Previously described				
Pure *meso* - 2,3 - dibromobutane	73.3[1]	1.5092[3]	.0544[3]	6.245[4]
Pure *dl* - 2,3 - dibromobutane	76.4[1]	1.5125[3]	.0297[3]	5.758[4]

the last of three intermediates.[2] In this paper is reported the preparation of the pure inactive *erythro*- and *threo*-3-bromo-2-butanols and a detailed study of their behavior with hydrobromic acid. These compounds were prepared by the action of hydrobromic acid upon the pure *trans*- and *cis*-2,3-epoxybutanes, respectively. The *threo* isomer was prepared also by the addition of hypobromous acid to *cis*-2-butene. With fuming, aqueous hydrobromic acid these bromobutanols were found to give *meso*- and *dl*-2,3-dibromobutanes, respectively, with complete retention of configuration. The identification of the resulting dibromobutanes is indicated in Table I, where their properties are compared with the already known properties of pure *meso*- and *dl*-2,3-dibromobutanes.[1,3,4]

Configurations of the *dl*-3-Bromo-2-butanols.—Of these two, one must have the *erythro* (or *cis*) configuration, the other the *threo* (or *trans*) configuration. The determination of the configuration of these bromobutanols is not absolute, but is reasonably certain. It is based upon the assumption that one stereomutation (inversion) accompanies the addition of hydrogen bromide to 2,3-epoxybutane (*trans* opening of the ring), in line with the effect of acetic acid[2] on 2,3-epoxybutane and with the known effect of water on oxide rings[5] in general; and also

(2) Winstein and Lucas, THIS JOURNAL, **61**, 1581 (1939).
(3) Dillon, Young and Lucas, *ibid.*, **52**, 1953 (1930).
(4) Winstein and Wood, unpublished work.
(5) (a) Kuhn and Ebel, *Ber.*, **58B**, 919 (1925); (b) Böeseken, *Rec. trav. chim.*, **47**, 683 (1928).

that one stereomutation accompanies the reaction of hypobromous acid with 2-butene (*trans* addition to the olefin bond) in line with the known behavior[6] of other reagents, especially bromine, toward the double bond. The configurations are known for the 2,3-epoxybutanes[1,7] and for the 2-butenes.[8] These conclusions are in agreement with those regarding configurations of other halohydrins,[9] in connection with cyclic compounds. The fact that the same product is predicted and obtained from both *cis*-2,3-epoxybutane and *cis*-2-butene shows that the assumed configurations are reasonably certain.

Mechanism of Formation and Opening of Oxide Rings.—Since *dl-threo*-3-bromo-2-butanol is converted by alkali to *cis*-2,3-epoxybutane, the same oxide which yields this bromobutanol with hydrogen bromide, it is reasonable to assume that a clean-cut inversion accompanies the formation of the oxide ring. The mechanisms shown below are proposed for the closing and opening of oxide rings

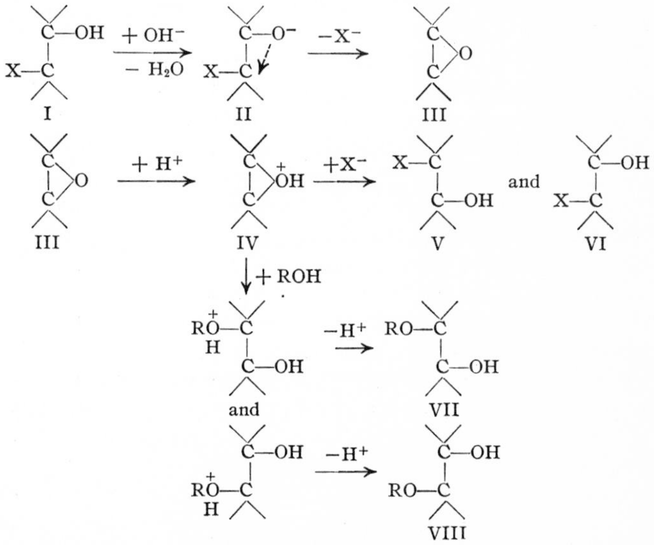

When the halohydrin, I, is converted into the oxide, III, by the action of alkali, the first step is the formation of an alcoholate ion II, for the presence of the halogen atom enhances the acidic

(6) (a) Michael, *J. prakt. Chem.*, **52**, 344 (1893); (b) Chavanne, *Rev. gen. sci.*, **35**, 229 (1924); (c) Terry and Eichelberger, THIS JOURNAL, **47**, 1067 (1925).
(7) Brockway and Cross, *ibid.*, **59**, 1147 (1937).
(8) (a) Young, Dillon and Lucas, *ibid.*, **51**, 2528 (1929); (b) Brockway and Cross, *ibid.*, **58**, 2407 (1936).
(9) (a) Suter and Lutz, *ibid.*, **60**, 1361 (1938); (b) Bartlett and White, *ibid.*, **56**, 2785 (1934); (c) Bartlett and Rosenwald, *ibid.*, **56**, 1892 (1934); (d) Bartlett, *ibid.*, **57**, 224 (1935).

character of the alcoholic hydroxyl group. The negatively charged oxygen atom of II attacks the adjacent carbon atom on the face opposite the bromine atom, thus leading to a Walden inversion of the usual bimolecular exchange type[10] except that in this case the reaction is intramolecular. Here the carbon atom to which the halogen atom originally was attached has been inverted. In the case of the *erythro* bromohydrin, one would expect the active forms to give rise to active forms of the *trans* oxide.

When the oxide, III, reacts with a hydrogen halide or with a compound having the hydroxyl group, the reactions are acid catalyzed. In this case the first step is believed to be the formation of the oxonium complex, IV, by the attachment of a proton. This cation may then be attacked by a negative ion (chloride, bromide, etc.) at the opposite face of either carbon atom, producing both halohydrins V and VI. Or it may be attacked by a solvent molecule (water, alcohol, organic acid, etc.) producing first the oxonium complexes which then lose the proton to form the hydroxy compounds VII and VIII. These may be glycols, glycol monoesters or glycol monoethers, depending upon the nature of ROH. In case the original oxide were *cis*-2,3-epoxybutane, the final product, in any case, would be a *dl*-mixture, for V and VI, also VII and VIII, are pairs of antipodes. In case it were a *d*- or *l*-*trans*-2,3-epoxybutane, the final product would be expected to be active, unless it were a glycol.

Retention of Configuration in the Conversion of *dl*-3-Bromo-2-butanol to 2,3-Dibromobutane.
—*erythro*-*dl*-3-Bromo-2-butanol with hydrobromic acid under the same conditions as 2,3-diacetoxybutane,[1] is converted into pure *meso*-2,3-dibromobutane, while the *threo* isomer yields pure *dl*-2,3-dibromobutane (see Table I). In this reaction, in which, unlike the reaction of 2,3-diacetoxybutane, the final product is formed directly from the initial compound without the complication of intermediates, complete retention of configuration unaccompanied by racemization (*i. e.*, partial inversion at one carbon atom) holds.

$$H_3C-\underset{\underset{H}{|}}{\overset{\overset{H}{|}\,\overset{Br}{|}}{C}}-\underset{\underset{H}{|}}{C}-CH_3 \quad \xrightarrow{HBr} \quad H_3C-\underset{\underset{H}{|}}{\overset{\overset{Br}{|}}{C}}-\underset{\underset{H}{|}}{\overset{\overset{Br}{|}}{C}}-CH_3$$

dl-erythro-3-Bromo-2-butanol   *meso*-2,3-Dibromobutane

(10) (a) Olson, *J. Chem. Phys.*, **1**, 418 (1933); (b) Bergmann, Polanyi and Szabo, *Z. physik. Chem.*, **20**, 161 (1933).

$$H_3C-\underset{\underset{H}{|}}{\overset{\overset{H}{|}\,\overset{O}{|}\,\overset{H}{|}}{C}}-\underset{\underset{Br}{|}}{C}-CH_3 \quad \xrightarrow{HBr} \quad H_3C-\underset{\underset{H}{|}}{\overset{\overset{Br}{|}\,\overset{H}{|}}{C}}-\underset{\underset{Br}{|}}{C}-CH_3$$

dl-threo-3-Bromo-2-butanol   *dl*-2,3-Dibromobutane

This striking phenomenon warrants discussion and also additional investigation because of its bearing upon the mechanism of substitution reactions.

In developing a mechanism to account for the retention of configuration in these two cases, one should bear in mind the difference in behavior of the bromobutanols and ordinary monohydric alcohols. When the latter[11] react with hydrobromic acid, inversion predominates, and more or less extensive racemization accompanies the reaction. The unusual behavior of the bromobutanols must be ascribed to the presence of the bromine atom. The following is offered as a plausible mechanism to account for the retention of configuration.

The proton converts the bromohydrin, IX, to an oxonium compound, X. The bromine atom may attack the back face of the carbon atom holding the hydroxonium group in the same way that an independent bromine anion may, giving rise to a cyclic, intermediate, positively charged complex, XI, which resembles closely the other intermediate, IV. A negatively charged ion, such as bromide ion, may attack the opposite face of either carbon atom of XI, giving rise to both dibromides XII and XIII. In either event, two inversions have accompanied the change, two on carbon atom C_1 when XII is the product, one each on carbon atoms C_1 and C_2, when XIII is the product. If the initial compound is an active *threo*-3-bromo-2-butanol, the resulting 2,3-dibromobutane is predicted[12] to be inactive, since XII and XIII are antipodes.

The extension of the idea of initial attack by one part of the molecule in substitution reactions at an asymmetric center in the neighborhood,

(11) (a) Cowdrey, Hughes, Ingold, Masterman and Scott, *J. Chem. Soc.*, 1252 (1937); (b) Winstein and Lucas, unpublished work.
(12) It is planned to investigate this reaction, for it constitutes a test of the hypothesis.

gives a satisfactory explanation of phenomena observed by others. Thus, the first order hydrolysis or alcoholysis of α-bromopropionate ion with complete retention of configuration observed by Cowdrey, Hughes and Ingold,[13] is due more likely to initial attack by the carboxylate ion group with formation of an α-lactone, than to the removal of bromine by ionization with the necessity of assuming stabilization of the resulting dipolar ion in a pyramidal form, as postulated by these authors.[11a] At the step of lactone formation, there is according to the point of view enunciated above complete inversion at the α-carbon atom. This is the slow, rate-determining step. Then the lactone reacts quickly with solvent molecules, again with complete inversion as in the case of oxides, and of β-lactones under some conditions.[14] Those two inversions would lead to the retention of the initial configuration, and the rate would be first order, as these workers observed.

The Positive Bromo-Olefin Complex.—Such a complex has been postulated by others as an intermediate in reactions of bromine with compounds having a double bond.[15] The formulation of this complex as a cyclic compound XI was first proposed by Roberts and Kimball.[15d] We believe that this intermediate is the same as the one assumed above in the reaction of the bromobutanol with hydrobromic acid, and we believe with Roberts and Kimball[15d] that the mechanism of the bromine addition to olefins, except for the initial attack by the bromine molecule, is shown satisfactorily by XI, XII and XIII. The existence of such a postulated intermediate seems more reasonable than formerly, now that a similarly constituted positive ion, the olefin-silver ion complex, has been shown to exist in aqueous solution.[16] The possibility of resonance among four forms, XIV, XV, XVI and XVII, contributes to the stability of the complex.

| XIV | XV | XVI | XVII |

The first form, XIV, probably contributes most, and the last form, XVII, least, because of the stabilizing effect arising from bond formation be-

tween bromine and carbon. In the case of the silver–olefin complex,[16] it was held that the form similar to XIV is not as important as the other three.

This bromo-olefin complex can be formed not only in the reaction of hydrobromic acid with bromohydrins and of bromine with ethylenic compounds, but also by the reaction of a variety of bromine donating substances with ethylenic compounds, as pointed out by Bartlett and Tarbell.[15b] To their list of bromine donating compounds should be added N-bromoacetamide,[17] and other compounds of similar structure.

Even an ion group in the same molecule may attack one or the other of the carbon atoms of XI. Thus Bartlett and Tarbell[15c] found that in the action of bromine upon sodium dimethylmaleate, a bromo-β-lactone is formed; moreover, this lactone is different from the one obtained from sodium dimethylfumarate. In these cases the negative carboxylate group is the attacking group.

The authors desire to express their appreciation of the advice given by Professor Linus Pauling, in connection with structural considerations.

Synthesis of Both 2-Butenes from the Same Oxide.—A practical result of the observation that a bromohydrin can be converted into a dibromobutane with retention of configuration is the possibility of preparing both cis- and trans-2-butenes from the same 2,3-epoxybutane, for example

Experimental

cis- and trans-2,3-Epoxybutanes.—These compounds were prepared as previously described,[1] and in a higher state of purity.[18] Some physical properties of these pure oxides are shown in Table II.

meso-2,3-Butanediol.—From 2 pounds of Lucidol butylene glycol, m. p. 27°, four crystallizations from a fourfold weight of isopropyl ether gave 300 g. of quite pure meso glycol, m. p. 34.0°.

(13) Cowdrey, Hughes and Ingold, *J. Chem. Soc.*, 1208 (1937).

(14) Olson and Miller, THIS JOURNAL, **60**, 2687 (1938).

(15) (a) Ingold, *Chem. Rev.*, **15**, 225 (1934); (b) Bartlett and Tarbell, THIS JOURNAL, **58**, 466 (1936); (c) Bartlett and Tarbell, *ibid.*, **59**, 407 (1937); (d) Roberts and Kimball, *ibid.*, **59**, 947 (1937).

(16) Winstein and Lucas, *ibid.*, **60**, 836 (1938).

(17) Schmidt, Knilling and Ascherl, *Ber.*, **59B**, 1280 (1926).

(18) We are indebted to Messrs. K. D. Johnson and W. T. Stewart for the preparation of a large amount of the mixed oxides and to Mr. H. S. Sargent, Jr., for the careful fractionation.

TABLE II

PROPERTIES OF THE ISOMERIC 2,3-EPOXYBUTANES

Property	Configuration	
	trans	cis
B. p., °C. (742 mm.)	53.5 ± 0.05	59.7 ± 0.05
$n^{20}D$	1.3736	1.3828
$n^{25}D$	1.3705	1.3802
d^{25}_4	0.8010	0.8226

cis-2-Butene.—This substance was obtained from the *meso* glycol by the series of reactions described previously.[1]

Preparation of the *dl*-3-Bromo-2-butanols from Oxides.[19]—190 ml. of 48% hydrobromic acid in a 3-necked 500-ml. flask is cooled with an ice-bath. Then 72 g. (1 mole) of pure oxide is dropped in with stirring over a period of about one hour, the reaction temperature being maintained below 5°. After all the oxide is added, the reaction mixture is left for one hour longer; then it is partially neutralized with solid sodium carbonate, the bottom phase is separated, and the aqueous phase is extracted with two 70-ml. portions of isopropyl ether. The bromohydrin layer and ether extracts are combined, neutralized with sodium carbonate and dried with sodium sulfate. Distillation through a 15-cm. column of glass helices yields 126–130 g. (82–85%) of bromohydrin, boiling range *ca.* 1°. On distillation of a portion of the bromohydrin through a 40-cm. Weston column,[20] constant-boiling material is obtained. The properties of the *erythro*-3-bromo-2-butanol (from *trans* oxide) and the *threo*-3-bromo-2-butanol (from *cis* oxide) and the melting points of their 3,5-dinitrobenzoates and α-naphthylurethans are given in Table III.

TABLE III

PROPERTIES OF THE *dl*-3-BROMO-2-BUTANOLS

Property	Configuration	
	erythro	threo
B. p., °C. (13 mm.)	53.1	50.5
$n^{25}D$	1.4767	1.4756
d^{25}_4	1.4474	1.4437
M_D	29.85	29.87
M_D, calcd.	29.96	29.96
M. p. of 3,5-dinitrobenzoate, °C.	85	109
M. p. of α-naphthylurethan, °C.	133	103

threo-3-Bromo-2-butanol from *cis*-2-Butene.—17.3 g. (0.31 mole) of *cis*-2-butene, an equivalent of N-bromoacetamide,[21] 250 ml. of water and 6 ml. of glacial acetic acid were kept under reflux for two hours in a 3-necked 500-ml. flask equipped with a carbon dioxide–alcohol reflux condenser and a mechanical stirrer and surrounded by an ice-bath. After this time butene still refluxed vigorously when the ice-bath was removed. This was contrary to expectations.[22] Then 2 ml. of 6 N sulfuric acid was added and this catalyzed the reaction so that the butene disappeared in less than an hour. The reaction mixture was extracted with two 100-ml. and one 50-ml. portions of ether, the extracts were neutralized with sodium bicarbonate and dried over sodium sulfate. Distillation at reduced pressure

yielded 34.4 g. (72.5%) of *threo*-3-bromo-2-butanol, b. p. (13 mm.) 49.5–51.0°, $n^{25}D$ 1.4748. The physical properties of the bromohydrin and its complete solubility in fuming aqueous hydrobromic acid show that dibromobutane was not a contaminant of the bromohydrin prepared as described.

cis-2,3-Epoxybutane from *threo*-3-Bromo-2-butanol.—15.3 g. (0.1 mole) of bromohydrin was converted to oxide as previously described in the case of the chlorohydrins. A 3-necked 100-ml. flask was used and a few minutes were sufficient for the experiment. To the oxide-water distillate was added potassium carbonate, and the oxide layer was separated and dried with potassium carbonate; yield 6.0 g. (83%). On distillation through the Weston column, 80% of the distillate was at 59.8–60.1° and 20% at 58.2–59.8°. Thus, the oxide was essentially pure *cis* oxide.

Preparation of the 2,3-Dibromobutanes from the Bromohydrins.—130 g. of 48% hydrobromic acid is saturated with hydrogen bromide gas (from tetralin and bromine) in a glass ampoule at 0°, then 23.0 g. (0.15 mole) of the bromohydrin is added, the ampoule is sealed and the mixture is left at room temperature with occasional shaking. After a day or more, the ampoule is opened, the dibromide layer at the bottom is separated, washed with water and potassium carbonate solution, and dried over calcium chloride. The average yield is 30.4 g. (94%). On distillation through the Weston column, more than 95% of the distillate is at constant temperature (Table I).

Analysis of the 2,3-Dibromobutanes.—The properties of the 2,3-dibromobutanes obtained from the bromohydrins are given in Table I. Reference to boiling point and refractive index indicates that the dibromobutanes are essentially pure. A better criterion of purity is K_2, the second-order reaction rate constant[3] for the reaction of the dibromobutane with potassium iodide in methanol at 74.93°, or ϵ, the dielectric constant,[4] a property by means of which the isomers are most accurately identified. From K_2 and ϵ, also, it can be concluded that these 2,3-dibromobutanes are pure.

Summary

It has been found that fuming hydrobromic acid converts *dl-erythro-* and *dl-threo-*3-bromo-2-butanol quantitatively into *meso-* and *dl-*2,3-dibromobutane, respectively, with complete retention of configuration.

It is proposed: (a) that the closing of an oxide ring brought about by the action of alkali, involves an intramolecular variety of the usual bimolecular exchange reaction in which the attacking group is the adjacent negatively charged oxygen atom; (b) that the acid catalyzed opening of the oxide ring involves attack by a negative ion or by a solvent molecule at one of the two ring carbon atoms of a cyclic intermediate positive oxonium complex; and (c) that the transformation of the bromobutanols to the dibromides involves attack by a bromide ion at one of two carbon atoms of a cyclic intermediate positive bro-

(19) See Cottle and Powell, THIS JOURNAL, **58**, 2267 (1936).

(20) Weston, *Ind. Eng. Chem., Anal. Ed.*, **5**, 179 (1933).

(21) The N-bromacetamide was prepared very satisfactorily by the method of Mauguin, *Ann. chim.*, [8] **22**, 302 (1911).

(22) Sikhosherstov and Alekseev, *J. Gen. Chem.* (U. S. S. R.), **3**, 927 (1933); see *C. A.*, **28**, 3054 (1934).

mine complex. This positive bromine complex is identical with the intermediate usually assumed in connection with halogen addition to olefins, and chemically is analogous to the oxide–proton complex.

PASADENA, CALIF.   RECEIVED MARCH 21, 1939

From: *J. Am. Chem. Soc.* **61**, 2845–48 (1939)

[CONTRIBUTION FROM THE GATES AND CRELLIN LABORATORIES OF CHEMISTRY, CALIFORNIA INSTITUTE OF TECHNOLOGY, No. 724]

The Loss of Optical Activity in the Reaction of the Optically Active *erythro*- and *threo*-3-Bromo-2-butanols with Hydrobromic Acid

BY S. WINSTEIN[1] AND H. J. LUCAS

Recently it was shown[2] that *dl-erythro*-3-bromo-2-butanol I is converted into *meso*-2,3-dibromobutane II, and *dl-threo*-3-bromo-2-butanol III, is converted into *dl*-2,3-dibromobutane IV, by the action of fuming hydrobromic acid, with complete retention of configuration.[3,4]

CH₃	CH₃	CH₃	CH₃
HCOH	HCBr	HCOH	HCBr
HCBr	HCBr	BrCH	BrCH
CH₃	CH₃	CH₃	CH₃
I	II	III	IV

In order to account for this unusual behavior, it was assumed that the replacement of the hydroxyl group by the bromine atom took place by a mechanism involving attack by the bromine atom on the adjacent carbon atom of the bromohydrin. This bromine atom, simultaneously with the removal of the OH_2^+ group V (which is formed from the OH group and a proton), forms a bond with the carbon atom on the face away from the OH_2^+ group, thus leading to the formation of the positively charged cyclic intermediate, VI,[5] of

Roberts and Kimball[6] which then reacts with bromide ion to produce the two possible dibromides VII and VIII.

On the basis of this mechanism two inversions take place, for the formation of the intermediate, VI, is accompanied by an inversion of carbon atom C_1, and the reaction of this with bromide ion is accompanied by a second inversion. If VII is the product, C_1 is inverted twice, while if VIII is the product C_1 and C_2 are each inverted once. This explains the formation of *meso*-2,3-dibromobutane from the *erythro*-bromohydrin, and of *dl*-2,3-dibromobutane from the *threo*-bromohydrin. In fact, each of the active forms of the *threo*-bromohydrin is predicted by this mechanism to give *dl*-2,3-dibromobutane, since VII and VIII would be formed in equal amounts.

It was pointed out that this feature could be used as a test for the mechanism by starting

(1) At present National Research Fellow in Chemistry at Harvard University.

(2) Winstein and Lucas, THIS JOURNAL, **61**, 1576 (1939).

(3) Only one of the two antipodes of the *dl*-compounds is shown.

(4) By retention of configuration in these cases is meant merely that an *erythro*-bromohydrin gives rise to a *meso*-dibromide and a *threo*-bromohydrin to a *dl*-dibromide. Strictly speaking, configuration is not retained.

(5) We propose to call the simplest ion having this structure, ethylenebromonium ion.

(6) Roberts and Kimball, THIS JOURNAL, **59**, 947 (1937).

with optically active *threo*-bromohydrin III. The predicted loss in activity in going from an active *threo*-bromohydrin to an inactive dibromide may be better understood perhaps by noting that the cyclic intermediate IX has the internally compensated *cis* configuration, and thus can give rise to only inactive products.

It has now been found that both the *erythro*- and *threo*-bromobutanols in the active form give rise to inactive dibromides. Moreover, optically active acetates of these two bromobutanols also give rise to inactive dibromides. The conversion was carried out with optically active forms of both the *erythro*- and *threo*-bromohydrins so as to make the test of the proposed mechanism free of any doubt that might be cast on it by questioning the assignment of configurations to the 3-bromo-2-butanols or the 2,3-dibromobutanes.

Optically active bromobutanols and acetates were obtained by partial acetylation of the bromohydrins with acetic anhydride in carbon tetrachloride containing brucine, according to the method which Wegler[7] used in other cases. The *dl-erythro*-3-bromo-2-butanol gave rise to a (+)-*erythro*-3-bromo-2-butanol and a (−)-*erythro*-3-acetoxy-2-bromobutane, while the *dl-threo*-3-bromo-2-butanol gave rise to a (−)-*threo*-3-bromo-2-butanol and a (−)-*threo*-3-acetoxy-2-bromobutane. The resolution to be expected from the method employed is of course quite incomplete.

The optical rotations of these compounds, as well as optical data on the oxides and dibromides, are given in Table I.

To make certain that the optical activity in the case of the (−)-*threo*-bromohydrin was not due largely to the presence of a quite small amount of an optically active *erythro* isomer, which would give optically inactive dibromobutane, some of the active *erythro*- and *threo*-bromohydrins were converted to oxides. One would expect active *erythro*-3-bromo-2-butanol I to yield an active *trans*-2,3-epoxybutane X, and active *threo*-3-bromo-2-butanol III to yield inactive internally compensated *cis*-2,3-epoxybutane XI since one inversion accompanies the formation of the oxide ring.[2]

The active bromobutanols behaved as expected on conversion to oxides. It was found that the *trans* oxide from (+)-*erythro*-3-bromo-2-butanol has a (+) rotation while the *cis* oxide from (−)-*threo*-3-bromo-2-butanol was inactive (Table I). Thus, the active *threo*-bromohydrin was not contaminated with appreciable amounts of an active *erythro*-bromohydrin.

The inactivity of the dibromide from the active *threo*-3-bromo-2-butanol (Table I) hardly can be explained on the basis of a low specific rotation for a *d*- or *l*-2,3-dibromobutane.[8] It seems quite unlikely that the rotation to be expected from (+)- or (−)-2,3-dibromobutane would be smaller than the rotation of (−)-*threo*-3-bromo-2-butanol by a factor of approximately 50 or 100, and thus be within experimental error of zero. Thus it must be that (−)-*threo*-3-bromo-2-butanol gives *dl*-2,3-dibromobutane. This definitely confirms

TABLE I

SUMMARY OF THE OPTICAL ROTATION DATA

	Substance	Config.	α_D (1 dcm.)
1	3-Bromo-2-butanol	*erythro*	$+1.91 \pm 0.02°$
2	2-Acetoxy-3-bromobutane	*erythro*	$-3.01 \pm .03$
3	2,3-Dibromobutane from 1	*meso*	$0.00 \pm .02$
4	2,3-Dibromobutane from 2	*meso*	$0.01 \pm .02$
5	2,3-Epoxybutane from 1	*trans*	$+4.37 \pm .01$
6	3-Bromo-2-butanol	*threo*	$-1.17 \pm .02$
7	3-Bromo-2-butanol	*threo*	$-1.04 \pm .01$
8	2-Acetoxy-3-bromobutane	*threo*	$-0.31 \pm .01$
9	2,3-Dibromobutane from 6	*dl*	$.00 \pm .01$
10	2,3-Dibromobutane from 7	*dl*	$.00 \pm .02$
11	2,3-Dibromobutane from 8	*dl*	$.00 \pm .01$
12	2,3-Epoxybutane from 7	*cis*	$.01 \pm .01$

(7) Wegler, *Ann.*, **506**, 77 (1933).

(8) In many cases, the optical activity of an alcohol is comparable to or less than that of the corresponding halide; see for example, Kenyon, Phillips and Pittman, *J. Chem. Soc.*, 1072 (1935); Levene and Rothen, *J. Biol. Chem.*, **127**, 237 (1939); Hughes, Ingold and Masterman, *J. Chem. Soc.*, 1196 (1937); Hughes, Ingold and Scott, *ibid.*, 1201 (1937); Cowdrey, Hughes and Ingold, *ibid.*, 1208 (1937); Stevens and McNiven, THIS JOURNAL, **61**, 1295 (1939).

the proposed mechanism, which involves the formation of 1,2-dimethylethylenebromonium ion, VI.

It is evident from Table I that the active bromoacetates behave as the bromohydrins do, to give inactive dibromides. This is to be expected since the bromoacetates presumably are converted to the dibromides by way of the bromohydrins.[9] It must be recognized that the butylenebromonium ion can react with water, as well as with bromide ion. The reaction with water, in the case of the *cis* ion, will give rise to *dl-threo*-3-bromo-2-butanol. Here then is a way for the active *threo*-bromohydrin to become inactive. It is probable, however, that the positive ion reacts practically exclusively with bromide ion in the present reaction medium. This statement is based upon the observations that the corresponding oxide is converted almost quantitatively to bromohydrin,[2] not glycol in concentrated hydrobromic acid, and that in bromine additions to double-bonded compounds, in which bromonium ions[10] are intermediates,[2,6,11] bromide ion competes much better than solvent molecules.

Other Possible Mechanisms.—The results obtained show that two other possible mechanisms, which have been proposed for the conversion of monohydric alcohols to bromides, are not operative here. One such mechanism is the internal, cyclic reaction of a bromohydrin–hydrogen bromide complex.[12] This type of reaction which seems to occur in some cases[8] cannot be operative here, otherwise the dibromide IV, resulting from optically active *threo*-3-bromo-2-butanol XII, would possess optical activity.

Another such mechanism is the dissociation[12] of the bromohydrin–proton complex, V, to give a halogen substituted carbonium ion XIII, with subsequent reaction of this ion with bromide ion. In the case of both the active *erythro-* and active *threo*-bromohydrins, this would lead to the production of a mixture of the *meso*-dibromide II and an active dibromide IV, unless one postulates that the configuration of the carbonium ion is stabilized in the pyramidal form. If it is possible for the configuration to be so stabilized, then the resulting dibromide from the active *threo*-bromohydrin would possess optical activity. Thus the carbonium ion mechanism, which has been postulated in other cases[12] but which has been the subject of considerable discussion recently,[13] definitely is not operative in the case of these 3-bromo-2-butanols.

While it might turn out to be useful to think that the chief "driving force"[14] of the reaction of formation of the butylenebromonium ion VI is the tendency for the —OH_2^+ group to be dissociated off as a water molecule, nevertheless we must not regard XIII as an intermediate. The bond between bromine and carbon is formed essentially simultaneously with the dissociation of the —OH_2^+ group from the rest of the molecule.

Other Changes Involving Halonium Ions.—In addition to the reactions of bromohydrins with acids and of bromine and bromine-donating substances with ethylenic compounds, as discussed previously,[2] there must be other situations in which bromonium ions are intermediates. This would be expected when there is a tendency to remove one group in a molecule in which there is a bromine substituent able to attack the back face of the carbon atom losing the group. Thus, for example, the production of *cis*-1,2-diacetoxycyclohexane from the action of silver acetate on 1,2-dibromocyclohexane in acetic acid does not necessarily indicate that the 1,2-dibromocyclohexane is the *cis* isomer.[15] We prefer the explanation that an odd number of inversions are involved in the transformation to the diacetate and that 1,2-dibromocyclohexane has the *trans* configuration. It seems plausible that the bromonium ion is produced by the action of a silver ion[14,16] simultaneously with the attack by the bromine

(9) Winstein and Lucas, THIS JOURNAL, **61**, 1581 (1939).

(10) Pfeiffer and co-workers have isolated and formulated salts which bear a formal resemblance to our bromonium salts, such as {[(CH₃)₂NC₆H₄]₂CCHBr}⁺ ClO₄⁻ [see Pfeiffer and Wizinger, *Ann.*, **461**, 132 (1928)] and [(C₆H₅C₆H₄)₂CCHBr]⁺Br₃⁻ [see Pfeiffer and Schneider, *J. prakt. Chem.*, **129**, 129 (1931)].

(11) (a) Bartlett and Tarbell, THIS JOURNAL, **58**, 466 (1936); (b) Read and Williams, *J. Chem. Soc.*, **117**, 359 (1920); (c) Ingold, *Chem. Rev.*, **15**, 225 (1934).

(12) Cowdrey, Hughes, Ingold, Masterman and Scott, *J. Chem. Soc.*, 1252 (1937).

(13) (a) Winstein, THIS JOURNAL, **61**, 1635 (1939); (b) Bartlett, *ibid.*, **61**, 1630 (1939). See these articles for further references.

(14) Roberts and Hammett, *ibid.*, **59**, 1063 (1937).

(15) Rothstein, *Ann. chim.*, **14**, 461 (1930).

(16) See Hughes, Ingold and Masterman, *J. Chem. Soc.*, 1236 (1937); Cowdrey, Hughes and Ingold, *ibid.*, 1243 (1937).

atom of carbon atom C_2 as shown by XIV and that this ion reacts with solvent as shown by XV. An inversion at the replacement of the second bromine atom by acetate would result in there being three inversions in the whole transformation. It seems plausible that presently the steric course of reactions of dihalides, halohydrins, etc., will be better understood when it is realized to what extent bromonium ions and hitherto unknown compounds of a similar sort play a part.

Besides bromonium ions there may be chloronium and iodonium ions of similar structure.

Experimental

Materials.—The *dl-erythro*-3-bromo-2-butanol was prepared from the pure *trans*-2,3-epoxybutane and the *dl-threo*-3-bromo-2-butanol from both pure *cis*-2,3-epoxybutane or *cis*-2-butene according to directions previously given.[2]

Merck brucine was employed and the acetic anhydride was purified by fractionation.

Partial Resolution of *erythro*-3-Bromo-2-butanol and Conversion to 2,3-Dibromobutane.—In 500 ml. of pure carbon tetrachloride was dissolved with heating 50 g. of brucine, then 50 ml. of *dl-erythro*-3-bromo-2-butanol and 22 ml. of acetic anhydride were added in turn and the reaction mixture was refluxed for two hours. After the reaction mixture was cool, it was washed first with dilute hydrochloric acid and then sodium carbonate solution. The mixture was dried over potassium carbonate, most of the carbon tetrachloride was distilled off through a 15-cm. column of glass helices at about 40°, and the residue was fractionated through a 40-cm. Weston[17] column. There was obtained 38 ml. of distillate, 12 ml. being essentially pure bromohydrin, b. p. (13 mm.) 53.1–53.7°, n^{25}D 1.4762 and 19 ml. being pure acetoxybromobutane, b. p. (13 mm.) 67.0–67.2°, n^{25}D 1.4488. Intermediate fractions made up the remainder of the material. The rotation αD (1 dcm.) of the bromohydrin was 1.91° and of the acetate −3.01°. Half of the bromohydrin sample was converted to oxide as previously described,[2] the oxide exhibiting αD (1 dcm.) +4.37°. The oxide and bromohydrin were dissolved in fuming hydrobromic acid, the dibromide b. p. (50 mm.) 73.2°, n^{25}D 1.5090, possessing αD (1 dcm.) 0.00°. The acetate similarly gave rise to dibromide b. p. (50 mm.) 73.2°, n^{25}D 1.5090 which possessed αD (1 dcm.) 0.00°. The intermediate fractions also were converted to dibromide. The combined and redistilled dibromobutane from the bromohydrin and oxide, acetoxybromobutane, and the intermediate fractions, b. p. (50 mm.) 73.3°, n^{25}D 1.5091 pos-

sessed a dielectric constant[2,18] of 6.208. This indicates a few % of *dl*-dibromobutane in the *meso*-dibromide. Some stereomutation from *erythro* to *threo* apparently takes place during the procedure for partial resolution of the bromohydrin.

Partial Resolution of *threo*-3-Bromo-2-butanol and Conversion to 2,3-Dibromobutane.—From the treatment of 44 ml. of *threo*-3-bromo-2-butanol with 44 g. of brucine and 22 ml. of acetic anhydride in 440 ml. of carbon tetrachloride as described above in the case of the *erythro*-bromohydrin and subsequent washing, drying and distillation was obtained 39 ml. of distillate, 8 ml. being quite pure bromohydrin, b. p. (13 mm.) 50.0–50.8°, n^{25}D 1.4757, 13 ml. being quite pure acetoxybromobutane, b. p. (13 mm.) 69.6°, n^{25}D 1.4491, the rest of the material consisting of intermediate fractions. The bromohydrin exhibited αD (1 dcm.) −1.17° while the acetoxybromobutane possessed αD (1 dcm.) −0.31°. The bromohydrin, acetoxybromobutane and the combined intermediate fractions were converted to dibromobutanes in the usual way. The dibromobutane b. p. (50 mm.) 76.1° from the bromohydrin exhibited αD (1 dcm.) 0.00°, that from the intermediate fractions, b. p. (50 mm.) 76.0° possessed αD (1 dcm.) 0.00°, and the dibromide b. p. (50 mm.) 76.2° from the bromohydrin acetate yielded αD (1 dcm.) 0.00°. The combined and redistilled dibromobutane b. p. (50 mm.) 75.9–76.2°, n^{25}D 1.5121, possessed a dielectric constant of 5.797. Here, too, a little stereomutation must have been involved in the procedure for the partial resolution of the bromohydrin.

When 46 ml. of *threo*-3-bromo-2-butanol was partially resolved with the aid of 46 g. of brucine, 20 ml. of acetic anhydride and 500 ml. of carbon tetrachloride and distillation was carried out, 10 ml. of bromohydrin fraction b. p. (13 mm.) 50.2–50.7°, n^{25}D 1.4749, αD (1 dcm.) −1.04° was obtained. Three ml. of this bromohydrin yielded an oxide having αD (1 dcm.) 0.01°. The remainder of the bromohydrin yielded a dibromide, b. p. (50 mm.) 76.3°, n^{25}D 1.5121, which showed αD (1 dcm.) 0.00°.

In Table I the indicated possible errors in the optical rotations are the sum of the mean deviations for a set of readings on the zero point and a set of readings on the substance in question. For the readings a Zeiss 0.01° instrument and a small capacity 1-dcm. tube were employed.

Summary

There is complete loss of optical activity when active *erythro*- or *threo*-3-bromo-2-butanol is converted to 2,3-dibromobutane. This confirms the mechanism previously proposed in connection with the conversion of *dl-erythro*- and *dl-threo*-3-bromo-2-butanol to *meso*- and *dl*-2,3-dibromobutane, respectively. The mechanism consists of the production of a butylenebromonium ion, and the subsequent reaction of this ion with bromide ion, two inversions occurring in the transformation. Other possible mechanisms for the transformation of bromohydrin to dibromide are discussed and rejected.

RECEIVED AUGUST 9, 1939

(17) Weston, *Ind. Eng. Chem., Anal. Ed.*, **5**, 179 (1933).

(18) Winstein and Wood, unpublished work.

4 | The Double Bond in Cholesterol

In 1946 in the steroids Shoppee recognized evidence that the carbon-carbon double bond as a neighboring group behaves analogously to other electron-donor substituents such as bromine and the carboxylate anion. That is, in ionizable compounds of appropriate geometry, it facilitates solvolysis with retention of configuration. By analogy to Ingold's treatment of α-bromopropionic acid, Shoppee wrote only an *ionic* bond from the double bond to C-3 of cholesterol in the postulated intermediate ion.

From: *J. Chem. Soc.* **1946**, 1147–51

254. *Steroids and the Walden Inversion. Part II. Derivatives of*
Δ⁵-*Cholestene and* Δ⁵-*Androstene.*

By C. W. SHOPPEE.

On the basis of the constitutions assigned in Part I, cholesteryl chloride is shown to be 3(β)-chloro-Δ⁵-cholestene. The steric orientation of substitution reactions at C_3 in Δ⁵-steroids is discussed; in striking contrast to the general occurrence of inversion in the replacement reaction ·Cl⟶·OR and the occurrence of inversion or retention according to the orientation rules of Cowdrey *et al.* (*J.*, 1937, 1252) for the substitution ·OR⟶·Cl in the saturated series, both these types of replacement take place in the Δ⁵-series with preservation of configuration and irrespective of the substituting agent within the range of reagents and conditions examined. It is suggested that the retention of configuration characteristic of the substitution reactions at C_3 of Δ⁵-steroids is due to polarisation of the C_5:C_6-double bond, the electrons of which interact with the cationic charge formed at C_3 by ionisation of the group substituted to produce a C_3-C_5 bond of mixed covalent–electrovalent type; this binding leads to a pyramidal configuration for the transition state and so to preservation of configuration.

On this basis, a consistent picture is obtained for substitution reactions at C_3 in the Δ⁵-steroid series, which harmonises with the configurations assigned (Part I) in the saturated series.

IN Part I (preceding paper), arguments were adduced to show that the so-called " α "-cholestanyl chloride, m. p. 115°, has the constitution 3(β)-chlorocholestane (III). When cholesterol (I) is treated with phosphorus pentachloride (Planer, *Annalen*, 1861, **118**, 25; Loebisch, *Ber.*, 1872, **3**, 510; Mauthner, *Monatsh.*, 1894, **15**, 87), or with thionyl chloride alone (Diels, Abderhalden, and Blumberg, *Ber.*, 1904, **37**, 3092; 1911, **44**, 287) or in presence of pyridine (Daughensbaugh and Allison, *J. Amer. Chem. Soc.*, 1929, **51**, 3665), high yields of one and the same product, cholesteryl chloride, m. p. 96°, are obtained. Since catalytic hydrogenation of cholesteryl chloride affords 3(β)-chlorocholestane (III) (Mauthner, *Monatsh.*, 1909, **30**, 635; Marker, Whitmore, and Kamm, *J. Amer. Chem. Soc.*, 1935, **57**, 2358) in quantitative yield (*vide infra*), cholesteryl chloride is to be regarded as 3(β)-chloro-Δ⁵-cholestene (II). Crystallographic evidence also supports this view : " from

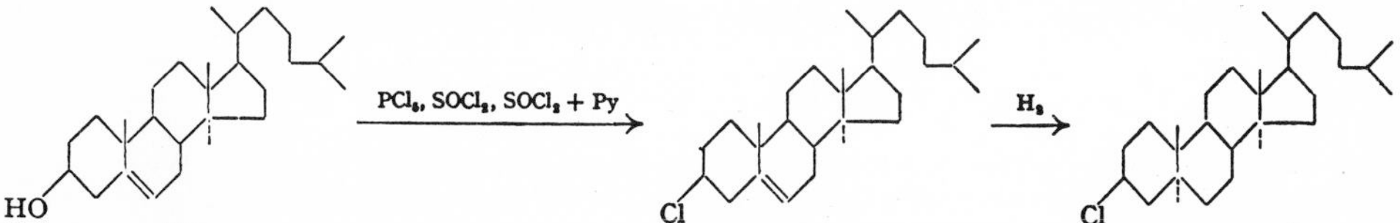

HO
(I.)
PCl₅, SOCl₂, SOCl₂ + Py ⟶
Cl
(II.)
H₂ ⟶
Cl
(III.)

the crystal unit cell dimensions and even more from the intensities of the *c* plane reflexions, it is clear that " α "-cholestanyl chloride has the same configuration (at C_3) as cholesteryl chloride " (Crowfoot, " Vitamins

17

and Hormones," New York, 1944, Vol. 2, p. 450). The hydroxyl group of cholesterol thus consistently undergoes replacement by chlorine with retention of configuration.

This relationship is unusual, inasmuch as although the three reagents specified can yield the same stereochemical product (*e.g.*, with β-*n*-octyl alcohol, ethyl lactate), they then cause inversion (mechanisms S_N1, S_N2). Retention of configuration according to the concepts laid down by Ingold *et al.* (*J.*, 1937, 1252) and recently summarised by Dostrovsky, Hughes, and Ingold (this vol., p. 186 *et seq.*) requires an intramolecular mechanism (S_Ni), leading to a transition state of pyramidal type, which is promoted by electron releasing groups and under conditions inhibitory to ionisation; retention of configuration with employment of all the three reagents specified is rational only if the structural influences favour mechanism S_Ni sufficiently, and would be the logical outcome of very powerful electron release—a circumstance which from inspection of the formula of cholesterol (I) would not be expected to arise.

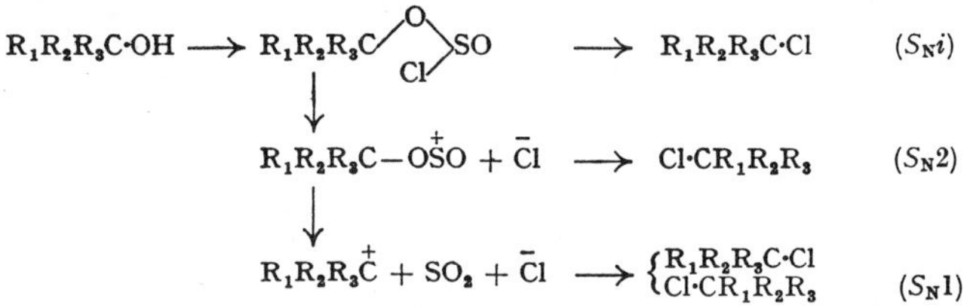

$$R_1R_2R_3C\cdot OH \longrightarrow R_1R_2R_3C\underset{Cl}{\overset{O}{\diagup}}SO \longrightarrow R_1R_2R_3C\cdot Cl \qquad (S_Ni)$$

$$R_1R_2R_3C - \overset{+}{O}SO + \overset{-}{Cl} \longrightarrow Cl\cdot CR_1R_2R_3 \qquad (S_N2)$$

$$R_1R_2R_3\overset{+}{C} + SO_2 + \overset{-}{Cl} \longrightarrow \begin{cases} R_1R_2R_3C\cdot Cl \\ Cl\cdot CR_1R_2R_3 \end{cases} \qquad (S_N1)$$

This singular behaviour of the Δ^5-cholestene system is not confined to the substitution of OR by Cl, but also appears in the replacement of Cl by OR. When cholesteryl chloride (II) is treated with acetate ions in acetic acid at 100°, the product is almost pure cholesteryl acetate (IV) (cf. Bergmann, *J. Amer. Chem. Soc.*, 1938, **60**, 1996), and hydrolysis furnishes a 91% overall yield of cholesterol * (I), unaccompanied by *epi*-cholesterol :

$$(II) \xrightarrow{\text{OAc}^\ominus} (IV; = II \text{ with OAc for Cl}) \xrightarrow{\text{OH}^\ominus} (I)$$

Thus here substitution occurs with apparently complete retention of configuration, and in sharp contrast with the corresponding substitution reactions of the cholestanyl chlorides, and secondary alkyl halides generally, which proceed (mechanisms S_N1, S_N2) with substantially complete inversion of configuration; and it is difficult to envisage the operation of some internal rearrangement mechanism analogous to S_Ni in an essentially ionic reaction such as the conversion of (II) to (IV) by acetate ions in an ionising medium.

A similar situation exists in the relations subsisting between other Δ^5-sterols and their 3-chloro-derivatives. Thus stigmasterol (V) by treatment with phosphorus pentachloride undergoes substitution with retention of configuration to furnish stigmasteryl chloride, which must possess the 3(β)-chloro-constitution (VI) because catalytic hydrogenation affords 3(β)-chlorostigmastane [3(β)-chlorositostane] (VII) (cf. Part I, *loc. cit.*). Treatment of stigmasteryl chloride (V) with acetate ions in acetic acid at 100°, with subsequent alkaline hydrolysis, regenerates stigmasterol (IV) with retention of configuration (Marker and Lawson, *J. Amer. Chem. Soc.*, 1937, **59**, 2711) :

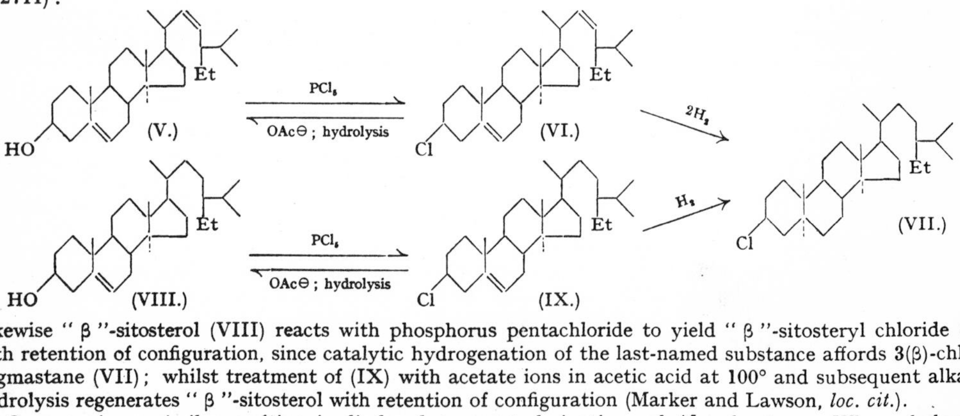

Likewise " β "-sitosterol (VIII) reacts with phosphorus pentachloride to yield " β "-sitosteryl chloride (IX) with retention of configuration, since catalytic hydrogenation of the last-named substance affords 3(β)-chloro-stigmastane (VII); whilst treatment of (IX) with acetate ions in acetic acid at 100° and subsequent alkaline hydrolysis regenerates " β "-sitosterol with retention of configuration (Marker and Lawson, *loc. cit.*).

Once again, a similar position is disclosed amongst derivatives of Δ^5-androstene. When cholesteryl chloride (II) is oxidised (as the dibromide) with chromium trioxide (Marker *et al.*, *J. Amer. Chem. Soc.*, 1936, **58**, 338) " α "-chloroandrostenone, m. p. 157°, is obtained; this must be regarded as 3(β)-chloro-Δ^5-androsten-17-one (X),† since (i) catalytic hydrogenation converts it into 3(β)-chloroandrostan-17-one (XI) (cf. Part I,

* The statement of Marker, Kamm, Fleming, Popkin, and Wittle (*J. Amer. Chem. Soc.*, 1937, **59**, 619) which is not supported by experimental evidence is thus confirmed.

† This compound has no androgenic activity in the comb test (Ruzicka, Goldberg, and Wirz, *Helv. Chim. Acta*, 1935, **18**, 998).

loc. cit.) and (ii) it is obtained from 3(β)-hydroxy-Δ⁵-androsten-17-one (dehydro*iso*androsterone) (XII) not only by treatment with thionyl chloride—a reagent which tends to substitute with retention of configuration—but also by use of phosphorus pentachloride (Wallis and Fernholz, *J. Amer. Chem. Soc.*, 1937, **59**, 764) and of hydrochloric acid (Butenandt *et al.*, *Z. physiol. Chem.*, 1935, **237**, 57).*

(Wallis and Fernholz, *J. Amer. Chem. Soc.*, 1935, **57**, 1504; Marker *et al.*, *ibid.*, 1936, **58**, 338).

In striking contrast to the reaction of (XI) with acetate ions in acetic acid, which proceeds with inversion to yield androsterone acetate and, after hydrolysis, androsterone (XIII)—a reaction which can be reversed by use of phosphorus pentachloride, a reagent which tends to substitute with inversion of configuration—3(β)-chloro-Δ⁵-androsten-17-one (X) reacts with benzoate ions in molten benzoic acid to give, after hydrolysis, 3(β)-hydroxy-Δ⁵-androsten-17-one (dehydro*iso*androsterone) (XII).

The situation outlined above may be summarised as follows. Of the replacement reactions at C_3: (a) $C \cdot OH \xrightarrow{SOCl_2} C \cdot Cl$, (b) $C \cdot OH \xrightarrow{PCl_5} C \cdot Cl$, (c) $C \cdot Cl \xrightarrow{OAc\ominus} C \cdot OAc$, in the saturated series (a) takes place with retention and (b) and (c) with inversion of configuration, but in the Δ⁵-series all three reactions (a), (b), and (c) take place with retention of configuration. Whilst a reaction mechanism ($S_N i$) is available to account for retention in (a), and a similar mechanism would be possible in the presence of groups able strongly to influence the geometry of the transition state (cf. the case of α-phenyl-*n*-amyl alcohol which reacts with phosphorus pentachloride with retention of configuration) but is therefore improbable here in respect of retention in (b), it appears impossible to invoke some analogous internal rearrangement mechanism in regard to retention in (c).

The sole constitutional feature distinguishing cholesterol and 3(β)-hydroxycholestanol, and the similar pairs of compounds referred to above, is the C_5:C_6-double bond. The incorporation of a double bond in a *cyclo*paraffin ring necessitates that the doubly-bound carbon atoms and those adjacent to them (C_4, C_7, C_{10}) lie in a plane, and that the angle C_4–C_5–C_{10} approximates to 120°. The influence of such a structural modification is to compel rings A and B to conform more nearly to flat hexagons in cholesterol than in 3(β)-hydroxycholestanol; the general effect will be to flatten further the already nearly flat steroid nucleus, and this has been confirmed crystallographically (Crowfoot, *op. cit.*, p. 422). But since it has been shown (Part I) that the approximately planar character of the steroid nucleus facilitates the formation of a transition state of linear, as opposed to pyramidal, type and hence tends to lead to replacement with inversion of configuration, the geometrical modification arising from the introduction of a C_5:C_6-double bond can have no part in the consistent retention of configuration exhibited in the substitution reactions of compounds of the Δ⁵-series.

The conclusion is inescapable that the apparently abnormal behaviour of cholesterol and its Δ⁵-analogues must be ascribed to the polarisability of the C_5:C_6-double bond. In support of this is the interaction known to occur between C_3 and C_5 in the production of derivatives of *i*-cholestane, *i*-stigmastane, and *i*-androstane. Further, the qualitatively increased reactivity displayed by the 3-chlorine atom in cholesteryl, stigmasteryl, and sitosteryl chlorides as compared with the cholestanyl and stigmastanyl chlorides must be attributed to electron-release by the C_5:C_6-double bond, and an indication that this is so is provided by 7-ketocholesteryl chloride (XIV); Marker *et al.* (*J. Amer. Chem. Soc.*, 1937, **59**, 619) note with some surprise that the chlorine atom in this compound exhibits the qualitatively lesser reactivity characteristic of the cholestanyl and stigmastanyl chlorides, a circumstance which clearly arises from the enforced polarisation of the double bond by the 7-carbonyl group, $C_5 = C_6 - C_7 = O$, in the direction opposite to that required to facilitate separation of the 3-chlorine atom. If this is true, then substitution of the 3-chlorine atom in (XIV) must proceed with inversion of configuration; and it is found (Marker *et al.*, *loc. cit.*) that the reaction of (XIV) with acetate ions in *n*-valeric acid furnishes 7-ketocholesterylene (XV) together with an acetate (XVI) which, after hydrolysis and reduction of the 7-keto-group, affords *epi*cholesterol (XVII); thus here inversion of configuration occurs in the manner characteristic of the saturated series.

* The polar influence of the 17-carbonyl group at C_3 is assumed to be negligible.

The suggestion that the retention of configuration uniformly observed in replacements at C_3 in the Δ^5-series is connected with the availability of electrons at C_3 arising from the polarisability of the C_5:C_6-double bond leads naturally to comparison with the first-order substitution reactions of the α-bromopropionate ion (Cowdrey, Hughes, and Ingold, *J.*, 1937, 1208). At this stage during private discussion with Professor Ingold the writer's attention was directed to a series of papers by Winstein *et al.* (*J. Amer. Chem. Soc.*, 1939, **61**, 1576, 1581, 1635, 2845; 1942, **64**, 2780, 2787, 2791, 2792, 2796; 1943, **65**, 613, 2196; 1946, **68**, 119) which show that the unshared electrons of an α-bromine atom are implicated in substitution reactions occurring at C_β in the system C_β–C_α·Br. It appeared therefore that the three examples (A), (B), and (C) illustrate essentially analogous processes.

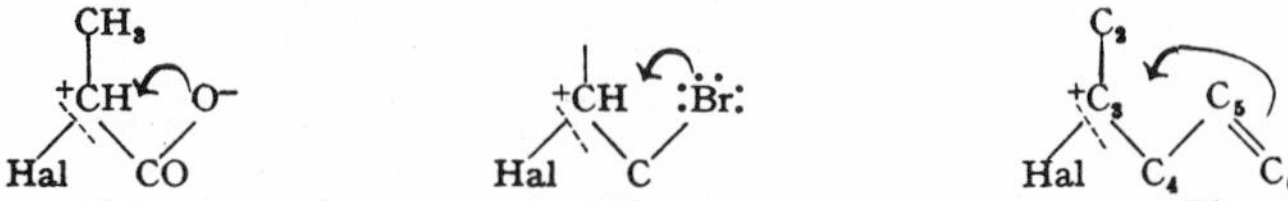

In regard to case (A), Cowdrey, Hughes, and Ingold (*loc. cit.*) showed by a kinetically controlled stereochemical examination that the first-order hydroxylation and methoxylation reactions of the α-bromopropionate ion are unimolecular and take place with 90—100% retention of configuration by mechanism S_N1 without detectable racemisation. In discussing this result, Cowdrey, Ingold, Hughes, Masterman, and Scott (*J.*, 1937, 1252, especially pp. 1256 and 1261) point out that it is in conformity with theory since, owing to the anionic charge, the most stable configuration of the intermediate carbon cation is now of the pyramidal type, which corresponds to retention of stereochemical form.

Winstein, Lucas, and their collaborators (*locc. cit.*) have adduced evidence to show that OH, OAc, and OMe groups, and bromine atoms, participate in replacement reactions at an adjacent saturated carbon atom. They have discovered a case of substitution involving an intermediate cation preserved as to configuration by an α-bromine atom; they formulate an intermediate bromonium ion, using the covalent extreme for a link which Cowdrey *et al.* regard as largely electrovalent; but this makes no essential difference to the stereochemical interpretation (cf. Bateman, Church, Hughes, Ingold, and Taher, *J.*, 1940, 1010).

In regard to case (C), examination of the product of the substitution of the chlorine atom in cholesteryl chloride by acetate ions in acetic acid at 100° discloses 91% retention and no detectable amount (after hydrolysis) of *epi*cholesterol, and hence no detectable racemisation. The mechanism of substitution therefore appears to be exclusively S_N1, for although mechanism S_N2 was shown to operate in the case of the α-bromopropionate anion for both hydroxylation and methoxylation, this mechanism furnished 80—100% inversion of configuration, and so appears qualitatively to be excluded here. If the suggested operation of mechanism S_N1 may be generalised for other replacement reactions in the Δ^5-series we have the following picture: as the ionisation of the group to be replaced passes over its energy barrier and before the reagent intervenes, the polarisable electrons of the C_5:C_6-double bond interact with the carbon cation sufficiently powerfully to overcome both the energetic and the geometrical factors, which normally operate to favour production of a transition state of linear type, and to lead to the formation of a transition state of pyramidal type, the consequence of which is retention of configuration following attack of the reagent and completion of the reaction.

The foregoing analysis of the facts provides a consistent picture of replacement reactions at C_3 in the Δ^5-steroid series (case C) resting on circumstantial evidence, but no proof that the interpretation suggested is correct. An examination of the kinetics and steric orientation of nucleophilic substitutions in the simpler aliphatic analogues of case (C)—the methylallylcarbinyl and benzylmethylcarbinyl series—is being undertaken by Hughes and Ingold; and the writer hopes to make a kinetic study of some suitable replacement reaction (hydrolysis, alcoholysis, or acetolysis) of cholesteryl chloride. It is also intended to examine the chemistry of *epi*cholesterol and *cis*-dehydroandrosterone, and of *i*-cholestane and *i*-androstane derivatives, from the point of view now developed.

EXPERIMENTAL.

(All m. ps. were determined thermoelectrically on a Kofler block and are therefore corrected; limit of error $\pm 2°$.)

Acetolysis of Cholesteryl Chloride.—Cholesteryl chloride (250 mg., chromatographically purified and recrystallised from acetone, m. p. 96°), 2 c.c. of a 20% solution of freshly fused potassium acetate in pure acetic acid, and sufficient pure acetic acid (redistilled over chromium trioxide) to give a homogeneous mixture, were heated with exclusion of moisture for 4 hours at 100°. After removal of most of the acetic acid under reduced pressure, water was added, and the product extracted with ether. The ethereal extract was washed with water, sodium bicarbonate solution, and again with water, dried (Na_2SO_4), and evaporated. The residue (263·5 mg.) was completely crystalline, had m. p. 112—114°, and appeared to be pure cholesteryl acetate. To confirm this, the product was heated under reflux for 0·5 hour with 4% methyl alcoholic potassium hydroxide (2·5 c.c. ≡ approx. 3 mols.); working up furnished apparently pure cholesterol, m. p. 147—148° (235 mg.), which was dissolved in methanol (7 c.c.) and treated with a solution of digitonin (700 mg.) in warm methanol (7 c.c.). Addition of water (1·4 c.c.) gave a large precipitate; the mixture was kept for 1 hour at 0°, and then separated by centrifuging. The precipitate was twice mixed with methanol and reseparated by centrifuging.

The digitonide was dried in a desiccator, dissolved in dry pyridine (4 c.c.), and decomposed by addition of dry ether (40 c.c.); the precipitated digitonin was filtered off and washed with ether, and the filtrate evaporated to yield cholesterol (217 mg.; yield, 91%), m. p. 148° after crystallisation from methanol.

The methyl alcoholic filtrates were combined and evaporated completely under reduced pressure, and the residue was extracted with boiling dry ether (5 portions of 20 c.c.); these extracts by evaporation gave a little oil (9 mg.), which was distilled at 140°/0·001 mm., and an attempt was made to crystallise the distillate from methanol. A trace of crystalline material, m. p. 80—90° (indefinite), was obtained; it gave a positive Beilstein test for halogen and possibly consisted essentially of unchanged cholesteryl chloride.

The yield of cholesterol was 91%, that of the digitonin non-precipitatable material 3·8%; losses, which appear to be unavoidable in digitonin separations, thus amounted to about 5%.

3(β)-*Chlorocholestane from Cholesteryl Chloride.*—Cholesteryl chloride, m. p. 96° (1·00 g.), was reduced by shaking with Adams's catalyst (100 mg.) in hydrogen at atmospheric pressure for 48 hours; the solvent used was pure ethyl acetate (10 c.c.) containing pure acetic acid (0·10 c.c.) (cf. Marker, Whitmore, and Kamm, *J. Amer. Chem. Soc.*, 1935, 57, 2358). The product obtained by filtration from the catalyst and complete evaporation had m. p. 111—112° (1·00 g.); recrystallisation from acetone afforded prisms, m. p. 112°, $[a]_D^{21°}$ +18°±2° (c, 1·809 in chloroform), which gave a pale but distinct yellow colour with tetranitromethane. Three recrystallisations from acetone gave a product, m. p. 112—113°, $[a]_D^{21°}$ +21°±2° (on material dried at 100°/10 mm.; c, 1·635 in chloroform), which still gave a pale yellow colour with tetranitromethane and so still presumably contained traces of unreduced cholesteryl chloride, $[a]_D^{20°}$ −27° (Beynon, Heilbron, and Spring, *J.*, 1936, 907). Part of the product (330 mg.) was therefore dissolved in pure acetic acid (4 c.c.) and treated with a 2% solution of chromium trioxide in acetic acid (4 c.c. ≡ 1·5 atoms of oxygen) at 60° for 0·5 hour with efficient stirring (cf. Ruzicka, Goldberg, and Brungger, *Helv. Chim. Acta*, 1934, 17, 1389). After working up, the neutral material was dissolved in pentane and purified from neutral oxidation products by filtration through a column of aluminium oxide (Merck–Brockmann, activity III—IV : 10 g.) prepared in pentane. After recrystallisation from acetone the pure chloro-compound had m. p. 114—115°, $[a]_D^{20°}$ +27°±1° (c, 1·911 in chloroform).

The author gratefully acknowledges the support of the British Empire Cancer Campaign, the Jane Coffin Childs Memorial Fund, and the Anna Fuller Fund.

The Chester Beatty Research Institute,   [*Received, August 8th*, 1946.]
The Royal Cancer Hospital (Free), London, S.W.3.

5, 6 | The Double Bond in Cholesterol

The paper of Winstein and Adams brings together stereochemical evidence of the type discussed by Shoppee with a kinetic analysis of the solvolysis and displacement reactions in the cholesteryl system. Of great importance is the concept of *driving force*—rate of reaction relative to a standard which has no neighboring group participation—as evidence of stabilization of the intermediate ion and hence of the transition state leading to it (also relative to a standard of comparison). The mere fact that cholesteryl tosylate solvolyzes 100 times as fast as cyclohexyl tosylate might have meant that the ion V was produced directly in the solvolysis and was somehow abnormally stable. But the abnormally fast conversion of the *i*-ether II to the normal ether III cannot simultaneously be explained as the direct formation of the cholesteryl ion VI, and an exceptional stability of the latter. A greatly enhanced rate (driving force) in *both directions* is one of the most characteristic signs of a resonance-stabilized intermediate. The conclusion that the homoallylic ion IV is involved rests upon the same kind of reasoning as that which infers the existence of a resonance-stabilized crotyl-α-methylcarbinyl cation in the allylic rearrangement.[1] These arguments are stated in the paper by Winstein and Adams and reinforced by the discovery of alkoxy exchange between *i*-cholesteryl ethers by Winstein and Schlesinger (No. 6). The study of driving forces has become a regular part of the testing for nonclassical ions; this kind of evidence gains in importance with increasing magnitude of the driving force. Some are known as high as 10^{14} (No. 45).

---

[1] R. H. DeWolfe and W. G. Young, *Chem. Revs.* **56**, 753 (1956).

From: *J. Am. Chem. Soc.* **70**, 838–40 (1948)

[CONTRIBUTION FROM THE CHEMISTRY DEPARTMENT OF THE UNIVERSITY OF CALIFORNIA, LOS ANGELES]

The Role of Neighboring Groups in Replacement Reactions. XIV. The 5,6-Double Bond in Cholesteryl p-Toluenesulfonate as a Neighboring Group

BY S. WINSTEIN AND ROWLAND ADAMS

Shoppee[1] has very recently pointed out the tendency toward a steric result of retention of configuration in nucleophilic displacements at C_3 in Δ^5-cholestene derivatives and similar systems. Also he has drawn an analogy which we also have been using between this phenomenon and our work, presented in previous papers of this series, on participation of such neighboring groups as bromine in nucleophilic displacement processes. We are prompted to report the results of a study of the kinetics of acetolysis of cholesteryl p-toluenesulfonate I which we carried out some time ago as part of an investigation which was unavoidably interrupted.

the action of the potassium acetate in the methanol where i-ether is formed from I is merely to buffer the solution so that high acidity is not developed.

The i-sterol rearrangement (I → II) represents a case of participation in a nucleophilic displacement reaction by a properly situated ethylenic linkage, a suitable example of which we had been seeking for study when we began the present investigation. The most likely general mechanism for this rearrangement would seem to involve either the hybrid carbonium ion IV or the rearranged carbonium ion V. The intermediate (IV or V) then reacts with nucleophilic agents more rapidly at C_6 than C_3.

It is known[2] that cholesteryl p-toluenesulfonate I on treatment with potassium acetate in methanol gives rise to a material which is best represented as the i-ether[3] II. In the absence of potassium acetate in the methanol, normal ether III is produced. By the action of potassium acetate in acetic anhydride, I is converted to i-acetate.[3c,d] Cholesteryl chloride, similarly to the toluenesulfonate, also[4] gives rise to i-ether. The i-ethers are relatively unstable, for example being converted to normal acetate on treatment with potassium acetate in glacial acetic acid.[3a,b] From the properties of the i-ethers it is apparent that

With regard to the formation of the intermediate IV or V, the alternatives (with no regard for stereochemistry) are a direct formation by ionization of I or prior formation of unrearranged carbonium ion VI, which then is converted to intermediate V (as though an energy barrier existed between V and VI). The specific reaction rate constants for the two modes of rate-determining ionization are symbolized by k_Δ and k_c, the symbols used previously[6] for other neighboring groups.

The kinetics of acetolysis of cholesteryl p-toluenesulfonate I support the general mechanism outlined and point to the direct ionization to intermediate IV or V (rate constant k_Δ). The acetolysis of I in glacial acetic acid proved to be very cleanly first-order, the first-order rate constants k at 35.00 and 50.00° being summarized in Table I.

The catalytic effect of water and sodium acetate on the acetolysis is quite marked. However, these effects are definitely solvent and ionic

(1) Shoppee, *J. Chem. Soc.*, 1117 (1946); journal received March 3, 1947.

(2) Stoll, *Z. physiol. Chem.*, **207**, 147 (1932).

(3) (a) Beynon, Heilbron and Spring, *J. Chem. Soc.*, 907 (1936); (b) Beynon, Heilbron and Spring, *ibid.*, 406 (1937); (c) Wallis, Fernholz and Gephardt, THIS JOURNAL, **59**, 137 (1937); (d) Ford and Wallis, *ibid.*, **59**, 1415 (1937); (e) Beynon, Heilbron and Spring, *J. Chem. Soc.*, 1459 (1937); (f) Ford, Chakravorty and Wallis, THIS JOURNAL, **60**, 413 (1938); (g) Heilbron, Hodges and Spring, *J. Chem. Soc.*, 759 (1938); (h) Ladenburg, Chakravorty and Wallis, THIS JOURNAL, **61**, 3483 (1939).

(4) Wagner-Jauregg and Werner, *Z. physiol. Chem.*, **213**, 119 (1932).

(5) (a) Winstein, Grunwald and Ingraham, THIS JOURNAL, **70**, 821 (1948); (b) Winstein and Grunwald, *ibid.*, **70**, 828 (1948).

TABLE I

RATE CONSTANTS OF ACETOLYSIS k OF ca. 0.01 M CHOLESTERYL p-TOLUENESULFONATE IN GLACIAL ACETIC ACID

Other solute	Temp., °C.	$10^3 k$, min.$^{-1}$
....	50.00	7.9[a]
0.50 M H$_2$O	50.00	12.2
.0100 M KOAc	50.00	19.8
.0100 M NaOAc	50.00	20.0
.0200 M NaOAc	50.00	20.0
.0100 M LiClO$_4$	50.00	24.1
....	35.00	1.19[a]
....	50.00	0.111[b]

[a] $\Delta H^{\ddagger} = 24.4$ kcal./mole. [b] Cyclohexyl p-toluenesulfonate.

strength effects. Thus the effect of sodium acetate is not even as large as that of lithium perchlorate. Also raising the concentration of sodium acetate from 0.01 to 0.02 M gives no further increase in rate, which is not too surprising for ionic strength effects[6] in a solvent of as low a dielectric constant as that of acetic acid (ca. 6).

The fact that acetic acid is such a poor nucleophilic agent, that the rate is still nicely first order on addition of sodium acetate and that the effect of sodium acetate (the same at 0.01 and 0.02 M) is less even than that of lithium perchlorate indicates that the acetolysis represents a reaction of the

VII

unimolecular type and that concerted mechanisms of the type shown in VII are not important here.

The rate of acetolysis of cholesteryl p-toluenesulfonate I is seen to be some 10^2 (depending on ionic strength) times as large as that for cyclohexyl p-toluenesulfonate[7] also determined at 50.00° for comparison (Table I). The latter compound represents at least one good choice of a model substance for comparison in order to estimate k_c. Now reactivities of ring compounds are not yet clearly understood so that other comparisons are desirable. Actually, there are other indications of enhanced reactivity due to the 5,6-ethylenic linkage. Thus, Stoll[8] compared cholesteryl p-toluenesulfonate I with cholestanyl and ergostanyl p-toluenesulfonates in ethanol (no added ethoxide) at 78° and from his first-order rate constants one calculates factors of the order of 40 in favor of the cholesteryl ester. In the solvent ethanol we had felt there was more reason to suspect mechanisms of the type VII. However, the rate constant of acetolysis of cholesteryl p-

toluenesulfonate I extrapolated to 78° is 0.176 min.$^{-1}$, a value nearly equal to Stoll's value of 0.18–0.19 min.$^{-1}$ in ethanol. Since ethanol and glacial acetic acid give comparable[9] solvolysis rates in unimolecular solvolyses, the indications are against mechanism VII in alcohol also. Further, in the case of chlorides, rather than toluenesulfonates, there are qualitative indications of greater reactivity of the Δ^5-compounds and Shoppee[1] refers to these.

The evidence then is that the 5,6-ethylenic linkage exerts a driving force[5] in favor of ionization of I, the main ionization being directly to intermediate IV or V (rate constant k_Δ). Thus a pair of electrons in an ethylenic linkage may play a role analogous to that of neighboring groups discussed in previous articles. There are further indications of the ionization by the k_Δ process. Thus the $\Delta H^{\ddagger}$ of activation for cholesteryl p-toluenesulfonate is less than that for the cyclohexyl ester[5a] by some 2.6 kcal./mole. This kind of a decrease with an increase in rate effected by a neighboring group has been noticed before.[5]

Also, the acetolysis of cholesteryl p-toluenesulfonate is much more sensitive to addition of water and salts than is the case with the cyclohexyl esters. While further comparison with medium effects in the case of higher molecular weight saturated esters such as cholestanyl are needed, one is led to compare the present situation with the one prevailing in the case of solvolysis of alkyl halides studied by Hughes, Ingold and co-workers.[6] In the latter case, the increase in rate by salt climbs as one proceeds from t-butyl to benzhydryl, separation of charge in the transition state being larger in the latter example. It is possible that the cyclohexyl-cholesteryl trend is analogous, the transition state for ionization of cholesteryl p-toluenesulfonate having positive charge both on C$_3$ and C$_6$.

Just as a pair of electrons of the 5,6 double bond in I imparts reactivity in ionization at C$_3$, the pair of electrons in the 3-membered rings of i-compounds such as II apparently imparts high reactivity at C$_6$. One very likely mechanism for the reverse i-sterol rearrangement of type II to type I, which we are also investigating, involves ionization followed by competitive reactions at C$_3$ and C$_6$. On this basis, judging by the high reactivity of i-compounds[3], V is not the intermediate. If these suppositions prove to be correct, the mesomeric ion IV would be the common intermediate for forward and reverse rearrangements, no energy barrier existing between the limiting resonance structures V and VI.

The over-all steric result of the conversion of cholesteryl p-toluenesulfonate I or chloride to an i-compound (type II) and back to a normal compound is clearly quite clean-cut retention of configuration. Thus, i-ether II gives cholesteryl

(6) Bateman, Church, Hughes, Ingold and Taher, J. Chem. Soc., 979 (1940).

(7) Winstein, Grunwald, Buckles and Hanson, THIS JOURNAL, 70, 816 (1948).

(8) Stoll, Z. physiol. Chem., 246, 6 (1937).

(9) Winstein, Hanson and Grunwald, THIS JOURNAL, 70, 812 (1940).

chloride[3a,b] on treatment with hydrogen chloride in acetic acid and also is easily converted to cholesteryl acetate.[3a,b] This steric result is analogous to that involving other neighboring groups and is expected from the mechanism outlined for the formation of the i-compound and a reverse rearrangement which requires nucleophilic attack on C_3 to completely sever the C_3–C_5 bond.

Over-all retention of configuration with Δ^5-materials is very general and Shoppee[1] has summarized[10] the displacement reactions at C_3 in which 3-OH is converted to 3-Cl and 3-Cl to 3-OCOR. However, in these cases there is still need for further scrutiny to determine whether i-product is not the first predominant one, which quickly is rearranged to normal product.

Experimental

Materials.—Cholesteryl p-toluenesulfonate, m. p. 132–133°, was prepared in the usual manner.[3e] This material generated 98.5% of the theoretical amount of acid in acetolysis.

Lithium perchlorate trihydrate was prepared by treatment of Merck reagent grade lithium carbonate with perchloric acid. The reaction mixture, pH 4.5, was filtered, concentrated to a small volume and then allowed to cool slowly. The deposited crystals were pressed dry and dried in an oven at 140° for four hours. The hot liquid product was allowed to cool with stirring to yield a white crystalline solid, m. p. 93–94.5°.

The acetic acid solvent was prepared from Grasselli reagent grade acid and pure acetic anhydride, the residual concentration[5a] of the latter being 1×10^{-3} M.

Rate Measurements.—The titration procedures were those used previously.[5a] In case lithium perchlorate or sodium acetate (sodium carbonate was used) was added to the solvent, water was destroyed by treatment with the proper amount of acetic anhydride.

In the case of cyclohexyl p-toluenesulfonate,[7] m. p. 44–45°, sealed ampoules were used, concentrations being approximately 0.03 M. With the cholesteryl p-toluenesulfonate, concentrations approximately 0.01 M were used due to low solubility and low rate of solution. The toluenesulfonate was added to the solvent already at bath temperature and the mixture was shaken violently in a glass-stoppered flask until solution of the toluenesulfonate was nearly complete. Then the mixture was filtered rapidly into a volumetric flask already in the bath. In this way a homogeneous solution of the toluenesulfonate at bath temperature could be achieved in approximately five minutes. The initial concentration of the material was determined by titration of a sample of the reaction mixture after ten half-life periods.

Rates were followed to approximately 70% completion, the mean deviation of the individual first-order rate constants in one run being within 3% even for the rapid cases.

---

(10) Bergmann [*Helv. Chim. Acta*, **20**, 590 (1937)] previously had remarked on such anomalous steric results and ascribed them vaguely to the unsaturated linkage.

It is a pleasure to acknowledge helpful discussions with Drs. Byron Riegel of Northwestern University and Sam Siegel of the Illinois Institute of Technology.

Summary

A study of the acetolysis of cholesteryl p-toluenesulfonate has shown that the first-order rate constant is *ca.* 10^2 (because of a corresponding decrease in $\Delta H^{\pm}$) times that for the cyclohexyl ester. Also the rate is quite sensitive to the addition of water, sodium or potassium acetate, or lithium perchlorate to the acetic acid solvent.

The poor nucleophilic character of acetic acid, the fact that the salt effect of sodium acetate in acetolysis is no greater than that of lithium perchlorate, and the near identity of acetolysis and alcoholysis rates of cholesteryl p-toluenesulfonate speak against a mechanism for the isosterol rearrangement involving nucleophilic attack at C_6 in the rate-determining step. Thus the isosterol rearrangement represents a case of participation by a pair of electrons of the 5,6-ethylenic linkage in a unimolecular type displacement reaction at C_3.

The relatively high rates of acetolysis and alcoholysis of cholesteryl p-toluenesulfonate and other qualitative indications of high reactivity of Δ^5-materials show that the double bond furnishes a substantial driving force. This speaks for the direct formation of intermediate IV or V in the ionization of the C_3-derivatives. It is highly pos-

$$IV \qquad V$$

sible that the reversed isosterol rearrangement (i-compounds to normal ones) normally proceeds through the same intermediate. On this basis, the high reactivity of i-compounds speaks for a driving force due to the pair of electrons in the 3-membered ring and thus intermediate IV is indicated.

The over-all steric result of the conversion to an i-compound and back to a normal compound is analogous to the retention of configuration observed with other neighboring groups.

Los Angeles 24, Calif.   Received April 3, 1947

From: *J. Am. Chem. Soc.* **70,** 3528–29 (1948)

EXCHANGE AT THE 6-POSITION OF
i-CHOLESTERYL METHYL ETHER

Sir:

We have recently[1] suggested that the predominant mechanism which operates for the conversion of cholesteryl *p*-toluenesulfonate to the *i*-ether involves ionization to an intermediate ion I which has the cationic charge distributed between positions 3 and 6 and which reacts more rapidly with methanol at position 6 than 3.

Postulating the same ion I as an intermediate in the well-known[2] rearrangement of an *i*-compound to a normal one, one would expect, in the acid-catalyzed conversion of *i*-methyl to *n*-ethyl ether, prior formation, to a large extent, of the *i*-ethyl ether. This we have now been able to confirm.

Thus, in a typical experiment, 2.00 g. of *i*-cholesteryl methyl ether, m. p. 79.0–79.5°, was subjected to a one-half hour reflux period in absolute ethanol to which was added ethanolic *p*-toluenesulfonic acid (total volume of final solution 37 ml.) 0.001 *M* in excess of the slight potassium acetate impurity present in the *i*-methyl ether as usually prepared.[3] The acid was neutralized, the solvent was evaporated, and the organic material

was taken up in hexane. Systematic separation of the products by chromatography with the aid of alumina gave rise to 1.09 g. of *i*-ethyl ether, m. p. 45.0–45.5° (reported[4] 47°), mixed m. p. with authentic material, 45.5–46.0°, $[\alpha]^{25}\mathrm{D}$ (chloroform) +47.10° (1 dcm., c = 2.65) (reported[4] $[\alpha]^{20}\mathrm{D}$ +49.78° (c = 1.607)), 0.18 g. of *i*-methyl ether, m. p. 78.5–79.5° and 0.48 g. of *n*-ethyl ether, m. p. 88.0–89.0°. Thus, under these conditions, the ethyl ether product was 68% *i*-ethyl. The latter ether is converted to *n*-ethyl at a very appreciable rate, but the results serve to indicate the initial conversion of *i*-methy ether predominantly to *i*-ethyl.

The *i*-ethyl ether product was indistinguishable in melting point and optical rotation from authentic *i*-ethyl ether and has, therefore, the same configuration as that of the product of the first reaction of ion I with ethanol under the usual conditions of preparation of *i*-ethyl ether. As far as we are aware this represents the first demonstration of exchange at the 6-position of *i*-compounds and suggests that, with care, it can be general.

The present work strengthens the case for an intermediate ion I in certain forward and reverse *i*-sterol rearrangements. It supplies evidence neither for nor against some contribution of bimolecular type mechanisms, and these remain possibilities for some rearrangements.

(4) Beynon, Heilbron and Spring, *J. Chem. Soc.*, 907 (1936).
(5) National Institute of Health Postdoctoral Fellow, 1947–1948.

DEPARTMENT OF CHEMISTRY
UNIVERSITY OF CALIFORNIA
LOS ANGELES 24, CALIFORNIA   S. WINSTEIN
    A. H. SCHLESINGER[5]

RECEIVED AUGUST 30, 1948

(1) Winstein and Adams, THIS JOURNAL, **70**, 838 (1948).
(2) McKennis, *ibid.*, **69**, 2565 (1947)
(3) Stoll, *Z. physiol. Chem.*, **207**, 147 (1932).

7 | The Norbornyl Cation

A paper in 1939 by T. P. Nevell, E. de Salas, and C. L. Wilson[1] contained the following statement concerning the rearrangement of camphene hydrochloride into isobornyl chloride:

Although the intermediate is represented as having the camphene structure, it is possible that it is mesomeric between this and the corresponding isobornyl structure. . . . One condition . . . would seem to be that, whatever the structure of the ion, the stereochemical identity of the carbon atom marked with an asterisk must be preserved.

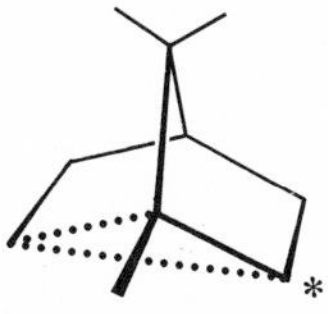

This first suggestion in the research literature of the existence of electronic delocalization in a saturated carbonium ion was not tested at the time, nor in any other paper for the following ten years. It was, however, discussed and advocated as the correct formulation of the rearrangement of pinene hydrochloride and of pinacol, by H. B. Watson[2] who credited the original suggestion to Ingold. In 1949 Winstein and Trifan (No. 7) published this preliminary announcement of stereochemical and kinetic evidence that the norbornyl cation possessed such a delocalized structure and plane of symmetry.

---

[1] T. P. Nevell, E. de Salas, and C. L. Wilson, *J. Chem. Soc.* **1939**, 1192. Their formula is here projected in the manner common elsewhere in this book.

[2] H. B. Watson, *Modern Theories of Organic Chemistry,* 2nd Edition (Oxford University Press, London, 1941), pp. 208–209.

From: *J. Am. Chem. Soc.* **71**, 2953 (1949)

from *exo*-norborneol (I, III, X = OH), m p. 127.6–128.5° (reported[3] 128–129°) on acetolysis yields *exo*-norbornyl acetate (I, III, X = OCOCH₃) (identified as the *exo*-norbornyl 3,5-dinitrobenzoate, m. p. 103.7–105.0°, reported[3] 105°) with no evidence of any *endo*-norbornyl acetate or norbornylene in the product. Also, *endo*-norbornyl *p*-toluenesulfonate, m. p. 28.1–29 2° yields only the *exo*-norbornyl acetate and *exo*-norbornyl alcohol in acetolysis and hydrolysis (aqueous acetone or dioxane), respectively.

The total resolution of the *exo*-norborneol is still in progress but sufficient resolution has been effected for the type of stereochemical test previously carried out in the case of bromonium ions[2a] and similar species. *Exo*-norborneol, $[\alpha]^{22}$D $-1.09°$ (chloroform, $c = 10.1$), prepared from acid phthalate, $[\alpha]^{23}$D $+ 3.33°$ (chloroform, $c = 10.0$), and which gives an acetate, $[\alpha]^{23}$D $+ 4.47°$ (acetic acid, $c = 5.36$), was converted to *p*-bromobenzenesulfonate, $[\alpha]^{25}$D $\cong + 1.29°$ (initially, in glacial acetic acid, $c = 20.08$). This *p*-bromobenzenesulfonate acetolyzes (with or without dissolved potassium acetate) to give completely inactive product, the activity of the solution disappearing at roughly the solvolysis rate. Examination of the concentrated product showed more precisely the completeness of the racemization under conditions where the fully survived activity would have been 100–200 times the experimental error.

The facts are at present best accommodated by the formulation of the intermediate ion from *exo*-norbornyl derivatives as II

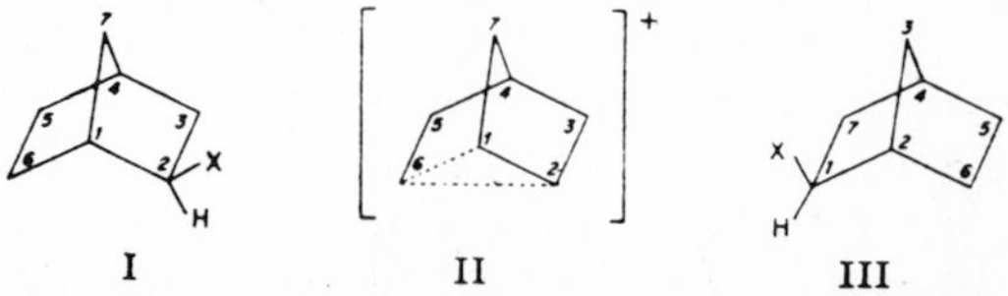

THE STRUCTURE OF THE BICYCLO[2,2,1]2-HEPTYL (NORBORNYL) CARBONIUM ION

Sir:

From a generalized viewpoint many rearrangements involve participation of electrons associated with a neighboring β-H,R, or Ar group in a unimolecular-type nucleophilic replacement process. Thus, in the Wagner–Meerwein rearrangement, ionization produces directly, or in a later stage, a rearranged ion or an ion with a bridged structure. The latter type formulation for a carbonium ion has been mentioned a number of times as a possibility or definitely proposed.[1] The same kinetic and stereochemical methods employed in the study of functional neighboring groups[2] are useful in this connection.

In the norbornyl system relative rates of acetolysis at 45° of *p*-toluenesulfonates or *p*-bromobenzenesulfonates are: *exo*-norbornyl (I, III, X = OSO₂C₆H₄Br), 350 > *endo*-norbornyl, 1 ≅ cyclohexyl. The driving force[2b] in the stereochemically favorable *exo*-isomer is a substantial fraction of that displayed by isobornyl chloride.

Exo-norbornyl *p*-bromobenzenesulfonate (I, III, X = OSO₂C₆H₄Br), m. p. 55.3–57.0°, prepared

I   II   III

which has a plane of symmetry through atoms 4, 5 and 6 and is therefore internally compensated. Attack at C-2 yields the original configuration, I; attack at C-1 yields the enantiomorph, III.

The solvolysis of the *endo*-norbornyl *p*-bromobenzenesulfonate is being subjected to the same kind of stereochemical scrutiny.

DEPARTMENT OF CHEMISTRY   S. WINSTEIN
UNIVERSITY OF CALIFORNIA   DANIEL S. TRIFAN[4]
LOS ANGELES 24, CALIFORNIA

RECEIVED JUNE 20, 1949

(1) E. g. (a) Winstein and Lucas, THIS JOURNAL, **60**, 836 (1938); (b) Nevell, de Salas and Wilson, *J. Chem. Soc.*, 1188 (1939); (c) Watson, "Annual Reports," 197 (1939); 120 (1941); (d) Eyring, *Ind. Eng. Chem.*, **35**, 511 (1943); (e) Dewar, *J. Chem. Soc.*, 406 (1946); (f) Walsh, *ibid.*, 89 (1947); (g) Arcus, *Chemistry and Industry*, 442 (1947).

(2) E. g. (a) Winstein and Lucas, THIS JOURNAL, **61**, 2845 (1939); (b) Winstein and Grunwald, *ibid.*, **70**, 828 (1948).

(3) Alder and Rickert, *Ann.*, **543**, 1 (1940).

(4) Postdoctoral Research Associate, 1948–1949.

8 | The 2-Norbornenyl Cation

Roberts, Bennett, and Armstrong in 1950 explored a rearrangement in the 2-norbornenyl-nortricyclyl system which is analogous to the *i*-sterol rearrangement. Two allusions in this paper to unpublished work indicate that driving forces, though small among these compounds, become much more dramatic with changes in structure (*exo/endo* ratio in norbornyl chloride, 10; in isobornyl/bornyl chloride, 10^5; nortricyclyl/*endo*-norbornenyl, about 0.9; cyclopropylcarbinyl/allylcarbinyl, 10^3–10^4). The driving forces also appear greater in less nucleophilic solvents than the 80% ethanol used here, and depend on the leaving group as well. A quite specific discussion is given of the stereochemical factors in what is later called homoallylic delocalization. The conclusions are modified in later discussions of the same theme (see Papers 22, 25, 40, 51).

From: *J. Am. Chem. Soc.* **72**, 3329–33 (1950)

[Contribution from the Department of Chemistry and Laboratory for Nuclear Science and Engineering of the Massachusetts Institute of Technology]

Solvolytic Reactivities of Nortricyclyl, Dehydronorbornyl and Norbornyl Halides. Possible Steric Requirements for Hyperconjugative Resonance[1]

By John D. Roberts, Winifred Bennett and Rose Armstrong .

The present investigation is concerned with the determination and interpretation of the solvolytic reactivities of nortricyclyl (I), *endo*-dehydronorbornyl (II), *exo*-dehydronorbornyl (III), *endo*-norbornyl (IV) and *exo*-norbornyl (V) halides.

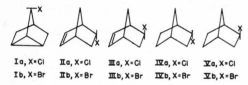

Ia, X=Cl   IIa, X=Cl   IIIa, X=Cl   IVa, X=Cl   Va, X=Cl
Ib, X=Br   IIb, X=Br   IIIb, X=Br   IVb, X=Br   Vb, X=Br

This series of structurally similar compounds provides an almost unique opportunity to observe the relationship between stereochemistry and solvolytic reactivities in alicyclic halides.

With X as a given halogen there are considerable differences in reactivity between some of the members of the series. In aqueous ethanol (20% water–80% ethanol, by volume) the sequence of reactivities shown below can be inferred from the rate constants in Table I. This sequence is only qualitative since different temperatures were used for the bromides and chlorides and a single halogen as X was not used throughout.

$$V > III > IV \sim II \sim I \qquad (1)$$

A significant feature of the rate sequence is the greater reactivities of the *exo*-compounds, III and V, as compared to the corresponding *endo*-compounds, II and IV. Ths spread between

Table I

Solvolysis Rates of Halides (RX) in 80% Ethanol–20% Water (by Volume) Solution

R	X	Temp., °C.	k_1, hr.$^{-1}$	% purity[a]
Nortricyclyl (I)	Br	55	0.015	100
endo-Dehydronorbornyl (II)	Br	55	.017	92[b]
	Cl	85	.017	97[c]
exo-Dehydronorbornyl (III)	Cl	85	.078	83[d]
endo-Norbornyl (IV)	Br	55	.020	80[b]
	Cl	85	.015	87[c]
exo-Norbornyl (V)	Br	55	.20	100
	Cl	85	.14	100

[a] Purity as indicated by analysis of reaction kinetics by the method of Brown and Fletcher, This Journal, **71**, 1845 (1949). [b] Impurity was a more reactive bromide, presumably the *exo*-bromide. [c] Impurity was a more reactive chloride, presumably the *exo*-chloride. [d] Impurity was a less reactive chloride which from infrared spectrum and hydrogenation data seemed to be nortricyclyl chloride (Ia).

exo- and *endo*-series is substantial although far less than the 10⁵ fold difference between isobornyl and bornyl chlorides in 80% ethanol–20% water solution.[2,3] The products of the solvolysis of the *exo–endo*-isomer pairs in water (which was used in the product determinations to avoid complications due to formation of ethyl ethers) were the same; thus, II[4] and III both gave principally (>90%) 3-hydroxynortricyclene (VI)

(1) (a) Supported in part by the joint program of the Office of Naval Research and the Atomic Energy Commission. (b) Preliminary results on *exo*-norbornyl chloride were reported by Roberts, Urbanek and Armstrong, This Journal, **71**, 3049 (1949).

(2) Unpublished experiments by Mrs. Hildegarde Harris.

(3) Detailed discussion of the solvolysis rates of *exo*- *vs.* *endo*-isomers will be deferred until completion of another investigation.

(4) Roberts, Trumbull, Bennett and Armstrong, *ibid.*, **72**, 3116 (1950).

while IV and V gave *exo*-norborneol (VII).[5] VI is also obtained in the hydrolysis of I.[4]

An interesting feature of sequence (1) is the slowness of the reactions of the unsaturated compounds, II and III, relative to those of the corresponding saturated compounds, IV and V. A quite different situation prevails in the solvolysis of cholesteryl (VIII) and cholestanyl (IX) compounds where the cholesteryl derivative reacts far more rapidly.[6] It is apparent from our results that the double bonds in II and III exert no very

substantial "driving force" (of the type postulated for cholesteryl compounds)[6] during the ionization of the C–X bonds in the solvolysis reactions. It is significant that the reactions result with carbon skeleton rearrangement and the formation of VI showing that the double bond becomes involved in the over-all reaction if not in the rate-determining step. The reactions of II and III might be formulated as involving the isomerization of a dehydronorbornyl cation (X) to a nortricyclyl cation (XI) or the formation of the conjugate acid of VI by attack of water on cation X after the rate-determining step. An

alternative scheme would have an intermediate ion such as XII[6] formed more or less directly in the rate-determining step. Since III is more favorably disposed structurally for the direct formation of a cation like XII than is II the larger solvolysis rate of III with respect to II could be accounted for on this basis. However, the effect on the rate is not large and the fact

that the saturated compounds IV and V are actually somewhat faster than II and III shows that the driving force is small.[7] Irrespective of the actual product of the rate-determining step in solvolysis reactions of compounds of the type $X-\overset{|}{C}-\overset{|}{C}-\overset{|}{C}=C\overset{}{\underset{}{\diagup}}$, the transition state for the ionization of the C–X bond can be considered to be stabilized to some extent by contributions of resonance forms such as XIII involving the

neighboring double bond. It is reasonable to expect that the importance of forms like XIII should be influenced by the spatial relationship between the double bond and the reacting center. In this connection it is interesting to note that the double bond and reactive center are spatially quite different for cholesteryl derivatives VIII and the dehydronorbornyl halides, II and III. Models of the compounds reveal that C-3 in VIII is located more nearly "endwise" to the 5,6-double bond than are the carbons holding the halogens in II and III are to the double bonds in these substances. While an *a priori* judgment as to the most favorable position is not easily made, the considerable reactivity of the cholesteryl derivatives indicates that the more endwise location results in an increased stabilization of the solvolysis transition state.

Perhaps the most striking characteristic of sequence (1) is the extraordinarily low relative reactivity of nortricyclyl bromide (Ia). It has been found that other cyclopropylcarbinyl-type compounds are exceptionally reactive. Thus, cyclopropylcarbinyl chloride solvolyzes in aqueous ethanol 10^3–10^4 times faster than allylcarbinyl chloride[8] and the *i*-sterols are generally far more reactive than the corresponding cholesteryl or cholestanyl derivatives.[6,9] The high reactivity of cyclopropylcarbinyl chloride has been ascribed to stabilization of the cyclopropylcarbinyl cation by contributions of resonance forms such as XIV.[8] This resonance involving the C–C bond

of the cyclopropane ring is similar to the hyperconjugative resonance such as XV which has been proposed to account for the stability of alkyl-substituted carbonium ions. Actually, forms like

(5) Alder and Stein, *Ann.*, **514**, 211 (1934), and Komppa and Beckmann, *ibid.*, **512**, 172 (1934), have reported the formation of VII from the *endo*- and *exo*-norbornylamines with nitrous acid while Winstein and Trifan, THIS JOURNAL, **71**, 2953 (1949), obtained VII as the acetate from the acetolysis of *exo*- and *endo*-norbornyl *p*-bromobenzenesulfonates. Schmerling, *ibid.*, **68**, 195 (1946), found that Va gave *exo*-norborneol with water.

(6) See Winstein and Adams, *ibid.*, **70**, 838 (1948), for references and discussion.

(7) The situation is not unlike that found to exist in the solvolysis of the *p*-toluenesulfonate of 3-phenyl-2-butanol studied by Cram, THIS JOURNAL, **71**, 3863 (1949), where rearrangement occurs but no driving force is evident.

(8) Roberts and Mazur, paper in preparation.

(9) *Cf.* Fieser and Fieser, "Natural Products Related to Phenanthrene," 3rd ed., Reinhold Publishing Corp., New York, N. Y., 1949, pp. 256–261.

XIV should be expected to be more effective in stabilizing the cyclopropylcarbinyl cation than XV is for the usual alkylcarbonium ions because

$$R_2C^{\oplus}\!-\!CH_2H \longleftrightarrow R_2C\!=\!CH_2\,H^{\oplus}$$

XV

of the relative "looseness" of the electrons in the three-membered ring bonds. Resonance forms similar to XIV can be written for the stabilization of the *i*-cholesteryl cation XVI and the nortricyclyl cation X which from their appearance

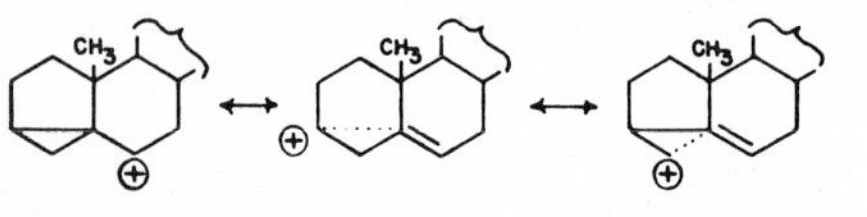

XVI   XVI a   XVI b

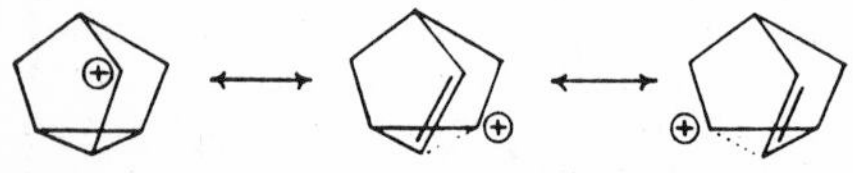

X   Xa

might be judged to be of comparable importance for each cation. Nonetheless, cation X is formed much less readily than XVI or the cyclopropylcarbinyl cation which fact suggests that the spatial relationship of the three-membered ring to the cationic center may be of considerable importance in determining the degree of resonance stabilization by forms XIV, XVIa, b and Xa.

So far, no clear statement of the steric requirements for hyperconjugative stabilization of carbonium ions has appeared although it has been stated without proof[10] that, for effective resonance interaction between an alkyl group and a benzene ring, the carbon atom which is directly attached to the benzyl group should be located *in the plane* of the ring. If it is considered that hyperconjugation in a carbonium ion can be ascribed to overlap of the vacant *p*-orbital of a planar cationic carbon with the σ-bonding or-

bitals of the adjacent carbon atom[11] then it seems likely that only one σ-bonding orbital on each group attached to the cationic carbon may be involved in the stabilization of a given ion. Thus, the overlap designated by XV and XIV may be represented by XVII and XVIII, respectively.

Similar formulation of the nortricyclyl cation **X** as in XIX indicates clearly that overlap of the

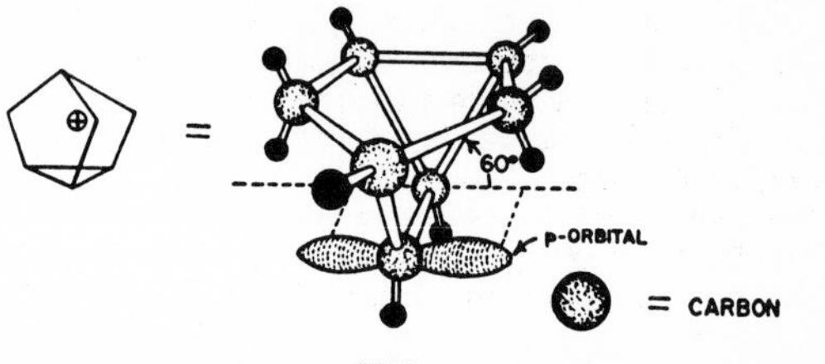

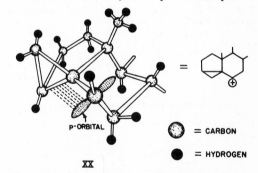

⊕ = CARBON   ● = HYDROGEN

XIX

vacant *p*-orbital with the bonding orbitals of the cyclopropane ring should not be very effective since the ring bonds are at about 60° angles to the *p*-orbital. A lack of resonance stabilization of this sort might be characterized as *steric inhibition of hyperconjugation*.

Application of these considerations to the *i*-cholesteryl cation XVI is particularly interesting. If *i*-cholesteryl derivatives are assigned the "chair" configuration for the B-ring, the *i*-cholesteryl cation may be represented by XX.

⊕ = CARBON   ● = HYDROGEN

XX

The relationship of the vacant *p*-orbital at C-6 to the three-membered ring is such that the 3,5-bond is particularly well positioned for effective overlap corresponding to resonance form XVIa. Clearly, the orbital picture agrees with the experimental facts in that it indicates that the *i*-cholesteryl cation can be stabilized by hyperconjugative resonance. Significantly, the 4,5-bond is poorly situated for effective overlap and as a result resonance corresponding to hyperconjugation of this bond as in XVIb is not likely to be important. Consequently, it is not surprising that no products corresponding to XVIb have been reported from the reactions of cholesteryl or *i*-cholesteryl derivatives.

⊕ = CARBON

● = HYDROGEN

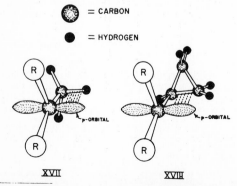

XVII   XVIII

(10) Baddeley, Chadwick and Rawlinson, *Nature*, **164**, 834 (1949).

(11) *Cf.* Dewar, "The Electronic Theory of Organic Chemistry," Oxford University Press, London, 1949, p. 19.

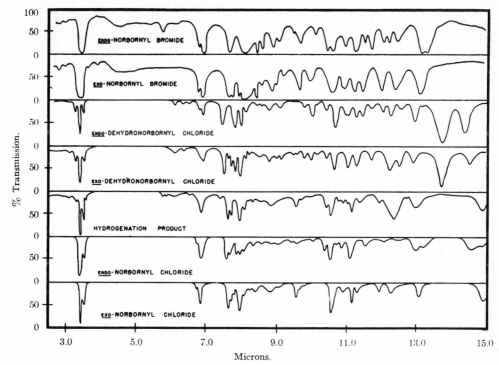

Fig. 1.—Infrared spectra: bromides determined with Perkin–Elmer spectrograph with NaCl prism, 0.1 mm. samples (no solvent); all others taken with Baird spectrometer with NaCl prism, 10% solutions in carbon disulfide except in the regions 4.2–5.0 μ and 6.2–7.2 μ where carbon tetrachloride was used as solvent.

Experimental

The preparations of several of the halides (Ib,[4] IIa,[4] IIb,[4] Va,[1] Vb[4]) used in the solvolysis rate studies have been described previously. The method of determining the solvolysis rates was the same as that used earlier.[1]

endo-**Norbornyl Halides** (IV) were obtained by hydrogenation in ethyl acetate over platinum oxide of the corresponding *endo*-dehydronorbornyl halides[4] prepared by the Diels–Alder reaction of vinyl halides and cyclopentadiene in sealed glass tubes. The impurities indicated by the kinetic analyses (Table I) are due to the slight nonstereospecificity of the Diels–Alder reaction.[4]

endo-Norbornyl bromide (IVb) had b. p. 69–70° (15.5 mm.) and n^{25}D 1.5198. The infrared spectrum is compared in Fig. 1 with that of the *exo*-isomer prepared by the addition of hydrogen bromide to norbornylene.[4] Hydrolysis of 4.0 g. of IVb by boiling for two and one-half days with 5.0 g. of lithium carbonate and 50 ml. of water gave 1.9 g. (76%) of *exo*-norborneol, m. p. 125.8–127.2°.

Anal. Calcd. for $C_7H_{11}Br$: C, 48.02; H, 6.33. Found: C, 48.43; H, 6.40.

endo-Norbornyl chloride had b. p. 51–53° (17 mm.), n^{25}D 1.4835, m. p. 28°. The infrared spectrum of the material is compared with that of *exo*-norbornyl chloride in Fig. 1.

Anal. Calcd. for $C_7H_{11}Cl$: C, 64.36; H, 8.49; Cl, 27.15. Found: C, 64.14; H, 8.48; Cl, 26.85.

exo-**Dehydronorbornyl Chloride** (IIIa).—It was reported previously[4] that the reaction of thionyl chloride with *endo*-dehydronorborneol gives principally nortricyclyl chloride (Ia). We now find that a somewhat modified procedure yields principally *exo*-dehydronorbornyl chloride (IIIa).

Redistilled thionyl chloride (14.7 g., 0.12 mole) was added dropwise to a stirred solution of 13.7 g. (0.12 mole) of *endo*-dehydronorborneol in 25 ml. of dry ether containing a few drops of pyridine. After the addition was complete, the mixture was refluxed for an hour and then distilled from a modified Claisen flask, b. p. 33–39° (8 mm.) On redistillation through a small Vigreux column 6.4 g. (42%) of chloride, b. p. 38° (9 mm.), n^{25}D 1.4909–1.4912, was obtained. The infrared spectrum of the product is shown in Fig. 1. The spectrum is distinctly different from that of the *endo*-isomer (IIa) and shows a weak band at 12.3 μ characteristic of the nortricyclene ring system.[4] On quantitative hydrogenation in ethyl acetate over platinum oxide, 81% of the theoretical quantity of hydrogen was absorbed and this result indicates that 19% of the material was nortricyclyl chloride. The hydrogenation product had b. p. 33° (8 mm.). Its infrared spectrum (Fig. 1) contained all of the bands of *exo*-norbornyl chloride as well as a band at 12.3 μ corresponding to the unreduced nortricyclyl chloride.

Hydrolysis of 1.7 g. of IIIa by boiling for three days with 1.1 g. of lithium carbonate and 15 ml. of water gave 1.0 g. (71%) of crude solid alcohol, m. p. 104–107°. The m. p. of 3-hydroxynortricyclene[4] is 108.8°. The product reacted with potassium permanganate in acetone and on quantitative hydrogenation absorbed 9% of the theoretical quantity of hydrogen calculated for a pure dehydronorborneol. The infrared spectrum of the material was practically identical with that of 3-hydroxynortricyclene[4] except for some weak absorptions which corresponded fairly well to the strong bands of *endo*-dehydronorborneol.

Summary

The solvolysis rates of some nortricyclyl,

endo- and *exo*-dehydronorbornyl and *endo*- and *exo*-norbornyl halides have been determined in aqueous ethanol solution.

The *exo*-isomers solvolyze considerably more readily than the *endo*-isomers. The double bond in the dehydronorbornyl halides appears to contribute less "driving force" in the ionization of the C–X bonds than does the 5,6-double bond in the solvolysis of cholesteryl derivatives.

Nortricyclyl bromide appears to be singularly unreactive relative to other substances containing the cyclopropylcarbinyl grouping. The cyclopropane ring in the nortricyclyl cation does not appear to contribute significantly to the stabilization of the ion. It is suggested that "steric inhibition of hyperconjugative-type resonance" may be involved.

CAMBRIDGE 39, MASS.   RECEIVED JUNE 1, 1950

9, 10 | Hughes and Winstein at Montpellier

Papers 9 and 10 are included for historical interest. They were presented at an international conference at Montpellier in April, 1950, and represent the best available simultaneous accounts of the state of research and thinking in the laboratories at UCLA and University College, London, on the subject of nonclassical ions. Both Hughes and Winstein report unpublished work on the accelerated solvolysis of β,β,β-triphenylethyl compounds (chlorides and arenesulfonates, respectively) by 10^4, and both quote the large *exo/endo* rate ratio for isobornyl and bornyl chlorides (see also Paper No. 7 and Paper No. 8, footnotes 2 and 3).

From: *Bull. soc. chim. France* [5] **18,** C39–43 (1951)

Anionotropy, and the Wagner Rearrangement,
par E. D. HUGHES.

(1) Anionotropy.

The mechanisms outlined in the preceding paper provide a basis for the discussion of these rearrangement reactions. A common mechanism of anionotropic change is related to the unimolecular mechanism (S_N1), ionisation being the rate-determining process (H. Burton and C. K. Ingold, *J. Chem. Soc.,* 1928, 904, 1650 ; 1934, 1268). In this instance, the cation is « mesomeric » (C. K. Ingold, *Chem. Reviews.* 1934, *15*, 250) and recombination with the anion may take place in either of two alternative positions, yielding one or other of the two tautomers :

$$X - CHR - CH = CH_2 \rightleftharpoons \bar{X} + [CHR \_\_ CH \_\_ CH_2]^-$$
$$\rightleftharpoons CHR = CH - CH_2 - X$$

Combination of the mesomeric cation with another anion, $\bar{Y}$, would lead to substitution with or without rearrangement. Isomeric rearrangement may therefore be regarded as a particular case of substitution with rearrangement and the mechanism described is a special case of the unimolecular type (S_N1). For substitution without rearrangement, there is an obvious alternative mechanism, namely, the common one-stage bimolecular mechanism (S_N2), *e. g.,*

$$\bar{Y} + X - CHR - CH = CH_2 \rightarrow \bar{X} + Y - CHR - CH = CH_2$$

The existence of these two mechanisms is demonstrated by the following observations :

mechanism involving the intermediate formation of a mesomeric cation (see, especially, A. G. Catchpole, E. D. Hughes and C. K. Ingold, *Trans. Faraday Soc.,* 1941, *37,* 627 ; *J. Chem. Soc.,* 1948, 4, 8 ; S. Winstein, W. G. Young and coworkers, *J. Amer. Chem. Soc.,* 1942, *64,* 2157 ; 1944, *66,* 421).

For rearrangement, an interesting alternative reaction path is possible (E. D. Hughes, *Trans. Faraday Soc.,* 1938, *34,* 185), namely, a one-stage bimolecular mechanism (S_N2') in which the bond-making and bond-breaking processes at C_α and C_γ are synchronous and are accompanied by an electronic adjustment in the carbon stucture, *e. g.,*

$$\bar{Y} + CH_2 = CH - CHR - X \rightleftharpoons Y - CH_2 - CH = CHR + Y^-$$

As written, this is a mechanism for substitution with rearrangement, but, when $\bar{Y} = \bar{X}$, it is also a possible mechanism of isomeric rearrangement.

The first attempts to obtain evidence for or against the operation of this mechanism were based mainly on the detection or isolation of substitution product formed by bimolecular substitution with rearrangement (S_N2') in the presence of competing (and generally predominating) substitution without rearrangement (S_N2). Depending on structural factors, both negative and positive evidence has, in this manner, been obtained in different cases. This does not indicate a fundamental inconsistency, for the relative importance of mechanisms S_N2 and S_N2', on which the outcome rests in this method, is expected to vary with structure in an understandable way. For instance, in the

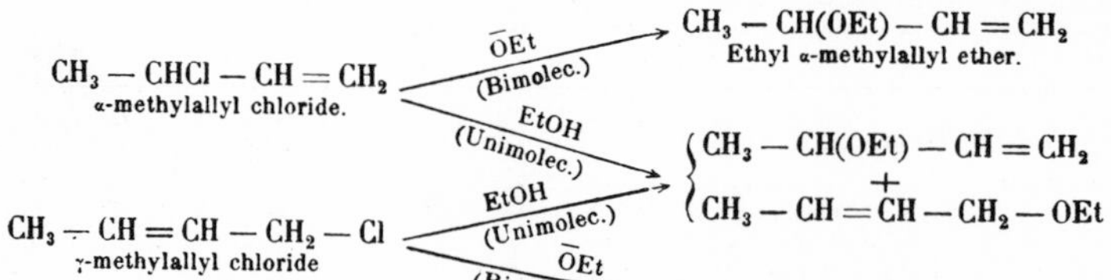

$$CH_3 - CHCl - CH = CH_2 \xrightarrow[\text{(Bimolec.)}]{\bar{O}Et} CH_3 - CH(OEt) - CH = CH_2$$
Ethyl α-methylallyl ether.

α-methylallyl chloride.

$$\xrightarrow[\text{(Unimolec.)}]{EtOH} \begin{cases} CH_3 - CH(OEt) - CH = CH_2 \\ + \\ CH_3 - CH = CH - CH_2 - OEt \end{cases}$$

$$CH_3 - CH = CH - CH_2 - Cl \xrightarrow[\text{(Unimolec.)}]{EtOH}$$
γ-methylallyl chloride

$$\xrightarrow[\text{(Bimolec.)}]{\bar{O}Et} CH_3 - CH = CH - CH_2 - OEt$$
Ethyl γ-methylallyl ether.

For the replacement of halogen by ethoxyl in α-and γ-methyl-allyl compounds, two reaction routes have been established, which are recognised kinetically as the mechanisms we have designated « bimolecular » and « unimolecular ». The bimolecular reaction with sodium ethoxide in ethyl alcohol gave, in each case, only the ether of corresponding structure to the chloride used. This is entirely consistent with a synchronous, one-stage replacement involving a single carbon atom, a process which provides no special opportunities for rearrangement in the carbon stucture. On the other hand, the first-order solvolytic reaction of each halide gave a mixture of isomeric ethers a result which is fully compatible with the presence of a

replacement of X by Y, in the example given, substitution with rearrangement is favoured, relatively to substitution without rearrangement, by steric hindrance from the substituent R (A. G. Catchpole, E. D. Hughes and C. K. Ingold, *loc. cit.* ; R. E. Kepner, S. Winstein and W. G. Young, *J. Amer. Chem. Soc.,* 1949, *71,* 115). The evidence derived in this way is not, however, wholly convincing.

With the aid of radiohalogens, this question may be conclusively settled. In « symmetrical » reactions of the type $\bar{X} + R - X \rightleftharpoons X - R' + \bar{X}$ (X = Hal.), bimolecular exchanges without rearrangement (S_N2; $R' = R$) do not cause complications, because the products of such reactions are, for ordinary purposes, identical with the reactants. Bimolecular isomerisation may then be investigated directly in such reactions and compared, as to rate, with substitution without rearrangement, wich may be followed by the tracer method. Results obtained in this way (B. D. England, E. D. Hughes and C. K. Ingold, unpublished) show conclusively that mechanism S_N2' exists. In simple structures, it is not as facile as bimolecular substitution without rearrangement (S_N2), and, for most conditions of anionotropic change in halogen compounds, it is not as important as the ionisation mechanism (cf. E. D. Hughes, C. K. Ingold and co-workers, *J. Chim. phys.*, 1949, 45, 236).

The foregoing discussion applies to conditions suitable for heterolysis. In the whole range of anionotropic phenomena, there are indications also of homolytic reactions, for which the following mechanism is suggested :

$$Br - CHS - CH = CH_2 + B°r \rightleftharpoons B°r + CHS = CH - CH_2Br$$

(2) The Wagner Rearrangement.

One of the mechanisms for rearrangements of the Wagner type is related to unimolecular substitution, the process depending on a rate-determining heterolysis of a carbon-halogen (or similar) bond. Important evidence for this, and for alternative types of rearrangement, depends on the interpretation of rate data, and a preliminary consideration of steric effects on reaction rates is necessary.

(2. 1) Steric Acceleration in Unimolecular Reactions.

The concept of the duality of mechanism in substitution reactions and its application to the stereochemistry of these changes has led to advances in our ideas of the effect of steric factors on reaction rates. In chemical reactions, the energies of the links which are involved in the processes are of major importance but account should also be taken of the « non-bonding » forces between atoms which are not directly linked. These additional forces are often sufficiently weak to be neglected, but in special structural circumstances non-bonded atoms are brought so close together that the non-bonding energy is of comparable order of magnitude to the bonding energy, and under these circumstances, steric effects on reaction rates become especially evident. Clearly, consideration should be given in this connection to the initial and transition states of reaction. The compression energy in the transition state may be either greater or less than that in the initial state, and possible steric effects may inhibit or facilitate reaction. In the past, the phenomenon of *steric hindrance* has received its due share of attention ; we shall show that analysis in terms of reaction mechanisms leads to the conclusion that *steric acceleration* may be equally important, especially for mechanisms of the type exemplified in unimolecular substitution (S_N1).

In their application to the two mechanisms of nucleophilic substitution reactions, the principles involved may be briefly described as follows : In the transition state of the bimolecular mechanism, five atoms or groups are wholly or partly attached by covalency forces to a single carbon atom and in certain structural circumstances the transition state involves considerably greater repulsion than does the initial state. A semi-quantitative theory of steric hindrance has been developed on this basis (I. Dostrovsky, E. D. Hughes, and C. K. Ingold, *J. Chem. Soc.*, 1946, 173). Unimolecular reactions on the other hand never entail the covalent attachment (wholly or partly) of more than four atoms or groups to the reactive centre, the additional forces involved being of the longer-range electrostatic type associated with

solvation. Consequently, steric hindrance is not conspicuous in reactions which proceed by this mechanism. Furthermore, if the structural factors are such that the compression energy of the initial state is considerable, a release of congestion may accompany the formation of the transition state of ionisation and steric acceleration by substituent groups which give rise to the initial state compression may be evident.

In practice, steric hindrance is more common than steric acceleration, the reason being that, while compression energy in the transition state of bimolecular substitution is considerable even for comparatively simple structures, comparable compressions in initial states are present only in complex compounds. For example, in the case of the neopentyl halides an inert behaviour of a very marked character, which was observed in substitution reactions (*e. g.*, neopentyl/ethyl = ca. 10^5), has been identified, both experimentally and theoretically, with the bimolecular mechanism. On the other hand, unimolecular reactions in structures which are not too intricate (but are at least as complex as that in the bimolecular case cited) exhibit no such marked steric effects, either inhibitive or accelerative. This is illustrated by the following approximate relative rates of solvolysis of tertiary halides in 80% aqueous ethyl alcohol at 25° : CMe_3Cl ; CMe_2EtCl, 1.6 ; CMe_2Pr^nCl, 1.5 ; CMe_2Bu^nCl, 1.4 ; CMe_2Pr^iCl, 0.9 ; CMe_2Bu^tCl, 1.2 ; $CMeEt_2Cl$, 2.4 ; CEt_3Cl, 2.8 ; CEt_2Pr^iCl, 2.0 (E. D. Hughes, *J. Chem. Soc.*, 1935, 255 ; K. A. Cooper, E. D. Hughes, C. K. Ingold, and B. J. MacNulty, *ibid.*, 1937, 1183, 1280, 1283 ; E. D. Hughes, C. K. Ingold and R. J. L. Martin, unpublished ; J. Shorter and Sir Cyril Hinshelwood, *J. Chem. Soc.*, 1949, 2412 ; H. C. Brown and R.S. Fletcher, *J. Amer. Chem. Soc.*, 1949, 71, 1843). Professor H. C. Brown (*loc. cit.*) has utilised a form of steric strain theory in a discussion of results of this type, taken in comjunction with data of a more conclusive character (see below). Large facilitating effects of substituent groups have been observed in other (usually more complex) cases, *e. g.*, ($CMe_3Cl = 1$), (i) $CMePr^iCl$ (?), 14 ; (ii) CEt_2Bu^tCl, 48 ; (iii) CBu^t_3Cl (?), 600 (Brown and Fletcher, *loc. cit.* (I and ii) ; I. Dostrovsky, O. J. Evans, and E. D. Hughes, unpublished (iii) ; P. D. Bartlett and co-workers — cf. Professor Bartlett's paper at this Colloquium). It is difficult to establish rigorously the structure of these complex halides isomerisation being possible in their preparation. The data as a whole support the structures given and the combined results provide evidence of the operation of effects which cannot readily be interpreted on the basis of polar influences alone.

In relation to these results for tertiary halides, the reactions of secondary structures are of interest. Taking account of the circumstance that the solvolytic rates of *iso*-propyl halides contain a bimolecular contribution, it has been established that the unimolecular reactions of pinacolyl halides are close to those to be expected for comparatively simple secondary structures (E. D. Hughes, C. K. Ingold, R. J. L. Martin and (Mrs.) M. G. Peeling, unpublished). In 80% aqueous ethyl alcohol at 100°, the unimolecular rates for ditert.-butyl carbinyl chloride (obtained by the chlorination of 2-2-4-4- tetramethylpentane) are greater than those observed for pinacolyl chloride under comparable conditions by a factor of 4.5 (cf. below). It is consistent with our thesis that the largest steric acceleration effects are observed when three bulky substituents are attached to the reaction centre.

In the reactions of di- and tri-*tert.* -butyl carbinols with hydrogen halides, fission of the carbon structure has been observed, giving, in addition to the expected products, *tert.* -butyl halides, *tert.* amyl halides, and unsaturated hydrocarbons (F. Brown, T. D. Davies, I. Dostrovsky, O. J. Evans, and E. D. Hughes, unpublished). In the tertiary structure this fission is extraordinarily facile. It has been suggested (H. C. Brown and R. S. Fletcher, *loc. cit.*) that ease of rupture of carbon structures is a consequence of steric strain. Pending the results of more extended investigations, which are in progress, our views on this subject must be of a tentative character. It is suggested that, in appropriate structures, fission of a suitable alkyl group (*e. g.*, CMe_3) may occur when it is one atom removed from a charged carbon centre (β-elimination, cf. proton removal), e. g.,

$$Me_2C(Me) - \overset{\cdot}{C}H . CMe_3 (1) \rightarrow Me_2\overset{+}{C} - CH(Me) . CMe_3 (2)$$
$$\rightarrow Me_2C = CHMe + \overset{+}{C}Me_3 \rightarrow Me_2C(Hal) . CH_2Me + CMe_4Hal.$$

Halides may also be formed from (1) and (2) and nonenes (probably reversibly) from (2). An alternative possibility is the fission of an alkyl group from a positively charged carbon atom to which it is directly attached, e. g.,

$$\overset{+}{C}H(CMe_3)_2 (1) \rightarrow \overset{+}{C}Me_3 + CMe_4C : (\rightarrow CMe_3\overset{+}{C}H_3)$$
$$\rightarrow CMe_3Cl + CMe.EtCl.$$

accompanied by a halide from (1), and an isomeric halide and nonenes by rearrangement of (1).

(2.2). — The Mechanism of the Rearrangement.

We shall now show that a mechanism of rearrangements of the Wagner type, $R - C - C - X \rightarrow X - C - C - R$, depends on preliminary ionisation, e. g.,

$$\begin{array}{c} CH_3 \\ | \\ (CH_3)2C - CH_2 - X \end{array} \rightarrow (CH_3)2\overset{CH_3}{\underset{}{C}} \overset{+}{\searrow} \overset{+}{C}H_2 + : X$$
$$\rightarrow (CH_3)2\overset{+}{C} - CH_3 - CH_3 + : X$$
$$\downarrow$$
$$(CH_2)2CX - CH_2 - CH_3$$

(Neopentyl compounds.)

It has been observed (I, Dostrovsky, E. D. Hughes, and C. K. Ingold, J. Chem. Soc., 1946, 157, et seq.) that, while no rearrangement of the carbon structure occurs in the reactions of neopentyl compounds in which the neopentyl group remains covalently bound continuously throughout the process (e. g., in the bimolecular reaction of neopentyl bromide whith sodium ethoxide), rearrangement to the tert.-amyl structure takes place in the unimolecular reactions of these compounds. The life of a neopentyl cation, before its rearrangement to the tert.-amyl cation, must be very short, because it yields no detected substitution products with an unrearranged neopentyl structure, and the question has been raised as to whether rearrangement accompanies or causes the separation of X (see, for example, Skell and C. R. Hauser, J. Amer. Chem. Soc., 1942, 64, 2633). It has been shown in the case of neopentyl bromide that the reactions which lead to rearrangement exhibit the characteristic behaviour of ionisation processes. If the migration of the methyl group with its bond electrons was a contributory cause, rather than a consequence of ionisation, an expected manifestation of this contribution would be an enhanced rate of reaction, by comparison with the ionisation rates of other primary halides under the same conditions. No substantial effect of this type has been observed in the neopentyl structure. Likewise, the reactions of pinacolyl halides, which similarly lead to rearrangement, have rates which are quite normal for the ionisation of secondary halide structures (preceding section).

In other cases, however, the rates of reaction are definitely higher than the ionisation rates of appropriate basic standards. In some instances it is difficult to decide whether or not the observed effects are larger than could be accounted for by the operation of other special facilitating influences such as steric acceleration. For example, although the observed effect is large, the results for tri-tert-butyl carbinyl chloride may be classified as ambiguous until further data, and a more quantitative treatment of steric factors, are forthcoming. The case of tritylmethyl chlo-

ride, $(C_6H_5)3C.CH_2.Cl$ (*), is more definite. For this halide in 70 % aqueous ethyl alcohol and in formic acid at 95°, the rates of reaction (leading to rearrangement) are greater than those of neopentyl chloride under the same conditions by factors of the order of 10^4 (J. C. Charlton, I Dostrovsky, and E. D. Hughes, unpublished). This seems larger than any possible combination of steric and polar factors (since a saturated carbon atom is interposed between the phenyl groups and the reaction centre).

In our work, the clearest and most striking examples of facilitating influences have been observed in investigations in the terpene field (F. Brown, E. D. Hughes, C. K. Ingold, and J. F. Smith, unpublished). For instance, while the rate for bornyl chloride in 80 % aqueous ethyl alcohol is little different from that of pinacolyl chloride, we have found that the rate for isobornyl chloride is larger by a factor of 10^5. The stereoelectronic requirements of a synchronous process are met in the isosobornyl structure and the contribution of bond-formation is clearly evident in the results. The case of camphene hydrochloride is not so clear cut. In alcoholic solvents the rates for this compound are greater than those for tert.-butyl chloride by factors of the order of $10^3 - 10^4$. In this tertiary halide structure, steric effects may, however, be large. The very reactive pinene hydrochloride, which is now under investigation, appears to provide another example of a synchronous process.

We conclude that two types of heterolytic rearrangements of the Wagner type exist, depending on the presence or absence of definite assistance (to the separation of X, cf. inset) from process (b). The situation is not unlike that governing the concept of the duality of mechanism in substitution reactions. Transformation of the pinacol type and rearrangements involving deamination (cf. the writer's preceding contribution) are similar in principle. Evidence of inversion at C_α (see, especially, H. I. Bernstein and F. C. Whitmore, J. Amer. Chem. Soc., 1939, 61, 1324) has generally been regarded as an indication of a synchronous mechanism, but this interesting observation may not be decisive in this respect even in the cases for which it has been found. Retention of configuration in the group R, which has been observed in changes of this type, is doubtless a manifestation of the circumstance that R migrates with the electrons of its bond with C_β. Interesting evidence of the existence of an intermediate hybrid structure of the form

$$\left[\overset{Ph}{\underset{C \quad C}{\diagdown}} \right]^+$$

in a Wagner rearrangement has recently been advanced by D. J. Cram (J. Amer. Chem. Soc., 1950, 71, 3863).

Sir William Ramsay and Ralph Forster Laboratories, University College, London, W. C. 1.

DISCUSSION

Intervention de M. le Pr Prévost au sujet de la communication de M. le Pr Hughes. — La très intéressante communication du Pr Hughes apporte des preuves expérimentales de la synionie parfaite des réactions S_N1, et des exemples de non isomérisation dans des réactions de type S_N2, portant sur des molécules allyliques.

Dans ma communication (p. 1), j'ai donné mon agrément sans restriction au premier point de vue, faisant toutes réserves sur la généralité du second.

(*) The compound prepared by Cone and Robinson (Ber., 1907, 40, 2164 — cf. Wooster and Mitchell, J. Amer. Chem. Soc., 1930, 52, 1042) has been shown to be $Ph_2C = C(Cl)Ph$. The course of its formation from $Ph_3C.CH_3$ and PCl_5 at 200° may be represented : $Ph_3C.CH_2Cl \rightarrow Ph_2C(Cl) - CH_2Ph \rightarrow Ph_2C = CHPh \rightarrow Ph_2C = C(Cl)Ph$.

Je tiens à présent à préciser la nature probable d'un complexe intermédiaire qui expliquerait les réactions S_N2', réactions bimoléculaires avec transposition allylique.

Si nous admettons le mécanisme S_N2 valable pour les molécules saturées :

$$Y^+ + R_2{\Large>}C - X \rightarrow Y^{\delta-} \cdots \underset{R_3}{\overset{R_1R_2}{C}} \cdots X^{\delta-}$$

(Complexe intermédiaire)

$$\rightarrow Y - C{\Large<}\overset{R_1}{\underset{R_3}{R_2}} + X^-$$

et si nous le généralisons sans modification aux molécules allyliques, nous retrouvons les conclusions du Pr Hughes au sujet des réactions S_N2., à savoir : inversion de Walden éventuelle, mais pas de transposition allylique.

Mais la possibilité d'une attaque de Y^- sur le carbone en β de X est tout aussi plausible, et conforme aux idées modernes :

$$R - CH = CH - CH_2X + Y^-$$

$$\rightarrow R - CH = CH - CH_2 \quad X^{\delta-}$$
$$Y^{\delta-}$$

(Complexe intermédiaire)

$$\rightarrow R - CHY - CH = CH_2 + X^-$$

Tel est, à mon avis, le mécanisme S_N2'.

Mais, dans le mécanisme S_N1, Y^- a l'alternative entre les pôles $+$ de l'ion commun mésomère (ou tripolaire) :

$$(R - CH - CH - CH_2)^+ \quad \text{ou} \quad R - CH^+ - CH^- - CH_2^+$$

Au contraire, sur le métamère $R - \underset{1}{CH} = \underset{2}{CH} - \underset{3}{CH_2}X$, Y^- aura l'alternative entre le carbone 3 et le carbone 1 (S_N2 ou S_N2'); sur le métamère $R - \underset{1}{CHX} - \underset{2}{CH} = \underset{3}{CH_2}$, Y^- aura aussi l'alternative entre les carbones 1 et 3. Mais, les deux métamères n'étant plus identiques, il n'y a plus de raisons pour qu'ils conduisent à un même mélange de métamères en Y ; on doit donc observer des phénomènes de synionie imparfaite.

On peut envisager comme cas limites :

a) La non-isomérisation [la présence de X favorise quantitativement l'attaque par Y^- du carbone qui le porte (S_N2 pur)] ;

b) Le double changement de structure (la présence de X entrave complètement l'attaque par Y^- du carbone qui le porte (S_N2' pur);

c) Synionie parfaite (la présence de X ne modifie pas l'affinité pour Y^- des deux carbones extrêmes du système allylique).

Ces cas limites ont fort peu de chances d'être quantitativement réalisés ; la synionie imparfaite semble devoir être la règle générale ; le cas de $Y^- = C_2H_5O^-$ serait un de ceux pour lesquels le mécanisme *a* est nettement prépondérant.

Réponse de M. le Pr Hughes. — In the whole range of observations on substitution and rearrangement in anionotropic systems there is evidence of the operation of mechanisms S_N1, S_N2, S_N2' and SH. Mechanism S_N2' is not expected to give the same mixture of products from both forms of allylic reactants and a combination of mechanisms S_N2 and S_N2' cannot account for the whole of the available data.

Intervention de M. le Doyen Kirrmann au sujet de la communication de M. le Pr Hughes. — Un mécanisme qui correspond pratiquement à S_N2' avait été envisagé autrefois par Meisenheimer et par moi-même. L'école d'Ingold a formellement contesté l'interprétation de Meisenheimer. L'adoption actuelle du type S_N2' doit-elle être considérée comme réservée à des réactions exceptionnelles?

Réponse de M. le Pr Hughes. — A mechanism of similar type to S_N2' was envisaged by Meisenheimer, but no unambiguous indication of its existence was contained in his work. As explained in my communication, we think that the S_N2' mechanism has a place in the interpretation of anionotropic phenomena, tough it is not a very common mechanism. An internal form of this mechanism may also be important in certain cases (cf. *Trans. Faraday Soc.* 1938, **34**, 185 and *J. Chem. Soc.*, 1948, 8).

M. le Pr Bartlett en réponse à M. Kirrmann. — It should be pointed out that a change in the status of the S_N2' reaction occured about a year ago. Up to that time it had not been possible to supplement the single case of Meisenheimer, to which M. Kirrmann refers, with any other allylic rearrangement proceeding unequivocally by the bimolecular mechanism. A year ago, however, it was shown by Kepner, Young and Winstein (*J. Am. Chem. Soc.*, **71**, 115 (1949) that sodium malonic ester is able to attack an allylic system according to the S_N2' scheme, and I believe that they have since found a number of other examples which will begin to show us when the S_N2' mechanism may be expected to occur.

Réponse de M. le Pr Hughes. — The factors which determine the importance of mechanism S_N2' and other processes in anionotropy are discussed in our papers. It remains to establish in detail the scope and limitations of the various mechanisms, and work to this end is in hand.

M. le Pr Winstein en réponse à M. Bartlett. — Regarding the work of Meisenheimer on the treatment of cinnamyl chloride with metal acetates in glacial acetic acid, it is not possible to decide wether the workers actually had in hand the S_N2' mechanism. Salt effects of various kinds are so serious under the conditions employed by Meisenheimer that it would require thorough reinvestigation to settle this point.

While it seems clear that there are examples of the S_N2' mechanism, it is not yet possible to say much regarding the eventual scope of this kind of displacement. Not only are steric effects serious but also there are specifities with regard to the nucleophilic agent. Professor Young and his students at the University of California at Los Angeles are investigating this matter. There are a number of cases where abnormal product is obtained with nucleophilic agents such as amines and thiourea. Each of these cases, however, requires thorough investigation for the possibility of prior rearrangement of reagent or subsequent rearrangement of product before the S_N2' mechanism is definitely established.

Intervention de M. Daudel au sujet de la communication de M. le Pr Hughes. — 1° MM. Hughes et Ingold ont expliqué la grande rareté des mécanismes S_N2' en faisant intervenir les électrons qui masquent le noyau des réactifs nucléophiles. J'aimerais savoir si le Pr Hughes a de nouvelles idées à ce sujet, compte tenu des expériences nouvelles.

2° Dans l'ion allylique ($CH_2 - CH - CH_2$)$^+$ l'indice de liaison (théorie des orbites moléculaires) est de 0,7, c'est-a-dire que l'énergie de la liaison C — C représente plus de 70 °/o d'une liaison éthylénique normale. On comprend donc qu'il soit peu probable qu'une inversion cis-trans ou vice-versa accompagne une réaction qui fait intervenir un tel ion (cf. P. et R. Daudel, N.-P. Buu Hoï et M. Martin, *Bull. Soc. Chim.*, 1948, p. 1210).

Réponse de M le Pr Hughes. — In the previous communication referred to by M. Daudel, a broad comparison of various mechanisms was made, particularly with regard to their stereoelectronic requirements. From our results (which were available before that date) obtained with the aid of the radioactive indicator method, and from theoretical considerations, it was concluded that mechanism S_N2' is usually not as facile in anionotropy as mechanisms S_N2 or S_N1 and that it was unimportant by comparison with a similar mechanism in prototropy (S_E2'). Our point of view is that mechanism S_N2' is generally difficult to realise; it is not our opinion that it is non-existent.

Intervention de M. Dewar au sujet de la communication de M. le Pr Hughes. — 1° The retention of cis-trans configuration in allylic cations seems to be demonstrated by the work of Craig (*J. Am. Chem. Soc.*, 1943, **65**, 100) who found that trans piperylene readily gave a normal Diels Alder reaction with maleic anhydride, whereas cis piperylene gave only a copolymer. There is evidence that the first step in these reaction is the formation of a zwitterion

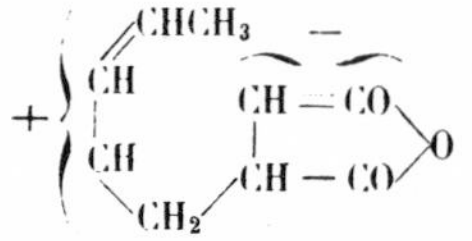

state A for the S_N2' disp'acement should be correlated with the transition state B for addition of a nucleophilic agent to such an

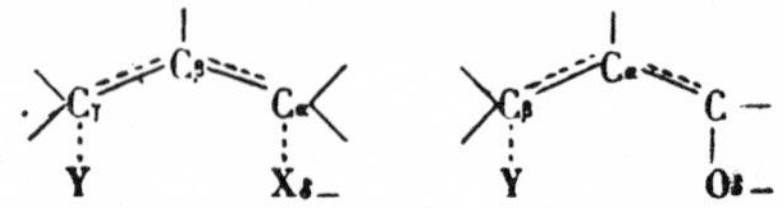

$$+ \begin{cases} CHCH_3 \\ CH \\ CH \\ CH_2 \end{cases} \begin{matrix} CH-CO \\ CH-CO \end{matrix} O$$

In the case of cis piperylene cyclisation is sterically inhibited, the cis configuration being maintained in the zwitter-ion.

2° The evidence for S_N2' reaction between allyl halide and sodiomalonic ester, given by WINSTEIN and his collaborators is not absolutely vigrous : since in theory reaction cou'd take place by normal S_N2 replacement to an enol ether

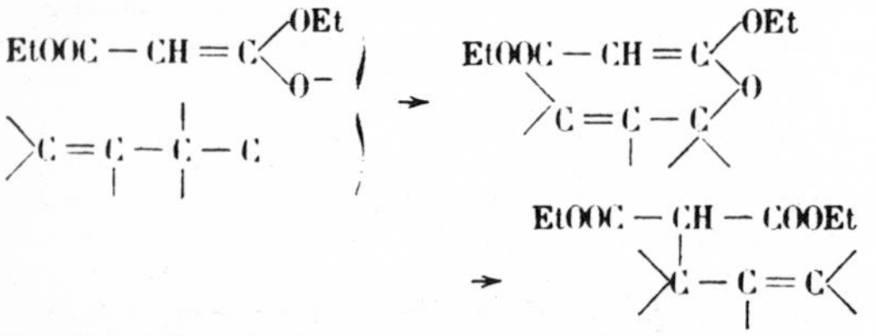

$$EtOOC-CH=C \begin{matrix} OEt \\ O^- \end{matrix} \qquad EtOOC-CH=C \begin{matrix} OEt \\ O \end{matrix}$$
$$\begin{matrix} C=C-C \end{matrix} \rightarrow \begin{matrix} C=C-C \end{matrix}$$

$$EtOOC-CH-COOEt$$
$$\rightarrow \begin{matrix} C-C=C \end{matrix}$$

this then undergoing CLAISEN rearrangement.

M. le Pr Winstein en réponse à M. Dewar. — The possible objection to the S_N2' interpretation of the formation of abnormal product from malonic ester anion and allylic halides, based on o-alkylation followed by rearrangement, occured to us also. While it is plained to investigate this possibility, it may be pointed out that the o-alkylation product would be a ketene acetal. While this ketene acetal would be expected to rearrange to carbonalkylated material in non-hydroxylic media, it would be expected to yield an orthoester in the ethanol solvent which was actually employed. Thus, it seems probable that the abnormal reaction product isolated would not arise from a combination of o-alkylation and subsequent rearrangement.

Intervention de M. le Pr Winstein au sujet de la communication de M. le Pr Hughes. — It may be of interest to point to intramolecular varieties of the S_N2' mechanism which made me confident of the eventual outcome of the search for this process. An intramolecular example is the following :

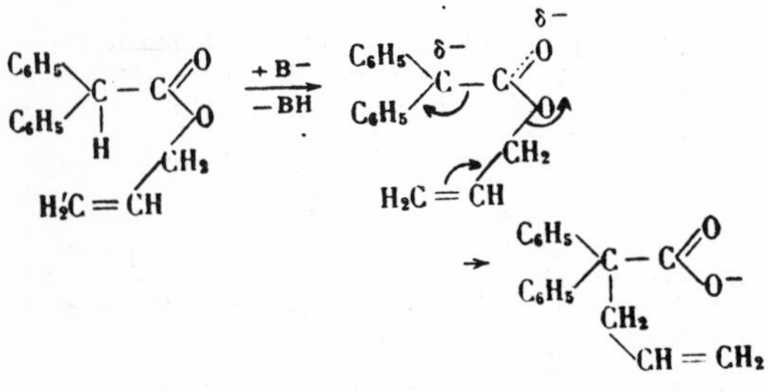

The stereo-electronic argument of HUGHES and INGOLD for the great difficulty or impossibility of operation of the S_N2' mechanism is not at all convincing. While the ethylenic linkage is in general no' susceptible to attack by nucleophilic agents, olefinic linkages conjugated with electron withdrawing groups such as the carbonyl group are so susceptible. It can be argued that the transition

α.β-unsaturated carbonyl compound, rather than with the transition state for the addition to the unconjugated olefinic linkage. Just as the original electron cloud around C_β has drifted away from C_β in B as indicated, so has the original electron cloud around C_γ drifted away from C_γ in the transition state A.

It may be energetically profitable to have an unusually high ionic character to the C_α-X linkage in transition state A relative to cases of substitution with simple saturated halides.

Réponse de M. le Pr Hughes. — It is, of course, realised that the case of mechanism S_N2' is different from the addition of a nucleophilic reagent to an ordinary unsaturated aliphatic bond. The analogy of the modification introduced by the presence of a substituent such as a carbonyl group has been considered also in our detailed publications.

M. le Pr Winstein (question a M. le Pr Prévost). — I would like to return to the question of the preservation of cis or trans geometry in displacements of allylic compounds which was mentionned by Professor PRÉVOST. It is very clear that S_N2 displacement on allylic compounds will preserve the cis or trans identity of the structure. The question arises, and is being actively investigated by Professor W.-G. YOUNG and his students at the University of California at Los Angeles, wether in reactions proceeding by a mesomeric carbonium ion B the product with the unrearranged structure C has the same cis or trans geometry as the initial reagent A. Theory predicts, since the C_β-C_γ bond

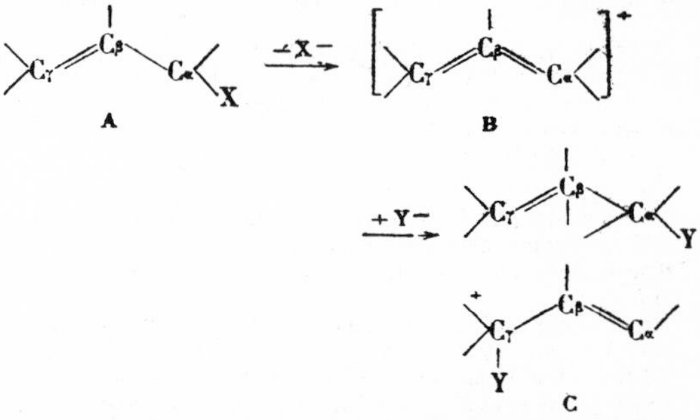

is still partly double in character, that a considerable energy barrier should exist for cis-trans isomerisation and that geometry should be preserved even in displacements proceeding by way of the carbonium ion. I would like to ask whether Professor PRÉVOST had the latter case of displacement in mind.

M. le Doyen Cornubert. — M. le Doyen CORNUBERT demande à M. le Pr PRÉVOST sur quelles bases il s'appuie pour accorder une configuration trans aux dérivés dont il a parlé.

From: *Bull. soc. chim. France* [5] **18**, C55–61 (1951)

Neighboring Groups in Displacements and Rearrangements,
par S. WINSTEIN.

Understanding of participation of a neighboring group and the associated electron cloud in unimolecular-type (Ib) nucleophilic displacement processes at a nearly center is important to both the WALDEN inversion and molecular rearrangement probleme. This paper deals with some aspects in which we have been interested, of such participation by ordinary functional neighboring groups, especially of the non-classical (Ib) type, and also H, R, Ar, and olefinic systems.

Chronologically, participation of neighboring functional groups, interested us first. The situation may be formulated as in I,

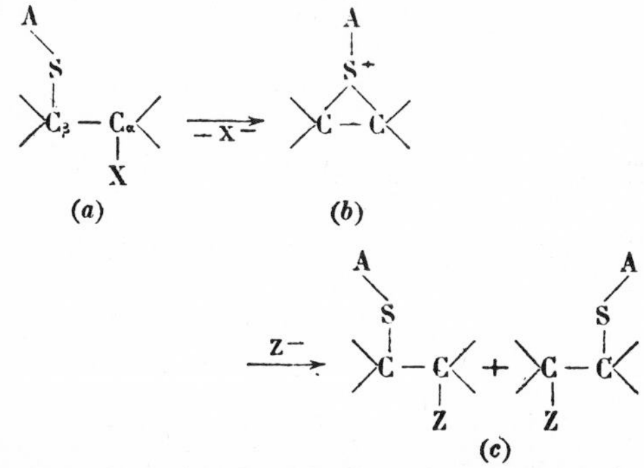

participation of the neighboring group SA in the displacement of X yielding a cyclic intermediate, Ib, the opening of which yields the final product Ic. The neighboring group may be of the classical type, such as O⁻, NR₂, and SR, the intermediate being an ethylene oxide, sulfonium ion or immonium ion, or of the non-classical type, such as Br, OCH₃, or OAc, the intermediate being an ethylene bromonium ion, IIa, oxonium ion IIb or IIc in the cited cases, respectively.

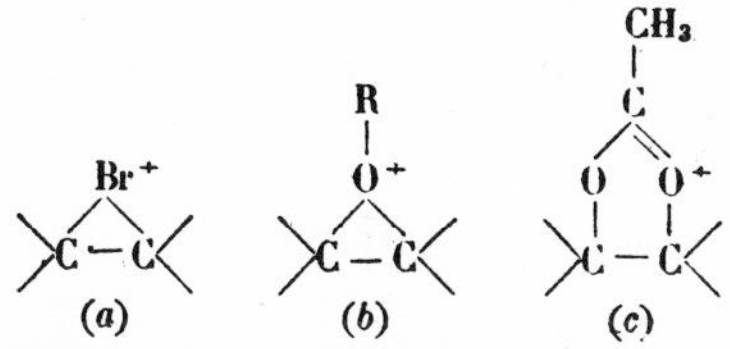

The ions Ib are regarded as mesomeric hybrids. For example, in the case of the bromonium ion, WINSTEIN and LUCAS (2) wrote the set of contributing structures (3) III.

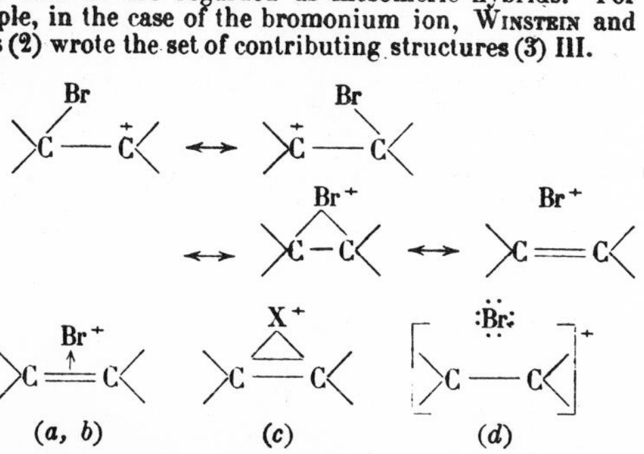

Of the implications to organic chemistry, perhaps the

most important has to do with the stereochemistry of the over-all replacement processes. In the closing and opening of the cycle, the fundamental principle applies that in each unit process of displacement at a carbon atom, the leaving and incoming electron clouds have the greatest separation (4). The equivalent statement is that WALDEN inversion occurs in the closing and opening of the cycle and thus the over-all stereochemical result from Ia to Ic involves two WALDEN inversions. Prior to our work, HUGHES, INGOLD and coworkers (4 a) recognized that retention of configuration observed in the hydrolysis of α-bromopropionate ion in dilute alkaline solution was somehow due to the neighboring carboxylate ion group, and subsequently, we discovered cases of over-all retention of configuration due to other neighboring groups. By 1942, it was clear this was a general phenomenon (5). We may cite the conversion of *dl-threo*-3-bromo-2-butanol to *dl*-2, 3-dibromobutane with fuming hydrobromic acid (2), the conversion of *dl-erythro*-3-acetoxy-2-bromobutane to *meso*-2-3-diacetoxybutane (5a) by treatment with silver acetate in anhydrous acetic acid and the similar conversion of *dl-trans*-2-acetoxycyclohexyl bromide to *dl-trans*-1-2-cyclohexanediol diacetate (5 a).

Analogous observations are available for a number of replacement reactions involving the following systems :

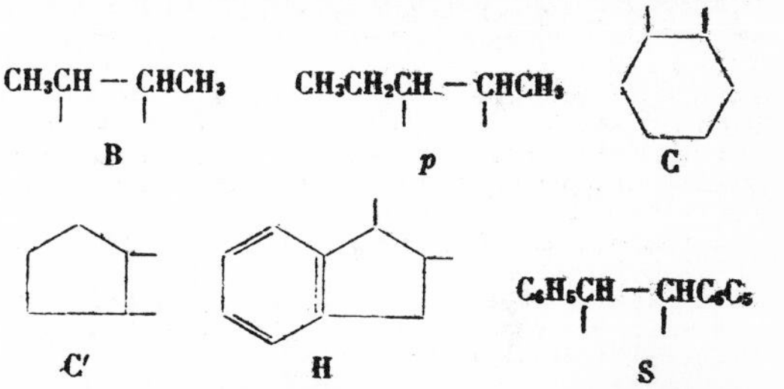

The systems are labelled with a letter by which they are characterized in Table I which represents a partial summary of observed reactions which proceed with over-all retention of configuration.

In the case that the *alpha* and *beta* carbon atoms of Ia or Ib are otherwise symmetrically substituted, one of the optically active diastereomeric starting materials (e. g., *d-threo*-3-bromo-2-butanol, V) gives rise to an internally compensated intermediate (e. g., VI). Thus the final product (e. g., 2-3-dibromobutane, VII) is optically inactive, even

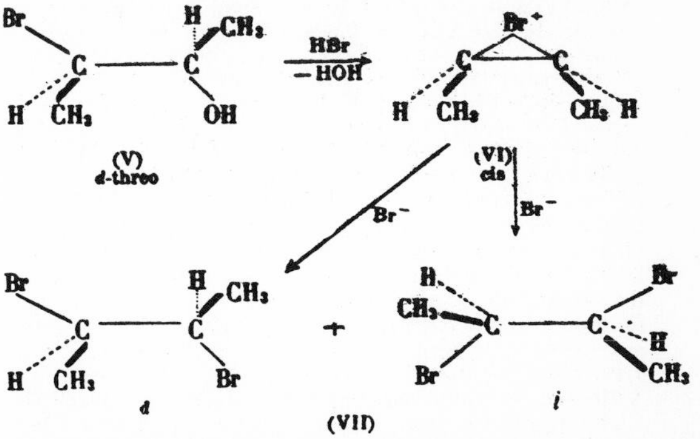

41

from an active *threo* starting material. The numbered cases 2, 3, 6, 8, 9, 10 in Table I have been subjected to this kind of stereochemical scrutiny (2, 5a, 6, 7b, 5e).

of solvolysis of *trans*-2-benzamidocyclohexyl *p*-toluene-sulfonate XX in acetic acid containing potassium acetate are analogous to those obtained with the acetoxy analog.

TABLE I.

Summary of Some Over-all
Retentions of Configuration due to Participation.

	Neighboring Group	System	Replaced Group	Entering Group	Reagent	Reference
1.	COO−	$CH_3CHBrCOO^-$	Br	OH, OC_2H_5	Solv., Ag$^+$	4a
2.	I	B	OH	Br, Cl	HBr, HCl	6
3.	Br	B, C, p	OH	Br	HBr	2, 5d, 7a
4.	Br	B, C	OH	Br	PBr$_3$	5c, d
5.	Br	C	OTs	Br	HBr	5d
6.	Br	B, C, C'	Br	OAc	AgOAc	5a, 8
7.	OH	B, C	Br	OAc	AgOAc	5b
8.	Cl	B	OH	Cl	SOCl$_2$ ·	7b
9.	OAc	B, C, C', H, S	Br, Cl	OAc	AgOAc	5a, 1b, 8, 5h
10.	OAc	B, C	OTs	OAc	AcOH, KOAc	5e, 6
11.	OCH$_3$ ·	B, C	Br	OAc	AgOAc	5g

In unsymmetrical systems rearrangements result from the formation of intermediate Ib and opening in the direction which leaves the neighboring group on a new carbon atom. An example is the conversion of 3-methyl-3-methoxy-2-bromobutane VIII to 3-methoxy-2-methyl-2-butanol X by treatment with aqueous silver nitrate (9).

The so-called complex neighboring groups are among the most interesting and important. The acetoxy group is one of the most investigated (4a, 5a, b, e, f, h, 8) one of these, and some of the relevant chemistry can be illustrated with *trans*-2-acetoxycyclohexyl *p*-toluenesulfonate XII. Ionization in acetic acid or ethanol as solvent is thought to yield the intermediate XIII (which may also be derived from ketene acetal XI or orthoester XVI). This, in the presence of a stoichiometric amount of water is thought to yield ortho-monoacetate XIV which collapses to *cis*-1-2-cyclohexanediol monoacetate XVII, which is obtained in good yield. Thus the over-all steric result is clean-cut inversion instead of retention of configuration which is observed in the absence of water and in the presence of potassium acetate. In ethanol as a solvent, buffered with potassium acetate, one obtains *cis*-cyclohexene ethyl orthoacetate XVI which is more stable than the orthomonoacetate XIV and which can there-fore be isolated. Acetic acid in the absence of water is thought to produce orthodiacetate XV which gives rise to *trans*-diacetate XIX under neutral or basic conditions, but, in the presence of toluenesulfonic acid, gives partly *cis*-diacetate XVIII and the original starting acetoxy-toluenesulfonate XII.

The acylamino group (10) is another example of these so-called complex neighboring groups. The steric results

Retention of configuration is observed in anhydrous solvent, inversion in the moist acetic acid. In this case, the analog of the intermediate ion XIII is the *cis*-oxazolinium ion XXI, which can be obtained in nearly quantitative yield as the picrate or toluenesulfonate or free oxazoline from several minutes warming of XX in acetic acid.

(XX)   (XXI)

The reactivities in unimolecular type reactions are tremendously affected by the neighboring groups and their participation. In the case of rates of acetolysis of 2-substituted cyclohexyl *p*-bromobenzenesulfonates (1 c), *trans*-Br or OAc give nearly unchanged reactivities from that of the unsubstituted ester, *trans*-Cl and *cis*-OAc lower the rate by roughly 10^4 and *trans*-I raises the rate by 10^3.

The effect of neighboring I or Br is sensitive to the state of substitution of C_α and C_β but that of Cl appears to be quite insensitive (1 d). Considering rate-determining ionization (1 b) process **A** and the limiting process **B**, the rate-determining ionization is approximated by the latter in

B   **A**

the case of neighboring chlorine. From electrostatic considerations it is possible to estimate k_c crudely and to obtain rough values for k_Δ/k_c and thus the driving force, $L = RT \ln (k_\Delta/k_c)$, due to participation. The estimates (1 c) of L at 25° for the *trans*-neighboring groups in the cyclohexane system are (kcals./mole): I, 8.49; OAc, 4.60; Br, 3.53; OCH$_3$, 0.86.

The driving force, as can be anticipated (1 d), decreases with *alpha* alkyl and increases with *beta* alkyl substitution, the variation being accounted for roughly by an equation of the type,

$$L = L_o - P_1 N_\alpha + P_2 N_\beta$$

where L_o is the standard driving force (in the ethane system) and N_α and N_β are the number of *alpha* and *beta* alkyl groups, respectively. Estimates (1 b) of L_o are (kcals./mole, 25°): HOCH$_2$CH$_2$S, 13; I, 8.7; NH$_2$, 8; O⁻, 6; Br, 4.5; OH, 1.3.

Consideration of both rates and stereo-chemical results brings up the possibility (1 d), whose range of applicability it is not yet possible to decide, of control of the stereochemical result by rapid equilibration of the type XXII ⇌ XXIII and restriction of rotation about the $C_\alpha — C_\beta$ bond.

(XXII)   (XXIII)

Turning to the other participations with which this paper is concerned, it is convenient first to mention π-electron neighboring systems. This phenomenon as it is encountered in the sterol field is presumably discussed in the paper by Professor Shoppee. For some of the conversions encountered, there has been suggested a mesomeric intermediate ion, *e. g.*, XXV.

(XXIV)   (XXV)

While we are familiar with the idea of a mesomeric allyl ion XXVI we are now referring to a mesomeric ion XXVII in the next homologous case. In the ion of the type XXVII

(XXVI)

(*a*)   (*b*)

or   or

(*c*)   (*d*)

(XXVII)

the 1,3-interaction may be considered, as a crude approximation (before further rehybridization) to involve overlap of the *p*-orbital on C-3 with what would have been a vacant *p*-orbital on C-1. This overlap tends to be a maximum when the axes of the respective *p*-orbitals are in the C-1, 2, 3 plane. The ion may be described by the contributing structures XXVII-a and b and by the symbol XXVII-c or by the symbol XXVII-d to use Dewar's π-complex notation (3a) for an internal π-complex.

The 3,5-interaction in the ion XXV accounts for the overall steric result from cholesteryl *p*-toluenesulfonate to normal ethyl ether; in other words, overall retention of configuration. Recognition of this role of the π-electron center at C_5 in the replacement reactions at C-3 of the Δ_5-sterols adds to the group of neighboring electronic systems (*e: g.*, neighboring CO$_2$, Br, etc.) which effect retention of configuration in nucleophilic displacements. It occurred independently to us and to C. K. Ingold (11) that a phenyl group, as in the classical system (12), C$_6$H$_5$CH$_2$CHXCH$_3$, might serve as the π-electron group. While the scope of this kind of control of steric result by a neighboring phenyl is still not clear, it can be reported that formolysis of C$_6$H$_5$CH$_2$CH(OTs)CH$_3$ proceeds with predominant retention of configuration (in contrast to ethanolysis or acetolysis). Formolysis of C$_6$H$_5$CH$_2$CH(OTs)CH$_3$ in 0.17 M solution, 0.20 M in sodium formate (otherwise racemization is serious) produces formate in 80 % yield. Saponification yields carbinol, $\alpha_D^{23} + 17.91$ (1 dcm.) compared to the original carbinol, $\alpha_D^{23} + 26.81$ (1 dcm.). The minimum amount of retention associated with formolysis is thus 83.4 %, accompanied by 16.6 % inversion.

In suitable systems, the i-sterol and Wagner-Meerwein phenomena will merge as is symbolised in XXVIII, leaving open the question of the number of discrete species that need explicit mention.

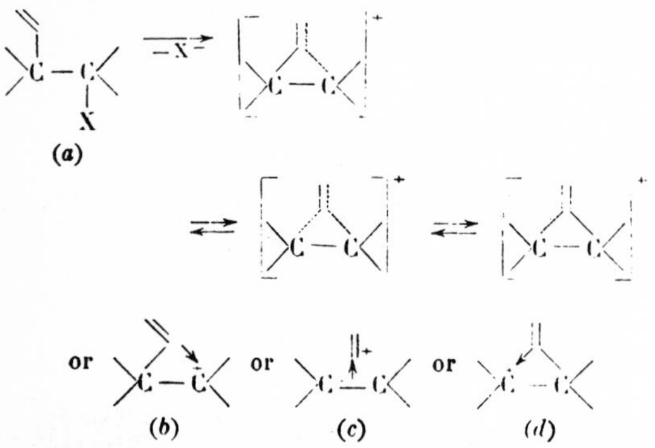

(a)

(b)   (c)   (d)

(XXVIII)

This brings us to the WAGNER-MEERWEIN rearrangement, the most general mechanism involving ionization to a carbonium ion. It would seem possible for participation of the electron cloud associated with a neighboring H, R or Ar to occur in the rate-determining ionization, producing directly either a rearranged ion XXIX-c or an ion with a bridged structure (13) XXIX-d. On the other hand, migration of a group may occur subsequent to ionization to an unrearranged carbonium ion XXIX-a.

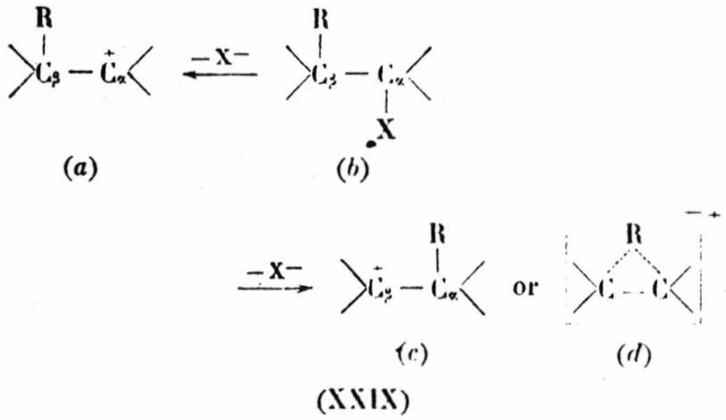

(a)   (b)

(c)   (d)

(XXIX)

Considering the contributing structures XXX-a, b, c in the case of a carbonium ion in the bridged state (also structures of type d in the case of a migrating aryl group),

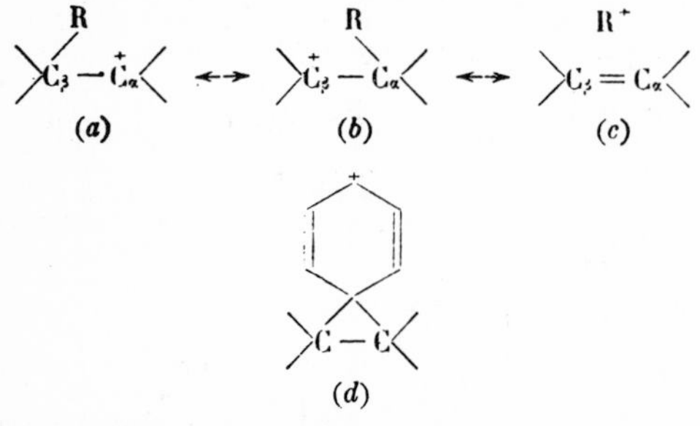

(a)   (b)   (c)

(d)

(XXX)

it is clear that the state of substitution of the *alpha* and *beta* carbons atoms should markedly affect any driving force

due to participation of the migrating group in the rate-determining ionization. The driving force can be expected to increase as we proceed from a tertiary leaving group to a primary, and as we place alkyl or aryl substituents on the β-carbon atom. Some orientation as to the order of magnitude of the driving forces attained may be derived from relative rates of acetolysis of arylsulfonates. That these may be substantial is shown by the primary series (14) XXXI (50°)

$$(C_6H_5)_2C - CH_2X \quad > \quad (CH_3)_2C - CH_2X$$
$$\quad\;\; C_6H_5 \qquad\qquad\qquad\;\; C_6H_5$$
$$\quad\;\; 10^4 \qquad\qquad\qquad\qquad 500$$

$$> \quad C_6H_5CH - CH_2X \quad > \quad (CH_3)_2C - CH_2X$$
$$\qquad\;\; C_6H_5 \qquad\qquad\qquad\quad CH_3$$
$$\qquad\;\; 50 \qquad\qquad\qquad\qquad 1$$

(XXXI)

(structures are written so as to indicate the migrating group). The relative rates are thought to represent minimum values for k/k_C due to the driving force from the migration of a methyl group which may already be occuring in the neopentyl case and the effect of variation of the β-structure k_C due to other causes (e. g. inductive effects, hyperconjugation, solvation energy of the carbonium ion).

To what extent the values of k reflect an enhancement due to steric strain effects, we are only now attempting to assess, but electronic factors seem the more important. There is an understandable serious increase in rate in case phenyl is the migrating group rather than methyl. Further, the rate increases logically with the changes in the remaining substituents on the β-carbon atom. Furthermore relative rates of acetolysis of series XXXII of secondary arylsulfonates, not yet extended to the most favorable cases show that driving forces here tend to appear later and be smaller (14).

(a)	(b)
C_6H_5	C_6H_5
$(CH_3)_2C - CHXCH_3,$	$C_6H_5CH - CHXCH_3,$
75	2

(c)	(d)
C_6H_5	C_6H_5
$CH_3CH - CHXCH_3,$	$CH_3CH - CHXCH_3,$
3/2	3/2

(e)	(f)
CH_3	H
$(CH_3)_2C - CHXCH_3,$	$(CH_3)_2C - CHXCH_3,$
4	6

(g)	(h)
$CH_3CH_2CHXCH_3,$	$CH_3CHXCH_3.$
2	1

(XXXII)

Of special interest are the strained bicyclic compounds where comparison of solvolysis rates (14, 15) gives series XXXIII. Isobornyl (a) and *exo*-norbornyl (b) with the ring member rigidly and nearly perfectly in the *trans* position for participation with inversion of the carbon atom losing X show very substantially enhanced rates. Bornyl (c) and *endo*-norbornyl (d) have a configuration such that the departing X is leaving the developing *p*-orbital in just the direction unfavorable to participation by the bonding electrons associated with the ring member in question and

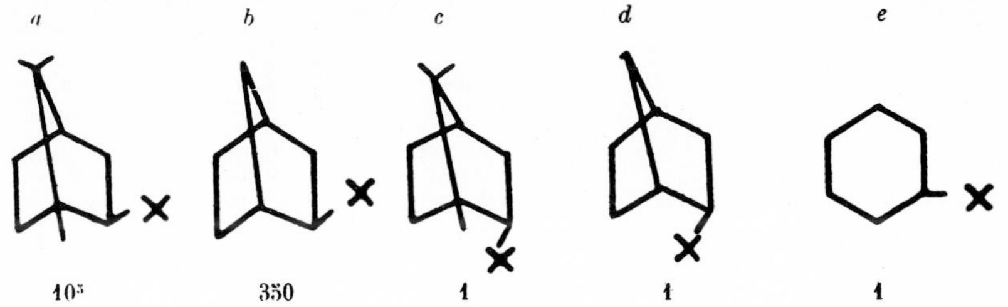

On the other hand, solvolysis of α-phenylneopentyl chloride or *p*-toluenesulfonate (14) yields unrearranged acetate XXXVI-a with a trace of predominant inversion and

(XXXIII)

these have unenhanced rates nearly identical with that for cyclohexyl.

It is now obvious that rearrangement is sometimes, but not necessarily, associated with a driving force. Isobornyl and *exo*-norbornyl rearrange in solvolysis reactions but so does bornyl and similarly so do some of the open chain cases with rates that are not seriously enhanced [*e. g.*, XXXII-b, c, d, e]. To answer a question which has been raised a number of times, rearrangement can accompany ionization, but it may also occur subsequent to ionization.

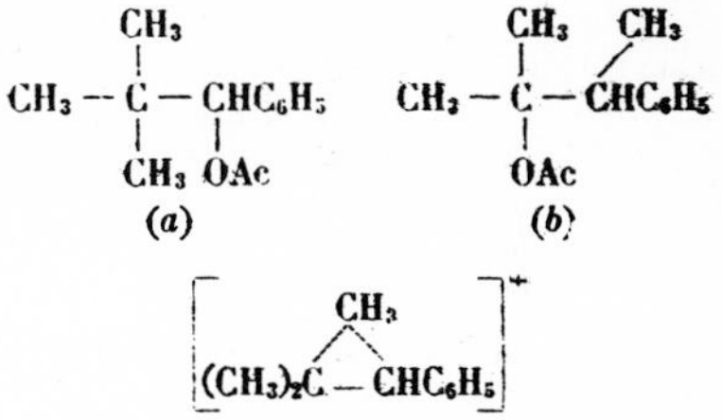

In considering the structure of the electron-deficient carbonium ion, the usual model has used a planar central atom with *sp.²* hybridization and stabilization by hyperconjugation and resonance. Recent suggestions (3, 13) of the bridged model make more specialized use of the bonding electrons of one of the β-bonds. While the relative advantages of the two models are not easy to weigh quantitatively, especially in a polar solvent, where due regard needs to be given to the relative very substantial solvation energies of the two structures, deductions may be based on rate measurements and stereochemical evidence. The stereochemical consequences of a bridged model wich is not dynamically in equilibrium with open modifications are just those observed with functional neighboring groups and thus recent stereochemical results are beginning to assist with the question where to apply the bridged model in the interpretation of carbonium ion reactions.

It has been observed that *exo*-norbornyl *p*-bromobenzenesulfonate yields *exo*-product of unchanged geometrical configuration but completely racemized. This stereochemical result and the rate are consistent with the formation of the norbornyl carbonium ion as a symmetrical species XXXIV and this lends credence to the earlier suggestion of WILSON and coworkers (13 b) that the rearrangement of camphene hydrochloride might proceed through a mesomeric ion.

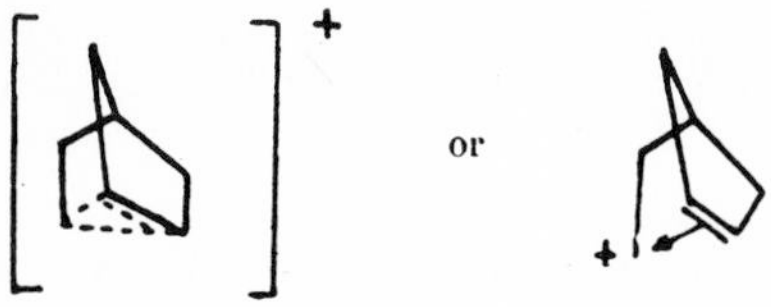

(XXXIV)

Similarly, CRAM (16) has shown that the solvolysis of 3-phenyl 2-butyl *p*-toluenesulfonate proceeds with WAGNER-MEERWEIN migration of the phenyl group and with maintenance of quite high stereochemical purity at the *alpha* and *beta* carbon atoms in question. The results are consistent with an intermediate XXXV (or intermediates: see XXVIII) *cis* (a) when formed from *threo*-sulfonate, *trans* (b) when formed from *erythro*-isomer.

rearranged material XXXVI-b in small amount which is completely racemic. Here the results do not correspond to formation and opening of a mesomeric structure XXXVI-c.

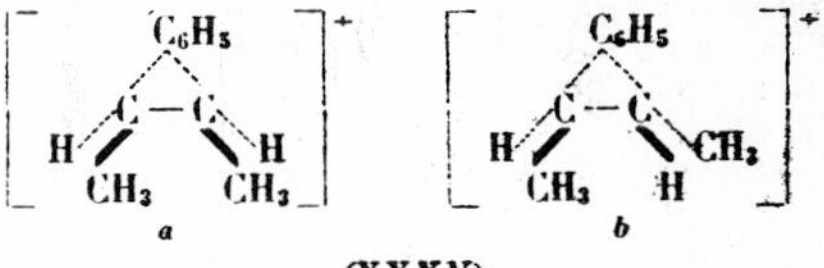

(XXXV)

In the case of a neighboring hydroxyl or methoxyl group, it is evident that there are possible competing partici-

(XXXVI)

pations. These are symbolised by XXXVII-a and b for this competition in the rate-determining ionization and by XXXVII-c and d for the competition subsequent to ioni-

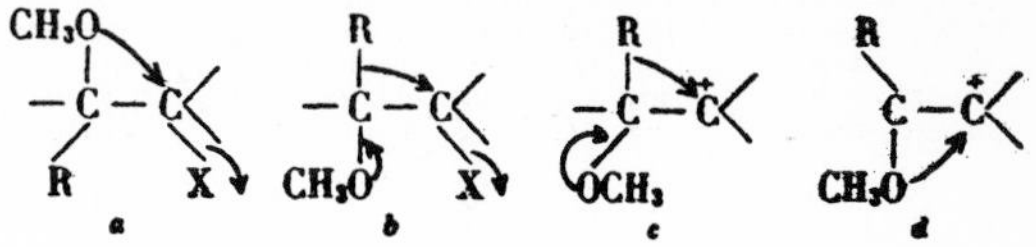

(XXXVII)

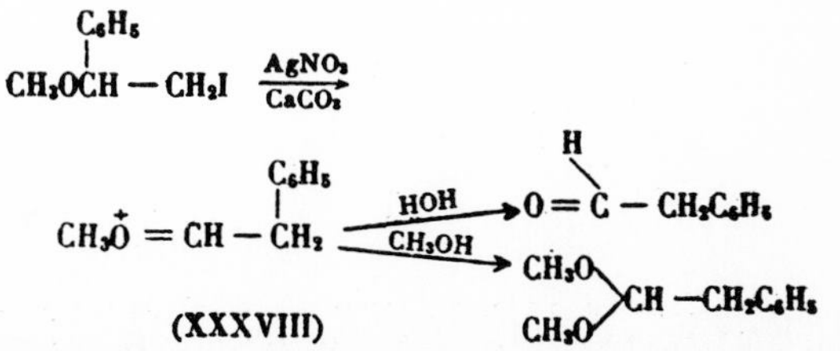

(XXXVIII)

zation. In the latter case, the indicated processes need to compete with other ordinary reactions of carbonium ions. such as association with solvents or solutes. We have so far given the most attention to the competition in the rate-determining ionization, where the phenomena may be discussed in terms of relative driving forces.

The sharp dependence of the competing relative driving forces on structure may be illustrated by the contrast between the reactions of 2-bromo 3-methyl 3-methoxybutane VIII and β-phenyl β-methoxyethyliodide XXXVIII, which, on treatment with silver nitrate, yields phenylacetaldehyde in aqueous solution and its acetal in methanolic solution (9).

Some feeling for the driving forces for pinacol rearrangement which are encountered can be derived from series XXXIX of relative acetolysis rates (9, 17) quite analogous to series XXXI in the WAGNER-MEERWEIN case. On the basis

$$
\begin{array}{cc}
\underset{\substack{| \\ O \\ | \\ CH_3}}{\overset{C_6H_5}{\underset{C_6H_5}{\big\backslash}}}\!\!C - CH_2OSO_2C_6H_4Br &
\underset{\substack{| \\ O \\ | \\ CH_3}}{\overset{C_6H_5}{|}}\!CH - CH_2OSO_2C_6H_4Br \\
150 & 3 \\
k/k_c > 10^4 & 10^2
\end{array}
$$

$$
CH_3 - \underset{\substack{| \\ CH_3}}{\overset{\substack{CH_3 \\ |}}{C}} - CH_2OSO_2C_6H_4Br
$$

1

(XXXIX)

of the estimated effect of a methoxyl group on k_C (a factor of approximately 10^{-2}) and the previous discussion, rough minimum figures for k/k_C are those listed.

BIBLIOGRAPHIE.

(1) WINSTEIN et al., *J. Am. Chem Soc.*, **70**, (a) 812, (b) 816. (c) 821. (d) 828, (e) 838, (f) 844, (g) 3528, (1948).
(2) WINSTEIN AND LUCAS, *ibid.*, **61**, (a) 1576. (b) 2845, (1939).
(3) Recently other notations for cases of this kind have been proposed. For the bromonium ion, for example, we have symbols IV. [(a) DEWAR, *J. Chem. Soc.*, 406, 777, (1946); (b) WALSH, *ibid.*, **89**, (1947); (c) ARCUS, *Chemistry and Industry*, 442, (1947); (d) PRICE, « *Mechanisms of Reactions at Carbon-Carbon Double Bonds* », Interscience Publishers, Inc., New-York, 1946, pp. 39-43.]
(4) This principle applies to the Walden inversion. [(a) HUGHES, INGOLD et al., *J. Chem. Soc.*, 1252, (1937)], elimination of the E₂ type [(b) WINSTEIN, PRESSMAN and YOUNG, *J. Am. Chem. Soc.*, **61**, 1645, (1939); (c) HUGHES, INGOLD et al., *J. Chem. Soc.*, 2093, (1948)], rearrangements [(d) BARTLETT and PÖCKEL, *J. Am. Chem. Soc.*, **59**, 820, (1937)] and will turn out to be important in other connections.

(5) WINSTEIN et al., *J. Am. Chem. Soc.*, **64**, (a) 2780. (b) 2787, (c) 2791, (d) 2792, (e) 2796, (1942); **65**, (f) 613, (g) 2196, (1943); **68**, (h) 119, (1946).
(6) LUCAS and GARNER, *private communication*.
(7) LUCAS et al., *J. Am. Chem. Soc.*, **63**, (a) 22, (b) 2541, (1941).
(8) R. ROBERTS and CORSE, *unpublished work*.
(9) INGRAHAM, *unpublished work*.
(10) WINSTEIN, BOSCHAN and GOODMAN, *J. Am. Chem. Soc.*, in press.
(11) C. K. INGOLD, *private communication*, spring of, 1947.
(12) PHILLIPS, *J. Chem. Soc.*, 44, (1923).
(13) The bridged structure for the carbonium ion has been a number of times considered a possibility or proposed in recent years. [E. G. (a) WINSTEIN AND LUCAS, *J. Am. Chem. Soc.*, **60**, 836, (1938); (b) NEVELL, DE SALAS and WILSON, *J. Chem. Soc.*, 1188 (1939); (c) WATSON, « Annual Reports », 197 (1939); 120 (1941); (d) EYRING, *Ind. Eng. Chem.*, 35, 511 (1943)] but only now is evidence beginning to appear on this question.
(14) CORSE, FRIESS, GRUNWALD and SCHREIBER, *unpublished work*.
(15) WINSTEIN and TRIFAN, *J. Am. Chem. Soc.*, **71**, 2953 (1949).
(16) CRAM, *J. Am. Chem. Soc.*, **71**, 3863 (1949).
(17) LINDEGREN, *unpublished work*

DISCUSSION

M. le Pr Winstein (en réponse à une question du Pr Paul). — The case which I quoted, of migration of a participating dialkylamino group in a nucleophilic replacement process is only one example. There are other such rearrangements in the literature.

Intervention de Mme Felkin au sujet de la communication de M. le Pr S. Winstein. — Je demande au Pr WINSTEIN s'il est possible de préciser le mécanisme de transformation du groupement methoxy lors de la déshalogénation des α-méthoxy iodures.

Réponse de M. le Pr Winstein à Mme Felkin. — In the reaction of β-methoxy-β-phenylethyl iodide A with silver salts under essentially neutral conditions the ion B is written as a direct product (or perhaps the structure C will represent a better description after the stereochemistry of the reaction at C3 is clear from the study under conditions where a mixed acetal will be the product). This ion yields aldehyde acetal in methanol through coordination of methanol. The general reaction course is clear from the fact that neither the vinyl ethers or styrene glycol mono-ethers, which are conceivable intermediates, nor phenyl-acetaldehyde yield the acetal under the reaction conditions. Since methanol coordinates with C3, water is presumed to react similarly to yield a hemiacetal which collapses to aldehyde. Thus the methanol which is produced contains the oxygen atom which originally existed in the starting material. In the example investigated by Mme FELKIN and about which inquiry is made, one would presume that the OH group is removed either as formate or as water. It would not be surprising if the first intermediate were represented to a fair approximation by the carbonium ion structure E. There can then be formulated rearrangement to structure F or G, which then follows a reaction course similar to the one outlined in the previous case. Either water or formic acid or formate ion coordinates at C3. In case acylal is produced the decomposition to the aldehyde or its hydrolysis to hemiacetal and subsequent decomposition to aldehyde needs to be formulated.

A   B   C   D

formic acid →

E   F   G

M. le Pr Winstein (en réponse à une question de M. Liebermann). — Oxazole formation from N-benzoyl-o-aminophenol is not analogous to the oxazoline formation from *trans*-2-benzamidocyclohexyl *p*-toluenesulfonate. The latter involves back-side participation (with Walden inversion) and this is true also of the treatment of *trans*-2-benzamidocyclohexanol with thionyl chloride. On the other hand, there is presumably no such breaking of the original C-O bond of the aminophenol in oxazole formation.

Intervention de M. Dewar au sujet de la communication de M. le Pr S. Winstein. — 1° An interesting parallel to Professor Winstein's internal SN2 replacements is provided by a series of rearrangements in the oxazole series which have been studied by Cornforth and his collaborators : they follow the general pattern

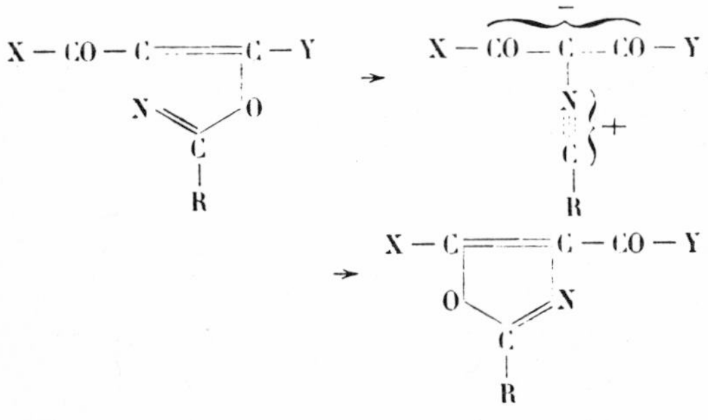

X — CO — C =====C — Y

N====O

C

R

X — CO — C — CO — Y

N

C

R

X — C =====C — CO — Y

O   N

C

R

and the mechanism must almost certainly be that indicated : that

is, an internal SN1 replacement. A considerable number of such reactions is now known.

2° It seems likely (?) on theoretical grounds that even if the π-complex form (I) of a carbonium ion is more stable that either form (II) or (III), the three forms may have independent existence and their interconversion may require activation.

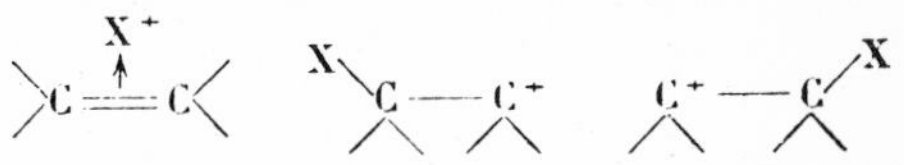

X[+]
>C ====== C<   >C — C[+]<   >C[+] — C<
                              X   X

(I)   (II)   (III)

For when one starts to convert (II) into (I) by C-X bond, initially energy well be required to the bond, and at first then will be no dividend, in increased overlap of the various electronic orbitals, to set against the bonding energy. It is therefore quite possible for the π-complex to be the more stable form of the ion, and yet for the group X not to facilitate SN1 reaction of a group attached to β-carbon (i. e. of Y in >CX — CY<) In such a case reaction will take place with more or less retention of configuration depending on height of the energy barrier which separates the initial ion (II) from the more stable isomeric π-complex (I), and consequently on the time that the ion (II) its stereochemistry is locked by conversion into (I). Therefore neither acceleration of SN1 reaction, nor complete retention of stereochemistry need necessarily be observed which in such a case the more stable form of the cation is a π complex. In this case resonance notation perhaps somewhat observes the fact that three stable isomeric forms of the cation are liable to occur ; and the possibility remains that the stable form any carbonium ions may be the π-complex isomer.

11 | Ingold on Synartetic Ions

Paper No. 11, published in July, 1951, was Ingold's first direct discussion of the role of carbon-bridged ions in molecular rearrangements and solvolyses. It is not a review of the pertinent literature, but a statement of principles. It again mentions the dramatic driving forces in isobornyl and β,β,β-triphenylethyl chlorides. At the end attention is called to the relation between the type of bonding in a carbon-bridged ion and that which prevails in the neutral molecules of boron compounds, an analogy which has become more compelling as examples of the three-center electron-deficient bonding in boron compounds have multiplied. This paper also proposes the term "synartetic" for carbon-bridged ions and the acceleration associated with their formation. See the discussion of Paper No. 13.

From: *Nature* **168**, 65–67 (1951)

WAGNER CHANGES, SYNARTETIC ACCELERATION AND SYNARTETIC IONS

By F. BROWN, Prof. E. D. HUGHES, F.R.S.,
Prof. C. K. INGOLD, F.R.S., and J. F. SMITH

University College, London, W.C.1

IT has been established[1] that the Wagner rearrangement is a form of unimolecular nucleophilic substitution or elimination (S_N1, $E1$); its primary step is that of all such unimolecular reactions, namely, a heterolysis with the production of a carbonium ion. Let us, for present convenience, call the obvious structure for this ion that of the 'first' carbonium ion. This ion might simply take up an anion (S_N1 substitution), or lose a proton ($E1$ elimination). However, the characteristic phenomenon of a Wagner change is that, prior to any such occurrence, a carbon atom with its full octet shifts over from an adjoining position to the charge-centre of the first ion. If nothing else happened, this would produce what we might call the 'second' carbonium ion. It is from this that the rearranged products may be considered as derived, either by uptake of the originally separating anion (Wagner isomerization), or by uptake of a different anion (Wagner substitution), or by loss of a proton (Wagner elimination):

$$
\begin{array}{c}
\underset{\underset{C_\beta}{|}-\underset{C_\alpha}{|}}{R\;\;X} \xrightarrow[\text{lysis}]{\text{hetero-}} \underset{\underset{C_\beta}{|}-\overset{+}{\underset{C_\alpha}{|}}}{R} \left(\substack{\text{1st} \\ \text{ion}}\right) \xrightarrow{\text{Case 1}} \underset{\underset{C_\beta}{|}-\underset{C_\alpha}{|}}{R\;\;Y}\;\;\text{etc.} \\[4mm]
\downarrow \\[4mm]
\underset{\overset{+}{\underset{C_\beta}{|}}-\underset{C_\alpha}{|}}{R} \left(\substack{\text{2nd} \\ \text{ion}}\right) \xrightarrow{\text{Case 2}} \underset{\underset{C_\beta}{|}-\underset{C_\alpha}{|}}{Y\;\;R}\;\;\text{etc.}
\end{array}
$$

As shown earlier[2], some primary heterolyses are 'accelerated'; that is, they occur much more rapidly than when the bond undergoing fission has the same local surroundings in simpler molecules; some heterolyses are not accelerated. Also, some heterolyses involve Wagner rearrangements, and some do not. The relationship between incidence of acceleration and of the Wagner change requires analysis.

One possible mechanism for the acceleration of a primary heterolysis depends on the release, during the process, of initially stored non-bonding energy: this has been defined[2] as 'steric acceleration'. Obviously it might operate whether a Wagner change is involved or not. Another mechanism of accelera-

49

tion, which could evidently operate when a Wagner rearrangement is involved, would gain the excess rate from a release of bonding energy during the bond-shift characteristic of the Wagner change : this we shall call 'synartetic acceleration', for a reason that will become clear later. We shall also note later, what is not immediately obvious, namely, that this mode of acceleration may operate even when a Wagner change is not involved. The ranges of incidence of the two accelerative mechanisms require consideration.

We have approached the two problems stated by trying experimentally to answer a number of simple guiding questions by the provision of examples. One might first ask : Can acceleration ever arise without a Wagner change ? The following example shows that it can. The rate of hydrolysis of camphene-hydrochloride in aqueous solvents to camphene-hydrate and camphene is too great to be easily measured ; it is obviously greater than the corresponding rate for simple tertiary alkyl chlorides. The rate of the analogous unimolecular ethyl-alcoholysis has been measured[3] (for example, $k_1 = 4 \cdot 0 \times 10^{-5}$ sec.$^{-1}$ at $0°$ in dry ethyl alcohol), and has been found to be about 6,000 times greater than the corresponding rate for tert.-butyl chloride.

The next question is complementary : Can a Wagner rearrangement ever occur without acceleration ? Again the answer is affirmative. The unimolecular solvolysis of neopentyl bromide[4], to give exclusively Wagner-rearranged tert.-amyl alcohol or tert.-amyl alkyl ethers and isoamylenes, takes place at rates ($k_1 = 1 \cdot 53 \times 10^{-6}$ sec.$^{-1}$, for hydrolysis at $95°$ in wet formic acid) which are of the same order of magnitude as those of the corresponding solvolytic reactions of ethyl bromide ($k_1 = 2 \cdot 70 \times 10^{-6}$ sec.$^{-1}$ in the same conditions). The unimolecular solvolysis of pinacolyl chloride, again to give exclusively Wagner-rearranged products, takes place at rates ($k_1 = 1 \cdot 94 \times 10^{-7}$ sec.$^{-1}$ in 80 per cent aqueous ethyl alcohol at $80°$) which are of the same order as those estimated for the unimolecular solvolysis of isopropyl chloride ($k_1 \sim 5 \times 10^{-7}$ sec.$^{-1}$ in the same conditions)[5]. A similar comparison could be given of pinacolyl iodide and isopropyl iodide[6].

These two types of examples show that the boundaries of the areas of incidence of acceleration and of Wagner rearrangements intersect.

Next we ask : Can an accelerated Wagner change be shown to derive its rate from 'steric acceleration' ? Theoretically, an affirmative answer is expected, because, given a sufficiently ramified structure, steric acceleration is a mechanism generally applicable to the primary heterolysis. However, an unambiguous example is difficult to provide. Probably the best available example is that of the isomerization of camphene-hydrochloride in aprotic solvents to iso-bornyl chloride. It has been found[7] that chlorine exchange between camphene-hydrochloride and chloride ions takes place more rapidly than the isomerization, which is not catalysed by chloride ions; and the conclusion has been drawn[8] that the heterolysis essentially precedes the Wagner rearrangement, which occurs during one of two competing forms of ionic reassociation. Now the initial heterolysis is identical, apart from the solvent difference, with the initial stage of the solvolysis of camphene-hydrochloride, which, as noted above, is strongly accelerated, but involves no Wagner change. Hence the acceleration could be a 'steric acceleration'. But even here, as we shall see later, 'synartetic

acceleration' is not excluded. However, having regard to the structure, and the large magnitude of the observed effect, we incline to the view that both mechanisms make substantial contributions.

The complementary question is : Can an accelerated Wagner change be shown to derive its rate from 'synartetic acceleration' ? Here the answer is definitely affirmative. As indicated in an earlier communication[8], tritylmethyl chloride, like neopentyl chloride, is incapable of easy bimolecular reactions ; and hence its unimolecular reactions, which give exclusively Wagner-rearranged products, may be studied, not only in formic acid, but also in aqueous alcoholic solvents. Charlton, Dostrovsky and Hughes found[9] that in formic acid it was hydrolysed by water at a rate ($k_1 = 2 \cdot 3 \times 10^{-3}$ sec.$^{-1}$ at $95°$) estimated as about 50,000 times that for neopentyl chloride. Comparisons referring to aqueous alcoholic solvents gave similarly large ratios. We assume that steric acceleration could not apply to the ionization of a primary halide, and that therefore synartetic acceleration is here responsible.

The following example[3] is especially instructive. First, the unimolecular solvolysis of bornyl chloride, to yield Wagner-rearranged products of the camphene series, takes place at rates ($k_1 \sim 1 \cdot 5 \times 10^{-7}$ sec.$^{-1}$ extrapolated for $80°$, in 80 per cent aqueous ethyl alcohol) which are of the same order as those of the solvolysis of pinacolyl chloride ($k_1 = 1 \cdot 94 \times 10^{-7}$ sec.$^{-1}$ in the same conditions). Secondly, the solvolysis of isobornyl chloride, also to give rearranged products, has rates ($k_1 \sim 1 \cdot 4 \times 10^{-2}$ sec.$^{-1}$ as above) which are about 70,000 times those of pinacolyl chloride. Steric acceleration seems here to be excluded, because isobornyl chloride, the exo-isomeride, can scarcely be supposed to have more non-bonding energy than bornyl chloride, the endo-compound : again we conclude that synartetic acceleration is responsible. Moreover, it neatly interprets the stereo-kinetic distinction. For in the exo-structure, a Wagner-type bond-shift could be initiated before the ionizing chlorine atom has attained the separation of the transition state of ionization (that is, before the chlorine atom has moved by more than about $0 \cdot 4$ A.) ; and therefore the initiation of the bond-shift could kinetically influence the heterolysis. But in the endo-structure, no such bond-shift could commence until the chlorine atom has passed out of the

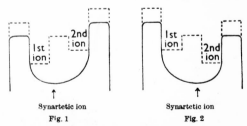

Synartetic ion   Synartetic ion
    Fig. 1   Fig. 2

(The reaction path enters from the left and leaves over which-ever transition state lies lower, that is, by the left in Fig. 1 and by the right in Fig. 2)

Case 1, nN (broken line). Non-rearranging $S_N1/E1$ without synartetic acceleration (for example, solvolysis of tert.-amyl bromide).

Case 2, nW (broken line). Wagner rearrangement, without synartetic acceleration (for example, solvolysis of neo-pentyl bromide).

Case, 3, aN (full line). Synartetically accelerated non-rearranging $S_N1/E1$ (for example, solvolysis of camphene-hydrochloride).

Case 4, aW (full line). Synartetically accelerated Wagner rearrangement (for example, solvolysis of iso-bornyl chloride).

way (that is, to well beyond the transition-state distance) ; and thus the shift could here have no kinetic influence.

While recognizing that marginal situations arise, we can divide the reactions discussed into four main classes, as illustrated by the schematic energy-reaction curves of Figs. 1 and 2. In unaccelerated unimolecular reactions, whether or not they involve a Wagner rearrangement, the 'first ion', and the transition state of its formation, are unaffected by the existence, or possibility of existence, of the 'second ion'. We assume that in unaccelerated Wagner changes there must be two ions ; but that when, in unaccelerated reactions, there are two, they are separated by an energy barrier substantial enough to preclude their energetically significant interaction. So we have either (case 1, nN) (the letters mean 'normal rate, normal structure') non-rearranging unimolecular reactions without synartetic acceleration (Fig. 1, broken line), or (case 2, nW) ('normal rate, Wagner change') Wagner rearrangements without such acceleration (Fig. 2, broken line), according as the transition state of the heterolysis which forms the 'first ion' lies energetically lower or higher than that of the co-ordination which destroys or would destroy the 'second ion'.

The other two classes can be most simply described by assuming that there is no resonance-stopping barrier between the first and second ionic structures, which interact according to a suggestion[10] made earlier, to produce a normal ion more stable than either—a *synartetic ion*, as we may call it, with a split single bond *fastening together* the locations of a split ionic charge. We then have not only a stabilized ion, but also stabilized transition states of ionization, and therefore either (case 3, aN) ('accelerated, normal structure') non-rearranging unimolecular reactions with synartetic acceleration (Fig. 1, full line), or (case 4, aW) ('accelerated, Wagner change') Wagner rearrangements with such acceleration (Fig. 2, full line), according, as before, to which of the two transition states lies lower. For these cases, we should modify our previous formulation :

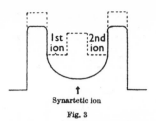

Fig. 3

(The reaction path enters, from the left, then divides, and leaves equally by the left and by the right)
Border cases 1, 2 (broken line) and 3, 4 (full line)

reaction having the described symmetry (border case 12) has been found by Cram[11] in the solvolysis with racemization (at both asymmetric centres) of that form of 2-phenyl-3-n-butyl p-toluenesulphonate for which the normal and rearranged substitution products would be enantiomers.

One usually thinks of CC-bond σ-electrons as having a much smaller tendency to enter into other orbitals than have CH-bond σ-electrons, or of course π-bond-electrons or unshared p-electrons. Yet it appears that CC-bond σ-electrons can interact strongly with a carbonium ionic centre to form what we have called a synartetic ion, at least when the stereoelectronic situation is favourable, and when the normal types of conjugation and hyperconjugation are more or less restricted. This seems somewhat less strange when we recall that the carbonium ion has the same electron configuration as the tercovalent boron atom, and that it is one of the lessons of boron chemistry that all low-lying orbitals will somehow achieve partial occupation, even when there are too few electrons to occupy them fully (this was recently pointed out to us by Dr. S. H. Bauer) : the same principle may apply in carbonium ion chemistry.

[Feb. 2.

[1] Dostrovsky, Hughes and Ingold, *J. Chem. Soc.*, 192 (1946).
[2] Brown, Davies, Dostrovsky, Evans and Hughes, *Nature*, [**167**, 987 (1951)].
[3] Results of present authors.
[4] Dostrovsky and Hughes, *J. Chem. Soc.*, 164, 166, 171 (1946).
[5] Martin, thesis (London, 1949) ; *Nature*, **166**, 679 (1950).
[6] Unpublished experiments by Mrs. M. G. Peeling.
[7] Nevell, de Salas and Wilson, *J. Chem. Soc.*, 1188 (1939).
[8] Bateman, Cooper, Hughes and Ingold, *J. Chem. Soc.*, 930 (1940).
[9] Charlton, Dostrovsky and Hughes, *Nature*, [**167**, 986 (1951)].
[10] Ingold, cited by Watson, *Ann. Rep. Chem. Soc.*, **36**, 197 (1939), and "Modern Theories of Organic Chemistry", Oxford Press, 2nd Ed., p. 208 (1941) ; also by Simonsen and Owen, "The Terpenes", Cambridge Press, 2nd Ed., p. 161 (1949).
[11] Cram, *J. Amer. Chem. Soc.*, **71**, 3836 (1949).

$$
\begin{array}{ccc}
R \;\; X & & R \\
| \;\;\; | & \xrightarrow[\text{lysis}]{\text{hetero-}} & \diagup \;\; \diagdown \\
C_\beta \!-\! C_\alpha & & C \!-\! C
\end{array}
$$

$$\underbrace{\qquad\qquad}_{\text{synartetic ion}} \; + $$

Case 3 →

$$\begin{array}{c} R \;\; Y \\ | \;\; | \\ C_\beta \!-\! C_\alpha \end{array} \text{ etc.}$$

Case 4 →

$$\begin{array}{c} Y \;\; R \\ | \;\; | \\ C_\beta \!-\! C_\alpha \end{array} \text{ etc.}$$

Marginal cases (between 1 and 3, and between 2 and 4) should arise when a tunnel effect permits weak resonance between the first and second ions ; but we shall not now discuss this phenomenon. Marginal cases of another sort (between 1 and 2, and between 3 and 4) arise when the two transition states lie on a common energy-level, so that the diagrams of Figs. 1 and 2 become symmetrical, as in Fig. 3. This happens when the unrearranged and Wagner-rearranged products are identical, but for some non-energetic distinction, as when they are enantiomeric, or are labelled isotopically. We then have either (border-case 12, $nN\bar{W}$) reactions without synartetic accelerations (Fig. 3, broken line), or (border case 34, $aN\bar{W}$) reactions with synartetic acceleration, leading, in either case, to 50 per cent of Wagner-rearranged product (for example, to racemization when the optical distinction is employed). A normal-rate

12 | The Cyclobutyl-cyclopropylcarbinyl System

The paper by Roberts and Mazur presents a concise account of exploratory work which, as later expanded, led to the conclusion that the ion from cyclobutyl and cyclopropylcarbinyl derivatives may have a common structure with three reactive, electron-deficient sites.

From: *J. Am. Chem. Soc.* **73,** 2509–20 (1951)

[Contribution from the Department of Chemistry and Laboratory for Nuclear Science and Engineering, Massachusetts Institute of Technology]

Small-Ring Compounds. IV. Interconversion Reactions of Cyclobutyl, Cyclopropylcarbinyl and Allylcarbinyl Derivatives

By John D. Roberts and Robert H. Mazur

A number of reactions have been investigated which lead to interconversion of cyclobutyl, cyclopropylcarbinyl and allylcarbinyl derivatives. Some degree of interconversion was observed in the following: vapor-phase light-catalyzed chlorination of methylcyclopropane; reaction of cyclopropylcarbinol with thionyl chloride, Lucas reagent, phosphorus tribromide and hydrobromic acid; cleavage of cyclopropylcarbinyl triethylsilyl ether with thionyl chloride; reaction of cyclobutanol with thionyl chloride and Lucas reagent; reaction of cyclopropylcarbinyl-, cyclobutyl- and allylcarbinylamines with nitrous acid; hydrolysis and acetolysis of cyclopropylcarbinyl and cyclobutyl chlorides; reaction of N-cyclopropylcarbinyl- and N-cyclobutylbenzamides with phosphorus pentabromide; and Grignard reactions of cyclopropylcarbinyl halides. No interconversion was observed in the following: reaction of allylcarbinol with thionyl chloride and phosphorus tribromide; vapor-phase light-catalyzed chlorination of cyclobutane; and Grignard reactions of allylcarbinyl and cyclobutyl halides. The products of those interconversion reactions which may reasonably be expected to involve carbonium ion intermediates have been correlated by consideration of carbonium ion stability and ease of interconversion, as well as the degree of reversibility of the reactions involved and the stabilities of the possible products. Cyclopropylcarbinyl halides have been shown to be unusually reactive in solvolysis reactions and, in fact, considerably more reactive than analogously constituted allylic halides.

Introduction

One of the principal limitations of carbonium-ion theory[1] as applied to rearrangement reactions occurring under the influence of polar catalysts or in polar media is the difficulty in deciding in advance which of several possible reaction paths should be most favorable. In no instance is this difficulty better exemplified than in the interconversion reactions of cyclobutyl, cyclopropylcarbinyl and allylcarbinyl derivatives where it has been reported that cyclobutyl- and cyclopropylcarbinylamines with nitrous acid give mixtures of cyclobutanol and cyclopropylcarbinol,[2] that cyclopropylcarbinol with phosphorus tribromide yields a bromide which on successive treatments with magnesium and carbon dioxide gives allylacetic acid,[3] and that cyclopropyldimethylcarbinol with hydrochloric acid forms (γ,γ-dimethylallyl)-carbinyl chloride which on hydrolysis with water regenerates cyclopropyldimethylcarbinol.[4] While simple *a posteriori* mechanistic interpretations of the above results may be made following the carbonium-ion theory of rearrangements, *prediction* of the product to be obtained from a given new carbonium-ion reaction must depend on a knowl-

edge of some or all of several important factors such as: (1) the relative carbonium-ion stabilities, (2) the energy barriers to interconversion of the carbonium ions, (3) the relative reactivities of the carbonium ions toward nucleophilic substances (4) the reversibility of the reaction in question and (5) the thermodynamic stabilities of the possible products. It was of interest, therefore, to determine, insofar as possible, the importance of these factors in directing rearrangements under a variety of conditions in reactions of cyclobutyl, cyclopropylcarbinyl and allylcarbinyl derivatives.

Preparation and Characterization of Allylcarbinyl, Cyclobutyl and Cyclopropylcarbinyl Halides

In order to determine qualitatively the relative stabilities of the cyclobutyl, cyclopropylcarbinyl and allylcarbinyl cations, one of the first objectives of the work was to prepare the corresponding halides and study their solvolytic reactivities. Allylcarbinyl chloride was readily obtained by the reaction of thionyl chloride with allylcarbinol prepared by the partial hydrogenation of 3-butyn-1-ol over palladium on calcium carbonate catalyst. Allylcarbinyl bromide was similarly obtained from the reaction of allylcarbinol with phosphorus tribromide. No rearrangements were noted in these reactions. The infrared spectra of the allylcarbinyl halides are shown in Figs. 1 and 2.

Cyclobutyl chloride was obtained by a vapor-phase light-catalyzed chlorination of cyclobutane. No other monochloride appeared to be formed in this preparation. Pure cyclobutyl bromide was obtained from the reaction of silver cyclobutane-

(1) (a) F. C. Whitmore, This Journal, **54,** 3274 (1932); *Chem. Eng. News,* **20,** 668 (1947); (b) L. P. Hammett, "Physical Organic Chemistry," McGraw-Hill Book Co., Inc., New York, N. Y., 1940, pp. 317–325.

(2) (a) N. J. Demjanow, *Ber.,* **40,** 4393 (1907); (b) N. J. Demjanow, *ibid.,* **40,** 4961 (1907); (c) R. Skrabal, *Monatsh.,* **70,** 420 (1937).

(3) L. I. Smith and S. McKenzie, Jr., *J. Org. Chem.,* **15,** 74 (1950).

(4) (a) P. Bruylants and A. Dewael, *Bull. classe Sci. Acad. roy. Belg.,* [5] **14,** 140 (1928); *Chem. Zentr.,* **99,** I, 2708 (1928); (b) T. A. Favorskaya and S. A. Fridman, *J. Gen. Chem. (U. S. S. R.),* **15,** 421 (1945).

carboxylate with bromine.[5] The infrared spectra of the cyclobutyl halides are given in Figs. 1 and 2.

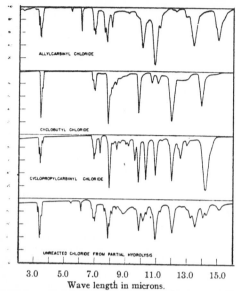

Fig. 1.—Infrared spectra: Baird spectrograph with NaCl prism, solutions of 50 mg. of compounds in 0.50 ml. of carbon disulfide except in the regions 4.2–5.0 μ and 6.2–7.2 μ where carbon tetrachloride was used as solvent.

Synthesis of pure cyclopropylcarbinyl chloride proved to be difficult. The reaction of the alcohol with thionyl chloride was unsatisfactory as was the cleavage of triethylsilyl cyclopropylcarbinyl ether with thionyl chloride,[6] both giving mixtures containing some cyclobutyl chloride. Chlorination of methylcyclopropane by the procedure used for cyclobutane gave a mixture of monochlorides which on fractional distillation yielded 21% of a mixture apparently comprised of 1- and 2-chloro-1-methyl-cyclopropane, 35% of allylcarbinyl chloride and 34% of a chloride (I), b.p. 87–89°, which from its properties and reactions (*vide infra*) was assigned the cyclopropylcarbinyl chloride structure.

$$\begin{array}{c}CH_2\\ |\\ CH_2\end{array}\!\!\!>\!\!CH{-}CH_3 \xrightarrow[h\nu]{Cl_2} \begin{array}{c}CH_2\\ |\\ CH_2\end{array}\!\!\!>\!\!CH{-}CH_2Cl + CH_2{=}CH{-}CH_2CH_2Cl + \left[\begin{array}{c}CH_2\\ |\\ CH_2\end{array}\!\!\!>\!\!CClCH_3 + \begin{array}{c}ClCH\\ |\\ CH_2\end{array}\!\!\!>\!\!CH{-}CH_3\right]$$

$$\underset{I}{34\%} \qquad\qquad 35\% \qquad\qquad\qquad \underset{21\%}{\text{(structures not proven)}}$$

I was saturated and its infrared spectrum (Fig. 1) showed none of the characteristic bands of cyclobutyl chloride although a small proportion (less than 5%) of cyclobutyl chloride might have remained undetected. However, analysis of the rate of solvolysis of I in 50% ethanol–50% water (by volume) at 50° indicated the presence of about

(5) This reaction was carried out by Dr. V. C. Chambers using a modification of the procedure of J. Cason and R. L. Way, *J. Org. Chem.*, **14**, 31 (1949).

(6) This reaction was suggested by the work of Dr. L. H. Sommer of Pennsylvania State College who has found that the cleavage of triethylsilyl alkyl ethers with thionyl chloride produces alkyl chlorides without rearrangement in other cases. We are indebted to Dr. Sommer for information about this reaction in advance of publication.

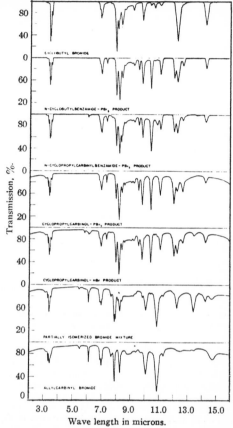

Fig. 2.—Infrared spectra: Baird spectrograph with NaCl prism, solutions of 50 mg. of compounds in 0.50 ml. of carbon disulfide except in the regions 4.2–5.0 μ and 6.2–7.2 μ where carbon tetrachloride was used as solvent.

80% of a very reactive chloride[7] and 20% of a considerably less reactive chloride (or chlorides). Analysis by fractional distillation and infrared spectra of the unreacted chloride from hydrolysis of I with boiling water showed about 45% allylcarbinyl chloride, 45% cyclobutyl chloride and 10% cyclopropylcarbinyl chloride. The infrared spectrum of the largest fraction which contains all three chlorides is shown in Fig. 1. The product (II) of the reaction of cyclopropylcarbinyl triethylsilyl ether with thionyl chloride which appeared to contain no allylcarbinyl chloride and about 15% of cyclobutyl chloride gave a similar

(7) It is unlikely that the reactive chloride could be either 1-chloro-1-methylcyclopropane or 1-chloro-2-methylcyclopropane since cyclopropyl chloride has been found by G. Gustavson, *J. prakt. Chem.*, [2] **43**, 396 (1891), and in unpublished experiments to be an exceptionally unreactive halide.

solvolysis rate curve in aqueous ethanol which indicated the presence of about 30% of a less reactive chloride. The fact that both I and II on solvolysis appeared to contain considerably more less-reactive chloride than was consistent with their infrared spectra indicates that the solvolysis reaction is accompanied by a rearrangement process similar to that discovered by Young, Winstein and Goering[8] for α,α-dimethylallyl chloride in acetic acid. It was possible to calculate the overall solvolysis rates of I and II to about the experimental error (Fig. 3) by assuming a unimolecular solvolysis with rate constant k_1 equal to 0.47 hr.$^{-1}$ competing with a unimolecular rearrangement having a rate constant k_1', equal to 0.14 hr.$^{-1}$ and yielding unreactive products. If, as indicated by the infrared spectra, the rearrangement results in cyclobutyl chloride with a k_1 of 0.017 hr.$^{-1}$ at 50° or allylcarbinyl chloride with $k_1 < 0.0005$ hr.$^{-1}$ at 50°, then only a slight error is introduced by assuming the rearrangement products to be unreactive.

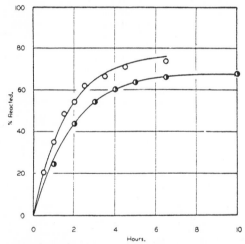

Fig. 3.—Solvolysis rates of chlorides I, O and II, ◑ in 50% ethanol–50% water (by volume) at 50°. Solid lines represent calculated reaction rate curves.

The rearrangement reaction was considerably faster than solvolysis in acetic acid in the presence of acetate ion at 100°, and I was essentially completely converted to cyclobutyl and allylcarbinyl chlorides by the time that 30% of the theoretical amount of chloride ion was formed (cf. Fig. 4). The ratio of formation of cyclobutyl chloride to allylcarbinyl chloride was about 1.7 as calculated from the rate of formation of unsaturated material in the reaction mixture (cf. Fig. 4) and confirmed by isolation and fractionation of the unreacted chloride. Cyclobutyl chloride was found to rearrange

(8) W. G. Young, S. Winstein and H. L. Goering, paper presented at the Philadelphia meeting of the American Chemical Society, April 12, 1950. Dr. S. Siegel of the Illinois Institute of Technology has kindly informed us that the solvolysis of cyclopropylcarbinyl benzenesulfonate in acetic acid competes with a similar rearrangement which yields a mixture of cyclobutyl and allylcarbinyl benzenesulfonates. Analogous behavior has been noted in this Laboratory for the corresponding p-toluenesulfonate as well as other p-toluenesulfonates in acetic acid.

to allylcarbinyl chloride at about the same rate as it solvolyzed in acetic acid at 100°. In 50% ethanol–50% water at 70°, the solvolysis rate curve of cyclobutyl chloride deviated slightly from the first-order law in the later stages of the reaction. This result could be explained on the basis of (1) the presence of about 5% of inert chloride in the original material or (2) the occurrence of a first-order rearrangement with k_1' equal to about a tenth of k_1.

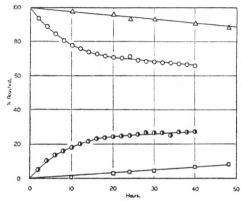

Fig. 4.—Solvolysis and isomerization (to allylcarbinyl chloride) rates of cyclopropylcarbinyl and cyclobutyl chlorides in acetic acid at 100°: O, solvolysis; ◑, isomerization for cyclopropylcarbinyl chloride. △, solvolysis: □, isomerization for cyclobutyl chloride.

The formation of allylcarbinyl chloride in the chlorination of methylcyclopropane appears to be a unique example of a carbon skeleton rearrangement occurring in a vapor-phase chlorination reaction. Similar results were obtained in three runs and since only one product was obtained in the chlorination of cyclobutane it appears unlikely that the abnormal products resulted from rearrangements in the isolation or distillation procedures.

Cyclopropylcarbinyl bromide has not as yet been prepared in purity comparable to that of the chloride. The reaction of cyclopropylcarbinol with phosphorus tribromide was found to give a mixture of cyclic bromides containing only a few per cent. of allylcarbinyl bromide. The b.p. of the bulk of the product (111–112°) agreed only fairly well with that (105–108°) previously reported[3] for material obtained from this reaction and inferred to be allylcarbinyl bromide. The b.p. of pure allylcarbinyl bromide obtained from allylcarbinol and phosphorus tribromide was 99–100°. The non-identity of the bromide mixture with allylcarbinyl bromide was confirmed by its saturated character and by infrared spectra (Fig. 2). Solvolysis rate data on the bromide indicated 65% of a very reactive bromide (presumably cyclopropylcarbinyl bromide). The presence of only about 20% of cyclobutyl bromide was indicated by the infrared spectrum (Fig. 2) and it is possible that here, also, solvolysis was accompanied by a rearrangement reaction although this has not yet been definitely established. Cyclopropylcarbinol and constant-boiling hydrobromic acid gave a mixture of bromides similar to that obtained in the phosphorus tribromide reaction (*cf.* infrared spectra in Fig. 2). The complexity of this reaction has been recognized previously by Demjanow and Demjanow.[9]

Attempts to characterize the pure halides by reaction of the corresponding Grignard reagents with phenyl isocyanate to yield the anilides of the next higher carboxylic acids were not completely successful. Cyclobutyl and allylcarbinyl halides reacted normally to give cyclobutylcarboxanilide and allylacetanilide, respectively. However, cyclopropylcarbinyl chloride appeared to give no cyclopropylacetanilide but only allylacetanilide. This behavior was observed repeatedly and, when mixtures of chlorides or bromides which contained cyclopropylcarbinyl, but not allylcarbinyl halides, were employed, allylacetanilide was formed in amount corresponding roughly to the proportion to cyclopropylcarbinyl halide present. The lack of rearrangement with cyclobutyl halides is surprising since in many other reactions, rearrangements are observed with *both* cyclobutyl and cyclopropylcarbinyl derivatives. It is not yet known at which step of the Grignard sequence rearrangement occurs. An attempt to induce an abnormal reaction with cyclobutyl bromide by isomerizing the halide with magnesium bromide in ether solution prior to formation of the Grignard reagent was unsuccessful.

A further point of interest in connection with the abnormal Grignard reactions of cyclopropylcarbinyl halides is the fact that they represent a rearrangement *opposite* in direction to that previously observed[10] in the Grignard reactions of *endo*-dehydronorbornyl halides which result with formation of cyclopropane ring-containing nortricyclene derivatives. Also in contrast is the finding[10] that nortricyclyl halides form Grignard reagents which react *without* rearrangements.

Solvolytic Reactivities of Halides

The relative solvolytic reactivities of cyclopropylcarbinyl, cyclobutyl and allylcarbinyl halides in 50% ethanol–50% water (by volume) are of particular interest (*cf.* Table I). The rate constant of cyclopropylcarbinyl chloride as calculated from the solvolysis rate of the high-boiling monochlorination product of methylcyclopropane was *27 times* that of cyclobutyl chloride and *40 times* that of β-methylallyl chloride at 50°. At the same temperature, allylcarbinyl chloride did not react at a measurable rate. Similarly cyclopropylcarbinyl bromide was found to be about 20 times more reactive than cyclobutyl bromide and 30 times more reactive than allyl bromide at 25°.

The high reactivity of cyclopropylcarbinyl halides is perhaps unexpected. Cyclobutyl halides could be anticipated to be more reactive than cyclopropylcarbinyl halides since secondary halides are customarily more reactive than primary halides in solvolytic reactions. However, since the cyclo-

propane ring has many of the physical and chemical characteristics[11] of the carbon–carbon double bond it can also be expected that a cyclopropylcarbinyl cation should be stabilized to some degree, at least, by resonance similar to that which stabilizes an allyl cation. The resonance forms here written for the cyclopropylcarbinyl cation are not con-

$$\left[CH_2\!=\!CH\!-\!\overset{\oplus}{C}H_2 \leftrightarrow \overset{\oplus}{C}H_2\!-\!CH\!=\!CH_2\right] \equiv$$
$$[CH_2\!\cdots\!CH\!\cdots\!CH_2]^{\oplus}$$

$$\left[\substack{CH_2 \\ | \\ CH_2}\!\!\!>\!CH\!-\!\overset{\oplus}{C}H_2 \leftrightarrow \substack{\overset{\oplus}{C}H_2 \\ | \\ CH_2}\!\!\!>\!CH\!=\!CH_2\right] \equiv$$

$$\left[\substack{CH_2 \\ | \\ CH_2}\!\!\!>\!CH\!\cdots\!CH_2\right]^{\oplus}$$

sidered to be energetically equivalent as are those of the allyl cation and this difference is indicated in the representation of the hybrid structure, where the cyclopropylcarbinyl form is weighted more heavily.[12] The considerable reactivity of cyclopropylcarbinyl chloride as compared to β-methylallyl chloride is unexpected and it will be interesting to see if cyclopropylcarbinyl derivatives are generally more reactive than analogously constituted allyl compounds.

It is possible to conclude from the relative solvolytic reactivities of cyclobutyl, cyclopropylcarbinyl and allylcarbinyl halides in aqueous ethanol that the order of stability of the carbonium ions corresponding to these substances is probably

$$\triangleright\!-\!\overset{\oplus}{C}H_2 \gtrsim \square^{\oplus} \gg CH_2\!=\!CH\!-\!CH_3\!-\!\overset{\oplus}{C}H_2{}^{13}$$

Irreversible Carbonium Ion Reactions

The major difficulty in obtaining information on the behavior of carbonium ions under conditions

(11) (a) E. P. Carr and C. P. Burt, *ibid.*, **40**, 1590 (1918); (b) I. M. Klotz, *ibid.*, **66**, 88 (1944); (c) J. D. Roberts and C. Green, *ibid.*, **68**, 214 (1946); (d) M. T. Rogers and J. D. Roberts, *ibid.*, **68**, 843 (1946); (e) M. T. Rogers, *ibid.*, **69**, 2544 (1947); (f) G. Gustavson, *J. prakt. Chem.*, [2] **62**, 273 (1900); (g) E. P. Kohler and J. B. Conant, THIS JOURNAL, **39**, 1404 (1917); (h) W. A. Bone and W. H. Perkin, *J. Chem. Soc.*, **67**, 108 (1895); (i) R. C. Fuson and F. N. Baumgartner, THIS JOURNAL, **70**, 3255 (1948); (j) C. A. Coulsen and W. E. Moffitt, *Phil. Mag.*, [7] **40**, 1 (1949); (k) A. D. Walsh, *Trans. Faraday Soc.*, **45**, 179 (1949).

(12) The reasons for writing only one bond of the cyclopropane ring as participating in the resonance stabilization of the carbonium ion have been given by J. D. Roberts, W. Bennett and R. Armstrong, THIS JOURNAL, **72**, 3329 (1950).

(13) It must be recognized that this sequence is purely qualitative since the solvolytic reactivities measure, at best, only the tendency toward partial ionization in the solvolysis transition state. Furthermore, under the conditions of our experiments, it is possible that part of the reactions involved a direct (non-ionization) replacement mechanism between solvent and halide. This latter complication is probably not of considerable importance with cyclopropylcarbinyl or cyclobutyl halides since, in common with many other carbonium ion processes, the solvolyses of these substances result in extensive rearrangement as will be shown later. A further complexity is introduced by the fact that the reaction rates do not depend on the absolute free energies of the solvolysis transition states but rather on the difference in free energy (ΔF)‡ between the ground and transition states. As a result, relative carbonium ion stabilities may be safely inferred from solvolytic reactivities only if there is reasonable assurance that the substances being solvolyzed have rather similar thermodynamic stabilities. In the present series of compounds, the order of increasing solvolytic reactivity corresponds to *decreasing* thermodynamic stability as will be shown later. Although this fact considerably weakens the basis for assignment of the sequence of carbonium ion stabilities, nonetheless, the sequence is useful in correlating the products of a number of interconversion reactions.

(9) N. Demjanow and J. Demjanow, *J. Russ. Phys.-Chem. Soc.*, **46**, 42 (1914); *Chem. Zentr.*, **85**, I, 1998 (1914).

(10) J. D. Roberts, E. R. Trumbull, Jr., R. Armstrong and W. Bennett, THIS JOURNAL, **72**, 3116 (1950).

where the ions can rearrange or react irreversibly with nucleophilic substances is the paucity of reactions which can be used to generate unstable primary as well as secondary and tertiary carbonium ions. The most generally suitable reactions seem to be the reaction of aliphatic primary amines with nitrous acid. Whitmore and others[14] have offered compelling evidence for the carbonium ion character of this reaction with amines such as n-propyl-, n-butyl- and neopentylamines. The characteristic nitrogen evolution and relatively mild conditions under which the reaction is usually run ensure complete irreversibility and freedom from rearrangements of the starting materials or products except during the reaction proper.

TABLE I

SOLVOLYSIS RATE CONSTANTS OF HALIDES IN 50% ETHANOL– 50% WATER (BY VOLUME)

Halide	Temp., °C. ($\pm 0.1°$)	k_1 (hr.$^{-1}$)
Allylcarbinyl chloride	90	0.0060
Cyclobutyl chloride	50	.017
	70	.15
Cyclopropylcarbinyl chloride (I)	50	.45^a
β-Methylallyl chloride	50	.011
Cyclobutyl bromide	25	.015
Cyclopropylcarbinyl bromide	25	.34^b
Allyl bromide	25	.013

^{a} Obtained from the initial slope of the rate curve of Fig. 3. ^{b} The value given is computed for a mixture containing 65% cyclopropylcarbinyl bromide and 35% cyclobutyl bromide. If the material contained 20% cyclobutyl bromide as indicated by the infrared spectrum and rearrangement accompanied solvolysis, the corrected k_1 would be about 0.27 hr.$^{-1}$.

We have utilized the amine–nitrous acid reaction to generate cyclopropylcarbinyl, cyclobutyl and allylcarbinyl cations in aqueous solution and, as a test of the reliability of the reaction for this purpose, crotyl- and α-methylallylamines were also studied. To avoid complications resulting from the formation of halides, the reactions were carried out by adding sodium nitrite solution to dilute aqueous solutions of the amines in perchloric acid. Crotylamine gave a mixture of alcohols which was found by fractional distillation to contain 47% of crotyl alcohol and 53% of α-methylallyl alcohol.[15] The over-all yield was 62%. α-Methylallylamine gave a similar but not identical mixture (73% yield) containing 31% of crotyl alcohol and 69% of α-methylallyl alcohol. The compositions of the alcohol mixtures correspond within our experimental error to those reported by Young and Andrews[16] for the products of the carbonium ion type reactions of crotyl and α-methylallyl chlorides with silver hydroxide in aqueous media.

It has been reported previously[2] that the reaction of cyclopropylcarbinyl- and cyclobutylamines with nitrous acid gives mixtures of cyclopropyl carbinol

and cyclobutanol. However, in earlier work[17] it was not possible to reproduce the melting points given[2a,18] for the N-phenylcarbamates which were used to separate and identify the cyclobutanol and cyclopropylcarbinol present in the reaction mixtures and reinvestigation of these reactions seemed desirable. Treatment of cyclopropylcarbinyl- and cyclobutylamines with sodium nitrite in dilute aqueous perchloric acid solution was found to give essentially identical mixtures of four-carbon alcohols from each amine. The total yields of alcohols ranged from 35–57%. The principal components of the mixtures were cyclobutanol (~47%) and cyclopropylcarbinol (~48%). The presence of about 5% of allylcarbinol was indicated by the infrared spectra. No crotyl or α-methylallyl alcohols were detected.

The reaction of allylcarbinylamine with sodium nitrite in dilute aqueous perchloric acid solution gave a complex mixture of alcohols which was analyzed partly by fractional distillation and partly by infrared spectra. The mixture (64% yield of alcohols) had approximately the following composition: 45% allylcarbinol, 18% α-methylallyl alcohol, 10% crotyl alcohol, 14% cyclopropylcarbinol and 13% cyclobutanol. The presence of α-methylallyl and crotyl alcohols among the products is particularly significant since it shows that the allylcarbinyl cation, when actually (or incipiently) formed, tends to undergo a hydride shift to the resonance-stabilized α-methylallyl-crotyl cation, as well as to undergo ring closure and form the cyclobutyl or cyclopropylcarbinyl cations. This fact appears to provide a useful diagnostic test for the free allylcarbinyl cation based on the formation or non-formation in a given reaction involving allylcarbinyl compounds of crotyl or α-methylallyl derivatives.

The results of the amine–nitrous acid reactions provide a qualitative idea of what is to be expected from carbonium ions in irreversible (or essentially irreversible) reactions with nucleophilic substances. The amounts of the various products appear to correspond roughly with relative carbonium ion stabilities. The energy barrier to the interconversion of the cyclobutyl and cyclopropylcarbinyl cations seems to be quite small since, starting with substances corresponding to either ion, the same mixture of final products is obtained.[19] The energy barrier to conversion of these ions to the allylcarbinyl cation seems to be high while that of the reverse process, as judged from the nearly equal ratio of allylcarbinol to cyclopropylcarbinol and cyclobutanol formed in the allylcarbinylamine–nitrous acid reaction, seems to have an intermediate value.

The information so far obtained is applicable to other irreversible carbonium ion reactions of cyclobutyl, cyclopropylcarbinyl and allylcarbinyl derivatives. For example, the solvolysis of the

(14) (a) F. C. Whitmore and D. P. Langlois, THIS JOURNAL, 54, 3441 (1932); (b) F. C. Whitmore and R. S. Thorpe, ibid., 63, 1118 (1941); (c) M. Freund and P. Leaze, Ber., 24, 2150 (1891).

(15) E. Galand, Bull. soc. chim. Belg., 39, 529 (1930), has reported that the reaction of crotylamine with nitrous acid gives only crotyl alcohol.

(16) W. G. Young and L. J. Andrews, THIS JOURNAL, 66, 421 (1944).

(17) J. D. Roberts and C. W. Sauer, ibid., 71, 3925 (1949).

(18) N. J. Demjanow and K. Fortunatow, Ber., 40, 4397 (1907).

(19) The possibility is being investigated that the cyclobutyl and cyclopropylcarbinyl cations have effectively no separate existence but are converted to an intermediate ion of the type suggested by T. P. Nevell, E. de Salas and C. L. Wilson, J. Chem. Soc., 1188 (1939), for the camphanyl cation.

chlorides in neutral or slightly alkaline aqueous media could reasonably be expected to be such a process, and it is not surprising to find that cyclopropylcarbinyl chloride and cyclobutyl chloride produce mixtures of alcohols of similar compositions to those formed from the corresponding amines with nitrous acid. Allylcarbinyl chloride was very unreactive and, in an attempt to speed the reaction by boiling with an aqueous suspension of silver carbonate, almost no alcohol was formed.

Reversible Carbonium Ion Reactions

In a reversible reaction, the relative stabilities of the possible products are of particular importance. It is perhaps surprising that, of the cyclopropylcarbinyl, cyclobutyl and allylcarbinyl halides, the last is most stable. This is strikingly demonstrated by complete conversion of a roughly equivalent mixture of cyclopropylcarbinyl and cyclobutyl chlorides or bromides at, or below, room temperature by Lucas reagent (a solution of zinc chloride in concentrated hydrochloric acid) or its bromide analog into allylcarbinyl halides. Allylcarbinyl chloride was also apparently the sole product of the reaction at room temperature between cyclopropylcarbinol or cyclobutanol with Lucas reagent. As expected from the estimates of the relative carbonium ion stabilities, allylcarbinol was by far the least reactive alcohol toward Lucas reagent. No reaction occurred below, or at, room temperature and, on boiling, extensive decomposition resulted. Cyclobutyl chloride is intermediate in stability between allylcarbinyl and cyclopropylcarbinyl chlorides, and it was found that a 2:1 mixture of cyclopropylcarbinyl and cyclobutyl chlorides was isomerized to a 1:1 mixture of allylcarbinyl and cyclobutyl chlorides by using a shorter reaction time and less Lucas reagent than was employed for complete isomerization to allylcarbinyl chloride.

The rearrangements of the chlorides and the reactions of the alcohols with Lucas reagent may be interpreted in several ways. The function of the zinc chloride is to facilitate the formation of carbonium ions from cyclobutanol, cyclopropylcarbinol and their respective chlorides. As one possibility, an equilibrium might be postulated between the various cations with a slow irreversible reaction between the allylcarbinyl cation and chloride ion or, to obviate the necessity of assuming a slow reaction of the allylcarbinyl cation, this entity could be considered to be formed slowly and to react rapidly and essentially irreversibly with chloride ion. An alternative and somewhat more attractive interpretation is similar to that proposed[20] for the analogous formation of isobornyl chloride from camphene hydrochloride. Here, the cyclobutyl and cyclopropylcarbinyl cations are postulated to be essentially in equilibrium with each other as well as with the respective chlorides. Allylcarbinyl chloride is formed by a direct and essentially irreversible slow reaction between either or both of the cations and chloride ion or hydrogen chloride as shown in the equations

This formulation is favored since, if the allylcarbinyl cation were actually an intermediate, some formation of crotyl and α-methylallyl chlorides would be expected, in accordance with the modes of reaction of the allylcarbinyl cation observed in the allylcarbinylamine–nitrous acid reaction.

Direct evidence that the rearrangement is not an intramolecular process was obtained by measurement of the extent of chlorine exchange between allylcarbinyl chloride and a mixture of cyclopropylcarbinyl and cyclobutyl chlorides with Lucas reagent containing Cl^{38}. Under conditions where the mixture of cyclopropylcarbinyl and cyclobutyl chlorides was 77% isomerized to allylcarbinyl chloride, 107%[21] of the theoretical chlorine exchange took place. However, under the same conditions, allylcarbinyl chloride showed but 13% exchange indicating that allylcarbinyl chloride is not readily converted to the corresponding carbonium ion in the presence of Lucas reagent.

Regardless of the mechanisms involved, the reactions of cyclopropylcarbinol and cyclobutanol with Lucas reagent to give allylcarbinyl chloride are obviously controlled by the relative stabilities of the possible products. It is likely that the same effects are operative in the formation of (γ,γ-dimethylallyl)-carbinyl chloride from dimethylcyclopropylcarbinol and hydrochloric acid.[4] In the hydrolysis of the chloride, where dimethylcyclopropylcarbinol is formed,[4] an irreversible carbonium ion type reaction is probably involved and the relative carbonium ion stabilities are the important factor in determining the reaction products.

Applications to Other Reactions

The reactions of alcohols with thionyl chloride do not generally seem to be considered[22] carbonium ion type reactions and, as pointed out earlier, allylcarbinol reacts with thionyl chloride (and also phosphorus tribromide) without rearrangement. Nonetheless, in some cases (as with isopropylmethylcarbinol[23a] and 2-methyl-2-phenyl-1-butanol[23b]) rearrangements occur which are characteristic of carbonium ion reactions. We find that cyclobutanol and cyclopropylcarbinol react with thionyl chloride to give mixtures of chlorides. Similar mixtures were obtained from each alcohol, with compositions on the order of cyclobutyl chloride (30%), cyclopropylcarbinyl chloride (67%) and allylcarbinyl chloride (3%). The compositions of the products were not altered by carrying out the

(20) (a) P. D. Bartlett and I. Pöckel, THIS JOURNAL, **60**, 1585 (1938). (b) W. E. Doering. Abstracts of 113th (Chicago) Meeting of the American Chemical Society, April 19 to 23, 1948, p. 41L.

(21) The difference between this figure and 100% may be due to experimental error or else some addition of HCl[38] to the double bond with Lucas reagent may have occurred.

(22) Cf. W. Gerrard, J. Chem. Soc., 688 (1936); 99 (1939); 218 (1940); 85 (1944); W. Gerrard and K. H. V. French, Nature, **159**, 263 (1947).

(23) (a) F. C. Whitmore and F. Johnston, THIS JOURNAL, **60**, 2265 (1938); (b) E. S. Wallis and P. I. Bowman, J. Org. Chem., **1**, 383 (1936).

reaction in the presence of a mole of pyridine for each mole of thionyl chloride used. The results indicate an irreversible carbonium ion type mechanism in the reaction of thionyl chloride with cyclobutanol and cyclopropylcarbinol. Presumably, similar considerations apply to the reaction of cyclopropylcarbinol with phosphorus tribromide.

Leonard and Nommensen[24] have shown that the von Braun synthesis of alkyl halides from N-substituted benzamides has some of the characteristics of a carbonium ion reaction and on this basis it is not unexpected that N-cyclobutyl- and N-cyclopropylcarbinylbenzamides give similar mixtures of bromides on treatment with phosphorus pentabromide.[25] The bromide mixtures are seen by their infrared spectra (Fig. 2) to be similar to cyclopropylcarbinol–phosphorus tribromide product.

Acknowledgment.—The radioactive exchange experiments were supported in part by the joint program of the Office of Naval Research and the Atomic Energy Commission.

Experimental

Cyclopropanecarboxylic Acid.—A procedure similar to that described by Jeffery and Vogel[26] was found to be more convenient than other large-scale preparations.[27] The yields in runs involving as much as 5 moles of ketone were 70–85% of material having b.p. 97–98° (40 mm.).

Cyclopropylcarbinol.—Lithium aluminum hydride reduction of cyclopropanecarboxylic acid and ethyl cyclopropanecarboxylate by the procedures of Nystrom and Brown[28] gave cyclopropylcarbinol, b.p. 123° (lit.[3] 122–123°), n^{25}D 1.4300 in 68 and 54% yield, respectively. The N-phenylcarbamate had m.p. 76.6–77.0° (lit. 100–104°,[18] 75.5–76°[3]) after crystallization from hexane.

Anal. Calcd. for $C_{11}H_{12}O_2N$: C, 69.11; H, 6.81. Found: C, 68.88; H, 6.77.

The 3,5-dinitrobenzoate had m.p. 101.2–101.4° after crystallization from hexane–benzene.

Anal. Calcd. for $C_{11}H_{10}O_6N_2$: C, 49.62; H, 3.76. Found: C, 49.96; H, 3.83.

Cyclobutanol was prepared from cyclobutanone as described previously.[17]

Allylcarbinol.—The starting material for the preparation of allylcarbinol was 3-butyne-1-ol which was obtained by distillation of commercial material (Farchan), b.p. 128°, n^{25}D 1.4388. The N-α-naphthylcarbamate of 3-butyn-1-ol was prepared and had m.p. 98.5–98.8° after crystallization from hexane–benzene.

Anal. Calcd. for $C_{16}H_{13}O_2N$: C, 75.29; H, 5.48. Found: C, 75.15; H, 5.52.

Hydrogenation of 3-butyn-1-ol mixed with an equal volume of methanol at 30 p.s.i. over 2% palladium-on-calcium carbonate catalyst was carried out in a water-cooled jacketed bottle until one mole of hydrogen per mole of butynol was absorbed. The catalyst which was too finely divided to be separated by filtration was removed by distillation of the organic material under reduced pressure into a Dry Ice-cooled trap. Fractional distillation through a glass-helix packed column gave allylcarbinol, b.p. 115° (770 mm.), 47.5° (41 mm.), n^{25}D 1.4182 (lit.[29] b.p.

112.5–113.5° (748 mm.), n^{20}D 1.4224). The yields averaged 65% in several preparations of varying size.

The N-α-naphthylcarbamate of allylcarbinol had m.p. 75.2–75.6° after crystallization from hexane–benzene.

Anal. Calcd. for $C_{15}H_{15}O_2N$: C, 74.69; H, 6.22. Found: C, 74.34; H, 6.29.

Allylcarbinyl Chloride.—A mixture of 8.0 g. (0.11 mole) of allylcarbinol with five drops of pyridine was cooled in an ice-bath and 13.2 g. (0.11 mole) of thionyl chloride added dropwise. The flask was shaken occasionally during the addition of the thionyl chloride and, after the addition was complete, the mixture was heated under reflux for 30 minutes. Fractional distillation of the products gave 7.3 g. (73%) of allylcarbinyl chloride, b.p. 73–74°, n^{25}D 1.4192 (lit.[29] b.p. 75.0°, n^{20}D 1.4233). The infrared spectrum of the product is given in Fig. 1.

Treatment of allylcarbinylmagnesium chloride with phenyl isocyanate gave allylacetanilide which had m.p. 91.4–91.8° (lit.[30] 91°) after crystallization from benzene–hexane.

Allylcarbinyl bromide was prepared in 43% yield from allylcarbinol by the method of Juvala[29]; b.p. 99–100°, n^{25}D 1.4573 (lit.[29] b.p. 98.5–99°, n^{20}D 1.4622). The infrared spectrum of the product is given in Fig. 2.

Cyclobutyl Chloride from the Chlorination of Cyclobutane.—Part of the apparatus used for the vapor-phase chlorination of cyclobutane is shown in Fig. 5. Joint A was connected to the top of a short vacuum-jacketed Vigreux column, a Dry Ice condenser was mounted on B and chlorine was passed in at C. The apparatus was covered with asbestos paper except for the glass spiral which was irradiated with an RS type G. E. Sunlamp at 5–10 cm.

Fig. 5.—Chlorination apparatus.

Cyclobutane[17] (8.4 g., 0.15 mole) was placed in the boiler of the Vigreux column and heated so that a rapid stream of reflux was evident at B. After allowing a few minutes for displacement of air from the system, chlorine was admitted at C from a gas buret at about 500 ml./hr. When 3700 ml. (measured at atmospheric pressure over saturated salt solution at room temperature) of chlorine had been run in, the thermometer in the head of the Vigreux column reached 60°. Distillation of the chlorination product gave 9.9 g. (73%) of cyclobutyl chloride; b.p. 82–83°, n^{25}D 1.4332. A middle fraction of b.p. 82.7–82.9° had d^{25} 0.991; MRD 23.75 (the calculated value of MRD was 23.66 using 0.32 for the exaltation of the cyclobutane ring[26]).[31]

Anal. Calcd. for C_4H_7Cl: C, 53.05; H, 7.79. Found: C, 53.35; H, 7.73.

Treatment of the Grignard reagent prepared from cyclobutyl chloride with phenyl isocyanate gave cyclobutanecarboxanilide, m.p. 109.0–110.6° after crystallization from benzene–hexane. This material did not depress the m.p. (113.8–114.0°) of an authentic sample prepared from the acid chloride of cyclobutanecarboxylic acid and aniline. The reported[32] m.p. for cyclobutanecarboxanilide is 111°. In some instances, particularly when the phenyl isocyanate was added to ice-cooled ethereal solutions of cyclobutylmagnesium chloride, a product of m.p. 99.6–100.2°, after crystallization from hexane, was isolated. This substance had the correct elemental analysis for N-cyclobutanecarboxyl-N,N'-diphenylurea which could reasonably arise through reaction between phenyl isocyanate and the chloromagnesium salt of cyclobutanecarboxanilide. Attempts to

(24) N. J. Leonard and E. W. Nommensen, This Journal, **71**, 2808 (1949).

(25) The reaction of N-cyclopropylcarbinyl benzamide with phosphorus pentabromide has been reported previously by J. A. Arvin and R. Adams, *ibid.*, **50**, 1983 (1928), and J. von Braun, R. Fuszgänger and M. Kühn, *Ann.*, **445**, 201 (1925), to give cyclopropylcarbinyl bromide. The purity of the earlier preparations is questionable.

(26) G. H. Jeffery and A. I. Vogel, *J. Chem. Soc.*, 1804 (1948).

(27) (a) M. J. Schlatter, This Journal, **63**, 1733 (1941); (b) C. M. McCloskey and G. H. Coleman, *Org. Syn.*, **24**, 36 (1944).

(28) R. F. Nystrom and W. G. Brown, This Journal, **69**, 1197, 2548 (1947).

(29) A. Juvala, *Ber.*, **63**, 1989 (1930).

(30) R. P. Linstead and H. N. Rydon, *J. Chem. Soc.*, 1995 (1934).

(31) Cyclobutyl chloride has previously been reported by W. H. Perkin, Jr., *ibid.*, **65**, 950 (1894), from the reaction of "cyclobutanol" (prepared from cyclobutylamine hydrochloride and silver nitrite) with phosphorus pentachloride. In view of the possibilities for rearrangement in these reactions the purity of Perkin's preparation is questionable.

(32) M. Freund and E. Gudeman, *Ber.*, **21**, 2697 (1888).

prepare authentic material by reaction of cyclobutanecar-boxanilide with phenyl isocyanate for 24 hours in refluxing dry xylene[33] or by successive treatments of cyclobutanecar-boxanilide with one equivalent of methylmagnesium iodide and phenyl isocyanate were unsuccessful. The substance depressed the m.p. (100°) of cyclopropylacetanilide pre-pared as described below.

Anal. Calcd. for $C_{18}H_{18}O_2N_2$: C, 73.44; H, 6.16; N, 9.52. Found: C, 73.74; H, 6.27; N, 9.37.

Isobutyl Triethylsilyl Ether and Cyclopropylcarbinyl Tri-ethylsilyl Ether.—In a 500-ml. three-necked flask equipped with stirrer, dropping funnel, reflux condenser and nitrogen inlet tube was placed 4.8 g. (0.20 mole) of sodium hydride and 100 ml. of dry ether and the air in the flask displaced by dry nitrogen. Isobutyl alcohol (13.0 g., 0.175 mole) was added dropwise to the stirred suspension and the mixture was then heated under reflux for two hours. Triethylbromo-silane[34] (39.0 g., 0.20 mole) was added to the rapidly stirred mixture at such a rate as to keep the ether refluxing gently. After the addition was complete, the mixture was refluxed for two hours and then treated with 100 ml. of water. The ether layer was separated, the aqueous layer extracted with ether and the combined extracts dried over magnesium sul-fate. The ether was distilled and the residue fractionated under reduced pressure. The forerun included 2.8 g. of triethylsilane, b.p. 42° (50 mm.). The yield of isobutyl triethylsilyl ether was 30.3 g. (92%); b.p. 76° (21 mm.); $n^{25}D$ 1.4169.

Anal. Calcd. for $C_{10}H_{24}OSi$: C, 63.76; H, 12.84. Found: C, 63.73; H, 12.86.

Cyclopropylcarbinyl triethylsilyl ether was prepared in a similar manner except that the treatment of the reaction mixture with water was omitted and instead the solids were filtered and the filtrate distilled. From 5.8 g. (0.080 mole) of cyclopropylcarbinol was obtained 7.0 g. (47%) of cyclo-propylcarbinyl triethylsilyl ether; b.p. 90–91° (22 mm.), $n^{25}D$ 1.4334.

Anal. Calcd. for $C_{10}H_{22}OSi$: C, 65.45; H, 11.90. Found: C, 64.32; H, 12.10.

Reaction of Silyl Ethers with Thionyl Chloride.—The cleavage of isobutyl triethylsilyl ether by thionyl chloride was found to give diisobutyl sulfite in the absence of pyri-dine and a low yield of isobutyl chloride in the presence of pyridine.

A.—To 23.5 g. (0.125 mole) of isobutyl triethylsilyl ether contained in a flask equipped with a reflux condenser was added 15.3 g. (0.13 mole) of thionyl chloride. A spontane-ous reaction occurred after which the mixture was heated under reflux for six hours. Fractionation under reduced pressure gave 17.6 g. (94%) of triethylchlorosilane, b.p. 60° (40 mm.) and 4.3 g. (40%) of diisobutyl sulfite, b.p. 89–90° (10 mm.), $n^{25}D$ 1.4253. An authentic sample of diisobutyl sulfite prepared by the method of Voss and Blanke[35] had b.p. 92–93° (12 mm.) and $n^{25}D$ 1.4242.

B.—A mixture of 5.5 g. (0.046 mole) of thionyl chloride and 0.8 g. of pyridine was heated to reflux and 8.7 g. (0.046 mole) of isobutyl triethylsilyl ether added dropwise. A vigorous reaction ensued with liberation of sulfur dioxide. The mixture was refluxed for one-half hour and then dis-tilled. The crude low-boiling material, 3 g., was washed with sodium bicarbonate solution to remove thionyl chlo-ride, dried over calcium chloride and distilled. The yield of isobutyl chloride was 0.6 g. (15%); b.p. 69.5°, $n^{25}D$ 1.3953 (lit.,[36] b.p. 68.9°, $n^{25}D$ 1.3958).

C.—The reaction of cyclopropylcarbinyl triethylsilyl ether with thionyl chloride was carried out in the presence of pyridine as described in the preceding preparation except that the reflux period was 1.5 hours. From 10.0 g. (0.081 mole) of thionyl chloride, 0.8 g. of pyridine and 15.5 g. (0.083 mole) of cyclopropylcarbinyl triethylsilyl ether there was obtained 6.1 g. of crude product, b.p. 84–86°, which on fractionation through an efficient center-tube column[37] gave

4.6 g. (61%) of material; b.p. 87–88.5°, $n^{25}D$ 1.4310–1.4323. A middle fraction had an infrared spectrum vir-tually identical with that of the product of cyclopropyl-carbinol with thionyl chloride. The solvolysis rate curve at 50° in aqueous alcohol indicated 63% of cyclopropylcar-binyl chloride (assuming no rearrangement).

Chlorination of Methylcyclopropane.—The methylcyclo-propane used in these experiments was prepared starting from 1,3-butyleneglycol by the procedures employed in the synthesis of 1,1-dimethylcyclopropane.[38] The over-all yield of methylcyclopropane, b.p. 2° (lit.[39] 4–5°), was 67%.

The chlorination procedure was similar to that described above for cyclobutane. 24.3 g. (0.43 mole) of methylcyclo-propane and 4900 ml. of chlorine were used and, at the con-clusion of the reaction, the column head temperature was 50°. The crude chlorination product was distilled rapidly through a short Vigreux column and the monochlorinated material which amounted to 31 g. (80%), b.p. 60–95°, was then carefully fractionated through an efficient center-tube column.[37] The following fractions were taken: b.p. 64–74°, $n^{25}D$ 1.4009–1.4045, 5.4 g. (21%), probably a mixture of 1- and 2-chloro-1-methylcyclopropane; b.p. 75–76°, $n^{25}D$ 1.4180–1.4198, 8.8 g. (35%), identified as allylcarbinyl chloride by its infrared spectrum; and b.p. 87–89°, $n^{25}D$ 1.4310–1.4328, 8.6 g. (34%) shown by its infrared spectrum (Fig. 1) to contain no cyclobutyl or allylcarbinyl chlorides and inferred to be cyclopropylcarbinyl chloride. Interme-diate fractions amounted to 2.2 g. (10%). The purest cyclopropylcarbinyl chloride had $n^{25}D$ 1.4328 and d^{25}_4 0.980, corresponding to MR$_D$ 24.00 (the calculated value of MR$_D$ was 23.94 using 0.60 for the exaltation of the cyclo-propane ring).[26]

Conversion of the material of b.p. 87–89° to the Grignard reagent and treatment with phenyl isocyanate gave allyl-acetanilide, m.p. 88.8–90.2°, after recrystallization from hexane–benzene. This material did not depress the m.p. of an authentic sample having m.p. 91.4–91.8°. The crude anilide (before recrystallization) absorbed 99% of the theoretical amount of hydrogen calculated for allylacetani-lide on quantitative hydrogenation in methanol over plati-num oxide.

Authentic cyclopropylacetanilide was obtained by treat-ment of cyclopropylacetic acid[40] with thionyl chloride in dry ether and reaction of the crude acid chloride with aniline. The material so obtained had m.p. 98.8–99.6° after crystalli-zation from benzene–hexane.

Anal. Calcd. for $C_{11}H_{13}ON$: C, 75.40; H, 7.48. Found: C, 75.26; H, 7.46.

Reaction of Cyclopropylcarbinol with Phosphorus Tri-bromide.—Cyclopropylcarbinol (4.2 g., 0.059 mole) was added dropwise to 7.0 g. (0.026 mole) of stirred ice-cooled phosphorus tribromide. Ten ml. of methylene chloride was added, the mixture was stirred for 30 minutes, and then the excess phosphorus tribromide was decomposed by addition of ice. The methylene chloride layer was separated, washed with water, dried over calcium chloride and fractionated through a center-tube column.[37] Three fractions were taken: 0.66 g., b.p. 102–110°, $n^{25}D$ 1.4568; 3.89 g., b.p. 110.8–111.6°, $n^{25}D$ 1.4750 and 0.97 g., b.p. 111.6–112.0°, $n^{25}D$ 1.4740. The total yield of bromide was 5.5 g. (70%).

The infrared spectra indicated that the first fraction con-tained about 50% allylcarbinyl bromide while the later fractions contained no allylcarbinyl bromide. The amount of allylcarbinyl bromide formed on this basis was 6% of the total yield. The spectrum of the middle fraction is shown in Fig. 2.

Solvolysis rate studies on the middle fraction in 50% ethanol–50% water (by volume) indicated the presence of a very reactive bromide to the extent of about 65%.

Conversion of 1.33 g. of the middle fraction to the Grig-nard reagent followed by treatment with 0.98 g. of phenyl isocyanate gave 1.03 g. of a mixture of anilides. Fractional crystallization of the anilide mixture from benzene–hexane yielded allylacetanilide, m.p. 90.2–90.6°, which did not de-press the m.p. of authentic material. Quantitative hydro-

(33) P. F. Wiley, THIS JOURNAL, **71**, 3746 (1949).

(34) This substance, b.p. 56–59° (23 mm.), was prepared in 64% yield by the method used by P. A. DiGiorgio, W. A. Strong, L. H. Sommer and F. C. Whitmore, *ibid.*, **65**, 1380 (1946), for triethylchloro-silane employing ammonium bromide in place of ammonium chloride.

(35) W. Voss and E. Blanke, *Ann.*, **485**, 258 (1931).

(36) J. Timmermans and F. Martin, *J. chim. phys.*, **23**, 747 (1926).

(37) The fractionating section of this column was similar to that described by E. A. Naragon and C. J. Lewis, *Ind. Eng. Chem., Anal. Ed.*, **18**, 448 (1946).

(38) R. W. Shortridge, R. A. Craig, K. W. Greenlee, J. M. Derfer and C. E. Boord, THIS JOURNAL, **70**, 946 (1948).

(39) W. A. Lott, W. G. Christiansen and L. F. Shackell, *J. Am. Pharm. Assoc.*, **27**, 125 (1938).

(40) The cyclopropylacetic acid was prepared by the procedure of Smith and McKenzie.[3] The diethyl cyclopropylmalonate was kindly furnished by Mr. Malcolm Chamberlain.

genation of a sample of the anilide mixture in methanol over platinum resulted with absorption of 58% of the theoretical quantity of hydrogen calculated for pure allylacetanilide. The presence of cyclobutanecarboxanilide in the anilide mixture was demonstrated by oxidation of the unsaturated material with potassium permanganate in acetone followed by removal of the manganese dioxide with sulfur dioxide and purification of the unoxidized anilide. The material so obtained had m.p. 112.0–112.6° and did not depress the m.p. (113.8–114.0°) of an authentic sample of cyclobutane-carboxanilide.

Cyclopropylcarbinol with Hydrobromic Acid.—A mixture of 4.1 g. (0.057 mole) of cyclopropylcarbinol and 51 g. (0.3 mole) of 48% hydrobromic acid was stirred in an ice-bath for 30 minutes and then extracted with methylene chloride. The extract was dried over calcium chloride and distilled. Two fractions were taken; 0.35 g., b.p. 102–110°, n^{25}D 1.4520 and 1.93 g., b.p. 110.5–112.0°, n^{25}D 1.4710. The total yield was 2.3 g. (28%) and assuming half of the first fraction to be allylcarbinyl bromide the extent of formation of this material was about 8%. The infrared spectrum of the second fraction (Fig. 2) indicates this material to be cyclopropylcarbinyl and cyclobutyl bromides in a ratio of about 2:1.

Attempted Isomerization of Cyclobutyl Bromide by Magnesium Bromide.—This experiment was designed to determine whether cyclobutyl bromide might be isomerized by magnesium bromide to allylcarbinyl bromide in a Grignard solution and thus give the over-all effect of an abnormal Grignard reaction such as was obtained with cyclopropylcarbinyl bromide.

The magnesium bromide was prepared by adding 0.59 g. (0.0037 mole) of bromine to 0.089 g. (0.0037 mole) of well-stirred magnesium turnings in 10 ml. of anhydrous ether. When the bromine color disappeared, 0.56 g. (0.0041 mole) of cyclobutyl bromide was added and the mixture heated under reflux for four hours. Additional magnesium (0.10 g., 0.0041 mole) was added and, after formation of the Grignard reagent was complete, 0.48 g. (0.0040 mole) of phenyl isocyanate was run in. The yield of crude anilide was 0.66 g. (94%). The product contained no allylacetanilide since no hydrogen was absorbed over platinum in methanol. Some of the by-product obtained in the cyclobutylmagnesium chloride reaction appeared to be present and pure cyclobutanecarboxanilide, m.p. 113.0–113.6°, was obtained only after sublimation and several crystallizations from hexane–benzene.

Solvolysis Rate Determinations.—The solvolysis rate experiments were carried out in 50% ethanol–50% water (by volume) using the procedure described previously.[41] The rate curve of the cyclopropylcarbinyl–cyclobutyl bromide mixture was treated by the procedure of Brown and Fletcher.[42]

The rate expression used for the calculated curves of Fig. 3 is

$$-(k_1 + k_1')t = \log \frac{k_1(a - b) - (k_1 + k_1')x}{k_1(a - b)}$$

where a = starting total concentration of chloride
   b = starting concentration of unreactive chloride
   x = concentration of hydrochloric acid formed by solvolysis
   t = time
   k_1 = first-order solvolysis constant
   k_1' = first-order rearrangement constant

The value of 0.47 hr.$^{-1}$ for k_1 was obtained from the initial slope of the solvolysis rate curve of 1. The value of 0.14 hr.$^{-1}$ for k_1' was obtained by successive approximations.

The solvolyses of cyclopropylcarbinyl, cyclobutyl and allylcarbinyl chlorides in acetic acid were followed by titration of the excess potassium acetate as described earlier.[43] With cyclopropylcarbinyl and cyclobutyl chlorides, the extent of formation of unsaturated material was determined by bromide–bromate titration. It was assumed that the unsaturated material was exclusively allylcarbinyl chloride formed by rearrangement (and not a solvolysis product) since other solvolysis reactions of cyclopropylcarbinyl and

cyclobutyl derivatives yield almost no unsaturated substances. The rate data are shown in Fig. 4. The rate constants computed from the slopes of the rate curves are given in Table II.

TABLE II

RATE CONSTANTS FOR SOLVOLYSIS AND REARRANGEMENT OF CHLORIDES IN ACETIC ACID IN THE PRESENCE OF ACETATE ION AT 100°

Chloride	RCl, mole/l.[a]	KOAc, mole/l.[a]	k_1, hr.$^{-1}$	k_1', hr.$^{-1}$
Cyclopropylcarbinyl	0.0267	0.0213	0.032	$\begin{cases} 0.027^b \\ .045^c \end{cases}$
Cyclobutyl	.0334	.0323	$\begin{cases} .0024 \\ (.004)^d \end{cases}$	$\begin{cases} .0018^b \\ (.002)^{b,d} \end{cases}$
Allylcarbinyl	.0252	.0213	<.0002	.....

[a] Initial concentrations. [b] For rearrangement to allylcarbinyl chloride. [c] For rearrangement to cyclobutyl chloride. [d] Calculated from the final slopes of the cyclopropylcarbinyl chloride rate curves.

Isolation of Solvolysis Products of Cyclopropylcarbinyl Chloride in Acetic Acid.—A solution of 5.94 g. (0.066 mole) of cyclopropylcarbinyl chloride and 2.13 g. (0.022 mole) of potassium acetate in 40 ml. of dry acetic acid was heated for 24 hours in a thermostat at 100°. It was calculated from the rate constants that the chloride should have been about 30% solvolyzed and 70% rearranged at the end of the heating period. The solution was cooled, neutralized with aqueous potassium hydroxide and extracted with ether. The extract was dried over magnesium sulfate and the ether distilled. The residue was fractionated through a center-tube column.[37] The chloride fractions, b.p. 76–88°, n^{25}D 1.4187–1.4232, amounted to 3.3 g. and were shown by their infrared spectra to contain cyclobutyl and allylcarbinyl chlorides in a ratio of about 1.7:1. The ratio calculated from the rate constants is 1.6:1. None of the characteristic infrared absorption bands of cyclopropylcarbinyl chloride were present in the chloride spectra. After an intermediate fraction of b.p. 88–120° amounting to 0.3 g., there was obtained 1.9 g. of a mixture of esters, b.p. 126–133° and n^{25}D 1.4050–1.4100. The infrared spectra of the ester mixture indicated the presence of cyclopropylcarbinyl and cyclobutyl acetates in a ratio of about 2.6:1. Little, if any, allylcarbinyl acetate appeared to be present. Infrared spectra of pure cyclopropylcarbinyl, cyclobutyl and allylcarbinyl acetates were obtained by Dr. Vaughan C. Chambers as part of a separate investigation and will be published later.

Crotylamine.—The procedure was based on those used by Sheehan and co-workers[44] for preparation of amino acids. A mixture of 35 g. (0.38 mole) of crotyl chloride, b.p. 43–45° (190 mm.), 74 g. (0.40 mole) of potassium phthalimide and 150 ml. of dimethylformamide was heated at 120° for 30 minutes and then at 160° for an additional 30 minutes. The hot mixture was poured over 200 g. of ice and extracted with four 50-ml. portions of chloroform. The combined extracts were washed successively with 1 N potassium hydroxide, water, 0.5 N hydrochloric acid and again with water. The chloroform solution was dried over magnesium sulfate and the chloroform distilled. The residual crude solid N-crotylphthalimide amounted to 70.4 g. (92%). A sample recrystallized from 95% ethanol had m.p. 75.2–75.8° (lit.[45] 76°).

A mixture of 69.2 g. (0.34 mole) of crude N-crotylphthalimide, 200 ml. of 95% ethanol and 21.9 g. (0.37 mole) of 85% hydrazine hydrate was heated under reflux for one hour, cooled, treated with 37 ml. of 10 N hydrochloric acid and filtered. The collected phthalhydrazide was triturated with 200 ml. of water, filtered and the combined filtrates evaporated to dryness under reduced pressure. The residue was treated with a solution of 26 g. (0.4 mole) of 85% potassium hydroxide in 50 ml. of water and then extracted with three 20-ml. portions of ether. The combined extracts were dried over potassium hydroxide and fractionated through a glass-helix packed column. The yield of crotylamine was 17 g. (70%); b.p. 81–82°, n^{25}D 1.4304 (lit.[45] b.p. 81–84°, n^{20}D 1.428–1.432).

(41) J. D. Roberts, L. Urbanek and R. Armstrong, THIS JOURNAL, **71**, 3049 (1949).

(42) H. C. Brown and R. S. Fletcher, *ibid.*, **71**, 1845 (1949).

(43) J. Steigman and L. P. Hammett, *ibid.*, **59**, 2536 (1937); J. D. Roberts, W. G. Young and S. Winstein, *ibid.*, **64**, 2157 (1942).

(44) (a) J. C. Sheehan and V. S. Frank, *ibid.*, **71**, 1856 (1949); (b) J. C. Sheehan and W. A. Bolhofer, *ibid.*, **72**, 2786 (1950).

(45) K. H. Slotta and R. Tschesche, *Ber.* **62**, 1398 (1929).

α-**Methylallylamine.**—The preparation of N-α-methyl-allylphthalimide paralleled that of N-crotylphthalimide except that the α-methylallyl chloride-potassium phthalimide reaction mixture was refluxed for three hours. The yield of crude N-α-methylallylphthalimide from 41 g. (0.45 mole) of α-methylallyl chloride, b.p. 28–29° (190 mm.), 88.8 g. (0.48 mole) of potassium phthalimide and 150 ml. of dimethylformamide was 70 g. (77%). A small sample recrystallized several times from 95% ethanol had m.p. 85.0–85.6° (lit.[46] 87–88°).

Treatment of 69 g. (0.34 mole) of N-α-methylallyl-phthalimide with 27 g. (0.45 mole) of 85% hydrazine hydrate in 300 ml. of 95% ethanol as described for the preparation of crotylamine gave 10.5 g. (44%) of α-methylallyl-amine; b.p. 62–64°, n^{25}D 1.4090 (lit.[47] b.p. 62.3°, n^{20}D 1.4150).

Allylcarbinylamine.—N-Allylcarbinylphthalimide was prepared in the same manner as N-crotylphthalimide except that potassium iodide was used as the catalyst and the reaction time was one hour. From 13 g. (0.14 mole) of allylcarbinyl chloride, 28 g. (0.15 mole) of potassium phthalimide, 0.2 g. of potassium iodide and 100 ml. of dimethylformamide there was obtained 23 g. (82%) of crude N-allylcarbinylphthalimide. A small sample was recrystallized twice from 95% ethanol and had m.p. 51.1–51.5°.

Anal. Calcd. for $C_{12}H_{11}O_2N$: C, 71.62; H, 5.51. Found: C, 71.51; H, 5.60.

Treatment of 27 g. (0.13 mole) of crude N-allylcarbinyl-phthalimide with 10 g. (0.17 mole) of 85% hydrazine hydrate in 125 ml. of 95% ethanol as described for the preparation of crotylamine yielded 6.4 g. (67%) of allylcarbinyl-amine; b.p. 75–77°, n^{25}D 1.4191 (lit.[15] b.p. 81–82.5°, n^{20}D 1.4273). Since the properties of the amine were quite different than those previously reported[15] the material was carefully characterized.

N-Allylcarbinyl-N'-phenylthiourea was obtained from the reaction of the amine with phenyl isothiocyanate and had m.p. 44.5–44.9° after crystallization from ethanol–water (lit.[15] m.p. 91°).

Anal. Calcd. for $C_{11}H_{14}N_2S$: C, 64.04; H, 6.84. Found: C, 63.93; H, 6.85.

N-Allylcarbinyl-N'-phenylurea from allylcarbinylamine and phenyl isocyanate had m.p. 94–95° after recrystallization from ethanol–water.

Anal. Calcd. for $C_{11}H_{14}ON_2$: C, 69.44; H, 7.42. Found: C, 69.39; H, 7.28.

The carbon-skeleton of the N-allylcarbinyl-N'-phenyl-urea was established by hydrogenation of a 0.14-g. sample over platinum at atmospheric pressure in methanol solution. The catalyst was removed by filtration, the filtrate concentrated to small volume and the product precipitated with water. Recrystallization from ethanol–water gave 0.097 g. (65%) of N-n-butyl-N'-phenylurea, m.p. 129.2–129.8° (lit.[48] 129–130°).

Cyclobutylamine.—The procedure of Zelinsky and Gutt[49] was used for the conversion of cyclobutanecarboxylic acid[50] to cyclobutylamine.

N-Cyclobutylbenzamide was obtained from the reaction of cyclobutylamine with benzoyl chloride by the Schotten-Baumann procedure. The product after crystallization from benzene–hexane had m.p. 120.6–121.6°.

Anal. Calcd. for $C_{11}H_{13}ON$: C, 75.41; H, 7.48. Found: C, 75.91; H, 7.53.

Cyclopropylcarbinylamine.—A solution of 27 g. (0.40 mole) of cyclopropyl cyanide[51] in 600 ml. of anhydrous ethanol[52] was treated with 46 g. (2.0 g.-atom) of sodium metal at such a rate as to maintain gentle refluxing of the solvent. After the sodium had dissolved, the solution was cooled and 240 ml. of 10 N hydrochloric acid added slowly. The precipitated sodium chloride was collected by filtration and washed with two portions of 95% ethanol. The filtrate and washings were combined and evaporated under reduced

pressure on a steam cone. The residue was made up to 100 ml. with water and 27 ml. of the solution was used to make N-cyclopropylcarbinylbenzamide as described above for N-cyclobutylbenzamide. The yield of N-cyclopropyl-carbinylbenzamide was 17.7 g. (94%); m.p. 67–70°, after evaporative distillation at 0.9–1.5 mm. Sublimation of a small sample gave material of m.p. 72.5–74.5° (lit.[25] 74–75°).

The remainder of the cyclopropylcarbinylamine hydrochloride solution was basified and steam-distilled into a receiver containing 28 ml. of 10 N hydrochloric acid. After 100 ml. of distillate had been collected, the solution was evaporated to dryness under reduced pressure on a steam cone. Benzene (50 ml.) was added, and the mixture again evaporated to dryness. The residue was taken up in 150 ml. of warm absolute ethanol, the solution filtered and the filtrate concentrated to 80 ml. Dry ether (50 ml.) was added and the mixture allowed to stand in a refrigerator for several hours. Three crops of **cyclopropylcarbinylamine hydrochloride** were obtained which amounted to 27.9 g. (89%) and had m.p. 203–204°. A small sample was recrystallized for analysis; m.p. 206–207.5°.

Anal. Calcd. for $C_4H_{10}NCl$: C, 44.65; H, 9.37. Found: C, 44.47; H, 9.23.

In one preparation, the free amine was isolated by treatment of the hydrochloride solution with potassium hydroxide and saturation with potassium carbonate. The crude product was dried over potassium hydroxide and distilled; b.p. 83.5°, n^{25}D 1.4300 (lit.[53] b.p. 86°, n^{19}D 1.4251).

Reactions of Amines with Nitrous Acid.—Similar procedures were used throughout and only the details of a single reaction will be given.

A. Crotylamine.—In a 500-ml. three-necked flask equipped with stirrer and a condenser set for downward distillation was placed an ice-cold solution of 9.3 g. (0.13 mole) of crotylamine in 50 ml. of water, 150 ml. of ice-cold 1 N perchloric acid and an ice-cold solution of 27.6 g. (0.40 mole) of sodium nitrite in 100 ml. of water. The stirrer was started, the solution was heated to boiling and the mixture distilled until about 50 ml. of distillate was collected. A Dry Ice-cooled trap was connected to the outlet of the receiver but no significant quantity of material was collected in the trap and it was concluded that no butadiene was formed in the reaction. The distillate was saturated with potassium carbonate and extracted with two 15-ml. portions of ether. The combined extracts were dried over magnesium sulfate, the ether distilled and the residue fractionated through a center-tube column.[37] The total yield of a mixture of α-methylallyl and crotyl alcohols was 5.8 g. (62%). The composition of the mixture as determined from the distillation and refractive index data was 53% α-methyl-allyl alcohol and 47% crotyl alcohol. The materials collected on the plateaus of the distillation curve had b.p. 98–99°, n^{25}D 1.4120 (lit. for α-methylallyl alcohol,[16] b.p. 97°, n^{25}D 1.4125) and b.p. 122–124°, n^{25}D 1.4270 (lit. for *trans*-crotyl alcohol,[16] b.p. 121°, n^{25}D 1.4270).

B. α-Methylallylamine.—From 10.5 g. (0.15 mole) of α-methylallylamine by a similar procedure was obtained 7.7 g. (73%) of a mixture of 69% α-methylallyl and 31% crotyl alcohols. The properties of the materials obtained on the distillation plateaus were in good agreement with those given above.

C. Cyclopropylcarbinylamine.—The cyclopropylcar-binylamine was generated from the hydrochloride (28 g., 0.26 mole) by shaking with freshly precipitated silver oxide prepared from 51 g. (0.30 mole) of silver nitrate and 12 g. (0.30 mole) of sodium hydroxide. The silver chloride was removed by filtration and the solution neutralized with 1 N perchloric acid. The procedure was not completely successful in that some silver chloride seemed to be carried along as an amine complex and precipitated on acidification with perchloric acid. The remainder of the procedure was similar to that used for crotylamine and 6.4 g. (35%) of a mixture of cyclobutanol and cyclopropylcarbinol of b.p. 57° (42 mm.) and n^{25}D 1.4316 was obtained. Analysis of the mixture by its infrared spectrum indicated approximately 47% cyclobutanol, 48% cyclopropylcarbinol and 5% allylcarbinol. No crotyl or α-methylallyl alcohol was detected.

D. Cyclobutylamine.—From 5.6 g. (0.08 mole) of cyclobutylamine was obtained 3.6 g. (64%) of alcohol mix-

(46) O. Mumm and H. Richter, *Ber.*, **73**, 843 (1940).

(47) J. Krueger and M. Schwarcz, THIS JOURNAL, **63**, 2512 (1941).

(48) T. L. Davis and N. D. Constan, *ibid.*, **58**, 1800 (1936).

(49) N. Zelinsky and J. Gutt, *Ber.*, **40**, 4744 (1907).

(50) J. Cason and C. F. Allen, *J. Org. Chem.*, **14**, 1036 (1949).

(51) M. J. Schlatter, *Org. Syntheses*, **23**, 20 (1943).

(52) The ethanol was dried by the method of E. L. Smith, *J. Chem. Soc.*, 1288 (1927).

(53) P. Dalle, *Rec. trav. chim.*, **21**, 123 (1902).

ture in two fractions; 1.3 g., b.p. 124–126°, n^{25}D 1.4310 and 2.3 g., b.p. 126°, n^{25}D 1.4319. The infrared spectra indicated 12% allylcarbinol in the first fraction and none in the second. Approximately equal amounts of cyclobutanol and cyclopropylcarbinol were present in each and the calculated composition of the over-all mixture was 48% cyclopropylcarbinol, 48% cyclobutanol and 4% allylcarbinol. No crotyl or α-methylallyl alcohol was detected.

E. **Allylcarbinylamine.**—From 8.9 g. (0.12 mole) of allylcarbinylamine was obtained 5.1 g. (57%) of a mixture of alcohols; b.p. 100–126°, n^{25}D 1.4110–1.4300. The mixture was found from distillation, refractive index, infrared and hydrogenation data to contain approximately 18% α-methylallyl alcohol, 10% crotyl alcohol, 45% allylcarbinol, 13% cyclobutanol and 14% cyclopropylcarbinol.

Since particular interest was attached to the formation of cyclobutanol and cyclopropylcarbinol in the reaction, an attempt was made to identify these substances more positively than possible by infrared spectra. The latter fractions, which amounted to 2.0 g. and had b.p. 123–126°, n^{25}D 1.4290–1.4300, were shown by infrared and quantitative hydrogenation data to contain about 10% allylcarbinol, 20% crotyl alcohol, and 35% each of cyclobutanol and cyclopropylcarbinol. One and one-half grams of the combined material was converted to a mixture of N-phenylcarbamates with 2.5 g. of phenyl isocyanate. The crude mixture was dissolved in 25 ml. of methylene chloride and stirred at room temperature for an hour with a solution of 4 g. of sodium permanganate trihydrate in 50 ml. of water. The mixture was cooled, the manganese dioxide destroyed by passing in sulfur dioxide, the methylene chloride layer separated, washed with water, washed with dilute potassium hydroxide solution and dried over magnesium sulfate. The residue obtained after removal of the methylene chloride was shown by its infrared spectrum (Fig. 6) to consist of approximately equal amounts of cyclopropylcarbinyl and cyclobutyl N-phenylcarbamates. No unsaturated material was present. Fractional crystallization of the material yielded the pure cyclobutyl compound, m.p. 130.2–130.8° which did not depress the m.p. of material previously prepared.[17] Attempts to separate the pure cyclopropylcarbinyl derivative from the mixture by fractional crystallization from several solvents, fractional sublimation and chromatographic adsorption were uniformly unsuccessful and the identification of this material in the mixture rests on the infrared spectra.

Hydrolysis of Chlorides. A. Cyclobutyl Chloride.—A mixture of 3.0 g. (0.033 mole) of cyclobutyl chloride, 1.2 g. (0.016 mole) of lithium carbonate and 10 ml. of water was refluxed for 30 hours, then saturated with potassium carbonate and extracted with ether. The ether extracts were dried over magnesium sulfate, the ether was distilled and the residue fractionated through a center-tube column.[37] The yield of a mixture of alcohols having an infrared spectrum practically identical with the spectra of the cyclobutylamine and cyclopropylcarbinylamine–nitrous acid products was 0.69 g. (29%); b.p. 125–127°, n^{25}D 1.4295–1.4329.

B. **Cyclopropylcarbinyl Chloride.**—Since cyclopropylcarbinyl chloride was found to rearrange to cyclobutyl and allylcarbinyl chlorides on solvolysis, complication in the interpretation of the reaction products by extensive hydrolysis of the cyclobutyl chloride was avoided by carrying the reaction only to 80% of completion. Under these conditions only a few per cent. of cyclobutyl chloride should have been hydrolyzed because of its relatively slow hydrolysis reaction rate compared to cyclopropylcarbinyl chloride.

A mixture of 10.2 g. (0.113 mole) of cyclopropylcarbinyl chloride, 3.3 g. (0.045 mole) of lithium carbonate and 40 ml. of water was refluxed until the lithium carbonate dissolved. The reaction mixture was extracted continuously with methylene chloride, the methylene chloride extract dried over magnesium sulfate and the methylene chloride distilled. The residue was fractionated through a center-tube column[37] giving 0.13 g., b.p. 73.5–77°, n^{25}D 1.4238; 0.65 g., b.p. 77–84.5°, n^{25}D 1.4264, and 0.38 g., b.p. 84.5–85°, n^{25}D 1.4297, of unreacted chlorides as well as 4.5 g. (69%) of a mixture of alcohols, b.p. 42–43° (31 mm.), n^{25}D 1.4324, which was shown by its infrared spectrum to have approximately the same composition as the products of the cyclobutylamine and cyclopropylcarbinylamine–nitrous acid reactions. Analysis of the chloride fractions by means of their refractive indexes and infrared spectra indicated 45% allylcarbinyl chloride, 45% cyclobutyl chloride and 10%

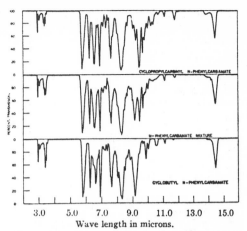

Fig. 6.—Infrared spectra: Baird spectrograph with NaCl prism, solutions of 50 mg. of compounds in 0.50 ml. of carbon disulfide except in the regions 4.2–4.0 μ and 6.2–7.2 μ where carbon tetrachloride was used as solvent.

cyclopropylcarbinyl chloride. The infrared spectrum of the largest fraction clearly shows the presence of all three halides (cf. Fig. 1).

C. **Allylcarbinyl Chloride.**—The reaction of allylcarbinyl chloride with water is extremely slow and an attempt was made to achieve a useful reaction rate by carrying out the reaction rate with silver carbonate instead of lithium carbonate. A reflux period of nine days was required for disappearance of the chloride layer. During the reaction a slight odor of 1,3-butadiene was apparent at the top of the reflux condenser and a silver mirror formed on the sides of the flask. A trace of starting material was the only organic product which could be isolated.

Reaction of Alcohols with Lucas Reagent.—The following experiment with cyclopropylcarbinol is illustrative of the procedure. Cyclopropylcarbinol (10.0 g., 0.14 mole) was added dropwise to 100 g. of ice-cooled stirred Lucas[54] reagent. An immiscible layer formed immediately. After the addition was complete the mixture was stirred at ice-bath temperature for an hour and then at room temperature for an additional hour. Ice water (100 ml.) was added, the upper layer was separated and the lower layer extracted with ether. The crude product and ethereal extracts were combined and dried over magnesium sulfate. After distillation of the ether the residue was distilled through a short Vigreux column. The yield of allylcarbinyl chloride, b.p. 75–75.4°, n^{25}D 1.4191, was 7.41 g. (59%). The only other products were high-boiling polymeric materials.

Cyclobutanol (2.54 g., 0.035 mole) was stirred with 25 g. of Lucas reagent at room temperature for two hours. The yield of allylcarbinyl chloride was 1.46 g. (46%); b.p. 75–76°, n^{25}D 1.4185.

Allylcarbinol did not appear to react with Lucas reagent at room temperature and, on heating, decomposition with formation of dark-colored products occurred.

Isomerization of Chlorides with Lucas Reagent.—Treatment of 11.0 g. of a mixture containing approximately 65% cyclopropylcarbinyl chloride and 35% cyclobutyl chloride with 80 g. of Lucas reagent for one hour at 0° and one hour at room temperature gave 5.1 g. (46%) of allylcarbinyl chloride; b.p. 75°, n^{25}D 1.4186.

With 2.8 g. of a similar mixture of cyclopropylcarbinyl and cyclobutyl chlorides and 2.8 g. of Lucas reagent and a reaction time of one hour at room temperature, there was obtained on fractionation through an efficient center-tube column[37] 0.62 g. of allylcarbinyl chloride, b.p. 77–78°, n^{25}D 1.4202 and 0.68 g. of material, b.p. 84–84.5°, n^{25}D 1.4329. Intermediate fractions amounted to 0.52 g., n^{25}D 1.4269. The material of b.p. 84–84.5° was shown by its infrared spectrum to contain 93% cyclobutyl chloride and 7% cyclopropylcarbinyl chloride.

(54) H. J. Lucas, THIS JOURNAL, 52, 802 (1930).

TABLE III

RESULTS OF EXCHANGE EXPERIMENTS USING Cl³⁸-CONTAINING LUCAS REAGENT AND ORGANIC CHLORIDES

Chloride	Wt., g.	G.-eq. of Cl	Layer	Elapsed time,d min.	Counts/min.e	Counts/min., cor. to zero time f	Fraction of layer counted g	Total counts/min.	Calcd. total counts at exchange equilibrium	Exchange, %
Mixture of cyclopropyl- carbinyl and cyclobutyl	6.36 LR^a	0.077^c	H₂O	0	4579	4579	0.420	10950	11200	107
	2.11 RCl^b	.023	CH₂Cl₂	2.0	1618	1679	.452	3650	3400	
Allylcarbinyl	6.34 LR^a	.077^c	H₂O	3.5	5534	5905	.421	14100	11100	13
	2.19 RCl^b	.024	CH₂Cl₂	5.0	212	233	.451	460	3500	
Blank	6.11 LR^a	.074^c	H₂O	7.0	4951	5637	.423	13300	13400	0.4
	.. RCl^b	....	CH₂Cl₂	8.5	21	27	.500	54	...	

[a] LR = Lucas reagent.   [b] RCl = organic chloride.   [c] The Lucas reagent contained 0.0121 g.-eq. of Cl/g.   [d] Elapsed time from beginning of counting period.   [e] Corrected for background.   [f] Using 37.4 min. for Cl³⁸ half-life.   [g] Calculated using d^{20} for Lucas reagent of 1.68, for cyclobutyl chloride of 0.99 and for allylcarbinyl chloride of 0.92.

Bromide Isomerizations with Zinc Bromide–Hydrobromic Acid Solutions.—The reagent was prepared by dissolving anhydrous zinc bromide in an equimolar amount of cold 48% hydrobromic acid. Isomerization of 2.0 g. of a mixture of about 2:1 cyclopropylcarbinyl and cyclobutyl bromides with 35 g. of zinc bromide–hydrobromic acid solution at 0° for one hour yielded 0.60 g. (29%) of bromides; b.p. 100–102° n^{25}D 1.4600. The infrared spectrum of the product (Fig. 2) indicates the product to contain about 30% of cyclobutyl bromide and 70% of allylcarbinyl bromide.

A similar experiment with 4.6 g. of the same bromide mixture and 25 g. of zinc bromide–hydrobromic acid solution at room temperature for one hour resulted in the formation of a bromide, b.p. 99–101°, n^{25}D 1.4600 which had an infrared spectrum which was identical with that of authentic allylcarbinyl bromide. The yield was 3.1 g. (67%).

Exchange Experiments Using Radioactive Chlorine (Cl³⁸).—One gram of potassium chloride was bombarded with deuterons in the M.I.T. cyclotron for ten minutes.[55] The target was allowed to stand for 30 minutes, and then the potassium chloride was transferred to an all-glass distillation apparatus. An excess of concentrated sulfuric acid was added and the resulting hydrogen chloride swept with a stream of carbon dioxide into a receiver containing 1 ml. of water. The radioactive hydrochloric acid so formed was then added to 30 g. of ordinary Lucas reagent.

The exchange reactions were carried out by stirring a halide sample with about three times its weight of radioactive Lucas reagent for one hour at room temperature. Twenty ml. each of water and methylene chloride was pipetted in, the mixtures shaken and the layers separated. The aqueous and methylene chloride layers were washed with methylene chloride and water, respectively, and the methylene chloride layer was dried over sodium sulfate. The washings were discarded. Ten-ml. aliquots were taken from each layer, placed in test-tubes and counted with a G–M counter at a standard distance. Appropriate corrections were made for the decay of the Cl³⁸ (half-life, 37 min.) during the counting period.

A mixture of cyclopropylcarbinyl ($\sim$ 65%) and cyclobutyl ($\sim$ 35%) chlorides was used in one of the exchange experiments and under the conditions (1 part of chloride to 3 parts of Lucas reagent for one hour at room temperature) about 80% of the material was isomerized to allylcarbinyl chloride. In the other exchange experiment, allylcarbinyl chloride was used. The results along with those obtained in a blank are given in Table III.

Reaction of Cyclopropylcarbinol and Cyclobutanol with Thionyl Chloride.—The procedure was similar to that used for the preparation of allylcarbinyl chloride.

(55) We are indebted to the M.I.T. cyclotron crew for the preparation and bombardment of the sample.

Cyclopropylcarbinol (15.0 g., 0.21 mole) with 24.8 g. (0.21 mole) of thionyl chloride yielded 13.7 g. (73%) of a mixture of chlorides, b.p. 84–86°, n^{25}D 1.4314–1.4324. Infrared spectra of the various fractions indicated the presence of 3% allylcarbinyl chloride, 67% cyclopropylcarbinyl chloride and 30% of cyclobutyl chloride. All of the allylcarbinyl chloride appeared in the first fraction which amounted to 2.08 g.

Treatment of the Grignard reagent prepared from a fraction containing no unsaturated material with phenyl isocyanate gave a mixture from which was isolated an anilide of m.p. 88.2–89.0° after crystallization from benzene–hexane. This material did not depress the m.p. of allylacetanilide.

A similar chloride mixture was obtained when equimolar amounts of pyridine, alcohol and thionyl chloride were used. Cyclobutanol (9.4 g., 0.13 mole) with 15.7 g. (0.13 mole) of thionyl chloride in the absence of pyridine gave 5.9 g. (50%) of chlorides, b.p. 83.5–84.8°. The infrared spectra of this material and that obtained in a similar preparation using an equimolar quantity of pyridine were almost identical with the spectrum of the products of the thionyl chloride–cyclopropylcarbinol reaction.

Reaction of Benzamides with Phosphorus Pentabromide.
A. N-Cyclopropylcarbinylbenzamide.—A mixture of 32 g. (0.18 mole) of N-cyclopropylcarbinylbenzamide and 51.5 g. (0.19 mole) of phosphorus tribromide was warmed until the amide dissolved and then cooled to 0°. Bromine (30.4 g., 0.19 mole) was added dropwise with shaking to the ice-cooled mixture. The crude products were distilled from the reaction mixture into a Dry Ice-cooled trap under reduced pressure. The organic layer was decanted and fractionated. The yield of material, b.p. 104°, n^{25}D 1.4759 (lit.,[55] b.p. 106°) was 4.3 g. (17%). The product was shown to contain about 30% of cyclobutyl bromide by its infrared spectrum (Fig. 2). Treatment of the Grignard reagent from the bromide with phenyl isocyanate gave a mixture of anilides, m.p. 70–77°, which after several recrystallizations yielded allylacetanilide, m.p. 88.8–89.6°. Since the bromide was saturated to permanganate and cyclobutyl bromide yields cyclobutanecarboxyanilide in the Grignard reaction, the allylacetanilide must have been formed from cyclopropylcarbinyl bromide.

B. N-Cyclobutylbenzamide.—A similar reaction using 41 g. (0.23 mole) of N-cyclobutylbenzamide, 63.5 g. (0.23 mole) of phosphorus tribromide and 37 g. (0.23 mole) of bromine yielded 18.5 g. (59%) of bromide mixture, b.p. 106–108°; n^{25}D 1.4760–1.4784. The infrared spectrum of this material (Fig. 2) indicated somewhat more (about 40%) cyclobutyl bromide than was formed in the preceding reaction.

CAMBRIDGE 39, MASSACHUSETTS   RECEIVED AUGUST 9, 1950

13 | Tracer Experiments on the Norbornyl Cation

The communication by Roberts and Lee is notable not only for its ingenious experiment and the remarkable results of it, but for the entrance of that word "nonclassical," with its varied and undefined meanings, into the language of organic chemistry. Roberts does not have Ingold's flair for nomenclature, yet "nonclassical" has many users, "synartetic" has few. This quirk of language development may come in part from a waning devotion to the classical in word roots as well in rules of valence. A generation emancipated enough to synthesize "barrelene" and "twistane" may feel that even earthy English is preferable to graceful Greek. Yet this is not the whole explanation; after getting along for several years with such words as "bridged" and "unclassical" for the ions, Winstein[1] proposed the term "anchimeric" to describe assistance to ionization from neighboring parts of a molecule. Thus, synartesis is a structural concept, anchimerism is a mechanistic one. But can a synartetic ion be formed with anchimeric assistance? Only if you come from a neutralist country.

The bridged norbornyl cation postulated by Winstein and Trifan requires that the radioactive label of Roberts and Lee be distributed in the solvolysis product equally between C-2 and C-1, and equally between C-3 and C-7 (see illustration on page 66). Setting out to test this minimum requirement, Roberts and Lee found that the required redistributions occurred completely, and some others partially which had not been anticipated. The authors were then in the position, not simply of checking predictions with experiment, but of looking for a theory which would predict the still more drastic isotopic scrambling which they found.

[1] S. Winstein, C. R. Lindegren, H. Marshall, and L. L. Ingraham, *J. Am. Chem. Soc.* **75**, 148 (1953).

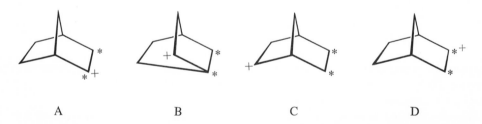

Without the work of Winstein and Trifan, and without knowledge of solvolysis rates, the facts might all have been explained by an instantaneous equilibrium between classical ions A and B, a reaction with solvent in competition with the hydride shift leading to C, and a trifling amount of D. The inadequacy of such a representation will be clear to the readers of Papers 7, 16, and 17. An appropriate intermediate ion must have a structure which accounts for its formation from

A   B   C   D

the *exo* so much faster than from the *endo* isomer, and should at best account also for the exclusive formation of *exo*-acetate as the kinetically determined product. Since the bridged ion accomplished these things and A–D did not, Roberts and Lee did not go back to A–D, but rather inquired whether the explanation might lie in still more symmetrical intermediates. The most searching NMR studies of 1964 on the unsubstituted norbornyl cation still show at low temperatures the apparent degree of symmetry required by the "nortricyclonium ion," VII, of Roberts and Lee.[2] Nevertheless we know from the incomplete equivalence of C-2

[2] P. von R. Schleyer, R. C. Fort, W. E. Watts, G. Olah, and M. B. Comisarow, *J. Am. Chem. Soc.* **86**, 4195 (1964).

and C-6 in the tracer work that if VII is present it is less important than some other ion with not more than C_s symmetry. Later workers have been disposed to get along with the three chemically equivalent bridged ions E, F, and G equilibrating too fast to be separately distinguishable in the NMR, but not fast enough to compete more than partially with attack of solvent in the formation of acetate product. These intermediates explain the driving force, the preference for *exo*

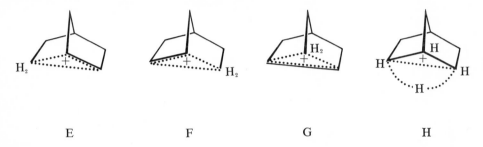

E F G H

product, the racemization, and the incomplete 6,2-shift. They even offer a reason why a hydride migration over an intervening atom, generally an elusive process in organic chemistry, chooses this particular system in which to come to the fore. In E, C-6 and C-2 are in fact neighboring atoms; the transition state (H) in the shift from E to F resembles a protonated cyclopropane, for which there is subtle modern evidence.[3]

[3] A. A. Aboderin and R. L. Baird, *J. Am. Chem. Soc.* **86**, 2300 (1964).

From: *J. Am. Chem. Soc.* **73**, 5009 (1951)

metry.[3] Actually, the reaction results in a more drastic shuffling of carbon atoms than can be accounted for solely on the basis of I or a combination of the customary 1,2-shifts of hydrogen or carbon not involving a 1-norbornyl cation. The finding that substantial C^{14}-activity was located in the 5,6-positions of the norbornyl acetate (III) is particularly significant.

An outline of the experimental results follows.

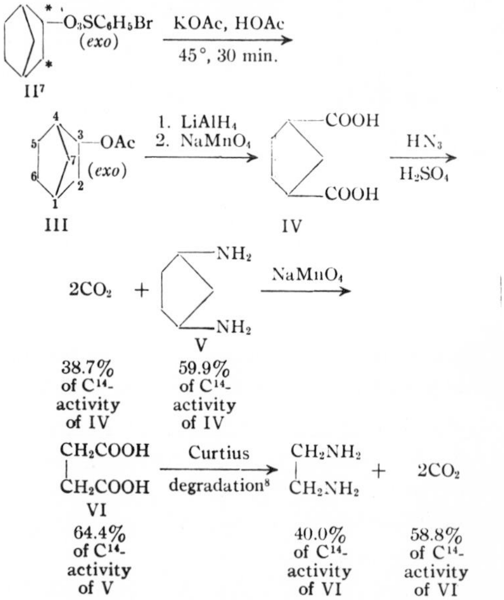

$$\text{II}^7 \quad -O_3SC_6H_5Br \ (exo) \quad \xrightarrow[45°, \ 30 \ \text{min.}]{\text{KOAc, HOAc}}$$

$$\text{III} \quad -OAc \ (exo) \quad \xrightarrow[2. \ NaMnO_4]{1. \ LiAlH_4} \quad \text{IV} \begin{array}{l} -COOH \\ -COOH \end{array} \quad \xrightarrow[H_2SO_4]{HN_3}$$

$$2CO_2 \ + \quad \text{V} \begin{array}{l} -NH_2 \\ -NH_2 \end{array} \quad \xrightarrow{NaMnO_4}$$

38.7% of C^{14}- activity of IV	59.9% of C^{14}- activity of IV

$$\begin{array}{l} CH_2COOH \\ | \\ CH_2COOH \end{array} \quad \xrightarrow[\text{degradation}^8]{\text{Curtius}} \quad \begin{array}{l} CH_2NH_2 \\ | \\ CH_2NH_2 \end{array} \ + \ 2CO_2$$

VI

64.4% of C^{14}- activity of V		40.0% of C^{14}- activity of VI	58.8% of C^{14}- activity of VI

THE NATURE OF THE INTERMEDIATE IN THE SOLVOLYSIS OF NORBORNYL DERIVATIVES[1,2]

Sir:

It has been suggested[3] on the basis of solvolysis rate and stereochemical considerations that the solvolysis of *exo*- and *endo*-norbornyl *p*-bromobenzenesulfonates in acetic acid proceeds by a bridged "non-classical" carbonium ion having a structure (I) like that proposed[4] for the cationic intermediate involved in the rearrangement of camphene hydrochloride to isobornyl chloride. The desirability of tracer experiments to confirm structure I has been pointed out earlier[5] and, as part of

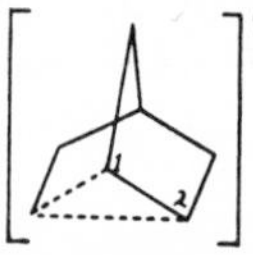

I

an investigation of the mechanisms of reaction of norbornyl derivatives, solvolysis reactions of *exo*- and *endo*-norbornyl-2,3-C_2^{14} *p*-bromobenzenesulfonates are being studied in several solvents.

Solvolysis of the *exo*-isomer (II) in acetic acid via intermediate I would be expected to yield equal[6] parts of *exo*-norbornyl-2,3-C_2^{14} and *exo*-norbornyl-1,7-C_2^{14} acetates since positions 1 and 2 must become equivalent if I is to have a plane of sym-

The C^{14}-activity distribution in III is calculated to be as follows: 2,3-positions, 40%; 1,4-positions, 23%; 5,6-positions, 16%; and 7-position, 21%.

An attractive interpretation of the present results is that the formation of I from II precedes, or possibly is competitive with the formation of a non-classical cation with a three-fold symmetry axis such as a "nortricyclonium" ion (VII). Preliminary results indicate that the relative importance of VII, or the equivalent, increases slightly in formic acid and decreases markedly in acetone–water.

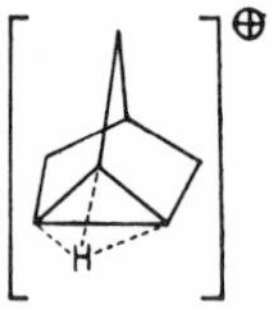

VII

DEPARTMENT OF CHEMISTRY AND LABORATORY FOR NUCLEAR SCIENCE AND ENGINEERING
MASSACHUSETTS INSTITUTE OF TECHNOLOGY
CAMBRIDGE 39, MASSACHUSETTS   JOHN D. ROBERTS
    C. C. LEE

RECEIVED AUGUST 20, 1951

(1) Supported by the program of research of the U. S. Atomic Energy Commission under Contract AT(30-1)-905.

(2) Presented at the Symposium on Reaction Mechanisms at the 75th Anniversary Meeting of the American Chemical Society, September 7, 1951.

(3) S. Winstein and D. S. Trifan, THIS JOURNAL, **71**, 2953 (1949); S. Winstein and D. S. Trifan, Abstracts of April, 1951, Meeting of the American Chemical Society, 53M, 54M.

(4) T. P. Nevell, E. de Salas and C. L. Wilson, *J. Chem. Soc.*, 1188 (1939).

(5) J. D. Roberts, R. E. McMahon and J. S. Hine, THIS JOURNAL, **72**, 4237 (1950).

(6) Neglecting differences in reaction rate between C^{12} and C^{14} atoms (isotope effect).

(7) The synthesis of II starting from barium carbide-C^{14} (obtained from Tracerlab, Inc., on allocation from the U. S. Atomic Energy Commission) will be described in detail later.

(8) A. A. Benson and J. A. Bassham, THIS JOURNAL, **70**, 3939 (1948).

14 | The Reactivity of Cyclopropylmethyl Benzenesulfonate

The paper of Bergstrom and Siegel (1952, Paper No. 14) focuses attention on the driving force toward ionization in cyclopropylmethyl benzenesulfonate. This compound shows the rare behavior, for a primary halide or sulfonate, of undergoing first-order solvolysis in the presence of a comparable concentration of strong base, here sodium methoxide. In the case of β,β'-dichlorodiethyl sulfide (mustard gas) such first-order hydrolysis in the presence of sodium hydroxide or other strong nucleophiles proved to be one of a series of compelling evidences of the formation of an ethylenesulfonium ion by participation of neighboring sulfur.[1-3] Bergstrom and Siegel seek to identify the special stabilization of the ion which so facilitates first-order solvolysis of cyclopropylmethyl benzenesulfonate and which must be associated at the same time with the ease of its rearrangement.

[1] R. A. Peters and E. Walker, *Biochem. J.* **17**, 260 (1923).
[2] R. C. Fuson, C. C. Price, and D. M. Burness, *J. Org. Chem.* **11**, 477 (1946).
[3] P. D. Bartlett and C. G. Swain, *J. Am. Chem. Soc.* **71**, 1406 (1949).

From: *J. Am. Chem. Soc.* **74**, 145–51 (1952)

[CONTRIBUTION FROM THE DEPARTMENT OF CHEMISTRY OF ILLINOIS INSTITUTE OF TECHNOLOGY]

The Effect of a Cyclopropyl Group on a Displacement Reaction at an Adjacent Saturated Carbon Atom. I. The Ethanolysis of Cyclopropylmethyl Benzenesulfonate[1]

BY CLARENCE G. BERGSTROM[2] AND SAMUEL SIEGEL

Cyclopropylmethyl benzenesulfonate isomerizes readily to a mixture which contains mainly 3-butenyl benzenesulfonate. It reacts with ethanol by a first order process to yield chiefly cyclopropylmethyl ethyl ether. The rate is faster than that of allyl or 3-butenyl benzenesulfonate by a factor of 10 and 10^3, respectively, at 20°. Therefore, in its effect upon displacement reactions at an adjacent carbon atom, the cyclopropyl group cannot be taken as a simple though less polarizable analog of a vinyl group. The implications of these results are discussed.

The interaction of cyclopropyl groups with other functional groups within a molecule has been clearly demonstrated to be analogous to the behavior of vinyl groups by a variety of experimental observations including comparison, using suitable derivatives, of the ultraviolet spectra,[3] electric polarizabilities[3b,4] and chemical reactions.[5] Recent studies of the displacement reactions undergone by derivatives of *i*-cholesterol[6] stimulated our interest in a study of the displacement reactions of simple analogs of these compounds. To this end cyclopropylmethyl benzenesulfonate was prepared and its alcoholysis in absolute ethanol was studied.[7]

Cyclopropylmethanol[8] was converted to the benzenesulfonate by a carefully controlled reaction of the alcohol with benzenesulfonyl chloride in the solvent 2,4,6-collidine.[9] The isolation of cyclopropylmethyl benzenesulfonate was complicated by its thermal instability. The compound could not be distilled, at 10^{-4} mm. in a molecular still, without causing considerable isomerization of the product. It was therefore necessary to study the product which was purified by extraction with methylene chloride followed by evaporation of the volatile solvent at diminished pressure. This gave a product which contained approximately 90% of the ester, the solvent being incompletely removed in the allotted time.

Cyclopropylmethyl benzenesulfonate isomerizes to a mixture which consists predominantly of 3-butenyl benzenesulfonate. A sample of the ester, stored over anhydrous K_2CO_3 at 20°, was 90% isomerized in 24 hours. The infrared absorption spectrum of the isomerized ester was compared with that of 3-butenyl benzenesulfonate prepared from 3-buten-1-ol. All absorption peaks found in the spectrum of 3-butenyl benzenesulfonate appear in the spectrum of the isomerized cyclopropylmethyl benzenesulfonate. This suggests that it

consists mainly of the former substance. However, the absorption peaks at 11.1 and 11.7 microns show the presence of an additional substance. It must be isomeric with 3-butenyl benzenesulfonate because of the excellent agreement between the data for the elementary analysis and the saponification equivalent weight with those calculated for butenyl benzenesulfonate. A likely candidate for this unidentified species is cyclobutyl benzenesulfonate. This identification is suggested by the findings of Roberts and Mazur[10] that both cyclopropylmethyl chloride and cyclobutyl chloride are formed in the reaction of cyclopropylmethanol with thionyl chloride. Further support for this interpretation of the identity of the products of isomerization is obtained from kinetic data. (See later discussion.)

The reaction of the isomerized cyclopropylmethyl benzenesulfonate with sodium ethoxide in absolute ethanol yielded 3-butenyl ethyl ether and 1,3-butadiene. A small amount of another ether, possibly cyclopropylmethyl ethyl ether, was indicated.

From the reaction of undistilled cyclopropylmethyl benzenesulfonate with a solution of sodium ethoxide in absolute ethanol, cyclopropylmethyl ether was isolated. This was identified by a comparison of its physical properties and its infrared spectrum with that of a sample prepared by the alkylation of sodium cyclopropylmethoxide. The spectra are identical except for a weak absorption peak at 8.2 μ which is not present in the authentic sample. The correspondence in spectra excludes the presence of an appreciable quantity of any substance other than cyclopropylmethyl ethyl ether.

Rate Studies.—To further explore the mechanism of the alcoholysis of cyclopropylmethyl benzenesulfonate, the kinetics of the reaction was examined and a comparison made with the kinetics of alcoholysis of two related compounds, allyl benzenesulfonate and 3-butenyl benzenesulfonate. In each of these compounds the benzenesulfonate group is attached to a primary carbon atom, and the predominant mode of reaction was expected to be of the S$_N$2 type, particularly in an alcoholic solution of sodium ethoxide.[11] Cyclopropylmethyl benzenesulfonate reacts more rapidly than allyl benzenesulfonate with ethanol or water. The first order rate constant in absolute alcohol was $6.0 \pm 0.4 \times 10^{-5}$ sec.$^{-1}$ at 20.1°

(1) Presented at the 119th Meeting of the American Chemical Society, Boston, Mass., April 4, 1951.

(2) From the dissertation of Clarence G. Bergstrom, submitted in partial fulfilment of the requirements for the Ph.D. degree at Illinois Institute of Technology.

(3) (a) I. M. Klotz, THIS JOURNAL, **66**, 88 (1944); (b) M. T. Rogers, *ibid.*, **69**, 2544 (1947); (c) J F. Music and F. A. Matsen, *ibid.*, **72**, 5256 (1950); (d) A. D. Walsh, *Trans. Faraday Soc.*, **45**, 179 (1949).

(4) M. T. Rogers and J. D. Roberts, THIS JOURNAL, **68**, 843 (1946).

(5) E. P. Kohler and J. B. Conant, *ibid.*, **39**, 1404 (1917).

(6) Studies in the laboratory of Professor Byron Riegel. *Cf.* R. M. Dodson and B. Riegel, *J. Org. Chem.*, **13**, 427 (1948).

(7) After this study was well under way, we learned that Professor John D. Roberts of the Massachusetts Institute of Technology was engaged in an extended study of the reactions of cyclopropylmethyl chloride. Occasional conversations and exchange of correspondence with him proved of value in our study.

(8) L. I. Smith and S. McKenzie, Jr., *J. Org. Chem.*, **15**, 74 (1950).

(9) C. G. Bergstrom and S. Siegel, THIS JOURNAL, **73**, in press (1951).

(10) J. D. Roberts and R. H. Mazur, *ibid.*, **73**, 2509 (1951).

(11) E. D. Hughes, *Trans. Faraday Soc.*, **37**, 603 (1941).

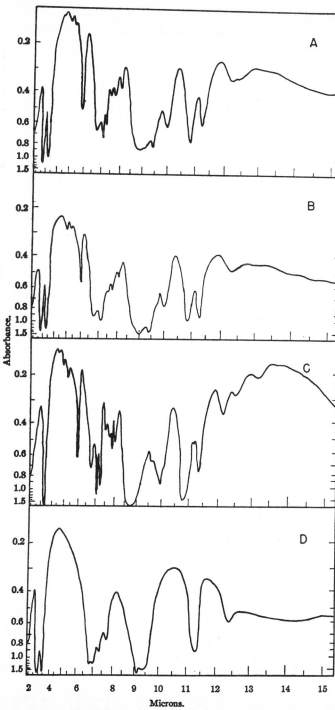

The rate remained first order in a solution containing approximately equivalent concentrations of ester and sodium ethoxide, although it was somewhat faster $(7.1 \times 10^{-5}$ sec.$^{-1})$. These results indicate the predominance of the S_N1 type of reaction. No attempt was made to obtain data from which activation energies for the solvolysis could be calculated because of the limited accuracy in the measurements of the rate constants.

3-Butenyl benzenesulfonate solvolyzes much more slowly than cyclopropylmethyl benzenesulfonate and a bimolecular rate constant for its reaction with sodium ethoxide was easily measured $(4.5 \times 10^{-4}$ l. mole^{-1} sec.$^{-1}$ at 34.8°). The rate of solvolysis at 20° $(5 \times 10^{-8}$ sec.$^{-1})$ was extrapolated by the use of the Arrhenius equation from the data obtained at 35 and 55°. The cyclopropylmethyl benzenesulfonate, therefore, solvolyzes at a rate over 10^3 times as rapidly as the 3-butenyl ester. The ratio compares well with that estimated by Roberts and Mazur for the ratio $(10^3–10^4)$ of the rates of solvolysis in aqueous ethanol of cyclopropylmethyl chloride and 3-butenyl chloride.[10]

Experimental[12]

Cyclopropanemethanol.—Cyclopropanemethanol was prepared according to the method of Nystrom and Brown,[13] by the reduction of cyclopropanecarboxylic acid (86 g.) with LiAlH$_4$ (47.5 g.) dissolved in 50 ml. of absolute ether. (See also ref. 8.) The alcohol was separated from the reaction mixture by steam distillation. The average yield for nine preparations was 69 $\pm$ 2% of the theoretical yield; b.p. 121–123°. The alcohol was purified by fractionation through a 12 $\times$ 915 mm. Todd column packed with glass helices. The properties of the material used were: b.p. 124°, n^{25}D 1.4308 and d^{25}_4 0.911.

Cyclopropylmethyl α-naphthylurethan was prepared in the usual way.[14] After it was recrystallized twice from carbon tetrachloride, it melted at 118–119°. *Anal.* Calcd. for $C_{15}H_{15}$-O_2N: N, 5.67. Found: N, 5.88.

(12) Elementary analyses were performed by the Micro-Tech Laboratory, Skokie, Illinois.

(13) R. F. Nystrom and W. G. Brown, THIS JOURNAL, **69**, 2548 (1947).

(14) R. L. Shriner and R. C. Fuson, "Identification of Organic Compounds," Second Edition, John Wiley and Sons, Inc., New York, N. Y., 1940, p. 136.

Absorbance.

Fig. 1.—Infrared spectra: A, ether–ethyl alcohol mixture obtained from the ethanolysis of "isomerized cyclopropylmethyl benzenesulfonate"; B, mixture of 3-butenyl ethyl ether and ethanol; C, 3-butenyl ethyl ether; D, ethanol.

Cyclopropylmethyl 3,5-dinitrobenzoate was prepared in pyridine from the alcohol and 3,5-dinitrobenzoyl chloride.[15] The product was recrystallized twice from alcohol and obtained in the form of brown plates, m.p. 97.5–99.0°. *Anal.* Calcd. for $C_{11}H_{10}O_4N_2$: N, 10.53. Found: N, 10.41.

3-Buten-1-ol.—3-Buten-1-ol was prepared by treating an ethereal solution of allylmagnesium chloride with gaseous formaldehyde. The alcohol boiled at 112–115° (lit. 112.5–113.5°).[16]

3-Butenyl Benzenesulfonate.—The conversion of 3-buten-1-ol to 3-butenyl benzenesulfonate was performed in the manner described for the preparation of allyl benzenesulfonate.[9] The properties of the ester were: b.p. 110° (1 mm.); $n^{20}D$ 1.5157; d^{20}_4 1.173. *Anal.* Calcd. for $C_{10}H_{12}O_3S$: C, 56.58; H, 5.70; S, 15.10; sapn. equiv., 212.3. Found: C, 56.60; H, 5.73; S, 14.63; sapn. equiv., 212.8.

Cyclopropylmethyl Benzenesulfonate.—The preparation of this ester was patterned after the procedure described for allyl benzenesulfonate.[9] However, chloroform used to extract allyl benzenesulfonate could not be removed effectively by vacuum distillation at room temperature and methylene chloride was a useful substitute for the chloroform. A mixture (26.4 ml.) of 2,4,6-collidine and cyclopropanemethanol (7.92 g.) was cooled to −5°, and freshly distilled benzenesulfonyl chloride (17.6 g.) was added. The rate of addition was such that the temperature was maintained between 0 and 5°. When all of the benzenesulfonyl chloride had been added (2 hours), 10 ml. of methylene chloride was added to give the mixture greater fluidity. The temperature was allowed to rise to 12° and was held there for one hour. The collidine was neutralized by 25 ml. of 10 N sulfuric acid, and the temperature did not rise above 18°. The two phases present were separated and the aqueous layer was extracted with methylene chloride. The combined extract was washed repeatedly with 2.5 N sulfuric acid and dried over anhydrous potassium carbonate. The solvent was removed under vacuum (0.5 mm.) at room temperature. The ester thus obtained was placed over anhydrous potassium carbonate and stored at −78° until it was used. The yield of ester was 70 ± 8%. Weighed samples of the ester were hydrolyzed in water at the reflux temperature and provided an estimate of its purity; hydrolysis equivalent weight, calcd.: 212.3. Found: 228.5.

The ester could not be distilled in a molecular still[17] at 10^{-4} mm. because of a tendency to decompose which caused the material to splatter. It decomposed more rapidly when ordinary methods of low pressure distillation were attempted.

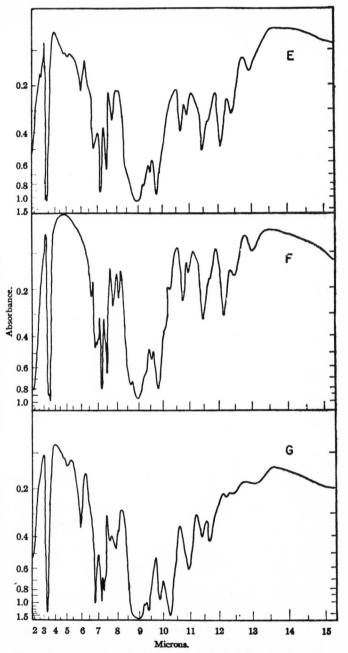

Fig. 2.—Infrared spectra: E, cyclopropylmethyl ethyl ether; F, the ether obtained in the ethanolysis of cyclopropylmethyl benzenesulfonate; G, crotyl ethyl ether.

The Isomerization of Cyclopropylmethyl Benzenesulfonate. —A chloroform solution of the product (obtained by the method described for allyl benzenesulfonate[9]) was dried over anhydrous potassium carbonate for 24 hours. After the solvent was removed under vacuum (20 mm.) the concentrate was distilled in approximately 5-g. portions from a 10-

(15) *Ibid.*, p. 138.

(16) H. Pariselle, *Compt. rend.*, **148**, 849 (1909).

(17) J. R. Matchett and J. Levine, *Ind. Eng. Chem., Anal. Ed.*, **16**, 820 (1944).

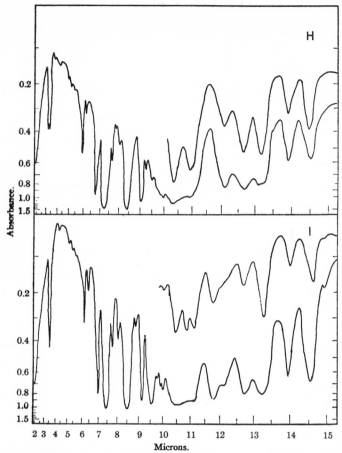

Fig. 3.—Infrared spectra: H, 3-butenyl benzenesulfonate; I, "isomerized cyclopropylmethyl benzenesulfonate." The upper curves were obtained from thin films.

alcohol (100 ml.) was added to the still pot (to prevent bumping). A total of 140 ml. of distillate was collected. It had an odor characteristic of the butenyl ethers. None of these fractions reacted with bromine in the manner of the butenyl ethyl ethers.

One-half of the distillate was diluted with water (300 ml.) and the mixture extracted with four 50-ml. portions of carbon bisulfide. The extract was dried over potassium carbonate. The dry solution was fractionated through an 8 × 915 mm. nickel spiral-packed Todd column. After removal of the carbon bisulfide, the product distilled at 95.7–99.4° (5.2 g.), mainly at 99.0–99.4° (2.8 g.). The infrared spectrum of the latter fraction was identical with that of cyclopropylmethyl ethyl ether prepared independently. The infrared spectrum of the fore fraction showed in· addition, the presence of carbon bisulfide. The yield of cyclopropylmethyl ethyl ether is 65% of the theoretical.

The Reaction of "Isomerized Cyclopropylmethyl Benzenesulfonate" with a Solution of Sodium Ethoxide in Absolute Alcohol.—The "isomerized cyclopropylmethyl benzenesulfonate" (17.1 g.), purified by distillation, and an alcoholic solution of sodium ethoxide (100 ml. of 1.4 M) were combined in a round-bottomed flask. The mixture of esters was not completely soluble in this medium. The flask was attached immediately to an 8 × 915 mm. nickel spiral-packed Todd column. The openings of the column were connected by rubber tubing and led into a trap held in Dry Ice. The temperature of the flask was raised until liquid refluxed in the column. The mixture was heated for five hours. A small amount of liquid (0.5 g.) condensed in the trap. It was transferred to a gas holder and an infrared spectrum of the vapor was obtained. Except for weak absorption bands characteristic of ethyl ether, the spectrum was identical with that reported for 1,3-butadiene.[18]

The reaction mixture was cooled and filtered to remove the large amount of solid which had separated from the solution. The crystalline material was washed with absolute alcohol, the washings were combined with the filtrate. The filtrate was returned to the still pot and 40 ml. of 1-hexanol (b.p. 158.0–159.5°) was added to serve as a "chaser." Distillate was obtained which boiled in the range 74–79° (120 g.). There was no appreciable intermediate fraction boiling between 79 and 158°. The amount of unsaturated ether present in the 74–79° fraction was measured by bromination, and the yield of unsaturated ether was 36%.

The first fraction taken, b.p. 74–78° (8.85 g.), contained approximately one-third by weight (2.9 g.) of an unsaturated ether. The infrared spectrum was identical with that of a synthetic mixture of one part 3-butenyl ethyl ether and two parts ethanol. The later fractions b.p. 78–79° (33.1 g.) contained less unsaturated ether (estimated by analysis for unsaturation, 1 g.). The solution was too dilute to provide a significant infrared spectrum. The ether was isolated by the procedure described above for the isolation of cyclopropylmethyl ethyl ether from an alcoholic solution. The product distilled at 92–95° (0.40 g.); n^{20}D 1.4010. Its infrared spectrum was almost identical with that of 3-butenyl ethyl ether. The fraction is therefore mainly 3-butenyl ethyl ether.

ml. distilling flask containing 0.2 g. of potassium carbonate. A clear, almost colorless distillate was obtained; b.p. 124° (0.9 mm.). The infrared spectrum was similar to that of 3-butenyl benzenesulfonate. *Anal.* Calcd. for C$_{10}$H$_{12}$O$_3$S: C, 56.58; H, 5.70; S, 15.10; sapn. equiv., 212.3. Found: C, 56.28; H, 5.64; S, 15.13; sapn. equiv., 211.9.

A portion of this ester was stored for 11 days at 55° over anhydrous potassium carbonate. It distilled in a molecular still when heated 50°(0.001 mm.); n^{20}D 1.5160; d^{20}_4 1.183. Its infrared spectrum had many features in common with that of 3-butenyl benzenesulfonate. *Anal.* Calcd. for C$_{10}$H$_{12}$O$_3$S: C, 56.58; H, 5.70; S, 15.10. Found: C, 56.54; H, 5.65; S, 15.46. These data suggest that cyclopropylmethyl benzenesulfonate isomerizes readily whenever an attempt is made to distil it.

The rate of alcoholysis of the ester provided a method for its· analysis. (See Rate Studies.) A freshly prepared sample of cyclopropylmethyl benzenesulfonate, in contact with anhydrous potassium carbonate at 20°, was 90% isomerized in 24 hours.

The Reaction of Cyclopropylmethyl Benzenesulfonate with a Solution of Sodium Ethoxide in Absolute Alcohol.—A solution of sodium ethoxide (200 ml., 1.7 M) was mixed with cyclopropylmethyl benzenesulfonate (38.1 g.; 93% by weight as determined by measurement of its hydrolytic equiv. wt.) and heated at 35° for 11 days. The alcoholic solution was fractionated through a 12 × 915 mm. glass helix packed Todd column. After 89 ml. of distillate (b.p. 78.5–78.4°) had been taken, a further quantity of absolute

(18) R. S. Rasmussen and R. R. Brattain, *J. Chem. Phys.*, **15**, 131 (1947).

TABLE I

PROPERTIES OF ETHYL ETHERS PREPARED IN THIS STUDY

Ethyl ether	B.p., °C.	n^{20}D	d^{20}_4	Carbon, % Calcd.	Found	Hydrogen, % Calcd.	Found
Cyclopropylmethyl[a]	99.5–100.8	1.4050	0.816	71.95	71.50	12.08	11.80
3-Butenyl[b]	90.7–90.8	1.3978	.779	71.95	71.72	12.08	11.57
Crotyl[c]	102–103	1.4036	.777	71.95	71.95	12.08	11.80

[a] Michiels[21] reports b.p. 98–101° for the ether obtained from the reaction of cyclopropylmethyl iodide and alcoholic potassium hydroxide. [b] Pariselle[22] prepared this ether from allylmagnesium bromide and chloromethyl ethyl ether; b.p. 90°; n^{17}D 1.396. [c] trans-Crotyl ethyl ether[23]; b.p. 100.4–100.5; n^{20}D 1.4040; d^{20}_4 0.7846.

3-Butenyl Ethyl Ether.—This ether was prepared by the reaction of the sodium salt of 3-buten-1-ol and diethyl sulfate. The salt was obtained from the reaction of the alcohol with "sodium naphthalene" in dioxane.[19]

To a mixture of carefully purified dioxane (250 ml.), and naphthalene (36 g.) maintained in an inert atmosphere, small lumps of sodium (6 g.) were added. The mixture was slowly heated to the reflux temperature. At the end of 20 hours, all of the sodium was dissolved and a brown sludge had separated from the solution. The solution was cooled in ice and 3-buten-1-ol (18.9 g.) was added cautiously. This was followed by 41.5 g. of diethyl sulfate. The mixture was allowed to stand at room temperature overnight.

The reaction mixture was distilled rapidly through a 12 × 915 mm. Todd column. The material boiling below 100° was purified by extraction with dilute sodium hydroxide and dried over Drierite. Fractionation of the material yielded a product of b.p. 90–91° (10.0 g., 26% of the theoretical). A central fraction had the properties given in Table I.

Cyclopropylmethyl Ethyl Ether.—Using the techniques described above, the lithium salt of cyclopropanemethanol was prepared from the alcohol (14.4 g.), and lithium hydride (1.59 g.) in butyl ether (100 ml.). A voluminous white precipitate formed when the flask was heated on a steam-bath for one-half hour. The mixture was heated for two hours longer and then cooled. Diethyl sulfate (30.0 g.) diluted with 25 ml. of n-butyl ether was added over a period of 40 minutes. The mixture was heated on the steam-bath and as the reaction proceeded more n-butyl ether was added to maintain a fluid mixture. The reaction was completed with the reaction flask attached to an 8 × 915 mm. nickel spiral-packed Todd column, and the material which boiled in the range 68–140° was collected (21.8 g.). The crude product was dried over solid sodium hydroxide and refractionated. The ether forms an azeotrope with ethyl alcohol; b.p. 78.0–78.1°; n^{20}D 1.3749. After the removal of the azeotrope (6.0 g.), cyclopropylmethyl ethyl ether distilled at 99.5–100.8° (5.0 g.); n^{20}D 1.4050. The properties of the product which was redistilled from sodium are given in Table I. Cyclopropylmethyl ethyl ether reacts slowly with bromine in carbon tetrachloride.

Crotyl Ethyl Ether.—This ether was prepared from crotyl chloride and sodium ethoxide in the way described by Roberts, Young and Winstein.[20] The properties are reported in Table I.

Rate Studies.

—The rate of reaction of 3-butenyl benzenesulfonate with sodium ethoxide in anhydrous ethanol was performed in the manner described for allyl benzenesulfonate.[9] The reactants were contained in volumetric flasks immersed in thermostats controlled to ±0.05°. Samples were removed by pipet for analysis. For the solvolysis of esters performed at 55° or followed for periods longer than 24 hours at 35 or 55°, the procedure was varied to avoid volatilization of materials. Aliquots were transferred to test-tubes and sealed using the usual techniques.

For the reaction of 3-butenyl benzenesulfonate

(19) (a) R. G. Stevens and S. A. V. Deans, *Canada J. Research*, 17B, 290 (1939); (b) N. D. Scott, J. F. Walker and V. L. Hansley, THIS JOURNAL, 58, 2442 (1936).

(20) J. D. Roberts, W. G. Young and S. Winstein, *ibid.*, 64, 2157 (1942).

(21) L. Michiels, *Bull. soc. chim. Belg.*, 24, 396 (1910).

(22) H. Pariselle, *Compt. rend.*, 150, 1066 (1910).

(23) M. Lepingle, *Bull. soc. chim. France*, [4] 39, 855 (1926).

with sodium ethoxide, the second-order rate constants calculated for sequential points in a run did not show a trend (Table II). However, "isomerized cyclopropylmethyl benzenesulfonate" (e.g., cyclopropylmethyl benzenesulfonate which had been allowed to stand at room or higher temperature for a day or more and then distilled) did not react with sodium ethoxide according to any simple reaction order. The calculated bimolecular rate constants decreased as the reaction proceeded (Table III) but was of the same order of magnitude as that of 3-butenyl benzenesulfonate. This may be explained if the isomeric esters include one such as cyclobutyl benzenesulfonate which would be expected to react more slowly with sodium ethoxide than the 3-butenyl ester.

TABLE II

RATE OF REACTION OF 3-BUTENYL BENZENESULFONATE WITH NaOEt IN ABSOLUTE ETHANOL AT 34.8°

3-Butenyl benzenesulfonate, 0.0289 M; sodium ethoxide 0.0472 M

Time, min.	Reacted, %	$k_2 \times 10^4$ (l. mole^{-1} sec.$^{-1}$)
210	22.0	4.55
479	40.2	4.42
710	52.6	4.60
1392	71.3	4.43
1643	76.2	4.48
1990	80.6	4.40
2200	82.0	4.23
2843	88.9	4.53
3099	92.1	5.03
	Average	4.52
	Weighted av.	4.55

TABLE III

RATE OF REACTION OF "ISOMERIZED CYCLOPROPYLMETHYL BENZENESULFONATE" WITH NaOEt IN ETHANOL AT 34.8°

Ester 0.0253 M; NaOEt 0.0446 M

Time, min.	Reacted, %	$k_2 \times 10^4$ (l. mole^{-1} sec.$^{-1}$)
354	26.1	3.47
1290	55.3	2.85
1798	62.5	2.60
2740	71.9	2.37
3314	75.4	2.20
4254	80.6	1.97
4722	79.8	1.83
8854	91.7	1.77

The Reaction of Cyclopropylmethyl Benzenesulfonate with Ethanol.—Since this ester hydrolyzes more rapidly than allyl benzenesulfonate, a modification was made in the quenching technique. A mixture of 25 ml. of carbon tetrachloride and 50 ml. of water was chilled in ice and made just basic to phenolphthalein. The sample tube was removed from the thermostat and at a recorded time 10 ml. of cold carbon tetrachloride was added to the tube. The contents of the tube were transferred quantitatively to the cold carbon tetrachloride–water mixture. The solution was titrated with 0.04 M sodium hydroxide. Because the end-point fades rather rapidly the rate of fading was measured and used to extrapolate the buret reading to the time of mixing of the reactants with water.

Because of the thermal instability of the ester, it was not obtained in a purity greater than about 90%. The remainder was probably solvent which was not removed. The initial concentration of the ester in a kinetic run was therefore calculated from the value of the titer of the reaction mixture which was attained at the end of eight to nine times the approximate half time for the reaction. If the sample of ester used had contained as much as 20% of either 3-butenyl benzenesulfonate or the mixture obtained when cyclopropylmethyl benzenesulfonate isomerizes, then the acid produced by their solvolysis would cause an error of about 1% in the calculated initial concentration of cyclopropylmethyl benzenesulfonate. Since the samples of ester used contained approximately 85% of cyclopropylmethyl benzenesulfonate, the error in

the probable uncertainty in the rate constants for the solvolysis of cyclopropylmethyl benzenesulfonate is estimated to be 10%. A typical run is given in Table IV.

Calculation of Rate Constants.—The bimolecular rate constants (k_2) were calculated from the equation

$$k_2 = \frac{2.303}{(a-b)t} \times \log \frac{b(a-x)}{a(b-x)}$$

where a and b are the initial concentrations of the ester and the sodium ethoxide, respectively, and x is the concentration of ester which has reacted at the time t.

The first order rate constant is a weighted average of all of the individual values for k. The initial concentration of ester is represented by a, the other symbols are as given above. The rate constants which are listed in Table V are weighted averages for each run.

Significance of Results

The data support the conclusion that cyclopropylmethyl benzenesulfonate solvolyzes in absolute alcohol by a process of the S_N1 type. The reactivity of the ester is remarkable, its rate of alcoholysis being greater than that of allyl benzenesulfonate by a factor of 10. The reverse order of reactivity was expected from considerations that the cyclopropyl group would behave as a less effective counterpart of the vinyl group in accelerating displacement reactions at an adjacent saturated carbon atom. The expected order of reactivity apparently is found for the S_N2 type of reaction.

Similar explanations have been offered to account for the enhanced reactivity toward solvolysis of allyl[24] and cyclopropylmethyl[10,25] halides relative to the solvolysis of saturated alkyl halides. The transition state for the solvolysis of an allyl halide is said to be stabilized by the contribution of the resonance forms I and II.

TABLE IV

THE SOLVOLYSIS OF CYCLOPROPYLMETHYL BENZENESULFONATE IN ANHYDROUS ETHYL ALCOHOL

Concentration of ester from "infinity" titer, 0.0160 M; unrearranged ester in sample, 84.0%

Time, min.	Reacted, %	$k_1 \times 10^5$ (sec.$^{-1}$)
21	9.4	(7.8)
34	15.0	(8.0)
59	22.5	7.2
97	31.9	6.7
161	46.8	6.5
246	61.2	6.5
326	72.5	5.5
441	83.7	6.7
1430	100.0	...
Average		6.5 (6.8)
Weighted av.		6.3

$$CH_2=CH-\overset{\oplus}{C}H_2 \ldots \overset{\ominus}{X} \longrightarrow \overset{\oplus}{C}H_2-CH=CH_2 \ldots \overset{\ominus}{X}$$

$$\text{I} \qquad\qquad\qquad \text{II}$$

TABLE V

REACTION RATES OF THE BENZENESULFONATES IN ABSOLUTE ETHANOL

Benzenesulfonate	Temp., °C.	Ester, mole/l.	NaOEt, mole/l.	k_1, sec.$^{-1}$	k_2, l./mole-sec.
3-Butenyl	34.79	0.0289	0.0472	....	4.55×10^{-4}
3-Butenyl	34.79	.0217	.0417	....	4.38×10^{-4}
3-Butenyl	34.79	.0298	....	2.2×10^{-7}	....
3-Butenyl	55.30	.0221	....	2.3×10^{-7}	....
3-Butenyl	55.30	.0198	....	2.0×10^{-7}	....
Cyclopropylmethyl	20.13	.0204	....	5.7×10^{-5}	....
Cyclopropylmethyl	20.13	.0160	....	6.3×10^{-5}	....
Cyclopropylmethyl	20.13	.0175	.0266	7.2×10^{-5}	....
"Isomerized cyclopropylmethyl"	34.79	.0215	....	7×10^{-7a}	....
Allyl	20.1	....	....	4.2×10^{-8b}	2.7×10^{-3}

[a] Apparent first order rate constant for early part of the reaction. [b] Constants are taken from reference 9.

the estimated initial concentration due to the presence of isomeric esters is less than one per cent.

The uncertainty caused by the incomplete quenching of the reaction provides a larger error, about 2 to 5% in the calculated rate constant and

The analogous forms for the solvolysis of cyclopropylmethyl halide are

(24) M. Polanyi, *Trans. Faraday Soc.*, 37, 377 (1941).
(25) J. D. Roberts, W. Bennett and R. Armstrong, THIS JOURNAL, 72, 3329 (1950).

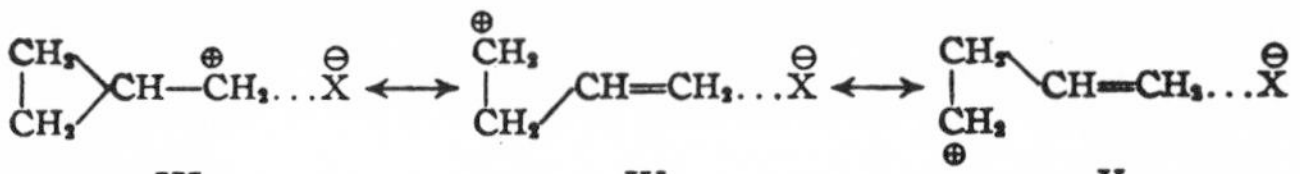

III   IV   V

The hyperconjugation which can be represented for saturated alkyl halides is thought to provide lesser stabilization of the transition state. Clearly, these formulations are intended to describe the interaction between an unsaturated center and a positive charge. Judging from the relative displacement of ultraviolet absorption bands for vinyl- and cyclopropylcarbonyl compounds,[20] or benzenes,[20] the interaction between a vinyl group and a positive center should be the more effective.

The remarkable facility with which cyclopropylmethyl benzenesulfonate solvolyzes, therefore, requires an explanation in which the cyclopropyl group is taken to be something other than a simple though less polarizable analog of the vinyl group. A clue to this problem may be gained from an examination of a possible structure for the cyclopropylmethyl carbonium ion represented by the hybrid VI—VII. The structure of this resonance hybrid is noteworthy for its symmetry, suggesting

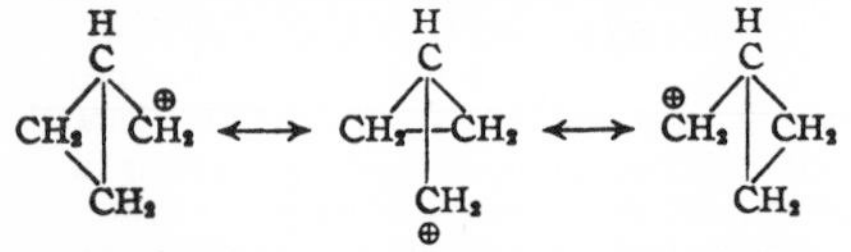

VI   VII   VIII

that the three methylene groups are equivalent. To gain this symmetry the bond angles and distances must be changed from those present in the parent compound. The importance of the symmetry factor in resonance stabilization of an ion has been stressed previously.[26]

The above argument for the structure of the carbonium ion can be transposed to a discussion of the transition state for solvolysis. In the transition state the structures IX → XI would be considered. Only two of the structures are equivalent but the third approaches the energy of the other two as the ions separate during the solvolysis.

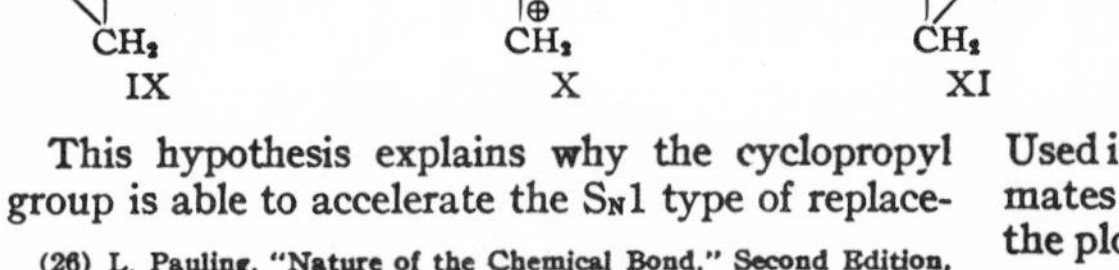

IX   X   XI

This hypothesis explains why the cyclopropyl group is able to accelerate the S_N1 type of replace-

(26) L. Pauling, "Nature of the Chemical Bond," Second Edition, Cornell University Press, Ithaca, New York, 1945, p. 214.

ment at a neighboring carbon atom more effectively than it can accelerate the S_N2 type of mechanism. It also explains the predominant formation of ethyl cyclopropylmethyl ether in the solvolysis; attack of a molecule of solvent at any one of three carbon atoms would lead to identical products. It does not exclude the possibility for rearranged products, for example an attack of the solvent at the carbon atom bearing only one hydrogen atom would yield a cyclobutane derivative.

The thermal isomerization of cyclopropylmethyl benzenesulfonate yields chiefly 3-butenyl benzenesulfonate. The ease with which this is accomplished suggests a mechanism of intramolecular rearrangement similar to the one postulated by Roberts, Young and Winstein[22] for the conversion of crotyl chlorosulfite XII to methylvinylcarbinyl chloride XIII. The geometry of the molecules of cyclopropylmethyl benzenesulfonate is so related as to suggest a common mechanism XIV → XV.

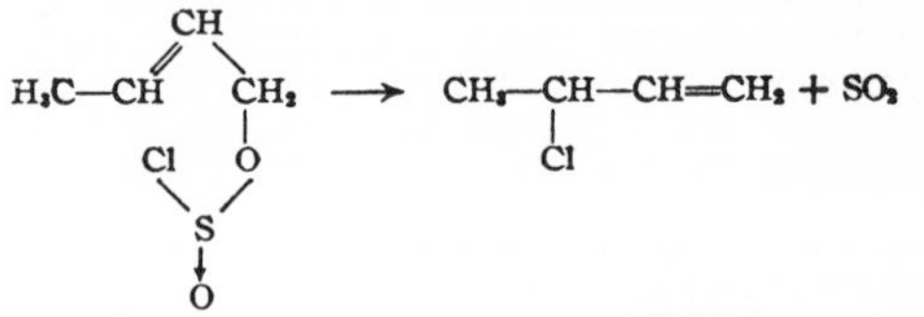

XII   XIII

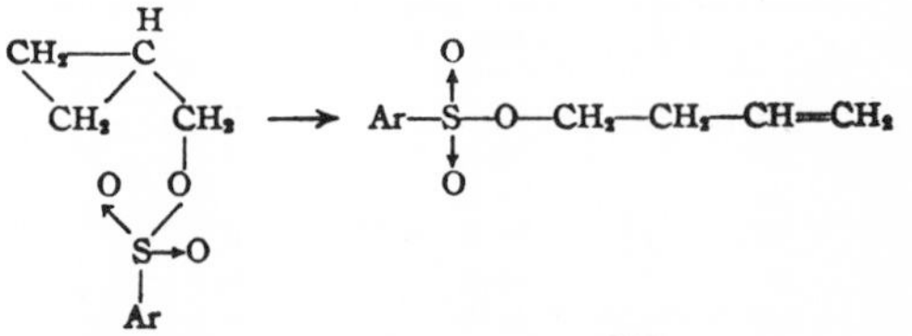

XIV   XV

Acknowledgment.—We are indebted to Mrs. Lorna Patterson of the Armour Research Foundation who determined most of the infrared absorption spectra. The infrared spectrum of 1,3-butadiene was determined by Dr. Richard Bernstein. We are also grateful for his assistance in the interpretation of the spectra.

Infrared Spectra.—The infrared spectra were determined with a Perkin–Elmer Model 12C single beam recording spectrophotometer. The mechanical slit drive was used and the cell length was 0.025 mm. Used in this way, the ordinate, absorbance, approximates a linear scale of per cent. transmission and the plot is suitable for "fingerprinting" compounds.

15 | Driving Forces in Neighboring Group Participation

The next three papers from Winstein's laboratory (Papers 15, 16, and 17) illustrate some of the patterns evolved for dealing with problems of mechanism and intermediates.

Winstein, Morse, Grunwald, Schreiber, and Corse (Paper No. 15) point out that whenever bridged ions are formed by participation of a neighboring group, they are formed in competition with unbridged ions, which in their turn may have either localized or delocalized charge. Different kinds of substitution in the starting material may have effects in stabilizing either or both of the competing ions. An assembly of experimental data is used to derive some generalizations assigning the effects observed among dipolar, steric, classical and nonclassical resonance causes. Although such assignments have been made more quantitatively in other special cases, this comprehensive paper allowed many correct predictions to be made. For example, noting the dwindling participational driving force as the α-carbon atom is changed from primary to secondary, one forecasts from this paper that bridged ions will not provide any important driving force in the benzpinacol rearrangement or other cases where the charge delocalization in a classical ion is overwhelmingly efficient. These anticipations were elegantly verified in tracer work by Collins and his co-workers (see Paper No. 24).

From: *J. Am. Chem. Soc.* **74,** 1113–20 (1952)

[CONTRIBUTION FROM THE DEPARTMENT OF CHEMISTRY OF THE UNIVERSITY OF CALIFORNIA AT LOS ANGELES]

Neighboring Carbon and Hydrogen.[1] V. Driving Forces in the Wagner–Meerwein Rearrangement[2,3]

BY S. WINSTEIN, BETSY K. MORSE,[4] E. GRUNWALD,[4] KURT C. SCHREIBER AND JOSEPH CORSE

Participation by a β-H, R or unsaturated group and its associated electron cloud in a nucleophilic replacement process has important analogies to the similar participation of functional neighboring groups. The driving force due to so-called participation of carbon in the rate-determining ionization can be substantial, and some orientation as to the order of magnitude of driving forces attained is supplied by rate measurements now reported. Solvolysis rate constants for a primary series and another secondary series of arylsulfonates illustrate the trends expected on the basis of participation. Driving forces decrease in the order of C_α: primary > secondary, and increase as C_β is substituted with conjugating groups in the order: $CH_3 < C_6H_5 \cong (CH_3)_2 < (C_6H_5)_2$. These effects modify tremendously the usual trends in reactivity with α- or β-substitution in the absence of driving forces due to participation.

Our work reported in another series of papers[5] has made it clear that participation of a functional neighboring group (*e.g.*, Br) and its associated electron cloud in nucleophilic displacement processes at a nearby center is a general phenomenon. The stereochemistry[6] of replacement processes (I → III) is often controlled by this phenomenon and, also, the

driving forces[7] due to this kind of participation are often of an important magnitude. Estimating k_0, the specific rate constant of ionization to IV without participation of the neighboring group, and defining the driving force L as $RT \ln k_\Delta/k_c$, one arrives at semi-quantitative figures for driving forces.

The participation of functional neighboring groups in displacement reactions is part of a more general phenomenon which includes participation of the electrons associated with a neighboring β-H, R, Ar or vinyl group. In this paper we are concerned with this participation as it applies to the Wagner–Meerwein rearrangement (V).

For the Wagner–Meerwein rearrangement there are conceivable special mechanisms which may prove to be operative for certain circumstances in the way of structure or conditions. One of these

(1) Previous papers in this series: (a) I, Winstein and Adams, THIS JOURNAL, **70**, 838 (1948); (b) II, Winstein and Schlesinger, *ibid.*, **70**, 3528 (1948); (c) III, Winstein and Trifan, *ibid.*, **71**, 2953 (1949); (d) IV, Winstein, Walborsky and Schreiber, *ibid.*, **72**, 5795 (1950).

(2) Supported in part by the Office of Naval Research and the Research Corporation.

(3) The material of this paper was presented in summary: (a) before the Organic Division of the American Chemical Society at St. Louis, September, 1948; (b) at the Eleventh National Organic Symposium, Madison, Wisconsin, June 21, 1949, page 65 of abstracts; and (c) at Montpellier, France, April 26, 1950 [*Bull. soc. chim. France*, **18**, 55 (1951)].

(4) Taken in part from Ph.D. theses, U. C. L. A., of Betsy Morse, 1949, and E. Grunwald, 1947.

(5) Winstein and Boschan, THIS JOURNAL, **72**, 4669 (1950), and previous papers.

(6) *E.g.*, Winstein, Hess and Buckles, *ibid.*, **64**, 2796 (1942).

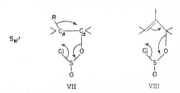

(7) (a) Winstein, Grunwald and Ingraham, *ibid.*, **70**, 821 (1948); (b) Winstein and Grunwald, *ibid.*, **70**, 828 (1948).

is $S_N i'$, illustrated by VII,[8] analogous to the $S_N i'$ mechanism in the allylic[9] rearrangement field (VIII). Another conceivable special mechanism is $S_N 2'$ illustrated by IX, analogous to $S_N 2'$ with allylic[10] materials (X). This is the type mechanism for which negative evidence was obtained by Bartlett and Pöckel[11] in the rearrangement of camphene hydrochloride.

$$S_N 2' \quad \overset{R}{\underset{\underset{Z}{\overset{\cdot\cdot}{\cdot}}}{>C_\beta}}\!\!-\!\!\underset{Y}{C_\alpha}< \qquad \underset{Z \quad X}{\times\!\!\!\times}$$

$$\text{IX} \qquad\qquad \text{X}$$

However, the most general mechanisms for the Wagner–Meerwein rearrangement would appear to involve preliminary ionization.[12-15] Whitmore,[14] who in 1932 formulated a consistent picture at the time of various rearrangements, visualized the Wagner–Meerwein rearrangement in terms of formation of a carbonium ion with the original structure XII, which rearranges, by shift of a β-electron pair and the accompanying group, to a carbonium ion with a rearranged structure XIII. The question has sometimes been raised whether rearrangement accompanies or occurs subsequent to ionization[16] and each alternative has at times been suggested.[15-17]

Our view has been[3] that it is possible for participation of the electron cloud associated with a neighboring H, R or Ar group to occur in the rate-determining ionization producing either the rearranged ion XIV (specific reaction rate constant k_R) or an ion XV (specific reaction rate constant k_Δ) with a bridged structure. This latter type formulation for a carbonium ion has been mentioned or proposed[18] a number of times, and evidence on this matter is presented in later papers in

$$\overset{R}{\underset{Y^-}{>C_\beta \overset{+}{-} C_\alpha<}} \xrightarrow[-Y^-]{k_c} \overset{R}{>C_\beta - C_\alpha<} \left\{ \begin{array}{l} \xrightarrow[-Y^-]{k_R} \overset{R}{>C_\beta^+ - C_\alpha<} \quad \text{XIV} \\ \\ \xrightarrow[-Y^-]{k_\Delta} \overset{R}{>C_\beta \cdots C_\alpha<} \quad \text{XV} \end{array}\right.$$

$$\downarrow \text{XII} \qquad\qquad \text{XI} \quad Y$$

$$\underset{\text{XIII}}{>C\overset{+}{-}C<} \quad \overset{Z:}{\underset{Z}{\longrightarrow}} \quad \overset{R}{\underset{Z}{>C_\beta - C_\alpha<}}$$

this series. On the other hand, migration of a group may also occur subsequent to ionization to an unrearranged carbonium ion XII (rate constant k_c).

(8) Wallis and Bowman, *J. Org. Chem.*, **1**, 383 (1936).

(9) Roberts, Young and Winstein, THIS JOURNAL, **64**, 2157 (1942).

(10) Kepner, Young and Winstein, *ibid.*, **71**, 115 (1949).

(11) Bartlett and Pöckel, *ibid.*, **60**, 1585 (1938).

(12) Meerwein and van Emster, *Ber.*, **53**, 1815 (1920); **55**, 2500 (1922).

(13) Ingold, "Annual Reports," **25**, 124 (1928).

(14) Whitmore, THIS JOURNAL, **54**, 3274 (1932).

(15) Dostrovsky, Hughes and Ingold, *J. Chem. Soc.*, 173 (1946).

(16) *E.g.*, Skell and Hauser, THIS JOURNAL, **64**, 2633 (1942).

(17) Swain, *ibid.*, **70**, 1119 (1948).

(18) (a) Winstein and Lucas, *ibid.*, **60**, 836 (1938); (b) Nevell, de Salas and Wilson, *J. Chem. Soc.*, 1188 (1939); (c) Watson, "Annual Reports," 197 (1939); 120 (1941); (d) Eyring, *Ind. Eng. Chem.*, **35**, 511 (1943); (e) Dewar, *J. Chem. Soc.*, 406 (1946); (f) Walsh, *ibid.*, 89 (1947); (g) Arcus, *Chemistry and Industry*, 442 (1947).

One of the keys to understanding the Wagner–Meerwein phenomenon is the assessment of the magnitude of the driving force due to so-called participation of carbon or hydrogen in the rate-determining ionization and here, as with functional neighboring groups,[7] rate measurements are helpful. This paper and the next two in the series report the results of a survey of solvolysis rates of a number of compounds of interest in the Wagner–Meerwein connection.

If there is participation[19] by neighboring carbon in the rate-determining ionization, whether the carbonium ion is best described by a structure of the type XIV or by one of the bridged type XV, the transition state for ionization of XI is the type XVI, structures such as XVIIa-d contributing to the hybrid. If there is no such participation, the

$$\overset{R}{\underset{\quad\quad Y^{\delta-}}{>C_\beta \overset{\delta+}{\cdots} C_\alpha<}}$$

$$\text{XVI}$$

$$\overset{R}{\underset{Y}{>C-C<}} \leftrightarrow \overset{R}{\underset{Y^-}{>\overset{+}{C}-C<}} \leftrightarrow \overset{R}{\underset{Y^-}{>C-\overset{+}{C}<}} \leftrightarrow \overset{R^+}{\underset{Y^-}{>C=C<}}$$

$$\text{a} \qquad\qquad \text{b} \qquad\qquad \text{c} \qquad\qquad \text{d}$$

$$\text{XVII}$$

transition state is the type XVIII. The effects of methyl substitution on C_α and C_β closely correspond to those observed in functional group par-

$$\overset{R}{\underset{\quad Y^{\delta-}}{>C_\beta \overset{\delta+}{-} C_\alpha<}}$$

$$\text{XVIII}$$

ticipation.[7] Alpha and beta substitution will both increase k_R or k_Δ, while alpha substitution will increase k_c more than k_R or k_Δ. Thus, the driving force due to participation will be increased by beta substitution and decreased by alpha substitution, and we can anticipate that it will increase as we proceed from a tertiary cleaving group to a primary. In this paper are reported rates of solvolysis of a series of primary arylsulfonates and a similar series of secondary arylsulfonates, which furnish some orientation on the order of magnitude of driving forces due to participation.

Unfortunately, the very variation of structure designed to vary the driving force due to participation changes other factors which affect rate, such as inductive effects, hyperconjugation[20] effects and steric effects and these need to be considered in interpreting the rates obtained.

To make the solvolyses of the compounds in question and the reference compounds used in estimating k_c as nearly limiting[21] (Lim.) with re-

(19) Participation amounts to delocalization of the C_β–R bonding electron pair as electron deficiency is created by ionization. Now in hyperconjugation,[20] involving β-linkages, there is also delocalization. Whether, in general, hyperconjugation and participation should be considered to merge depends on the still unsettled preferred geometry in hyperconjugation.

(20) (a) Baker and Nathan, *J. Chem. Soc.*, 1844 (1935); (b) Mulliken, Rieke and Brown, THIS JOURNAL, **63**, 41 (1941).

(21) Winstein, Grunwald and Jones, *ibid.*, **73**, 2700 (1951).

TABLE I

SOLVOLYSIS RATES OF p-TOLUENESULFONATES AND p-BROMOBENZENESULFONATES

Compound	Concn. M	Temp., °C.	Solvent	$k_1(\text{sec.}^{-1})$	$\Delta H^{\ddagger}$	$\Delta S^{\ddagger}$
$(CH_3)_3CC_2HOTs$	....	49.60[a]	AcOH	2.17×10^{-9}	31.5	-1.0
	0.0403	74.71	AcOH	$(7.7 \pm 0.4) \times 10^{-8}$		
	.0796	74.71	AcOH	$(8.32 \pm 0.08) \times 10^{-8}$		
	.418	99.58	AcOH	$(1.72 \pm 0.06) \times 10^{-6}$		
	.0796	99.58	AcOH	$(1.60 \pm 0.13) \times 10^{-6}$		
	.0555	99.58	EtOH	$(4 \pm 1) \times 10^{-7}$		
$(C_6H_5)_2CHCH_2OTs$	....	49.60[a]	AcOH	1.15×10^{-7}	27.1	-6.4
	.0155	74.71	AcOH	$(2.61 \pm 0.05) \times 10^{-6}$		
	.0144	99.58	AcOH	$(3.81 \pm 0.27) \times 10^{-5}$		
	.0080	99.58	EtOH	2×10^{-5}		
$(CH_3)_2C_6H_5CCH_2OTs$	....	49.60[a]	AcOH	9.92×10^{-7}	25.7	-6.4
	.0411	74.71	AcOH	$(1.93 \pm 0.05) \times 10^{-5}$		
	.0524	99.58	AcOH	$(2.47 \pm 0.05) \times 10^{-4}$		
	.0426	74.72	EtOH	$(5.2 \pm 0.2) \times 10^{-6}$		
$(C_6H_5)_3CCH_2OTs$	.0087	49.60	AcOH	$(1.68 \pm 0.09) \times 10^{-5}$	25.2	-2.5
	.0085	74.72	AcOH	$(3.09 \pm 0.11) \times 10^{-4}$		
	.0107	49.60	EtOH	$(7.5 \pm 0.4) \times 10^{-6}$		
$CH_3CH(OBs)CH_3$	.0427	34.94	AcOH	$(1.02 \pm 0.01) \times 10^{-6}$	24.8	-5.5
	....	49.60[a]	AcOH	6.44×10^{-6}		
	.0267	70.0[b]	AcOH	6.90×10^{-5}		
$CH_3CH_2CH(OBs)CH_3$	.0229	40.0	AcOH	$(4.05 \pm 0.02) \times 10^{-6}$		
	....	49.60[a]	AcOH	1.29×10^{-5}		
	.0281	70.0	AcOH	$(1.23 \pm 0.01) \times 10^{-4}$	23.7	-7.7
	.0369	70.0	AcOH 0.025 M KOAc	$(1.27 \pm 0.02) \times 10^{-4}$		
$(CH_3)_2CHCH(OBs)CH_3$	.0162	34.94	AcOH	$(5.85 \pm 0.05) \times 10^{-6}$		
	....	49.60[a]	AcOH	3.83×10^{-5}		
	.0162	70.0	AcOH	$(4.02 \pm 0.09) \times 10^{-4}$	24.7	-2.3
	.0157	70.0	AcOH 0.025 M KOAc	$(4.14 \pm 0.04) \times 10^{-4}$		
$(CH_3)_3CCH(OBs)CH_3$	....	49.60[a]	AcOH	2.27×10^{-5}		
	.0343	50.0	AcOH	$(2.37 \pm 0.03) \times 10^{-5}$		
	.0226	70.0[b]	AcOH	(2.73×10^{-4})	26.3	1.5
$(CH_3)C_6H_5CHCH(OTs)CH_3(I)$	.035	49.60	AcOH	$(2.38 \pm 0.05) \times 10^{-6}$	26.3	-2.9
	.030	74.71	AcOH	$(4.95 \pm 0.17) \times 10^{-5}$		
$(CH_3)C_6H_5CHCH(OTs)CH_3(II)$	.029	49.60	AcOH	$(2.72 \pm 0.05) \times 10^{-6}$	26.5	-2.1
	.032	74.72	AcOH	$(5.77 \pm 0.26) \times 10^{-5}$		
$(C_6H_5)_2CHCH(OBs)CH_3$	....	49.60[a]	AcOH	1.17×10^{-5}		
	.0145	49.30	AcOH	$(1.134 \pm 0.015) \times 10^{-5}$		
	.0145	74.81	AcOH	$(2.31 \pm 0.05) \times 10^{-4}$	25.7	-1.7
	.0244	74.81	EtOH	$(1.12 \pm 0.04) \times 10^{-4}$		
$(CH_3)_2(C_6H_5)CCH(OBs)CH_3$	.0104	24.95	AcOH	$(2.03 \pm 0.03) \times 10^{-5}$	23.6	-1.0
	.0292	24.95	AcOH	$(2.05 \pm 0.02) \times 10^{-5}$		
	.0147	49.61	AcOH	$(4.64 \pm 0.08) \times 10^{-4}$		
	.0274	49.61	AcOH	$(4.67 \pm 0.09) \times 10^{-4}$		

[a] Extrapolated from data at other temperatures.   [b] Previously reported.[48]

spect to the solvent role and thus to bring out most clearly the assistance derived from participation, we have studied acetolysis of benzenesulfonates.[7a] Also, in some cases we have compared the acetolysis rates with rates of ethanolysis.

Table I lists first order rates of acetolysis and ethanolysis for four primary toluenesulfonates including neopentyl, prepared by conventional methods. The value of the ratio of acetolysis rate to ethanolysis rate ($ca.$ 2–4) suggest that the acetolysis reactions approach the desired type. Acetolysis rates, if not available at 49.60°, have been extrapolated to this temperature for comparison, the figures being given in Table I. In Table II, the acetolysis rates at 49.60° relative to neopentyl p-toluenesulfonate are given for the four primary p-toluene-

sulfonates A, B, C and D. It is clear that substantial increases of rate attend the structural changes represented by the sequence A:B:C:D. Thus β,β-diphenylethyl toluenesulfonate B, is some 50 times as reactive as neopentyl A, neophyl C some 500 times and the β,β,β-triphenylethyl D more reactive by a factor of nearly 4 powers of ten.

Table I also lists first order rates of acetolysis of a number of secondary p-toluenesulfonates or p-bromobenzenesulfonates, E — M. The esters were derived from alcohols prepared by conventional methods, except for the dl-3-phenyl-2-butanols I and II which were furnished by Dr. Donald Cram. The configurations indicated in Table III for 3-phenyl-2-butyl p-toluenesulfonates

TABLE II
RELATIVE ACETOLYSIS RATES OF PRIMARY p-TOLUENE-SULFONATES

		Rel. k_{AcOH} 49.6°	10^n rel. k or est. k/k_c
A	$(CH_3)_2C-CH_2OTs$ (with CH_3 above and phenyl below)	1	1
B	$C_6H_5-CH-CH_2OTs$ (with phenyl below)	53	5.3×10^3
C	$(CH_3)_2CH-CH_2OTs$ (with phenyl below)	460	4.6×10^3
D	$(C_6H_5)_2C-CH_2OTs$ (with phenyl below)	7.7×10^3	7.7×10^6

J I and J II are based on Cram's stereochemical evidence.[22] Acetolysis rate constants adjusted to 49.60° are given in Table I and the relative rates compared to isopropyl p-bromobenzenesulfonate E are shown in Table III (allowing a factor of 3

TABLE III
RELATIVE ACETOLYSIS RATES OF SECONDARY p-TOLUENE-SULFONATES AND p-BROMOBENZENESULFONATES

		Rel. k_{AcOH} 49.6°	k/k_H	10^n k/k_H or est. k/k_c
E	$CH_3-CH(OBs)CH_3$	1.0		
F	$CH_3-CH_2-CH(OBs)CH_3$	2.0		
G	$(CH_3)_2\overset{H}{C}-CH(OBs)CH_3$	6.0		
H	$(CH_3)_2\overset{CH_3}{C}-CH(OBs)CH_3$	3.5		
J I	structure with phenyl, $H-\overset{H}{\underset{CH_3}{C}}-\overset{CH_3}{\underset{OTs}{C}}-H$	1.1	0.55	6
J II	structure with phenyl, $CH_3-\overset{H}{\underset{H}{C}}-\overset{CH_3}{\underset{OTs}{C}}$	1.3	0.63	6
K	$C_6H_5CH-CH(OBs)CH_3$ (with phenyl below)	1.8	1.8	180
M	$(CH_3)_2C-CH(OBs)CH_3$ (with phenyl below)	73	12.2	120

[22] Cram, THIS JOURNAL, 71, 3863, 3883 (1949).

between acetolysis rates of p-bromobenzenesulfonates and p-toluenesulfonates). In the series E — H of bromobenzenesulfonates, $RCH(OBs)CH_3$, variation of R from CH_3 to t-Bu leads to the sequence of relative rates: 1:2:6:3.5. Other substitution of C_β also gives little effect on rate until M, $(CH_3)_2C(C_6H_5)CH(OBs)CH_3$, is reached, this having a relative rate of 73.

It is clear that the solvolysis of the primary p-toluenesulfonates A — D is associated with rearrangement. Neopentyl derivatives give rearranged tertiary amyl compounds in solvolytic reactions[15,23] and acetolysis of neopentyl toluene-sulfonate A should be no exception. From acetolysis of β,β-diphenylethyl toluenesulfonate B was isolated a high yield of trans-stilbene, the olefin derived after migration of a phenyl group, a result which recalls the reported dehydrations of β,β-diphenylethyl alcohol to stilbene.[24] We assume solvolysis of neophyl toluenesulfonate C largely involves migration of the phenyl group, by analogy with the almost exclusive formation of β,β-dimethylstyrene in the dehydration of neophyl alcohol.[24a] The situation is similar in the case of the triphenylethyl[25] derivative D. All four toluenesulfonates are written in Table II to indicate the migrating group on this basis. With the secondary arylsulfonates (Table III), rearrangement attends the solvolysis of most of the materials. The acetolysis products from methyl-i-propyl-carbinyl (G) and pinacolyl (H) p-bromobenzene-sulfonates are at least largely rearranged.[26]

With the 3-phenyl-2-butyl p-toluenesulfonates J I and II, at least a very substantial part of solvolysis involves phenyl group migration.[22] This same thing is true for 1,1-diphenyl-2-propyl p-bromobenzenesulfonate[27] K and is assumed for 3-methyl-3-phenyl-2-butyl p-bromobenzenesulfonate M. On this basis, compounds G — M are written in Table III to indicate the migrating group.

In discussing the significance of the substantial enhancement of rates in the primary series A — D and the effects in the secondary series E — M, we must first consider the possibility that participation is not the governing consideration. With the highly branched structures involved we must consider possible enhancement of rate due to relief of steric strain[28] in ionization without participation. For example, in the series of alkyl chlorides, $R_1R_2R_3CCl$, substantial enhancement of solvolysis rate is observed by the time (i — $Pr)_3CCl^{28b,d}$ is reached. If the governing consideration was simply steric acceleration of rate, then an effect observed in the primary series A — D should be accentuated, if anything, by α-methyl substitution to a more substituted structure. This

(23) (a) Whitmore and Fleming, J. Chem. Soc., 1269 (1934); (b) Whitmore, Wittle and Popkin, THIS JOURNAL, 61, 1586 (1939); (c) Dostrovsky and Hughes, J. Chem. Soc., 164, 166, 171 (1946).

(24) (a) Ramart and Amagat, Ann. chim., [20] 8, 263 (1927); (b) Kharasch and Clapp, J. Org. Chem., 3, 355 (1938).

(25) Danilov, C. A., 18, 1488 (1924).

(26) D. Gelfer and H. Marshall, unpublished work.

(27) Kurt Schreiber, unpublished work.

(28) (a) Brown, Science, 103, 385 (1946); (b) Bartlett, Paper before 10th National Organic Symposium, Boston, Mass., June, 1947, p. 22 of Abstracts; (c) Brown and Fletcher, THIS JOURNAL, 71, 1845 (1949); (d) Bartlett, Paper delivered at Montpellier, France, April 28, 1950.

is just the opposite of what is observed to be the effect of α-methyl substitution. For example, the C:A comparison gives relative rates

CH$_3$—C—CH$_2$OTs, 460 > CH$_3$—C—CH$_2$OTs, 1

C   A

The analogous comparison (M:H) in the secondary series gives relative rates

CH$_3$—C—CHCH$_3$, 21 > CH$_3$—C—CHCH$_3$, 1

M   H

Alpha methyl substitution acts to depress markedly the enhancement of rate attending the change of a β-CH$_3$ to a β-phenyl group. This can be accounted for on the basis of participation. In fact, the main trends in rate in the A — D series and much of the trend in the E — M series are well explained by participation.

It appears that rearrangement is attended by substantial driving forces in the primary series A — D. The main trend in rate is due to changes in $\Delta H^{\ddagger}$, $\Delta S^{\ddagger}$ being -4.1 ± 2.3 e.u. for the series. The C:A comparison (460:1) shows the serious increase in rate when phenyl is the migrating group rather than methyl. This much greater driving force for a migrating phenyl over migrating methyl may be understood on the basis, long realized, that the migration represents internal electrophilic displacement and has some analogy to external electrophilic substitution on the benzene ring or on saturated carbon (for example, the reaction of RHgI or ArHgI with triiodide ion[29]). The superiority of phenyl over alkyl lies in the availability of an electron supply for contribution of structures of the type XIXabc to the transition state. The stabilization of the transition state by this device apparently usually outweighs the ad-

>C—C<   >C—C<   >C—C<
   Y$^-$ Y$^-$ Y$^-$
XIX a   b   c

vantage of leaving the aryl group on C$_\beta$ for conjugation purposes.[30] The relative rates in the A — D series in Table II represent the first approximation to values of k/k_c, and the approximation

(29) J. Keller, Dissertation, U. C. L. A., 1948.

(30) We prefer this viewpoint to the one of Dewar, who explains the greater migration aptitude of phenyl by the greater electron attraction of cationic phenyl over cationic alkyl in a π-complex. Carried further, this viewpoint predicts incorrectly relative migration aptitudes of substituted aryl groups. [Dewar, "The Electronic Theory of Organic Chemistry," Oxford Univ. Press, Oxford, 1949, p. 215.]

may be improved. One correction has to do with the electron-attracting inductive effect usually attending the replacement of a hydrogen atom by a phenyl substituent. A crude estimate of one power of ten for the depressing effect of a phenyl substituent on k_c may be obtained from the fact that a phenyl substituent in acetic acid is ca. one-fourth as acid strengthening (logarithmically) as a chlorine substituent and the estimate that the latter decreases k_c by 4 powers of ten.[7a] Applying this correction for one phenyl substituent in C, two in B and 3 in D gives the steeper rate sequence, A:B:C:D, of 1:ca. 5 × 10^3: ca. 5 × 10^3: 8 × 10^6. Thus, on this basis, β,β,β-triphenylethyl p-toluenesulfonate D is ca. 10^7 as reactive as it would be without participation.

The rate constant for neopentyl p-toluenesulfonate A is used as the reference compound because the solvolysis of, for example, ethyl p-toluenesulfonate is far from limiting[21] in type. This rate constant may be high as an estimate of k_c because of whatever driving force may already be in evidence in the neopentyl case. Thus the estimated values of k/k_c in the last column of Table II represent lower limits.

Going over to the secondary compounds, we consider first the series, RCH(OBs)CH$_3$ (E — H). The compounds (CH$_3$)$_2$CH-CH(OBs)CH$_3$ (G) and (CH$_3$)$_3$C(CH$_3$)CH(OBs)CH$_3$ (H) have structures which we originally expected might lead to the appearance of a driving force due to participation. However, the departure from constancy in the rate sequence, E:F:G:H, of 1:2:6:3.5 is very slight and there are several effects outside of participation, the net result of which could conceivably give the observed trend. While there may be some rate enhancement in G and H, and this matter is discussed further in a following article which reports more data, any such assistance from participation is small.

Driving forces become more clearly indicated as we move down the E — M series in Table III. The diastereomeric 3-phenyl-2-butyl p-toluenesulfonates J I and II are, in a sense, borderline. They are approximately equal to i-Pr (E) in reactivity and ca. half as reactive as s-butyl (F); $k/k_H = 0.55$ or 0.63 for J I and J II, respectively. Correction for the effect a phenyl group may have on k_c raises the estimated k/k_c to ca. 6.

With 1,1-diphenyl-2-propyl p-bromobenzenesulfonate K, the driving force is larger. The acetolysis rate is already larger than that of the isopropyl compound and correction for the effect of two phenyl groups on k_c gives a corrected relative reactivity of 180. The situation is similar with 3-methyl-3-phenyl-2-butyl p-bromobenzenesulfonate M whose rate is 73 times that of the isopropyl standard and 12.2 times that of (CH$_3$)$_2$CHCH-(OBs)CH$_3$ (k_H). Correcting k/k_H by the factor for a phenyl group gives a value of 120, which is a lower limit to k/k_c to the extent a driving force exists in the reference compound G. For the cases J — M, $\Delta S^{\ddagger}$ is -1.9 ± 0.6 e.u., the rate trend being mainly due to changes in $\Delta H^{\ddagger}$.

The estimates for k/k_c in the last columns of Tables II and III are apt to be low because the values employed for k_c have probably been too high for still other reasons. Substitution of a hydrogen by carbon can be expected to reduce k_a slightly for hyperconjugative reasons. Further, this will increase steric hindrance to solvation and reduce k_c.

Besides the greater driving force for migrating phenyl vs. methyl, the estimated values of k/k_a illustrate other features in line with participation. Alpha-methyl substitution decreases (by a factor of ca. 30 or 40) the apparent driving force. For example, the k/k_c estimates are: B, $5.3 \times 10^3 >$ K, 180; C, $4.6 \times 10^3 >$ M, 120. The effect of a β-methyl group is illustrated by the k/k_c values: M, $120 >$ J, 6. Beta-substitution increases the apparent driving forces pretty much in the order of relative power for conjugation with a cationic or olefinic center. Reference to B, C, D and J, K, M gives the order of relative effectiveness of β-substituents other than the migrating group: $(C_6H_5)_2 > (CH_3)_2 \cong (C_6H_5) > CH_3$.

Looking not at driving forces but at over-all reactivities, we notice how the phenomenon of participation markedly affects the reactivity pattern in solvolysis. The effect of an α-methyl group, which ordinarily, in solvolysis of the limiting[21] or near-limiting variety, has a large rate-enhancing effect, may vary widely. As the comparisons show,

$(CH_3)_3CCH(OBs)CH_3$, $3500 > (CH_3)_3CCH_2OBs$, 1

$(CH_3)_2(C_6H_5)CH(OBs)CH_3$, $156 >$
$(CH_3)_2C(C_6H_5)CH_2OBs$, 1

$(C_6H_5)_2CHCH(OBs)CH_3$, $34 > (C_6H_5)_2CHCH_2OBs$, 1

introduction of an α-methyl group into neopentyl p-bromobenzenesulfonate still increases the acetolysis rate by a factor of 3500, but the effect is reduced to a factor of 34 in β,β-diphenylethyl. Similarly, a β-methyl group which usually has a small effect in solvolysis may have a large effect in cases of participation. This is illustrated by the comparison

$(CH_3)_2C(C_6H_5)CH(OTs)CH_3$, $60 >$
$CH_3CH(C_6H_5)CH(OTs)CH_3$, 1

While we believe the large rate trends observed involve participation and the driving forces have mainly the electronic origin discussed, nevertheless the observed rates (involving participation) can be influenced by steric effects to an extent we still have to assess. If steric strain is relieved by migration of a group from C_β to C_α, there can be an enhancement of rate of a reaction involving participation. To put it another way, participation may provide a mechanism for relief of steric strain.[28d]

As we mentioned already in connection with functional neighboring groups,[31] in a reaction involving participation, the bonds on C_α and C_β are becoming more eclipsed and interaction between groups, one on C_α and one on C_β, can increase on going to the transition state. The observed rates of reactions involving participation will reflect this interaction and further consequences of it, such as steric inhibition of resonance in the transition state.[32] While the cases are not quantita-

tively comparable, we can obtain some idea of the order of magnitude this effect may reach from existing information on other reactions. Thus for CH_3,CH_3 interaction, we know that meso-2,3-dibromobutane reacts with iodide ion to eliminate bromine only 1.8 times as rapidly as the dl-dibromide.[33] Similarly, it is interesting to note in

the case of the 3-phenyl-2-butyl p-toluenesulfonates J, that the diastereomer J I which eclipses the two methyl groups as a phenyl group participates is ca. 0.9 as reactive as the other diastereomer J II.

That the CH_3, C_6H_5 interaction of this kind can be serious, we know, for example, from the factor of ca. 70 which exists between acyl migration rates of benzoyl-ψ-ephedrine and benzoylephedrine.[34]

That the C_6H_5, C_6H_5 interaction is similarly serious we know, for example, from the factor of ca. 20 between equilibrium constants in the reaction of the dl- and meso-stilbene glycols with acetone,[35] the substantial difference in rate of reaction with potassium iodide between meso- and dl-stilbene dibromides,[36] and the inertness of meso-stilbene dichloride to elimination with pyridine relative to the dl-isomer.[37]

Participation by neighboring carbon in the rate-determining ionization step is important not only to our understanding of reactivity but also for stereochemical reasons. The general principle, applicable to the Walden inversion,[38] elimination (E2)[39] and rearrangement,[40] that activation energy is minimized when the incoming and leaving electron clouds in each unit displacement on a carbon atom have a trans relationship, will hold here. Therefore, definite evidence of a driving force due to participation should also be associated with Walden inversion at C_α.

Experimental

Neopentyl p-Toluenesulfonate.—Neopentyl alcohol, b.p. 110–111.5°, m.p. 51.6° (reported 52°)[41] was prepared by reduction of pivalyl chloride with lithium aluminum hydride by the procedure of Nystrom and Brown.[42] The p-toluenesulfonate, m.p. 48–49°, was prepared in 78% yield.

Anal. Calcd. for $C_{12}H_{18}SO_3$: C, 59.48; H, 7.79. Found: C, 59.51; H, 7.84.

2,2-Diphenylethyl p-Toluenesulfonate.—The alcohol, m.p. 59.1–59.5° (reported 59–60°),[43] was prepared in 84%

(31) Winstein and Seymour, THIS JOURNAL, 68, 119 (1946).
(32) Pollak and Curtin, ibid., 72, 961 (1950).

(33) (a) Dillon, Young and Lucas, ibid., 52, 1953 (1930); (b) Young, Eighth Nat. Org. Symposium, St. Louis, Mo., Dec., 1939, Abstracts of Papers, pp. 92–95.
(34) Welsh, THIS JOURNAL, 71, 3500 (1949).
(35) Hermans, Z. physik. Chem., 113, 338 (1924).
(36) Young, Pressman and Coryell, THIS JOURNAL, 61, 1640 (1939).
(37) Pfeiffer, Ber., 45, 1816 (1912).
(38) Hughes, Ingold, et al., J. Chem. Soc., 1252 (1937).
(39) (a) Winstein, Pressman and Young, THIS JOURNAL, 61, 1645 (1939); (b) Hughes, Ingold, et al., J. Chem. Soc., 2093 (1948).
(40) Bartlett and Pöckel, THIS JOURNAL, 59, 820 (1937).
(41) Huntress and Mulliken, "Identification of Pure Organic Compounds, Order I," John Wiley and Sons, Inc., New York, N. Y., 1941.
(42) Nystrom and Brown, THIS JOURNAL, 69, 1197 (1947).
(43) Bergmann, J. Chem. Soc., 412 (1936).

yield by reduction of diphenylacetic acid with lithium aluminum hydride, the reaction mixture being worked up with potassium hydroxide solution. Some less pure material, m.p. 53–54°,[44] used in some of the earlier work, was prepared from methyl benzhydryl ether by cleavage with excess sodium under nitrogen and treatment with formaldehyde. The p-toluenesulfonate, m.p. 116°, equivalent weight in acetolysis within 0.3% of theory, was prepared in the usual way.

Anal. Calcd. for $C_{21}H_{20}SO_3$: C, 71.56; H, 5.72. Found: C, 71.31; H, 5.71.

Neophyl p-Toluenesulfonate.—The alcohol was prepared in 62% yield by the oxidation of neophylmagnesium chloride according to the directions of Whitmore, Weisgerber and Shabica.[45] The toluenesulfonate, m.p. 74–75°, was prepared in the conventional manner. The equivalent weight in acetolysis agreed to 0.05 and 1.7% with the calculated value in different runs.

Anal. Calcd. for $C_{17}H_{20}SO_3$: C, 67.08; H, 6.62. Found: C, 66.96; H, 6.79.

2,2,2-Triphenylethyl p-Toluenesulfonate.—Triphenylmethylsodium was prepared in anhydrous ether according to the method of Hauser[46] from 1.5% sodium amalgam and trityl chloride, which had been recrystallized from ligroin and acetyl chloride. The solution of triphenylmethylsodium was decanted under nitrogen from the excess sodium and a threefold excess of formaldehyde, generated by heating dried polyoxymethylene, was passed over the vigorously stirred solution. Addition of ice water, drying of the ether layer over potassium carbonate, and removal of the ether, followed by several recrystallizations of the residue from methanol, gave triphenylethanol, m.p. 104–105° (reported 107°).[47] The toluenesulfonate, m.p. 106°, equivalent weight in solvolysis within 1.8% of theoretical, was prepared in 51% yield.

Anal. Calcd. for $C_{27}H_{24}SO_3$: C, 75.67; H, 5.65. Found: C, 75.65; H, 5.80.

Isopropyl and Pinacolyl p-Bromobenzenesulfonates.—These materials, m.p. 32.3–34.1° and 53.2–53.5°, respectively, have been described previously.[48]

2-Butyl p-Bromobenzenesulfonate.—Prepared in 50% yield from 2-butanol, this material tended to be a viscous oil, $n^{25}D$ 1.5323, d^{25}_4 1.4394; equiv. wt., calcd. 293.2; obsd. 299.6 (solvolysis in 80% acetone), 299.4 (acetolysis), m.p. 31–32° after crystallization.

Anal. Calcd. for $C_{10}H_{13}SO_3Br$: C, 40.96; H, 4.47. Found: C, 40.77; H, 4.47.

Methyl-i-propylcarbinyl p-Bromobenzenesulfonate.—The necessary carbinol, b.p. 111.8–111.9 (754 mm.) was prepared from acetaldehyde and isopropylmagnesium bromide. The bromobenzenesulfonate was prepared in 55% yield in the form of a viscous oil, which could not be induced to crystallize, $n^{24}D$ 1.5292, d^{24}_4 1.389; equiv. wt., calcd. 307.2; found 309.6 (acetolysis).

Anal. Calcd. for $C_{11}H_{15}SO_3Br$: C, 43.00; H, 4.92. Found: C, 43.07; H, 5.20.

From the refractive indices and densities of the two esters described above, the molar refraction of the p-$BrC_6H_4SO_3$ group is found to be 43.79 ± 0.22.

3-Phenyl-2-butanols and 3-Phenyl-2-butyl p-Toluenesulfonates.—The alcohols, b.p. of both racemates, 114° (20 mm.), were obtained by the saponification of the acid phthalates furnished by Dr. Donald Cram. The distilled alcohols were converted to toluenesulfonates by the conventional procedure.

I. Racemate I from acid phthalate, m.p. 130–131°, gave rise to p-toluenesulfonate, m.p. 51°, in 58% yield.

Anal. Calcd. for $C_{17}H_{20}SO_3$: C, 67.08; H, 6.62. Found: C, 67.24; H, 6.57.

II. Racemate II from acid nitrophthalate, m.p. 156–157°, gave rise to p-toluenesulfonate, m.p. 42.5–43° in 48% yield.

Anal. Found: C, 67.09; H, 6.75.

Toluenesulfonate I displayed equivalent weights in acetolysis within 0.68–0.75% of theoretical and toluenesulfonate II within 0.78–2.0%.

1,1-Diphenyl-2-propanol and p-Bromobenzenesulfonate.—1,1-Diphenylacetone was prepared by addition of a solution of diphenylacetyl chloride, prepared from 106 g. (0.5 mole) of diphenylacetic acid, in 250 ml. of benzene in a nitrogen atmosphere, to a solution of dimethylcadmium in benzene prepared from 24 g. (1 mole) of magnesium and excess methyl iodide according to the directions of Cason.[49] The addition required 15 minutes and the reaction mixture was allowed to stand 1 hour at room temperature. Decomposition was effected with ice and hydrochloric acid. The organic layer was washed with water, sodium hydroxide solution, water, sodium sulfite solution and again with water, and finally dried over magnesium sulfate. Removal of the solvent on the steam-bath and distillation *in vacuo* yielded 66 g. of 1,1-diphenylacetone, b.p. 142–144° (2 mm.).

In more recent work, 1,1-diphenylacetone, b.p. 138–145° (1.5–3 mm.), m.p. 57–60° (reported 61°),[50] was prepared from phenylacetone by the method of Schultz and Mickey.[51]

The 66 g. of liquid ketone was dissolved in 120 ml. of anhydrous ether and added over 30 minutes to 3.8 g. of lithium aluminum hydride suspended in 120 ml. of ether. After stirring for 20 minutes, the reaction mixture was decomposed with water and cold dilute sulfuric acid. The organic layer was washed with water and potassium carbonate solution and dried over potassium carbonate. Evaporation of the ether left 62.9 g. of crude liquid 1,1-diphenyl-2-propanol. Similar reduction of 190 g. (0.90 mole) of solid ketone yielded 164 g. (84.5%) of 1,1-diphenyl-2-propanol, m.p. 62° from Skellysolve B (reported 62–63°).[52]

Preparation of the p-bromobenzenesulfonate from the carbinol in the usual way, allowing a reaction period of four days in the refrigerator, gave rise to the ester in 69% yield, m.p. 98–99°; equiv. wt., 428.8 (ethanolysis), 433.1 (acetolysis); calcd., 431.3.

Anal. Calcd. for $C_{21}H_{19}BrO_3S$: C, 58.47; H, 4.44. Found: C, 58.47; H, 4.61.

2-Phenyl-2-methyl-3-butanol and Derivatives.—To a methyl Grignard solution, prepared from methyl iodide (5 g., 0.055 mole), magnesium (5 g., 0.037 mole) and ether (100 cc.), was added 2-phenyl-2-methylpropionaldehyde (5 g., 0.034 mole) (kindly furnished by Mr. Lee Kent) in ether (50 cc.). The resulting mixture was stirred for one hour at room temperature after the addition was complete and it was then poured into ice-water containing sulfuric acid (15 cc., 6 N). The ether layer was separated, and the aqueous layer extracted with ether. The combined ethereal layers were washed with 5% sodium bicarbonate solution and dried over sodium sulfate. The ether was distilled on a steam-bath, the last traces under reduced pressure at room temperature. The residual oil, 3.9 g., represented a 71% yield of crude carbinol based on the starting aldehyde.

The crude alcohol (0.7 g., 4.3 mmol.) in 5 cc. of anhydrous pyridine was mixed with 0.9 g., 4.8 mmols., of p-nitrobenzoyl chloride and allowed to stand at room temperature for 12 hr. There was obtained in the usual way 0.9 g. (65%) of p-nitrobenzoate, m.p. 94–100°, m.p. 105.5–106.4° after several recrystallizations from ethanol.

Anal. Calcd. for $C_{18}H_{19}O_4N$: C, 68.67; H, 6.11. Found: C, 68.81; H, 6.03.

The crude 2-phenyl-2-methyl-3-butanol was left with p-bromobenzenesulfonyl chloride in pyridine for one week. Working up in the usual way gave a precipitate which was filtered and dissolved several times in chloroform and reprecipitated with petroleum ether (20–40°). The material crystallized slowly in the cold to yield 0.9 g. (28%) of p-bromobenzenesulfonate, m.p. 55–56°, decomposing after several days at room temperature. The equivalent weight of this material in acetolysis was 389 (calcd. 383.3).

Anal. Calcd. for $C_{17}H_{19}O_3SBr$: C, 53.27; H, 5.00. Found: C, 53.21; H, 4.97.

3,3-Diphenyl-2-butanol.—A 67-g. quantity of 3,3-diphenyl-2-butanone, m.p. 40.4–41° (reported 41–41.5°),[53]

(44) Kostanecki and Lampe, *Ber.*, **39**, 4019 (1906).

(45) Whitmore, Weisgerber and Shabica, This Journal, **65**, 1469 (1943).

(46) Hauser and Hudson, "Organic Reactions," Vol. I, John Wiley and Sons, Inc., New York, N. Y., 1942, p. 286.

(47) Schlenk and Ochs, *Ber.*, **49**, 610 (1916).

(48) Grunwald and Winstein, This Journal, **70**, 846 (1948).

(49) Cason, *ibid.*, **68**, 2078 (1946).

(50) Tiffeneau, *Compt. rend.*, **143**, 127 (1898).

(51) Schultz and Mickey, *Org. Syntheses*, **29**, 38 (1949).

(52) Levy, Callais and Abragam, *Bull. soc. chim.*, **43**, 874 (1928).

(53) Tiffeneau and Levy, *ibid.*, [4] **41**, 1362 (1927); **45**, 732 (1929).

in 200 ml. of anhydrous ether was added to 11.4 g. of lithium aluminum hydride suspended in 360 ml. of ether with stirring over a 40-minute period and the reaction mixture was stirred one hour longer. Then it was decomposed with water and cold dilute sulfuric acid. The ether layer was separated, washed with water and dried over potassium carbonate. Evaporation of the ether left 58.2 g. of crude 3,3-diphenyl-2-butanol.

Attempts to prepare the toluenesulfonate or *p*-bromobenzenesulfonate from the above material were without success. Distillation of the alcohol gave, as a main fraction, material, b.p. 125–126° (0.7 mm.), which did not crystallize and which was somewhat impure, probably containing olefin (% C: calcd., 84.91; found, 86.60. % H: calcd., 8.00; found, 8.15). Attempted preparation of the toluenesulfonate from this material gave a solid, m.p. 94–96°, which analyzed near that of an olefin $C_{16}H_{16}$.

Product of Acetolysis of β,β-Diphenylethyl *p*-Toluenesulfonate.—In this experiment, for which we are indebted to Mr. William Beidler, a solution of 8.8 g. (0.02 mole) of toluenesulfonate in 500 ml. of glacial acetic acid was held at 100° for 35 hours. It was cooled and poured into water to yield 3.75 g. (83.5%) of a white solid after washing with water and drying, m.p. 122.8–124°, m.p. 123–124° after recrystallization from ethanol, no depression on admixture with Eastman Kodak Co. *trans*-stilbene, m.p. 123–124°. Fur-

ther dilution and neutralization of the aqueous acetic acid phase and extraction with ether gave rise to 0.60 g. of more solid, m.p. 114–121°.

Rate Measurements.—Acetic acid solvent, usually 0.2% in acetic anhydride, was prepared as previously described.[7a] Absolute ethanol was prepared from commercial absolute ethanol with sodium and ethyl phthalate.[54] Titrations in acetic acid were carried out with standard sodium acetate in acetic acid.[7a] In ethanol, brom thymol blue was used as indicator.

The sealed-ampoule technique was used in the rate runs, and acetolyses were followed to 70–90% completion, except with neopentyl *p*-toluenesulfonate which was followed to 17% completion at 75° and 44% at 100°. Good first-order behavior was observed in acetolysis, the mean deviation in the constants obtained from the integrated first-order expression being shown in Table I.

The ethanolyses were followed less nearly to completion, especially with neopentyl *p*-toluenesulfonate, and the ethanolysis rate constants listed in Table I are much less precise than for acetolysis. These were considered sufficient for the purpose and were not studied further.

(54) Fieser, "Experiments in Organic Chemistry," The Macmillan Co., New York, N. Y., 1937, pp. 359, 360, 368.

LOS ANGELES 24, CALIF.   RECEIVED JUNE 11, 1951

16, 17 | *endo*- and *exo*- Norbornyl Arenesulfonates

The two papers of Winstein and Trifan (Papers 16 and 17) treat four important phenomena associated with the solvolysis of norbornyl arenesulfonates: (1) the exclusive formation of *exo* product,[1] (2) the total racemization attending solvolysis of *exo*-norbornyl arenesulfonates and the extensive (92%) racemization from the *endo* isomer, (3) the 350-fold difference in rate constant of solvolysis between these isomers, and (4) internal return of optically active to racemic *exo*-norbornyl arenesulfonate attending solvolysis in solvents of high ionizing power but low nucleophilic reactivity. Some of the simplest alternatives to the norbornyl bridged ion are considered and eliminated. A question remaining for later quantitative treatment is that of the possible role of transannular steric effects in determining the relative strain associated with approach of a reagent in the *endo* compared to the *exo* position. It should be noted, however, that it was never possible to conclude that the preference for *exo* in the norbornyl ring system was associated with the smaller steric hindrance at that position. In the camphenyl-isobornyl interconversion the *endo* position is the less hindered on account of the *gem*-dimethyl group at position 7, as has been verified by equilibrium measurements on borneol (*endo*) and isoborneol (*exo*); yet the *exo* product, though the more hindered sterically, is still the strongly preferred product kinetically.[2]

[1] This work was done without the benefit of vapor phase chromatography, but advantage was taken of the large difference in rates of solvolysis between *exo*- and *endo*-sulfonates to test kinetically for small amounts of *endo*-norbornyl acetate in the acetolysis product of the *endo-p*-bromobenzenesulfonate. The estimate that the product of hydrolysis in 75% acetone was at least 99.7% *exo* was refined twelve years later, by means of VPC, to 99.98% [S. Winstein, E. Clippinger, R. Howe, and E. Vogelfanger, *J. Am. Chem. Soc.* **87**, 376 (1965)].

[2] Compare also the situation with apoisobornyl bromobenzenesulfonate [R. Howe, E. C. Friedrich, and S. Winstein, *J. Am. Chem. Soc.* **87**, 379 (1965)]. The acetolysis product is at least 99.95% *exo* while borohydride attacks apocamphor 78.4% on the *endo* side and the equilibrium mixture of the alcohols is 63% *endo*.

From: *J. Am. Chem. Soc.* **74**, 1147–54 (1952)

[CONTRIBUTION FROM THE DEPARTMENT OF CHEMISTRY, UNIVERSITY OF CALIFORNIA AT LOS ANGELES]

Neighboring Carbon and Hydrogen. X. Solvolysis of *endo*-Norbornyl Arylsulfonates[1,2,3]

BY S. WINSTEIN AND D. TRIFAN

Solvolysis of *endo*-norbornyl arylsulfonates proceeds in glacial acetic acid, aqueous acetone and aqueous dioxane to give completely the corresponding *exo*-derivative. That this *endo* to *exo* change involves rearrangement is clear from the complete resolution of *endo*-norbornyl alcohol and the solvolysis of optically active *endo*-norbornyl *p*-bromobenzenesulfonate in glacial acetic acid, ethanol and 75% aqueous acetone. Nearly complete loss of activity attends the formation of *exo*-products, first-order polarimetric rate constants agreeing with titrimetric rate constants within experimental error. The facts are most simply explained with carbon migration in the norbornyl cation. While the geometry in the *endo*-norbornyl *p*-bromobenzenesulfonate is unfavorable to participation of the C_1–C_6 bonding electron cloud in the ionization process, ionization is, for the most part, followed by rearrangement to the presumably more stable bridged structure. Solvent intervention, with 7–8% inversion, competes with carbon migration in acetolysis.

Among the norbornyl derivatives, the *exo*-configuration is the one associated with an enhanced rate of solvolysis.[3,4] Also, as reported previously in preliminary form[3] and in detail in the following paper,[5] the indications from stereochemical scrutiny of the solvolysis are that solvolysis proceeds with Wagner–Meerwein rearrangement. It would be instructive to know whether with the *endo* configuration, which is not associated with an enhanced solvolysis rate, rearrangement nevertheless accompanies solvolysis. The use of optically active *endo*-norbornyl derivatives represents one of the approaches to this problem, and, in this paper, we report the study of the solvolysis of *dl* and resolved *endo*-norbornyl arylsulfonates.

endo-Dehydronorbornyl acetate was prepared from cyclopentadiene and vinyl acetate with only slight modification of the method of Alder

and Rickert.[6] Hydrogenation[6] of this material gave *endo*-norborneol (I) but this material was clearly not homogeneous, the Diels–Alder reaction being not completely stereospecific as was also noted recently by Roberts and co-workers.[7] The crude acid phthalate was a mixture and the crude toluenesulfonate (III, X = *p*-CH₃) was contaminated with material which solvolyzed much more rapidly than the *endo*-*p*-toluenesulfonate.

Solvolysis of the crude *endo*-*p*-toluenesulfonate (III) gave rise to products at least very largely *exo*. Thus acetolysis in glacial acetic acid gives acetate product IV (obtainable in 86% yield) which is at least largely *exo* as shown by comparison of the infrared spectrum of the acetolysis product (Fig. 1) with those of *endo*-norbornyl acetate (Fig. 1) and *exo*-norbornyl acetate.[5] Treatment of the acetate with lithium aluminum hydride and conversion of the carbinol product to 3,5-dinitrobenzoate gave 3,5-dinitrobenzoate of *exo*-norborneol (II) with no evidence of contamination with the *endo*-isomer. Similarly, hydrolysis in aqueous dioxane or aqueous acetone yielded *exo*-norborneol (II) either as the 3,5-dinitrobenzoate or as the acid phthalate in yields of 76–78% with no evidence for the presence of *endo*-isomer in the product. The results of solvolysis of pure *endo*-

(1) Supported in part by the Office of Naval Research and the Research Corporation.

(2) Much of the material of this paper was presented in summary: (a) at the Eleventh National Organic Symposium, Madison, Wisconsin, June 21, 1949, page 65 of Abstracts; (b) at Montpellier, France, April, 26, 1950, *Bull. soc. chim.*, [5] **18**, C55 (1951); (c) presented before Organic Division of American Chemical Society, Boston, Mass., April 2–5, 1951, page 54M of Abstracts.

(3) Preliminary communication, Winstein and Trifan, THIS JOURNAL, **71**, 2953 (1949).

(4) Winstein, Morse, Grunwald, Jones, Corse and Marshall, *ibid.*, **74**, 1127 (1952).

(5) Winstein and Trifan *ibid.*, **74**, 1154 (1952).

(6) Alder and Rickert, *Ann.*, **543**, 1 (1940).

(7) Roberts, *et al.*, THIS JOURNAL, **72**, 3116 (1950).

Wave number, cm.$^{-1}$

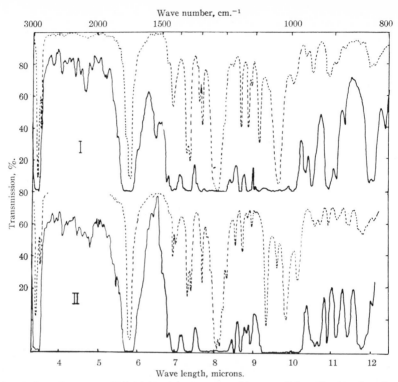

Fig. 1.—Infrared absorption spectra (Baird infrared spectrometer; 0.1 mm. cell length): I, *endo*-norbornyl acetate; II, acetolysis product from *endo*-norbornyl *p*-bromobenzenesulfonate; —, pure liquid; – – – 10% in CCl₄.

norbornyl *p*-bromobenzenesulfonate (III) (X = Br) were entirely analogous to those with the *p*-toluenesulfonate. Large scale solvolysis of the sulfonate esters in aqueous acetone and isolation of the norborneol II as acid phthalate was convenient for preparative purposes, saponification of the acid phthalate yielding pure *exo*-norborneol (II). A little more quantitative idea of the completeness of the change from *endo*- to *exo*-configuration accompanying the solvolysis is available from the refractive index of the product of acetolysis. The value n^{25}D 1.4565 agreed perfectly with the value for authentic *exo*-norbornyl acetate.[5] Since the value for the *endo*-isomer is n^{25}D 1.4583, the *exo*-product is pure within the experimental error of *ca.* 6%.

The most accurate estimate of the completeness of the *endo* → *exo* change in solvolysis depended on reconversion of the solvolysis product to *p*-bromobenzenesulfonate and scrutiny of the kinetics[4] of acetolysis of this material. This method was applied to the product of solvolysis of *endo-p*-bromobenzenesulfonate (III) (X = *p*-Br) in 75% acetone. The first order rate constant for acetolysis of the product was $(9.02 \pm 0.09) \times 10^{-5}$ sec.$^{-1}$ at $25.10 \pm 0.05°$; $(8.84 \pm 0.21) \times 10^{-5}$ sec.$^{-1}$ at $25.00 \pm 0.05°$ in good agreement with the value reported previously[4] $(8.79 \pm 0.90) \times 10^{-5}$ at $24.96°$ for *exo*-norbornyl-*p*-bromobenzenesulfonate. Furthermore, the acid liberation after 24 hours

at 25° (11 half-lives for *exo*-material; 2% reaction for *endo*-isomer) was equal to that after 24 hours at 100° (complete reaction of *endo*-isomer). From this it is clear that the *endo* → *exo* change in the solvolysis in 75% acetone was at least 99.7% complete.

Other analogous transformations, which proceed with the *endo* → *exo* configurational change, have been reported although less quantitative evidence is available in these cases. This is true of the treatment of *endo*-norbornylamine with nitrous acid[8,9] and the hydrolysis of *endo*-norbornyl halides.[10]

For the work with optically active benzene-

(8) Alder and Stein, *Ann.*, **514**, 211 (1934).

(9) Komppa and Beckmann, *ibid.*, **512**, 172 (1934).

(10) Roberts, Bennett and Armstrong, THIS JOURNAL, **72**, 3329 (1950).

TABLE I

EFFECT OF SOLUTES ON ACTIVE MATERIALS IN ACETIC ACID SOLVENT AT 74.57°

Other solute	Active compound	M	Time, hr.	Observed α, degrees Initial	Final
None	*exo*- (A) acetate	0.370	13.0	−0.813	−0.815
None	*endo*- (A) acetate	.373	14.0	− .802	− .805
0.755 M HOTs[a]	*exo*- (A) acetate	ca. .370	1.30	− .751	− .073
.755 M HOTs	*exo*- (A) acetate	ca. .370	3.40	− .751	− .001
.758 M HOTs	*exo*- (B) acetate[c]	ca. .370	17.0	+ .726	+ .675
.758 M HOTs	*endo*- (A) acetate	ca. .373	14.0	− .763	− .758
.427 M KOAc	*exo*- (A) acetate	ca. .370	14.0	+ .743	+ .746
.666 M PyHOBs[b]	*exo*- (A) acetate	ca. .370	14.0	− .678	− .681
.673 M PyHOBs[b]	*endo*- (A) acetate	ca. .373	27.0	− .732	− .734
.453 M HOTs	*exo*- (A) alcohol[d]	ca. .302	3.55	+ .077	+ .078
.453 M HOTs	*exo*- (A) alcohol[d]	ca. .302	11.77	+ .077	+ .075

[a] *p*-Toluenesulfonic acid. [b] Pyridinium *p*-bromobenzenesulfonate. [c] Temperature was 24.96°. [d] Solvent was 75% acetone.

TABLE II

TITRIMETRIC AND POLARIMETRIC SOLVOLYSIS RATES OF *endo*-NORBORNYL *p*-BROMOBENZENESULFONATE AT 74.57°

Solvent	Concn., M	Other solute	Procedure	Isomer	Observed α, degrees Initial	Final	k sec. $^{-1}$
AcOH	0.020[4]		Titrimetric	*dl*			$(1.54 \pm 0.02) \times 10^{-4}$
	.301		Polarimetric	(B)	1.260	0.001	$(1.53 \pm .08) \times 10^{-4}$
	.301		Titrimetric	(B)			$(1.70 \pm .10) \times 10^{-4}$
	.301		Titrimetric	*dl*			$(1.71 \pm .10) \times 10^{-4}$
	.301	0.409 M KOAc	Polarimetric	(B)	1.199	.043	$(2.07 \pm .08) \times 10^{-4}$
	.302	0.415 M KOAc	Titrimetric	(B)			$(1.87 \pm .06) \times 10^{-4}$
75% (CH₃)₂CO	.301		Polarimetric	(B)	1.076	.002[a]	$(2.31 \pm .19) \times 10^{-4}$
	.301		Titrimetric	(B)			$(2.51 \pm .13) \times 10^{-4}$
EtOH	.301		Polarimetric	(B)	1.139	.002[b]	$(6.05 \pm .23) \times 10^{-5}$
	.301		Titrimetric	(B)			$(6.38 \pm .20) \times 10^{-5}$

[a] 0.002 ± 0.005°. [b] 0.002 ± 0.004°

sulfonates, *endo*-norborneol (I) was resolved in the conventional manner. Preliminary tests on *endo*-norbornyl acid phthalate using the organic bases cinchonidine, brucine, cinchonine, quinine and *l*-menthylamine failed to yield crystallizable salts with the last three compounds but indicated that the cinchonidine and brucine alkaloids concentrated the (A) and (B) enantiomorphs, respectively. After concentrating the (A) and (B) enantiomorphs to *ca.* 65–80% purity, final purification was possible by recrystallizations of the active acid phthalates until they were free of the less soluble racemic material. The rotations of the (A) and (B) enantiomorphs agreed well and there are other indications that the resolution was complete. Saponification of the (A) and (B) acid phthalates made available the *endo*-(A) and (B)-norborneols IA and IB which were converted to bromobenzenesulfonates III A and B.

Examination of the optical stability of *endo*-norbornyl acetate, *exo*-norborneol, whose resolution is described elsewhere,[5] and the corresponding acetate under conditions for solvolysis of *endo*-norbornyl *p*-bromobenzenesulfonate disclosed how much the stereochemical result of solvolysis could be influenced by racemization of the product subsequent to its formation. As summarized in Table I, *exo*-acetate is not optically stable at 75° in acetic acid solution 0.755 M in toluenesulfonic acid, being 90% racemized in 1.3 hours and completely racemized after 3.40 hours. On the other hand, it is only 7% racemized by the same solution after 17 hours at 25°. Both *exo*- and *endo*-acetates are completely optically stable at 75° in

acetic acid alone or in the presence of potassium acetate or pyridinium *p*-bromobenzenesulfonate, while the *endo*-acetate is stable even in the presence of 0.758 M toluenesulfonic acid. The *exo*-norborneol is optically stable at 75° to the more weakly acidic medium represented by 0.453 M toluenesulfonic acid in 75% acetone.

Examination of the solvolysis of optically active *endo*-(B)-norbornyl *p*-bromobenzenesulfonate showed that it was attended by loss of optical activity to a very large extent. Some of the information is summarized in Table II, which includes initial and final rotation readings on solvolysis solutions. Hydrolysis in 75% acetone is attended by essentially complete loss of activity. However, because of the low specific rotation of *exo*-norborneol, complete survival of activity would have led in this case to a rotation of only *ca.* 0.080° (see Table I). Even so, with the accuracy obtainable with the polarimeter which was available for this work (see data, Table II), it is clear that racemization attending the hydrolysis to *exo*-norborneol is at least 90% complete. Activity is similarly lost in ethanolysis, but no work was carried out on norbornyl ethers which would permit more quantitative evaluation of this result.

In acetolysis, in the absence of potassium acetate, activity is completely destroyed, but this result loses most of its significance because of the optical instability of *exo*-acetate under the solvolysis conditions. However, in the presence of 0.409 M potassium acetate, under conditions where *exo*-acetate is completely optically stable, solvolysis of 0.301 M *endo*-norbornyl *p*-bromobenzenesulfonate is still attended by nearly complete loss of activity, the rotation reading dropping from 1.199 to 0.043° (see Table II). From data in Table I it is clear that *ca.* 93% racemization attends the acetolysis to *exo*-acetate. The result was similar when 96.5% resolved *endo*-(B)-bromobenzenesulfonate was acetolyzed in 0.10 *M* solution, 0.12 *M* in potassium acetate and the acetate product isolated. The rotation α^{24}D +0.793° (1 dm.) of the acetate product, compared with the magnitude of 10.39° for pure *exo*-acetate,[5] indicates that *ca.* 92% racemization attends the acetolysis.

To verify that racemization is inherent in the solvolysis process and not due to racemization of the bromobenzenesulfonate, the change in rotation attending solvolysis was followed polarimetrically for comparison of polarimetric rate constants with titrimetric solvolysis rate constants. Polarimetric rate constants were calculated from equation 1, the change in rotation of the solutions following good first-order kinetics.

Table II summarizes the comparison between polarimetric and titrimetric solvolysis rate con-

$$2.303 \log \frac{\alpha_0 - \alpha_\infty}{\alpha - \alpha_\infty} = kt \qquad (1)$$

stants. At the top of Table II is listed the rate constant for acetolysis[4] of *endo*-norbornyl *p*-bromobenzenesulfonate in 0.02 *M* solution, and it is seen that titrimetric rates at higher concentration (appropriate for polarimetric observation) and with potassium acetate present are somewhat higher by about the magnitude of medium effects. In acetolysis with and without potassium acetate, as also in solvolysis in 75% acetone and in ethanolysis, the polarimetric rate constants agreed within experimental error with those from the titrimetric procedure.

Thus it is clear that the solvolysis of *endo*-norbornyl *p*-bromobenzenesulfonate is not complicated by a polarimetric rate constant in excess of the titrimetric one, as we observe in other cases, including *exo*-norbornyl *p*-bromobenzenesulfonate.[5] This means that no racemization of *endo*-norbornyl *p*-bromobenzenesulfonate takes place during or before solvolysis. This rules out such over-all processes, resulting in racemization of original *endo*-bromobenzenesulfonate, as the one symbolized in V (regardless of mechanism).

V

It is still necessary to inquire whether *endo*-norbornyl *p*-bromobenzenesulfonate somehow solvolyzes by way of the *exo*-isomer, which we know[3,5] does give racemic *exo*-product in solvolysis. *exo*-Norbornyl *p*-bromobenzenesulfonate is sufficiently more reactive in solvolysis[4] than the *endo*-isomer that formation of *exo*-isomer from *endo* would contribute to the measured solvolysis rate.

One of the conceivable disturbances is a bimolecular displacement by *p*-bromobenzenesulfonate ion (OBs⁻) on IIIA to yield *exo*-bromobenzenesulfonate as symbolized in VI. This can be ruled

out because it requires the titrimetric solvolysis rate constant to climb as OBs⁻ builds up in a run. Also, were racemization attending solvolysis due to this cause, there would be no agreement between polarimetric and titrimetric rate constants early in a run.

VI

Another conceivable disturbance which can be ruled out on the basis of the observed kinetics, is the formation of *exo*-bromobenzenesulfonate from an intermediate cation and external *p*-bromobenzenesulfonate ion.

Still another conceivable route to *exo*-norbornyl *p*-bromobenzenesulfonate is by way of an ion pair from ionization of IIIA which achieves the proper orientation to give back *exo*-bromobenzenesulfonate. This does not involve external OBs⁻ and cannot be dismissed on simple kinetic grounds. However, the extent of a similar kind of return to *exo*-*p*-bromobenzenesulfonate is known in the much more favorable case where one start with *exo*-*p*-bromobenzenesulfinate.[5,11] Even this much return either to active or inactive *exo*-*p*-bromobenzenesulfonate (which then gives racemic solvolysis product) is far from sufficient to account for the racemization which attends solvolysis of *endo*-norbornyl *p*-bromobenzenesulfonate (III).

The data on the stereochemical outcome of solvolysis of III and the previous discussion make it clear that racemization is due to some rearrangement of the cation VII produced by ionization of III. In this system, racemization would result either from H: shifts (VII → VIII or VII → IX) or from migration of the C-6 ring member. There is conceivable even further structural reshuffling

III   VII   VIII   IX

by H: and carbon shifts, either consecutive or coupled, and other tracer work is necessary here. We are informed that some of this is being carried out by Dr. J. D. Roberts of the Massachusetts Institute of Technology. Pending results of this work, the simplest interpretation[5] of the presently observed racemization attending solvolysis of *endo*-norbornyl *p*-bromobenzenesulfonate (III) involves C-6 migration in the cation VII giving either the bridged[12] intermediate X or the mirror image ion XI, the former being preferred.[5]

XI   VII   X

On this basis, the solvolysis of *endo*-norbornyl *p*-bromobenzenesulfonate (III) illustrates re-

(11) Winstein and Schreiber, THIS JOURNAL, in press (1952).
(12) Winstein and Morse, *ibid.*, **74**, 1133 (1952).

arrangement, not associated with a driving force, which follows a rate-determining ionization. The geometry of III is unfavorable[4] for delocalization of the C-1–C-6 bonding electron cloud in the rate-determining ionization. The bromobenzenesulfonate ion, departing with the pair of electrons previously shared with C-2, leaves the developing *p*-orbital on C-2 in just the direction unfavorable to participation by the C-1–C-6 bonding pair. Essentially after ionization, however, this involvement does occur. The behavior here parallels that in the solvolysis of bornyl derivatives.[4]

It is interesting how well rearrangement competes with solvent intervention—in other words how little do the stereochemical results of solvolysis differ from complete racemization. Examination of the small amount of activity which survives in acetolysis with the aid of the stereochemical relationships brought out in this paper and the following one[5] shows that it is in accord with a slight excess of either simply inverted product [*exo*-(A)-acetate IVA from IIIA and *exo*-(B)-acetate IVB from IIIB], or product with retained configuration [slight amount of *endo*-(A)-acetate from IIIA or *endo*-(B)-acetate from IIIB]. That the surviving activity is associated with *exo* or inverted product is clear from the fact that the product is completely racemized by toluenesulfonic acid in glacial acetic acid under conditions toward which *endo*-acetate is completely optically stable (Table I). On this basis, the proportion of predominantly inverted acetate in the product of acetolysis of active *p*-bromobenzenesulfonate III is calculated to be *ca.* 7% in the experiment employing 0.409 M potassium acetate and *ca.* 8% in the one employing 0.12 M potassium acetate. Thus the 7–8% inversion in the acetolysis is not due to acetate ion attack, but is inherent in the solvolysis.

Writing the first intermediate VII to include the 2 species most important in the solvation sphere,[13] we have XII which can give XIII, SOH indicating a solvent molecule. Involvement of the C-1–C-6 bonding electron pair gives eventually racemic product. Prior collapse gives active *exo*-acetate IVA. Even with α-phenylethyl chloride, we estimate from the data of Steigman and Hammett[14]

that acetolysis proceeds with *ca.* 16% of predominant inversion. Thus the participation of carbon is more serious in the later steps of the acetolysis process for IIIA than in the process XIV → XV is in acetolysis of α-phenylethyl chloride.

Experimental

endo-**Dehydronorbornyl Acetate.**—A typical batch run in a steel bomb with a glass liner consisted of 164 g. of freshly distilled cyclopentadiene and 322 g. of distilled vinyl acetate (molar ratio of 1.00:1.50 instead of the 1.00:1.15 molar ratio[15] employed by Alder and Rickert[6]) and a reaction time of 10–19 hours at 168–178° was employed instead of 10 hours at 185–190°. It was noted that the crude reaction mixture was very dark in cases where the heating period was 10–12 hours but was markedly lighter when the heating period was extended to 15–19 hours. In two separate preparations, each involving four and six batches, respectively, yields of the 1:1 dehydronorbornyl adduct (b.p. range 73–77° at 14 mm.) were 45.0 and 44.8% (reported[6] 43.5%).

endo-**Norbornyl Acid Phthalate.**—In a typical preparation, 194 g. (1.274 moles) of crude *endo*-dehydronorbornyl acetate was hydrogenated in 300 ml. of glacial acetic acid with 0.07 g. of platinic acid and agitated with external air cooling for 18 hours, the major hydrogen uptake occurring during the first hour. The solution was diluted with 1 l. of water, the salted aqueous phase extracted six times with ether, and the combined ether extracts washed with aqueous potassium carbonate and dried over anhydrous magnesium sulfate. The ether solution of the crude *endo*-norbornyl acetate was directly reduced with lithium aluminum hydride.[16] The reaction mixture was treated with excess dilute sulfuric acid in ice and the aqueous phase, heavily salted with sodium chloride, was extracted seven times with 50–100-ml. portions of ether. After washing the combined ether extracts with aqueous potassium carbonate and drying over anhydrous magnesium sulfate, the ether solution was concentrated using a fractionating column. When the volume was reduced to *ca.* 250 ml., 125 ml. of anhydrous pyridine was added and the distillation continued until ethyl alcohol was completely expelled.

The pyridine solution of the crude *endo*-norbornyl alcohol was diluted with an additional 75 ml. of the pyridine and heated with 189.0 g. (1.274 moles) of phthalic anhydride at 100° for four hours. The reaction mixture was diluted with several volumes of water and shaken with a mixture of excess dilute sulfuric acid and benzene. After five additional extractions, the combined benzene extract was washed several times with water, dried, and evaporated to an oil. Crystallization from ethyl acetate–petroleum ether (30–60°) gave 242 g., 73.1%, of crude *endo*-norbornyl acid phthalate.

The crude acid phthalate, on fractional crystallization, indicated the presence of a small but definite amount of a second acid phthalate. The principal isomer present was purified by recrystallization six times from ethyl acetate–petroleum ether followed by an effective recrystallization from warm aqueous acetic acid to yield 122 g. of pure *endo*-norbornyl acid phthalate, m.p. 109.1–109.9° (reported[6] 109–110°).

endo-**Norbornyl Alcohol.**—In a typical experiment for liberation of pure *endo*-norbornyl alcohol from the corresponding *endo*-norbornyl acid phthalate, *endo*-norbornyl acid phthalate, 20.0 g., m.p. 109.1–109.9°, was dissolved in a solution of 25 g. of sodium hydroxide in 100 ml. of water and steam distilled at once. The liberated alcohol, which distilled rapidly, was collected together with *ca.* 100 ml. of water, and the water phase was quickly decanted from the 5.86 g. of solid alcohol. The aqueous decantate was saturated with sodium chloride and extracted with five portions of pet. ether (b.p. 20–40°), which were combined, dried, and concentrated with the aid of a fractionating column to yield 2.58 g. of additional alcohol. The combined 8.44 g. of pure *endo*-norbornyl alcohol, m.p. 152.0–153.0° (reported[6,9] 149–150°), corresponded to a yield of 97.8%.

Racemic *endo*-Norbornyl Acetate.—A mixture of 0.9 g. (0.008 mole) of *endo*-norbornyl alcohol, 20 cc. of acetic acid, and 5 cc. of acetic anhydride was kept at 75° for 8 hours. The reaction mixture was diluted with water and extracted

(13) Winstein, Grunwald and Jones, THIS JOURNAL, **73**, 2700 (1951).
(14) Steigman and Hammett, *ibid.*, **59**, 2536 (1937).
(15) Incorrectly reported as 1:1.5.
(16) Nystrom and Brown, THIS JOURNAL, **69**, 1197 (1947).

with pet. ether (30–40°); the pet. ether solution was washed with water, aqueous sodium bicarbonate and dried by filtration through magnesium sulfate. The solvent was removed and the residue was distilled *in vacuo* to yield 1.2 g. (0.007 mole, 89%) of product, n^{25}D 1.4583. The infrared spectrum was taken on this material.

endo-Norbornyl *p*-Toluenesulfonate.—This material was prepared in one instance from 10.1 g. of crude *endo*-norbornyl alcohol. A quantitative yield of crude oil was obtained from which 14.9 g. of solid *endo*-norbornyl *p*-toluenesulfonate, m.p. 28.1–29.2°, was crystallized with difficulty from ethyl ether–low boiling petroleum ether. The equiv. wt. of this material in acetolysis was 266.3, 267.2 (calcd. 266.3). The solvolysis kinetics of this material indicated contamination with *ca.* 19% *exo*-norbornyl *p*-toluenesulfonate. The figure of 19% is not perfectly representative, however, since the crude *endo*-norbornyl alcohol was derived from the first 53% of dehydronorbornyl acetate obtained in distillation of the Diels–Alder reaction product.

Solvolyses of *endo*-Norbornyl *p*-Toluenesulfonate. Glacial Acetic Acid.—Solvolysis of 4.78 g. of the crude *endo*-norbornyl *p*-toluenesulfonate was carried out in 187.6 g. of dry glacial acetic acid for 99.5 hours at 45° followed by 22 hours at 100°. The solvolysis product was extracted with seven portions of ethyl ether after dilution and neutralization of the acetic acid reaction medium. The combined ether extract was dried after several washings with aqueous potassium carbonate and water and the ester product reduced directly with 0.45 g. of lithium aluminum hydride. After working up the resulting alcohol product in the usual manner and concentrating the ether solution to an oil through use of a fractionating column, the oil was converted to the corresponding 3,5-dinitrobenzoate by reaction with 6.00 g. of 3,5-dinitrobenzoyl chloride in 30 ml. of dry pyridine for 10 minutes at *ca.* 80–100°. Cooling and dilution with several volumes of water precipitated a solid which was washed with dilute aqueous sodium carbonate, water and dried to yield 2.64 g. (48.1% yield from *p*-toluenesulfonate) crude *exo*-norbornyl 3,5-dinitrobenzoate, m.p. 99.5–102°, m.p. 104–105° (needles) after recrystallization from acetic acid–water (reported[6] for *exo*-norbornyl 3,5-dinitrobenzoate 105°). No isomeric *endo*-norbornyl 3,5-dinitrobenzoate (thin, pearly plates) was detectable.

65% Aqueous Dioxane.—Solvolyses in 65% aqueous dioxane (Eastman Kodak Co., white label dioxane) were carried out in sealed flasks at *ca.* 0.1 *M* for 148 hours at 45° and 6 hours at 100° on 2.750- and 2.879-g. quantities of *endo*-norbornyl *p*-toluenesulfonate. Each solution was diluted with *ca.* 400 ml. of water, extracted five times with 75-ml. portions of ethyl ether and converted to the 3,5-dinitrobenzoates in the same manner already described. Over-all yields based on the crude derivatives for the 45 and 100° solvolyses were 76.6% (needles, m.p. crude, 94.5–98.0°) and 69.2% (needles, m.p. crude, 100–103°), respectively. Recrystallization from acetic acid–water again gave in both cases with good recovery pure *exo*-3,5-dinitrobenzoate, m.p. 104–105° with no evidence for the presence of any of the *endo*-derivative.

65% Aqueous Acetone.—Solvolysis of 1.94 g. of crude *p*-toluenesulfonate in 75 ml. of 65% aqueous acetone (*ca.* 0.1 *M*) in the presence of excess powdered calcium carbonate for 18 hours at 63–64° yielded in the usual manner 1.73 g. (77.5%) *exo*-norbornyl 3,5-dinitrobenzoate (m.p. crude, 98–101°).

Similarly, solvolysis of 98.5 g. (0.370 mole) of crude *endo*-norbornyl *p*-toluenesulfonate was carried out in 2310 ml. of 65% aqueous acetone (0.16 *M*) for 40.0 hours at 63.5° under reflux in the presence of excess powdered calcium carbonate. The *exo*-norbornyl alcohol was extracted with ether, concentrated through use of a fractionating column with dry pyridine as a chaser for the ether and ethanol, and reacted with 0.370 mole of phthalic anhydride in a *ca.* twofold molar excess dry pyridine for four hours at 96°. Dilution and neutralization of the pyridine with dilute hydrochloric acid in ice, followed by extraction with benzene and isolation of the acid phthalate in several crops from ethyl acetate–petroleum ether gave a yield of 75.6% crude *exo*-norbornyl acid phthalate, m.p., on one recrystallization from the same solvent pair, 80.5–83.5° (reported[6] 80–81°, 102–103°[9,17]). Saponification of a 20.0-g. portion of the

exo-norbornyl acid phthalate and isolation *via* steam distillation, gave directly very pure *exo*-norbornyl alcohol, m.p. 127.6–128.5° (reported 128–129°,[8] 127–128°[6]) in 95% yield.

Solvolyses of *endo*-Norbornyl *p*-Bromobenzenesulfonate in 75% Aqueous Acetone.—In a manner identical to that described above for the preparation of *endo*-norbornyl acid phthalate from crude *endo*-dehydronorbornyl acetate, 421 g. of this same latter material was carried through to the pyridine solution of the crude *endo*-norbornyl alcohol at which point it was treated in the usual manner with 727 g. of *p*-bromobenzenesulfonyl chloride (5% excess of theoretical) to yield six crops of crude *endo*-norbornyl *p*-bromobenzenesulfonate totaling 795.4 g. with a calculated yield of 88.8% from the starting dehydronorbornyl acetate.

The entire 795.4 g. of the *p*-bromobenzenesulfonate was solvolyzed in 74.9% aqueous reagent acetone at 0.76 *M*, the approximate maximum concentration permitted by solubility of the *p*-bromobenzenesulfonate in the medium, in the presence of excess powdered calcium carbonate for 44 hours at 61.5–62.0° under reflux. Isolation of the resulting *exo*-norbornyl alcohol as the acid phthalate as in the case of the solvolysis of the *p*-toluenesulfonate gave rise to 448.9 g. (71.7%) of crude *exo*-norbornyl acid phthalate.

Pure *endo*-norbornyl *p*-bromobenzenesulfonate (4.50 g.) was dissolved in 68 ml. of 75% aqueous acetone (0.20 *M*), sealed in a pressure tube, and immersed in a 75° thermostat for 14.5 hours. Shaking with several portions of anhydrous potassium carbonate served to remove the water from the solution and, after a final overnight drying over anhydrous magnesium sulfate, the solution was concentrated through a fractionating column and the acetone removed using dry pyridine as a chaser. An equimolar amount of *p*-bromobenzenesulfonyl chloride was added to the cold pyridine solution containing the product alcohol and after standing 37 hours in the ice-box, the resulting *p*-bromobenzenesulfonate was isolated by diluting the pyridine with several volumes of ice and scratching. The *p*-bromobenzenesulfonate separated from the solution as a clean white solid and was washed thoroughly on a sintered glass funnel and promptly dried *in vacuo* over phosphorus pentoxide. In this manner, 3.27 g. (72.6%) of *exo*-norbornyl *p*-bromobenzenesulfonate was obtained. The solvolysis rate of this product in dry acetic acid was measured at concentrations of *ca.* 0.03 to 0.037 *M*. In two runs the infinity titers in ml. of base were: I, calcd. 3.679, 3.546 after 24 hr. at 25°, 3.556 after 24 hr. at 100°; II, calcd. 4.391, 4.251 after 24 hr. at 25°, 4.243 after 24 hr. at 100°. The material assays 96.7–96.8% exo, 0.0% endo and 3.2–3.3% inert materials.[18]

Complete Resolution of *endo*-Norbornyl Acid Phthalate.—69.3 g. of pure racemic *endo*-norbornyl acid phthalate, m.p. 109.1–109.9°, was dissolved in 350 ml. of hot acetone followed by an equivalent amount of brucine (104.8 g.). The initial 79.7 g. (45.7%) of brucine salt was recrystallized from hot acetone with overnight standing an additional four times, the amount of starting alkaloid salt at this stage having decreased to 28.6 g. (16.4% of theoretical).

At the same time, the combined mother liquors from the first two brucine salt crystallizations were combined, shaken with 150 ml. of 2 *N* hydrochloric acid, diluted considerably with water, and extracted with seven portions of chloroform. The combined extract, after washing with dilute acid and water was concentrated and evaporated to dryness (36.1 g.). This partially active *endo*-(A)-norbornyl acid phthalate was in turn dissolved in 180 ml. of hot acetone together with an equimolar quantity of 40.75 g. of cinchonidine and also crystallized slowly, with overnight standing, four times to yield a 25.5-g. quantity (19.3% of theoretical) of cinchonidine salt.

Polarimetric examination of the liberated acid phthalates from 5-g. portions of the brucine and cinchonidine salts gave rotations of $[\alpha]^{25}$D −3.96° (chloroform, *c* 0.97) and $[\alpha]^{25}$D +3.28° (chloroform, *c* 10.00) corresponding (on the basis of later data) to only 79.2 and 65.5% resolution, respectively, at this stage. The remaining amounts of partially resolved acid phthalates were liberated from their brucine and cinchonidine salts by shaking the benzene solutions several times in turn with excess dilute hydrochloric acid and water. The acid phthalates were further purified through their sodium salts by extraction of the benzene solution with excess aqueous sodium bicarbonate, acidifi-

---

(17) This crystalline form of *exo*-norbornyl acid phthalate was also prepared and is described in the following paper.[6]

(18) We are indebted to Dr. Kurt Schreiber for this analysis.

cation with excess dilute sulfuric acid to reliberate the acid phthalates, extraction with five portions of reagent benzene, washing, and evaporation of the benzene solvent to dryness with a 95–98% recovery of the partially active acid phthalates. Fractional crystallization of the individual enantiomorphs away from the racemate was then carried out with each of the partially resolved *endo*-acid phthalates. The crystalline racemate was slightly but sufficiently less soluble in ethyl ether–petroleum ether (20–40°) mixtures than the crystalline enantiomorphs (m.p. 98.3–99.7°) to permit successful separation, although a considerable number of fractionations, recombinations of fractions, and refractionation cycles were necessary to achieve a successful complete resolution of both the (A) and (B) enantiomorphs. The melting point was used on all fractions to indicate the progress of the fractionation and polarimetric checks were required only at the last stages in these separations. To keep mechanical losses at a minimum all fractions were separated, washed, etc., by decantation procedures and quantitatively recovered from all glassware. In this manner, starting with 11.45 g. of 65.5% initially resolved *endo*-(A)-acid phthalate, 4.01 g. 100% resolved (A) enantiomorph, together with 4.28 g. of low activity acid phthalate (and 2.94 g. of middle fractions) were finally obtained through manipulation of *ca.* 56 intermediate fractions with a loss of only 1.9% material.

The completeness of this resolution was indicated by the fact that the last three crops of a total of five obtained at a late stage of the fractionation had rotations of $[\alpha]^{24}$D +5.02° (chloroform, *c* 10.03), $[\alpha]^{24}$D +5.00° (chloroform, *c* 10.02), and $[\alpha]^{24}$D +4.97° (chloroform, *c* 10.00). The first two crops which had rotations of $[\alpha]^{24}$D +4.27° (chloroform, *c* 10.01) and $[\alpha]^{24}$D +4.84° (chloroform, *c* 10.00) on further multiple recrystallization yielded an additional amount of enantiomorph $[\alpha]^{23}$D +4.97° (chloroform, *c* 10.03).

Anal. Calcd. for $C_{15}H_{16}O_4$: C, 69.21; H, 6.20. Found for *endo*-(A)-norbornyl acid phthalate: C, 69.16; H, 6.34.

A less thorough but sufficient separation of the (B) enantiomorph yielded from an initial 10.66 g. of 79.2% resolved *endo*-acid phthalate only 2.33 g. of 100% resolved (B) enantiomorph, $[\alpha]^{24}$D −4.99° (chloroform, *c* 10.03), 6.82 g. of several combined fractions corresponding to 81.8% resolution, together with 1.36 g. of low activity acid phthalate with an over-all 98.6% recovery of material through an intermediate *ca.* 31 fractions. The concentration of the *endo*-(B)-norbornyl acid phthalate was discontinued at this point and the 2.33 g. of pure enantiomorph combined with the 6.82-g. quantity above to give optically active compound of known per cent. resolution (calcd. 86.5%).

Conversion of *endo*-Acid Phthalate Enantiomorphs into the Corresponding Alcohols and *p*-Bromobenzenesulfonates.—By methods described above, 3.47 g. of optically pure *endo*-(A)-acid phthalate, m.p. 98.3–99.7°, $[\alpha]^{24}$D +5.00° (chloroform, *c* 10.0) and 8.33 g. of 86.5% resolved *endo*-(B)-acid phthalate were saponified and steam distilled to yield 1.44 g. (96.3% yield) of optically pure *endo*-(A)-norbornyl alcohol, m.p. 151.2–152.5°, $[\alpha]^{24}$D −1.89° (chloroform, *c* 10.05) and 3.46 g. (96.4% yield) *ca.* 86.5% resolved *endo*-(B)-norbornyl alcohol.

Anal., *endo*-(A)-norbornyl alcohol. Calcd. for $C_7H_{12}O$: C, 74.95; H, 10.79. Found: C, 74.67; H, 10.74.

0.95 g. of *endo*-(A)-norbornyl alcohol and 3.00 g. of *ca.* 86.5% resolved *endo*-(B)-norbornyl alcohol were converted in the usual manner to 2.73 g. (97.4%) of pure *endo*-(A)-norbornyl *p*-bromobenzenesulfonate, recrystallized, m.p. 60.6–62.0°, $[\alpha]^{24}$D −11.78° (chloroform, *c* 9.97), $[\alpha]^{24}$D −13.52° (glacial acetic acid, *c* 10.09) and 96.5% resolved *endo*-(B)-norbornyl *p*-bromobenzenesulfonate.

Anal., *endo*-(A)-norbornyl *p*-bromobenzenesulfonate. Calcd. for $C_{13}H_{15}O_3SBr$: C, 47.14; H, 4.57. Found: C, 46.98; H, 4.72. Mol. wt. Calcd.: 331.23. Found by ∞ titration in solvolysis: 332.9, 331.4.

Acetolysis of Active *endo*-(A)-Norbornyl *p*-Bromobenzenesulfonate in Glacial Acetic Acid and Examination of Product.—A mixture of 1.00 g. of optically pure *endo*-(A)-norbornyl *p*-bromobenzenesulfonate and 3.00 g. of racemic *endo*-norbornyl *p*-bromobenzenesulfonate was solvolyzed in 120 ml. of dry glacial acetic acid (0.10 *M*) containing potassium acetate (0.085 *M*, inadvertently insufficient) in a 75° thermostat for 18.5 hours. The acetic acid solution was diluted to four times its volume with water; then it was extracted four times with 50-ml. portions of petroleum ether

(b.p. 34–39°). The combined extract was washed with water and aqueous sodium bicarbonate, then dried over magnesium sulfate. The petroleum ether solution was concentrated through a fractionating column and the residue distilled *in vacuo* to give 1.60 g. (85.9%) of *exo*-norbornyl acetate, n^{25}D 1.4565, α^{25}D −0.129°. This material was completely racemized (α 0.000 ± 0.002°) by 0.75 *M* toluenesulfonic acid in gl. acetic acid after 10 hours at 75°.

When the acetolysis was repeated on 4.00 g. of 96.5% resolved *endo*-(B)-norbornyl *p*-bromobenzenesulfonate in 0.10 *M* solution, 0.12 *M* in potassium acetate, for 17.3 hours at 75°, there was obtained 1.38 g. (74%) *exo*-norbornyl acetate, n^{25}D 1.4565, α^{24}D 0.793° (1 dcm.).

Active *exo*- and *endo*-Norbornyl Acetates in Acetic Acid.—0.2076 g. of active *exo*-norbornyl alcohol[5] and 0.2094 g. of active *endo*-(A)-norbornyl alcohol were each weighed into 5-ml. volumetric flasks and dissolved in *ca.* 1 ml. of dry glacial acetic acid. Then 0.328 g. and 0.325 g. (*ca.* 50% excess of theoretical) of acetic anhydride (Baker's Analyzed) were also weighed into each volumetric flask, respectively, followed by *ca.* 0.03 g. of dry pyridine. The characteristic odor of the norbornyl acetates could be detected at once. The flasks were stoppered and warmed at 40° for *ca.* 24 hours and then made up to volume with more dry acetic acid to produce 0.370 *M* and 0.373 *M* stock solutions of the respective *exo*-norbornyl acetate, $[\alpha]^{24}$D 14.20° (acetic acid, *c* 5.72) and *endo*-(A)-norbornyl acetate, $[\alpha]^{24}$D −14.00° (acetic acid, *c* 5.73).

Effect of Solutes on Active Acetates in Acetic Acid and on Active *exo*-Alcohol in Aqueous Acetone.—Appropriate quantities of *p*-toluenesulfonic acid monohydrate, anhydrous potassium acetate and pyridinium *p*-bromobenzene-sulfonate (prepared by reaction of reagent pyridine with *p*-bromobenzenesulfonic acid monohydrate) were weighed out to 0.1 mg. and made up to the mark at room temperature in a calibrated constricted test-tube (1.628 ml.) with either the stock 0.370 *M* active *exo*-norbornyl acetate or 0.373 *M* active *endo*-norbornyl acetate in acetic acid. The solutions were homogenized with the aid of a drawn-out medicine dropper and the initial observed rotation measured in the polarimeter in a 1-decimeter, semimicro polarimeter tube. The solution was then sealed in a clean ampoule and immersed in the 74.57° thermostat for a measured period of time, after which the ampoule was opened and the optical rotation remeasured.

The corresponding test on active *exo*-norbornyl alcohol with *p*-toluenesulfonic acid in 75% aqueous acetone was performed similarly (Table I).

Solvolysis Rate Measurements.—The solvents and procedures for acetolysis[19] and ethanolysis[13] rate measurements were the same as those previously employed.

In acetolysis involving high salt concentrations, the difficulty resulting from the gradual color change of the brom phenol blue indicator was minimized by diluting the 1-ml. aliquots during the first half of the run with 5 ml. of glacial acetic acid prior to titration and with 10 ml. of glacial acetic acid during the last half of the run. The measurements were carried out by first titrating with standard *p*-toluenesulfonic acid in acetic acid beyond the equivalence point to colorless followed by backtitration with standard sodium acetate to the usual yellow end-point color.

The 75% aqueous acetone was prepared by mixing 60 ml. of reagent grade acetone and 20 ml. of distilled water, each delivered by pipet. The solvolysis in this solvent was followed by titration with standard 0.05 *N* methanolic sodium methoxide using brom thymol blue as indicator.

Polarimetric Measurements.—Polarimetric determinations carried out in this work were done with the aid of a new Hilger polarimeter, with Lippich triple-field polarizer reading directly to 0.01 and estimating to 0.001°, and a *ca.* 1.2-ml. semimicro 1-dcm. polarimeter tube. In a completely dark room, individual settings made with care seldom varied more than ±0.005° and the average of five or six readings invariably were reproducible to 0.002–0.004° or better when the solutions were completely colorless. Decreased accuracy resulting from slight thermal gradients, developing in the solution during measurements, was avoided by intentionally introducing a small air bubble in the polarimeter tube during filling. Between readings the solution was occasionally mixed with the aid of the bubble by inverting the tube a number of times and then returning the air bubble to

(19) Winstein, Grunwald and Ingraham, THIS JOURNAL, **70**, 821 (1948).

a recess provided in the glass wall at the middle of the polarimeter tube.

Polarimetric Racemization Rates of *endo*-(**B**)-**Norbornyl** *p*-**Bromobenzenesulfonate.**—In these rate runs, the 96.5% resolved *endo*-(B)-norbornyl *p*-bromobenzenesulfonate was employed and the appropriate quantities of reagent involved were weighed out to 0.1 mg. and made up to the mark in a 10-ml. volumetric flask with the corresponding solvent. Approximate volumes (*ca.* 1.4–1.6 ml.) were introduced by means of a roughly calibrated medicine dropper into carefully cleaned Pyrex ampoules. The ampoules were simultaneously introduced into the 74.57 ± 0.01° thermostat in a wire basket which was then rocked for 6–8 minutes before the first ampoule ($t = 0$) was removed and quenched in ice and the time recorded. Soon thereafter, the ampoule was brought to room temperature in a water-bath, opened, and the polarimeter tube filled and the rotation measured.

Los Angeles 24, Calif.   Received June 11, 1951

From: *J. Am. Chem. Soc.* **74**, 1154–60 (1952)

[CONTRIBUTION FROM THE DEPARTMENT OF CHEMISTRY, UNIVERSITY OF CALIFORNIA AT LOS ANGELES]

Neighboring Carbon and Hydrogen. XI. Solvolysis of *exo*-Norbornyl *p*-Bromobenzenesulfonate[1,2,3]

BY S. WINSTEIN AND DANIEL TRIFAN

Solvolysis of *exo*-norbornyl *p*-bromobenzenesulfonate in acetic acid and aqueous acetone gives the corresponding *exo*-derivatives with great steric specificity. Complete resolution of *exo*-norborneol has been carried out and the solvolysis of active *exo*-norbornyl *p*-bromobenzenesulfonate shown to proceed with complete loss of optical activity. Part of the loss in activity attending solvolysis is due to internal rearrangement, involving racemization, of the *exo*-norbornyl *p*-bromobenzene-sulfonate, for first-order polarimetric rate constants exceed titrimetric first-order solvolysis rate constants by factors of 3.46, 2.94 and 1.40 in acetic acid, ethanol and 75% acetone, respectively. The facts are most readily interpretable in terms of a bridged structure for the norbornyl cation. The *exo*-norbornyl *p*-bromobenzenesulfonate with the favorable geometry for participation of the C_1–C_6 bonding electron pair in the rate-determining ionization process, giving it an enhanced ionization rate, ionizes to the bridged carbonium ion. This intermediate, with a plane of symmetry, leads to racemic *exo*-product.

Isobornyl chloride (*exo*), with the proper geometry for delocalization of the neighboring β-bonding electron cloud in the rate-determining ionization, is more reactive in solvolysis[4] by 5 powers of ten relative to bornyl chloride (*endo*). In the simpler analogous norbornyl system, a gap in rate between *exo* and *endo* configurations still persists, the *exo*-norbornyl *p*-bromoben-zenesulfonate being 350 times as rapid in acetolysis at 25° as the *endo*-isomer.[4] For our understanding of participation of carbon[5] in displacement reactions, it is necessary to know whether Wagner–Meerwein rearrangement attends the solvolysis of *exo*-norbornyl *p*-bromobenzene-sulfonate. As in the case of the *endo*-isomer,[6] we studied the solvolysis of *dl*- and active *exo*-norbornyl *p*-bromoben-zenesulfonate[3] and this work is reported in the present paper. This study, together with the previous one,[6] furnishes a picture of the nature of the solvolysis of the simple pair of

isomers with the geometrical features of the more heavily substituted isobornyl–bornyl pair.

Solvolysis of the arylsulfonates of *endo*-norborneol (I), most conveniently carried out in 75% acetone

as already described,[6] provided useful quantities of *exo*-norborneol (II) and its derivatives.

The solvolysis of *exo*-norbornyl *p*-bromobenzene-sulfonate (III), as in the case of the *endo*-isomer,[6] gave rise essentially exclusively to *exo*-products. Thus the acetolysis product IV (obtainable in 80% yield) was at least 94% *exo*, as shown by infrared spectrum[6] (Fig. 1), refractive index,[6] and saponi-fication and conversion to the 3,5-dinitrobenzoate. In the case of solvolysis in 75% acetone, a more quantitative estimate of the completeness of main-tenance of the *exo*-configuration was obtained from reconversion of the crude norborneol to *p*-bromo-benzenesulfonate and kinetic analysis of the latter.

(1) Supported in part by Office of Naval Research and Research Corporation.

(2) Much of the material of this paper was presented in summary (a) at the Eleventh National Organic Symposium, Madison Wisconsin, June 21, 1949, page 65 of Abstracts; (b) at Montpellier, France, April 26, 1950 (*Bull. soc. chim.*, [5] **18**, C55 (1951)). Presented before Or-ganic Division of American Chemical Society, Boston, Mass., April 2–5, 1951, page 53 M of Abstracts.

(3) Preliminary communication, Winstein and Trifan, THIS JOURNAL, **71**, 2953 (1949).

(4) Winstein, *et al.*, *ibid.*, **74**, 1127 (1952).

(5) Winstein, Morse, Grunwald, Schreiber and Corse, *ibid.*, **74**, 1113 (1952).

(6) Winstein and Trifan, *ibid.*, **74**, 1147 (1952).

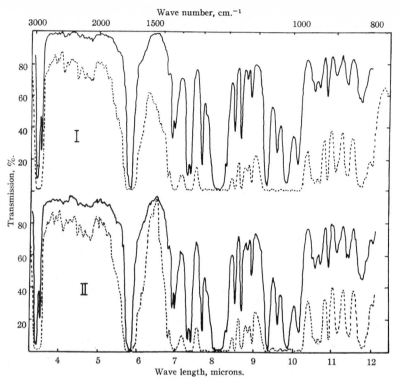

Fig. 1.—Infrared absorption spectra (Baird infrared spectrometer; 0.1 mm. cell length): I, *exo*-norbornyl acetate; II, acetolysis product from *exo*-norbornyl *p*-bromobenzenesulfonate; - - - -, pure liquid; —— 10% solution in CCl₄.

As shown in Table I, the first-order acetolysis rate constant for this product agreed well with the previously[4] reported value for *exo-p*-bromobenzenesulfonate. Moreover, early and late infinity titers indicated that the proportion of *endo* derivative in the product was very small and possibly as large as $1.6 \pm 0.5\%$. Thus the *exo*-configuration survived in hydrolysis at least to the extent of 98.4%.

Other analogous transformations in which *exo* configuration is maintained, but where less quantitative evidence is available, are the conversion of *exo*-norbornylamine[7,8] to *exo*-norborneol (II) and the hydrolysis of *exo*-norbornyl halides.[9]

For the study of optically active *exo-p*-bromobenzenesulfonates (III) A and B, *exo*-norborneol (II) was resolved through the acid phthalate in the conventional manner. Small scale tests with brucine, strychnine, cinchonine, cinchonidine, quinine and *l*-menthylamine showed cinchonidine to be the most useful resolving agent. Using this alkaloid for partial resolution, fractional crystallization of the partially resolved acid phthalate as in the *endo*-case,[6] yielded completely resolved (A) and (B) isomers, the specific rotations of the enantiomorphs agreeing closely. Saponification of the (A) and (B) acid phthalates yielded the enantio-

morphic *exo*-(A) and (B)-norborneols IIA and B from which *p*-bromobenzenesulfonate or acetate were prepared.

The stereochemical relationship between the *exo*-norborneols IIA and B and the *endo*-norborneols IA and B described in the preceding paper[6] was established by oxidation to norcamphor V and VI. *Ca.* 60–80% resolved *endo*-(A)-norborneol IA and optically pure *exo*-(B)-norborneol IIB were oxidized with potassium dichromate and sulfuric acid.[10] The norcamphor (predominantly V) from IA displayed a rotation $[\alpha]^{24}$D $-15.73°$, while the norcamphor (predominantly VI) from IIB displayed a rotation $[\alpha]^{24}$D $+8.66$. This proves that *endo*-(A) is related to *exo*-(A) and *endo*-(B) to *exo*-(B) and the representation of IAB and IIAB and their derivatives in this paper and the preceding one[6] takes account of this relationship. It is interesting that the 100% resolved *exo*-(B)-norborneol yielded a norcamphor of lower rotation than the one from the less fully resolved *endo*-(A)-norborneol. This is undoubtedly due to racemization of the *exo*-alcohol in the acidic medium prior to oxidation, this alcohol being more rapidly racemized.[6]

Solvolysis of optically active *exo*-(B)-norbornyl *p*-bromobenzenesulfonate IIIB proceeded with complete loss of optical activity, even under conditions toward which the solvolysis products are

(7) Alder and Stein, *Ann.*, **514**, 211 (1934).

(8) Komppa and Beckmann, *ibid.*, **512**, 172 (1934).

(9) (a) Roberts, Bennett and Armstrong, THIS JOURNAL, **72**, 3329 (1950); (b) Schmerling, *ibid.*, **68**, 195 (1946).

(10) Alder and Rickert, *Ann.*, **543**, 1 (1940).

TABLE I

TITRIMETRIC AND POLARIMETRIC SOLVOLYSIS RATES OF *exo*-NORBORNYL *p*-BROMOBENZENESULFONATE AT $24.98 \pm 0.02°$

Solvent	Concn., M	Other solute	Isomer	Procedure	Rotations, degree Initial	Final	k(sec.$^{-1}$)	k_α/k_t
AcOH	0.020		dl	Titrimetric[4]			$(8.79 \pm 0.09) \times 10^{-5}$	
	.037		a	Titrimetric			$(8.64 \pm 0.08) \times 10^{-5}$	
	.037		a	Titrimetric			$(8.90 \pm 0.01) \times 10^{-5}$	
	.201	0.252 M KOAc	(B)	Polarimetric	0.265	-0.001	4.25×10^{-4}	
	.200	.249 M KOAc	(B)	Titrimetric			$(1.22 \pm 0.03) \times 10^{-4}$	3.46
EtOH	.300		(B)	Polarimetric	.279	$-$ .003	7.83×10^{-5}	
	.300		(B)	Titrimetric			$(2.66 \pm 0.03) \times 10^{-5}$	2.94
75% $(CH_3)_2CO$	.200		(B)	Polarimetric	.119	.002	7.56×10^{-4}	
	.200		(B)	Titrimetric			$(5.41 \pm 0.35) \times 10^{-4}$	1.40

a *p*-Bromobenzenesulfonate of product of solvolysis in 75% acetone.

optically stable. This is shown in Table I which lists initial and final rotations for solvolysis runs in acetic acid, 75% acetone and absolute alcohol. In the case of the latter solvent, no rotation data are available on norbornyl ethers to give quantitative significance to the loss of optical activity. In acetolysis the high degree of completeness of the loss of optical activity was more quantitatively demonstrated by isolation of the acetate and measurement of the rotation of the homogeneous material. The acetate from a 1:1 mixture of *exo*-(B) and *dl-exo*-norbornyl *p*-bromobenzenesulfonates gave a rotation of $0.001 \pm 0.004°$ whereas 50% active *exo*-acetate would have corresponded to a rotation of $5.20°$.

To probe whether loss of activity was indeed to be ascribed to solvolysis and not to prior racemization of the bromobenzenesulfonate, the solvolyses were followed polarimetrically. In preliminary work,[3] there was some indication that the polarimetric drop in rotation in solvolysis of *exo*-norbornyl bromobenzenesulfonate III somewhat exceeded the titrimetric rate. Careful comparison of polarimetric rate constants, k_α, defined by equation 1, with titrimetric rate constants

$$2.303 \log \alpha_0/\alpha = k_\alpha t \qquad (1)$$

k_t brought to light an interesting disturbance, k_α indeed exceeding k_t.

Table I gives the titrimetric rate constants for solvolysis at $24.98°$ at concentrations of 0.200 to

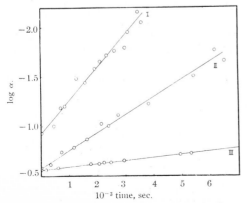

Fig. 2.—Polarimetric observation of solvolysis of *exo*-norbornyl *p*-bromobenzenesulfonate: I, in 75% acetone; II, in AcOH; III, in EtOH.

0.300 M in III, high enough for polarimetric scrutiny. In the case of acetolysis, potassium acetate at 0.25 M was included, and the rate constant here was, as is proper, some 40% higher than the one previously reported.[4] The titrimetric rates displayed good first-order behavior, and the polarimetric rates were also nicely first-order. Figure 2 shows plots of log α *vs.* time for hydrolysis in 75% acetone, acetolysis and ethanolysis. The points fall nicely on first-order straight lines, especially when one considers that rotations down to $0.02°$ in acetolysis and $0.01°$ in aqueous acetone are involved. The polarimetric rate constants derived from the slopes of these plots are the ones given in Table I.

The available data (Table I) show that steady first-order polarimetric rate constants k_α exceed the steady first-order titrimetric rate constants k_t by factors of 3.46, 2.94 and 1.40 in acetolysis, ethanolysis and hydrolysis in 75% acetone, respectively. The data also show that in this extra racemization *exo*-bromobenzenesulfonate (III) remains *exo*, for *endo*-ester is so much less reactive[4] in solvolysis that the titrimetric rate constant would reflect any *exo* → *endo* change.

It is evident from the kinetic behavior that the excess racemization of the *exo*-norbornyl *p*-bromobenzenesulfonate does not involve external *p*-bromobenzenesulfonate ion. The process is, kinetically, an intramolecular one. The rate of the so-called internal racemization is very dependent on the ionizing character of the solvent, as shown, for example, by the optical stability of *exo*-norbornyl *p*-bromobenzenesulfonate in the solvent pyridine which is used in the preparation of the material. Thus the *exo*-(B)-norbornyl *p*-bromobenzenesulfonate (IIIB) possessed the identical rotation whether isolated after 16 hours or 7 days in the pyridine solvent. This whole phenomenon is discussed[11] more fully in the following article and the concern here will be with the effect of the excess racemization of the *p*-bromobenzenesulfonate concurrent with solvolysis on the quantitative significance to be attached to the racemic character of the final solvolysis product.

We can calculate what fraction of the final solvolysis product has come from *exo*-(B)-material (IIIB), and what fraction has arisen from *dl-exo*-bromobenzenesulfonate IIIAB. Taking $k_\alpha - k_t$ as a rate constant for the extra racemization of *p*-bromobenzenesulfonate not associated with sol-

(11) Winstein and Schreiber, THIS JOURNAL, in press.

volysis, the optical purity **P**, starting with optically pure material, of residual p-bromobenzenesulfonate at time t is given by equation 2.

$$\mathbf{P} = e^{-(k_\alpha - k_t)t} \tag{2}$$

This is the optical purity of the p-bromobenzene-sulfonate undergoing solvolysis at time t. The average optical purity $\overline{\mathbf{P}}$ of the p-bromobenzene-sulfonate which has solvolyzed over a long interval is given by equation 3.

$$\overline{\mathbf{P}} = \frac{\int \mathbf{P}[-d(\text{ROBs})]}{\int -d(\text{ROBs})} = \frac{\int e^{-(k_\alpha - k_t)t} k_t (\text{ROBs})_0 e^{-k_t t} dt}{\int k_t (\text{ROBs})_0 e^{-k_t t} dt} \tag{3}$$

At time t, $\overline{\mathbf{P}}$ is given by equation 4, and at total reaction, $\overline{\mathbf{P}}$ is expressed by equation 5.

$$\overline{\mathbf{P}} = (k_t/k_\alpha)(1 - e^{-k_\alpha t})/(1 - e^{-k_t t}) \tag{4}$$

$$\overline{\mathbf{P}} = k_t/k_\alpha \tag{5}$$

Another way to put it is that, on complete solvolysis, the fraction of solvolysis product which has arisen from prior racemized bromobenzenesulfonate is $(1 - k_t/k_\alpha)$, while the fraction which has arisen from active material is (k_t/k_α).

Thus we see from the rate constants in Table I that in solvolysis of exo-norbornyl p-bromobenzenesulfonate (III), the solvolysis product arises from active material only to the extent of 29, 34 and 71% in acetolysis, ethanolysis and hydrolysis in 75% acetone, respectively.

In Table II are given the data relating to the loss in activity attending solvolysis in acetic acid and 75% acetone. In the third column are given the rotations ($\alpha_{\text{theor.}}$) which would be expected from previous[6] and present data if III did not racemize and solvolysis proceeded with complete retention of configuration. In the next column this figure is corrected for racemization of the III. The values of $\overline{\mathbf{P}}$ $\alpha_{\text{theor.}}$ are still sufficiently large compared to the uncertainties in reading with the instrument available for this work, that it is clear that loss in activity attends solvolysis itself to within $ca.$ 10% in 75% acetone and within 0.3% in acetic acid.

TABLE II

SUMMARY OF EXTENT OF RACEMIZATION ATTENDING ACETOLYSIS AND HYDROLYSIS OF exo-NORBORNYL p-BROMOBENZENESULFONATE

Solvent	ROBs concn.	α theor.	$\overline{\mathbf{P}}_\alpha$ theor.	α obsd.	% Rac. att. solv.
AcOH	0.201	0.440	0.127	−0.001	100 ± 4
AcOH	.100^a	5.20	1.51	+ .001	100 ± 0.3
75% acetone	.200	0.051	0.036	.002	100 ± $ca.$ 10

^{a} Acetate isolated and α_D (1 dcm.) of homogeneous material taken.

Actually, there are several possible rearrangements which could conceivably account for the racemization that attends the solvolysis of exo-norbornyl p-bromobenzenesulfonate by way of a carbonium ion. One of them involves C_2, C_6 equivalence by 2,6-hydrogen equilibration as shown in VII⇌VIII. This is the type shift once called on[12] to explain the isobornyl chloride racemization

(12) Meerwein and Montfort, $Ann.$, **435**, 207 (1924).

which is now much better understood on the basis of the Nametkin rearrangement.[13] Another possible racemization mode involves C_2, C_3 equivalence by 2,3-hydrogen equilibration as shown in VII ⇌ IX. Still another involves C_1, C_2 equivalence by carbon migration as, for example, in VII ⇌ X. While other labelling techniques in addition to the polarimetric one are necessary, there are reasons to favor carbon migration.

Stereo-electronically, carbon migration is more likely than hydrogen for C_6, C_1 and C_2 are more nearly in the favorable situation of planarity with the axis of the vacant p-orbital on C_2 than is the case for a 3-hydrogen atom, C_3 and C_2. Further, there is the example of the cation from camphene hydrochloride or isobornyl chloride, where the Nametkin rearrangement,[13] involving a methyl migration analogous to the 3-hydrogen migration, competes only poorly with other reactions of the cation. Thus it is expected that hydrogen migration will be slower and subsequent to carbon involvement in the system in hand.

On the basis of carbon migration, racemization alone could be due to a dynamic equilibrium between two one-sided cationic species VII and X. Further qualifications regarding these species and their reactions would be necessary to account for the other striking aspects of the present results, namely, the essentially exclusive formation of exo-product, and the enhanced solvolysis rate of the exo-p-bromobenzenesulfonate.[4] While our precise chemical and thermodynamic knowledge of bicyclic systems is still limited, it is attractive to account for all of these results by way of the bridged formulation[14] XI for the norbornyl cation. This structure would, in this system,[4] be more stable[15] than the classical one VII. The exo-norbornyl

(13) W. Hückel, "Theoretische Grundlagen der Organischen Chemie," Vol. I, Akademische Verlagsgesellschaft m. B. H., Leipzig, 1940, pp. 295–299.

(14) Winstein and Morse, THIS JOURNAL, **74**, 1133 (1952).

(15) One of the contributory causes of this could be relief of strain attending the greater flattening of the $C_{1,2,3,4,7}$ ring in the species XI.

p-bromobenzenesulfonate III has the proper geometry for delocalization of the C_1–C_6 bonding electron pair directly in the rate determining ionization process, and thus is the more reactive isomer. Like the *cis*-2-butene bromonium ion,[2,16] the bridged ion XI is internally compensated, attack on C_2 giving original configuration XII, attack on C_1 giving inverted configuration XIII.

In the present system, favorable to carbon participation, the dominance of this over solvent intervention is very large and greater than in solvolysis of the *endo-p*-bromobenzenesulfonate. In 75% acetone, the indications are that *ca.* 1.5% of *endo*-norborneol is produced in solvolysis of *exo*-norbornyl *p*-bromobenzenesulfonate. This is being investigated further, but it would seem that carbon participation has not yet taken over completely in 75% acetone. More complete dominance of carbon participation could be expected[17] in the less nucleophilic acetic acid solvent and the facts seem to be in line with this. While the technique for disclosing small amounts of *endo* material in *exo* has not yet been applied to the acetolysis product, the polarimetric results indicate that any proportion of active *endo*-acetate in the *exo*-acetate product must be very small indeed. Starting with *exo*-(B)-norbornyl *p*-bromobenzenesulfonate (IIIB), the acetate product IV A B is completely optically inactive. Now, either no active acetate of *endo*-(B)-norborneol[6] (IB) is present, or its activity is just balanced, by coincidence, by that due to active *exo*-acetate. The *exo*-acetate cannot be the *exo*-(B) for its sign of rotation is the same as that of *endo*-(B). It would need to be the inverted *exo*-(A)-acetate. On the whole, the cancellation of activities seems likely than the absence of active materials in the *exo*-acetate product and, on this basis, allowing for the possible error in rotation reading and multiplying by (k_α/k_t), the proportion of *endo*-(B)-acetate in the solvolysis product must be less than 5 parts per thousand.

The evidence for an unclassical structure XI for the norbornyl cation lends credence to the earlier suggestion of Christopher Wilson[18] of a possible mesomeric cation from camphene hydrochloride. Such a formulation (XIV), while again not uniquely required by any one result, takes account the most simply of products and reactivities. On this basis, one can understand: (a) the formation from the cation of isobornyl and camphene hydrate derivatives and not bornyl and methylcamphenilol derivatives[13]; (b) the formation of traces of tricyclene from the cation[19]; (c) the rate sequences, isobornyl > bornyl,[4] and camphene hydrate > methylcamphenilol,[20] to electrophilic reagents.

There are similar but less well known cations which may be best described by a bridged structure. One of these, for example, would be the internally compensated species XV from 2-methyl-

isofenchol.[21] Another would be the species XVI from either methylborneol or methylfenchyl alcohol.[22]

XIV   XV   XVI

The number of known cases of carbonium ions[23] the stereochemistry of whose reactions is best accounted for, under some circumstances, by so-called non-classical structures, is still small. The known examples mostly have the special feature of the bicyclic ring structure in the systems discussed in this article or the feature that the neighboring group is an unsaturated electron source, vinyl, as in cholesteryl cation,[2,24] or phenyl, as in the benzylmethylcarbinyl[17] or 3-phenyl-2-butyl cations.[25] Thus it remains to be seen how general this situation may become.

ADDED IN PROOF.—Since our first publications[3,24] dealing with neighboring carbon, Hughes and Ingold have also recognized the possibility of acceleration of ionization due to carbon participation. They reported several cases of such acceleration (2,2,2-triphenylethyl chloride, isobornyl chloride and possibly camphene hydrochloride) at the Conference on the Walden Inversion and Molecular Rearrangements at Montpellier, France, April, 1950, which paralleled some of the results in the present series of papers presented at the same time.[2b] More recently they have discussed the possibility of bridged structures for certain ions, for example, the one from camphene hydrochloride (XIV) [F. Brown, E. D. Hughes, C. K. Ingold and J. F. Smith, *Nature*, 168, 65 (1951)]. Hughes and Ingold employ the terms, "synartetic acceleration" and "synartetic ions."

Very recently further evidence has appeared on the question of 2,6-hydrogen shifts[12] in [2,2,1]bicycloheptane systems. J. D. Roberts and C. C. Lee report that solvolysis of *exo*-norbornyl-2,3-C_2[14] *p*-bromobenzenesulfonate in 75% acetone results in a shuffling of carbon atoms slightly more than expected on the basis of the structure XI, while the extra shuffling is increasingly drastic in acetic and formic acid solvents [J. D. Roberts, Paper at 120th Meeting of the American Chemical Society, New York, N. Y., September 3–7, 1951, page 24M of Abstracts; J. D. Roberts and C. C. Lee, THIS JOURNAL, 73, 5009 (1951)]. The equivalent of 2,6-hydrogen shifts are required to account for the extra shuffling. Similarly, some 2,6-type hydrogen shift occurs in the dehydration of β-fenchol [W. Doering and A. P. Wolf, XIIth International Congress of Pure and Applied Chemistry, New York, N. Y., September 10–13, 1951, page 437 of Abstracts]. The action of nitrous acid on camphenilyl amine has now been reported to give, in addition to camphenilol and the Wagner rearrangement product apoisoborneol, a small amount of a material which could owe its formation to 2,6-type hydrogen shift, namely, β-isofenchocamphorol, the quantity of the latter decreasing markedly under the mildest conditions [S. Beckmann and R. Bamberger, *Ann.*, 574, 65 (1951)]. In the hydration of para-santen, addition of hydrogen chloride, followed by hydrolysis with lime-water, gives no α-santenol (which may arise from a 2,6-type hydrogen shift), whereas the action of acetic acid-sulfuric acid gives some α-santenol and formic acid gives α-santenol essentially completely [S. Beckmann and R. Bamberger, *Ann.*, 574, 76 (1951)].

While we are now investigating related sulfonic acid esters, all of the above results are perhaps most simply explained by prior formation of a structure of the type XI which can rearrange further if the conditions are conducive

(16) Winstein and Lucas, THIS JOURNAL, 61, 1576, 2845 (1939).

(17) Winstein, Brown, Schreiber and Schlesinger, *ibid.*, 74, 1140 (1952).

(18) Nevell, de Salas and Wilson, *J. Chem. Soc.*, 1188 (1939).

(19) Moycho and Zienkowski, *Ann.*, 340, 25 (1905).

(20) Hückel, "Theoretische Grundlagen der Organischen Chemie," Vol. I, Akademische Verlagsgesellschaft m. B. H., Leipzig, 1940, p. 291.

(21) Komppa and Nyman, *Ann.*, 533, 290 (1938).

(22) Ruzicka, *Helv. Chim. Acta*, 1, 110 (1918).

(23) Excluding cations with functional neighboring groups.

(24) (a) Winstein and Adams, THIS JOURNAL, 70, 838 (1948); (b) Winstein and Schlesinger, *ibid.*, 70, 3528 (1948).

(25) Cram, *ibid.*, 71, 3863 (1949).

to long life of the carbonium ion, perhaps by way of intermediates like XVII.

Considering the wave-mechanical description of the cyclopropane ring, structure XVII illustrates one of the attractive ways to protonate a cyclopropane, and changes of the type XI ⇌ XVII could be important in certain closures and openings of the cyclopropane ring. Also, the distance between Cα and a γ-hydrogen atom in a carbonium ion is substantially decreased in the bridged structure of type XI, and changes of the type XI → XVII → XVIII may represent one general way in which so-called 1,3-shifts could arise.

Experimental

exo-Norbornyl Alcohol and *exo*-Norbornyl Acid Phthalate. —The solvolysis of *endo*-norbornyl *p*-toluenesulfonate to *exo*-norborneol isolated as the acid phthalate in the 80–81° crystalline form described by Alder and Rickert[10] has been described already.[6] In the second large preparation, the 448.9 g. of crude *exo*-norbornyl acid phthalate proved to be this same crystalline form. After several recrystallizations from ethyl acetate–petroleum ether, which failed to effectively remove the phthalic acid impurity, recrystallization from aqueous acetic acid yielded a second crystalline form, m.p. 98.6–99.7° (probably corresponding to the 102–103° form reported by Komppa and Beckmann[8]), m.p. unchanged on recrystallization from ethyl acetate–petroleum ether.

Anal. Calcd. for $C_{15}H_{16}O_4$: C, 69.21; H, 6.20. Found: C, 69.21; H, 6.44.

exo-Norbornyl acid phthalate (20.0 g.), m.p. 80.5–83.5°, and *exo*-norbornyl acid phthalate (10.0 g.), m.p. 98.6–99.7°, gave, on saponification,[6] 8.37 g. (98.0%) and 4.17 g. (96.9%) of the same *exo*-norbornyl alcohol, m.p. 127.8–128.5°.

Solvolysis of *exo*-Norbornyl *p*-Bromobenzenesulfonate. Glacial Acetic Acid.—*exo*-Norbornyl *p*-bromobenzenesulfonate[4] (1.50 g.) was allowed to solvolyze in dry glacial acetic acid at 25° for 24 hours. Extraction from the neutralized acetic acid solvent with ether, reduction with lithium aluminum hydride, and conversion of the norborneol to the 3,5-dinitrobenzoate yielded 0.828 g. (59.3%) of *exo*-norbornyl 3,5-dinitrobenzoate, m.p., crude, 97–102°; m.p. 103.4–105.0° after recrystallization from aqueous acetic acid.

A 0.60 M *exo*-norbornyl *p*-bromobenzenesulfonate[4] solution in dry acetic acid and a solution 0.60 M in *exo*-norbornyl *p*-bromobenzenesulfonate and 0.70 M in potassium acetate in dry acetic acid were each allowed to solvolyze to completion at 25° and then examined for unsaturation by quantitative bromination. Carefully weighed amounts of the solvolyzed solution (*ca.* 0.15–0.24 g.) were added to 15 ml. of acetic acid containing 2 ml. of 10% aqueous sulfuric acid in bromination flasks followed by 10 ml. of standard bromate-bromide solution delivered by pipet. The bromination was allowed to proceed in the dark for 12–40 minutes, excess solid potassium iodide introduced after sufficient water (*ca.* 30 ml.) was added to reduce acidity, and then the solution was titrated with standard 0.0509 M thiosulfate to a starch end-point.

In the absence and presence of potassium acetate, bromine consumption equivalent to 0.27 ± 0.27 mole % and 4.53 ± 0.22 mole % norbornylene was observed, respectively.

75% Aqueous Acetone.—*exo*-Norbornyl *p*-bromobenzenesulfonate[4] (3.4 g.) was dissolved in 75% aqueous acetone to a concentration of 0.30 M and the solution held at 25° for *ca.* 12 hours. Isolation of the norborneol as in the case of the analogous experiment with the *endo*-*p*-bromobenzenesulfonate[6] and conversion to the *p*-bromobenzenesulfonate gave 1.45 g. (42.6%) of *exo* ester. A portion of this *exo*-norbornyl *p*-bromobenzenesulfonate[4] product was then solvolyzed in dry glacial acetic acid in duplicate runs at 0.037 M (Table I). Early and late infinity titers[6] yielded assays of the material of 2.1, 0.9 and 1.9% *endo*-derivative.

Complete Resolution of *exo*-Norbornyl Acid Phthalate.—Racemic *exo*-norbornyl acid phthalate (207.0 g.) was refluxed in 1000 ml. of acetone with an equivalent amount of cinchonidine alkaloid (234 g.) and allowed to stand overnight in the cold room. The initial 387.6 g. of alkaloid salt

(87.9% theoretical) was recrystallized from warm acetone with overnight standing three more times, ending with 165.6 g. (37.5%) of cinchonidine salt. A 5-g. quantity of this salt was dissolved in 25 ml. of hot benzene, extracted with excess 2 N hydrochloric acid, washed and dried, and the liberated *exo*-norbornyl acid phthalate was isolated in two crops after addition of 20–40° petroleum ether to the concentrated benzene solution. Polarimetric examination of the two successive crops of 1.15 g. and 0.88 g. acid phthalate gave rotations of $[\alpha]^{25}$D +0.89° and +8.39° (chloroform, c 10.04), respectively.

Both pure *exo*-norbornyl acid phthalate enantiomorphs were obtained by fractionally crystallizing the liberated partially active acid phthalates from the recrystallized cinchonidine salt and from the combined mother liquors. The procedure used in working up the active *exo*-(A)-norbornyl acid phthalate enantiomorph from the combined mother liquors from the alkaloid salt recrystallization is typical and the results were strictly analogous to those obtained in the isolation of the (B) isomer. In the former case, the four mother liquors were combined, diluted with water and 100% excess dilute hydrochloric acid and extracted with chloroform seven times. The combined chloroform phase was washed several times with dilute hydrochloric acid and then several times with water and finally dried over magnesium sulfate. The chloroform solution was evaporated under suction to a concentrated oil, dissolved in ethyl acetate and petroleum ether and brought to turbidity. Overnight standing in the ice-box yielded a first crop of 77.25 g. of *exo*-norbornyl acid phthalate which was essentially pure racemic compound, $[\alpha]^{25}$D −0.04° (chloroform, c 9.98). The next three crops were combined and refractionated several times to remove racemic impurity and all of the remaining acid phthalate fractions (33.6 g.) were combined and purified through the sodium salt by extracting the compound from an ether solution with excess aqueous sodium carbonate. After the addition of excess dilute sulfuric acid, the liberated acid phthalate was extracted thoroughly with ether, washed, dried and evaporated to dryness. The resulting 32.85 g. of acid phthalate was crystallized from ether–petroleum ether and 31.66 g. of pure *exo*-(A)-norbornyl acid phthalate was obtained in five successive crops, m.p. 89.3–90.3°. The specific rotations, $[\alpha]^{24}$D, of crops 1, 2, 3 and 5 were −8.49°, −8.49°, −8.42° and −8.46° (chloroform, c 10.04), respectively.

In like manner, the *exo*-(B)-norbornyl acid phthalate enantiomorph was obtained by fractional crystallization of the partially active acid phthalate obtained from the recrystallized cinchonidine salt to yield in this case 29.15 g. of pure enantiomorph, m.p. 89.0–90.2°, $[\alpha]^{25}$D +8.45° (chloroform, c 10.02).

Anal. Calcd. for $C_{15}H_{16}O_4$: C, 69.21; H, 6.20. Found for *exo*-(A)-norbornyl acid phthalate: C, 69.35; H, 6.30. Found for *exo*-(B)-norbornyl acid phthalate: C, 69.19; H, 6.45.

Conversion of *exo*-Norbornyl Acid Phthalate Enantiomorphs into the Corresponding Alcohols and *p*-Bromobenzenesulfonates.—Employing the usual procedure,[6] 28.29 g. of *exo*-(A)-norbornyl acid phthalate and 28.15 g. of *exo*-(B)-norbornyl acid phthalate were saponified and steam distilled to give 11.93 g. (97.8%) of *exo*-(A)-norbornyl alcohol, m.p. 126.0–126.6°, $[\alpha]^{24}$D +2.44° (chloroform, c 9.99) and 11.36 g. (93.7%) of *exo*-(B)-norbornyl alcohol, m.p. 126.0–126.8°, $[\alpha]^{24}$D −2.41° (chloroform, c 10.04).

Anal. Calcd. for $C_7H_{12}O$: C, 74.95; H, 10.79. Found for *exo*-(A)-norborneol: C, 74.93; H, 10.57. Found for *exo*-(B)-norborneol: C, 74.90; H, 10.88.

exo-(B)-Norborneol (6.0 g.) was dissolved in *ca.* 40 ml. of dry pyridine and 14.32 g. (5% excess) of *p*-bromobenzenesulfonyl chloride was added with cooling of the flask in an ice-bath. The flask was left in the ice-box for seven days and the *exo*-(B)-norbornyl *p*-bromobenzenesulfonate was then isolated by dilution of the pyridine solution with several volumes of ice in the original flask. The product was induced to crystallize and then promptly collected on a sintered glass funnel, washed thoroughly with water and dried without phosphorus pentoxide in a vacuum desiccator. A 16.31-g. yield (92.2%) of *exo*-(B)-norbornyl *p*-bromobenzenesulfonate, m.p. 55.3–56.4°, was thus directly obtained, $[\alpha]^{24}$D +1.89° (chloroform, c 10.15).

Anal. Calcd. for $C_{13}H_{15}O_3SBr$: C, 47.14; H, 4.57. Found: C, 46.88; H, 4.71.

Repetition of the above procedure with 2.0 g. of *exo*-(B)-norbornyl alcohol, 4.77 g. (5% excess) of *p*-bromobenzenesulfonyl chloride and 15 ml. of dry pyridine and a reaction time of 16 hours yielded 5.16 g. (87.5%) of *exo*-(B)-norbornyl *p*-bromobenzenesulfonate with the identical optical activity, $[\alpha]^{24}$D +1.85° (chloroform, *c* 10.21).

Relation of Configuration of *exo*- and *endo*-Norbornyl Enantiomorphs by Oxidation to Active Norcamphor.—1.93 g. of *ca*. 60–80% resolved *endo*-(A)-norbornyl acid phthalate[6] from middle fractions was saponified and steam distilled. The combined solid and *ca*. 20 ml. of aqueous distillate was treated with 8 ml. of acetic acid followed by 1.4 g. of potassium dichromate and 1.8 g. of concentrated sulfuric acid. After one hour standing with occasional warming to *ca*. 40°, excess norcamphor and the norcamphor steam distilled. Only the 0.32 g. of solid norcamphor in the distillate was saved and dried *in vacuo* over potassium hydroxide, m.p. 95.5–96.2°, $[\alpha]^{24}$D −15.73° (chloroform, *c* 9.79).

Anal. Calcd. for $C_7H_{10}O$: C, 76.29; H, 9.16. Found: C, 76.08; H, 9.37.

In similar manner, 1.42 g. of optically pure *exo*-(B)-norborneol was oxidized and 0.68 g. of solid norcamphor separated by decantation from the steam distillate and dried, m.p. 107.1–109.3°, $[\alpha]^{24}$D +8.66 (chloroform, *c* 10.00).

Active (B) and Racemic *exo*-Norbornyl Acetates.—Optically pure *exo*-(B)-norborneol (1.00 g.) was dissolved in a mixture of 5 ml. of acetic anhydride and 20 ml. of dry glacial acetic acid in a 50-ml. volumetric flask and heated in a 75° bath for 10.0 hours. The solution was diluted with *ca*. five volumes of water, extracted four times with 50-ml. portions of pet. ether (b.p. 34–39°) and the extract washed in turn with water, aqueous sodium bicarbonate, and water. It was dried over anhydrous magnesium sulfate, and then concentrated to *ca*. 5 ml. through a fractionating column. The residue was carefully distilled *in vacuo* through a small all-glass apparatus to give 1.24 g. (90.2%) of *exo*-(B)-norbornyl acetate, α^{25}D +10.39° (1 dcm.), n^{25}D 1.4565.

Anal. Calcd. for $C_9H_{14}O_2$: C, 70.09; H, 9.15. Found: C, 69.95; H, 9.25.

The same procedure was used to prepare a sample of pure racemic *exo*-norbornyl acetate whose infrared spectrum was taken (Fig. 1).

Acetolysis of Active *exo*-(B)-Norbornyl *p*-Bromobenzenesulfonate in Glacial Acetic Acid.—Optically pure *exo*-(B)-norbornyl *p*-bromobenzenesulfonate (2.00 g.) was mixed with 2.00 g. of racemic *exo*-norbornyl *p*-bromobenzenesulfonate and the combined 4.00 g. dissolved in 120 ml. of dry glacial acetic acid (0.10 *M*) to which was added potassium acetate (0.085 *M* inadvertently insufficient) and the solution warmed in a 40° bath for 18 hours. The acetate was iso-

lated as in the preparation from norborneol to yield 1.50 g. (80.5%) racemic *exo*-norbornyl acetate, α^{24}D +0.001° (1 dcm.), n^{25}D 1.4565, infrared spectrum in Fig. 1.

Actually, the amount of excess acid prevailing in this solvolysis because of the deficiency of potassium acetate employed in the run was insufficient to cause more than several per cent. racemization of the final acetate. This is clear from control experiments previously described[6] on the behavior of *exo*-acetate toward much more concentrated (0.76 *M*) toluenesulfonic acid at 75 and 25°, and also from the effect even at 75° of just this excess acid concentration on the surviving activity in the *exo*-acetate product from solvolysis of the *endo*-*p*-bromobenzenesulfonate.[6]

Kinetic and Polarimetric Measurements.—The general procedures for the titrimetric rate measurements were those previously employed.[4,6]

In most of the acetolysis runs, the solution aliquot was drained directly into at least an equal volume of pure pet. ether (b.p. 30–60°) which served to reduce the solvolysis rate very markedly. Cooling the pet. ether-diluted aliquot further slowed the solvolysis reaction so that titration could be postponed for at least an hour without error. Tests showed that the brom phenol blue indicator color and color change at the equivalence point were identical in 1:1 acetic acid–pet. ether and acetic acid.

In the case of the rapid solvolysis in 75% acetone, room temperature was kept close to 25° and the titrations concluded without delay. Time was taken at the titration endpoint.

Routine polarimetric measurements were carried out with the Hilger instrument[6] in semimicro or micro 1 dcm. polarimeter tubes.

Polarimetric racemization rates of *exo*-(B)-norbornyl *p*-bromobenzenesulfonate in various solvents were carried out in a specially constructed 4-dcm. all-glass jacketed polarimeter tube of *ca*. 22-ml. capacity with sealed-on optically plane ¼-inch Pyrex end pieces. Water from a 24.98 ± 0.01° thermostat was continuously circulated through the outer jacket during the course of the racemization rate runs. In each such rate run, solvent first brought to temperature in the thermostat was used to dissolve the weighed quantity of the active *p*-bromobenzenesulfonate to the mark in a 25-ml. volumetric flask. The resulting solution was then transferred as rapidly as possible to the polarimeter tube through the glass-stoppered opening at the center of the tube and then carefully located in place in the polarimeter trough. Readings were taken at appropriate intervals.

LOS ANGELES 24, CALIF.   RECEIVED JUNE 11, 1951

18 | 3-Phenyl-2-butanol; the Phenonium Ion

This is a good place to remind the reader that to gain appreciation of the field of nonclassical ions, one must read many papers beside those in this collection. This is nowhere more true than of Parts I–IV of the series of one-man papers by Cram, of which Part V (Paper No. 18) is here reproduced.

The unique interest of the derivatives of 3-phenyl-2-butanol is revealed by a study of the chart on page 110 of Paper No. 18. Something happens during solvolysis to cause the optically active *threo*-tosylates (I) to yield racemic *threo*-acetates, while the intimately related optically active *erythro*-tosylates (II) yield the *active erythro*-acetates of retained configuration and asymmetry. As the chart shows, this result is uniquely predicted by the mechanism which involves a butylenephenonium ion which is both formed and opened with inversion of configuration as with an ethylene oxide. The phenonium ion from *threo* starting material has a plane of symmetry; that from *erythro* starting material does not, and this is responsible for the striking difference in the two cases. The driving force from phenyl in 3-phenyl-2-butyl tosylate is not so large but that some leakage of material through a nonphenonium mechanism would be expected. In this paper the extent of such leakage is measured and found to amount to several per cent. Recovered *threo*-tosylate after partial solvolysis is found to be extensively racemized, showing internal return from an ion pair having the stereochemical characteristics of the phenonium ion itself. Although capture of the intermediate ion by solvolyzing solvent is efficient in competition with sulfonate ions, in the non-solvolyzing solvent acetonitrile it is possible to make a second sulfonate ion play the role of product determination. Olefin formation attending these ionizations is treated in other papers of the series. This paper is largely devoted to exploring the role of ion pairs in several solvents.

The kind of ion pairs which are here differentiated from free ions are the ones later characterized as "intimate," i.e., immune to any intervention by other ions outside the pair.

From: *J. Am. Chem. Soc.* **74**, 2129–37 (1952)

[Contribution from the Department of Chemistry of the University of California at Los Angeles]

Studies in Stereochemistry. V. Phenonium Sulfonate Ion-pairs as Intermediates in the Intramolecular Rearrangements and Solvolysis Reactions that Occur in the 3-Phenyl-2-butanol System

By Donald J. Cram

When the p-toluenesulfonates or p-bromobenzenesulfonates of the stereoisomers of 3-phenyl-2-butanol are dissolved in ionizing solvents (acetic and formic acids or acetonitrile) an intramolecular rearrangement occurs in which the phenyl and the p-toluenesulfonate (or p-bromobenzenesulfonate) groups exchange places. A comparison of the stereochemical structures of the products and reactants indicates the rearrangement to be highly stereospecific. When the reaction of the p-bromobenzenesulfonate is carried out in the presence of a large concentration of p-toluenesulfonate ion, minor amounts of p-toluenesulfonate of the same configuration as the p-bromobenzenesulfonate product are obtained. The configurations of the recovered p-bromobenzenesulfonates (or p-toluenesulfonates) are in each case qualitatively the same as the configurations of the solvolyzed products (acetates or formates). These facts are rationalized in terms of a series of reversible reactions between starting material, bridged ion-pairs (phenonium p-toluenesulfonates or p-bromobenzenesulfonates) and rearranged p-toluenesulfonate or p-bromobenzenesulfonate products. The solvolysis reaction is interpreted as going by an exchange reaction between phenonium sulfonate ion-pairs and solvent to give new ion-pairs which collapse to product.

In Papers I and III[1] of this series evidence was presented for the existence of a cyclic bridged ion (A)[2] as a discrete intermediate in the phenyl migration that occurs during the solvolyses of the tosylates (p-toluenesulfonates) of the various stereomers of 3-phenyl-2-butanol, 2-phenyl-3-pentanol and 3-phenyl-2-pentanol. In Paper IV[3] the stereochemical structures of the four stereo-

IA $[\alpha]^{25}$D +30.9   IB $[\alpha]^{25}$D −30.2   IIA $[\alpha]^{25}$D + 0.68   IIB $[\alpha]^{25}$D −0.69

mers of all three compounds were interrelated, and structural assignments were made on the basis of both the stereochemistry of the rearrangement reaction[1] and of the Chugaev elimination reaction.[4] The numbering system (IA and IB representing one set of enantiomorphs and IIA and IIB designating the second pair) adopted in the previous papers is maintained here.

The present investigation deals with a more detailed study of the mechanism of the solvolysis reaction, and with the concomitant transformations. This paper reports the results that pertain to the reactions giving rise to the oxygen containing products, whereas Paper VI in this series will deal with the mechanism by which the olefinic products are produced.

Methods

The physical properties and analyses of the starting materials are reported in Table I. The tosylates, brosylates (p - bromobenzenesulfonates) and acetates as well as the alcohols (IA, IB, IIA and IIB) from which these derivatives were prepared were synthesized by methods that have already been reported.[1] The brosylate of IIA was inordinately unstable, and had to be used as soon as prepared and, when obtained as a product, its properties had to be recorded without delay. Table II records the

(1) D. J. Cram, This Journal, **71**, 3863, 3875 (1949).

(2) This type of ion subsequently will be referred to as a "phenonium ion."

(3) D. J. Cram, This Journal, **71**, 3883 (1949).

(4) Further substantiation of the correctness of these assignments will be found in Papers VII and VIII of this series.

TABLE I

PHYSICAL PROPERTIES AND ANALYSES OF STARTING MATERIALS

Compound	$n^{25}D$	M.p., °C.	Rotation, $[\alpha]D$	Mol. form.	Calcd. Carbon	Calcd. Hydrogen	Found Carbon	Found Hydrogen
IA tosylate[e]	....	62-63	+16.97[ob]	....	...	..	...	..
IB tosylate[e]	....	62-63	−16.89[b]	$C_{17}H_{20}O_3S$	67.08	6.62	66.97	6.59
I tosylate	....	46-47	....	$C_{17}H_{20}O_3S$	67.08	6.62	67.22	6.77
IIA tosylate[d]	....	36-37[f]	−17.41[b]	....	...	..	...	..
IIB tosylate[e]	....	46-47[f]	+17.72[b]	$C_{17}H_{20}O_3S$	67.08	6.62	67.07	6.77
IA acetate[e]	1.4877	....	− 8.08[g,i]	$C_{12}H_{16}O_2$	74.96	8.38	74.89	8.65
IIB acetate[e]	1.4877	....	+32.55[g,i]	$C_{12}H_{16}O_2$	74.96	8.38	74.89	8.57
IB brosylate[e]	....	74-75[h]	−21.7[b]	$C_{16}H_{17}O_3SBr$	52.03	4.93	51.73	4.77
I brosylate	....	93-94	....	$C_{16}H_{17}O_3SBr$	52.03	4.93	51.98	4.63
IIA brosylate[d]	....	57-58	−19.6[b]	$C_{16}H_{17}O_3SBr$	52.03	4.93	52.02	4.64

[e] Prepared from alcohol IA, $[\alpha]^{23}D$ +32.1°. IA tosylate was previously reported (ref. 1). [b] Benzene solution, $c = 5\%$; $T = 23-25°$. [c] Prepared from alcohol IB, $[\alpha]^{23}D$ −31.8°. [d] Prepared from alcohol IIA, $[\alpha]^{23}D$ 0.36°. IIA tosylate was previously reported but was erroneously labeled IB (see Table I, ref. 1). [e] Prepared from alcohol IIB, $[\alpha]^{23}D$ −0.51°. [f] These enantiomers were each isolated in two polymorphic forms, one set melting at 36-37°, the other at 46-47°. [g] These rotations were taken on the pure liquid sample, $l = 1$ dm., $\lambda = $ D, $T = 23°$. [h] The compound seemed to solidify and remelt at 77-78°. [i] αD.

conditions of each experiment and the results.

The sulfonate esters were isolated from the reaction medium through extraction and crystallization procedures. The carboxylate esters and olefins were first isolated by distillation as mixtures, which were converted by lithium aluminum hydride to mixtures of alcohol and olefin. These two classes of components were then quantitatively separated by chromatographic methods with alumina. The alcohols were submitted to infrared analysis. **Figure 1** records the infrared spectra of the two diastereomeric 3-phenyl-2-butanols (I and II) and of 2-phenyl-2-butanol,[5] and enough differences

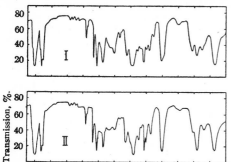

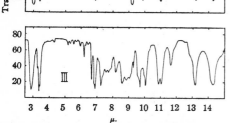

3 4 5 6 7 8 9 10 11 12 13 14
μ.

Fig. 1.—Infrared spectra of the two diastereomeric 3-phenyl-2-butanols (I and II, the numbers designating the configurations as in text) and 2-phenyl-2-butanol (III). Spectra were taken on liquid films (0.01 mm. thickness) in NaCl cells on a Baird Spectrophotometer.

(5) This alcohol could have arisen in the reaction by migration of a hydrogen instead of a phenyl group during the course of solvolysis. Evidence that such a process does indeed take place is presented in paper VI of this series.

between the spectra exist to allow analyses for the three components. Table III reports the results of this analysis taken at the most advantageous wave lengths. The absence of any 2-phenyl-2-butanol in the mixtures (as shown by inspection of the optical densities of the pure substances and unknown mixtures at all four wave lengths) resolved the problem into an analysis of a two-component system (carbinols I and II).

The results of conducting the solvolysis reaction with the brosylates of IB and IIA in acetic acid and in the presence of ten parts (brosylate = 1 part) of tosylate ion are recorded in Table IV. In these experiments the acetate products were not examined, attention being given to only the analysis of the brosylate–tosylate mixtures that were isolated after about two thirds of the ester had solvolysed. The vast differences between the percentage of carbon and of bromine in the tosylates and brosylates of the isomers ($\Delta = 15.05\%$ for carbon and $\Delta = 21.64\%$ for bromine) allow two independent methods of analysis for the balance between the two derivatives in the crystalline products. The identity of these products was determined from their rotatory power, and from a series of mixed melting point experiments.

Results

A high degree of stereospecificity for the reaction that produces the acetates is apparent in runs 3–6. Both IA and IB tosylates (runs 3 and 4) give ultimately alcoholic products, 96% of which possess the I configuration and 4% the II configuration. It is clear from the low rotation of the alcoholic fraction ($\alpha^{23}D$ 0.20°, $l = 1$ dm.) that the component belonging to the I series is almost completely racemic. Thus the small residual rotation in the alcoholic product of run 3 amounts to αD = +0.20° ($l = 1$ dm.), and must be due to a preponderance of IA over IB to the extent of 0.64%.[6] The maximum contribution that the IIA present could make to the rotation is 0.002° and this value is within the experimental error. From the rotations of the

(6) In this and subsequent calculations of a similar sort, the assumption has been made that the rotational contributions of the two components are additive. The structural similarity of the two diastereomeric alcohols lends substance to this assumption.

TABLE II: THE OXYGEN-CONTAINING PRODUCTS OF SOLVOLYSIS

Run no.	Start mat. Config. tos.	Start mat. Wt. g.	Solution	Moles[a] base added	Temp., °C.	Time,[b] hr.	αD[d] alc.	Yld.[e] alc.	%I[e] mixt.	%II[e] mixt.	αD[d] mixt.	αD[d] acet.	1st crop rec. tos. Yld. %	M.p., °C.	[α]D[d]	2nd crop rec. tos. Yld. %	M.p., °C.	[α]D[d]
1	IA	10	Gl. acetic	0.8	75	36	+0.14°	43										
2	IIB	10	Gl. acetic	0.8	75	36	−1.92	58										
3	IA	14	Gl. acetic	1.2	75	33	+0.20	53	96	4		−0.43[g]						
4	IB	12	Gl. acetic	1.2	75	33	−0.19	53	96	4								
5	IIA	12	Gl. acetic	1.2	75	33	+1.91	68	5	94								
6	IIB	14	Gl. acetic	1.2	75	33	−1.82	69	5	94		+32.49°						
7	IA	5	Gl. acetic	1.2	75	3⅓						+1.09°	30	46–49°[h]		0.5	47–49°[h]	
8	IIB	5	Gl. acetic	1.2	75	3⅓						+18.1	32	46–47°[i]		2.1	46–47°[i]	
9	IA	5	Dry formic	1.2	25	24	+0.03	70[j]				−0.01°		55–59[j]	+13.9	Trace		
10	IIB	5	Dry formic	1.2	25	24	.73	71[k]				+33.50[g]		45–46[m]	−6.43	3.6	Oil	
11	IA	2.5	Dry formic	1.2	25	0.72		33					40	45–46°	−17.56	7	42–45°	−16.67°
12	IB	5	Acetonitrile	2	82	67		0					52					
13	IIA	5	Acetonitrile	2	82	67		0					45	45–46[n]	−4.33	15	45–48[p]	−4.31
14	IA	1.0	Acetonitrile + TosOH (1 mole)	0	82	2		0					40	45–48[h]				
15	IA	0.5	Chloroform	0	62	53		0					92	62–63°[g]	+16.77			

[a] Starting material = 1 mole. In runs 1–8 the base was added in the form of potassium carbonate along with more than enough acetic anhydride to consume the water produced. Anhydrous sodium formate was employed in runs 9–11, and anhydrous potassium carbonate was present as a second phase in runs 12–15. In each case the solvent was preheated. [b] For every sample of alcohol, n^{25}_D 1.5168 ± 0.0006. [c] c = 5% (benzene), T = 23–25°. [d] Pure sample, l = 1 dm., T = 23–25°. [e] Values obtained from infrared data (see Table III). [g] For every sample of acetate, n^{20}_D 1.4877 ± 0.0003. [h] M.m.p. with I tosylate ... distinguish between the enantiomorphs in each racemate series.

(racemic) 46–48°. [f] M.m.p. with authentic sample of IIB tosylate, 46–47°. [i] This material was converted to the acid phthalate, 1st crop, yield 62%, 2nd crop, yield 3%, m.p. (both crops) 130–131°, not depressed by admixture with an authentic sample. The residue was extracted into NaHCO₃ solution, acidified, and a trace of material crystallized, m.p. 128–130°, not depressed by admixture with IA acid phthalate. [k] Converted to the acid phthalate: 1st crop, yield 64%, [α]²⁵D +65.6° (c 3%, in ethanol), m.p. 101–102°, m.m.p. with an authentic sample of the acid phthalate of IIB, 101–102°; residue extracted into NaHCO₃ solution, acidified, and a trace of material crystallized, m.p. 98–100° (not depressed by admixture with the first crop). [l] M.m.p. with IA tosylate, 58–62°. [m] M.m.p. with tosylate of I (racemic), 45–47°. [n] M.m.p. with authentic IIA tosylate, 45–46°. [o] M.m.p. with IIA tosylate, 44–46° (filtrates produced 5% yield of non-distillable, non-acidic oil). [p] M.m.p. with I tosylate (racemic), 45–47°. M.m.p. with IA tosylate 62–63° (filtrates produced a 4% yield of non-distillable, non-acidic oil). [q] M.m.p. with I tosylate, 62–63°.

TABLE III

INFRARED ANALYSES FOR THE DIASTEREOMERIC 3-PHENYL-2-BUTANOLS AND 2-PHENYL-2-BUTANOL

Sample[a] alcohol	Optical density (Cell thickness = 0.03 mm., slit = 0.92 mm.)				% I[b]	% II	% Total[b]
	λ = 8.10 μ	λ = 8.60 μ	λ = 10.38 μ	λ = 11.67 μ			
I	1.11	0.322	0.589	0.190	..	..	..
II	0.806	.399	1.01	.211	..	..	..
2-Phenyl-2-butanol	.609	1.29	0.330	.821	..	..	..
50% I, 50% II	.920	0.373	.783	.204	46	51	97
From run 3	1.09	.334	.598	.189	95.5	3.5	99
From run 4	1.09	.333	.598	.186	95.5	3.5	99
From run 5	.816	.391	.981	.189	4.9	94.6	99.5
From run 6	.815	.392	.984	.202	4.5	94.9	99.4

[a] No solvent was employed. [b] These values were calculated using the data at λ = 8.10 μ and λ = 10.38 μ, assuming that Beer's law holds, and that no 2-phenyl-2-butanol was present. That the first assumption is valid is shown by the facts that the sum of I and II are very close to 100% and that the deviation from Beer's law at 50% I, 50% II is small (and hence much smaller at low concentrations of I in II or II in I). The second assumption is demonstrated to be valid by the values of the optical density at λ = 8.60 μ and λ = 11.67 μ.

TABLE IV

SOLVOLYSES OF BROSYLATES OF IA AND IIB IN PRESENCE OF HIGH CONCENTRATIONS OF TOSYLATE IONS[a]

Run no.	16	17
Bros.[b]	IB	IIA
% yld., ac. + ol.[c,d]	63	59
Wt. % recov. { cryst. mat.[d]	25	27
Wt. % recov. { non.-cryst. mat.[e]	2	1
Crystalline material recrystallized — 1st crop { Wt. %[d] yld.	19	20
{ [α]D[f]	−2.05°	−18.8
{ M.p., °C.	79–86[i]	43–50[i]
{ Wt. %[g] tos. { Brom.	15	26
{ Wt. %[g] tos. { Carb.	16	25
2nd crop { Wt. % yld.[d]	1.5	4.3
{ [α]D[f]	....	−17.8°
{ M.p., °C.	43–45[i]	42–44[i]
{ Wt. %[g] tos. { Brom.	87	48
{ Wt. %[g] tos. { Carb.	91	50
Over-all yields,[h] % { Bros.	16	17
Over-all yields,[h] % { Tos.	5	9

[a] Ten moles of KO Tos. to one of brosylate in dry glacial acetic acid (see Experimental). [b] See Table I for properties. [c] Yields are calculated on the assumption that the ratios of acetate to olefin are the same as those found in runs 3 and 5 (Table II and unpublished results). [d] Wt. starting material = 100%. [e] This material was non-acidic. [f] T = 23–25°, c 5%, in benzene. [g] These wt. %'s are based on bromine and carbon analyses for the mixtures, total crop = 100%. [h] These are yields of recrystallized material including both crops, and take into consideration the difference in molecular wt. of the tosylate and brosylate esters. [i] See experimental part for mixed melting point determinations.

acetate made from the alcohol mixture of run 3 and the rotations of the acetates of pure IA and IIA, it is evident that of the 4% of material of the II configuration in the mixture, 2.8% is II (racemic) and 1.2% is IIA. The data are summarized below. A similar treatment of the data from run 6 produces the results shown in the diagram.

$$
\text{IB Bros. (run 16)} \xrightarrow[\text{1.5 half-lives}]{\substack{\text{O Tos.}^- \\ \text{CH}_3\text{COOH}}} \underbrace{\underset{\text{(racemic)}}{15\% \text{ I Bros.}} + \underset{\text{(optically pure)}}{1.5\% \text{ IB Bros.}}}_{\text{Ratio of about 3.7 to 1}} + \underset{\text{(racemic)}}{4.5\% \text{ I Tos.}} + \underset{\text{olefin}}{\text{acetate,}}
$$

$$
\text{IIA Bros. (run 17)} \xrightarrow[\text{1.5 half-lives}]{\substack{\text{O Tos.}^- \\ \text{CH}_3\text{COOH}}} \underbrace{\underset{\text{(optically pure)}}{17\% \text{ IIA Bros.}} + \underset{\text{(optically pure)}}{9\% \text{ IIA Tos.}}}_{\text{ratio of about 2 to 1}} + \text{acetate, olefin}
$$

$$
\begin{array}{l}
\text{IA Tos.} \\
\text{(run 3)}
\end{array}
\xrightarrow[\substack{3,\ \text{Al}_2\text{O}_3 \\ \text{sep.}}]{\substack{1,\ \text{AcOH} \\ 2,\ \text{LiAlH}_4}}
\begin{array}{l}
\text{3-phenyl-2-} \\
\text{butanol}
\end{array}
\quad
\begin{array}{l}
\sim 95\% \text{ I (racemic)} \\
\sim 0.6\% \text{ IA} \\
\sim 2.8\% \text{ II (racemic)} \\
\sim 1.2\% \text{ IIA}
\end{array}
$$

$$
\begin{array}{l}
\text{IIB Tos.} \\
\text{(run 6)}
\end{array}
\xrightarrow[\substack{3,\ \text{Al}_2\text{O}_3 \\ \text{sep.}}]{\substack{1,\ \text{AcOH} \\ 2,\ \text{LiAlH}_4}}
\begin{array}{l}
\text{3-phenyl-} \\
\text{2-butanol}
\end{array}
\quad
\begin{array}{l}
\sim 94\% \text{ IIB} \\
\sim 4\% \text{ IB from rotation} \\
\sim 5\% \text{ IB from infrared} \\
\text{data}
\end{array}
$$

An even higher degree of stereospecificity for the solvolysis reactions that were conducted in formic acid was experienced.

$$
\begin{array}{l}
\text{IA Tos.} \\
\text{(run 9)}
\end{array}
\xrightarrow[\substack{3,\ \text{Al}_2\text{O}_3}]{\substack{1,\ \text{HCOOH} \\ 2,\ \text{LiAlH}_4}}
\begin{array}{l}
\text{3-phenyl-} \\
\text{2-butanol}
\end{array}
\quad
\begin{array}{l}
\sim 100\% \text{ I (racemic)} \\
< 0.02\% \text{ IA (calcd. from} \\
\quad \text{rot. of alcohol)} \\
< 0.01\% \text{ IIA (calcd.} \\
\quad \text{from rot. of acetate)}
\end{array}
$$

$$
\begin{array}{l}
\text{IIB Tos.} \\
\text{(run 10)}
\end{array}
\xrightarrow[\substack{3,\ \text{Al}_2\text{O}_3}]{\substack{1,\ \text{HCOOH} \\ 2,\ \text{LiAlH}_4}}
\begin{array}{l}
\text{3-phenyl-} \\
\text{2-butanol}
\end{array}
\quad
\begin{array}{l}
\sim 100\% \text{ IIB} \\
\sim 0.5\% \text{ IB}
\end{array}
$$

A new feature of the solvolysis reaction was brought to light when IA tosylate was recovered from a partially acetolyzed mixture. This sulfonate ester had undergone *94% racemization* during the period of one solvolytic half-life. The tosylate of IIA was recovered optically pure in a similar

$$
\text{IA Tos. (run 7)} \xrightarrow[\text{1 half-life}]{\text{AcOH}} \underbrace{\underset{\text{(racemic)}}{28\% \text{ I Tos.}} + \underset{\text{(optically pure)}}{2\% \text{ IA Tos.}}}_{\text{94\% racemized}} + \text{acetate} + \text{olefin}
$$

$$
\text{IIB Tos. (run 8)} \xrightarrow[\text{1 half-life}]{\text{AcOH}} \underset{\text{(optically pure)}}{34\% \text{ IIB Tos.}} + \text{acetate} + \text{olefin}
$$

$$
\text{IA Tos. (run 11)} \xrightarrow[\text{1 half-life}]{\text{HCOOH}} \underbrace{\underset{\text{(racemic)}}{7\% \text{ I Tos.}} + \underset{\text{(optically pure)}}{33\% \text{ IA Tos.}}}_{\text{18\% racemized}} + \text{acetate} + \text{olefin}
$$

$$
\text{IB Tos. (run 12)} \xrightarrow[\text{2/3 half-life}]{\text{CH}_3\text{CN}} \underbrace{32\% \text{ I Tos.} + \underset{\text{(optically pure)}}{20\% \text{ IB Tos.}}}_{\text{ratio of about 1.5 to 1}} + \text{olefin}
$$

$$
\text{IIA Tos. (run 13)} \xrightarrow[\text{2/3 half-life}]{\text{CH}_3\text{CN}} \underset{\text{(optically pure)}}{52\% \text{ IIA Tos.}} + \text{olefin}
$$

$$
\text{IA Tos. (run 14)} \xrightarrow[\text{2/3 half-life}]{\substack{\text{CH}_3\text{CN} \\ \text{TosOH}}} \underbrace{\underset{\text{(racemic)}}{41\% \text{ I Tos.}} + \underset{\text{(optically pure)}}{14\% \text{ IA Tos.}}}_{\text{ratio of about 3 to 1}} + \text{olefin}
$$

experiment. When formic acid was used as solvent, the unreacted IA tosylate was racemized to the extent of 18% during one solvolytic half-life.[7]

(7) The half-lives in formic and acetic acids were calculated from the rate data obtained by S. Winstein, et al., [S. Winstein, B. Morse, E. Grunwald, K. Schreiber and J. Corse, ibid., **74**, 1113 (1952)]. The

When the esters were heated in acetonitrile, a nonsolvolytic medium, a slow reaction to give olefins took place. Again IA tosylate was shown to undergo racemization more rapidly than elimination. Both reactions were found to be strongly catalyzed by p-toluenesulfonic acid.

Since it was of interest to learn whether or not the racemization of IA tosylate involves the separation of tosylate ion from the molecule, the partial solvolysis of the corresponding brosylate was carried out in the presence of a high concentration of tosylate ion. Both tosylate and brosylate esters were isolated from the reaction mixture, and both sulfonate esters had approximately the same configuration.

Discussion

Evidence has been accumulated in the foregoing experiments that exclusive of olefin formation, four discrete sets of products can be realized when tosylate or brosylate esters of 3-phenyl-2-butanol are allowed to react in glacial acetic acid. Although several of the reactions undoubtedly have common intermediates, they can best be discussed in terms of names which refer more to the product than to the mechanism by which the product comes into being. In the present discussion the four reactions will be referred to as follows: the solvolysis reaction (C) in which sulfonate esters are converted to carboxylate esters, both asymmetric carbon atoms being involved in the process, the isomerization reaction (D) in which tosyl and phenyl groups exchange places in half of the molecules; the exchange reaction (E) in which a tosylate anion outside of the molecule exchanges with a brosylate group within the molecule, with or without stereoisomerization of the system, and the simple replacement reaction (F) in which a tosyl group is replaced by an acetoxyl group, the stereochemistry of no carbon atom other than the one at the seat of reaction being involved in the process.

The Solvolysis Reaction.—In view of the recently discovered isomerization reaction of IA tosylate to I tosylate (runs 7 and 11)[8] the evidence presented

author is indebted to S. Winstein for suggesting the use of formic acid as a solvolytic medium.

(8) Such a reaction was considered improbable until W. G. Young, S. Winstein and H. L. Goering [ibid., **73**, 1958 (1951)] discovered the somewhat similar intramolecular rearrangement of α,α-dimethylallyl chloride in acetic acid. The experiments were conducted by the author to ascertain the existence of an isomerization in the tosylate of IA after S. Winstein and D. Trifan had made the observation that the rate of loss of optical activity was greater than the rate of appearance of p-bromobenzenesulfonic acid during the solvolysis of active exo-norbornyl brosylate in acetic acid [S. Winstein and D. Trifan, ibid., **74**, 1154 (1952)].

in Papers I and III[1] of this series for a bridged ionic intermediate (a phenonium ion) in the solvolysis reaction requires elaboration. If k_i, the rate of isomerization, is much greater than k_s, the rate of solvolysis, then the racemic nature of the I acetate produced (e.g., in runs 3 and 4) could be explained without recourse to mechanisms involving bridged ions as intermediates in the solvolysis reaction. The results of the present

$$\text{IA Tos.} \xrightarrow{k_i} \text{I Tos. (racemic)}$$

$$\downarrow k_s \qquad\qquad \downarrow k_s$$

	I Acetate	I Acetate
In acetic acid	20%	80%
In formic acid	75%	25%

investigation remove this ambiguity from the former interpretation. Thus in runs 3 and 4 in glacial acetic acid (the reaction went to completion) the preponderance of IA over IB in the final product was negligible. Yet in experiment 7, where the reaction was run for one solvolytic half-life, the isomerization reaction had passed through about four half-lives (the recovered tosylate of I was 94% racemized). Therefore in acetic acid the isomerization reaction must be four times as fast as the solvolysis reaction, or $k_i/k_s = 4/1$. Since the solvolysis reaction is irreversible and the isomerization is in effect irreversible (I Tos.—X→IA Tos.), then the ratio of I acetate produced directly from IA tosylate to I acetate produced via I tosylate must be one to four. In other words, 20% of I acetate must have arisen by a route not involving I tosylate as an intermediate. Clearly the isomerization reaction in itself cannot account for the virtually racemic character of the solvolysis product.

Similar reasoning applied to the data obtained in formic acid (runs 9 and 11) reveals that in this solvent $k_i/k_s = 1/3$, and that 75% of I formate produced must not have involved I tosylate as an intermediate. Therefore the argument previously advanced[1] for a phenonium ion intermediate, internally compensated in the I series, but asymmetric in the II series becomes valid.

The Isomerization and Exchange Reactions.— Four general mechanisms are compatible with the stereochemistry of the isomerization reaction.

$$\text{IA Tos.} + {}^-\text{OTos.} \rightleftarrows \text{IB Tos.} + {}^-\text{OTos.} \quad (1)$$

IA Tos. ⟶ [structure] + ⁻OTos ⟶ I Tos. (racemic)   (2)

dissociated **ions**

$$\text{IA Tos.} \rightleftarrows \text{IB Tos.} \quad (3)$$

IA Tos. ⟶ [structure] ⟶ I Tos. (racemic)   (4)

Experiment 16 in which IB brosylate was solvolyzed in the presence of ten moles of tosylate ion (starting material = one mole) gave after about 1.5 solvolytic half-lives a ratio of about 3.7 to 1 of recovered brosylate to tosylate, both substances being almost completely racemic. Thus the isomerization reaction took place in the presence of large amounts of a different but very similarly constituted ion without that ion being involved in the isomerization process to any large degree. Had the reaction been intermolecular, conditions would have been favorable for the production of predominantly tosylate ester.[9] Mechanisms 1 and 2 are therefore incompatible with the evidence.

If mechanism 3 applies then the transition state would have to be somewhat like (S), in which a phenyl group bridges two atoms on one side and the tosyl group does the same on the other side of the carbon–carbon bond. Yet in the solvolysis process a somewhat similarly constituted species (a pheno-

[structure (S)]

nium ion) was shown to be a distinct intermediate and not a transition state. Furthermore, the rates of solvolysis and isomerization are very close together indicating that the activation energies for the rate-controlling steps are similar. If mechanism 3 were operating no ionic bonds would be formed in the isomerization, whereas in the solvolysis reaction a covalent bond is being broken and a largely ionic bond being formed. Mechanism 3 also lacks the virtue of explaining the exchange reaction, and requires that the exchange take place by some independent process.

In contrast to the other three, mechanism 4 offers an internally consistent explanation of not only the isomerization but also the solvolysis and exchange reactions. In this mechanism a distinct intermediate exists between the starting material and product in the isomerization reaction. This intermediate is an ion-pair (a phenonium tosylate or brosylate) which sometimes exchanges its anion for a solvent molecule (solvolysis) or a solvent anion (acetate or formate anions), sometimes it exchanges its anion for either a different anion that has been dissolved in the solvent (exchange reaction) or the same anion that has previously been liberated by the solvolytic process, and sometimes the ion-pair collapses to sulfonate ester (isomerization reaction). With such a mechanism the rate of formation of the ion-pair would be very sensitive to the ionizing power of the solvent. Thus the rates of ion-pair formation have been found to fall off rapidly in going from formic acid to acetic acid

(9) At the beginning of the reaction the ratio of tosylate to brosylate ion was infinity, and after one half-life the ratio was 20:1. The tosylate ion is probably somewhat more nucleophilic than brosylate ion as evidenced by the higher acidity of p-bromobenzenesulfonic acid as compared to p-toluenesulfonic acid and by the fact that brosylate esters solvolyze about three times as fast as tosylate esters. Were the isomerization reaction mainly intermolecular, tosylate ester would accumulate very rapidly and the only brosylate ester recoverable would be optically active and unisomerized starting material.

to acetonitrile to chloroform. The distribution of products once the ion-pair had formed should be sensitive to both the ionizing power and nucleophilic character of the solvent. The greater the ionizing power of the solvent, the greater the tendency of the ion-pair to dissociate, thereby allowing the solvent or dissolved anions to assert their nucleophilic tendencies in more open competition with the nucleophilic properties of the anion of the original ion-pair. In the experiments at hand it was found that in acetic acid, roughly for every five ion-pairs formed, four collapsed to tosylate ester, and one went to acetate. In formic acid on the other hand, for every four ion-pairs formed, only one collapsed to tosylate ester and the other three went to formate. Since acetic acid is more nucleophilic than formic, the ionizing power seems to be more important than the nucleophilic character of the solvent in determining the fate of an ion-pair.

The roughly thirty-fold increase in the rate of the isomerization reaction when carried out in the presence of *p*-toluenesulfonic acid in acetonitrile (run 14) is an interesting example of acid catalysis, and suggests that the conjugate acid of the tosylate might be the species involved in at least the initiating stage of the isomerization reaction.[10] Although about the same amount of tosylate ester had been consumed in runs 12 and 14, in the acid catalyzed experiment the isomerization reaction had progressed about twice as far. Thus although the acid catalyzes both the isomerization and the competing reactions (those leading to olefins), the isomerization reaction is enhanced twice as much as the competing reactions.

The mechanism of the exchange reaction has a bearing on the fate of the initially formed ion-pair.

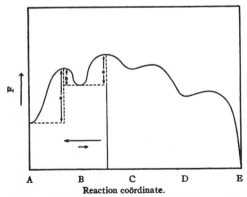

Fig. 2.—Energy—reaction coördinate diagram for the solvolysis reaction in acetic acid: A = tosylate or brosylate ester; B = phenonium tosylate (or brosylate) ion pair; C = hypothetical dissociated or partially dissociated ions; D = phenonium acetate; a = activation energy for the isomerization reaction; b = activation energy for the collapse of phenonium tosylate (or brosylate) to starting material; c = activation energy for the dissociation (or partial dissociation) of phenonium tosylate (or brosylate).

(10) In paper I of this series (ref. 1) a similar suggestion was mistakenly made for the solvolysis reaction in acetic acid.

The fact that an exchange reaction took place at all is evidence in favor of a second reversible reaction in which one ion-pair goes to a second. In experiment 16 since phenonium brosylate went to phenonium tosylate (and probably to a very small extent in the reverse direction), it seems likely

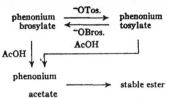

that the solvolysis reaction takes place through the formation of a second ion-pair (phenonium acetate) which then collapses to stable ester. Two limiting mechanisms can be envisioned to account for the conversion of one ion-pair to a second: the second ion-pair could be formed by either a dissociation of the first ion-pair and combination of the appropriate species (two transition states), or by a concerted displacement reaction (one transition state). Either possibility is consistent with the greater importance of the ionizing power of the solvent over the nucleophilic character of the solvent. In the first case, the dissociation of the first ion-pair would certainly be favored in the more ionizing solvent. In the second case, the more ionizing the solvent, the more ionic the character of the bond holding the ion-pair together, and the more amenable the anion of the pair would be to nucleophilic displacement, and *vice versa*.

Figure 2 is a crude plot of free energy *vs*. reaction coördinate for the solvolysis, isomerization and exchange reactions in acetic acid, and represents a mechanism, in part speculative, and in part substantiated by experiment. That B (phenonium tosylate ion-pair) is produced reversibly is well substantiated. The minima in the curve represented by C (partially or fully dissociated ions) and D (phenonium acetate) are suggested as reasonable but as yet unsubstantiated further stages in the reaction. The question of whether a minimum can intervene between A (starting tosylate ester) and B seems to be at least partially answered by the stereochemistry of the reaction. Such a minimum would represent a carbonium tosylate ion-pair, and to make the stereochemistry of the reaction compatible with the existence of such an "open" ion-pair would necessitate the following assumptions: first, that the configuration of the carbon atom involved in the open ion-pair was almost completely preserved throughout the lifetime of the species; second, that the anion of the open ion-pair can be displaced by the phenyl group only from the rear. Such a stage in the mechanism is not necessitated by any experimental evidence in the present investigation.

It is interesting to note that although the isomerization reaction could not be detected when IIA (or IIB) brosylate (or tosylate) was solvolyzed because collapse of the ion-pair gave back sulfonate of the same configuration as that of the starting material, yet the exchange reaction was detected in this system (run 17). Although IB and IIA brosylates were solvolyzed in the presence of tosylate ion (runs 16 and 17) under identical conditions, with the former starting material the ratio of recovered brosylate to tosylate ester was about 3.7 to 1 whereas with the latter the ratio was 2 to 1. Other than in these experiments, the yields and product balances seem to be comparable from either stereomeric starting material. The mechanistic argument is summarized in the following formulation.

(0.6%) produced in run 3 (IA Tos. completely solvolyzed in acetic acid) gives a means of estimating the extent to which acetate of I configuration was produced by a simple S_N1 mechanism. If k_r is the rate at which IA tosylate goes to IA acetate (or I tosylate goes to I acetate) by an S_N1 mechanism, then $k_s/k_r = 20/0.6 = 80/2.4$. Therefore about 2.4% of the I acetate produced must have come from I tosylate by an S_N1 mechanism, and a total of about 3% of acetate of I (A and B)

The Simple Substitution Reaction.—The small excess of acetate of configuration IA over that of IB configuration must have been produced by an S_N1 mechanism.

Since the simple S_N1 process would also be expected to produce amounts of acetate of the II configuration (run 3) of the same order of magnitude as those of acetate of the I configuration, it is probable that the acetate of II configuration produced also arose by the simple S_N1 process. The ratio of II to IIA acetate found in run 3 is about two and one-half to one which is not highly divergent from the ratio of four to one which would be expected. A small amount of acetate of the II configuration might also have been produced by an S_N2 reaction of acetate ion with IA and I tosylates, but it seems improbable that more than a trace of acetate arose by such a path. It is interesting that the amounts of diastereomeric material produced from IA tosylate (run 3) and IIB tosylate (run 6) were approximately equal.

The absence of diastereomeric products when the solvolyses were conducted in formic acid is attributable to the weaker nucleophilic character and the enhanced power to dissociate ion-pairs of this acid as compared to acetic acid. Noteworthy in this connection is the relative freedom from non-crystallizable material of the tosylate recovered from the formic acid solvolysis (run 11) as compared to that material recovered from the experiments conducted in acetonitrile (runs 12 and 13).

The possible general implications of the existence of ion-pairs as intermediates in these reactions are many. First, the isomerization reaction can be looked upon as an aromatic substitution in which one methylene group is displaced by electrophilic attack on the benzene ring of a second methylene group bearing an incipient positive charge. Possibly many of the aromatic substitution reactions, both those occurring by intramolecular processes (e.g., the Claisen rearrangement) and those involving intermolecular mechanisms (e.g., the Friedel-Crafts reaction) go through similarly constituted ion-pairs as distinct intermediates in the reaction sequence. Second, the solvolysis reaction can be looked upon as an S_N1 replacement reaction, and the possibility that many S_N1 replacement reactions go through ion-pairs as intermediates is suggested by the present investigation. Third, the isomerization reaction is an intramolecular rearrangement, and the intermediate ion-pair of this reaction suggests that many molecular rearrangements (e.g., the pinacol, Beckmann and allied rearrangements) may go through analogous intermediate stages.

Experimental

Solvolyses of Tosylates (Runs 1–8) in Acetic Acid.—Anhydrous potassium carbonate (14.1 g.) was allowed to react with 1000 ml. of glacial acetic acid and 25 ml. of acetic anhydride. The solution (20 ml. per g. of tosylate) was warmed in a constant temperature bath (75°) for one-half hour, tosylate was added, and the mixture was allowed to stand for the times specified in Table II (in runs 1 and 2 the proportion was 13 ml. of solution to 1 g. of tosylate). At the end of this time the mixture was quenched in an ice-bath, diluted threefold with water, and the aqueous solution was extracted three times with pure pentane. In the cases where tosylate was to be recovered (runs 7 and 8) a 75% pentane-25% ether mixture was employed. The organic extracts were combined, washed twice with water, twice with bicarbonate solution, again with water, dried, and the solvent was removed at atmospheric pressure through a column (without a small column olefin losses amount to 10-20%) until a volume of 20 ml. remained. In runs 1–6,

this solution was added dropwise to a mixture of 30 ml. of dry ether and 1 g. of lithium aluminum hydride, and the resulting mixture was decomposed in a mixture of sodium hydroxide solution and ice. The organic layer was separated, the aqueous suspension was extracted twice with ether, the extracts were combined, dried, the solvent was removed at atmospheric pressure through a column, and the residue was flash distilled at 20 mm. (the mixture was never heated above 100° at any point). This mixture was submitted to separation on an alumina column (80 g. of alumina per g. of mixture) made up in pentane. The olefin fraction appeared in the column eluate, and the alcohol remained on the alumina when pentane was used as a developer. The alcohol was removed by elution with methyl alcohol. The pentane eluate was evaporated (through a column) and flash-distilled at 20 mm. to give the olefin fraction. This material was set aside.

The methyl alcohol was removed by distillation through a column, and the alcohol fraction was flash-distilled at 20 mm. This material was used directly for infrared analysis and preparation of acetate. In every case where either the olefin, alcohol or a mixture of the two was distilled, the small residue left in the pot was not acidic.

In those runs where tosylate was recovered (7 and 8), the concentrated solution (from the extractions) was cooled, and the crystalline tosylate was collected, further material being crystallized from the filtrates. When no more crystalline tosylate could be obtained the filtrates were combined, evaporated and submitted to distillation at 0.1 mm., the pot temperature never getting above 80°. Additional amounts of tosylate ester were recovered from the still residue. All tosylate ester fractions were combined and recrystallized, and two crops were taken. All filtrates when combined and evaporated gave only traces of a non-acidic residue.

Solvolysis of Tosylates (Runs 9–11) in Formic Acid.—These experiments were conducted in a manner analogous to those reported above except that the solvolysis solution was prepared by dissolving 2.52 g. of anhydrous sodium formate in 200 ml. of anhydrous formic acid, 20 ml. of solution per g. of tosylate being employed. The isolation procedures were completely analogous to those reported above.

Reaction of Tosylates (Runs 12–14) in Acetonitrile.—Mixtures made in the proportions of 10 ml. of acetonitrile to 1 g. of tosylate to 0.45 g. of anhydrous potassium carbonate (runs 12 and 13) were held at reflux, cooled, shaken with four volumes of water and one volume of a 50%-ether-50%-pentane mixture, and the layers were separated. The aqueous layer was again extracted with the ether mixture, the extracts were combined, washed three times with water, once with dilute acid, once with dilute base, and again with water. From here the isolation procedure was completely analogous to that used in runs 7, 8 and 11.

In run 14, in place of the potassium carbonate was added one mole (based on tosylate) of anhydrous p-toluenesulfonic acid (prepared from the monohydrate, the water being eliminated by azeotropic distillation with toluene). The isolation procedure was analogous to the other runs.

Solvolyses of Brosylates (Runs 16 and 17) in the Presence of Tosylate Ion.—Anhydrous potassium carbonate (84.20 g.) was allowed to react with a mixture of 207 g. of p-toluenesulfonic acid monohydrate, 600 ml. of glacial acetic acid, and 286 ml. of pure acetic anhydride. The resulting mixture was made up to 1000 ml. with acetic acid (glacial) and 25 ml. of this solution per g. of brosylate was used in the solvolysis experiments. The solvent was preheated to 75°, the brosylate was added, and after 40 minutes the reaction mixture was quenched. The products were isolated in exactly the same manner as in runs 7 and 8. In each case the sulfonate ester products were identified through their rotations (see Table IV) and through the following mixed melting point experiments. About equal amounts of each component were used, and whenever IIA Tos. was involved, the polymorphic form melting at 46–47° was employed. Melting points of mixtures of knowns: Bros. I and Bros. IB, 87–92°; Bros. I and Tos. I, 88–92°; run 16, 1st crop and Bros. IB, 68–73°; run 16, 1st crop and Tos. I, 44–60°; run 16, 1st crop and Tos. IB, 60–64°; run 16, 2nd crop and Tos. I, 45–47°; run 17, 1st crop and Bros. IIA, 44–56°; run 17, 1st crop and Tos. IIA, 39–41°; run 17, 2nd crop and Bros. IIA, 43–54°; run 17, 2nd crop and Tos. IIA, 40–42°. In run 17, the first crop gave oils when mixed with Bros. I, Bros. IB, Tos. IB or Tos. I; the second crop gave oils with Bros. I, Bros. IB, Tos. IB and Tos. I.

Control Experiments.—Demonstration of the complete separation of the olefinic and alcoholic products was accomplished by mixing 2 parts of IA alcohol $\alpha^{25}D$ +31.5° ($l = 1$ dm.) with one part of an equimolar mixture of the four 2-phenyl-2-butenes and by submitting the resulting mixture (3.0 g.) to the chromatographic separation described above, followed by distillation of each fraction: alcohol fraction, $\alpha^{25}D$ +31.6° ($l = 1$ dm.); olefin fraction, $\alpha^{25}D$ 0.02° ($l = 1$ dm.). Thus there is no detectable contamination of olefin with alcohol, and less than 0.1% contamination of alcohol with olefin.

To ascertain whether experiments 12 and 13 were carried out in the presence of base, a large excess of finely divided potassium carbonate was refluxed for four hours with 500 ml. of dry acetonitrile, the mixture was filtered quickly while still at the boiling temperature, and the solvent was removed by distillation. No weighable residue remained in the flask. Water was added to the flask and titration of the resulting solution with dilute acid gave no more acid consumption than a blank run. It can be concluded that the reaction was conducted in the absence of base. To determine whether secondary acetate could be produced from olefin, and whether the acetates of 3-phenyl-2-butanol once formed were stable under the conditions of the acetolysis, a mixture of 2 g. of the acetate of IA ($\alpha^{25}D$ −8.08°, $l = 1$ dm.) 1 g. of cis-2-phenyl-2-butene[4] and 1 g. of trans-2-phenyl-2-butene[4] were held at 75° in the acetic acid solvolysis mixture for 36 hours. The acetate–olefin mixture that was recovered was reduced with lithium aluminum hydride, the alcohol and olefin separated (see above procedure), and the alcohol recovered ($\alpha^{25}D$ +31.5°, $l = 1$ dm.), wt. 1.48 g.

Acknowledgment.—It is a pleasure to acknowledge stimulating and helpful discussions of problems related to this paper with Drs. W. G. McMillan, K. N. Trueblood and G. S. Hammond.

LOS ANGELES, CALIFORNIA   RECEIVED JUNE 22, 1951

19-21 | Where Non-classical Ions Are Absent

How general are nonclassical ions? Three papers (Papers 19–21) by Roberts and his co-workers are here included which surveyed various aspects of this question in 1952 and 1953 by means of radioactive tracers. In the first two cases a few per cent of rearrangements were found which might or might not have involved bridged ion intermediates. The conclusion of these papers, however, was that bridged intermediates are of little if any importance in the solvolysis of *sec*-butyl tosylate or the nitrous acid deamination of ethylamine.

In the deamination of *n*-propylamine it was found that 8.5% of the label originally at carbon atom 1 was no longer at that position in the product. Assuming that it was at position 2, the authors surmised that this increased rearrangement (compared to 1.5% for ethylamine) might mean that the methyl-bridged nonclassical ion III was stabler than the hydrogen-bridged structure I. It was

III   I

shown later (Reutov and Shatkina, Paper No. 60) that the missing ^{14}C was not at position 2, but at position 3, indicating an interesting isomerization but not a methyl-bridged cation.

From: *J. Am. Chem. Soc.* **74**, 4283–86 (1952)

[Contribution from the Department of Chemistry and Laboratory for Nuclear Science and Engineering, Massachusetts Institute of Technology]

Rearrangements in the Solvolysis of 2-Butyl-1-C14 p-Toluenesulfonate[1,2]

By John D. Roberts, Winifred Bennett, Robert E. McMahon and Edmond W. Holroyd, Jr.

Received February 8, 1952

Solvolysis of 2-butyl-1-C14 p-toluenesulfonate in acetic acid in the presence of acetate ion under conditions where the reaction rate is essentially independent of the acetate ion concentration leads to a mixture of $91 \pm 1\%$ of 2-butyl-1-C14 acetate and $9 \pm 1\%$ of the rearranged product, 2-butyl-4-C14 acetate. It has been shown that the rearrangement is not due to rearrangement of the starting material or to elimination to yield butenes followed by addition of acetic acid. Much less rearrangement occurs in the hydrolysis of 2-butyl-1-C14 p-toluenesulfonate in 75% acetone–25% water (by volume). It is concluded that a non-classical cation of the type $CH_3\overset{\oplus}{\underset{H}{C}H\text{---}CHCH_3}$ is not an important intermediate in the unimolecular hydrolysis or acetolysis of 2-butyl p-toluenesulfonate.

In an earlier investigation,[3] it was shown that isotope position rearrangements do not occur in the usual essentially irreversible, carbonium ion-type metathetical or elimination reactions of *t*-butyl and *t*-amyl derivatives. Such behavior was expected on the basis of the carbonium ion theory[4] of molecular rearrangements since any isotope position rearrangements with *t*-butyl or *t*-amyl derivatives would involve interconversion of tertiary to less stable secondary (or primary) cations under unfavorable conditions. The situation with 2-butyl derivatives is quite different in that the interconversion equilibrium of, for example, 2-butyl-1-C14 (I) and 2-butyl-4-C14 (II) cations could be established by simple 1,2-hydride shifts. The role of a more or less stable "ethyleneprotonium" ion[5] intermediate like III[6] in such processes has not yet been established. It is possible that III is no more than

$$CH_3CH_2\overset{\oplus}{C}HC^{14}H_3 \rightleftarrows CH_3\overset{\oplus}{C}HCH_2C^{14}H_3$$

$$\text{I} \qquad\qquad \text{II}$$

$$CH_3\overset{\overset{H}{\diagup\oplus\diagdown}}{CH\text{===}CH}C^{14}H_3$$

$$\text{III}$$

a transition state through which rearrangement could occur more or less readily as shown schematically in the top curve of the energy diagram (Fig. 1). Alternatively, III and the isomeric cations I and II could have similar energies and be in more or less a dynamic equilibrium[7] as indicated by the middle curve of Fig. 1. As a final clear-cut possibility, III could be substantially more stable than either of the cations I and II and could be formed directly and react without their intervention as indicated by the lowest curve of Fig. 1.

Information as to the best approximation to the actual state of affairs was sought in the present research by measurement of the extent of rearrangement in solvolyses of 2-butyl-1-C14 p-toluenesulfonate (IV) under conditions where these processes are irreversible. It was expected that extensive rearrangement to yield 2-butyl-4-C14 derivatives would be observed if reasonably free cationic intermediates were involved and if III possesses comparable or greater stability than I or II.

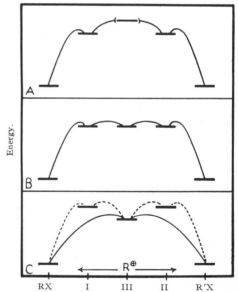

Fig. 1.—Schematic energy diagram for extreme and intermediate formulations of reactions involving possible cations from 2-butyl derivatives labeled with C14. RX and R'X represent 2-butyl-1-C14 and 2-butyl-4-C14 derivatives, respectively. Curve A depicts a situation where cation III is less stable than I or II. Curve B has III of comparable stability and readily interconvertible with I and II. Curve C has III much more stable than I or II with solid lines representing the usual course of reaction, *i.e.*, III being formed directly from RX or R'X without intervention of I or II being required.

(1) Supported in part by the joint program of the Office of Naval Research and the United States Atomic Energy Commission.

(2) Presented in part at the Symposium on Reaction Mechanisms at the 75th Anniversary Meeting of the American Chemical Society, September 7, 1951.

(3) J. D. Roberts, R. E. McMahon and J. S. Hine, This Journal, **71**, 1896 (1949); **72**, 4237 (1950).

(4) *Cf.*, L. P. Hammett, "Physical Organic Chemistry," McGraw–Hill Book Co., Inc., New York, N. Y., 1940, pp. 317–325; G. W. Wheland, "Advanced Organic Chemistry," John Wiley and Sons, Inc., New York, N. Y., 1949, pp. 451–534.

(5) *Cf.*, D. J. Cram, This Journal, **74**, 2137 (1952).

(6) For refs. to some other situations where intermediates similar to III have been proposed see S. Winstein and D. S. Trifan, *ibid.*, **71**, 2953 (1949).

(7) M. J. S. Dewar, "The Electronic Theory of Organic Chemistry," Oxford University Press, London, 1949, pp. 211–213.

Synthetic and Degradative Methods

The 2-butyl-1-C14 p-toluenesulfonate was pre-

TABLE I

RATE CONSTANTS FOR SOLVOLYSIS OF 2-BUTYL p-TOLUENESULFONATE (ROTs)

Solvent	Temp., °C.	Initial [ROTs], M	Initial [KOAc], M	Initial [KOTs],[a] M	k_1, hr.$^{-1}$	k_2, (mole/l.)$^{-1}$ hr.$^{-1}$	Olefin,[b] %	F_1[c]
HOAc[d]	60.0	0.62	0.61	..	0.06	0.14	...	0.63
HOAc[d]	65.0	.46	.46	..	.11	.22	...	.71
HOAc[d]	65.0	.51	.46	0.45	.16	.19	38	.81
HOAc[d]	65.0	.099	.100	.89	.22	(.19)[e]	33	.95
H$_2$O-acetone[f]	65.0	.148	...	..	.32	...	(23)[g]	1.00

[a] Potassium p-toluenesulfonate. [b] Percentage of theoretical amount of olefin formed at practical completion of solvolysis; determined by the hydrogenation procedure of J. D. Roberts, THIS JOURNAL, 71, 1980 (1949). [c] Fraction of reaction proceeding by first-order processes at practical completion; calculated from k_1 and k_2 by the equation given in ref. 10. [d] Acetic acid containing 1% acetic anhydride. [e] Assumed to be the same as in the preceding run. The kinetics in this run were quite accurately first-order to over 90% reaction after a small correction for the infinity titer was made. [f] 25% water–75% acetone (by volume). [g] Calculated from the C[14]-activity of the carrier-diluted product from the hydrolysis of IV.

pared starting with methyl-C[14] iodide[8] by the following series of reactions. The solvolysis reactions were carried out in acetic acid and aqueous acetone

$$C^{14}H_3I \xrightarrow{Mg} C^{14}H_3MgI \xrightarrow[\text{2. H}_2\text{O, NH}_4\text{Cl}]{\text{1. CH}_3\text{CH}_2\text{CHO}}$$

$$CH_3CH_2CHOHC^{14}H_3 \xrightarrow[\text{2. CH}_3\text{C}_6\text{H}_4\text{SO}_2\text{Cl}]{\text{1. NaH}}$$

$$\underset{\underset{OSO_2C_6H_4CH_3}{|}}{CH_3CH_2CHC^{14}H_3}$$
IV

and yielded 2-butyl acetate or 2-butanol. In the former event, the ester was converted to 2-butanol by alkaline hydrolysis for degradation. The most satisfactory degradation procedure involved oxidation of labeled 2-butanol with excess sodium hypobromite to yield carbon tetrabromide, the C[14]-activity of which gives the activity at C-1 of the 2-butanol. Purification of carbon tetrabromide was found to be somewhat simpler than that of the iodoform obtained in the analogous oxidation with sodium hypoiodite solution.

Experimental Results and Discussion

It was considered particularly desirable to study the unimolecular solvolysis products of IV in acetic acid since much work has been done on reaction rates and rearrangements of benzenesulfonate esters in this solvent.[6,9] Some difficulty was encountered in selecting appropriate reaction conditions since it was considered imperative to use at least one equivalent of acetate ion to each equivalent of IV to avoid formation of the free sulfonic acid. However, complications were then introduced by bimolecular substitution (S$_N$2) and elimination (E2) reactions between acetate ion and IV. Presumably, bimolecular substitution would proceed without rearrangement and suitable corrections could be made if the appropriate rate constants were known. However, since both the unimolecular and bimolecular reactions may lead to substitution and elimination, complete analysis of the kinetics would be difficult and it was deemed preferable to find conditions where the bimolecular reaction is essentially negligible. The kinetics of the reaction of

(8) The methyl-C[14] iodide was obtained from Tracerlab, Inc., on allocation from the United States Atomic Energy Commission.

(9) (a) S. Winstein, E. Grunwald and H. W. Jones, THIS JOURNAL, 73, 2700 (1951); (b) E. Grunwald and S. Winstein, ibid., 70, 846 (1948); (c) S. Winstein and co-workers, ibid., 70, 812, 816, 821, 839 (1948), and earlier papers.

unlabeled IV with potassium acetate were studied[10] under several different conditions (see Table I) and, as would be expected, the most satisfactory circumstances for practical elimination of the bimolecular reaction involved low concentrations of IV and acetate ion with considerable neutral salt present.

The extent of rearrangement in the acetolysis of IV was measured at ionic strengths of 0.9 and 1.0 M using acetate ion concentrations of 0.46 and 0.10 M. The experimental results along with those obtained in the hydrolysis of IV in aqueous acetone and some controls are given in Table II. At 0.10 M acetate,

TABLE II

EXTENT OF REARRANGEMENT IN THE SOLVOLYSIS OF 2-BUTYL-1-C[14] p-TOLUENESULFONATE AT 65°

Solvent	Initial [ROTs] M	Initial [KOAc], M	Initial [KOTs], M	Radioactivity[a] 2-butanol	Radioactivity[a] CBr$_4$	Rearrange.,[b] %
HOAc[c]	0.51	0.46	0.45	{ 1005 ± 15[d]	915 ± 5	7.9[f]
				980 ± 20[e]		
HOAc[c]	.10	.10	.89	656 ± 4	603 ± 4	8.8
HOAc[c]	.18	.10	.89	1557 ± 21[g]	1540 ± 8	1.1[h]
HOAc[c]	{ .72[i]	.10	.89	−1 ± 4[k]	......	(<1)[l]
	.62[j]					
H$_2$O-acetone[m]	.15	..	..	636 ± 12	617 ± 8	3.0[n]

[a] C[14]-activities determined with a windowless methane-filled counter ("Nucleometer") with standard deviations; corrected for background, self-absorption and dilution by non-labeled carbon atoms and expressed in dis./min./mg. of barium carbonate. The samples were of "infinite" thickness, had cross-sectional areas of 2.90 cm.^{2} and were prepared as described by J. D. Roberts, W. Bennett, E. W. Holroyd and C. H. Fugitt, Anal. Chem., 20, 904 (1948). The methods of calculation of the activities are described in ref. 3. [b] % Rearrangement = [Activity of 2-butanol − activity of CBr$_4$)/activity of 2-butanol] × 100. [c] Acetic acid containing 1% acetic anhydride. [d] Activity of 2-butanol. [e] Activity of 2-butyl N-phenylcarbamate prepared from the 2-butanol. [f] Calculated using the average activity of the 2-butanol and the N-phenylcarbamate. [g] Activity of the 2-butanol obtained by hydrolysis in water-acetone of the unreacted p-toluenesulfonate after two half-lives. [h] % Rearrangement of the p-toluenesulfonate over two half-lives of the solvolysis reaction. [i] Concentration of butene mixture with activity of 308 ± 6 counts/min./mg. of barium carbonate present in reaction medium. [j] Concentration of non-labeled 2-butyl acetate in reaction medium. [k] Activity of 2-butanol obtained from the hydrolysis of the recovered 2-butyl acetate. [l] % of labeled butene which was converted to 2-butyl acetate by reaction with acetic acid. [m] 25%-75% acetone. [n] This figure may be slightly high due to the presence of a small amount of acetone in the 2-butanol.

(10) The procedures were similar to those used previously, J. D. Roberts, W. G. Young and S. Winstein, ibid., 64, 2157 (1942); J. D. Roberts and V. C. Chambers, ibid., 73, 5034 (1951).

where the reaction proceeded about 95% by first-order kinetics, the amount of rearrangement was 9% which corresponds to 9% of formation of II or 18% of III. As would be expected from the rarity of carbon skeleton rearrangements in bimolecular displacement reactions of saturated halides, the amount of rearrangement drops somewhat at 0.46 M acetate ion under conditions where 81% of the reaction is first-order. Quantitative comparison of the results at different acetate concentrations is difficult since it is not certain how much of the 19% second-order reaction at 0.46 M acetate ion yielded butenes. The acetolysis rearrangement is unlikely to be due to isomerization of the final product, 2-butyl acetate, since norbornyl-2,3-C_2^{14} acetate, which is expected to be considerably more labile, does not rearrange significantly with comparable salt concentrations in refluxing acetic acid.[11] The rearrangement cannot be due to the type of "internal return" isomerization process postulated by Trifan and Winstein[12] for the racemization of exo-norbornyl p-bromobenzenesulfonate, which might convert IV into the isomeric 2-butyl-4-C^{14} p-toluene-sulfonate (V), since the unreacted labeled 2-butyl p-toluenesulfonate isolated from the reaction mixture containing 0.10 M acetate ion after two half-lives on hydrolysis in aqueous acetone actually gave slightly less-rearranged 2-butanol than was found in the corresponding hydrolysis of IV. Furthermore, the rearrangement on acetolysis does not result by formation of 2-butene and subsequent addition of acetic acid since no measurable amount of labeled 2-butyl acetate was formed under the solvolysis conditions from a C^{14}-containing butene mixture at a concentration several-fold greater than was present in the solvolysis of IV. Considerably less rearrangement was observed in the hydrolysis of IV in 25% water–75% acetone than in the acetolysis reactions.

The present results agree well with the conclusions of Winstein, Grunwald and Jones[9a] as to the mechanism of solvolysis of isopropyl halides and arylsulfonates in good-ionizing solvents possessing different degrees of nucleophilic character. In a medium like 25% water–75% acetone, solvolysis of IV (here considered as a single stereoisomer) would be expected to proceed through a transition state in which a water molecule (or molecules) would be substantially covalently bonded to the backside of the carbon undergoing displacement. The first intermediate (VI) may then collapse giving inverted, unrearranged product or partially proceed to a symmetrically solvated intermediate (VII) which would give racemic, unrearranged product.

Apparently the degrees of covalent bonding in VI and VII are at all times sufficient to preclude substantial rearrangement. The importance of VII is indicated by the partial racemization accompanying the solvolysis of s-alkyl derivatives in aqueous solvents.[9a,13]

In acetic acid, the degree of covalent bonding involving solvent in the transition state and the first intermediate (VIII) is expected to be considerably less than in aqueous media and VIII, besides yielding inverted, unrearranged acetate has more of an opportunity to be converted to symmetrically solvated IX[15] or X by a 1,2-hydride shift.[4] IX like VII would give racemic, unrearranged acetate while X would yield racemic, rearranged product.[16]

X is probably formed from VIII or IX by way of III; however, because of the low tendency for rearrangement, it is doubtful that III is an important intermediate of comparable or greater stability to IX or X (I or II) and the situation seems described by the top curve of Fig. 1.[17] It is interesting to contrast the solvolysis of IV with the corresponding reactions of secondary derivatives where the non-classical cations appear to be particularly stable. Thus, with endo-norbornyl derivatives, even though a non-classical cation analogous to III cannot be

(11) Unpublished experiments by Dr. C. C. Lee; cf. J. D. Roberts and C. C. Lee, THIS JOURNAL, **73**, 5009 (1951).

(12) D. S. Trifan and S. Winstein, Abstracts of the 119th Meeting of the American Chemical Society, April, 1951, p. 53M. An example of this type of process yielding products with rearrangement of carbon skeleton is afforded by J. D. Roberts and R. H. Mazur, ibid., **73**, 2509 (1951).

(13) E. D. Hughes, C. K. Ingold and S. Masterman, J. Chem. Soc., 1196 (1937).

(14) For economy of representation, the water molecules which solvate VI and VII have been omitted.

(15) IX and X are essentially equivalent to I and II, respectively, solvated by acetic acid.

(16) The reasoning leads to prediction of more racemization in the solvolysis of optically-active 2-butyl derivatives in acetic acid than in aqueous acetone. Our projected investigation of this point was abandoned when we learned that Professor S. Winstein and his co-workers were already engaged in a critical scrutiny of the stereochemistry of the solvolysis of 2-butyl derivatives.

(17) Similar conclusions have been reached by Bartlett and Lefferts in a study of the interconversion of cyclohexyldimethylcarbinyl and α-isopropylcyclohexyl derivatives; P. D. Bartlett, paper presented at the Organic Symposium at Denver, June, 1951.

formed directly in the rate-determining step, very extensive rearrangement is noted even in aqueous acetone.[11]

Acknowledgment.—We are pleased to acknowledge the aid of Dr. G. R. Coraor and Mrs. Clare M. Regan with some of the experimental work.

Experimental

2-Butanol-1-C[14] and 2-Butyl-1-C[14] *p*-Toluenesulfonate.— To a stirred Dry Ice-cooled solution of methyl-C[14]-magnesium iodide in 300 ml. of ether prepared from 26 g. (0.18 mole) of methyl-C[14] iodide[8] and 5.0 g. (0.21 gram-atom) of magnesium turnings was added slowly 10.2 g. (0.18 mole) of freshly-distilled propionaldehyde. The mixture was brought to 0° and 30 ml. of saturated solution of ammonium chloride added dropwise. The ethereal layer was siphoned off and the salt cake washed with three 100-ml. portions of fresh ether. The combined extracts were dried over calcium sulfate, filtered and the ether removed through a glass-helix packed column. The residue was fractionated through an efficient center-tube column[18] and yielded, besides 0.5 g. of forerun, b.p. 98.5–100.3°, 6.89 g. (53%) of 2-butanol-1-C[14], b.p. 100.3–100.5° (uncor.). The product had an activity of 16,090 ± 90 dis./min./mg. of barium carbonate.

In 500-ml. three-necked flask equipped with stirrer, reflux condenser and dropping funnel was placed 2.0 g. (0.086 mole) of sodium hydride and 50 ml. of dry ether. A nitrogen atmosphere was maintained and 4.9 g. (0.066 mole) of 2-butanol-1-C[14] dissolved in 20 ml. of ether was added. The mixture was refluxed for six hours, allowed to stand overnight and then treated dropwise with an ethereal solution of 11.4 g. (0.060 mole) of *p*-toluenesulfonyl chloride. After the addition was complete, the mixture was refluxed for 30 min. and 40 ml. of water added cautiously. The ethereal layer was separated, washed with 10% sodium carbonate solution and dried over a mixture of magnesium sulfate and potassium carbonate. The ether was removed under reduced pressure and the residue transferred to the boiler of a molecular still containing 1 g. of anhydrous potassium carbonate. The 2-butyl-1-C[14] *p*-toluenesulfonate distilled at 3 microns with a bath temperature of 59–61°; the yield was 9.9 g. (72%). The product was shown to be free of *p*-toluenesulfonyl chloride by lack of reaction with alcoholic silver nitrate. The C[14]-activity was 15,290 ± 88 dis./min./mg. of barium carbonate.

The rate runs with this material were carried out as described earlier.[10]

Acetolysis of 2-Butyl-1-C[14] *p*-Toluenesulfonate.—The details of a single typical experiment will be given. 2-Butyl-1-C[14] *p*-toluenesulfonate (2.23 g., 0.010 mole) was dissolved in 100 ml. of an acetic acid stock solution (used also for the rate runs) containing 0.100 *M* potassium acetate, 0.89 *M* potassium *p*-toluenesulfonate and 1% of acetic anhydride and the mixture heated at 65° for 24 hours. The acetic acid was then neutralized with strong potassium hydroxide solution and about 0.2 mole of excess potassium hydroxide added. Water was run in until the salts dissolved and the mixture was heated at 100° for six hours. Unlabeled, redistilled 2-butanol (5.0 g.) was added as a carrier and the mixture extracted continuously with ether for six hours. The ether extract was dried over magnesium sulfate, the ether removed through a glass helix-packed column and the residue fractionated through a center-tube column.[18] The yield of 2-butanol of b.p. 100.0–101.0° (uncor.) was 1.74 g.

Hydrolysis of 2-Butyl-1-C[14] *p*-Toluenesulfonate.—A solution of 1.715 g. (0.0075 mole) of 2-butyl-1-C[14] *p*-toluenesulfonate in 50 ml. of 25% water–75% acetone was heated in a sealed tube at 65° for 26 hours. The mixture was cooled, 10.00 g. of unlabeled redistilled 2-butanol added as a carrier and the *p*-toluenesulfonic acid neutralized with sodium hydroxide solution. The solution was saturated with so-

dium chloride and extracted continuously with ether for 60 hours. The extract was dried over magnesium sulfate, the ether removed through a stainless-steel helix-packed column and the residue fractionated through a center-tube column.[18] The yield of 2-butanol of b.p. 100.5–101.0° (uncor.) was 4.9 g. The C[14]-activity of this material was 636 dis./min./mg. of barium carbonate while that of the sulfonate ester was 15,290. The amount of 2-butanol formed in the hydrolysis was thus 0.434 g. (77%). The balance of the reaction product was presumed to be butene.

Degradation Procedure for 2-Butanol.—A typical experiment is described. Labeled 2-butanol (0.62 ml., 0.5 g.) in 5 ml. of water was added to a stirred solution maintained below 10° of sodium hypobromite prepared by dissolving 4.3 g. of bromine in 6 ml. of clear saturated sodium hydroxide solution diluted with 20 ml. of boiled water. The mixture was kept at 10° or below for 6 hours and then steam distilled. The carbon tetrabromide in the steam distillate was collected by filtration and purified by sublimation at 55° (2 mm.). The yield was 0.13 g.

Investigation of the Rearrangement of 2-Butyl-1-C[14] *p*-Toluenesulfonate during the Acetolysis Reaction.—2-Butyl-1-C[14] *p*-toluenesulfonate (3.015 g.) was dissolved in 75 ml. of acetic acid solution containing 0.100 *M* potassium acetate, 0.89 *M* potassium *p*-toluenesulfonate and 1% acetic anhydride and the mixture was heated at 65° for 3.0 hours (two half-lives). The stirred mixture was cooled in an ice-bath and carefully neutralized with potassium hydroxide solution. The salts were dissolved by addition of cold water and 1.02 g. of carrier unlabeled 2-butyl *p*-toluenesulfonate added. The mixture was extracted continuously for 17 hours with ether. At the start of the extraction, the extraction flask was ice-cooled. The extract was dried over magnesium sulfate and the bulk of the ether distilled. The residue was placed under reduced pressure to remove any 2-butanol which was present and finally degassed at one micron for an hour with a mercury vapor pump.

The crude residual 2-butyl *p*-toluenesulfonate was hydrolyzed with 10 ml. of 25% water–75% acetone at 65° for 18 hours. The mixture was neutralized with potassium carbonate and extracted with ether. The extract was dried over magnesium sulfate and the ether removed. The residue on fractionation yielded 0.95 g. of 2-butanol, b.p. 98–99°, after 0.1 g. of forerun, b.p. 87–98°. The activity data are given in Table II.

Investigation of the Reaction of C[14]-Labeled Butenes with Acetic Acid.—2-Butanol-1-C[14] (5.0 g., C[14]-activity of 308 dis./min./mg. of barium carbonate) was dehydrated by heating with 15 ml. of water and 20 ml. of concd. sulfuric acid.[19] The resulting butenes were passed through 10% sodium hydroxide solution, 50% sulfuric acid, a Drierite tube and finally condensed in a Dry Ice-cooled trap. The yield was 2 g. (50%). The butenes were then transferred by distillation into a Dry Ice-cooled heavy-walled glass tube equipped with a pressure stopcock and containing 3.65 g. of unlabeled 2-butyl acetate and 50 ml. of the acetic acid stock solution used in the preceding experiment. The mixture was cooled with liquid nitrogen and degassed by evacuation with an oil pump. The pump was disconnected, the mixture warmed to room temperature then cooled with liquid nitrogen and degassed again. The cycle was repeated and the mixture then heated at 65° for 24 hours. The solution was cooled, just neutralized with potassium hydroxide solution and continuously extracted with ether. The ethereal solution was dried over calcium chloride and the ether distilled through a glass-helix packed column. The residue was fractionated through a center tube column and yielded 1.0 g. of 2-butyl acetate, b.p. 113.5°, *n*[25]D 1.3860. The C[14]-activity of this material was equal to background within experimental error and showed that no detectable addition of acetic acid to butenes occurs under these conditions.

CAMBRIDGE 39, MASSACHUSETTS

---

(18) The fractionating section of this column was similar to that described by E. A. Naragon and C. E. Lewis, *Ind. Eng. Chem., Anal. Ed.*, **18**, 448 (1946).

(19) C. E. Wilson and H. J. Lucas, THIS JOURNAL, **58**, 2396 (1936), report that with 1-butanol these conditions give 68% *trans*- and 32% *cis*-2-butene.

From: *J. Am. Chem. Soc.* **74**, 5943–45 (1952)

[Contribution from the Department of Chemistry and Laboratory for Nuclear Science and Engineering, Massachusetts Institute of Technology]

The Reaction of Ethylamine-1-C^{14} with Nitrous Acid[1,2]

By John D. Roberts and Joel A. Yancey

Received July 18, 1952

Ethylamine-1-C^{14} on treatment with perchloric acid and sodium nitrite in aqueous solution gave ethylene and a 38% yield of C^{14}-labeled ethanol which was shown by degradation and C^{14}-analysis to contain 1.5% of the rearrangement product, ethanol-2-C^{14}. The rearrangement product was demonstrated not to be formed in the degradation procedure or by hydration of the ethylene produced in the amine–nitrous acid reaction. It is concluded that the ethyl cation is not converted to ethyleneprotonium ion (II) at a rate which is comparable to that of its reaction with water. The reaction of ethylamine with perchloric acid and sodium nitrite in 99.8% deuterium oxide gave ethanol which contained only 1.1 atom % of deuterium attached to carbon. This result indicates that less than 10% of the ethanol could have been formed *via* diazoethane as an intermediate.

Recent interest in the structures of carbonium ions[3] has led to speculation as to whether the ethyl cation is most appropriately formulated as a simple solvated electron-deficient entity (I), a "non-classical" bridged ethyleneprotonium ion (II) or possibly as an equilibrium mixture of the two forms.[3a,4]

$$CH_3{-}\overset{\oplus}{C}H_2 \qquad \overset{\diagup \ \ H \ \ \diagdown}{CH_2{=}CH_2}$$
$$\text{I} \qquad\qquad \text{II}$$

Isotopic tracer techniques for use in problems of this type have been developed[3a,5] and the only important difficulty was a method for irreversible generation of the desired cation in as "free" a state as possible. The reaction of ethylamine with nitrous acid was chosen for this purpose since the corresponding reactions of a number of primary alkylamines such as *n*-propylamine,[6] *n*-butylamine,[7] isobutylamine,[8] neopentylamine[9] and cyclopropylcarbinylamine[5b,10] lead to rearrangement products which are characteristic of carbonium ion processes.

With ethylamine-1-C^{14} and nitrous acid, decom-

(1) Supported in part by the program of research of the Office of Naval Research and the U. S. Atomic Energy Commission.

(2) Presented at the Symposium on Reaction Mechanisms at the 75th Anniversary Meeting of the American Chemical Society, September 7, 1951.

(3) (a) J. D. Roberts, R. E. McMahon, W. Bennett and E. W. Holroyd, Jr., This Journal, **74**, 4283 (1952); (b) *cf.* S. Winstein and co-workers, *ibid.*, **74**, 1113, 1120, 1127, 1133, 1140, 1147, 1154 (1952), for other references.

(4) M. J. S. Dewar, "The Electronic Theory of Organic Chemistry," The Oxford University Press, London, 1949, pp. 211–213. See D. J. Cram, This Journal, **74**, 2137 (1952), for an exceptionally thorough discussion of hydrogen-bridged cations and elimination reactions in the 3-phenyl-2-butanol system.

(5) (a) J. D. Roberts, R. E. McMahon and J. S. Hine, This Journal, **72**, 4237 (1950); (b) J. D. Roberts and R. H. Mazur, *ibid.*, **73**, 3542 (1951); (c) J. D. Roberts and C. C. Lee, *ibid.*, **73**, 5009 (1951).

(6) A. Siersch, *Ann.*, **144**, 137 (1867).

(7) F. C. Whitmore and D. P. Langlois, This Journal, **54**, 3441 (1932).

(8) E. Linnemann, *Ann.*, **162**, 12 (1872).

(9) M. Freund and F. Lenze, *Ber.*, **24**, 2150 (1891).

(10) J. D. Roberts and R. H. Mazur, This Journal, **73**, 2509 (1951).

TABLE I
RADIOACTIVITY ANALYSES

Reaction sequence	Compound	Measured activity, counts/min.[a]	Activity/labeled C-atom[b]	% rearrangement[c]
$CH_3C^{14}H_2NH_2$ + HONO	$C_2H_5ODNB^d$	379.1 ± 3.4	1180 ± 11	
	CHI_3	51 ± 2.6	18 ± 1	1.5 ± 0.1
$CH_2C^{14}H_2$ + HONO	C_2H_4	....	(1180)[e]	
	$C_2H_5ODNB^{d,f}$	0.6 ± 1.5	1.8 ± 5	(0.0 ± 0.4)[g]
	$C_2H_5ODNB^{d,h}$	1.7 ± 1.2	5.3 ± 4	
	(carrier)	3.2 ± 3.8	10.0 ± 11	
		0.5 ± 1.2	1.6 ± 4	
$CH_3C^{14}H_2OH^i$	C_2H_5ODNB	696.9 ± 12	2165 ± 37	
	CHI_3	11.5 ± 2	4.0 ± 1	0.18 ± 0.04

[a] Activity (corrected for background) with standard deviations of "infinitely thick" barium carbonate samples having a cross-sectional area of 2.90 cm.[2] measured with a methane-filled windowless proportional counter, cf. J. D. Roberts, W. Bennett, E. W. Holroyd and C. H. Fugitt, Anal. Chem., 20, 904 (1948). [b] Activities in dis./min. corrected for self absorption and dilution by the carbon atoms at the unlabeled positions. [c] % rearrangement = activity of iodoform/activity of ethanol derivative × 100. [d] C_2H_5ODNB = ethyl 3,5-dinitrobenzoate. [e] Assumed to be the same as the activity of the ethanol. [f] Activity given for derivative prepared from ethanol isolated from the nitrous acid reaction mixture by carrier technique. [g] Calculated amount of ethylene hydration. [h] Activity of carrier ethanol before use in nitrous acid reaction. [i] Prepared by lithium aluminum hydride reduction of $CH_3C^{14}O_2H$.

position of the intermediate diazonium ion (III) could lead directly either to the classical ion (Ia) or the bridged cation (IIa).[3a] The isomeric ion (Ib) might be formed from Ia or IIa. Loss of a proton from any of these entities would yield ethylene-C[14] while reaction with water would yield ethanol-1-C[14] from Ia, ethanol-2-C[14] from Ib and equal amounts of the two isomers from IIa (neglecting the isotope effect on the reactivity of C-1 and C-2). The tracer technique cannot, of course, distinguish between formation of IIa and just half as much Ib but can give information as to how readily IIa and Ib are obtained from Ia relative to its rate of reaction with water to yield ethanol.

or Ib. Although the formation of IIa is expected to proceed from Ia with a low activation energy,[4,11] the activation energy for the reaction of a primary cation with water should be essentially negligible. In any event, IIa is certainly not formed directly in the decomposition of III in the manner familiar in some analogous reactions.[3,5] The second possibility is that the extent of rearrangement is small because III reacts directly with water by the SN2(N)[12] type mechanism without yielding any free carbonium ions at all. While not excluded by the available evidence for III itself, this hypothesis is made rather unlikely by the results obtained with other primary alkylamines as mentioned earlier.

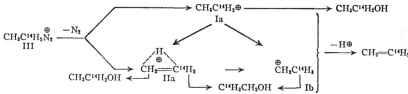

Treatment of ethylammonium-1-C[14] perchlorate with sodium nitrite in aqueous solution gave ethylene and a 38% yield of C[14]-labeled ethanol. Degradation of the ethanol with sodium hypoiodite to iodoform (C-2 of the ethanol) and radioactivity analysis (cf. Table I) indicated the presence of 1.5 ± 0.1% of ethanol-2-C[14] in the reaction product. The amount of rearrangement in the reaction was small but nonetheless almost certainly real since degradation of authentic ethanol-1-C[14] prepared by reduction of acetic-1-C[14] acid gave iodoform containing but 0.18 ± 0.04% of the activity of the ethanol. The observed rearrangement was not apparently due to hydration of the ethylene formed in the decomposition of the diazonium salt since ten passes of a sample of C[14]-labeled ethylene through a simulated reaction mixture gave no detectable amount of C[14]-labeled ethanol.

There are a number of ways in which the results may be explained. First, and to us most likely, is the possibility that the ethyl cation Ia when formed reacts with the solvent to give ethylene or ethanol considerably more rapidly than it rearranges to IIa

A third formulation of the reaction which would not lead to extensive rearrangement is conversion of III by loss of a proton to diazoethane which conceivably could go directly to ethanol by reaction with acidulated water in a manner analogous to certain diphenyldiazomethane reactions.[13] This route is substantially eliminated by the finding that ethylamine with nitrous acid in 99.8% deuterium oxide solution yields ethanol containing only 1.1 atom % of deuterium bound to carbon. If all of the ethanol were formed by way of diazoethane, the product would be expected to contain about 12.5 atom % of deuterium and therefore less than 10% of the reaction could have proceeded by this path.

Acknowledgment.—We are indebted to Mrs. C. M. Regan for the C[14]-analyses and to Mr. D. B. Kellom for the deuterium analysis.

(11) H. Eyring, H. M. Hulburt and R. A. Harman, Ind. Eng. Chem., 35, 511 (1943).

(12) S. Winstein, E. Grunwald and H. W. Jones, THIS JOURNAL, 73, 2700 (1951).

(13) J. D. Roberts and W. Watanabe, ibid., 72, 4869 (1950); J. D. Roberts, W. Watanabe and R. E. McMahon, ibid., 73, 760, 2521 (1951).

Experimental

Reaction of Ethylamine-1-C^{14} with Nitrous Acid.—An aqueous solution of ethylamine-1-C^{14} was prepared from sodium cyanide-C^{14} (100 μcuries of C^{14}) by the procedure of Kilmer and du Vigneaud[14] on a 0.23-mole scale. About 40% of the reduction mixture was acidified with hydrochloric acid, diluted with 6.1 g. of ethylamine hydrochloride and evaporated almost to dryness under reduced pressure. The residue was treated with excess 20% sodium hydroxide solution and steam distilled until all of the ethylamine was removed. The steam distillate was titrated with dilute perchloric acid (0.112 eq., 68%) to pH 4. The solution was cooled to 3° and 23 g. (0.34 mole) of sodium nitrite in 50 ml. added rapidly. After one-half hour, the mixture was heated at 50° for an hour and then distilled slowly for 2.5 hours. The ethylene which was evolved during the reaction was absorbed in a gas washing bottle equipped with a fritted disk and containing liquid bromine at 10°. During the distillation, the last of the ethylene was swept out of the system into the trap with a stream of nitrogen. The recovery of ethylene as the dibromide was 1.1 g. after purification by distillation.

The aqueous distillate was neutralized and steam distilled. The distillate was saturated with potassium carbonate and continuously extracted with ethanol-free diethyl ether for three days. The extract was dried over magnesium sulfate and fractionated. The yield of ethanol, b.p. 77–78°, was 1.94 g. (38%). Part of the material was converted to the 3,5-dinitrobenzoate, m.p. 92.5–92.8°, for C^{14}-assay.

The labeled ethanol was degraded as follows. A solution of 0.5 g. of ethanol-C^{14} in 30 ml. of water was treated simultaneously with 10% sodium hydroxide and iodine–potassium iodide solutions (100 g. of potassium iodide, 50 g. of iodine in 400 ml. of water) at 50° until a persistent iodine color was obtained. The mixture was poured into ice-water, the iodoform collected and crystallized twice from ethanol–water, m.p. 118° (dec.).

A check degradation was performed on ethanol-1-C^{14} obtained by lithium aluminum hydride reduction of acetic-1-C^{14} acid prepared as described earlier.[15]

(14) G. W. Kilmer and V. du Vigneaud, *J. Biol. Chem.*, **154**, 247 (1944).

(15) J. D. Roberts, D. R. Smith and C. C. Lee, THIS JOURNAL, **73**, 618 (1951).

The radioactivity analyses are given in Table I.

Action of Nitrous Acid on Ethylene-C^{14}.—The ethylene dibromide obtained above was converted back to ethylene by the action of zinc powder in boiling ethanol then mixed with nitrogen and passed ten times through a fritted disk immersed in a solution at 60° containing 1.2 g. (0.017 mole) of sodium nitrite, 11.2 ml. of 1.57 N perchloric acid (0.018 mole) and 1.23 g. of ordinary ethanol over a period of an hour. The ethanol in the reaction mixture was isolated as described above and converted to the 3,5-dinitrobenzoate for C^{14}-assay. For comparison, the ethanol used as a carrier was also assayed (Table I). The ethylene used amounted to 0.0049 mole (activity of 1180 dis./min./labeled C-atom) and if it were all hydrated the recovered ethanol would be expected to have an activity of 180 dis./min./labeled C-atom. Since the recovered ethanol did not have an activity significantly different from the carrier ethanol it is unlikely that any hydration occurred under the reaction conditions.

Reaction of Ethylamine with Nitrous Acid in Deuterium Oxide.—Ethylamine hydrochloride (9.3 g., 0.11 mole) was dissolved in 120 ml. of water and treated with 30 ml. of 20% sodium hydroxide solution. The liberated ethylamine was steam distilled, the distillate neutralized with perchloric acid and evaporated to dryness under reduced pressure. After one hour at room temperature at 1 mm., 2 ml. of 99.8% deuterium oxide[16] was added and the mixture allowed to stand for 0.5 hour. The water was removed under reduced pressure as before and the residue dissolved in 40 ml. of 99.8% deuterium oxide. Sodium nitrite (23 g., 0.34 mole) was added and the balance of the reaction and isolation of the products were carried out as described above. The yield of ethanol was 1.2 g. (45%). The product was converted to the 3,5-dinitrobenzoate for deuterium analysis which was carried out by combustion and assay of the resulting water by the "falling-drop" procedure. The ester contained 0.70 atom % deuterium which after correction for the hydrogens of benzene ring gave 1.1 atom % deuterium for the hydrogens bound to carbon in the ethanol.

(16) Obtained on allocation by the U. S. Atomic Energy Commission.

CAMBRIDGE 39, MASSACHUSETTS

From: *J. Am. Chem. Soc.* **75**, 5759–60 (1953)

if the ethyl cation is an important intermediate in the reaction of ethylamine with nitrous acid it reacts with water considerably more rapidly than it is converted to the ethyleneprotonium ion (I). Much more rearrangement is found with 2-phenylethylamine-1-C[14] with nitrous acid and about 56% of the 2-phenylethanol formed appears to result from a symmetrical intermediate such as II.[5]

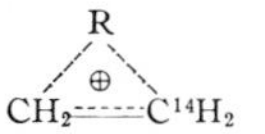

$$\underset{CH_2 \text{------} C^{14}H_2}{\overset{R}{\triangle}} \overset{\oplus}{}$$

I, R = H
II, R = C₆H₅ → II, R = C_6H_5
III, R = CH₃ → III, R = CH_3

Alkyl-bridged cations analogous to III ("ethylenealkonium" ions) have been proposed[6] to account for a wide variety of rearrangement reactions of alkyl derivatives but there are very few data which indicate the degree of stability of such ions relative to the isomeric classical carbonium ions like R–$CH_2CH_2^{\oplus}$.

In the present research, the tendency of the n-propyl cation to be converted to III was tested in the reaction of 1-propylamine-1-C[14] (IV) with nitrous acid. The reaction is complicated by elimination and rearrangement to 2-propyl derivatives,[7] but if III is formed from the n-propyldiazonium ion (V) or cation VI the 1-propanol obtained from IV should contain at least some 1-propanol-2-C[14] (VII). A possible reaction sequence for propanol formation is given below in which, for simplicity, it has been assumed that all of the cation isomerization processes are irreversible[8] and further that all of the propanol is formed by carbonium ion processes. The validity of the latter assumption has been discussed before.[4,5]

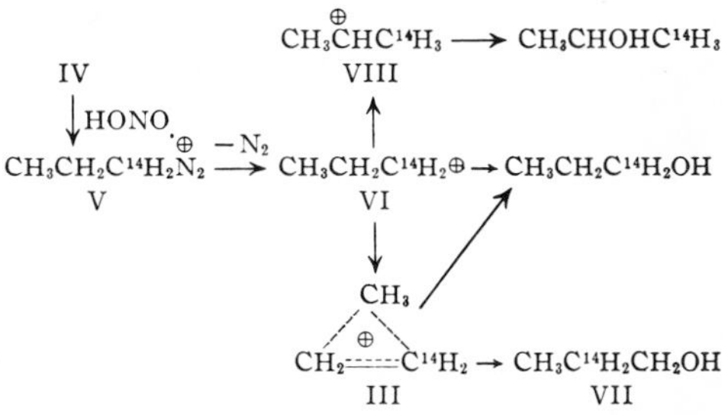

$$CH_3\overset{\oplus}{C}HC^{14}H_3 \longrightarrow CH_3CHOHC^{14}H_3$$
$$\text{VIII}$$

IV

$\downarrow$HONO

$$CH_3CH_2C^{14}H_2\overset{\oplus}{N_2} \xrightarrow{-N_2} CH_3CH_2C^{14}H_2^{\oplus} \rightarrow CH_3CH_2C^{14}H_2OH$$
$$\text{V} \qquad\qquad \text{VI}$$

$$\underset{III}{\overset{CH_3}{\underset{CH_2 \text{------} C^{14}H_2}{\triangle}}} \overset{\oplus}{} \rightarrow \underset{VII}{CH_3C^{14}H_2CH_2OH}$$

The following reactions were carried out in the present investigation. The substances represented by formulas in bold-face type were analyzed for radioactive carbon. The degradation procedure was checked for rearrangement as indicated by a blank experiment on authentic 1-propanol-1-C[14]. The results are presented in Table I. The 1-propanol from the amine–nitrous acid reaction was found to contain 8.5% of isotope-position rearrangement product such as would be expected from hav-

Rearrangement in the Reaction of C14-Labeled n-Propylamine (1-Aminopropane-1-C14) with Nitrous Acid[1]

By John D. Roberts[2] and Martin Halmann[3]

Received June 24, 1953

Ethylamine-1-C[14] on treatment with aqueous nitrous acid has been shown[4] to yield, besides ethylene, a mixture of 98.5% of ethanol-1-C[14] and 1.5% of ethanol-2-C[14]. It was concluded that

(1) Supported in part by the program of research of the U. S. Atomic Energy Commission.

(2) Gates and Crellin Laboratories, California Institute of Technology, Pasadena 4, Calif.

(3) Foreign Students Summer Project, Massachusetts Institute of Technology, 1952. The Weizmann Institute of Science, Rehovoth, Israel.

(4) J. D. Roberts and J. A. Yancey, This Journal, **74**, 5943 (1952).

(5) J. D. Roberts and C. M. Regan, ibid., **75**, 2069 (1953).

(6) (a) A number of references have been given previously[4,5]; (b) D. P. Stevenson, C. D Wagner, O. Beeck and J. W. Otvos, ibid., **74**, 3269 (1952).

(7) A. Siersch, Ann., **144**, 137 (1867); F. C. Whitmore and R. S. Thorpe, This Journal, **63**, 1118 (1941).

(8) The assumption only becomes important to the qualitative interpretation of the tracer results if VI and VIII are in rapid equilibrium, which event is unlikely since 2-propylamine with nitrous acid gives no 1-propanol and, in other processes, primary and secondary cations do not appear to be at all readily interconvertible; cf. J. D. Roberts, R. E. McMahon and J. S. Hine, ibid., **72**, 4237 (1950).

ing 17% of the 1-propanol originating from III[9] and 83% by way of VI.

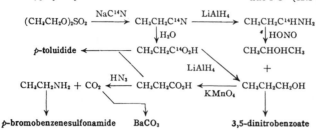

1-Propyl-1-C[14]-ammonium Perchlorate.— The procedure was based on that of Amundsen and Nelson.[11] Propionitrile-1-C[14] (12.1 g.) dissolved in 30 ml. of ether was added dropwise with stirring to 9 g. of lithium aluminum hydride in 300 ml. of dry ether in a flask cooled in ice-water. After 3 hours, 8 ml. of water, 6 ml. of 20% sodium hydroxide solution and 25 ml. more of water were added successively. The mixture was distilled and the distillate collected in a flask containing 20 ml. of 70% perchloric acid. The volatile material was removed at 30–35° under reduced pressure and the residual perchlorate salt recrystallized from *n*-hexyl alcohol by adding *n*-heptane. The yield of 1-propyl-1-C[14]-ammonium perchlorate was 11 g. (31%), m.p. 167°.

TABLE I

RADIOACTIVITY DETERMINATIONS

Reaction		1-Amino-propane-1-C[14] + nitrous acid	Degradation of 1-propanol-1-C[14]
C[14]-Activities,[a] mc. per millimole × 10⁸	1-Propanol[b]	139	.....
	Propionic acid[c]	142 ± 4[f]	11380
	Barium carbonate[d]	127 ± 2[f]	11070
	N-Ethyl-*p*-bromo-benzenesulfonamide	12 ± 1[f]	16
	Rearrangement,[e] %	8.5 ± 1	0.15

[a] Measured by the procedure of O. K. Neville, THIS JOURNAL, **70**, 3051 (1948), using a vibrating reed electrometer (Applied Physics Corp.). Corrected for background. [b] Assayed as the 3,5-dinitrobenzoate. [c] Assayed as the *p*-toluidide. [d] Since the barium carbonate samples are particularly subject to contamination their activities are only considered to be useful as a qualitative check on the other activities. [e] % rearrangement = activity of N-ethyl-*p*-bromobenzenesulfonamide/activity of *p*-toluidide × 100. [f] Average of four or five different combustions with standard deviations.

It is clear that rather more rearrangement (8.5%) occurs in the process of forming 1-propanol through the reaction of 1-propylamine with nitrous acid than in the corresponding reaction[4] with ethylamine.[4] The results probably reflect a greater stability of III compared to I under similar reaction conditions. This amounts to saying that the intrinsic migratory aptitude of methyl is likely to be greater than that of hydrogen in circumstances where the degree of substitution of the methylene groups of the intermediates (I or III) is the same.

Experimental

Propionitrile-1-C[14].—Ethyl sulfate (66 ml.) was added dropwise to a solution of 25 g. of sodium cyanide[10] containing 1 mc. of C[14] in 50 ml. of water and 50 ml. of ethylene glycol at 35°. The mixture was allowed to stand overnight and the low-boiling material was distilled out. The distillate was diluted with 20 ml. of 18 *N* sulfuric acid, the upper layer separated, dried over calcium chloride and distilled. The yield of propionitrile-1-C[14] was 12.1 g. (44%), b.p. 94–97°.

(9) It is possible that some or all of the rearranged 1-propanol might arise from an intermediate such as $CH_2 \overset{\oplus}{\underset{CH_2}{\overset{H}{\diagup}}} C^{14}H_2$. Such intermediates may be important in special sterically favorable conditions; J. D. Roberts and C. C. Lee, *ibid.*, **73**, 5009 (1951), J. D. Roberts and J. A. Yancey, *ibid.*, **75**, 3165 (1953); but are rendered unlikely with alkyl derivatives by the finding[4] that the presumably more stable ion I does not seem to play a very important role in the reaction of ethylamine with nitrous acid.

(10) The radioactive sodium cyanide was obtained from Tracerlab, Inc., Boston, Mass., on allocation from the U. S. Atomic Energy Commission.

***n*-Propylamine–Nitrous Acid Reaction.**—To a stirred solution at 25° of 22.5 g. of 1-propyl-1-C[14]-ammonium perchlorate in 20 ml. of 35% perchloric acid was added dropwise over 2 hours 21 g. of sodium nitrite dissolved in 30 ml. of water. The solution was then distilled and 25 ml. of distillate was collected. The distillate was acidified with hydrochloric acid and redistilled to remove any excess amine. Potassium fluoride was added to the distillate to salt out the organic products which were then separated and diluted with 2.0 ml. of 1-propanol as a carrier. The products were fractionated through a Podbielniak Micro Column and yielded, besides 3.4 g. (41%) of 2-propanol with b.p. 80–84°, 0.76 g. of pure 1-propanol, b.p. 95–96°. The 1-propanol was diluted with 20 g. of carrier 1-propanol for the degradation reactions. Part of the 1-propanol was converted to the 3,5-dinitrobenzoate, m.p. 73°, for radioactive assay.

Degradation Procedure.—A stirred solution of 20 g. of labeled propanol in 300 ml. of water containing 30 ml. of concd. sulfuric acid was cooled to 5° with an ice-bath and 54 g. of potassium permanganate added in small portions at a rate slow enough to keep the temperature below 15°. The mixture was stirred for 1.5 hours, after which time sulfur dioxide was passed in until the manganese dioxide dissolved. The solution was extracted continuously with ether for 10 hours. The extract was dried with sodium sulfate and distilled. The yield of propionic acid, b.p. 135.5–139.5°, was 8.1 g. (42%). The product was assayed as the *p*-toluidide, m.p. 124°.

A mixture of 1.44 g. of labeled propionic acid, 5 ml. of chloroform and 3 ml. of concd. sulfuric acid was stirred magnetically at 45–55° in a 200-ml. flask equipped with a dropping funnel and gas inlet and outlet tubes while a stream of carbon dioxide-free nitrogen was passed through. The outlet was connected to two absorption flasks containing 0.07 *N* barium hydroxide solution. The nitrogen flow was stopped and 35 ml. of a solution of 1.2 *N* hydrazoic acid in chloroform added over 70 minutes. After two additional hours at 50°, nitrogen was passed through to sweep out the balance of the carbon dioxide. The barium carbonate precipitate in the absorption flasks was filtered, washed with boiling water and acetone, then dried at 120°. The yield was 2.8 g. (73%). The material in the reaction flask was cooled with ice, cautiously basified with 5% sodium hydroxide solution and stirred with a solution of 2 g. of *p*-bromobenzenesulfonyl chloride in 5 ml. of chloroform. After 2 hours, the mixture was acidified with concd. hydrochloric acid, the chloroform layer separated, dried over sodium sulfate and evaporated to dryness. The residue was dissolved in 5% sodium hydroxide solution, the crude N-ethyl *p*-bromobenzenesulfonamide precipitated with hydrochloric acid, dried and crystallized from a benzene–*n*-hexane mixture. The yield was 1.4 g. (30%), m.p. 80.5°.

The degradation procedure was checked in the following way. 1-Propionitrile-1-C[14] (see above) was hydrolyzed with 90% sulfuric acid to propionic-1-C[14] acid in 67% yield. The acid was reduced with lithium aluminum hydride to give a 50% yield of 1-propanol-1-C[14]. The above degradation was then carried through on the 1-propanol-1-C[14] and, as may be seen from the data given in Table I, a negligible fraction of the activity of the N-propionyl-*p*-toluidide was found in the N-ethyl-*p*-bromobenzenesulfonamide.

DEPARTMENT OF CHEMISTRY AND LABORATORY
  FOR NUCLEAR SCIENCE AND ENGINEERING
MASSACHUSETTS INSTITUTE OF TECHNOLOGY
CAMBRIDGE 39, MASSACHUSETTS

(11) L. H. Amundsen and L. S. Nelson, *ibid.*, **73**, 282 (1951).

22 | MO Calculations on Homo-allylic Cations

Simonetta and Winstein (Paper No. 22) consider the nature of the bonding in a homoallylic cation, and show by Hückel MO calculations that stabilizing electron delocalization may be expected in a molecular orbital made up of σ overlap between an atomic orbital on C-1 and the one on C-3 which is also involved in π overlap with C-4. It is pointed out, as had been discussed before, that delocalization with different degrees of symmetry can exist in systems of the same type; what is the most probable degree of symmetry, and whether certain configurations become transition states or intermediates, remain experimental problems.

From: *J. Am. Chem. Soc.* **76**, 18–21 (1954)

[CONTRIBUTION FROM THE INSTITUTO DI CHIMICA GENERALE E ANALITICA OF THE POLITECNICO DI MILANO, ITALY, GATES AND CRELLIN LABORATORIES, CALIFORNIA INSTITUTE OF TECHNOLOGY, AND THE DEPARTMENT OF CHEMISTRY, UNIVERSITY OF CALIFORNIA AT LOS ANGELES]

Neighboring Carbon and Hydrogen. XVI. 1,3-Interactions and Homoallylic Resonance

BY M. SIMONETTA[1] AND S. WINSTEIN[2]

RECEIVED MARCH 16, 1953

Evidence from stereochemistry and reaction kinetics suggests the existence of an important 1,3-interaction between a carbonium ion center and a π-electron-containing β-substituent. A semi-empirical molecular orbital method has been used to estimate the stabilization due to π-electron delocalization in the case of a vinyl, diolefinic or phenyl group beta to a cationic carbon center. Even at the unmodified 1,3 C–C distance of 2.5 Å., a slight stabilization due to electron delocalization is found, the 1,3-overlap integrals, with proper orientation, being appreciable. Considerable compression of the 1,3-distance is more than compensated for by increase in resonance energy; the intervening methylene group is in effect a poor insulator against interaction of the unsaturated centers. The net stabilizations are estimated as *ca.* 10, 6 and 4 kcal./mole for β-dienyl, β-vinyl and β-phenyl, in accord with the rate-enhancing effects of these substituents in solvolysis.

Evidence from stereochemistry and reaction kinetics suggests the existence of an important interaction between a carbonium ion center and a π-electron-containing β-substituent such as a vinyl or phenyl group. This is true for *homoallylic* cases such as cholesteryl I[3] and dehydronorbornyl V[4] and *homobenzyl* cases such as benzylmethylcarbinyl VI.[5,6] Thus cholesteryl derivatives have enhanced

rates of ionization,[3] ascribed to delocalization of the electron cloud of the neighboring olefinic group in the rate-determining step.[3] This participation of the 5,6-olefinic group in the substitution process gives rise to a non-classical ion[3,5] which has been written as II (canonical structures IIa and IIb) with partial 3,5-bonding and weakened 5,6-bonding. This intermediate reacts[3] with nucleophilic species at C_6 to yield 3,5-cyclosteroids III or at C_3 to yield cholesteryl derivatives IV with over-all retention[3,5] of configuration from I to IV.

The concept of the hybrid allyl ion VII is familiar, but the non-classical structure II represents a hybrid structure for the next homologous case, with a methylene group interposed between the cationic center and the π-electron system; this is the reason

(1) Arthur A. Noyes Fellow in Chemistry. California Institute of Technology, 1951–1952.

(2) Research supported in part by the Office of Naval Research.

(3) (a) S. Winstein and R. Adams, THIS JOURNAL, **70**, 838 (1948); (b) S. Winstein and A. H. Schlesinger, *ibid.*, **70**, 3528 (1948).

(4) S. Winstein, H. M. Walborsky and K. C. Schreiber, *ibid.*, **72**, 5795 (1950).

(5) S. Winstein, *Bull. soc. chim.*, **18**, 55C (1951).

(6) S. Winstein, M. Brown, K. C. Schreiber and A. H. Schlesinger, THIS JOURNAL, **74**, 1140 (1952).

for the *homoallylic designation*. The possible existence of an important 1,3-interaction even in the

homoallylic case has interesting implications in organic chemistry. We report in the present paper

the results of semi-empirical calculations of the stabilization to be expected from such interaction of a cationic center with an olefinic group, a diolefinic group and a phenyl group.

The 1,3-interaction in the homoallylic ion VIII can be considered[5,7] in a first approximation to involve overlap of the p-orbital on C_3 with what would have been a vacant orbital on C_1, resulting in delocalization of the 3,4-π-electron cloud. With regard to preferred geometry there can be expected a fundamental difference between the allyl and homoallyl cases. The allyl cation is planar, for this is the configuration favorable to π-electron delocalization. On the other hand, a planar arrangement for atoms C_1, C_2, C_3, C_4, a and b is unfavorable in the homoallylic ion because it makes 2pπ-overlap the

(7) R. Dodson and B. Riegel, *J. Org. Chem.*, **13**, 424 (1948).

basis of the 1,3-interaction and π-overlap falls off rapidly with increasing internuclear distance. (For example, the Slater overlap integral[8] for 2pπ-overlap is smaller than for 2pσ-overlap by factors of 3 at a distance of 2.00 Å., 4 at 2.41 Å. and 5 at 2.78 Å.) If the axes of the vacant p-orbital of C_1 and the p-orbital of C_3 are made to lie in the C_1–C_2–C_3 plane as illustrated in IX, considerably improved overlap,[5] intermediate between π and σ, is attained. Our calculations have been made for this orientation with various values of the 1,3-interatomic distance $R_{1,3}$ (the overlap is naturally improved[9] by decrease in $R_{1,3}$), the calculated delocalization or resonance energy, R.E., at each $R_{1,3}$ being corrected for the estimated strain energy, S.E., due to compression of the corresponding C_1–C_2–C_3 angle α, to yield a total energy, T.E. The estimates of both R.E. and S.E. would naturally be affected, and therefore the estimate of the net stabilization, $-$T.E., due to the 1,3-interaction would be increased, by proper rehybridization of atomic orbitals on atoms C_1, C_2, C_3 and C_4. However, sp²-hybridization on C_1, C_3 and C_4 and sp³-hybridization on C_2 have been maintained throughout the present calculations. While the latter are admittedly crude for this and other reasons, the results are nevertheless quite instructive.

The delocalization energies R.E. for the two-electron, three-orbital problem presented by the electrons and orbitals of the double bond and the p-orbital of C_1 were calculated by a semi-empirical molecular orbital (LCAO) method.[10] All Coulomb integrals were assumed equal. Overlap integrals S between the p-orbitals of C_1 and C_3 were numerically evaluated with Kopineck's tables,[11] assuming Z, the effective nuclear charge, to be 3.09 for 2 p-orbitals on C atoms. The exchange integrals β were estimated by using Mulliken's assumption[12] that the energy B of an electron-pair bond is given by equation 1 and the assumption that the exchange integral is a nearly constant fraction of the bond energy. On this basis the β's are related by equa-

$$B = AIS/(1 + S) \qquad (1)$$

tion[13] 2, where the prime refers to the 1,3-interac-

$$\frac{\beta'}{\beta} = \frac{B'}{B} = \frac{A'I'S'/(1 + S')}{AIS/(1 + S)} \qquad (2)$$

tion and its absence to the 3,4-interaction. In equation 2, A' and A and I' and I were cancelled, as is appropriate enough for the valence-state ionization potentials if perhaps not for the constants[12b] A and A' (Mulliken's values being 1.16 for σ-bonds and 1.5 for π-bonds), and S and β were set equal to 0.28 and the usual value -20 kcal./mole, respec-

(8) R. S. Mulliken, *et al.*, *J. Chem. Phys.*, **17**, 1248 (1949).

(9) S. Winstein, *Bull. soc. chim.*, **18**, 123C (1951).

(10) (a) R. S. Mulliken, *Phys. Rev.*, **41**, 49 (1932); (b) R. S. Mulliken, *J. Chem. Phys.*, **3**, 375 (1935); (c) C. A. Coulson, "Valence" Oxford Press, New York, N. Y., 1952, Chapter IV and further.

(11) H. J. Kopineck, *Z. Naturforsch.*, **5A**, 420 (1950).

(12) (a) R. S. Mulliken, THIS JOURNAL, **72**, 4493 (1950); (b) R. S. Mulliken, *J. Phys. Chem.*, **56**, 295 (1952).

(13) This assumption seems a reasonable one. In a treatment of the butadiene molecule it gives a value for the delocalization energy of 7.6 kcal./mole, superior to the value obtained by the usual molecular orbital LCAO method of 9.6 kcal./mole, and in agreement with the valence-bond value of 7.9 kcal./mole [M. Simonetta, *J. chim. phys.*, **49**, 68 (1952)].

tively. The secular equation was then solved (with omission of the term $-SW$ in the off-diagonal matrix elements) to obtain the energy levels for the three resultant molecular orbitals, and the value $2(Q + \beta)$ for a pair of electrons in a localized 3,4-π-bond was subtracted from twice the lowest energy level to obtain R.E.

We have estimated S.E. by the method of Kilpatrick and Spitzer,[14] which, following Pauling's discussion,[15] assumes that the energy of the angle-strained system is just the sum of energies of the "bent" σ-bonds, each being proportional to the product of the angle-dependent factors, measured along the lines joining the two nuclei, of the bond orbitals involved. In particular, we have used equation 3 where B is the normal C–C bond energy, θ and θ' are the angles by which the axes of

$$S.E. = 2B[0.996 - (0.5 + 1.5 \cos \theta)(0.577 + \sqrt{2} \cos \theta')/4] \quad (3)$$

the bond orbitals, respectively sp^3 and sp^2, at the two ends of each σ-bond deviate from the internuclear line ($\theta = \theta'$ was assumed[16]) and the two trigonometric factors are the relevant orbital strengths. Since the appropriate value for B is in some doubt[17] for several reasons, the calculation was made for two values, 59 and 66.6 kcal./mole.[18]

Similar calculations were made for the system with two olefinic linkages X and the homobenzyl system XI. The 1,3-integrals and S.E. were treated as before, the 5,6- and intraphenyl-integrals were treated like the 3,4-integral before, and the 3,4- and 4,5-integrals were set equal to 0.89 β.

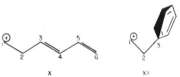

$$\text{X} \qquad \qquad \text{XI}$$

The calculations are summarized in Tables I and II.

TABLE I

SUMMARY OF CALCULATIONS FOR HOMOALLYL CATION IX

$R_{1,3}$, Å.	S'	β'/β	$-$R.E.^{a}	S.E.^{a} $B = 59$	$B = 66.6$	T.E.^{a} $B = 59$	$B = 66.6$
2.51	0.072	0.30	1.8	0.0	0.0	1.8	1.8
2.35	.117	.47	4.2	0.9	1.1	3.3	3.1
2.15	.180	.68	8.3	2.8	3.2	5.5	5.1
1.95	.247	.88	13.2	6.1	7.0	7.1	6.2*
1.75	.302	1.03	17.4	10.2	11.6	7.2*	5.8
1.63	.322	1.08	18.8	12.9	14.7	5.9	4.1
1.54	.332	1.11	19.7	14.7	16.8	5.0	2.9

^{a} R.E., S.E. and T.E. values are in kcal./mole.

(14) J. E. Kilpatrick and R. Spitzer, *J. Chem. Phys.*, **14**, 463 (1946). See J. D. Dunitz and V. Schomaker, *ibid.*, **20**, 1703 (1952).

(15) L. Pauling, "The Nature of the Chemical Bond," Cornell University Press, Ithaca, N. Y., 1939, chapter III.

(16) This assumption was of course also made in the calculation of S' and β'

(17) See for example, L. Pauling and W. F. Sheehan, *Proc. Nat. Acad. Sci.*, **35**, 359 (1949).

(18) Other modifications were explored. In one calculation, for example, θ' was varied so as to maximize $S_{1,3}$; equation 3 was evaluated with $B = 80$ kcal./mole; and $I = I'$ and $A = 1.5$ were assumed in equation 2, while A' was varied to suit the σ-character of the 1,3-bond. The resulting $-$T.E. values go through a maximum of 8.90 kcal./mole at $R_{1,3} = 1.75$ Å

TABLE II

SUMMARY OF CALCULATIONS FOR X AND XI

$R_{1,3}$, Å.	X $-$R.E.^{a}	T.E.^{a} $B = 59$	$B = 66.6$	XI $-$R.E.^{a}	T.E.^{a} $B = 59$	$B = 66.6$
2.51	2.0	2.0	2.0	1.2	1.2	1.2
2.35	5.2	4.3	4.1	3.6	2.7	2.5
2.15	10.4	7.6	7.2	6.8	4.0	3.6
1.95	16.4	10.3	9.4	11.2	5.1*	4.2*
1.75	21.2	11.0*	9.6*	15.2	5.0	3.6
1.63	22.8	9.9	8.1	16.4	3.5	1.7
1.54	24.0	9.3	7.2	17.2	2.5	0.4

^{a} In kcal./mole.

The calculated values of S' and R.E. show that the 1,3-overlap is great enough to be of some chemical importance[9] even at the normal distance 2.5 Å., and for smaller values of $R_{1,3}$ (and α) the net stabilization rises to quite sizable maxima, indicated by asterisks in Tables I and II, where the forces of angle strain and C$_1$–C$_3$ stretching balance.

The present calculations are instructive in stressing how little insulation against interaction between unsaturated centers may be provided by an intervening methylene group[19] if the assumed orientation is accessible. Indeed, the $-$T.E. of $ca.$ 6 kcal./mole for the homoallylic ion is 40% as great as the corresponding delocalization energy [$(2\sqrt{2} - 2)\beta = 16.4$ kcal./mole] of the allyl cation. 1,3-Interactions may well give rise to other effects such as the interaction between non-adjacent chromophores[20,21] observed for 9,10-dihydroanthracene, triptycene,[20] 2,5-dihydroacetophenone,[21] etc., as pointed out by Bartlett and Lewis.[20] There has been a certain tendency,[21] however, to reject direct 1,3-interactions in the excited state in light absorption and to stress hyperconjugation.

As might have been expected, the order of stabilization dienyl > vinyl > phenyl found for these groups in the β-position is the same as the order found previously for ordinary (α) conjugation of these groups with an olefinic linkage (ref. 10c, p. 235; ref. 15, p. 202). Furthermore, it is the order of the rate-enhancing effects of the β-substituents in solvolysis.[3–6,22] For example, the rates of solvolysis of cholestanyl XII, cholesteryl XIII and 7-dehydrocholesteryl[23] XIV p-toluenesulfonates are in the ratio 1:100:3000. These figures correspond to stabilization of the transition states for XIII and XIV by $ca.$ 3 and 5 kcal./mole even though the orientation of the β-substituent is not the ideal one.

(19) Although no calculations are presented here for 1,4-interactions across two methylene groups, it is clear that the configuration favors relatively strong interaction, as was first pointed out to us by L.

deVries. The 1,4-distance is no larger than the original $R_{1,3}$ in IX, X, and XI, and the relative orientation of orbitals on C$_1$ and C$_4$ is more conducive to effective overlap. Considerations of this sort are pertinent to valency tautomerism questions.

(20) E.g., P. D. Bartlett and E. S. Lewis, THIS JOURNAL, **72**, 1005 (1950).

(21) E.g., E. A. Braude, et al., J. Chem. Soc., 607, 1902 (1949).

(22) S. Winstein, et al., THIS JOURNAL, **74**, 1113 (1952).

(23) N. J. Holness, unpublished work.

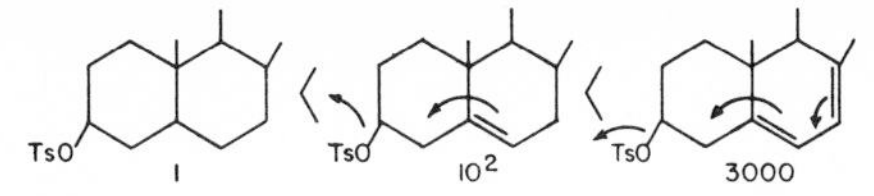

The electron distributions for the most stable configurations of IX, X and XI were obtained by calculating the coefficients of the atomic orbitals in the bonding molecular orbital. The following resonance descriptions correspond to the same net atomic charges:

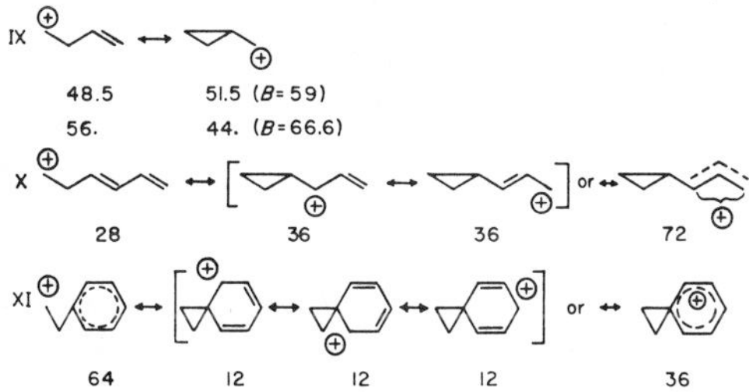

The possibility of substantial stabilization *via* 1,3-interaction does not, of course, guarantee that reaction will proceed only in the indicated way; other, competing paths of reaction must, as usual, be considered. These may involve displacement by solvent or another nucleophilic reagent (XV), hydrogen participation (XVI), assisted[5,22] by a β-vinyl or similar group, or other kinds of cyclization, *e.g.*, XVII. Thus the simplest homoallyl alcohol, allylcarbinol, reacts without rearrangement[24]

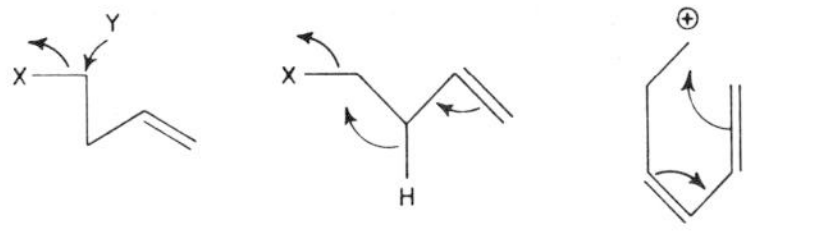

with reagents such as thionyl chloride or phosphorus tribromide. Benzylmethylcarbinyl *p*-toluenesulfonate solvolyzes predominantly without phenyl participation in ethanol and acetic acid, but predominantly with phenyl participation in formic acid.[6] When allylcarbinylamine is diazotized, hydrogen shift, with formation of crotyl and α-methyl-

allyl alcohols is a competing process.[24] Similarly, hydrogen shift is more or less important in solvolysis of epicholesteryl[25] and 3-phenyl-2-butyl[26] derivatives. With (γ,γ-dimethylallyl)-carbinyl,[27] cholesteryl[3,7,25] and dehydronorbornyl[28] derivatives, other competing processes are apparently much more nearly completely excluded.

Moreover, the present calculations do not preclude further delocalization leading to different or additional structures. Thus, homoallyl and homobenzyl effects can merge[5,6] with the Wagner–Meerwein rearrangement. Additional delocalization involving the bonding electrons "a" in XIX, (formed from XVIII) can lead to the symmetrical ion XX. Similarly, further electron delocalization in a homobenzyl ion can lead to a phenyl-bridged structure.[6,29] As pointed out previously,[5,6] in neither the homoallyl nor homobenzyl cases is it entirely clear how many cationic species require explicit mention in any specific case. In the dehydronorbornyl,[28,30,31] β-phenylethyl[30b,32] and 4-phenyl-3-hexyl[33] cases, there has been some discussion of possible evidence for both symmetrical (*e.g.*, XX) and unsymmetrical (*e.g.*, XIX) non-classical cations.[34]

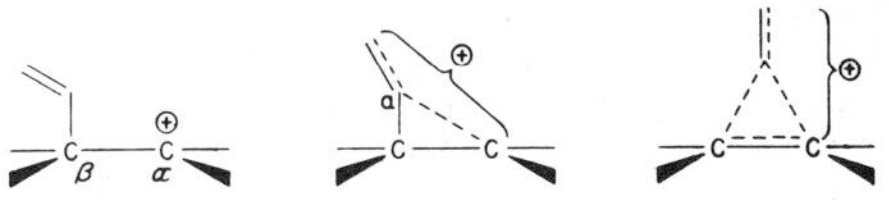

(24) J. D. Roberts and R. H. Mazur, THIS JOURNAL, **73**, 2509 (1951).

(25) E. Kosower, Ph.D. Thesis, U.C.L.A., 1952; D. D. Evans and C. W. Shoppee, *J. Chem. Soc.*, 540 (1953).

(26) D. J. Cram, THIS JOURNAL, **74**, 2137 (1952).

(27) (a) P. Bruylants and A. Dewael, *Bull. classe. sci. acad. roy, Belg.*, [5] **14**, 140 (1928); (b) T. A. Favorskaya and S. A. Fridman. *J. Gen. Chem.* (*U.S.S.R.*), **15**, 421 (1945).

(28) H. J. Schmid, unpublished work.

(29) D. J. Cram, THIS JOURNAL, **71**, 3863 (1949).

(30) J. D. Roberts, (a) Organic Reaction Mechanisms Symposium, New York, Sept., 1951; (b) Organic Reaction Mechanisms Conference, Bryn Mawr, Pa., Sept., 1952.

(31) S. Winstein, Organic Reaction Mechanisms Conference, Bryn Mawr, Pa., Sept., 1952.

(32) J. D. Roberts and C. M. Regan, THIS JOURNAL, **75**, 2069 (1953).

(33) D. J. Cram, Organic Reaction Mechanisms Conference, Bryn Mawr, Pa., Sept., 1952; D. J. Cram and F. A. Abd Elhafez, THIS JOURNAL, **75**, 3189 (1953).

(34) With the simplest homoallyl derivatives there is a further complication, since, for example, allylcarbinylamine gives rise to cyclobutanol as well as cyclopropylcarbinol.[24] The number of cationic species involved and their formulation are not yet clear[30a] [J. D. Roberts and R. H. Mazur, THIS JOURNAL, **73**, 3542 (1951); M. J. S. Dewar, *Ann. Repts.*, **48**, 120 (1951)].

23 | Tracer Experiments on the Norbornyl Cation

On the Roberts, Lee, and Saunders paper (Paper No. 23) see the previous comments on the Communication by Roberts and Lee. In this paper the results are discussed in more detail and experiments are included which show that the nitrous acid deamination of the norbornylamines also leads to functional scrambling of the carbon atoms in the products, but the 6,2- and 6,1-rearrangement (or that which in this paper is described in terms of the nortricyclonium ion) is less prevalent than in solvolysis of the p-bromobenzenesulfonate, suggesting that the "higher-energy," potentially less solvated ion from deamination is shorter lived and can form product directly in competition with the nonclassical delocalization. This is consistent with the picture developed by more recent studies of the deamination reaction, such as that of Corey and co-workers (Paper No. 64); but see also Berson and Remanick (Paper No. 68).

Interestingly enough, these tracer studies set a lower limit on the symmetry of the norbornyl cation than do the later NMR studies of Schleyer, Watts, Fort, Comisarow, and Olah (Paper No. 74) on the long-lived norbornyl cation in SbF_5-SO_2 solution. At $-60°$ the NMR spectrum divides the protons into three types numbering 1, 6, and 4, respectively. The tracer results tell us that there is an intermediate less symmetrical than this, since the radioactivity at atom 6 in the product is not equal to that at atoms 1 and 2. The combination of the two studies shows that the conversion of IIIa into IIIb and IIIc,[1] over whatever type

---

[1] The notation IIIa–c has evolved to the point where it is now commonly used without definition. In each case the dotted triangle denotes a three-center, electron-deficient bond made up by an electron pair in an orbital formed by overlap of one atomic orbital from each of the three atoms. The one solid side of the triangle is a σ bond superposed on the three-center bond. The two carbon atoms joined by the solid line bear one hydrogen atom each; the third carbon atom

128

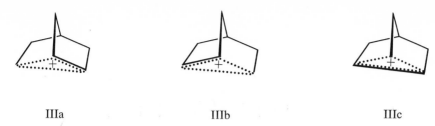

IIIa   IIIb   IIIc

of transition state, must be a hydride shift with a rate constant at $-120°$ greater than 3×10^5 sec^{-1} (Paper No. 75).

---

bears two hydrogen atoms. Thus the interconversion of IIIa, IIIb, and IIIc involves a shift of the extra hydrogen atom around among the three carbons of the triangle. To depict the product of attachment of a nucleophile at any of the three carbon atoms, eliminate the two dotted lines to that atom and replace the one on the opposite side with a solid line:

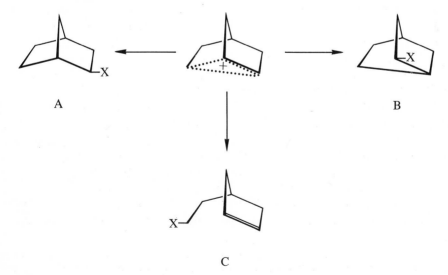

A   B

C

The product C is not normally formed; see the discussion later of the π route to the three-center ion.

From: *J. Am. Chem. Soc.* **76**, 4501–10 (1954)

[CONTRIBUTION FROM THE DEPARTMENT OF CHEMISTRY AND LABORATORY FOR NUCLEAR SCIENCE AND ENGINEERING, MASSACHUSETTS INSTITUTE OF TECHNOLOGY]

Rearrangements in Carbonium Ion-Type Reactions of C14-Labeled Norbornyl Derivatives[1,2]

BY JOHN D. ROBERTS,[3] C. C. LEE AND W. H. SAUNDERS, JR.

RECEIVED FEBRUARY 1, 1954

The extents of isotope-position rearrangement have been determined in solvolyses of *exo*- and *endo*-norbornyl-2,3-C_2^{14} *p*-bromobenzenesulfonates and nitrous acid reactions of *exo*- and *endo*-norbornyl-3-C^{14}-amines. The bridged "norbornonium" ion proposed by Winstein and Trifan as the intermediate in cationic reactions of norbornyl derivatives does not suffice to account for the C^{14}-distributions in the reaction products. The formation of norbornyl derivatives with C^{14} in the 5- and 6-positions along with the observed percentages of rearrangement require 1,3-type hydride shifts which may occur by way of a "nortricyclonium" ion or its equivalent. The extent of rearrangement was found to increase in the solvolytic reactions as nucleophilic character of the solvent decreased. The rearrangement in the amine–nitrous acid reactions was relatively independent of solvent. More rearrangement was observed when the starting norbornyl derivatives had the *exo*-configuration. Possible interpretations of the experimental results are presented.

Introduction

Carbonium ion-type reactions of *exo*- and *endo*-norbornyl derivatives (I and II, respectively) have been found to have unusual stereochemical and kinetic characteristics. Solvolyses of the chlorides[4] (Ia, IIa) and *p*-bromobenzenesulfonates (Ib, IIb) as well as the reaction of the amines[6] (Ic, IIc) with nitrous acid yield exclusively substitution products with the *exo*-configuration (I), irrespective of the configuration of the starting material. The solvolysis rates of the *endo* compounds (II) approximate those of the corresponding cyclohexane derivatives,[7] while those of the *exo* compounds (I) are up to 350 times greater.[4,5,7] Of particular significance is the observation[5] that solvolysis of optically active *exo*-norbornyl *p*-bromobenzenesulfonate

EXO-
I

ENDO-
II

Ia, X = Cl
Ib, X = –SO$_2$C$_6$H$_4$Br
Ic, X = –NH$_2$
Id, X = –OAc
Ie, X = –OH
If, X = –NO$_2$

IIa, X = Cl
IIb, X = –SO$_2$C$_6$H$_4$Br
IIc, X = –NH$_2$
IId, X = –OAc
IIe, X = –OH
IIf, X = –NO$_2$

gives only racemic *exo*-norbornyl derivatives. The *endo* derivatives solvolyze with predominant racemization although a small fraction ($\sim$8%) of the optical activity survives, the amount being rather solvent dependent.

Winstein[5] has demonstrated that all of the above experimental results may be accounted for by assuming intermediate formation of the non-classical "norbornonium"[8] cation (III) analogous to that previously suggested for the conversion of camphene

(1) Preliminary reports of this work were given at the Symposium on Reaction Mechanisms at the 75th Anniversary Meeting of the American Chemical Society, September 7, 1951, and by J. D. Roberts and C. C. Lee, THIS JOURNAL, **73**, 5009 (1951).

(2) Supported in part by the joint program of the Office of Naval Research and the U. S. Atomic Energy Commission.

(3) Gates and Crellin Laboratories, California Institute of Technology, Pasadena 4, California.

(4) J. D. Roberts, L. Urbanek and R. Armstrong, THIS JOURNAL, **71**, 3049 (1949); J. D. Roberts, W. Bennett and R. Armstrong, *ibid.*, **72**, 3329 (1950). See also J. D. Roberts and W. Bennett, *ibid.*, **76**, 4623 (1954).

(5) S. Winstein and D. Trifan, *ibid.*, **71**, 2953 (1949); *ibid.*, **74**, 1147, 1154 (1952).

(6) (a) K. Alder and G. Stein, *Ann.*, **514**, 211 (1934); (b) G. Komppa and S. Beckmann, *ibid.*, **512**, 172 (1934).

(7) S. Winstein, B. K. Morse, E. Grunwald, H. W. Jones, J. Corse, D. S. Trifan and H. Marshall, THIS JOURNAL, **74**, 1127 (1952).

(8) The present use of this and similar names stems from our feeling that non-classical carbonium ion intermediates of this general type are best designated as "*onium*" ions to indicate their relationship to ethylenebromonium, ethyleneacetoxonium, etc., intermediates. While names like "norbornonium," "nortricyclonium" or "tricyclobutonium" (for the ion postulated earlier, J. D. Roberts and R. H. Mazur, *ibid.*, **73**, 3542 (1951)) do not represent an extension of the system used for "ethylene–onium" intermediates, they seem justifiable on the basis of the fairly loose general usage of the *-onium* suffix as well as from the descriptive and euphonic advantages.

hydrochloride to isobornyl chloride.⁹ III has a plane of symmetry (defined by C-4,5,6 and the mid-point of the 1,2-bond) and can be expected to be formed from *exo*-norbornyl derivatives with substantial "driving force" in the ionization process.⁴,⁵,⁷

III

It has been pointed out¹⁰ that III does not uniquely account for the stereochemical and kinetic results with norbornyl systems. Indeed, several other cationic intermediates could explain the observed behavior although these are not as well supported by analogies from other systems as is III. In the present investigation, more definite information as to the nature of the intermediate was sought through study of carbonium ion-type reactions of C¹⁴-labeled *exo*- and *endo*-norbornyl derivatives.

Synthetic and Degradative Procedures

Synthesis of norbornyl-2,3-C₂¹⁴ *p*-bromobenzenesulfonates started from barium carbide-C₂¹⁴. Acetylene-1,2-C₂¹⁴ generated from the carbide was converted to vinyl-1,2-C₂¹⁴ acetate by treatment with acetic acid and mercuric phosphate.¹¹ The Diels–Alder reaction between vinyl-1,2-C₂¹⁴ acetate and cyclopentadiene¹² afforded a mixture of *exo*- and *endo*-dehydronorbornyl-2,3-C₂¹⁴ acetates (IVa and

IV	V
IVa, X = –OAc	Va, X = –OAc
IVb, X = OH	Vb, X = OH
IVc, X = –NO₂	Vc, X = –NO₂

Va, respectively). Hydrogenation of the Diels–Alder adduct gave a mixture of norbornyl-2,3-C₂¹⁴ acetates (Id, IId) which with lithium aluminum hydride⁵ afforded a mixture of norborneols (Ie, IIe). The product with *p*-bromobenzenesulfonyl chloride in pyridine¹³ yielded a *p*-bromobenzenesulfonate mixture (Ib, IIb). The solvolysis rate curve of the sulfonate ester mixture in 75% acetone–25% water indicated the presence of 19% of the reactive *exo*-isomer (essentially completely solvolyzed in 30 minutes at 45°) in agreement with Winstein and Trifan.⁵ The pure *endo* isomer (IIb) was readily obtained by selective solvolysis of the *exo* isomer in the mixture.

A norborneol-2,3-C₂¹⁴ mixture enriched in the *exo* isomer (Ie) was obtained from the lithium aluminum hydride product by a stereochemical equilibration procedure based on that of Doering and Aschner.¹⁴ Analysis of the mixture by the solvolysis rate curve of its *p*-bromobenzenesulfonate indicated the presence of 70% of the *exo* isomer. The large difference in rate⁵ between the *exo*- and *endo*-norbornyl *p*-bromobenzenesulfonates permitted use of the sulfonate ester mixture in place of the pure *exo* isomer for product isolations since the initial rapid solvolysis was almost entirely due to the *exo* material and the unreacted *endo* ester could be readily separated from the reaction products.

To prepare *exo*- and *endo*-norbornyl-3-C¹⁴-amine, formaldehyde-C¹⁴ was converted to 2-nitroethanol-1-C¹⁴ with nitromethane in high dilution by a procedure similar to that used by Hays, *et al.*¹⁵ The 2-nitroethanol-1-C¹⁴ was dehydrated to 2-nitroethylene with phthalic anhydride.¹⁶ The product was found to add readily to cyclopentadiene in ether at room temperature¹⁷ and afforded 5-nitronorbornene-6-C¹⁴ (IVc, Vc) in excellent yield. No suitable procedure was found for determination of the ratio of *endo* to *exo* isomers formed in this Diels–Alder addition nor were the isomers obtained pure. The unsaturated character of the nitro group would be expected to lead to a high degree of stereospecificity in the addition of nitroethylene to cyclopentadiene¹⁸ so that the *endo* isomer might be expected to predominate to the extent of >90%. In the absence of more specific information, the product will be designated as *endo*-5-nitronorbornene-6-C¹⁴ (Vc).

Hydrogenation of Vc afforded *endo*-2-nitronorbornane-3-C¹⁴ (IIf) which on reduction with iron and hydrochloric acid was converted to *endo*-norbornyl-3-C¹⁴-amine (IIc). The *exo* isomer (Ic) was obtained by isomerization of IIf with triethylamine and reduction. Pure Ic (>90% *exo*) was afforded by fractional crystallization of the acetylated reduction product. The yields of acetyl derivative indicated the isomerization product of IIf to have the composition 70–80% If and 30–20% IIf.

Solvolysis of the labeled norbornyl *p*-bromobenzenesulfonates in 75% acetone–25% water, acetic acid and formic acid yielded *exo*-norborneol, *exo*-norbornyl acetate and *exo*-norbornyl formate, respectively, as previously reported.⁵ The infrared spectrum of the product of the aqueous norbornyl-amine–nitrous acid reaction indicated it to be *exo*-norborneol contaminated with 2–5% of norcamphor. The latter substance might be formed by an α-elimination from norbornyl nitrite (or nitrate).¹⁹ Deamination of the norbornylamines in acetic acid gave *exo*-norbornyl acetate. The esters were cleaved to *exo*-norborneol with lithium aluminum hydride for degradation.

(9) T. P. Nevell, E. de Salas and C. L. Wilson, *J. Chem. Soc.*, 1188 (1939).

(10) J. D. Roberts, R. E. McMahon and J. S. Hine, THIS JOURNAL, **72**, 4237 (1950).

(11) (a) G. O. Morrison and T. P. G. Shaw, *Trans. Electrochem. Soc.*, **63**, 425 (1933); (b) B. S. Groth and S. B. H. Johanson, U. S. Patent 2,376,964 (May 29, 1945); *C. A.*, **39**, 3303 (1945).

(12) K. Alder and H. F. Rickert, *Ann.*, **543**, 1 (1939).

(13) R. S. Tipson, *J. Org. Chem.*, **9**, 235 (1944).

(14) W. v. E. Doering and T. E. Aschner, THIS JOURNAL, **71**, 838 (1949).

(15) J. T. Hays, G. F. Hager, H. M. Engelmann and H. M. Spurlin, *ibid.*, **73**, 5369 (1951).

(16) G. D. Buckley and C. W. Scaife, *J. Chem. Soc.*, 1471 (1947).

(17) Previously run at 105–115° for 8 hours by K. Alder, H. F. Rickert and E. Windemuth, *Ber.*, **71**, 2451 (1938).

(18) M. C. Kloetzel in R. Adams, "Organic Reactions," Vol. IV, John Wiley and Sons, Inc., New York, N. Y., 1948, pp. 10–12.

(19) J. W. Baker and D. M. Easty, *J. Chem. Soc.*, 1193 (1952).

Table I

Radioactivity Analyses of Degradation Products of *exo*-Norbornyl Derivatives from Solvolyses of Norbornyl-2,3-C_2^{14} *p*-Bromobenzenesulfonates

Exp.	Reactant	Config.	Solvent	Temp., °C.	Acid VI[a] Meas. act.[c]	Acid VI[a] Cor. act.[d]	Diamine VII[b] Meas. act.[c]	Diamine VII[b] Cor. act.[d]	BaCO₃ VIII Meas. act.[c]	BaCO₃ VIII Cor. act.[d]	Re-arr., %
A	Norborneol mixture from *endo–exo*[e] Diels–Alder synthesis (blank)	....	....	..	362	876	0.5	1	1226	847	0.1
B	Norborneol mixture from *exo–endo*[f] stereochemical equilibration (blank)	....	....	..	489	1181	4.4	7	1615	1115	0.6
C	Sulfonate ester[g]	*exo*[h]	75% acetone–25% water	45	586	1417	444	767	815	563	54.1
					470	1138	361	623	759	525	54.8
D	Sulfonate ester[g]	*endo*	75% acetone–25% water	Reflux	650	1571	397	684	1160	800	43.6
					593	1433	376	650	1007	696	45.3
E	Sulfonate ester[g]	*exo*[h]	HOAc	45	493	1190	421	727	664	458	61.1
					496	1199	416	718	671	464	60.0
F	Sulfonate ester[g]	*endo*	HOAc	Reflux	663	1603	522	900	924	638	56.3
					510	1232	398	688	744	514	55.8
G	Sulfonate ester from norborneol stereochemical equilibration product[g]	*exo–endo*[f]	HCOOH	45	504	1216	412	712	736	508	58.5
					425	1023	336	580	596	405	56.5
H	Sulfonate ester from norborneol equilibration product[g]	*exo–endo*[f]	HCOOH	Reflux	498	1203	484	835	532	365	69.4
					498	1203	485	838	543	375	69.7
I	Sulfonate ester[g]	*endo*	HCOOH	Reflux	552	1333	503	870	622	457	65.2
					493	1190	455	786	495	342	66.0
J	Sulfonate ester from norborneol mixture obtained from Diels–Alder Synthesis	*endo–exo*[e]	HOAc	Reflux	622	1505	488	840	892	616	55.8
K	Sulfonate ester from product J	*exo*	HOAc	Reflux	658	1590	582	1000	798	550	63.0
L	Sulfonate ester from product K	*exo*	HOAc	Reflux	312	753	293	505	362	242	67.1
M	Sulfonate ester from product H	*exo*	HOAc	Reflux	223	539	209	361	221	153	67.0
N	Norbornyl formate (30.8% rearranged)	*exo*	HCOOH[i]	45[j]	629	1520	242	418	1465	1011	27.5 (0.0)[k]
O	Norbornyl formate (30.8% rearranged)	*exo*	HCOOH[i]	Reflux[l]	669	1617	402	693	1319	910	42.8 (17)[k]
P	Norbornyl acetate from norborneol equilibration	*exo–endo*[f]	HOAc[m]	Reflux[n]	662	1600	24	42	2168	1500	2.6

[a] *cis*-Cyclopentane-1,3-dicarboxylic acid. [b] *cis*-Cyclopentane-1,3-diamine as the stannous chloride derivative. [c] Measured C^{14}-activities in counts/min., determined using a windowless methane-filled counter ("Nucleometer"), of "infinitely thick" barium carbonate samples with a cross-sectional area of 2.90 cm.² prepared as described by J. D. Roberts, W. Bennett, E. W. Holroyd and C. H. Fugitt, *Anal. Chem.*, **20**, 904 (1948). The activities are corrected for background and have standard deviations of less than 3% or ±5 counts/min., whichever is larger. [d] C^{14}-activities in dis./min./mg. of barium carbonate corrected for self-absorption and dilution by non-labeled carbon atoms as described by J. D. Roberts, R. E. McMahon and J. S. Hine, This Journal, **72**, 4237 (1950). [e] Approximately 81% *endo* and 19% *exo*. [f] Approximately 70% *exo* and 30% *endo*. [g] C^{14}-Activities given in duplicate represent either parallel solvolyses or separate combustions on the products of a single solvolysis reaction. [h] Selective solvolysis of *exo* isomer in a mixture of ~70% *exo*- and ~30% *endo*-norbornyl-2,3-C_2^{14} *p*-bromobenzenesulfonates. [i] Solution contained 0.46 *M* sodium *p*-toluenesulfonate and 0.46 *M* sodium formate. [j] The reaction time was 0.33 hr. [k] Corrected for rearrangement in starting material. [l] The reaction time was 20 hr. [m] Solution contained 0.37 *M* potassium *p*-toluenesulfonate and 0.41 *M* potassium acetate. [n] The reaction time was 20 hr.

The degradation scheme for location of the C^{14} in the *exo*-norborneol samples follows.

The radioactivity of VI represents that of the norborneol, while VII contains the C^{14} which migrated from its original location at the 2,3-positions. Consequently, the figures (activity of VII/activity of VI) × 100 are designated as "% rearrangement."

(20) A. A. Benson and J. A. Bassham, This Journal, **70**, 3939 (1948).

The carbon dioxide VIII, isolated as barium carbonate, provides a check on the % rearrangement but was not used in the calculations since values for C^{14}-activities of barium carbonate samples from the Schmidt reaction by our procedures are always 3–5% low. The remainder of the degradation scheme was carried through for several selected cases to provide a more exact picture of the C^{14}-distribution. The difference in activity between VII and IX gave the activity of the 7-position. X represents the 5,6-positions of the starting material and the carbon dioxide (XI) activity is derived from that of the 1,4-carbons.

Experimental Results

Data for the % rearrangement in the solvolyses of *exo*- and *endo*-norbornyl *p*-bromobenzenesulfonates in 75% acetone–25% water, glacial acetic acid and anhydrous formic acid are presented in Table I. Corresponding figures for the reactions of *exo*- and *endo*-norbornylamines with nitrous acid in water and acetic acid are given in Table II. The results of the complete degradations are shown in Table III.

TABLE II

RADIOACTIVITY ANALYSES OF *exo*-NORBORNEOL FROM RE-
ACTIONS OF *exo*- AND *endo*-NORBORNYL-3-C^{14}-AMINES WITH
NITROUS ACID

Config. of amine	Solvent	Temp., °C.	C^{14}-Activities^a			
			Acid VI^b	Diamine VII^c	BaCO$_3$ VIII	Rearr., %
endo^d	....	..	0.1905	0.000	0.1714	0.0
endo	HBF$_4$–H$_2$O	25	.3706	.1711	.1716	46.2
endo	HOAc	25	.0432	.0180	.0232	41.6
		25	.1470	.0659	.0795	44.9
endo	HOAc	90–100	.0505	.0222	.0263	43.9
exo	HBF$_4$–H$_2$O	25	.0648	.0330	.0281	50.9
exo	HOAc	25	.0366	.0176	.0178	48.0
exo–*endo*^{e}	HBF$_4$–H$_2$O	25	.4039	.2105	.1804	52.1

^{a} Activities in microcuries/millimole (μc./mmole) determined by the vibrating reed electrometer method as described by O. K. Neville, THIS JOURNAL, **70**, 3499 (1948).
^{b} *cis*-Cyclopentane-1,3-dicarboxylic acid. ^{c} *cis*-Cyclo-
pentane-1,3-diamine as the dibenzoyl derivative. ^{d} Blank
degradation on amine. ^{e} Approximately 70–80% *exo*-
amine.

extents of rearrangement corresponded to those
which would obtain at equilibrium under the solvolysis conditions, several repetitive reactions were
run. Acetolysis of a predominantly *endo*-nor-
bornyl *p*-bromobenzenesulfonate yielded an acetate
which was 56% rearranged. Conversion of the
acetate (*exo*) to the sulfonate ester and further solvolysis gave a material which was 63% rearranged.
A further repetition yielded 67% rearranged acetate. An attempt to further rearrange an *exo*-
norbornyl formate, made by solvolysis in refluxing
formic acid which showed 69% rearrangement,
through conversion to the *p*-bromobenzenesul-
fonate and solvolysis in acetic acid resulted in no
significant change. It appears that the *equilibrium*
extent of rearrangement under these conditions is
around 67–70%.

Discussion

In the absence of evidence to the contrary, it will

TABLE III

RADIOACTIVITY ANALYSES OF DEGRADATION PRODUCTS

Reaction		Acid VI^a	Diamine VII^b	BaCO$_3$ VIII	Acid IX^c	Diamine X^d	BaCO$_3$ XI
exo-Norbornyl *p*-bromobenzene-	Meas. act.^{e}	496	416, 244^g	671	197, 136^g	109	160
sulfonate in HOAc at 45°	Cor. act.^{f}	1199	718, 422^g		271, 188^g	75	111
	% of total	(100)	60	39	38	15	23
Sulfonate ester from norborneol mix-	Meas. act.^{e}	2376	2284	2613	2083	2334	1742
ture^h obtained from Diels–Alder	Cor. act.^{f}	5740	3940	1805	2880	1610	1202
synthesis in formic acid at reflux	% total act.	(100)	68.7	31.5	50.2	28.1	21.0
exo–*endo*-Amine mixture^i with HO-	Meas. act.^{i}	0.4039	0.2105^k	0.1804	0.02377^l	....	....
NO in HBF$_4$–H$_2$O	% of total act.	(100)	52.1	44.7	5.9	....	....

^{a} *cis*-Cyclopentane-1,3-dicarboxylic acid. ^{b} *cis*-Cyclopentane-1,3-diamine as stannous chloride derivative. ^{c} Succinic
acid. ^{d} Ethylenediamine as dihydrobromide. ^{e} See footnote (*c*) of Table I. ^{f} See footnote (*d*) of Table I. ^{g} Lower
activity figures are for the material which was carried through the complete degradation sequence. ^{h} Approximately 81%
endo and 19% *exo*. ^{i} Approximately 70–80% *exo*-amine. ^{j} See footnote (*a*) of Table II. ^{k} As dibenzoyl derivative. ^{l} As
di-*p*-bromophenacyl succinate.

A consistent feature of the rearrangement pattern is a 5–10% difference in % rearrangement between the *endo* and *exo* series. It is probable that
the difference is due to some direct displacement of
the leaving group by solvent which would lead to
unrearranged product with the *exo*-configuration.
This conclusion is strongly supported by the observation of Winstein and Trifan[5] that the acetolysis
of *endo*-norbornyl *p*-bromobenzenesulfonate yields
7–8% of optically active *exo*-norbornyl acetate
while the *exo*-sulfonate ester gives only racemic
exo-acetate.

The substantially greater rearrangement on solvolysis of norbornyl *p*-bromobenzenesulfonate in
refluxing formic acid as compared with formic acid
at 45° is clearly due to further rearrangement of
the first-formed *exo*-norbornyl formate at the
higher temperature. A blank run with 31% rearranged *exo*-norbornyl formate in refluxing formic
acid for 20 hours yielded 43% rearranged ester.
No corresponding rearrangement was detected at
45°, nor was labeled *exo*-norbornyl acetate altered
when heated to reflux with acetic acid. Winstein
and Trifan[5] have noted that optically active *exo*-
norbornyl acetate is not racemized in similar conditions.

In order to determine how closely the observed

be assumed that the only mechanistic difference
between the solvolyses of *exo*- and *endo*-norbornyl
p-bromobenzenesulfonates is the previously reported[5] direct replacement reaction which takes
place with the *endo* isomer, and, consequently, that
the part of the reaction which leads to rearrangement is independent of the configuration of the
starting materials. It should be clear that the
observed extents of rearrangement, along with the
substantial C^{14}-activity in the 5- and 6-positions of
the solvolysis product, cannot be accounted for
on the assumption that the only carbonium ion intermediate is the norbornonium cation III. With

III, the probability of reaction at the 1- and 2-
positions is equal (neglecting the isotope effect)
and thus a maximum of 50% rearrangement would

be predicted, with no possibility of isotope-position rearrangement to the 5- and 6-positions. Indeed, no combination of the customary 1,2-alkyl or 1,2-hydrogen shifts can lead to 5,6-labeled norbornyl derivatives if the unstable 1-norbornyl cation is excluded as an intermediate. The only reasonable mode of formation of 5,6-labeled products is by way of 2,6-hydrogen migrations and the present work offers convincing evidence that "1,3-type" hydrogen migrations will proceed in favorable circumstances.[21] Hydrogen migration might take place *via* a non-classical hydrogen-bridge cation

such as XII which could account for the formation of a product with C^{14} at the 5- and 6-positions, but *direct* formation of this intermediate, alone or in competition with III, could not lead to more than 50% rearrangement. Although the extent of rearrangement and formation of products with C^{14} at the 5- and 6-positions can be rationalized by some contribution of a concerted attack at the 6-position with concomitant hydride shift as shown in the following equation, such eventuality is ruled out by the finding of Winstein and Trifan[5] that the product is completely racemized.

Any intermediate or intermediates which would tend to lead to a statistical distribution of the C^{14} over the entire norbornyl carbon skeleton may be excluded by the following argument. If the C^{14} were distributed evenly over the norbornyl skeleton, 71.5% rearrangement would be observed. Although this figure is equal within experimental error to the observed equilibrium distribution (see above) there is strong circumstantial evidence that no C^{14} is present at the 4-position. Total degradation (see Table III) reveals that, under near-equilibrium conditions, the activity of the 7-position is within experimental error equal to the sum of the activities of the 1- and 4-positions. If *all* the carbon atoms were becoming "scrambled" in the rearrangement process, the activity at the 7-position would be just one-half the sum of the activities at the 1- and 4-positions. The only reasonable interpretation of the near-equilibrium C^{14}-distribution is that an intermediate or intermediates are involved which tend to spread the C^{14} initially at position 2 over positions 1, 2 and 6 and the activity

at position 3 over positions 3, 5 and 7.[22] In this event, the activity at C-7 would be equal to the sum of the activities of C-1 and C-4 as observed. The finding that rearrangement is not complete in a given solvolysis reaction militates against the postulation of a single cationic intermediate, and supports the suggestion of two or more intermediates being formed either simultaneously or consecutively.

All of the experimental results which have been so far obtained can be accommodated if it is assumed that important roles in the rearrangement processes are played by both intermediates III and the non-classical "nortricyclonium" ion XIII (or its equivalent). XIII has a 3-fold symmetry axis and, acting

alone, it would be expected to react with solvent at the 1-, 2- and 6-positions with equal probability thus leading to 66.7% rearrangement. The C^{14} distributions actually observed for most of the "single-pass" reactions are intermediate for what would be expected from III or XIII. For example, the C^{14}-distribution in the carbon skeleton of the acetolysis product of *exo*-norbornyl *p*-bromobenzenesulfonate (Ib) can be calculated within experimental error if it is assumed that 45% of the reaction proceeds *via* XIII and 55% by III (see Fig. 1).

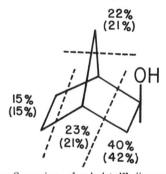

Fig. 1.—Comparison of calculated[22] (in parentheses) and found C^{14}-distributions in solvolysis of *exo*-norbornyl-2,3-C^{14} *p*-bromobenzenesulfonate in acetic acid assuming 45% of the reaction proceeds *via* XIII and 55% *via* III.

The fact that the percentages of the rearrangement observed in the solvolyses in aqueous acetone are less than those in acetic acid suggests that III is the initial intermediate[1,5] and that XIII is formed

(22) The observed near-equilibrium distribution rules out any 2,3-hydrogen shift which would be associated with such an intermediate as

shown [M. J. S. Dewar, *Ann. Reports* (*Chem. Soc.*), 121 (1951)], since cations of this type in combination with III and XIII would lead to "scrambling" of all of the atoms.

(21) See also W. A. Mosher and J. C. Cox, Jr., THIS JOURNAL, **72**, 3701 (1950); W. v. E. Doering and A. P. Wolf, Abstracts of the XII International Congress of Pure and Applied Chemistry, 1950, p. 437.

from it in a subsequent step. The aqueous solvent is more nucleophilic than acetic acid and III would then have a shorter lifetime and a smaller opportunity to rearrange to XIII. The rearrangement data (Table I) indicate that XIII is involved to the extent of 27% in the solvolysis of Ib in aqueous acetone.

The "nortricyclonium" ion (XIII) is interesting as the equivalent of the historically important but frequently discredited cyclopropane mechanism for Wagner–Meerwein rearrangements.[23] A possible formulation of XIII which is analogous to Walsh's[24] model of the cyclopropane ring and recent molecular orbital models for boron hydrides[25] is shown in Fig. 2. Here, the proton may be considered to be embedded in a molecular orbital containing two electrons and formed by the overlap of three sp^2 orbitals protruding from 1-, 2- and 6-positions.

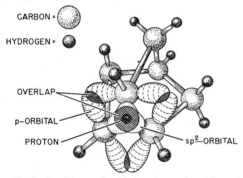

CARBON =

HYDROGEN =

OVERLAP

p-ORBITAL

PROTON sp^2-ORBITAL

Fig. 2.—Possible atomic orbital representation of "nortricyclonium" ion (XIII) formulated with the aid of Prof. M. J. S. Dewar.

Winstein[5,26] has suggested an alternative representation of the hydride shifts here associated with XIII, which involves equilibration of three ions of type III (IIIa–IIIc). In this formulation, the interconversions are written as proceeding by way of

IIIa   IIIb   IIIc

hydride shifts from the 6- to 2- to 1-positions through intermediates like XII. The consequences of this hypothesis are very much the same as those expected for XIII, and we have been unable to arrive at any experimental method of distinguishing between these formulations. The essential point of difference is a rather subtle one, namely, whether XIII is a true intermediate, that is, occupies a "valley" in the potential energy diagram for the reaction, or is merely a transition state in the

interconversion of IIIa–IIIb–IIIc. Certainly, XIII is the more economical representation.

There are some interesting differences between the rearrangements associated with the solvolyses of the sulfonate esters and the reactions of the amines with nitrous acid. In the deamination processes, the percentage of rearrangement is comparatively insensitive to differences in configuration or reaction medium. Thus, the spread in the extent of rearrangement between the *exo* and *endo* isomers is comparatively slight, and acetic acid as a solvent actually leads to slightly less rearrangement than is observed in aqueous fluoboric acid. Furthermore, ion XIII appears to be less important in the amine–nitrous acid reactions than in the solvolysis processes. Whereas XIII accounts for nearly half of the reaction path in acetolysis of the *exo*-norbornyl sulfonate, it is probably not involved to an extent of greater than 20% in the amine–nitrous acid reaction.[27]

There are several possible explanations of the differences between the solvolysis and amine–nitrous acid reactions.[28] The 5–12% smaller extent of rearrangement in the deamination reaction may be partially due to (1) an unlikely non-rearranging formation of norcamphor, (2) energy differences between the carbonium ions obtained in deamination and solvolysis processes or, (3) "internal return" isomerization. The insensitivity of the rearrangements to ionizing power of the solvent in the amine–nitrous acid reactions observed in this and other[29] work as well as the lack of selectivity in migration-aptitude studies[30] with β,β-diarylethylamines suggest that carbonium ions obtained by decomposition of alkyldiazonium ions are of high energy relative to those obtained in solvolysis. This is to be expected from the high energy of formation of nitrogen from the diazonium ions and should result with less need for assistance from solvent and neighboring groups in cation formation. It seems possible that part of the greater proportion of direct replacement found in the amine–nitrous acid reaction may arise from direct formation of a small amount of "classical" norbornyl cation which could react with solvent before rearranging to the more stable isomers III and XIII.[31] An important

(23) For some examples of the utility of the cyclopropane formulation in accounting for the products of Wagner–Meerwein rearrangements with terpenes see L. Ruzicka, *Helv. Chim. Acta*, **1**, 110 (1918). See also, J. L. Simonsen and L. N. Owen, "The Terpenes," Vol. II, 2nd Ed., Cambridge University Press, London, 1949, pp. 156–165.

(24) A. D. Walsh, *Trans. Faraday Soc.*, **45**, 179 (1949).

(25) H. C. Longuet-Higgins, *J. chim. phys.*, **46**, 268 (1949).

(26) See also, P. D. Bartlett in H. Gilman, "Organic Chemistry," Vol. III, John Wiley and Sons, Inc., New York, N. Y., 1953, pp. 68–69.

(27) The percentage of participation of XIII (or its equivalent) may be calculated from the data in Table III and the following considerations. If XIII were the only intermediate, the C^{14}-activity at the 5-position (represented by diamine X) would be 33.3% of the activity of the norborneol. Therefore the fraction of the reaction which proceeds *via* XIII (or its equivalent) is three times the percentage activity of X. Degradation of the *exo*-norborneol from the reaction of the norbornyl-3-C^{14}-amine with nitrous acid was carried only to succinic acid IX, since the product should be labeled with C^{14} only at the 2-, 5- and 7-positions. Therefore, the carboxyl groups of IX should contain no C^{14}-activity and the total activity of IX would be equal to that of the diamine X. The participation of intermediate XIII is easily calculated from the activity of IX to be about 18%.

(28) A minor source of discrepancy would be an isotope effect in reactions at the 2-position of the doubly labeled norbornyl derivatives used in the solvolysis processes. The labeled position (3) of the amines is away from the immediate reaction site so that practically no isotope effect would be expected. It seems unlikely that isotope effects should introduce deviations much greater than our experimental error.

(29) J. D. Roberts and C. M. Regan, THIS JOURNAL, **75**, 2069 (1953).

(30) L. S. Ciereszko and J. G. Burr, Jr., *ibid.*, **74**, 5431 (1952).

(31) This possibility could be tested experimentally since any amount of the reaction proceeding by such a path would lead to optically active norborneol if one started with optically active *exo*-norbornylamine.

difference between the solvolyses and amine–nitrous acid reactions is the "internal return" process demonstrated by Winstein and Trifan[5] in the solvolysis of *exo*-norbornyl *p*-bromobenzenesulfonate. The observation that the optically active sulfonate ester is racemized more rapidly than it is solvolyzed led to the conclusion that the reaction proceeded through an internally compensated ion-pair consisting of the cation III and *p*-bromobenzenesulfonate anion. This ion-pair could react with solvent to give the solvated cation III or could collapse to give racemized sulfonate ester. Any given molecule of sulfonate ester could thus arrive at the ion-pair stage several times before reacting irreversibly with solvent to give cation III and subsequently the solvolysis product. Clearly, we are not dealing with a strictly irreversible carbonium ion process in the solvolysis reactions and the possibility of some rearrangement at the ion-pair stage must be considered. Presumably, the ion-pair is more stable and longer-lived than a simple carbonium ion and this fact provides some chance for rearrangement, perhaps by conversion to an isomeric ion-pair corresponding to structure XIII. On the other hand, the decomposition of the norbornyldiazonium ion is likely to be a completely irreversible process. The "internal return" phenomenon should be absent and less rearrangement expected.

Acknowledgment.—We are greatly indebted to Professor S. Winstein of the University of California at Los Angeles for discussions and much valuable information regarding the solvolysis of norbornyl *p*-bromobenzenesulfonates well in advance of publication. Several discussions with Professor M. J. S. Dewar have been very helpful.

Experimental

Vinyl-1,2-C_2^{14} Acetate.—Acetylene-C_2^{14} was generated by addition of water under reduced pressure to barium carbide[32] containing 1 mc. of C^{14} in a 100-ml. round-bottomed reaction flask fitted with a dropping funnel and connected in series with a Dry Ice trap and two liquid nitrogen traps. The reaction mixture was boiled gently for 10 minutes, frozen in Dry Ice and the system evacuated to 1.0 mm.
Mercuric oxide (0.30 g.) was heated with 4.0 ml. of glacial acetic acid and 1.0 ml. of acetic anhydride in a 1-l. flask until all of the solid dissolved. Five milliliters of a 5% solution of 1:1 phosphorus pentoxide–sirupy phosphoric acid in glacial acetic acid was added whereby mercuric phosphate precipitated. The mixture was frozen in a Dry Ice bath, the flask was evacuated to 0.05 mm. and attached to the vacuum system. The acetylene was allowed to vaporize into the flask and the system brought to atmospheric pressure by flushing with inactive acetylene.
The reaction flask was shaken overnight, during which time the pressure fell to 60 mm. The product was removed with a pipet, mixed with 1.0 g. of anhydrous potassium acetate and distilled through a semi-micro column. The yield of vinyl-1,2-C_2^{14} acetate, b.p. 72–74°, was 2.73 g. (71% based on 1 l. of acetylene). The distillation residue was mixed with about 5 g. of inactive vinyl acetate and distilled to scavenge out any remaining labeled product. A further 10 ml. of the mercuric phosphate–acetic acid mixture was added to the reaction flask which was then cooled with liquid nitrogen, evacuated, warmed to room temperature, and the system filled with inactive acetylene at atmospheric pressure. The flask was again shaken overnight and the product isolated as before. The reaction flask was washed with inactive vinyl acetate which was then used to scavenge the distillation residue. The yield of radioactive vinyl ace-

(32) Obtained from Tracerlab, Inc., on allocation from the United States Atomic Energy Commission.

tate was not determined, but was at least 40% based on barium carbide-C^{14}.

Dehydronorbornyl-2,3-C_2^{14} acetate was prepared by heating 14 g. of cyclopentadiene and 21 g. of labeled vinyl acetate in a sealed tube at 200° for 10 hours. There was obtained 10.5 g. of unreacted vinyl acetate and 13.5 g. (73%, based on unrecovered vinyl acetate) of dehydronorbornyl-2,3-C_2^{14} acetate, b.p. 82–83° (17 mm.), $n^{25}D$ 1.4667. Several subsequent reactions were carried out using the recovered labeled vinyl acetate. Radioactivity assays of the adducts indicated an over-all C^{14}-yield of 25% based on barium carbide.

Norbornyl-2,3-C_2^{14} acetate was obtained in 97% yield by low-pressure hydrogenation of dehydronorbornyl-2,3-C_2^{14} acetate over platinum oxide at room temperature in ethyl acetate. The product had b.p. 69° (6 mm.), $n^{25}D$ 1.4578.

Norborneol-2,3-C_2^{14} was produced by cleavage of norbornyl-2,3-C_2^{14} acetate with lithium aluminum hydride in ether in 90% yield.

Partial Isomerization of *endo*- to *exo*-Norborneol.—A mixture of 15 g. of norborneol-2,3-C_2^{14}, 0.30 g. of fluorenone and 0.15 g. of sodium in 35 ml. of toluene was heated under reflux for 48 hours. Most of the toluene was removed under reduced pressure and the residue washed into a sublimation tube with methanol. Removal of the methanol followed by sublimation yielded 13.2 g. (88%) of isomerization product which was found to contain 74% of the *exo* isomer by analysis of the solvolysis rate curve of its *p*-bromobenzenesulfonate in 75% acetone–25% water.

Norbornyl-2,3-C_2^{14} *p*-bromobenzenesulfonates were prepared by the general method of Tipson.[13] The reaction between the alcohols and *p*-bromobenzenesulfonyl chloride was allowed to proceed for two days at 0°. The extractions and washings of the product were carried out at 0° to minimize hydrolysis. Recrystallization from ether–pentane mixtures gave 80–85% yields of the mixed *exo*–*endo*-norbornyl *p*-bromobenzenesulfonates. The product from pure *exo*-norborneol had m.p. 60° (lit.[5] 55.7–57.0°) while that from pure *endo*-norborneol had m.p. 62–63° (lit.[5] 60.0–61.7°).

Selective Solvolysis of the Mixed Sulfonates in 75% Acetone.—A solution (about 7% by weight) of *endo*- and *exo*-sulfonate ester mixture in 75% acetone–25% water (by volume) was heated at 45° for one-half hour. Under these conditions the *exo* isomer was essentially completely solvolyzed while the *endo* isomer was practically unreacted (the first-order solvolysis rate constants at 45 ± 0.1° are 7.8 × 10^{-6} sec.$^{-1}$ and 2.41 × 10^{-3} sec.$^{-1}$ for the *endo*- and *exo*-norbornyl *p*-bromobenzenesulfonates, respectively). Titration of the liberated *p*-bromobenzenesulfonic acid with sodium hydroxide gave the *exo* content of the mixture. The unreacted *endo*-sulfonate ester was recovered by neutralization of the reaction mixture with sodium hydroxide solution and extraction with alcohol-free ether. The extract was dried over magnesium sulfate, concentrated, and pentane added to precipitate the *endo*-sulfonate ester. The filtrate was evaporated to dryness and the residue sublimed to yield *exo*-norborneol, m.p. 127–128°, in 60–65% yields based on reacted *exo*-sulfonate. The recovery of the unreacted *endo*-sulfonate was nearly quantitative.

Solvolysis of *endo*-Norbornyl-2,3-C_2^{14} *p*-Bromobenzenesulfonate in 75% Acetone–25% Water.—A solution of 4.97 g. of *endo*-norbornyl-2,3-C_2^{14} *p*-bromobenzenesulfonate in 75 ml. of 75% acetone–25% water (by volume) was refluxed for 48 hours. The products were isolated as described above. Sublimation of the residue from the ether extraction yielded 0.91 g. (54%) of *exo*-norborneol, m.p. 127–128°, phenylurethan, m.p. 145–146°.

Solvolysis of *exo*-Norbornyl-2,3-C_2^{14} *p*-Bromobenzenesulfonate in Acetic Acid.—A solution of 7.9 g. of the mixed norbornyl-2,3-C_2^{14} *p*-bromobenzenesulfonates from the isomerization reaction described above, 2.5 g. of potassium acetate (10% excess) and 50 ml. of glacial acetic acid was heated at 45° for 20 minutes. Most of the acetic acid was removed under reduced pressure at 45°. The residue was diluted with ice-water, basified with cold sodium hydroxide solution, and extracted with alcohol-free ether. The extract was dried and concentrated to a few ml. Addition of pentane caused the unreacted *endo*-sulfonate ester (2.1 g., 27%) to crystallize. Fractional distillation of the mother liquors yielded 1.6 g. (44%) of *exo*-norbornyl acetate, b.p. 60–61° (5 mm.).

Solvolysis of *endo*-Norbornyl-2,3-C_2^{14} *p*-Bromobenzenesulfonate in Acetic Acid.—The procedure for solvolysis of the *exo*-sulfonate ester was followed except that the reaction mixture was heated under reflux for 20 hours. From 4.97 g. of *endo*-norbornyl-2,3-C$_2^{14}$ *p*-bromobenzenesulfonate was obtained 1.53 g. (66%) of *exo*-norbornyl acetate.

Solvolysis of Norbornyl-2,3-C$_2^{14}$ *p*-Bromobenzenesulfonates in Formic Acid.—A solution of 6.8 g. of the mixed norbornyl-2,3-C$_2^{14}$ *p*-bromobenzenesulfonates from the isomerization reaction described above and 1.4 g. of sodium formate in 40 ml. of anhydrous formic acid (98–100% reagent grade distilled from Drierite) was heated at 45° for 20 minutes. The resulting solution was worked up as described for the acetic acid solvolyses. The yield of *exo*-norbornyl formate, b.p. 79–80° (25 mm.), was 1.9 g. (66%). No unreacted *endo*-sulfonate ester could be recovered.

In other experiments, using mixed or pure *endo*-sulfonate esters, the reaction mixtures were refluxed for 20 hours. *exo*-Norbornyl formate was obtained in 70–75% yields.

2-Nitroethanol-1-C^{14}.—The procedure for the preparation of this compound was a modification of that described by Hayes, *et al.*,[15] and employed the apparatus shown in Fig. 3. The boiler was charged with 100 g. of redistilled nitromethane, 40 g. of dioxane and 1.5 ml. of 10% citric acid solution. The system was then evacuated to 175 mm., the boiler heated with an oil-bath at 120–130° and the stirrer started. A solution of 1.27 mc. of formaldehyde-C^{14} (0.133 mmole in about 4.5 ml. of water)[33] was mixed with 12 g. of ordinary 36% formaldehyde, 16 g. of dioxane and 0.4 ml. of 10% sodium hydroxide solution; the last 10 ml. of the diluent mixture was used to wash the solution into the dropping funnel. The basic formaldehyde solution was added dropwise over a two-hour period to the refluxing nitromethane in the reaction tube. Finally, a mixture of 4 g. of 36% formaldehyde solution, 4 g. of dioxane and 0.1 ml. of 10% sodium hydroxide solution was added over 20 minutes; refluxing was then continued for an additional 15 minutes. The yellow solution in the boiler was filtered and the solvent removed under reduced pressure. The residue was washed into a 100-ml. distillation flask with 6.0 g. of inactive nitroethanol in two portions. The material was then distilled under reduced pressure taking, as 2-nitroethanol, the fraction of b.p. 59–63° (1.0 mm.). The residue was scavenged three times with a total of 13.0 g. of inactive 2-nitroethanol. The total yield of 2-nitroethanol-1-C^{14} was 29.0 g. (58% after making allowance for the material used as carrier). Radioactivity assay indicated a C^{14}-yield of 45% based on the reported activity of the formaldehyde-C^{14}.

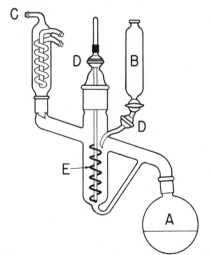

Fig. 3.—Apparatus for formaldehyde-C^{14}–nitromethane reaction: A, nitromethane boiler; B, formaldehyde-C^{14} solution; C, vacuum connection; D, ball joints; E, heavy wire spiral stirrer.

(33) Obtained on allocation from the Los Alamos Scientific Laboratories of the United States Atomic Energy Commission.

Nitroethylene-2-C^{14} was prepared from 2-nitroethanol-1-C^{14} substantially as previously described.[16] In order to minimize polymerization of the nitroethylene by water formed in the dehydration reaction, the product was condensed in an ice-cooled receiver containing a few grams of anhydrous calcium chloride. In a typical experiment, the dehydration product from 40 g. of 2-nitroethanol-1-C^{14} and 90 g. of phthalic anhydride was filtered from the calcium chloride and a small amount of polymer, the residue washed several times with dry ether and the combined filtrates dried over fresh calcium chloride. The resulting ethereal solution of nitroethylene-2-C^{14} was used directly in the next synthetic step.

endo-5-Nitronorbornene-6-C^{14}.—The ethereal solution (about 50 ml.) of nitroethylene-2-C^{14} from the above preparation was added with stirring over 1.5 hours to a solution of 30 g. of freshly distilled, dried cyclopentadiene dissolved in 75 ml. of dry ether. The reaction mixture warmed to the refluxing temperature during the addition and was then allowed to stand overnight. After removal of the ether and excess cyclopentadiene, distillation of the residue through a short vacuum-jacketed Vigreux column afforded 37.0 g. (61% based on 2-nitroethanol) of almost colorless *endo*-5-nitronorbornene-6-C^{14}; b.p. 74–77° (4.3 mm.). The product was semi-solid at room temperature.

endo-2-Nitronorbornane-3-C^{14}.—A mixture of 26.5 g. of *endo*-5-nitronorbornene-6-C^{14}, 150 ml. of glacial acetic acid and 0.2 g. of platinum oxide was shaken with hydrogen at two atmospheres. The uptake of hydrogen was rapid and several pauses for cooling of the reaction mixture were necessary. Hydrogen absorption practically ceased after the quantity calculated for one double bond was taken up. The catalyst was removed by filtration and most of the acetic acid distilled under reduced pressure. The residue was taken up in 50 ml. of ether and washed with 25 ml. of water. It was then dried over magnesium sulfate, the ether removed, and the residue sublimed. The yield of colorless, solid *endo*-2-nitronorbornane-3-C^{14} was 21.7 g. (81%). The m.p. of the product was not very well-defined even after repeated sublimation. Most of the material melted from 64–67°.

Anal. Calcd. for C$_7$H$_{11}$NO$_2$: C, 59.55; H, 7.86. Found: C, 59.84; H, 8.13.

Isomerization of *endo*-2-Nitronorbornane-3-C^{14}.—A mixture of 32 g. of *endo*-2-nitronorbornane-3-C^{14} and 1.6 g. of triethylamine was heated on a steam-cone overnight. The material was taken up in 100 ml. of pentane and shaken with 50 ml. of 20% acetic acid containing 10 g. of urea.[34] The pentane solution was dried over Drierite, the pentane removed and the residue distilled under reduced pressure. The yield of a colorless liquid mixture of *exo*- and *endo*-2-nitronorbornane-3-C^{14} was 31.0 g. (97%); b.p.78° (4 mm.).

endo-Norbornylamine-3-C^{14}.—To a mixture of 35 ml. of water, 35 ml. of dioxane and 10 ml. of concentrated hydrochloric acid was added 30 g. of 20-mesh iron filings. When the gas evolution ceased, there was added 21 g. of 2-nitronorbornane-3-C^{14} and the mixture refluxed for two days. Several milliliters of hydrochloric acid was added and the mixture steam distilled until 75 ml. of distillate was collected. The residue in the flask was basified with sodium hydroxide solution and an additional 125 ml. of steam distillate collected. The second distillate was extracted three times with ether and the combined extracts dried over potassium carbonate. Removal of the ether through a short column left a colorless liquid residue which on sublimation yielded 11.5 g. (70%) of a hygroscopic white solid which softened at 43° and melted mostly in the range 53–59°. The acetyl derivative of the product had m.p. 123–126°. After repeated recrystallizations from ligroin (b.p. 90–100°), the m.p. was 125–126° (lit.[6a] m.p. 124°).

exo-Norbornylamine-3-C^{14}.—Reduction of 31 g. of the isomerized 2-nitronorbornane-3-C^{14} described above with iron and hydrochloric acid was performed as in the preceding experiment. The dried ethereal solution of the amine was diluted to 31 ml. with dry ether and added over one-half hour with stirring to 22 g. of acetic anhydride dissolved in 300 ml. of dry ether. The mixture was refluxed for 1 hour, washed with 10% potassium carbonate solution and dried over anhydrous potassium carbonate.

The ethereal solution was concentrated on a steam-bath

(34) Recommended for the regeneration of nitroparaffins from their salts by N. Kornblum and G. E. Graham, THIS JOURNAL, **73**, 4041 (1951).

until solid appeared and then allowed to cool. Recrystallization of the first crop of solid gave 5.4 g. of acetyl derivative, m.p. 140–141°. Further systematic crystallization of the material from the mother liquors from ether and later from heptane–ethyl acetate mixtures yielded a total of 11.4 g. of acetyl derivative having m.p. 140–141° (lit.[6a] m.p. 139°). Repeated recrystallizations of a small sample gave a product of m.p. 141–142.4°.

Regeneration of the amine was effected by heating 11.0 g. of the acetyl derivative with 100 ml. of 10% sulfuric acid under reflux for 24 hours. The reaction mixture was basified with sodium hydroxide solution and extracted with five 40-ml. portions of ether. The extracts were dried over potassium carbonate, and the ether removed through a short column. Distillation of the residue yielded 6.3 g. (79%) of exo-norbornylamine-3-C[14] as a colorless liquid, b.p. 78° (55 mm.), which solidified when stored in a refrigerator.

Diazotization of Norbornylamines in Aqueous Fluoboric Acid.—Essentially the same procedure was used for all of the experiments and only a typical reaction with endo-norbornylamine-3-C[14] will be described. A mixture of 3.4 g. of the amine and 10 ml. of water was neutralized with 2 N fluoboric acid and then an extra equivalent of acid was added. The mixture, which contained some precipitated amine fluoborate, was stirred with a magnetic stirrer and a solution of 2.4 g. (10% excess) of sodium nitrite in 10 ml. of water was added over a period of one hour. The whole was allowed to stand for two days at room temperature and then extracted five times with ether. The combined extracts were dried over magnesium sulfate, the ether removed and the yellow semi-solid residue steam distilled from 20% sodium hydroxide solution. The solid in the receiver was separated by decantation. The residual aqueous phase was saturated with sodium chloride and extracted with ether. The ether extract was combined with the solid and dried over magnesium sulfate. The ether was removed and the residue sublimed. The yield of exo-norborneol, m.p. 117–121° (lit., 127–128°,[6] 127.8–128.5°)[5] was 2.6 g. (77%). The infrared spectrum of the crude norborneol indicated the presence of a few per cent. of norcamphor.

Diazotization of Norbornylamines in Glacial Acetic Acid.—The following procedure is typical. endo-Norbornylamine-3-C[14] (6.0 g.) was dissolved in 40 ml. of glacial acetic acid. The solution was stirred with a magnetic stirrer, and 6.0 g. of solid sodium nitrite added portionwise over one hour. The mixture was then allowed to stand overnight at the end of which time was added a final 1.5 g. of sodium nitrite (making a total of two equivalents). Water (15 ml.) was added and the mixture was then poured into 150 ml. of cold 20% sodium hydroxide solution. The whole was extracted with five 40-ml. portions of pentane and the combined extracts washed with 1 N hydrochloric acid to remove any unreacted amine (generally less than 10%). The pentane solution was dried over Drierite and the pentane removed through a short column. Fractionation of the residue afforded 4.0 g. (50%) of exo-norbornyl acetate, b.p. 77–79° (15 mm.).

An analogous procedure was employed for the reaction at 90–100°. A three-necked flask heated in an oil-bath and fitted with a reflux condenser and a solid addition tube was used. A total of four equivalents of sodium nitrite was added and the yield of exo-norbornyl acetate was 60%.

cis-Cyclopentane-1,3-dicarboxylic Acid.—To a solution of 1.0 g. of norborneol in 5 ml. of pentane were added 4.0 g. of solid potassium permanganate and 40 ml. of cold 20% potassium hydroxide solution. During the reaction, the flask was cooled in an ice-bath and stirred with a magnetic stirrer. After 1–3 hours, sulfur dioxide was bubbled through the reaction mixture to remove the excess permanganate and manganese dioxide. The whole was extracted with eight 25-ml. portions of ether. The combined extracts were dried over magnesium sulfate and concentrated on a steam-cone to about 10 ml. The balance of the solvent was removed under reduced pressure at room temperature. The solid residue (a dark, intractable sirup resulted when the evaporation was not performed carefully) was dissolved in alcohol-free ether and filtered through a layer of charcoal supported on a sintered glass funnel. Addition of pentane to the filtrate caused the cis-cyclopentane-1,3-dicarboxylic acid to crystallize. The product had m.p. 120–121° (lit.[35]

119–120.6°). Occasionally, it was necessary to recrystallize the product once or twice to obtain pure material. The yields generally ranged from 40–70%.

Decarboxylation of cis-Cyclopentane-1,3-dicarboxylic Acid.—In a 100-ml. flask equipped with a magnetic stirrer and a 2-hole stopper carrying a dropping funnel and a gas outlet tube were placed 0.5 g. of cis-cyclopentane-1,3-dicarboxylic acid and a solution of 10 mmoles (50% excess) of hydrazoic acid in 10 ml. of alcohol-free chloroform. The gas outlet was connected to a gas–washing bottle containing saturated barium hydroxide solution. The mixture was stirred and 1.5 ml. of concentrated sulfuric acid added dropwise under slight nitrogen pressure. After all of the acid had been added, nitrogen was passed slowly through dropping funnel to sweep the evolved carbon dioxide into the gas-washing bottle. After the initial reaction subsided, the mixture was heated at 40–45°. The total reaction time was 1–2 hours and in the middle of this period an additional 5 mmoles of hydrazoic acid in 5 ml. of chloroform was added to ensure complete reaction.

The barium carbonate was separated by filtration, washed repeatedly with boiled distilled water, and then digested in boiling distilled water overnight. The precipitate was collected, washed well with boiled distilled water and after a final washing with acetone, dried at 100° at 1 mm. for 2–3 hours. The yields of purified barium carbonate ranged from 70–80%.

The material in the reaction flask was chilled in ice and diluted with 30 ml. of water. The chloroform layer was separated and washed with water. The combined aqueous extracts were basified and distilled into 5 ml. of 2 N hydrochloric acid. When the distillation flask was dry, the residue was cooled and 30 ml. of water added. The distillation was again carried to dryness, water was added and the process repeated. The combined distillates were evaporated to dryness in a stream of air on a steam-cone. cis-Cyclopentane-1,3-diamine dihydrochloride was obtained as a hygroscopic yellow powder in 70–90% yields.

In some of the work the diamine was converted to the stannous chloride complex[36] for radioactivity assay by the following procedure. A solution of 0.35 g. of cis-cyclopentane-1,3-diamine dihydrochloride in 2.0 ml. of water was mixed with 1.1 g. (2 equiv.) of stannous chloride dihydrate in 2.0 ml. of water. The whole was heated on a steam-bath for five minutes and then cooled in ice. Crystallization of the stannous chloride complex was initiated by scratching, and the resulting long needles were collected by suction filtration and air-dried. The yield was 0.88 g., m.p. 145–146°.

Anal. Calcd. for $C_5H_{14}N_2Cl_6Sn_2 \cdot H_2O$: C, 10.52; H, 2.83; N, 4.92. Found: C, 10.26; H, 2.90; N, 4.95.

When these reaction conditions were not used, partially hydrated material of indefinite m.p. (about 170°) often was obtained. The reported melting point of the monohydrate is 172°.[36] The dibenzoyl derivative of the diamine was more readily obtainable in analytically pure form and so was used in the later stages of the work for characterization and radioactivity assay of the diamine. The dibenzoyl derivative was obtained by shaking 0.1 g. of cis-cyclopentane-1,3-diamine dihydrochloride with 0.4 g. of benzoyl chloride and 10 ml. of 10% sodium hydroxide solution until the odor of benzoyl chloride disappeared. The solid was separated by filtration, washed with water and recrystallized from an ethanol–water mixture. The yield of purified dibenzoyl derivative as colorless plates of m.p. 213–215° was 70–90 mg.

Anal. Calcd. for $C_{19}H_{20}O_2N_2$: C, 74.00; H, 6.54. Found: C, 74.11; H, 6.49.

Oxidation of cis-Cyclopentane-1,3-diamine Dihydrochloride.—To a solution of 0.85 g. of cis-cyclopentane-1,3-diamine dihydrochloride in 68 ml. of water was added 6.8 g. of potassium permanganate. The mixture was heated under reflux for 15 minutes and then cooled. The manganese dioxide was collected by filtration and washed thoroughly with water. The filtrates were acidified with hydrochloric acid and decolorized with sulfur dioxide. The resulting solution was extracted continuously with alcohol-free ether for two days. The extract was dried over magnesium sulfate, evaporated to near dryness under reduced pressure at room temperature, and the resulting precipitate of succinic

(35) S. F. Birch, W. J. Oldham and E. A. Johnson, *J. Chem. Soc.*, 818 (1947).

(36) O. Diels, J. H. Blom and W. Koll, *Ann.*, **443**, 242 (1925).

acid collected by filtration. The yield was 0.080 g., m.p. 180–185°. Recrystallization from water afforded 0.045 g. of material with m.p. 188–189°. The melting point of the product was not depressed by admixture with an authentic sample. In some instances, the succinic acid was converted to the corresponding di-*p*-bromophenacyl ester which after recrystallization from dioxane–ethanol had m.p. 213–214° (lit.[37] m.p. 211°).

(37) W. L. Judefind and E. E. Reid, THIS JOURNAL, **42**, 1043 (1920).

Degradation of succinic acid was achieved by the procedure previously described.[20] The ethylenediamine was converted to the dihydrobromide, colorless plates from alcohol, for radioactive assay. Since the product did not melt but decomposed, the purity was verified by analysis.

Anal. Calcd. for $C_2H_{10}N_2Br_2$: C, 10.81; H, 4.50; N, 12.61; Br, 72.07. Found: C, 10.91; H, 4.67; N, 12.90; Br, 72.00.

CAMBRIDGE 39, MASS.

24 | The 1,2,2-Triphenylethyl Cation

The paper by Bonner and Collins (Paper No. 24), Part IV of a substantial series, illustrates a group of critical tests which showed, in the present case, that the acid-induced reversible ionization of 1,2,2-triphenylethyl acetate in acetic acid proceeds by way of ions whose charge is delocalized by the benzyl, and not by the phenonium, or hydrogen-bridged, mechanism. This conclusion follows from the fact that acetic acid containing an equivalent of *p*-toluenesulfonic acid removes labeled acetate in the ester at the same rate as labeled phenyl or labeled chain carbon approaches equilibration between the 1- and 2-positions. Only an intermediate ion which comes to equilibrium during its lifetime with the six possible distributions of its three phenyl groups will yield the observed result. Although this evidence does not specifically exclude the six possible phenonium ions from joining the six classical ions in a rapid equilibration, it does exclude the participation of phenonium ions which have the stereochemical property essential in the original experiments of Cram—a singleness of structure and the ability to react only with inversion at two definite points.[1]

---

[1] It has long been clear from migration aptitudes that the Wagner-Meerwein or pinacol rearrangement of an aryl group is essentially an electrophilic aromatic substitution in which the β carbon is replaced at C-1 of the aryl group by the electron-deficient α carbon. Accordingly, the reaction begins with attack by C-α and passes through a phenonium-ion stage. The discussion in this paper and in other mechanistic studies of carbonium ion systems centers on the relative stabilities and lifetimes of the phenonium and benzylic species, including the question of whether the former in particular cases may be a transition state rather than an intermediate.

From: *J. Am. Chem. Soc.* **77,** 99–103 (1955)

[Contribution from the Chemistry Division of Oak Ridge National Laboratory]

Molecular Rearrangements.   IV.   Triple-labeling Experiments on the Isotope Position Isomerization of 1,2,2-Triphenylethyl Acetate[1]

By William A. Bonner and Clair J. Collins

Received April 26, 1954

1,2,2-Triphenylethyl acetate, separately labeled in the chain, phenyl and acetate portions of the molecule, has been studied kinetically with respect to the rates of radiochemical isomerization and of acetoxyl exchange under the influence of an acid catalyst.   Confirmatory experiments, using combinations of these three differently labeled species, have also been carried out.   It is found that the rates of radiochemical equilibration of the ring-labeled and chain-labeled acetates are equal, and each is identical to the rate of loss of the labeled acetoxyl group.   The data are explainable in terms of open carbonium ion intermediates in which the cation undergoes radiochemical isomerization prior to product formation.   It is shown that, as expected, no internal return accompanies the isomerization.

Introduction

In the previous paper[2] a study was reported of a number of irreversible carbonium ion-type proc-esses with doubly labeled 1,2,2-triphenylethyl de-rivatives.   That is, a comparison was made of the distributions of the radioactive labels when derivatives of 1,2,2-triphenylethanol-1-C[14] and of 1-phenyl-C[14]-2,2-diphenylethanol undergo certain irreversible carbonium ion-type reactions.   These reactions have included tosylate acetolysis, tosylate

(1) This paper is based upon work performed under Contract Number W-7405-eng-26 for the Atomic Energy Commission at Oak Ridge National Laboratory.   Reprint requests should be addressed to C. J. C.

(2) C. J. Collins and W. A. Bonner, This Journal, **77,** 92 (1955).

hydrolysis, carbinol dehydration and elimination of acetic acid from the acetates. The observed radiochemical results could be explained completely and quantitatively in terms of open carbonium ions which undergo radiochemical isomerization to a varying degree depending on their lifetimes (eq. 1). There was no evidence for the existence of bridged ions[3-6] in any of the reactions studied. In

$$Ph-CH-\overset{\oplus}{C}{}^{*}H-Ph^{*} \underset{\underset{Ph}{|}}{\overset{\underset{Ph}{|}}{\rightleftarrows}} Ph-\overset{\oplus}{C}H-C^{*}H-Ph^{*} \rightleftarrows$$

$$\overset{*}{Ph}-CH-\overset{\oplus}{C}{}^{*}HPh \quad (1)$$
$$\underset{Ph}{|}$$

certain reactions, e.g., formic acid catalyzed dehydrations of chain- and ring-labeled[2] 1,2,2-triphenylethanols, the intermediates seemed to be sufficiently long-lived to permit statistical redistribution of the radioactive labels prior to irreversible formation of the final olefinic products. In other reactions, for example, hydrolysis or acetolysis of chain- and ring-labeled 1,2,2-triphenylethyl p-toluenesulfonates, the shorter-lived intermediates were permitted only a partial equilibration before occurrence of the final irreversible step. In such reactions, the chain-labeled compound proceeded faster toward equilibrium than did the ring-labeled compound and the degree of rearrangement observed during reaction in the chain-labeled system could be calculated with considerable precision, knowing the extent of rearrangement occurring during reaction in the phenyl-labeled system. The calculations were based on a simple kinetic relationship involving equilibrating cationic intermediates.

Acetoxyl group removal from 1,2,2-triphenylethyl acetate appears to be a process in which the equilibration of labeled phenyl groups is complete, during the lifetime of the intermediates.[2] Thus when 1-phenyl-C^{14}-2,2-triphenylethyl acetate (II) is heated with formic acid with or without p-toluenesulfonic acid as catalyst, the triphenylethylene obtained is found[2] to have a statistical distribution of the radioactive label

$$\overset{*}{Ph_2}C=CHPh\overset{*}{}$$
$$2/3 \qquad 1/3$$

In addition, both 1,2,2-triphenylethyl-1-C^{14} acetate (I) and 1-phenyl-C^{14}-2,2-triphenylethyl acetate (II), when warmed in acetic acid containing p-toluenesulfonic acid, give 1,2,2-triphenylethyl acetate samples having a statistical distribution of radioactivity.[2] The isomerization of this acetate labeled in various positions seemed to offer promise in the study of internal return in the present system for at least one set of conditions. By a comparison of the rates of radioactivity redistribution both of the chain-labeled and of the ring-labeled acetates with the rate of acetoxyl exchange with environment during this reaction, it was hoped that the presence or absence of internal return could be demonstrated, and that, in addition,

(3) D. J. Cram, This Journal, 71, 3863 (1949).

(4) J. D. Roberts and C. M. Regan, ibid., 75, 2069 (1953).

(5) (a) S. Winstein and D. Trifan, ibid., 74, 1154 (1952); (b) D. J. Cram and F. A. Abd Elhafez, ibid., 75, 3189 (1953).

(6) F. A. Abd Elhafez and D. J. Cram, ibid., 75, 339 (1953).

further information might be obtained regarding the validity of the proposed mechanism.[2] To this end, the triply labeled system of 1,2,2-triphenylethyl acetates, $Ph_2CHC^{*}H(OAc)Ph$ (I, chain-labeled), $Ph_2CHCH(OAc)Ph^{*}$ (II, ring-labeled) and $Ph_2CHCH(OCOC^{*}H_3)Ph$ (III, acetyl-labeled), has been studied kinetically with regard to the comparative rates of label migration and of acetoxyl exchange. Methyl rather than carbonyl labeling in the acetoxyl group of III was selected in order to reduce any possible complications which might arise from an isotope effect during acetoxyl removal.

Methods and Results

The kinetic studies were conducted at 54.6 ± 0.4°, using the appropriate 1,2,2-triphenylethyl acetate, in acetic acid solution containing one equivalent of p-toluenesulfonic acid. Aliquots of the reaction mixture were then quenched in aqueous sodium chloride solutions after various time intervals. The acetate from each aliquot was recovered and, for those runs in which it was necessary to determine carbon-14 at this point, crystallized one or two times. The crude acetate obtained quantitatively on quenching the aliquots was quite pure; recrystallization prior to radioactivity assay was carried out chiefly to remove p-toluenesulfonic acid and sodium chloride which might possibly have been occluded during the quenching procedure. The extent of carbon-14 equilibration in the chain- and ring-labeled acetates was ascertained by deacetylating the recovered acetate, oxidizing the resulting carbinol and assaying the benzophenone oxidation product for radioactivity. The extent of acetoxyl exchange of the acetyl-labeled acetate with its non-radioactive environment was ascertained by assaying for total radioactivity the acetate recovered from each aliquot. Both isomerization reactions, as well as the acetoxyl exchange reaction, were found to obey first-order kinetic expressions with respect to acetates I, II or III under the reaction conditions employed. First-order rate constants at the time of each aliquot removal were calculated as described in the Experimental section. The results of these kinetic experiments are presented in Tables I–III.

Examination of Tables I–III indicates that the first-order rates of equilibration of the chain-labeled acetate and the ring-labeled acetate are equal within experimental error and each is essentially the same as the first-order rate of acetoxyl exchange for the acetyl-labeled acetate, although the data for acetoxyl exchange seem to be subject to a larger external error than do the data of Tables I or II. These results demonstrate that during the p-toluenesulfonic acid catalyzed isomerization of labeled 1,2,2-triphenylethyl acetates, *statistical equilibration of each label occurs each time an acetoxyl group is removed from the discretely labeled starting material.*

Although the possibility was considered extremely unlikely, there was a chance that a consistent external error was operative during the gathering of the data of Tables I and II which would make it seem that the rates of equilibration of the ring-labeled and chain-labeled acetates

TABLE I

FIRST-ORDER RATE CONSTANTS FOR THE EQUILIBRATION OF
1,2,2-TRIPHENYLETHYL-1-C^{14} ACETATE

	$k_I \times 10^2$, hours^{-1}
Run 1	2.22 ± 0.02
Run 2	$2.22 \pm .06$
Average	$2.22 \pm .05$

TABLE II

FIRST-ORDER RATE CONSTANTS FOR THE EQUILIBRATION OF
1-PHENYL-C^{14}-2,2-DIPHENYLETHYL ACETATE

	$k_{II} \times 10^2$, hours^{-1}
Run 1	2.22 ± 0.09
Run 2	$2.08 \pm .07$
Average	$2.15 \pm .08$

TABLE III

FIRST-ORDER RATE CONSTANTS FOR ACETOXYL EXCHANGE
OF 1,2,2-TRIPHENYLETHYL ACETATE-2-C^{14}

	$k_{III} \times 10^2$, hours^{-1}
Run 1	1.97 ± 0.06
Run 2^a	$2.56 \pm .03$
Run 3^b	$2.39 \pm .07$
Average	$2.31 \pm .05$

^{a} Value obtained running the ring-labeled and acetyl-labeled 1,2,2-triphenylethyl acetates in the same reaction vessel. ^{b} One-half of the value obtained using two equivalents of p-toluenesulfonic acid.

were equal when in reality they should bear the 0.75 ratio which might be predicted on the basis of the previously derived kinetic reaction.[2] This possibility has now been definitely and completely excluded by the results of an experiment in which the two differently labeled acetate samples, I and II, were mixed homogeneously in solution and then subjected to the conditions of the acid-catalyzed isomerization in the same reaction vessel. The degradative procedure and the radiochemical results of this experiment are outlined in Chart I. Radioactivity data are shown for each molecule or for each portion thereof as millicuries per mole. The reaction conditions were identical to those employed in gathering the data of Tables I and II except that only one aliquot was removed—after 72 hours. From these data k_I is calculated to be 0.0203 ± 0.0012 hour^{-1}, while k_{II} is calculated as 0.0211 ± 0.008 hour^{-1}. The errors in the values of the two constants are calculated from the average errors of the radioactivity determinations shown in Chart I. Allowing for these average errors, the ratio $k_{II}/k_I = 1.04$ lies between the extreme limits 0.945 and 1.14, excluding the ratio 0.75 as a possibility.

CHART I

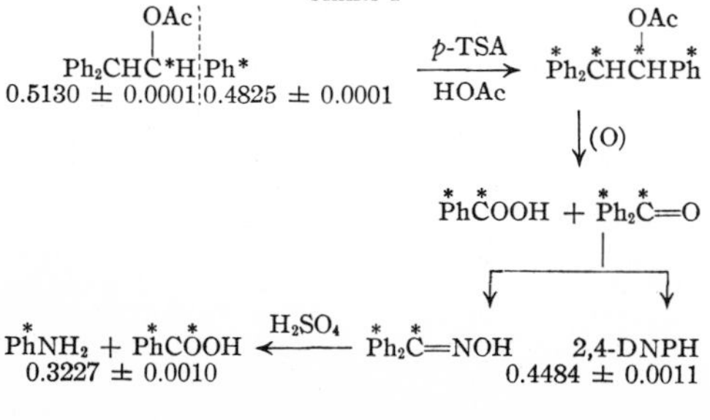

OAc
|
Ph$_2$CHC*H Ph* $\xrightarrow[\text{HOAc}]{p\text{-TSA}}$ Ph$_2$CHCHPh

0.5130 ± 0.0001 0.4825 ± 0.0001

$\downarrow$(O)

PhCOOH + Ph$_2$C=O

PhNH$_2$ + PhCOOH $\xleftarrow{\text{H}_2\text{SO}_4}$ Ph$_2$C=NOH   2,4-DNPH

0.3227 ± 0.0010 0.4484 ± 0.0011

Discussion

The kinetic data of the preceding section allow the following conclusions to be drawn concerning the nature of the intermediates in the isomerization of the several labeled species of 1,2,2-triphenylethyl acetate: (1) Internal return[5] does not occur during the isomerization, since the rate of acetoxyl loss is the same as the rate of equilibration of the acetates I and II. If internal return should take place during these reactions, then the rate of acetoxyl loss, k_{III}, would be expected to be considerably slower than the two equilibration rates k_I and k_{II}. This conclusion might have been anticipated, since the leaving group is undoubtedly an acetic acid molecule. Thus an ion pair is not formed on ionization and ion-pair collapse is, of course, impossible. These same considerations do not apply to the solvolyses reported in the preceding paper,[2] during which it is possible that internal return does occur.

(2) Symmetrical[3] or unsymmetrical[4,5] bridged ions can be ruled out as the sole cationic intermediates since, in the absence of internal return, and whether or not they demonstrate stereospecificity,[7] their postulation would demand that k_I should be *greater than* k_{II}.[8] In the event that the *trans*-phenonium ion were formed to the complete exclusion[2] of the *cis*-phenonium ion, then the ring-labeled acetate II could never exhibit more than 50% rearrangement of the radioactive label.

(3) A completely concerted process in which one phenyl group migrates totally as it assists in the removal of an acetoxyl group

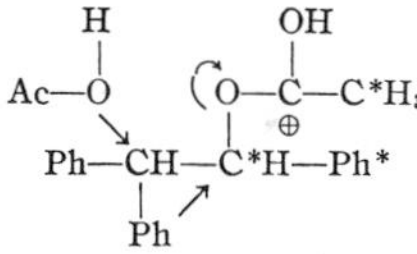

$$\begin{array}{ccc} H & & OH \\ | & & | \\ Ac-O & (O-C-C^*H_3 \\ & & \oplus \\ Ph-CH-C^*H-Ph^* \\ & | \\ & Ph \end{array}$$

is excluded as an explanation for the present data since it would require that the rate of *isomerization* of both the ring-labeled and chain-labeled acetates be equal to the rate of acetoxyl exchange (k_{III}). Such a mechanism would then require that the rate of *equilibration* (k_I) of the chain-labeled acetate be twice the rate of acetoxyl exchange, and the rate of *equilibrium* (k_{II}) for the ring-labeled acetate be 3/2 the rate of acetoxyl exchange, again contrary to observation.

(4) The general mechanism proposed in the previous paper[2] in which the classical carbonium ion intermediates undergo more or less equilibration, depending upon their lifetimes, receives support. During the isomerizations of acetates I and II, it is obvious from the present kinetic data, that the ionic intermediates are sufficiently long-lived in

(7) P. I. Pollak and D. Y. Curtin, THIS JOURNAL, **72**, 961 (1950); D. Y. Curtin and P. I. Pollak, *ibid.*, **73**, 992 (1951); D. Y. Curtin, E. E. Harris and P. I. Pollak, *ibid.*, **73**, 3453 (1951); D. Y. Curtin and E. K. Meislich, *ibid.*, **74**, 5905 (1952); D. Y. Curtin and D. B. Kellom, *ibid.*, **75**, 6011 (1953); D. J. Cram and F. A. Abd Elhafez, *ibid.*, **76**, 30 (1954). See also discussion of stereospecificity in ref. 2.

(8) A symmetrical phenonium-ion mechanism in which a complete lack of stereospecificity is postulated would require that the rate of equilibration for the chain-labeled acetate be given by the relation $k_I = 2k = (1/t) \ln (x_0/x_0 - x)$, and that for the ring-labeled acetate by the relation of $k_{II} = 3k/2 = (1/t) \ln y_0/(y_0 - y)$ where k, x_0, x, y_0 and y have the same significance as in the identical relations derived in the preceding (ref. 2) paper. Thus, $k_I:k_{II}$ should be in the ratio 4:3.

acetic acid solution, in the absence of acetate ion, to permit statistical redistribution of both the chain and ring labels before reaction of these intermediates with non-radioactive acetic acid. Thus, each mole of acetate product is fully equilibrated radiochemically for each mole of radioactive acetoxyl lost.

Experimental

1,2,2-Triphenylethyl-1-C¹⁴ Acetate.—A synthesis for this acetate was employed which differs slightly from that previously reported.[9] 1,2,2-Triphenylethanol-1-C¹⁴ (4.5 g.) was dissolved in pyridine (20 ml.) and the solution was treated with acetic anhydride (15 ml.). The mixture was allowed to stand for 24 hours, then diluted with water and the product was filtered, rinsed and dried. The crude product was dissolved in excess hot acetone, then the solution was concentrated and treated with an equal volume of hot ethanol. The pure acetate (5.14 g., 99%, m.p. 155–156°) crystallized as splendid needles. In other experiments giving comparable results, the original reaction mixture was allowed to stand for one hour, then heated on the steambath for one hour prior to dilution. Such procedures were employed in the synthesis of all three alternatively labeled acetates studies except, of course, that radioactive acetic anhydride was employed in the preparation of the acetyl-labeled acetate. The radiochemical structure of one of the acetates prepared by this method was confirmed by deacetylation and oxidative degradation of the resulting carbinol. Isolation and assay of the benzophenone fraction from the oxidation by the usual procedures indicated that only 0.66% of the total radioactivity was found in the supposedly non-radioactive fraction, a result in accord with our previous observations.

Radioactivity Assays of the Three Alternatively Labeled Acetate Species

	Assay, mc./mole
1,2,2-Triphenylethyl-1-C¹⁴ acetate	2.161 ± 0.006
1-Phenyl-C¹⁴-2,2-diphenylethyl acetate	0.991 ± .004
1,2,2-Triphenylethyl acetate-2-C¹⁴	0.549 ± .003

Kinetic Investigations.—The kinetic experiments leading to the rate data in Table I–III were conducted as follows. The 1,2,2-triphenylethyl acetate under study (3.000 g.) was dissolved in hot glacial acetic acid (70.00 ml.) and the solution was allowed to reach the thermostat temperature of 54.6 ± 0.4°. At this point 6.00 ml. of catalyst solution was added, and the time was recorded. The catalyst solution consisted of 9.89 g. of desiccated p-toluenesulfonic acid dissolved in 32.4 ml. of glacial acetic acid containing 4.00 ml. of acetic anhydride. The reaction mixture was thus 0.1260 M in p-toluenesulfonic acid and 0.1250 M in starting acetate. At various time intervals 15.0-ml. aliquots were pipetted from the thermostated reaction mixture and drained into water. In those runs in which the recovered acetate was assayed for carbon-14, the precipitate was filtered and crystallized from an acetone–alcohol mixture. For acetoxyl-exchange data the acetate was assayed at this point, or after a second recrystallization. For phenyl equilibration data the acetate (including that recovered from the recrystallization mother liquors) was deacetylated with ethereal lithium aluminum hydride, and the crude carbinol obtained was oxidized in the usual fashion[2] with an acetone–water solution of potassium permanganate. The benzophenone oxidation fraction was isolated as usual and converted to its 2,4-dinitrophenylhydrazone, which was recrystallized once or twice from dioxane prior to radioactivity assay.

In one acetoxyl exchange run the volume of catalyst solution employed was doubled and the volume of acetic acid decreased accordingly, giving a solution 0.2714 M in p-toluenesulfonic acid and 0.1250 M in starting acetate. In several of the experiments the size of the run was scaled to exactly ²/₃ that indicated above.

Kinetic Calculations.—The rates of equilibration for the chain-labeled acetate were calculated by means of the integrated first-order expression

(9) W. A. Bonner and C. J. Collins, This Journal, **75**, 5376 (1953).

$$k_I = \frac{2.303}{t} \log \frac{x_e}{x_e - x}$$

where k_I is the specific rate for the conversion of 1,2,2-triphenyl-1-C¹⁴ acetate I into an equilibrium mixture of 1,2,2-triphenylethyl-1,2-C₁¹⁴ acetate, x is the radioactivity assay of the benzophenone fraction isolated at time t, and x_e is the radioactivity assay of the benzophenone fraction at complete equilibrium (0.500 times the assay of the starting acetate).

The rates of equilibration for the ring-labeled acetate were calculated by means of the equation

$$k_{II} = \frac{2.303}{t} \log \frac{y_e}{y_e - y}$$

where k_{II} is the specific rate constant for the conversion of acetate II to its equilibrium mixture, y is the radioactivity assay of the benzophenone fraction at time t, and y_e is the assay of the benzophenone fraction at complete equilibrium (0.667 times the assay of the starting acetate).

The rates of acetoxyl exchange for the acetyl-labeled acetate were calculated by the first-order expression

$$k_{III} = \frac{2.303}{t} \log \frac{a}{a - x}$$

where a is the original radioactivity assay of the starting acetyl-labeled acetate, and x is the quantity of radioactive acetoxyl lost at time t. The radioactivity assay of the acetate recovered at time t thus defines the value of $a - x$.

Kinetic Data.—In Tables IV–VI are given the equilibration or exchange rates calculated for each time t from the corresponding radioactivity assays of the products isolated at each time t. The averages of these values appear in Tables I–III.

Table IV

Equilibration Constants for 1,2,2-Triphenylethyl-1-C¹⁴ Acetate

Run	Assay of starting acetate, mc./mole	Time, hours	Ph₂C*O assay (x), mc./mole	$k_I \times 10^2$, hours⁻¹
1	2.161	6	0.172	(2.900)
	(x_e 1.081)	22	.419	2.229
		30	.529	2.243
		46	.689	2.207
		70	.848	2.192
				2.218 ± 0.018
2	1.000	9	0.0996	(2.460)
	(x_e 0.500)	21	.191	2.296
		44	.314	2.250
		48	.317	2.130
		52	.347	2.280
		57.5	.365	2.272
		70	.398	2.268
		76	.402	2.130
		95	.435	2.164
				2.224 ± 0.062

Isomerization of Ph₂CHC*HPH*.—The doubly labeled acetate (2.4459 g. containing 0.5130 ± 0.001 mc./mole carbon-14 in the C-1 ethyl carbon and 0.4825 ± 0.0001 mc./mole in the C-1 phenyl group) was dissolved in 57 ml. of glacial acetic acid in a 200-ml. flask and, after having been placed in a thermostat at 54.6 ± 0.4° for one hour, 4.9 ml. of the catalyst solution (described previously in this section) was added, and the mixture was well shaken to ensure homogeneity. After 72 hours, a 32-ml. aliquot was removed, and poured into excess water containing sodium chloride to congeal the precipitate. The acetate was filtered, dried and added to an ethereal solution of lithium aluminum hydride, from which the carbinol was recovered. The crude carbinol was dissolved in 60 ml. of acetone, and to it was added 3.8 g. of KMnO₄ in 32 ml. of water containing 0.2 ml. of acetic acid. After four days, the oxidation mixture was worked up in the usual fashion. The benzo-

TABLE V

EQUILIBRATION CONSTANTS FOR 1-PHENYL-C14-2,2-DIPHENYLETHYL ACETATE

Run	Assay of starting acetate, mc./mole	Time, hours	$1.009 \times$ Ph$_2$*CO assay (y), mc./mole	$k_{II} \times 10^2$, hours^{-1}
1	0.991	6	0.107	(2.950)
	(y_e 0.661)	22	.270	2.385
		30	.318	2.190
		46	.419	2.186
		71.5	.510	2.100
				2.215 ± 0.092
2	0.991	9	0.119	2.208
	(y_e 0.661)	21	.241	2.162
		44	.399	2.102
		48	.414	2.120
		52	.435	2.062
		57.5	.457	2.045
		70	.501	2.028
		76	.518	2.018
		95	.560	1.978
				2.080 ± 0.070

TABLE VI

ACETOXYL EXCHANGE CONSTANTS FOR 1,2,2-TRIPHENYLETHYL ACETATE-2-C14

Run	Assay of starting acetate, mc./mole	Time, hours	Assay of recovered acetate $(a - x)$ mc./mole	$k_{III} \times 10^2$, hours^{-1}
1	0.549	6.5	0.483	1.982
		23	.344	2.035
		30.75	.293	2.042
		47	.224	1.905
		54	.198	1.890
				1.971 ± 0.059
2	0.495	6	0.282	(4.318)
		22	.278	2.621
		30	.230	2.560
		46	.153	2.553
		71.5	.083	2.500
				2.558 ± 0.032
3	0.549	4.5	0.438	5.00
	(p-toluenesulfonic acid	23	.178	4.90
	concn. doubled)	27	.151	4.77
		30	.137	4.51
				4.79 ± 0.15
		(Divided by 2)		2.39 ± 0.07

phenone fraction was dissolved in 8 ml. of ethanol, treated with Norit and filtered through Celite, then 1.5 ml. of this solution was converted to the 2,4-dinitrophenylhydrazone (189 mg.) which was twice crystallized from dioxane and dried in an Abderhalden. The radioactivity assay was: 0.4495; 0.4473 average 0.4484 ± 0.0011 mc./mole. The remaining 6.5 ml. of ethanolic benzophenone was heated under reflux for 24 hours with 1 ml. of pyridine and 0.5 g. of hydroxylamine hydrochloride. The mixture was then poured into water and filtered, yielding 647 mg. of crude benzophenone oxime. This was not purified, since several model experiments had demonstrated that the crude oxime gave satisfactory yields in the Beckmann rearrangement. The oxime was dissolved in 12 ml. of concd. sulfuric acid and the solution was warmed on a steam-bath for one hour, after which time the cooled solution was poured over crushed ice. The resulting mixture was extracted three times with ether, the ether was clarified and concentrated, yielding 232 mg. of pure benzoic acid. This was twice crystallized from water, and identified by melting point and mixed

melting point. The radioactivity assay was: 0.3238; 0.3217, average 0.3227 ± 0.0010 mc./mole of carbon-14. From these data it was calculated that $k_I = 2.03 \pm 0.12 \times 10^{-2}$ hours^{-1}, and $k_{II} = 2.11 \pm 0.08 \times 10^{-2}$ hours^{-1}, and that $k_{II}/k_I = 1.04 \pm 0.095$.

Radioactivity Determinations.—These were carried out in the normal fashion as described in the previous paper.[2] For the determination of the isomerization of doubly labeled acetate (I and II) described in the preceding section, the highest precision was necessary. This was obtained by weighing large samples (20–50 mg.) of analytical material on a micro-balance, and using the technique described for previous double-labeling experiments.[2]

OAK RIDGE, TENNESSEE

25 | Tracer Experiments on the 2-Nor-bornenyl Cation

In the second paper of Roberts, Lee, and Saunders (Paper No. 25) the difference between the two discussed ions, VII and VIII, is that in VII the bond between C-1 and C-6 is considered largely intact and the homoallylic system includes an overlap between orbitals of C-2 and C-6. In VIII the C1–C6 and C2–C6 bonds are regarded as identical, leading to the prediction of equal amounts of products derived from VII and from IX. Solvolysis of *exo*-dehydronorbornyl brosylate-2,3-$^{14}C_2$ yielded, in addition to nortricyclyl product, *exo*-dehydronorbornyl ester which was 38% rearranged when acetate and 48% when formate. Thus the structure VIII could account for most, but not all, of the dehydronorbornyl product. In later work by dePuy, Ogawa, and McDaniel (Paper No. 51) and by Giddings and Dirlam[1] the structure and stereochemistry of products from starting materials of norbornenyl and benzonorbornenyl type seem most compatible with a structure of type VIII.

[1] W. P. Giddings and J. Dirlam, *J. Am. Chem. Soc.* **85**, 3900 (1963).

From: *J. Am. Chem. Soc.* **77**, 3034–37 (1955)

[CONTRIBUTION FROM THE DEPARTMENT OF CHEMISTRY AND LABORATORY FOR NUCLEAR SCIENCE AND ENGINEERING, MASSACHUSETTS INSTITUTE OF TECHNOLOGY]

Rearrangements in Carbonium Ion-Type Reactions of C^{14}-Labeled Dehydronorbornyl Derivatives[1]

BY JOHN D. ROBERTS,[2] C. C. LEE AND W. H. SAUNDERS, JR.

RECEIVED OCTOBER 11, 1954

Solvolysis of *exo*- and *endo*-dehydronorbornyl-2,3-C_2^{14} *p*-bromobenzenesulfonates in acetic acid and formic acid solutions and nitrous acid deaminations of *endo*-dehydronorbornyl-3-C^{14}-amine in acetic acid and aqueous fluoboric acid were found to yield 4–17% of dehydronorbornyl derivatives with 30–48% of the C^{14} located at other than the 2,3-positions. The C^{14}-rearrangements are discussed in terms of unsymmetrical "dehydronorbornium" intermediates.

In conjunction with our investigation of rearrangements in carbonium ion-type reactions of C^{14}-labeled norbornyl derivatives,[3] studies were made of solvolyses of *exo*- and *endo*-dehydronorbornyl-2,3-C_2^{14} *p*-bromobenzenesulfonates (Ia and IIa) and nitrous acid deamination of *endo*-2-amino-$\Delta^{5,6}$-norbornene-3-C^{14} (*endo*-dehydronorbornyl-3-C^{14}-amine, IIb).

Ia, IIa, X = p-BrC$_6$H$_4$SO$_3$-
Ib, IIb, X = –NH$_2$
Ic, IIc, X = –OH
Id, IId, X = –OAc
Ie, IIe, X = –O$_2$CH

Synthetic Procedures and Experimental Results

A mixture of *exo*- and *endo*-dehydronorborneols-2,3-C_2^{14} (Ic and IIc) was obtained by the lithium alu-minum hydride reduction of mixed labeled dehydronorbornyl acetates (Id and IId) from the Diels–Alder reaction between cyclopentadiene and vinyl-1,2-C_2^{14} acetate.[3] Equilibration of the alcohol mixture in refluxing toluene with sodium and fluorenone effected enrichment in the *exo*-isomer,[3,4] the latter amounting to 47% of the recovered product. With *p*-bromobenzenesulfonyl chloride in pyridine,[5] the alcohols yielded the desired sulfonates Ia and IIa.

The stereoisomeric *p*-bromobenzenesulfonate mixtures were not separated for the solvolysis experiments since the published[6] relative solvolysis rates of Ia and IIa indicated that Ia easily can be solvolyzed preferentially at 45° in the presence of IIa. Acetolysis of Ia or IIa gave principally 3-acetoxy-nortricyclene (IIIa) with lesser amounts of *exo*-dehydronorbornyl acetate (Id).[6] Conversion of the product mixtures to the corresponding alcohols and hydrogenation gave mixtures of 3-hydroxynortricyclene (IIIb) and *exo*-norborneol (IV). The hydro-

(1) (a) Supported in part by the joint program of the Office of Naval Research and the U. S. Atomic Energy Commission. (b) Presented in part at the Symposium on Reaction Mechanisms at the 75th Anniversary Meeting of the American Chemical Society, September 7, 1951.

(2) Gates and Crellin Laboratories, California Institute of Technology, Pasadena 4, Calif.

(3) J. D. Roberts, C. C. Lee and W. H. Saunders, Jr., THIS JOURNAL, **76**, 4501 (1954).

(4) (a) W. v. E. Doering and T. C. Aschner, *ibid.*, **71**, 838 (1949); (b) J. D. Roberts, E. R. Trumbull, Jr., W. Bennett and R. Armstrong, *ibid.*, **72**, 3116 (1950), erroneously infer that the equilibrium product is substantially pure *exo*-dehydronorborneol.

(5) R. S. Tipson, *J. Org. Chem.*, **9**, 235 (1944).

(6) S. Winstein, H. M. Walborsky and K. Schreiber, THIS JOURNAL, **72**, 5795 (1950).

TABLE I

RADIOACTIVITY ANALYSES OF DEGRADATION PRODUCTS OF DEHYDRONORBORNYL COMPOUNDS FROM CARBONIUM ION-TYPE
REACTIONS OF DEHYDRONORBORNYL-2,3(OR 3)-C¹⁴ DERIVATIVES

Reactant	Con-fig.	Solvent	Temp., °C.	Time, hr.	Dehydro prod.,[a] %	Acid V, activity Meas.[b]	Acid V, activity Cor.[c]	Diamine VI, activity Meas.[b]	Diamine VI, activity Cor.[c]	BaCO₃, activity Meas.[b]	BaCO₃, activity Cor.[c]	Rearr., %[d]
p-Bromobenzenesulfonate	endo	HOAc	Reflux	48	17	850	2050	358[e]	618	1941	1342	30.1
p-Bromobenzenesulfonate	exo	HOAc	45	1.0	11	442	1065	236[e]	407	877	602	38.2
p-Bromobenzenesulfonate	exo	HCO₂H	45	1.0	4	530	1278	355[e]	613	937	646	48.0
Amine	endo	HOAc	Room	12	17	0.03946[f]		0.01521[f,g]		0.02298[f,h]		38.5
Amine	endo	H₂O–HBF₄	Room	48	7	.06905[f]		.02416[f,g]		.04306[f,h]		35.0

^{a} As determined by quantitative hydrogenation; remainder of product presumed to be nortricyclyl derivatives. ^{b} Measured C¹⁴-activities in counts/min., determined with a windowless methane-filled counter (Nucleometer), of "infinitely thick" barium carbonate samples of cross-sectional area equal to 2.90 cm.² and prepared as described by J. D. Roberts, W. Bennett, E. W. Holroyd, Jr., and C. H. Fugitt, *Anal. Chem.*, **20**, 904 (1948). The activities are corrected for background and have standard deviations of less than 2%. ^{c} C¹⁴-Activities in dis./min./mg. of barium carbonate, corrected for self absorption and dilution by non-labeled carbon atoms as described by J. D. Roberts, R. E. McMahon and J. S. Hine, THIS JOURNAL, **72**, 4237 (1950). ^{d} Figures are for (activity of VI/activity of V) × 100. The BaCO₃ activities were used only as a rough check on the activity balance.³ ^{e} Determined by combustion of the stannous chloride complex of VI.³ ^{f} Activities in microcuries/millimole (μc./min.) determined by the procedure of O. K. Neville, *ibid.*, **70**, 3499 (1948). ^{g} Combustion of the dibenzoyl derivative of VI.³ ^{h} Corrected for a statistical factor of two.

gen absorptions indicated that the product from the acetolysis of Ia contained 11% Id, whereas

IIIa, X = OAc
IIIb, X = OH
IIIc, X = OCHO

the acetolysis of IIa, Id amounted to 17% of the total product.

The *exo*-isomer Ia was solvolyzed also in formic acid. Hydrogenation showed the product to contain only 4% unsaturated material, presumably *exo*-dehydronorbornyl formate (Ie), the remainder being nortricyclyl formate (IIIc). Cleavage of the ester mixture with lithium aluminum hydride followed by hydrogenation gave a mixture of IIIb and IV.

endo-Dehydronorbornyl-3-C¹⁴-amine (IIb) was prepared by the iron and hydrochloric acid reduction of the Diels–Alder adduct of nitroethylene-2-C¹⁴ and cyclopentadiene.³ IIb was treated with nitrous acid in acetic acid and in aqueous fluoboric acid. As in the solvolyses, the products were mixtures of the corresponding nortricyclyl and dehydronorbornyl derivatives⁷ which eventually were converted to IIIb and IV. Quantitative hydrogenation showed the proportion of dehydronorbornyl derivatives, Id from the reaction in acetic acid and Ic from the reaction in aqueous fluoboric acid, to be 17 and 7% of the total product, respectively.

The radioactive *exo*-norborneol in the hydrogenated reaction products was degraded by the method previously reported.³

Appropriate amounts of non-radioactive norborneol were added as carrier to aid the degradation. Alcohol IIIb appeared to cause no complications in the oxidation of IV to V. The C¹⁴-content of the diacid V is equivalent to the total activity of IV,

while that of VI represents the C¹⁴-activity which migrated from its original location at the 2,3-positions. Consequently, the figures for (activity of VI/activity of V) × 100 are designated as "% rearrangement." Data from the C¹⁴-assays and the "% rearrangements" for the reactions studied are given in Table I.

Discussion

As with the norbornyl derivatives,³ it appears reasonable to assume that the only mechanistic difference between solvolysis reaction of the *p*-bromobenzenesulfonates Ia and IIa is that 6–10% of direct displacement reaction may take place with the *endo*-isomer IIa. With this assumption, the part of the reaction which leads to rearrangement is considered mechanistically independent of the configuration of the starting material. Rearrangement of the C¹⁴-activity from carbons 2 and 3 amounted to 38% in the acetolysis of *exo*-sulfonate Ia and 30% rearrangement was found in the acetolysis of the *endo*-isomer IIa (Table I). The 8% difference in rearrangement between the isomers is attributable to the above-mentioned direct non-rearranging displacement reaction between solvent molecules and the *endo*-sulfonate (IIa). The quantitative hydrogenation data also tend to support this interpretation since more Id is formed in the acetolysis of IIa than in the acetolysis of Ia.

Simonetta and Winstein⁸ have reviewed the stereochemical and kinetic evidence for important conjugative interaction between a carbonium ion center and an appropriately oriented II-electron-bearing β-substituent such as the vinyl group in dehydronorbornyl derivatives. A non-classical "dehydronorbornonium" ion with the structure VII has been proposed¹ᵇ,⁹ as a possible reaction intermediate in the solvolyses of dehydronorbornyl halides. To accommodate the observed rearrangements in the carbonium ion-type reactions reported here, it is necessary to postulate also either ion VIII or a relatively slow equilibration of VII with its enantiomorph IX. The failure to achieve complete rearrangement indicates ion VII to be the initial

(7) *Cf.* W. E. Parham, W. T. Hunter and R. Hanson, THIS JOURNAL, **73**, 5068 (1951).

(8) M. Simonetta and S. Winstein, *ibid.*, **76**, 18 (1954).

(9) J. D. Roberts, W. Bennett and R. Armstrong, *ibid.*, **72**, 3329 (1950).

intermediate in the ionization process. Either VII, VIII or IX can react with the conjugate base of

VII

the solvent at position 5 to give a nortricyclyl derivative. With VII, the alternative is reaction at position 2, giving rise to an unrearranged dehydronorbornyl derivative.

VII   VIII   IX

With VIII, besides position 5, reaction may occur with equal probability at positions 1 and 2, leading to a 50% rearrangement of the labeled atoms in the unsaturated product if isotope effects are neglected. IX can only yield nortricyclyl or rearranged dehydronorbornyl (X) derivatives.

VIII   X

Since the system, acetic acid–acetate ion, is more nucleophilic than formic acid–formate ion, the activation energy for the product–controlling reaction between a cationic intermediate and either solvent or anion should be lower with acetic acid than with formic acid. Thus, in the acetolysis of Ia or IIa, the first intermediate VII can react partly with acetate ions to give unrearranged dehydronorbornyl acetate and partly be converted to intermediates VIII or IX. In such circumstances, the product shows less than 50% rearrangement of C14 atoms. In formic acid, the activation energy for the product-forming reaction is higher, and a better opportunity is available for the first intermediate to proceed successively through VIII (and/ or IX) before giving the final products. The larger observed rearrangement of 48.0% in the formolysis of Ia is in accord with this idea.[10] Nitrous acid deamination of IIb in acetic acid gave similar extents of rearrangement and dehydronorbornyl acetate formation to those obtained in acetolysis of the endo-sulfonate ester IIa. In aqueous fluoboric acid, IIb gave somewhat more rearrangement and a substantially smaller fraction of dehydronorbornyl product. The difference in extent of rearrangement with acetic acid and water as solvents correlates with the behavior of labeled norbornylamines in corresponding reactions[3] but is not yet satisfactorily explicable.

(10) The situation in these reactions is very similar to that encountered in carbonium ion reactions of β-phenylethylamines, see J. D. Roberts and C. M. Regan, THIS JOURNAL, 75, 2069 (1953).

It is of interest to note that, if intermediate VIII is solely responsible for the observed rearrangements as postulated above, complete degradation of the norborneol IV should show no C14 in positions 5 and 6. Also, since VII is asymmetric and VIII has a plane of symmetry, acetolysis of optically active Ia may be predicted to lead to only partial loss of optical activity whereas formolysis should give a practically completely racemized product.

The lack of complete isotope-position rearrangement in the acetolysis of dehydronorbornyl-2,3-C2^14 sulfonates coupled with the tendency of exo-dehydronorbornyl sulfonate to be interconverted with the corresponding nortricyclyl sulfonate ester[11] indicates that either the "internal return" process studied by Winstein and co-workers[12] does not lead to rearranged sulfonate (as X) or else that the actual degree of rearrangement in the solvolyses is substantially less than appears from the C14-data.

Experimental

Dehydronorborneol-2,3-C2^14 was prepared in 82% yield by lithium aluminum hydride cleavage of dehydronorbornyl-2,3-C2^14 acetate obtained from Diels–Alder addition of vinyl-1,2-C2^14 acetate to cyclopentadiene.[3]

Partial Isomerization of endo- to exo-Dehydronorborneol-2,3-C2^14.—A mixture of 4.5 g. of dehydronorborneol-2,3-C2^14 (from Diels–Alder adduct, exo-isomer content about 19%), 0.09 g. of fluorenone and 0.045 g. of sodium in 20 ml. of toluene was refluxed for 45 hours. The equilibration product was isolated as previously described.[3] The yield was 3.4 g. (76%). The proportion of exo-isomer, as measured by the acid liberated when the p-bromobenzenesulfonate was solvolyzed in 75% acetone–25% water at 45° for one hour, was 47%.

Dehydronorbornyl-2,3-C2^14 p-bromobenzenesulfonates were prepared as described for the norbornyl-2,3-C2^14 p-bromobenzenesulfonates.[3]

Solvolysis of exo-Dehydronorbornyl-2,3-C2^14 p-Bromobenzenesulfonate in Acetic Acid.—Eight grams (0.024 mole) of a mixture of exo- and endo-p-bromobenzenesulfonates prepared from isomerized dehydronorborneol-2,3-C2^14 and 2.5 g. (10% excess) of potassium acetate in 50 ml. of acetic acid were heated at 45° for 1 hour. The resulting solution was worked up as described for the acetolysis of exo-norbornyl-2,3-C2^14 p-bromobenzenesulfonate.[3] The recovery of endo-norbornyl-2,3-C2^14 p-bromobenzenesulfonate, m.p. 88–89°, was 4.1 g. (51%). The yield of mixed acetates (nortricyclyl and dehydronorbornyl), b.p. 70–72° (8 mm.), amounted to 1.3 g. (35%). Treatment of the crude product with lithium aluminum hydride yielded 0.80 g. (85%) of 3-hydroxynortricyclene and exo-dehydronorborneol which absorbed 11% of one molar equivalent of hydrogen in ethyl acetate over platinum oxide. The yield of hydrogenated alcohols was 0.71 g. (89%). Non-radioactive norborneol (0.70 g.) was added and the total of 1.41 g. of norborneol and 3-hydroxynortricyclene mixture was oxidized with 5.6 g. of potassium permanganate and 5.6 g. of potassium hydroxide in 56 ml. of water as in the oxidation of pure norborneol.[3] The isolated cis-cyclopentane-1,3-dicarboxylic acid amounted to 0.60 g. (55% based on the norborneol present). It melted alone and in admixture with an authentic sample at 119–120°. Its infrared absorption spectrum (Nujol mull) was also identical with that of an authentic sample.

The decarboxylation of the cis-cyclopentane-1,3-dicarboxylic acid and the radioactivity assays of the degradation products were carried out as previously described.[3] The results are given in Table I.

Solvolysis of endo-Dehydronorbornyl-2,3-C2^14 p-Bromobenzenesulfonate in Acetic Acid.—A mixture of 4.1 g. (0.012 mole) of endo-dehydronorbornyl-2,3-C2^14 p-bromo-

(11) S. Winstein, paper presented at the Organic Reaction Mechanisms Symposium.[1b]

(12) (a) See for example, S. Winstein and K. C. Schreiber, THIS JOURNAL, 74, 2156 (1952); (b) S. Winstein and D. S. Trifan, ibid., 74, 1154 (1952).

benzenesulfonate and 1.35 g. (10% excess) of potassium acetate in 25 ml. of acetic acid was heated under reflux for 48 hours. The products were isolated as in the acetolysis of *endo*-norbornyl-2,3-C_2^{14} *p*-bromobenzenesulfonate.[3] The yield of the mixture of nortricyclyl and *exo*-dehydronorbornyl acetate was 1.2 g. (63%). The corresponding alcohol mixture (0.76 g.) obtained after lithium aluminum hydride reduction absorbed 17% of a molar equivalent of hydrogen. The hydrogenation product (0.64 g.) was mixed with 0.70 g. of inactive norborneol and the whole was oxidized with potassium permanganate, giving 0.69 g. (60% based on the norborneol present) of *cis*-cyclopentane-1,3-dicarboxylic acid. Results of radioactivity analyses of the degradation products are given in Table I.

Solvolysis of *exo*-**Dehydronorbornyl-2,3-C_2^{14}** *p*-**Bromobenzenesulfonate in Formic Acid.**—A mixture of 7.0 g. (0.021 mole) of mixed *p*-bromobenzenesulfonates prepared from the isomerized *exo*- and *endo*-dehydronorborneol-2,3-C_2^{14}, 1.45 g. (0.021 mole) of sodium formate and 40 ml. of anhydrous formic acid was heated at 45° for 1 hour. The products were isolated as for the acetolysis experiment. The recovered *endo*-dehydronorbornyl-2,3-C_2^{14} *p*-bromobenzenesulfonate weighed 2.5 g. (36%). The yield of nortricyclyl and *exo*-dehydronorbornyl formate mixture, b.p. 60° (8 mm.), was 1.0 g. (34%). The mixture of formates was converted to the corresponding alcohols which absorbed 4% of a molar equivalent of hydrogen. The hydrogenation product and 0.40 g. of norborneol carrier was oxidized to give 0.40 g. of *cis*-cyclopentane-1,3-dicarboxylic acid. Degradation and radioactivity assays were carried out the usual way.

endo-**Dehydronorbornyl-3-C^{14}-amine with Nitrous Acid.**— The experiment using acetic acid as solvent was carried out as with *endo*-norbornyl-3-C^{14}-amine.[3] The crude ester from 2.5 g. of *endo*-dehydronorbornyl-3-C^{14}-amine and sodium nitrite in acetic acid was cleaved with lithium aluminum hydride and yielded 0.56 g. of mixed alcohols, m.p. 85–95°. The product absorbed 17% of one molar equivalent of hydrogen. The hydrogenated material was diluted with carrier *exo*-norborneol and degraded as before.

The aqueous fluoboric acid deamination employed the previously described procedure[3] and 2.5 g. of amine afforded 0.60 g. of crude alcohol mixture, m.p. 95–103°. On quantitative hydrogenation, 7% of one molar equivalent of hydrogen was absorbed. The reduction product was degraded in the usual way.

CAMBRIDGE 39, MASS.

26 | 7-Norbornyl and 7-Norbornenyl Tosylates

The first synthesis of 7-norbornanol (Paper No. 26) was a truly exploratory piece of work, with the betting fairly even. It was anticipated from the rigidity of the ring system and the possible hindrance to solvation that the arenesulfonates of this alcohol might be very unreactive in solvolysis. At other times by some of the same investigators, it was anticipated that the geometry might be especially favorable to four-way carbon-carbon hyperconjugation, thus making these sulfonates exceptionally reactive in solvolysis. The tosylate is in fact about one ten-millionth as reactive in acetolysis as cyclohexyl tosylate; the reason is now thought to be the narrow carbon bond angle at C-7, rigidly unfavorable for the sp^2 hybridization normal for a carbonium ion. (See C. S. Foote, Paper No. 69.)

The first entry into the 7-norbornenyl halides was made by Roberts and co-workers in 1954.[1] The *syn* isomer was the first to be characterized; it gave little indication of the spectacular reactivity which marks the *anti*. *anti*-7-Norbornenyl tosylate, described in Paper No. 26, undergoes acetolysis with complete retention of configuration, and at a rate 10^{11} times that of the saturated compound. Because of the unfavorable polar effect of a nonparticipating double bond on ionization, the driving force k_Δ/k_c will be several times larger than this. The presence of a second double bond (in 7-norbornadienyl tosylate) raises this ratio further to 10^{14} (Winstein and Ordronneau, Paper No. 45). This largest homo-allylic driving force known suggests the superiority of symmetrical over unsymmetrical three-center electron-deficient bonds. Further indications of the importance of symmetry are found in the later observed solvolytic ring closures of Δ^4-cyclo-

---

[1] J. D. Roberts, F. O. Johnson, and R. A. Carboni, *J. Am. Chem. Soc.* **76**, 5692 (1954); see also W. G. Woods, R. A. Carboni, and J. D. Roberts, *ibid.*, **78**, 5653 (1956).

heptenylmethyl[2] and 2-(Δ^3-cyclopentenyl)ethyl[3] arenesulfonates, compared with 5-hexenyl and 5-heptenyl compounds.[4]

[2] G. LeNy, Paper No. 44.

[3] R. G. Lawton, Paper No. 53.

[4] P. D. Bartlett, S. Bank, R. J. Crawford, and G. H. Schmid, *J. Am. Chem. Soc.* **87**, 1288 (1965); P. D. Bartlett and G. D. Sargent, *ibid.,* **87**, 1297; P. D. Bartlett, W. D. Closson, and T. J. Cogdell, *ibid.,* **87**, 1308; P. D. Bartlett, W. S. Trahanorsky, D. A. Bolon, and G. H. Schmid, *ibid.,* **87**, 1314 (1965).

From: *J. Am. Chem. Soc.* **77,** 4183–84 (1955)

7-NORBORNENYL AND 7-NORBORNYL CATIONS

Sir:

We wish to record the synthesis of *anti*-7-norbornenol (I) and 7-norborneol (II), and *a ratio of 10^{11} in the solvolytic reactivities of the corresponding toluenesulfonates.*

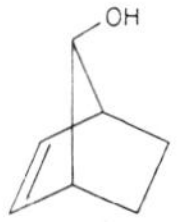

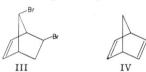

I 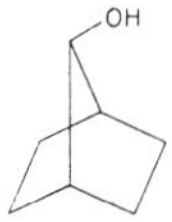   II

anti-7-Norbornenol, m.p. 117–118°, was obtained: (i) as its acetate by reaction of ethylene with acetoxycyclopentadiene,[1] generated *in situ* from acetoxydicyclopentadiene, at 190°, and (ii) by selective hydrolysis of the unsaturated dibromide (III), one of the products of addition of bromine to bicycloheptadiene (IV), followed by zinc debromination of the resulting bromohydrin.

III   IV

7-Norborneol, m.p. 150–151°, was obtained by catalytic hydrogenation of *anti*-7-norbornenol (I).

The first order rate constants (k_1) for acetolysis of the corresponding *p*-toluenesulfonates in acetic acid (0.1 *M* in potassium acetate, containing 1% Ac_2O), and other pertinent data, are

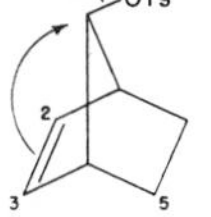

V   VI

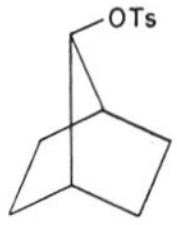

m.p. 60.5–61.0°   m.p. 54.7–55.7°

	$k_1(205°)$	8.40×10^{-5} sec.$^{-1}$
23.3 ± 0.3 kcal./mole	$\Delta H^{\ddagger}$	35.7 ± 0.6 kcal./mole
5.7 ± 2.0 e.u.	$\Delta S^{\ddagger}$	−3.5 ± 1.7 e.u.
9.04×10^{-4} sec.$^{-1}$	$k_1(25°)$	6.36×10^{-15} sec.$^{-1}$

(1) Dissertations (Harvard): P. Wilder, Jr. (1950), R. E. Vanelli (1950), C. J. Norton (1955).

(2) S. Winstein, H. M. Walborsky and K. Schreiber, THIS JOURNAL, **72,** 5795 (1950); H. J. Schmid and K. Schreiber, unpublished work.

The striking situation brought to light by the new measurements is emphasized by the following reactivities at 25°

p-TOLUENESULFONATE	
anti-7-Norbornenyl	10^4
exo-5-Norbornenyl[2]	10^3
Cyclohexyl[2]	1
endo-5-Norbornenyl[2]	10^{-1}
7-Norbornyl[3]	10^{-7}

It is clear that the geometry of the norbornyl system is uniquely unfavorable for stabilization of a cationic center at C.7.

We attribute the high reactivity of the *anti*-7-norbornenyl derivatives to powerful anchimeric assistance to ionization at C.7, involving the 2,3 π-electron cloud (V, *arrow*). It will be noted that a homoallylic system[4] is present, which is geometrically unique in that a vacant orbital on C.7 can overlap the *p* orbital systems of the double bond symmetrically. The 7-norbornenyl cation may be represented by (VII). It reacts with solvent

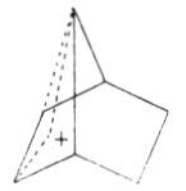

VII

stereospecifically; complete retention of configuration was observed in the hydrolysis of the dibromide (III) to the alcohol, and in the acetolysis of 7-norbornenyl toluenesulfonate (V).

(3) Qualitative mention of low reactivity for 7-norbornyl chloride and *syn*-7-norbornenyl chloride has been made by J. D. Roberts, F. O. Johnson and R. A. Carboni, *ibid.*, **76,** 5695 (1954).

(4) M. Simonetta and S. Winstein, *ibid.*, **76,** 18 (1954).

DEPARTMENT OF CHEMISTRY
UNIVERSITY OF CALIFORNIA   S. WINSTEIN
LOS ANGELES 24, CALIFORNIA   M. SHATAVSKY

CONVERSE MEMORIAL LABORATORY   C. NORTON
HARVARD UNIVERSITY   R. B. WOODWARD
CAMBRIDGE, MASSACHUSETTS

RECEIVED JULY 13, 1955

27 | The Classical Pentamethylethyl Cation

Roberts and Yancey (Paper No. 27) provided one more calibration point with the demonstration that the conversion of pentamethylethanol into its chloride at 0° under irreversible conditions does not proceed to any important extent through a methyl-bridged nonclassical ion.

From: *J. Am. Chem. Soc.* **77**, 5558–62 (1955)

[Contribution from the Department of Chemistry and Laboratory for Nuclear Science and Engineering, Massachusetts Institute of Technology]

Rearrangements in Carbonium-ion Type Reactions of C^{14}-Labeled Pentamethylethanol (2,3,3-Trimethyl-2-butanol-1-C^{14})[1]

By John D. Roberts[2] and Joel A. Yancey

Received May 9, 1955

Treatment of 2,3,3-trimethyl-2-butanol-1-C^{14} with concentrated hydrochloric acid and zinc chloride (Lucas reagent) yielded 2-chloro-2,3,3-trimethylbutane with the C^{14} distributed essentially equally among the five methyl groups. Under the conditions used, the aliphatic chloride equilibrated completely with Lucas reagent containing radioactive chloride ion. The rearrangement and chloride exchange may be accounted for by the following equilibria involving solvated carbonium ions.

Treatment of 2,3,3-trimethyl-2-butanol-1-C^{14} with concentrated hydrochloric acid at 25° for 20 minutes and 0° for one minute gave 36% and 12–16% of methyl group rearrangement, respectively. At 0° and one minute, the reaction was essentially irreversible since chloride exchange between the aliphatic chloride and radioactive concentrated hydrochloric acid was negligible. Hydrolysis of 2-chloro-2,3,3-trimethyl-2-butane by shaking with water at room temperature gave no additional methyl group rearrangement. It is concluded that the non-classical cationic intermediate VIII is not an important intermediate in *irreversible* carbonium ion type reactions of pentamethylethyl derivatives in aqueous solution and that such an intermediate is unlikely to be as stable as the classical cations shown in the equations above.

A large part of our program of research[3] on carbonium-ion type reactions has been devoted to elucidation of the structural and environmental factors which are important for the occurrence of non-

(1) Supported in part by the joint program of research of the Office of Naval Research and the U. S. Atomic Energy Commission. Presented at the Symposium on Reaction Mechanisms at the 75th Anniversary of the American Chemical Society, September 13, 1951.

(2) Gates and Crellin Laboratories, California Insitute of Technology, Pasadena 4, Calif.

(3) (a) J. D. Roberts, R. E. McMahon and J. S. Hine, This Journal, **72**, 4237 (1950); (b) J. D. Roberts and R. H. Mazur, *ibid.*, **73**, 2509, 3542 (1951); (c) J. D. Roberts and C. C. Lee, *ibid.*, **73**, 5009 (1951); (d) J. D. Roberts, W. Bennett, R. E. McMahon and E. W. Holroyd, Jr., *ibid.*, **74**, 4283 (1952); (e) J. D. Roberts and G. R. Coraor, *ibid.*, **74**, 3586 (1952); (f) J. D. Roberts and J. A. Yancey, *ibid.*, **74**, 5943 (1952); (g) J. D. Roberts and C. M. Regan, *ibid.*, **75**, 2069 (1953); (h) J. D. Roberts and J. A. Yancey, *ibid.*, **75**, 3165 (1953); (i) J. D. Roberts and M. Halmann, *ibid.*, **75**, 5759 (1953); (j) J. D. Roberts, C. C. Lee and W. H. Saunders, Jr., *ibid.*, **76**, 4501 (1954); **77**, 3034 (1955).

classical cationic intermediates of the "ethyleneonium" variety I. Very substantial progress toward

II, $R_1 = C_6H_5$; $R_2 = H$; $R_3 = CH_3$
IV,[3f] $R_1 = H$; $R_2, R_3 = H$
V,[3d] $R_1 = H$; $R_2 = CH_3$; $R_3 = H$
VI,[3g] $R_1 = C_6H_5$; $R_2, R_3 = H$
VII,[3i] $R_1 = CH_3$; $R_2, R_3 = H$
VIII, $R_1 = CH_3$; $R_2, R_3 = CH_3$

similar objectives has been made, principally by Winstein,[4] Cram,[5] Collins[6] and their co-workers, using reaction rate and stereochemical techniques. Non-classical cationic intermediates of one variety

(4) (a) As a leading reference to a number of papers see S. Winstein, C. R. Lindgren, H. Marshall and L. L. Ingraham, *ibid.*, **75**, 147 (1953); (b) S. Winstein and D. Trifan, *ibid.*, **71**, 2953 (1950); **74**, 1147, 1154 (1952).

(5) *Cf.* D. J. Cram, *ibid.*, **71**, 3863 (1949); **74**, 2129, 2159 (1952); and later papers.

(6) C. J. Collins and W. Bonner, *ibid.*, **75**, 5372 (1953); **77**, 72, 99 (1955).

or the other have been decisively demonstrated by these methods, notably "phenonium" (II)[4a,5] and "norbornonium" (III)[4b] cations.

III

With many substances, the stereochemical and reaction rate procedures are not readily applicable and the isotopic tracer technique[3] can yield information of value.[7] By this means, intermediates such as I have been shown to be of relatively minor importance in carbonium ion type processes where R_1 = H (IV, V)[3d,f] but possibly of more significance where R_1 = C_6H_5(VI).[3g] The state of affairs for *symmetrical* cations such as I, with R_1 = alkyl, is as yet unsettled. Although there is strong evidence for "methylene participation" in the strained norbornyl system (*i.e.*, to give III)[3c,j46] the tendency to form VII is relatively smaller.[3i]

In the present investigation, the stability of the methyl-bridged cation VIII with respect to its classic isomers IX and X has been studied. This

IX   VIII

X

system is particularly interesting since it provides an unusual opportunity to distinguish experimentally between the non-classical cation VIII and an equilibrium mixture of the classical cations IX and X. Thus, if one carries out a cationic reaction with a 2,3,3-trimethyl-2-butyl-1-C^{14} derivative (XI) and the intermediate were the symmetrical nonclassical cation VIII, with equivalent carbon atoms at positions 2 and 3, it should be clear that a 50–50 mixture of the two possible C^{14}-labeled products (corresponding to XI and XII) would be expected. On the other hand, if an equilibrium mixture of the classical cations IX and X is involved, one would expect a product mixture corresponding to statistical mixing of methyl groups, *i.e.*, 60% of the C^{14}-label at position 4 and 40% at position 1. The argument is only valid for irreversible carbonium reactions, *i.e.*, where the intermediate is formed irreversibly from the starting material and is converted irreversibly to the final product. If the initial formation of the intermediate is reversible, we could have an isotope-position rearrangement of the starting material and if the product-forming reaction is reversible, we might have a rearrangement of the first-formed product. In either case, a reversible reaction involving intermediate VIII would lead to the same products as from an equilibrium mixture of ions IX and X.

(7) A relatively complete discussion (for which no great originality is claimed) has been given earlier.[3d]

XIa, X = OH   XIIa, X = OH
XIb, X = Cl   XIIb, X = Cl

Synthetic and Degradative Methods

2,3,3-Trimethyl-2-butanol-1-C^{14} was synthesized through the reaction of pinacolone with methyl-C^{14}-magnesium iodide.[8] The method of locating the C^{14} in the methyl groups of pentamethylethyl derivatives depended on their conversion to 2,3,3-trimethyl-1-butene. With alcohol XIa, this was achieved reasonably satisfactorily by dehydration with phenyl isocyanate. With the chlorides, the most satisfactory procedure involved dehydrohalogenation with dimethylaniline. The subsequent degradation of the alkene is shown in the equation

2,4-dinitrophenylhydrazone   ***p*-bromophenacyl ester**

The substances whose formulas are printed in boldfaced type were analyzed for C^{14}. The C^{14}-analyses on the degradation products obtained by dehydration of alcohol XIa with phenyl isocyanate are given in Table I. Clearly, the rearrangement in the preparation of XIa and its degradation was relatively small (3–6%).

Results and Discussion

The extent of rearrangement in the carbonium ion type reactions of 2,3,3-trimethylbutyl-1-C^{14} derivatives (XI) was found to depend markedly on the degree of reversibility of the processes as defined by the reaction conditions. For example, treatment of the alcohol XIa with Lucas reagent (concentrated hydrochloric acid–zinc chloride solution) for three hours at room temperature gave a chloride in which the methyl groups were completely equilibrated, *i.e.*, a 60:40 mixture of XIb and XIIb (Table I). The experiment gives no real information regarding the role of the non-classical ion VIII since the reaction was completely reversible as shown by the fact that, under the same conditions, the chloride was completely equilibrated with Lucas reagent containing radioactive chloride ion (Table II). In circumstances where the reaction was less reversible, less rearrangement was observed. Thus, with concentrated hydrochloric acid at room temperature in 20 minutes, 36% of the rearranged chloride XIIb was detected and the extent of exchange with radioactive hydrochloric acid

(8) The methyl iodide used in the preparation of the Grignard reagent was obtained from Tracerlab, Inc., on allocation from the U. S. Atomic Energy Commission.

TABLE I

REARRANGEMENT IN REACTIONS OF 2,3,3-TRIMETHYL-2-BUTYL-1-C14 DERIVATIVES

Reaction	2,3,3-Trimethyl-1-butene[a]	Pinacolone DNPH[a,b]	CBr4[a]	BrPA[c] trimethyl acetate[a]	Rearr., % A[d]	B[e]	Av.
2,3,3-Trimethyl-2-butanol-1-C14 dehydrated with	3510 ± 16	1748 ± 21	1327 ± 9	109 ± 12	3.1	3.5	3
C6H5NCO	2918 ± 14	1468 ± 17	1283 ± 14	174 ± 9	6.0	6.3	6
2,3,3-Trimethyl-2-butanol-1-C14 with Lucas reagent, room temp., 3 hr.	2946 ± 27	2363 ± 8	586 ± 3	1706 ± 54	57.9	57.9	58
2,3,3-Trimethyl-2-butanol-1-C14 with concd. HCl, 25°, 20 min.	2172 ± 15	1817 ± 25	412 ± 4	1291 ± 15	59.4	57.9	59
2,3,3-Trimethyl-2-butanol-1-C14 with concd. HCl, 0°, 1 min.	3340 ± 36	2122 ± 24	928 ± 6	1136 ± 5	34.0	37.3	36
2,3,3-Trimethyl-2-butyl-1-C14 chloride[h] with water, room temp.	2404 ± 18	1294 ± 2	1023 ± 21	273 ± 5	11.4	11.7	12
	.......[f]	0.1256[g]	0.0905[g]	0.0344[g]	..	15.9	(16)[i]
	.......[f]	0.1080[g]	0.0767[g]	0.0265[g]	..	14.4	(14)[i]

[a] Corrected C14-activities with standard deviations in c./min./labeled carbon atom calculated as described earlier[3a] from activities (corrected for background) of "infinitely-thick" barium carbonate precipitates prepared as described by J. D. Roberts, W. Bennett, E. W. Holroyd, Jr., and C. H. Fugitt, *Anal. Chem.*, **20**, 904 (1948), and measured in a window-less methane-filled proportional counter ("Nucleometer," Radiation Counter Laboratories). [b] DNPH = 2,4-dinitrophenylhydrazone. [c] BrPA = *p*-bromophenacyl. [d] A = activity of bromophenacyl ester/activity of alkene × 100. [e] B = activity of bromophenacyl ester/(activity of dinitrophenylhydrazone plus carbon tetrabromide) × 100. [f] The alkene gave erratic results in the Van Slyke oxidation. [g] C14-Activity in μc./millimole determined with vibrating-reed electrometer (Applied Physics Corp.) as described by O. K. Neville, THIS JOURNAL, **70**, 3499 (1948). [h] The chloride was part of the product which showed 15.9% rearrangement on degradation *via* dehydrohalogenation with dimethylaniline. [i] Single value.

was 17%.[9] Treatment of the alcohol XIa with concentrated hydrochloric acid at 0° for one minute gave still less rearrangement (12–16%) and about 2% of exchange with radioactive hydrochloric acid (see Tables I and II).[9] The system is clearly labile, but the tendency for rearrangement can be greatly reduced by working under mild conditions.[10] The small extent of rearrangement under mild conditions obviously indicates that the symmetrical non-classical cation VIII is not the principal cationic intermediate in the irreversible reactions of the alcohol XIa with hydrochloric acid. At *most*, only one of about four alcohol molecules could be converted to the cation VIII in reaction with concentrated hydrochloric acid. This is obviously an *upper* limit since, although conditions were found where the chloride-forming step appeared to be essentially irreversible, there is a good possibility of reversibility (and rearrangement) in carbonium ion formation from the starting alcohol as shown in the equations

CH3—C(CH3)(CH3)—C(OH)(CH3)... $\overset{H^{\oplus},\, -H_2O}{\underset{H_2O,\, -H^{\oplus}}{\rightleftarrows}}$

CH3—C(CH3)(CH3)—C$^{\oplus}$(CH3)... $\overset{\overset{\ominus}{Cl}}{\rightarrow}$ CH3—C(CH3)(CH3)—C(Cl)(CH3)...

Thus, when the cation is formed from the alcohol in hydrochloric acid solution, it may return to alcohol

(9) The extents of exchange in these experiments may be low because the reactions were heterogeneous. As a result, it does not seem desirable to attach more than qualitative significance to the ratios of exchange and isomerization reaction rates.

(10) In a recent paper, H. C. Brown and R. B. Kornblum, THIS JOURNAL, **76**, 4510 (1954), report substantially less rearrangement in the reactions of 2,2,3-trimethyl-3-pentanol and 2,3,3-trimethyl-2-pentanol with hydrogen chloride than we observed with 2,3,3-trimethyl-2-butanol-1-C14 under similar conditions. One possible difference between the two systems is that interconversion of the *t*-amyldimethylcarbinyl and *t*-butylethylmethylcarbinyl cations through methyl migration necessitates eclipsing an ethyl and three methyl groups in two pairs which would be sterically less favorable than eclipsing four methyls in two pairs as in VIII.

or pick up chloride ion (irreversibly) to yield organic chloride. If water competes favorably (as it should) with chloride ion for the carbonium ion, then each molecule of alcohol might be converted many times to cation (each time with slight rearrangement) before being converted to chloride. This interpretation is favored by the lack of rearrangement in neutral hydrolysis of the chloride (see below) where all of the reaction steps are likely to be irreversible.

We infer from the foregoing that the non-classical ion VIII is less stable than its classical isomers IX and X *provided* that reversibility of the reaction in question is adequately indicated by the exchange experiments and the mechanism involves a carbonium ion intermediate rather than a SN*i*-type process between the alcohol and undissociated hydrogen chloride molecules as shown in the equation

CH3—C(CH3)(CH3)—C(CH3)(O—H···Cl···H)—C14H3 → CH3—C(CH3)(CH3)—C(CH3)(Cl)—C14H3 + H2O

Although there is not much direct evidence for the participation of carbonium ion intermediates in the reaction of tertiary alcohols with hydrochloric acid, the general character of such processes is in harmony with a carbonium ion mechanism. Ample evidence is available for the carbonium-ion character of hydrolyses of tertiary chlorides[11] and we have used the hydrolysis reaction as a test of whether the alcohol–hydrochloric acid reaction behaves differently from a *bona fide* carbonium ion process. This experiment was carried out in the following way. 2,3,3-Trimethyl-2-butanol-1-C14 (XIa) was converted to the chloride with hydrochloric acid at 0° (one minute) and the chloride divided into two portions. One part was dehydrohalogenated with dimethylaniline and the isotope position C14-distribution of the resulting alkene compared with that of material obtained by hydrol-

(11) C. K. Ingold, "Structure and Mechanism in Organic Chemistry," Cornell University Press, Ithaca, N. Y., 1953, Chap. VII.

TABLE II

EXCHANGE BETWEEN HCl³⁶ AND 2,3,3-TRIMETHYL-2-BUTYL CHLORIDE

Reagent	Millimoles of chloride ion	Millimoles of organic chloride	CH₂Cl₂, ml.	Time, min.	Temp., °C.	AgCl³⁶ activities[a]		Exch., %
						Starting HCl solution	Organic chloride after reaction	
Concd. HCl[b]	98	7.4	2.0	1.0	0	1310 ± 44	15 ± 10	~1
Concd. HCl[b]	97	8.3	1.5	20	Room	978 ± 32	156 ± 15	17
Lucas reagent[c]	215	9.0	1.5	180	Room	1601 ± 54	1674 ± 56	110

[a] Measured activities corrected for background (~45 c./min.). For procedure see Experimental part. [b] 12.1 M hydrochloric acid. [c] Made from 9.60 g. of anhyd. zinc chloride and 6.0 ml. of concd. (12.1 N) hydrochloric acid.

ysis of another portion of the chloride with water at room temperature and treatment of the product with phenyl isocyanate (to convert the resulting mixture of alkene and alcohol to alkene). No significant difference in the amount of rearrangement by the two separate paths was observed and this fact provides another link in the chain of evidence that the *symmetrical* non-classical cation VIII is a relatively unimportant intermediate in the irreversible carbonium type reactions of pentamethylethyl derivatives in aqueous solution.[12] For all practical purposes, it seems valid to consider that VIII is less stable than the classical cations IX and X. Indeed, VIII may only be a transition state through which the latter ions are interconverted. From the accumulated evidence,[3] we may expect that similar situations will be encountered generally with aliphatic compounds, except where stereochemical, solvent or steric factors tend to make the non-classical cations more stable relative to their classical isomers.

Acknowledgment.—We are indebted to Mrs. Clare Regan and Mr. E. C. Stivers for the C¹⁴-analyses.

Experimental

2,3,3-Trimethyl-2-butanol-1-C¹⁴.—Pinacolone (24 g.) dissolved in 70 ml. of anhydrous ether was added dropwise over 3 hours to a solution of methyl-C¹⁴-magnesium iodide prepared under a nitrogen atmosphere by the reaction of 40 g. of methyl-C¹⁴ iodide (containing about 0.3 mc. of C¹⁴) with 7 g. of magnesium in 160 ml. of anhydrous ether. The mixture was refluxed for an hour after the addition was complete and the complexes were decomposed by shaking with saturated ammonium chloride solution and ice in a separatory funnel. The ether layer was separated and the aqueous solution extracted four times with 20-ml. portions of ether. The combined extracts were dried with magnesium sulfate, 70 ml. of anhydrous benzene was added and the ether removed by distillation. Barium oxide (45 g.) was added to the benzene solution, the mixture refluxed for three hours, and then distilled at 5–10 mm. Inactive alcohol (14.2 g.) was added to the distillate and the mixture distilled through a carefully-dried 60 × 1-cm. helix-packed column. The yield of 2,3,3-trimethyl-2-butanol-1-C¹⁴ was 88.5 g., b.p. 129–131°. The yield was 74% when account was taken of the carrier carbinol. The product must be carefully protected from moisture since it very readily forms the crystalline hydrate, m.p. 80.9–81.2°.

2-Chloro-2,3,3-trimethylbutane-x-C¹⁴.—The following experiment is typical and illustrates the isolation procedure. 2,3,3-Trimethyl-2-butanol-1-C¹⁴ (4.1 g.) was stirred vigorously for 20 minutes at room temperature with 10 ml. of methylene chloride and 50 ml. of concentrated hydrochloric acid. The aqueous layer was separated and extracted with fresh methylene chloride. The combined methylene chloride extracts were dried over magnesium sulfate and the solvent distilled, the latter part under reduced pressure. The residue was sublimed under reduced pressure and yielded 4.5 g. (94%) of chloride, m.p. 130.2–132.6° (sealed tube).

2,3,3-Trimethyl-1-butene-x-C¹⁴. A. From 2,3,3-Trimethyl-2-butanol-1-C¹⁴.—A mixture of 4.8 g. of the C¹⁴-labeled alcohol, 14 g. of phenyl isocyanate and 2–4 drops of pyridine was refluxed for four hours in an oil-bath at 150°. The material then was distilled and the fraction boiling below 90° collected. The distillate was washed three times with 10-ml. portions of cold water and dried over calcium chloride. Distillation from barium oxide through a semi-micro column[13] yielded 2.6 g. (62%) of alkene, b.p. 78°. A sample of this material absorbed 99.2% of the calculated amount of hydrogen over platinum oxide.

B. From 2-Chloro-2,3,3-trimethylbutane-x-C¹⁴.—2-Chloro-2,3,3-trimethylbutane-x-C¹⁴ (5 g.) was refluxed with 40 ml. of dimethylaniline for 1.75 hours. The mixture was distilled through a semi-micro column[10] and gave 3.2 g. (88%) of 2,3,3-trimethyl-1-butene-x-C¹⁴, b.p. 78°.

The infrared spectra of samples of the alkene prepared from the alcohol and chloride were identical except for faint carbonyl absorption in the material prepared by the phenyl isocyanate dehydration.

Degradation Procedure for 2,3,3-Trimethyl-1-butene-x-C¹⁴.—The alkene (2.6 g.) was shaken mechanically with a solution of 17 g. of sodium permanganate trihydrate in 170 ml. of water contained in a glass-stoppered bottle for 1.5 hours. During the reaction period, the mixture was maintained at 10–20°. The unreacted permanganate and manganese dioxide were destroyed by bubbling sulfur dioxide through the ice-cooled reaction mixture. The organic material was extracted with five 20-ml. portions of ethanol-free ether. The combined extracts were dried with anhydrous magnesium sulfate, the ether removed through a short column and the residue distilled through a semi-micro column.[10] The yield of pinacolone was 0.84 g. (33%), b.p. 102–106°. The product was converted to the 2,4-dinitrophenylhydrazone, m.p. 127°, for C¹⁴-analysis.

Pinacolone-x-C¹⁴ (1.0 g.) was stirred for three hours with a mixture of 1.8 ml. of bromine, 12 g. of sodium hydroxide and 40 ml. of water at 0–10°. The resulting precipitate of carbon tetrabromide was steam distilled, collected by filtration, pressed between filter papers and sublimed twice. The yield was 1.5 g. (46%), m.p. 95°.

The residue from the steam distillation was cooled and then cautiously acidified by addition of concentrated sulfuric acid. Silver sulfate (13 g.) was added and the mixture again steam distilled. The distillate was neutralized and the water removed under reduced pressure. The residual sodium trimethylacetate was converted to the p-bromophenacyl ester (m.p. 77.0–77.4° after three recrystallizations from ethanol–water) for C¹⁴-analysis.

Exchange Reactions between HCl³⁶ and 2-Chloro-2,3,3-trimethylbutane.[14]—The following experiment is illustrative of the procedures used in the exchange reactions for which no great accuracy is claimed because of the heterogeneity of the reactions and difficulty of obtaining reproducible mixing.

An aliquot of a radioactive sodium chloride solution (containing Cl³⁶) was evaporated to dryness in a 50-ml. flask. The flask was evacuated and the residual salt (5.4 millimoles) was treated with 5 ml. of concentrated sulfuric acid. The resulting hydrogen chloride was condensed in a liquid air-cooled trap containing 9.0 ml. of ordinary concentrated hydrochloric acid. The trap was allowed to warm to room temperature, thoroughly mixed, and 8.2 ml. of the resulting radioactive hydrochloric acid was shaken vigorously with 1.00 g. of 2-chloro-2,3,3-trimethylbutane and 2.0 ml. of

(12) A similar situation has been noted by D. J. Cram and J. D. Knight, THIS JOURNAL, **74**, 5839 (1952), with regard to formation of cations like VIII in solvolysis reactions of 3,4-dimethyl-3-phenylhexyl derivatives.

(13) C. W. Gould, G. Holzman and C. Niemann, *Anal. Chem.*, **20**, 361 (1948).

(14) The Cl³⁶ used in these experiments was obtained from the Oak Ridge National Laboratory on allocation from the U. S. Atomic Energy Commission.

methylene chloride at 0° for 1.0 minute in a separatory funnel. The layers were separated, and the aqueous portion extracted several times with 5-ml. portions of methylene chloride. The combined methylene chloride extracts were washed with water, dried over magnesium sulfate and concentrated. The residual 2-chloro-2,3,3-trimethylbutane was purified by sublimation under reduced pressure. The recovery was 0.60 g.

The following procedures were used to convert the chloride samples to silver chloride for radioactive assay. A portion of the aqueous hydrochloric acid solution containing about 1–2 millimoles of chloride ion was diluted to 5 ml. with water containing 1 ml. of 6 N nitric acid. The solution was warmed to about 50° and 10 ml. of 10% silver nitrate solution added rapidly with stirring. The precipitate of silver chloride was collected on a sintered-glass funnel, rinsed several times with acetone and dried in an evacuated desiccator over phosphorus pentoxide. The organic chloride (about 0.1–0.2 g.) was dissolved in 5 ml. of ethanol, warmed to 50–60° and a warm solution of 10 ml. of 10% silver nitrate containing 1 ml. of 6 N nitric acid was added with stirring. The precipitated silver chloride was collected and dried as above.

The samples for counting were prepared by weighing out identical amounts of silver chloride on copper dishes previously checked for radioactive contamination. The samples were counted in a methane-filled proportional counter ("Nucleometer," Radiation Counter Laboratories). Trials indicated that the manner of spreading of the samples in the sample dish was not critical provided the samples were spread reasonably evenly. In the experiment described above, the measured activities for 29.0-mg. samples of silver chloride corrected for background with standard deviations were 1309 ± 44 and 15 ± 10 counts per minute for the silver chloride from the original aqueous solution and the organic chloride from the reaction mixture, respectively.

In this experiment, the initial reaction mixture contained 98.5 millimoles of hydrochloric acid and 7.4 millimoles of organic chloride. If complete equilibration had occurred, the activity of the organic chloride would be (98.5/106) × 1310 ± 44 = 1220 ± 41 counts per minute. The extent of exchange was thus (15 ± 10/1220) × 100 or 1.2 ± 0.8%. Further experimental results regarding the exchanges are presented in Table II.

CAMBRIDGE 39, MASS.

28 | cis- and trans-2-Phenyl-cyclohexanols

Schaeffer and Collins, "Molecular Rearrangements VI" (Paper No. 28), using isotopic carbon labeling and isotope dilution to obtain a complete product analysis of the dehydration of *cis*- and *trans*-2-phenylcyclohexanol, show how much more complicated this reaction is than had been formerly supposed. The superficial analogy to 3-phenyl-2-butanol is largely destroyed by the relative conformational rigidity of the cyclohexane ring, which causes the equatorial phenyl in the *trans* isomer to be located unfavorably, for the most part, for participation compared to the ring-contracting migration of a ring methylene group. The phenonium ion mechanism here is limited to about 10% of the total dehydration, and about half of the 1-phenylcyclohexene is formed by a secondary isomerization of 3-phenyl-cyclohexene. The relatively clean dehydration of *cis*-2-phenylcyclohexanol-2-^{14}C proceeds without phenyl migration and hence without phenonium ion formation.

From: *J. Am. Chem. Soc.* **78**, 124–33 (1956)

[Contribution from the Chemistry Division of Oak Ridge National Laboratory]

Molecular Rearrangements. VI. The Dehydration of *cis*- and of *trans*-2-Phenylcyclohexanol[1]

By Howard J. Schaeffer[2] and Clair J. Collins

Received July 11, 1955

The dehyration of *cis*-2-phenylcyclohexanol-2-C[14] (Ia) with phosphoric acid has been shown to produce 88% 1-phenyl-cyclohexene (III) and 2% 3-phenylcyclohexene (IV), in qualitative agreement with the results of Price and Karabinos (ref. 3). When *trans*-2-phenylcyclohexanol-2-C[14] (IIa) was subjected to the same dehydrating conditions there was produced 21% of 1-phenylcyclohexene (III) but only 9% of 3-phenylcyclohexene (IV). These results are in disagreement with those of previous investigators (ref. 3). In addition to III and IV, the *trans*-alcohol IIa was shown to yield 4-phenylcyclohexene (V), 6%; 1-benzylcyclopentene (VI), 32%, and benzalcyclopentane (VII), approximately 20%. Phenyl migration was shown to occur during the formation of 1-phenylcyclohexene-1,2-C[14] (IIIab) from the *trans*-alcohol IIa. The same mixture of olefins as was produced from the dehydration of the *trans*-alcohol IIa was obtained when labeled 3-phenylcyclohexene (IV) was subjected to the dehydration conditions. These results are discussed, in terms of a mechanism which is consistent with the foregoing observations.

Introduction and Preliminary Results

The dehydrations, with phosphoric acid, of *cis*- and of *trans*-2-phenylcyclohexanol (I and II, respectively) were reported in 1940 by Price and Karabinos.[3] The results of this study were interpreted as evidence for the *trans* elimination of the elements of water in such dehydrations, since the *cis*-alcohol was reported to yield chiefly 1-phenyl-cyclohexene (III) whereas the *trans*-alcohol was said to yield predominantly 3-phenylcyclohexene (IV).

It was suggested[3] that the small amount of isomeric olefin formed in each dehydration was the result either of (a) isomerization of the alcohols I ⇌ II before dehydration, or (b) competitive *cis* elimination of the elements of water from each carbinol.

The Chugaev reactions of the methyl xanthates, and the thermal decompositions of the acetates of I and II were not studied by Alexander and

Mudrak,[4] who showed that in each of these reactions *cis* elimination occurred, for the results were the reverse of those reported for the phosphoric acid-catalyzed dehydrations of I and II. Thus, both the acetate and the methyl xanthate of the *cis*-alcohol I yielded primarily 3-phenylcyclohexene (IV), whereas the corresponding *trans* compound yielded principally 1-phenylcyclohexene (III).

The difficulties of determining the yields and identities of liquid, isomeric olefins are indicated by Alexander and Mudrak,[4] who measured the refractive indices of the redistilled products from each reaction for this purpose. These authors point out that the yields calculated by Price and Karabinos[3] are based upon an incorrect refractive index for 3-phenylcyclohexene, but state that the general conclusions[3] concerning the acid-catalyzed dehydrations of I and II remain valid.[5]

By the use of the carbon-14 dilution technique,[6] a method not available to Price and Karabinos at the time of their experiments, it should be possible, by employing carbon-14 labeled reactants, to gain accurate information concerning the yields of olefins III and IV upon dehydration of *cis*-2-phenylcyclohexanol (Ia) and *trans*-2-phenylcyclohexanol (IIa). It should be possible also to determine whether the small amount of 1-phenylcyclohexene (IIIab) obtained upon dehydration of alcohol IIa is the consequence of *cis* elimination of the elements of water, or of participation of the phenyl group during removal of the hydroxyl ion. This latter possibility has been speculated upon by Cram.[5] Thus, in the dehydration of *trans*-2-

(1) This paper was presented at the 128th meeting of the American Chemical Society, Minneapolis, Sept., 1955, and is based upon work performed under Contract Number W-7405-eng-26 for the Atomic Energy Commission at Oak Ridge National Laboratory; previous paper, C. J. Collins, This Journal, **77**, 5517 (1955).

(2) Graduate Fellow of the Oak Ridge Institute of Nuclear Studies from the University of Florida, Gainesville. This paper is taken from the Ph.D. dissertation of H. J. Schaeffer. Senior advisor, University of Florida, Professor W. M. Lauter.

(3) C. C. Price and J. V. Karabinos, This Journal, **62**, 1159 (1940).

(4) E. R. Alexander and A. Mudrak, *ibid.*, **72**, 1810 (1950).

(5) See, however, D. J. Cram, *ibid.*, **74**, 2137 (1952), footnote 2.

(6) R. H. Mayor and C. J. Collins, *ibid.*, **73**, 471 (1951).

phenylcyclohexanol-2-C^{14} (IIa) the contribution of such an intermediate ion[5] as A, for example, should

A

lead to the formation of 1-phenylcyclohexene-1,2-C$_1^{14}$ (IIIab) in which the radioactive carbon is equally divided between the 1- and 2-positions of the cyclohexene ring.

We have repeated the experiments of Price and Karabinos[3] employing *cis*-2-phenylcyclohexanol-2-C^{14} (Ia) and *trans*-2-phenylcyclohexanol-2-C^{14} (IIa), and have determined the yields, for the dehydration of each alcohol, of olefins III and IV. In addition, for the dehydration of IIa, three further olefins have been identified as products, and the extent of phenyl participation in the formation of 1-phenylcyclohexene (IIIab) has been determined. On the basis of our experiments, it has been necessary to modify certain conclusions of the previous investigators.[3] The experimental methods employed, the results of these experiments, and the conclusions drawn from the present work are discussed in the following sections.

Yields of 1-Phenylcyclohexene (IIIa) and 3-Phenylcyclohexene (IVa) on Dehydration of Alcohols Ia and IIa.—The dehydrations of the *cis*- and the *trans*-alcohols Ia and IIa each labeled with carbon-14 in the 2-position were carried out by heating under reflux for four hours equal weights of the appropriate alcohol and 85% phosphoric acid. The mixture from dehydration of each alcohol was analyzed for olefins IIIa and IVa by means of the radioactivity dilution technique,[6] which is described in detail (as are the synthetic procedures), later in this paper. The results of these experiments are given in Table I, and are compared with those of Price and Karabinos.[3]

Although the results of the dehydration of the *cis*-alcohol Ia are in qualitative agreement with those of Price and Karabinos,[3] the results of dehydration of the *trans* compound IIa are in disagreement. Thus, in our hands, the *trans*-alcohol underwent dehydration to produce more 1-phenylcyclohexene (IIIa) than the 3-isomer IVa in the ratio of 2:1. In addition, the two olefins IIIa and IVa previously reported as the sole products of these reactions, account for only 30% of the material yield in the dehydration of the *trans*-alcohol IIa.

Molecular weight determinations of the oil from the dehydration of IIa suggested that this product was a mixture of monomers of the same approximate molecular weight as the olefins IIIa and IVa. The ease of oxidation of this mixture with permanganate suggested the presence of unsaturation.

Our attack on the problem, therefore, was to (1) synthesize a number of olefins isomeric with III and IV, which we suspected by reason of our ability to justify them mechanistically might be

present in this mixture; (2) add a weighed amount of each purified olefin to a separate aliquot of the mixture obtained on dehydration of II; (3) re-isolate the olefin after homogenizing the solution; (4) convert this olefin to a solid derivative and purify to constant radioactivity content; (5) calculate, from the foregoing data, the yield of the particular olefin.

TABLE I

YIELDS OF 1-PHENYLCYCLOHEXENE (III) AND OF 3-PHENYL-CYCLOHEXENE (IV) UPON PHOSPHORIC ACID DEHYDRATION OF *cis*-2-PHENYLCYCLOHEXANOL (Ia) AND OF *trans*-2-PHENYLCYCLOHEXANOL (IIa)

Expt.	Reactant	Yield, %	
		Of III	Of IV
1	*cis*-Alcohol Ia	88	2.4
Ref. 3	*cis*-Alcohol I	56–62	9–17
2	*trans*-Alcohol IIa	18.8	9.6
3	*trans*-Alcohol IIa	20.8	Av. 21.0	9.0 Av. 9.3
4	*trans*-Alcohol IIa	23.4		
Ref. 3	*trans*-Alcohol II	10–18	59–68

Additional Methods and Results

Synthetic and Degradative Methods.—The syntheses of *cis*- and *trans*-2-phenylcyclohexanol-2-C^{14} (Ia and IIa) were accomplished as shown in Chart I, the carbon-14 being introduced in the preparation of pimelonitrile-1,7-C$_2^{14}$. The radiochemical structures of the products were established by oxidation of 1-phenylcyclohexene-1-C^{14}, of 2-phenylcyclohexanone-2-C^{14} and of Ia and IIa to benzoic acid. The benzoic acid fractions obtained from these oxidations possessed lower molar radioactivities than the compounds oxidized by about 2–3%. These results indicate that the alcohols Ia and IIa are discretely labeled with carbon-14 in the 2-position at least to the extent of 97–98%. The lower radioactivity assays of the benzoic acid fractions are caused in all probability by isotope effects occurring during the oxidation of these compounds.

1-Phenylcyclohexene-1-C^{14} (IIIa) was prepared as indicated in Chart I. The degradation of IIIa and the conversion of it to a derivative suitable for radioactivity assay were accomplished in three ways: (a) oxidation of the olefin with potassium permanganate to δ-benzoylvaleric acid (VIII), (b) preparation of the solid 1-phenylcyclohexene nitrosochloride (X), and (c) preparation of 2-phenyl-2-cyclohexenone oxime (XI), followed by oxidation of these derivatives to benzoic acid.

3-Phenylcyclohexene (IV) labeled with carbon-14 was prepared by a modification of the Berlande[7a,b]

(7) (a) A. Berlande, *Bull. soc. chim.*, [V] **9**, 644 (1942). (b) In this paper Roman numerals have been used to designate the names of the various compounds where repetition of their names would be cumbersome. In the case of radioactive compounds, letters have been appended to the Roman numerals to indicate the position of labeling. Thus, IIa represents *trans*-2-phenylcyclohexanol-2-C^{14} discretely labeled in the 2-position whereas IIIab represents a mixture of 1-phenylcyclohexene-1,2-C^{14} labeled at both the 1- and 2-positions.

In the tables, radioactive 3-phenylcyclohexene has been labeled IVa although the amount of carbon-14 adjacent to the phenyl group is only 26% of the total radioactivity. In the synthesis of radioactive 3-phenylcyclohexene an allylic rearrangement probably occurs so that the carbon-14 is distributed among the 1-, 2- and 3-positions in the ratio of 1:2:1. For an example of this type of rearrangement in symmetrical molecules, see R. F. Nystrom and J. C. Leak, THIS JOURNAL, **75**, 3039 (1953).

CHART I

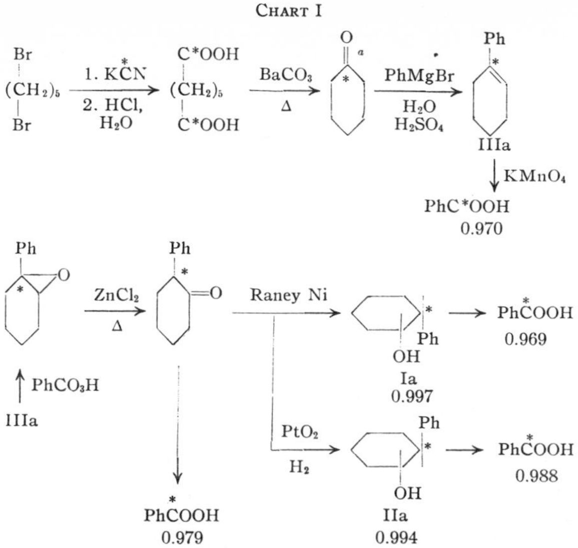

Br
|
(CH$_2$)$_5$ $\xrightarrow{\substack{1.\ KC^*N \\ 2.\ HCl,\ H_2O}}$ C*OOH
| |
Br   (CH$_2$)$_5$ $\xrightarrow{\substack{BaCO_3 \\ \Delta}}$
                                                      |
                                                      C*OOH

$\xrightarrow{\substack{PhMgBr \\ H_2O \\ H_2SO_4}}$ (IIIa) $\xrightarrow{KMnO_4}$ PhC*OOH   0.970

PhCO$_3$H (up arrow) ← (from epoxide)

$\xrightarrow{\substack{ZnCl_2 \\ \Delta}}$ (ketone =O) $\xrightarrow{Raney\ Ni}$ (Ia OH, Ph) 0.997   → PhČOOH 0.969

IIIa

$\xrightarrow{\substack{PtO_2 \\ H_2}}$ (IIa Ph, OH) 0.994   → PhČOOH 0.988

PhČOOH 0.979

a The molar radioactivity of this compound was taken as 1.000. The molar radioactivities of the other compounds listed in this chart are expressed as fractions of the original radioactivity of cyclohexanone-1-C^{14}.

method. Owing to the fact that the position of labeling was unimportant for the isomerization and stability experiments, the radiochemical structure of 3-phenylcyclohexene was not proven exhaustively. It was shown, however, that 26% of the carbon-14 in the cyclohexene nucleus was adjacent to the phenyl group (Table VI). In order to obtain a solid derivative suitable for radioactivity assay, 3-phenylcyclohexene was converted to the solid methoxychloromercury derivative XII, which was also oxidized to benzoic acid.

The synthesis of 4-phenylcyclohexene V was accomplished by the method of Konigsberger and Salmon.[8] This compound was converted to the solid β-phenyladipic acid upon oxidation with chromium trioxide.

1-Benzylcyclopentene (VI) was prepared as described by Denisenko and co-workers.[9,10] This compound was converted to its solid nitrosochloride and the radioactivity content of VI was determined by assay of this derivative.

Benzalcyclopentane (VII) was synthesized by a two-step reaction with benzylcyclopentene (VI) as the starting material. Anhydrous hydrogen bromide was added to VI to give 1-bromo-1-benzyl-cyclopentane which upon dehydrohalogenation with methanolic potassium hydroxide formed benzalcyclopentane (VII). Benzalcyclopentane is a difficult compound to prepare in pure form since (a) surprisingly, the double bond apparently is more stable in the unconjugated position (compound VI), and (b) most preparations of this material by the present authors contained appreciable amounts of a material, probably an oxidation

(8) C. Konigsberger and G. Salmon, *J. Polymer Sci.*, **1**, 353 (1946).
(9) Ya. I. Denisenko, *Ber.*, **69B**, 1668 (1936).
(10) Ya. I. Denisenko and V. M. Kotel'nikoma, *J. Gen. Chem.* (*U.S.S.R.*), **7**, 1357 (1937).

product, which was difficult to remove (see Experimental section). This compound was degraded by ozonolysis to benzaldehyde whose 2,4-dinitrophenyl-hydrazone was assayed for radioactivity. This latter assay was taken as a measure of the radioactivity content of olefin VII obtained as a dehydration product of IIa.

In order to ensure that the derivatives of the olefins were radiochemically pure, it was necessary to prepare the various derivatives from mixtures of non-radioactive and radioactive olefins whose radioactivity content was known and determine that no contamination had occurred. For example (see the Experimental section), the radiochemical purity of derivative VIII of 1-phenyl-cyclohexene was determined by oxidizing a mixture of 1-phenylcyclohexene-1-C^{14} (IIIa) and 3-phenylcyclohexene (IV) to δ-benzoyl-valeric acid (VIII). A 1% decrease in radioactivity was observed, the same decrease observed upon oxidation of pure IIIa, and most probably caused by an isotope effect. This showed that there was no dilution of the radioactivity by an oxidation product of IV.

Identification of Further Products in the Dehydration of *trans*-2-Phenylcyclohexanol-2-C^{14} (IIa).—In order to determine which compounds, other than IIIa and IVa, were formed as a result of the dehydration of *trans*-2-phenylcyclohexanol, this reaction was repeated using labeled IIa, and the product was divided into several aliquots. To each aliquot a different one of the non-radioactive olefins, 1-phenylcyclohexene (III), 3-phenylcyclo-hexene (IV), 4-phenylcyclohexene (V), 1-benzyl-cyclopentene (VI) and benzalcyclopentane (VII) was added. Each of the aliquots was usually subjected to some initial physical method for separating the compound which had been added (and which now was mixed with the radioactive olefin of identical structure which has been formed on dehydration). After this initial partial purification, the liquid compound in question was converted to its appropriate solid derivative. After repeated crystallization of this derivative until its radioactivity content was constant between crystallizations, the yield could be determined with high accuracy. The results of these experiments are given in Table II, together with those results included previously in Table I. The total material yield of these products is about 90%, leaving 10% of the reaction mixture unaccounted for. It is possible, therefore, that one or more unknown products of this reaction may require future identification.

Effect of Dehydrating Conditions on 1- and 3-Phenylcyclohexenes (III and IV).—The stability of 1-phenylcyclohexene (III) was determined by subjecting equal weights of the olefin III and phosphoric acid to the dehydration conditions. The experiments were performed in two ways: (a) by refluxing equal weights of non-radioactive 1-

TABLE II

PRODUCTS FORMED UPON DEHYDRATION OF *trans*-2-PHENYLCYCLOHEXANOL (IIa)

Expt.					
2	18.8%				
3	20.8	9.6%			
4	23.4	9.0	6.0%	31.6%	
5			5.7	32.5	*ca.* 20%
Average	21.0	9.3	5.8	32	

phenylcyclohexene and phosphoric acid for 4 hours, diluting with a known weight of 1-phenyl-cyclohexene-1-C[14], and oxidizing the mixture to δ-benzoylvaleric acid (VIII); and (b) by the reverse of the above procedure, that is, by subjecting 1-phenylcyclohexene-1-C[14] (IIIa) to the dehydrating conditions and diluting with 1-phenylcyclohexene before preparing the derivative. From each of these experiments, the loss of 1-phenylcyclohexene under the dehydration conditions was calculated.

The stability of a mixture of 1-phenylcyclohexene-1-C[14] (IIIa) and non-radioactive 3-phenylcyclohexene (IV) was next examined. In this case it was necessary to prepare two derivatives of 1-phenylcyclohexene (III). One derivative of III was prepared from an undiluted aliquot of the olefins and the other was prepared from a diluted aliquot. With these two assays both the loss of 1-phenylcyclohexene (III) and the isomerization of 3-phenylcyclohexene (IV) to 1-phenylcyclohexene (III) were then calculated.

In order to test the stability of 3-phenylcyclohexene (IV), the radioactive olefin IV was heated with phosphoric acid under the same conditions used for dehydrating alcohols Ia and IIa. With the aid of the dilution technique the presence as well as the yields of each of the olefins III, IV, V, VI and VII were determined. It is to be noted that a mixture of the same five isomeric olefins was obtained from the isomerization of radioactive 3-phenylcyclohexene (IV) as was obtained from the dehydration of *trans*-2-phenylcyclohexanol-2-C[14] (IIa). All of these stability experiments are summarized in Table III.

That the isomerization of 3-phenylcyclohexene (IV) is not measurably reversible was demonstrated in two ways: (a) by subjecting a mixture of 1-phenylcyclohexene-1-C[14] (IIIa) and non-radioactive 3-phenylcyclohexene (IV) to the dehydrating conditions, diluting with 3-phenylcyclohexene (IV), and preparing the methoxychloromercury derivative XII of 3-phenylcyclohexene; and (b) by refluxing equal weights of non-radioactive benzalcyclopentane (VII) and phosphoric acid for 4 hours, diluting with radioactive 3-phenylcyclohexene (IV) and preparing the same derivative XII. Thus, it was found that neither 1-phenylcyclohexene (IIIa) nor benzalcyclopentane (VII) is isomerized to 3-phenylcyclohexene (see Table VI).

Determination of Phenyl Migration in Reactions Yielding 1-Phenylcyclohexene (III).—*cis*-2-Phenylcyclohexanol-2-C[14] (IIa) was dehydrated with phosphoric acid as described previously (see Tables I and II) to yield 87.7% of 1-phenylcyclohexene (IIIa). No phenyl migration occurred during this reaction since the benzoic acid obtained on oxidation of IIIa so prepared contained only 2.6% less radioactivity than the parent alcohol Ia, the same decrease of radioactivity observed on oxidation of both the discretely labeled alcohol and the discretely labeled olefin IIIa to benzoic acid, and explainable on the basis of an isotope effect (Chart II). Dehydration of *trans*-2-phenylcyclohexanol-2-C[14] (IIa) afforded 1-phenylcyclohexene (IIIab) which was oxidized to benzoic acid containing an average of 24.4% less carbon-14 than the parent alcohol (see Chart II). Radioactive 3-phenylcyclohexene (IV)[7b] was isomerized under the de-

TABLE III

ISOMERIZATION PRODUCTS OF 1-PHENYLCYCLOHEXENE AND OF 3-PHENYLCYCLOHEXENE IN REFLUXING PHOSPHORIC ACID

Expt.		Mole % reactant				Isomerization of IV to form, %			CH₂Ph	CHPh	Loss of, %
6	0.548	..	..	0.452	12.4[b]	..	..	..	..		6.6[c]
7	0.476	..	..	0.524	12.3[b]	...	..	..	..		7.9[c]
8	..	1.00	..	...	...	...	..	..	..		18.3
9	1.00	..	..	...	...	...	..	..	..		11.4
10	...	..	..	1.00	11.2	...	..	..	..		..
11	...	..	1.00	...	17.2	58.6[a]	11.5	5.9	*ca.* 3		..
12	...	..	1.00	...	6.8	76.2[a]	..	..	..		..

[a] This figure represents the 3-phenylcyclohexene remaining after isomerization.   [b] Av. 12.35.   [c] Av. 7.3.

hydration conditions to 1-phenylcyclohexene (III) and subsequent oxidation of III to benzoic acid indicated that phenyl migration had not occurred.

CHART II

DETERMINATION OF PHENYL MIGRATION IN 1-PHENYL-CYCLOHEXENE [III]

Expt.

1   I   OH   III a (1.000)^a (0.974)^b

2	1.000	0.767
3	1.000	.737
4	1.000	.765
II	IIIab Av.	.756^c

12   1.000   1.000   0.257

IV   IV

+

1.000   0.266

III

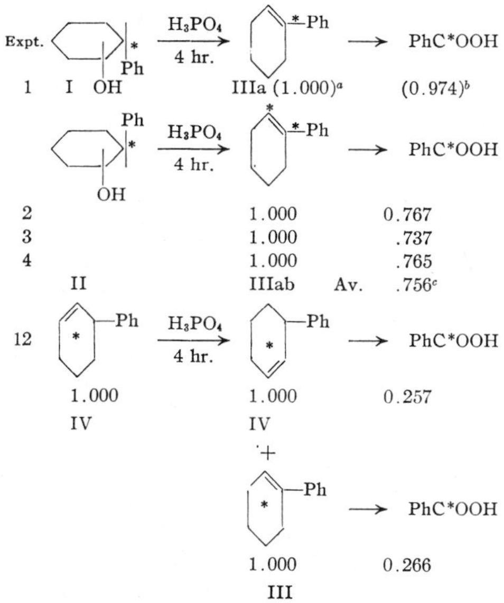

^{a} The molar radioactivity of product III is actually less than that of I, II or IV, owing to the use of carrier technique in which a known weight of non-radioactive olefin was added to an aliquot from the reaction mixture to facilitate preparation of a solid derivative. This procedure will be fully explained in the Experimental section. ^{b} The figure was obtained by dividing the molar radioactivity of the benzoic acid by that of IIIa. ^{c} This corresponds to a *net* phenyl migration of 24%, neglecting the small error introduced by the oxidative isotope effect.

Discussion

From Tables I, II and III it is apparent that the mechanism of dehydration of the *cis*- and *trans*-2-phenylcyclohexanols (I and II) is more complicated than had been previously thought.[3] The implications of these data are as follows: 1. From the fact that Ia and IIa yield the products III–VII in widely differing amounts, we may conclude that these two alcohols do not produce, upon dehydration, a common classical carbonium ion intermediate B. At least one of these alcohols and possibly both must, therefore, undergo dehydration *via* concerted processes.

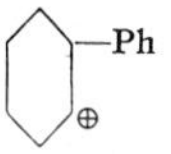

B

2. If a bridged ion (or its equivalent) were the only intermediate in the formation of 1-phenylcyclohexene (III) from the *trans* alcohol IIa, it is obvious that the radioactivity should be distributed equally between the 1- and the 2-positions of the cyclohexene ring. That the observed

phenyl migration is only 24%, however, is readily explainable by reason of the two paths of formation of 1-phenylcyclohexene during the dehydration of IIa. Let us consider that portion of the 1-phenylcyclohexene (IIIab) which is formed by participation of the phenyl group during dehydration, and assume that it has a 50:50 distribution of radioactivity between the 1- and the 2-positions. We have shown experimentally that the portion which is formed by the isomerization of 3-phenylcyclohexene yields unrearranged 1-phenylcyclohexene IIIa. With a knowledge of the total yield of 1-phenylcyclohexene (III) from the dehydration of *trans*-2-phenylcyclohexanol-2-C^{14} (IIa), it is possible to calculate the fraction of radioactivity which should be observed to be lost from the 1-position of the olefin IIIa and IIIab, if we assume that the extent of isomerization of IV → III during this reaction is the same as that observed when labeled IV is placed under similar conditions. Given in Table IV (column 2) are the data for the observed losses of radioactivity in the 1-position of 1-phenylcyclohexene (IIIa and IIIab) during dehydration experiments 2, 3 and 4 (Chart II). The average yield of III in these experiments was 21% (see Tables I and II). From Table III, the yields of III in experiments 6, 7, 10, 11 and 12 have been employed to calculate the percentages given in column 4 of Table IV.

TABLE IV

THE OBSERVED AND CALCULATED PERCENTAGE LOSS OF RADIOACTIVITY IN THE BENZOIC ACID OBTAINED FROM 1-PHENYLCYCLOHEXENE UPON DEHYDRATION OF *trans*-2-PHENYLCYCLOHEXANOL-2-C^{14}

Expt.	Obsd. C^{14} loss, %	Expt.	Calcd. C^{14} loss, %
2	23.3	6	20.5
3	26.3	7	21.0
4	23.5	10	23.7
Av.	24.4	11	9.6
		12	29.1
		Av.	20.8

These calculations, although admitting of much uncertainty, yet may be taken as evidence that the assumption is valid that the labeled 1-phenylcyclohexene formed directly from IIa upon dehydration possesses equal amounts of radioactivity in the 1- and 2-positions.

3. It is apparent that 4-phenylcyclohexene (V) must have 3-phenylcyclohexene IV as a precursor. A similar situation obtains for the formation of 1-benzylcyclopentene (VI); that is, it must have benzalcyclopentane (VII) as a precursor (Chart III). It is interesting and surprising that VII should isomerize to VI, with the migration of a double bond from a conjugated to a non-conjugated position. This isomerization is supported, however, by the fact (see Experimental section) that the olefin obtained upon acid-catalyzed dehydration of either phenylcyclopentylcarbinol or 1-benzylcyclopentanol could not be ozonized to produce significant yields of benzaldehyde.

4. The reaction mechanism outlined in Chart III is the simplest mechanism for the dehydration which is consistent with all of the experimental

observations. This mechanism, however, leaves unexplained the following facts: (a) that phenyl migration accompanies the dehydration of *trans*-2-phenylcyclohexanol (II) to 1-phenylcyclohexene (III), whereas phenyl migration does not accompany the isomerization of 3-phenylcyclohexene (IV) to the same olefin III; and (b) that ring contraction of II is preferred over phenyl participation by a factor of about five. By a consideration of the possible conformations which may be assumed by II and IV, these questions are capable of rationalization.

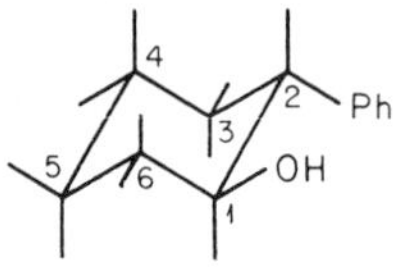

II-1 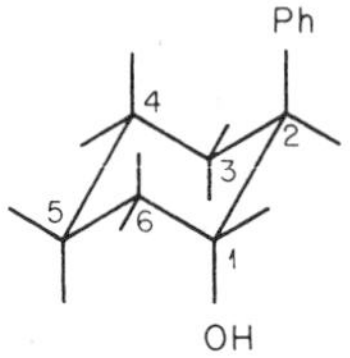   II-2

CHART III

PROPOSED MECHANISM FOR THE PHOSPHORIC ACID-CATALYZED DEHYDRATION OF *cis*- AND *trans*-2-PHENYLCYCLOHEXANOL

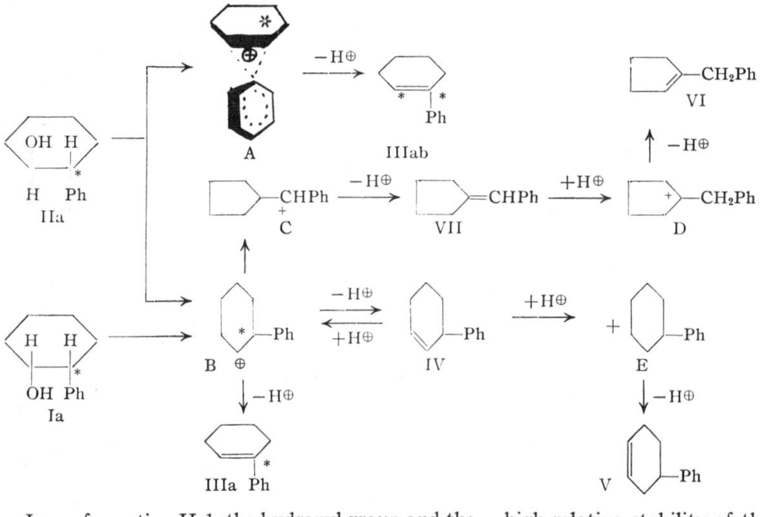

In conformation II-1, the hydroxyl group and the 1-, 2- and 3-carbon atoms all lie in the same plane, thus permitting easy access of the 3 carbon to backside attack on carbon 1, with resultant expulsion of the hydroxyl group and ring contraction. Although these conformations are undoubtedly in equilibrium, II-1 must surely be preferred over II-2, in which both phenyl and hydroxyl are in axial rather than in equatorial positions. It is only II-2, moreover, which can permit phenyl participation during hydroxyl removal, for only in this conformation are phenyl, hydroxyl and the 1 and 2 carbons in the same plane, thus permitting back-side attack of phenyl on carbon 1 with resultant hydroxyl expulsion and formation of 1-phenylcyclohexene (III). That ring contraction is preferred over phenyl participation by a factor

of approximately 5 may, therefore, be rationalized if one assumes a lowered activation energy for ring contraction in II-1 through the "equatorial effect" and an increased activation energy for phenyl migration through the "axial effect."[11a,b]

That ring contraction is preferred over simple elimination is not surprising, since it is only conformation II-2 which allows one of the hydrogens on the 6-carbon ready access to back-side attack on carbon 1. The question of the relative ability of hydrogen to migrate with respect to either alkyl or aryl groups, however, is anomalous, since it has been shown in a previous paper[1] that for the pinacol rearrangement of triphenylethylene glycol, the phenyl/hydrogen migration ratio may vary from 7.3 to 0.04, depending upon the acid catalyst used to effect the rearrangement.

Considering next the conversion of IV[7b] to 1-phenylcyclohexene III *without phenyl migration*, to V and to ring-contracted products, we are again faced with the peculiar position of hydrogen as a migrating group[1] relative to phenyl. It seems, however, that a concerted protonation of the double bond and concurrent ejection of hydrogen from the adjacent 3- or 6-positions of IV is a likely explanation for this result. That hydrogen ejection and ring contraction should be favored to the exclusion of phenyl migration seems reasonable in view of the possible conformations[11a] of a protonated 3-phenyl-cyclohexene structure. These facts are certainly not predictable, however, on the basis of conformational knowledge. Undoubtedly one of the factors favoring formation of 5-membered rings in this instance is the high relative stability of the potential benzyl-type carbonium ion produced upon contraction of the protonated form of IV.

5. Curtin and Schmukler[11b] have shown ring-contraction to be favored over phenyl migration by a factor of at least 100 in the deamination of *cis*-2-amino-1-phenylcyclohexanol, and by a factor of about 3 in the rearrangement of *cis*-2-chloro-1-phenylcyclohexanol. The latter is in the expected qualitative agreement with the ring contraction/

(11) (a) See, for example, H. D. Orloff, *Chem. Revs.*, **54**, 347 (1954), and D. H. R. Barton, R. C. Cookson, W. Klyne and C. W. Shoppee, *Chemistry & Industry*, 21 (1954); (b) D. Y. Curtin and S. Schmukler, THIS JOURNAL, **77**, 1107 (1955), have pointed out the importance of the "axial effect" in increasing the activation energy for phenyl participation in conformation II-2. Equally important is the "equatorial effect" for conformation II-1 by which the activation energy for ring contraction is decreased (see also references 11a).

phenyl migration ratio of about 5 for the dehydration of IIa.

6. Dehydration of the *cis* isomer Ia to produce labeled 1-phenylcyclohexene (IIIa) in preponderant yield, and without phenyl migration, is very simply rationalized. In the chair form, the *cis*-alcohol I may assume two conformations: (a) axial phenyl, equatorial hydroxyl and (b) equatorial phenyl, axial hydroxyl. In neither of these does the phenyl group have access to the back-side of carbon 1. Thus phenyl migration can never occur. In the latter conformation, however, *trans*-elimination of water is possible. To explain the high preference for elimination over ring contraction (a factor of greater than 10) it need only be assumed that the "axial-effect" of the phenyl group[11b] causes a preference for that reaction produced through the conformation in which phenyl is equatorial.

Acknowledgment.—The authors wish to acknowledge support and the helpful interest given this research by Professor W. M. Lauter. The authors also acknowledge helpful discussions with Dr. J. F. Eastham.

Experimental

1-Phenylcyclohexene-1-C[14] (IIIa).—Cyclohexanone-1-C[14], prepared by the method of Speer and co-workers,[12] was converted with phenylmagnesium bromide to 1-phenylcyclohexanol-1-C[14], and the latter alcohol was dehydrated to the olefin as previously described by Sabatier and Mailhe.[13] Thus, from 42.5 g. (0.43 mole) of the ketone there was obtained 58.7 g. (85%) of twice-distilled 1-phenylcyclohexene-1-C[14], b.p. 132–134° (20 mm.). This preparation was repeated several times yielding products whose molar radioactivities were 1–3 mc.

2-Phenylcyclohexanone-2-C[14].—By the method of Levy and Sfiras,[14] 45.5 g. (0.46 mole) of IIIa was converted to 51.0 g. (63%) of once-distilled 2-phenylcyclohexanone-2-C[14], b.p. 155–161° (15 mm.). After four crystallizations from petroleum ether (30–60°) a pure product was obtained, m.p. 63–64.5°.

cis-**2-Phenylcyclohexanol-2-C[14] (Ia).**—2-Phenylcyclohexanone-2-C[14] (8.0 g.) was dissolved in 100 ml. of absolute ethanol. Raney nickel catalyst (1.2 g.) was added and the mixture was hydrogenated at atmospheric pressure until the theoretical amount of hydrogen had been absorbed (37 hours). The catalyst was removed by filtration, the solvent was removed from the filtrate with the aid of an air stream, and the last traces of the solvent were removed in vacuum. The residue partially crystallized on cooling, the oil was removed by filtration, and the solid was recrystallized from petroleum ether (30–60°) to yield a first crop of the *cis*-alcohol (4.16 g.), m.p. 42–44°.[3] Concentration of the mother liquor yielded two further crops, m.p. 40–42° (total yield, 72%); phenylurethan; m.p. 127–128°.[3]

trans-**2-Phenylcyclohexanol-2-C[14] (IIa).**—2-Phenylcyclohexanone-2-C[14] (16 g., 0.14 mole) was dissolved in 75 ml. of absolute ethanol and 500 mg. of platinum oxide was added. The mixture was reduced overnight in a Parr hydrogenator with an initial pressure of 37.1 p.s.i. of hydrogen. The catalyst was removed by filtration and the solvent was evaporated so that 16.1 g. of a white solid was obtained. The alcohol was recrystallized from petroleum ether (30–60°) several times to yield 11.4 g. (70.5%) of *trans*-2-phenylcyclohexanol-2-C[14], m.p. 56–57°. The phenylurethan prepared from IIa had a m.p. of 137–138°.[13,15,16]

3-Phenylcyclohexene-C[14] (IV).—Cyclohexanone-1-C[14] (28.4 g., 0.29 mole) was dissolved in 75 ml. of absolute

methanol and 400 mg. of platinum oxide was added. The mixture was reduced overnight in a Parr hydrogenator with an initial pressure of 53.5 p.s.i. of hydrogen. In the morning the theoretical amount of hydrogen had been absorbed, so the catalyst was filtered, and the methanol was removed by distillation through an 18-inch Vigreux column. To the residue (28.4 g.), which was almost pure cyclohexanol-1-C[14], was added 12 g. of powdered fused potassium hydrogen sulfate and the mixture was distilled through an 18-inch Vigreux column at such a rate that the temperature at the top of the column remained between 75 and 80°.[17] In this way 23.6 ml. (83%) of cyclohexene-C[14] distilled. Non-radioactive cyclohexene (2 ml.) was added to the residue and it was distilled to scavenge the carbon-14 cyclohexene. The water in the distillate was separated from the cyclohexene-C[14], washed once with ether, the ether wash was combined with the cyclohexene-C[14], dried with magnesium sulfate and distilled. Pure cyclohexene-C[14] (23 ml.) distilled at 81–82°. Non-radioactive cyclohexene (2 ml.) was again added to the residue and distilled until the total volume of cyclohexene-C[14] was 25 ml. (0.246 mole). N-Bromosuccinimide (43.8 g., 0.246 mole), 25 ml. (0.246 mole) of cyclohexene-C[14] and 100 ml. of carbon tetrachloride were heated under reflux on a steam-bath for 1 hour, cooled, and the succinimide was removed by filtration. The carbon tetrachloride was removed from the filtrate by distillation and 21.4 g. (0.133 mole) of 3-bromocyclohexene-C[14] was obtained, b.p. 60–63° (12 mm.).[18] To the phenyl Grignard reagent (0.146 mole, 10% excess) prepared from 3.55 g. of magnesium and 22.9 g. of bromobenzene in 100 ml. of ether was added with cooling 21.4 g. (0.133 mole) of 3-bromocyclohexene-C[14]. After addition was completed the mixture was refluxed for 0.5 hour and decomposed with dilute hydrochloric acid. The ether solution was dried with anhydrous sodium carbonate, filtered, the ether was removed from the filtrate by distillation and the residue was distilled. 3-Phenylcyclohexene distilled at 76–79° (2 mm.) and weighed 14.8 g. (0.094 mole or 32% based on cyclohexanone-1-C[14]), n^{20}D 1.5448.

4-Phenylcyclohexene (V).—This olefin was prepared by a modification of the method of Konigsberger and Salmon.[8] 1,3-Butadiene (109 g., 2.2 moles), styrene (68 g., 0.64 mole) and 40 mg. of N-phenyl-2-naphthylamine were heated in a sealed tube at 100° for 120 hours, after which time the tube was cooled and opened. The plastic product was dissolved in hot benzene and most of the polystyrene was precipitated by the addition of methanol. The clear supernatant liquid was decanted, and the precipitate was subjected to the benzene–methanol treatment two more times. The solvent was removed from the decanted liquid by flash distillation and the residue was distilled. There was obtained 23.7 g. (0.15 mole) of 4-phenylcyclohexene, b.p. 115–116.6° (15 mm.), n^{20}D 1.5412.

1-Benzylcyclopentene (VI).—To 0.57 mole (20% excess) of benzylmagnesium chloride was added 40 g. (0.48 mole) of cyclopentanone. The excess Grignard reagent was decomposed by the addition of just sufficient water to completely hydrate the magnesium salts. The ether solution was decanted and the ether was removed in an air stream. After removal of the last traces of ether in a vacuum, the residue crystallized, and after repeated crystallizations from hexane, 82 g. (98%) of the pure 1-benzylcyclopentanol was obtained, m.p. 58–60°.

Anal. Calcd. for $C_{12}H_{16}O$: C, 81.77; H, 9.15. Found: C, 82.04, 82.00; H, 9.13, 9.20.

Denisenko[9] reported that this compound was a liquid, b.p. 129–130° (11 mm.). 1-Benzylcyclopentanol (44.4 g., 0.25 mole) was refluxed for 4 hours with 200 ml. of 20% aqueous oxalic acid. The two layers were separated and the aqueous layer was extracted with ether, the ether extract was combined with the olefin, washed with water, 5% aqueous sodium bicarbonate, again with water and dried with anhydrous magnesium sulfate. The ether was removed by distillation at atmospheric pressure and the residue was distilled through an 18-inch Vigreux column. 1-Benzylcyclopentene (23.9 g., 66%) distilled at 103–107° (11 mm.), n^{20}D 1.5367.[9,10]

Benzalcyclopentane (VII).—To 23.9 g. (0.15 mole) of 1-benzylcyclopentene at 0° was added 14.0 g. of dry hydrogen

(12) R. J. Speer, N. L. Humphries and A. Roberts, This Journal, **74**, 2443 (1952).

(13) P. Sabatier and A. Mailhe, *Compt. rend.*, **138**, 1323 (1904).

(14) J. Levy and J. Sfiras, *ibid.*, **187**, 45 (1928).

(15) J. von Braun, H. Gruber and G. Kirschbaum, *Ber.*, **55**, 3668 (1922).

(16) J. W. Cook, C. A. Lawrence and C. L. Hewitt, *J. Chem. Soc.*, 71 (1936).

(17) L. Brunel, *Bull. soc. chim.*, [III], **33**, 270 (1905).

(18) K. Ziegler, A. Spaeth, E. Schaaf, W. Schumann and E. Winklemann, *Ann.*, **551**, 80 (1942).

bromide over a 30-minute period. The cloudy solution was refluxed with 25% methanolic potassium hydroxide for 1.5 hours and allowed to stand overnight. Water (300 ml.) was added and the lighter olefin layer was separated. The aqueous layer was extracted with ether, the ether extract was combined with the olefin layer, washed with water and dried with anhydrous sodium carbonate. The ether was removed by distillation at atmospheric pressure and the residue was distilled through an 18-inch Vigreux column. There was obtained 7.8 g. of benzalcyclopentane, b.p. 108–118° (8.5 mm.), n^{20}D 1.5518.[19]

Preparation of Solid Derivatives of Olefins III, IV, V, VI and VII. (a) Potassium Permanganate Oxidation of 1-Phenylcyclohexene (III) to δ-Benzoylvaleric Acid (VIII).— In a typical experiment, 500 mg. (3.16 mmoles) of 1-phenyl-cyclohexene was dissolved in 40 ml. of acetone and a solution of 2.5 g. of potassium permanganate in 80 ml. of water was added. The mixture was stirred for 15 minutes after which time the oxidation was complete. The manganese dioxide was removed by filtration, and the filtrate was heated on a steam-bath to remove most of the acetone. The basic filtrate was extracted with chloroform, made acid with dilute sulfuric acid and extracted with ether. The ether extract was washed with water and the ether was evaporated leaving 205 mg. (31%) of δ-benzoylvaleric acid which was recrystallized alternately from hexane and water until its melting point was 77–78°.[20]

(b) 1-Phenylcyclohexene Nitrosochloride (X).—In one of several experiments 910 mg. (5.77 mmoles) of 1-phenylcyclohexene was dissolved in 2 ml. of glacial acetic acid and 0.6 ml. of hydrochloric acid was added. The flask was cooled in an ice-bath while 2.5 g. of isoamyl nitrite dissolved in 2 ml. of glacial acetic acid was added, with stirring, over a 15-minute period. The reaction mixture was stirred for an additional 15 minutes at 0°, 5 ml. of methanol was added, and the nitrosochloride (629 mg.) which precipitated was filtered, washed with methanol, with water and dried, m.p. 128–131° dec. Recrystallization from a mixture of methanol and chloroform produced the pure nitrosochloride, m.p. 134–135° dec. in agreement with the literature.[21]

(c) 2-Phenyl-2-cyclohexenone Oxime (XI).—To 1-phenyl-cyclohexene nitrosochloride (629 mg., 2.8 mmoles) prepared as previously described was added 10 ml. of ethanol and 450 mg. of potassium hydroxide dissolved in 2 ml. of water. The mixture was refluxed for 2 hours, poured into 100 ml. of water, cooled and filtered. The 2-phenyl-2-cyclohexenone oxime (313 mg. or 60%) obtained had a melting point of 151–153°. After two recrystallizations from methanol, the pure product was obtained, m.p. 156.5–157.5°.[21]

(d) Methoxychloromercury Derivative of 3-Phenylcyclohexene (XII).—3-Phenylcyclohexene (300 mg., 1.9 mmoles) was dissolved in 5 ml. of absolute methanol, 606 mg. (1.9 mmoles) of mercuric acetate was added, and the mixture was shaken until solution was complete. It was allowed to stand at room temperature for 46 hours, filtered, and to the filtrate was added 70 ml. of 10% aqueous sodium chloride solution. The resulting cloudy solution was allowed to stand for 4 hours before it was filtered. The crude derivative weighed 749 mg. (93%) after being washed with water and dried. Two recrystallizations from ethanol gave the pure compound, m.p. 154–155°. The above procedure is a modification of the method of Wright.[22]

(19) (a) We were unable to obtain a sample of benzalcyclopentane (VII) which contained more than 70% of the olefin (see Additional Methods and Results section). That the most satisfactory preparation did in fact contain VII, however, was evidenced by the yield (66%) of benzaldehyde 2,4-dinitrophenylhydrazone obtained upon ozonolysis of this material. The data of Tables V and VI for compound VII, therefore, were multiplied by two-thirds to obtain the percentage yields of this compound given in Tables II and III. We are indebted to C. C. Price, E. L. Eliel and J. A. McCoy for the information that they have experienced similar difficulty in preparing VII in a pure form. They report n^{20}D of 1.5752 for the purified samples of VII. (b) L. H. Groves and G. A. Swan, J. Chem. Soc., 871 (1951), report the preparation of this compound by the oxalic acid-catalyzed dehydration of cyclopentylphenylcarbinol. We were unable, however, to obtain a significant yield of benzaldehyde on ozonolysis of the product obtained by their method. Similar difficulties were encountered in the attempted dehydrations of 1-benzylcyclopentanol.

(20) K. von Auwers and W. Treppman, Ber., 48, 1217 (1915).

(21) C. F. Koelsch, THIS JOURNAL, 73, 2951 (1951).

(22) G. F. Wright, ibid., 57, 1993 (1935).

Anal. Calcd. for $C_{13}H_{17}OHgCl$: C, 36.71; H, 4.03; Hg, 47.16. Found: C, 36.72, 36.49; H, 4.08, 4.00; Hg, 47.02, 47.20.

(e) β-Phenyladipic Acid from 4-Phenylcyclohexene.—In a typical experiment 500 mg. (3.16 mmoles) of 4-phenylcyclohexene was dissolved in 10 ml. of glacial acetic acid and cooled in an ice-bath. A solution of chromium trioxide (850 mg.) in 0.5 ml. of concentrated sulfuric acid, 3 ml. of water and 5 ml. of glacial acetic acid was added dropwise over a 10-minute period while the reaction mixture was being stirred. The reaction mixture was allowed to warm to room temperature and was stirred for an additional 15 minutes, after which time it was poured into 200 ml. of water and extracted with ether. The ether extract was washed with water and extracted with 10% sodium hydroxide solution. The basic extract was made acid with dilute sulfuric acid and extracted with ether. The ether extract was washed with water and evaporated to dryness. There was obtained by this method 232 mg. (33%) of a solid, m.p. 137–140°. After two recrystallizations from a mixture of ether and benzene, a pure sample of β-phenyladipic acid was obtained, m.p. 147–148°.[23]

(f) 1-Benzylcyclopentene Nitrosochloride.—To a stirred solution of 500 mg. (3.16 mmoles) of 1-benzylcyclopentene (VI) in 1 ml. of glacial acetic acid and 1 g. of isoamyl nitrite cooled in an ice-bath was slowly added 1 ml. of concentrated hydrochloric acid. The mixture was stirred for an additional 15 minutes, 20 ml. of methanol was added, and the mixture was filtered. The white nitrosochloride (96 mg. or 14%) was washed with methanol, water and again with methanol; m.p. 108–109° dec. Two recrystallizations from a mixture of chloroform and methanol gave the pure product, m.p. 109.5–110.5° dec.

Anal. Calcd. for $C_{12}H_{14}ONCl$: C, 64.43; H, 6.31; Cl, 15.85. Found: C, 64.15, 63.86; H, 6.40, 6.35; Cl, 16.03, 16.19.

(g) Ozonolysis of Benzalcyclopentane to Benzaldehyde 2,4-Dinitrophenylhydrazone.—Benzalcyclopentane (0.9157 g.) was dissolved in 30 ml. of ethanol and a solution of 2.65 g. of 2,4-dinitrophenylhydrazine in 9 ml. of concentrated sulfuric acid, 5 ml. of water and 40 ml. of ethanol was added. The clear solution was ozonized for 45 minutes at room temperature after which the solid was filtered, washed with ethanol, hot water, hot ethanol and dried. The yield was 1.092 g. (66%), m.p. 211–218°. Two crystallizations from dioxane gave pure benzaldehyde 2,4-dinitrophenylhydrazone, m.p. 237–238°.[24] The melting point was not depressed when mixed with an authentic sample of benzaldehyde 2,4-dinitrophenylhydrazone.

Oxidation of Various Derivatives of 1-Phenylcyclohexene and 3-Phenylcyclohexene to Benzoic Acid. (a) Oxidation of δ-Benzoylvaleric Acid to Benzoic Acid.—In a typical experiment, 400 mg. (1.94 mmoles) of δ-benzoylvaleric acid, 2 g. of potassium permanganate, 2 ml. of 10% aqueous sodium hydroxide solution and 30 ml. of water were refluxed for 3 hours, cooled, and the excess potassium permanganate was destroyed with sodium bisulfite. The manganese dioxide was removed by filtration and washed with water. The basic filtrate was extracted with chloroform, made acid with dilute sulfuric acid and extracted with ether. The ether extract was washed with water and the solvent was evaporated so that 210 mg. (88%) of crude benzoic acid was obtained. Two recrystallizations from water produced the pure compound, m.p. 121–122°.

(b) Oxidation of 1-Phenylcyclohexene Nitrosochloride to Benzoic Acid.—To 147 mg. (0.62 mmole) of 1-phenylcyclohexene nitrosochloride was added a solution of 1 g. of chromium trioxide in 3 ml. of concentrated sulfuric acid, 3 ml. of water and 20 ml. of glacial acetic acid. The mixture was refluxed for 1 hour, cooled, poured into 200 ml. of water and extracted with ether. The ether extract was washed with water and extracted with 10% sodium hydroxide solution. The basic extract was made acid with dilute sulfuric acid and extracted with ether. On solvent evaporation there was 70.6 mg. (93%) of crude benzoic acid. One crystallization from water, followed by vacuum sublimation at 100° (12 mm.) produced the pure acid, m.p. 121–122°.

(23) R. H. Manske, ibid., 53, 1104 (1931).

(24) R. L. Shriner and R. C. Fuson, "The Systematic Identification of Organic Compounds," John Wiley and Sons, Inc., New York, N. Y., 3d Edition, 1948, p. 229.

TABLE V

RADIOCHEMICAL AND DILUTION DATA FOR THE PHOSPHORIC ACID DEHYDRATION OF *cis*-2-PHENYLCYCLOHEXANOL-2-C^{14} (Ia) AND OF *trans*-2-PHENYLCYCLOHEXANOL-2-C^{14} (IIa)

Expt.	Reactant and wt.	Carrier olefin and wt., g.^{a}	Aliquot of reacn. mixt., %	Radioactivity assay of deriv. mc./mole	Yield of added olefin from dehydration, %	Radioactivity assay of benzoic acid mc./mole
1	Ia, 2.8855 g.	III 0.6606	10	0.3401 ± 0.0004^b	87.7	0.3312
	1.330 mc./mole	IV 0.6118	40	.0519 ± .0002	2.4	
2	IIa, 2.0684 g.	III 1.4669	40	.1161 ± .0007^c	18.8	.0890 ± 0.00005
	1.334 mc./mole					
3	IIa, 2.1107 g.	III 0.9204	50	.2338 ± .0002^c	20.8	.1723 ± .0012
	1.326 mc./mole	IV .8285	20	.0554 ± .0004	9.6	
4	IIa, 4.9099 g.	III .7128	40	.9228 ± .0008^c	23.4	.7057 ± .0022
	2.518 mc./mole	IV .7831	20	.2315 ± .0001	9.0	
		V 1.0533	11.2	.0686 ± .0004	6.0	
		VI 2.0280	5.6	.0933 ± .0006	31.6	
5	IIa, 2.5957 g.	V 0.8810	30	·.1082 ± .00005	5.7	
	2.518 mc./mole	VI 1.0466	10	.1700 ± .00005	32.5	
		VII 0.8458		.1908 ± .0006	29.8	

^{a} The olefin in this column was added to the aliquot of the reaction mixture specified in column four. ^{b} Assayed as 2-phenyl-2-cyclohexenone oxime. ^{c} Assayed as 1-phenylcyclohexene nitrosochloride.

TABLE VI

RADIOCHEMICAL AND DILUTION DATA FOR THE PHOSPHORIC ACID ISOMERIZATION OF 1-PHENYLCYCLOHEXENE (III), 3-PHENYLCYCLOHEXENE (IV) AND BENZALCYCLOPENTANE (VII)

Expt.	Reactant and wt.	Carrier olefin and wt., g.^{d}	Aliquot of reacn. mixt., %	Radioactivity assay of deriv., mc./mole	Radioactivity assay of benzoic acid, mc./mole	Radioactivity in benzoic acid, %
6	IIIa, 2.2922 g.	III 0.5539	20	0.4140 ± 0.0025^a	....	....
	1.004 mc./mole	IV, 1.8858 g.	40	.8973 ± .0046^b	....	....
7	IIIa, 1.8946 g.	III .5316	20	.3756 ± .0007^a	....	....
	1.004 mc./mole	IV, 2.0852 g.	40	.8825 ± .0025^b	....	....
		IV .5636	40	.0004	....	....
8	III, 3.8703 g.	IIIa .3737	100	.1409 ± .0004^a	....	....
		1.334 mc./mole				
9	IIIa, 3.1477 g.	III 2.0729	100	.5707 ± .0007^a	....	....
	1.004 mc./mole					
10	IV, 1.1580 g.	IIIa 0.5875	100	1.088 ± 0.0010^a	....	....
		1.334 mc./mole				
11	IVa, 4.7652 g.	III 0.6340	15	0.3716 ± 0.0016^c	....	....
	2.293 mc./mole	IV .8094	15	.7816 ± .0024	....	....
		V .7874	15	.2168 ± .0002	....	....
		VI .9761	25	.1543 ± .0006	....	....
		VII .3080	30	.0990 ± .0006	....	....
12	IVa, 4.5558 g.	III 2.1201	60	.1860 ± .0008^e	0.0495 ± 0.0001	(26.6)^f
	2.293 mc./mole	IV 2.0946	40	.9143 ± .0005	.2346 ± .0005	(25.7)^e
13	VII, 2.4431 g.	IV 0.8132	100	2.235	....	....
	2.293 mc./mole					

^{a} Diluted with carrier olefin—assayed as δ-benzoylvaleric acid. ^{b} Undiluted olefin IIIa—assayed as δ-benzoylvaleric acid. ^{c} Diluted with carrier olefin—assayed as 1-phenylcyclohexene nitrosochloride. ^{d} The olefin in this column was added to the aliquot of the reaction mixture specified in column IV. ^{e} Percentage radioactivity adjacent to the phenyl group in IV. ^{f} Percentage radioactivity adjacent to the phenyl group in III obtained from the isomerization of IV.

(c) **Oxidation of 2-Phenyl-2-cyclohexenone Oxime to Benzoic Acid.**—The oxime (171 mg.) and a solution of 2.5 g. of potassium permanganate in 40 ml. of water were refluxed for 5 hours. The mixture was then cooled, the excess permanganate was destroyed with sodium bisulfite, and the manganese dioxide was filtered. The basic filtrate was extracted with chloroform, made acid with dilute sulfuric acid and extracted with ether. The ether extract was washed with water and the solvent was evaporated. In this way 53 mg. (47%) of crude benzoic acid was obtained. Crystallization from water followed by vacuum sublimation at 100° (12 mm.) produced the pure compound, m.p. 121–122°.

(d) **Oxidation of the Methoxychloromercury Derivative of 3-Phenylcyclohexene.**—The oxidation of the compound was performed in exactly the same way as was the oxidation

of 1-phenylcyclohexene nitrosochloride described above. In general, the yields of benzoic acid were 90–95%.

Dehydration of *cis*- and *trans*-2-Phenylcyclohexanol-2-C^{14} (Ia and IIa).—Equal weights of Ia or IIa and 85% phosphoric acid were mixed in a 25-ml. flask and refluxed for 4 hours. After the dehydration was complete the contents of the flask were cooled, water and ether were added, the layers were separated, and the aqueous layer was extracted with ether which was combined with the original ether extracts. The ether extract was washed with water until it was free of acid and made up to volume with ether in a 100-ml. volumetric flask.

The isolation of the olefins was accomplished by the following method: an accurately measured sample was removed from the volumetric flask and diluted with a known weight of non-radioactive olefin. The mixture then was usually subjected to some preliminary purification and the derivative was prepared as previously described. In the case of olefin III, the crude mixture was partially purified by the use of a column of alumina; for olefins IV, V and VI, the crude mixture of olefins was distilled, and for olefin VII, the derivative was prepared without preliminary purification. In Table V are summarized the details of the above-described experiments.

The calculation of the yields of the olefins may best be illustrated by a sample calculation for 1-phenylcyclohexene in experiment 1 (Table V). In the equation[6] $A_1(D_1 + X) = A_0X$

A_0 = specific act. of undiluted IIIa = spec. act. of starting material [Ia] = 1.330 mc./mole

A_1 = measd. spec. act. of deriv. = 0.3401 mc./mole (column V)

D_1 = wt. of non-radioactive 1-phenylcyclohexene (III) added = 0.6606 g. (column III)

X = wt. of 1-phenylcyclohexene-1-C^{14} (IIIa) of specific act. 1.330 mc./mole

then

$(0.3401)(0.6606 + X) = 1.330(X)$

$$X = \frac{(0.3401)(0.6606)}{0.990} = 0.227 \text{ g. of III in } 10\% \text{ of the}$$
reacn. mixt. (col. IV) or 2.27 g. of III in total reacn. mixt.

Theoretical yield of olefins = 2.59 g.

$(2.27/2.59) \times 100 = 87.7\%$ yield of III

Determination of Phenyl Migration Occurring during the Dehydration of cis- and trans-2-Phenylcyclohexanol-2-C^{14} (Ia and IIa).—The derivatives of 1-phenylcyclohexene (III) obtained from the dehydration of Ia and IIa (Table V) were oxidized to benzoic acid by one of the methods previously described. The radiochemical data are given in Table VI. The latter calculations are straightforward, and are thus not included in the present write-up.

Isomerization of 3-Phenylcyclohexene (IV) and Mixtures of 1- and 3-Phenylcyclohexene (III and IV).—The isomerization experiments of the olefins III and IV were performed under the same conditions that were used for the dehydration. Equal weights of the olefin and phosphoric acid were refluxed for 4 hours. The isolation and the derivative preparation of the olefins was accomplished as previously described in this section for the dehydration reactions. The radiochemical and dilution data are summarized in Table VI.

Determination of Purity of 1- and 3-Phenylcyclohexene (III and IV).—In order to ensure that the derivatives pre-

pared from the various olefins were not contaminated with "spurious" radioactivity, it was necessary to prepare a number of synthetic mixtures of radioactive and non-radioactive olefins, convert them into the corresponding derivatives, and prove that contamination was not a source of error. The results of these experiments are listed in Table VII and signify that these derivatives are almost certainly radiochemically pure.

TABLE VII

RADIOCHEMICAL DATA ON THE PURITY OF 1- AND 3-PHENYL-CYCLOHEXENE AND THEIR DERIVATIVES

Expt.	Reactant and wt.	Deriv.	Radioactivity assay of deriv., mc./mole	Calcd. radio-activity of deriv., mc./mole
14	IIIa 4.0 g. 1.004 mc./mole	VIII	0.9955 ± 0.0016	1.004
15	IIIa 0.9931 g. 1.004 mc./mole III 1.0139 g.	VIII	0.4953 ± .0011	0.4968
16	IIIa 0.8624 g. 1.004 mc./mole IV 0.3252 g.	X	1.004 ± .000	1.004
17	IIIa 0.8665 g. 1.334 mc./mole IV 0.3201 g.	VIII	1.320 ± .0015	1.334
18	IVa 0.2198 g. 2.293 mc./mole IV 0.1707 g.	XII	1.286 ± .009	1.291
19	IIIa 1.8946 g. 1.004 mc./mole IV 2.0852 g.	XII	0.0004	0.000

The radioactivity assays reported in this paper were performed with a vibrating reed electrometer using a modification of the wet combustion procedure as described by Neville.[25]

The elemental analyses reported herein were performed by the Huffman Microanalytical Laboratories, Wheatridge, Colorado.

(25) O. K. Neville, THIS JOURNAL, **70**, 3501 (1948).

OAK RIDGE, TENNESSEE

Erratum

Page 165, right-hand column, line 22 from bottom *should read:*

uncertainty, yet may be taken as evidence that the labeled 1-phenyl-

29 | *7-anti-* Norbornenol

Winstein and Shatavsky (Paper No. 29) present the detailed account of the synthesis and reactions of 7-*anti*-norbornenol and its derivatives reported in part in the communication with Norton and Woodward.

The interesting dibromide II appears to be extremely dangerous.[1] It shares with β,β'-dichlorodiethyl sulfide and the "nitrogen mustards" the property of being a highly reactive bifunctional alkylating agent, both bromines being subject in succession to ionization assisted by the double bond.

---

[1] S. Winstein, *J. Am. Chem. Soc.* **83**, 1516 (1961).

From: *J. Am. Chem. Soc.* **78**, 592–97 (1956)

[CONTRIBUTION FROM THE DEPARTMENT OF CHEMISTRY OF THE UNIVERSITY OF CALIFORNIA AT LOS ANGELES]

Neighboring Carbon and Hydrogen. XXI.[1] *Anti*-7 Derivatives of Norbornene[2] (Bicyclo[2.2.1]heptene) as Homoallylic Systems[3a]

BY S. WINSTEIN AND M. SHATAVSKY[3b]

RECEIVED JULY 7, 1955

The mixture of dibromides obtained from bromine addition to bicycloheptadiene contains an unsaturated component which is very reactive in solvolysis. The solid glycol derived from treatment of the dibromide with aqueous permanganate is no longer unusually reactive in solvolysis. Debromination of the dibromoglycol with zinc–copper couple yields initially a very unreactive monobromoglycol. Further debromination yields *exo-cis*-2,3-dihydroxynorbornane. On the basis of this evidence and the dipole moment of the acetonide of the dibromoglycol the unsaturated dibromide is taken to be *exo-5-anti-7*-dibromonorbornene. Selective hydrolysis of the more reactive halogen atom of the unsaturated dibromide gives rise to *exo*-5-bromo-*anti*-7-hydroxynorbornene. This bromohydrin yields a toluenesulfonate which is very reactive in acetolysis. Zinc debromination of the bromohydrin and hydrogenation of the *anti*-7-hydroxynorbornene gave rise to 7-hydroxynorbornane, identical with a specimen supplied by R. B. Woodward and C. Norton. The toluenesulfonate of the 7-hydroxynorbornene is twenty-five times as reactive as the *exo*-5-norbornenyl ester and 2 × 10⁵ times as reactive as the *endo*-5-norbornenyl derivative. The *anti*-7-norbornenyl system should be classed as a homoallylic one along with others like cholesteryl and 5-norbornenyl. However, it is geometrically quite unique. The full extent of anchimeric assistance to ionization of *anti*-7-norbornenyl *p*-toluenesulfonate may be appreciated from the factor of *ca.* 10¹¹ between acetolysis rates of *anti*-7-norbornenyl *p*-toluenesulfonate and its saturated analog which has been studied by Woodward and Norton.

As shown elsewhere,[4] the dibromide from addition of bromine to bicycloheptadiene I contains an unsaturated component which has been concentrated somewhat but not isolated separately. This unsaturated dibromide is unusually reactive in solvolysis by comparison with the saturated dibromonortricyclenes also obtained. Similarly,[4] the bromoether obtained on treatment of bicycloheptadiene I with N-bromosuccinimide in methanol also contains a highly reactive unsaturated component. In Table I are given the relative reactivities of the unsaturated dibromide and the unsaturated bromoether relative to *exo*-5-bromonorbornene[4] in 80% alcohol. The dibromide is twenty-three times as reactive, and the bromoether 190 times as reactive, as the *exo*-5-bromonorbornene

even before correction for the rate-retarding polar effect of the second halogen atom[5] or the methoxyl group[5] on solvolysis rate.

TABLE I

COMPARISON OF REACTIVITY OF SOME DEHYDRONORBORNYL BROMIDES IN 80% EtOH

Compound	Temp., °C.	k, hr.⁻¹	Rel. rate[a] 25°
XIV	75.0	1.0	1
XV	75.0	1.90 ± 0.02	2
II	24.8	0.043	23
	50.0	1.0	
exo-5-Methoxy-*anti*-7-nor-			
bornene[4]	25.1	0.36	190

[a] Approximated on the basis of identical $\Delta S^{\pm}$ for the first three compounds.

Considerations of mechanism of halogen addition[4] with or without carbon participation suggested II, III and IV as possible structures of the reactive

(1) Paper XX: S. Winstein, M. Shatavsky, C. Norton and R. B. Woodward, THIS JOURNAL, **77**, 4183 (1955).

(2) See A. M. Patterson, *Chem. Eng. News*, **30**, 930 (1952), for nomenclature.

(3) (a) Research supported by grants from Julius Hyman and Co., Denver, Colo., and later the Julius Hyman Division of Shell Chemical Co.; (b) deceased, summer, 1954.

(4) S. Winstein and M. Shatavsky, *Chemistry and Industry*, in press.

(5) *E.g.*, S. Winstein, *et al.*, THIS JOURNAL, **70**, 816, 821, 828 (1948); E. Grunwald, *ibid.*, **73**, 5458 (1951).

TABLE II

COMPARISON OF SOLVOLYSIS RATES OF SOME NORBORNYL BROMIDES

Compound	Solvent	Temp., °C.	k, hr.$^{-1}$	Rel. rate k_2, H$_2$O, 25°	Rel. rate, k_1, 80% EtOH, 25°
exo-2-Bromo-norbornane[a,b]	80% EtOH	50.0	0.0828		
	80% EtOH	75.0[c]	1.36		1.0
	80% EtOH	99.9[c]	10.4		
XII	80% EtOH	75.0	0.021		7.7×10^{-3}
	H$_2$O	25.0	.0043		
	H$_2$O[d]	25.0	$10,400 \pm 600^e$	5.4×10^3	
V	80% EtOH	75.0	0.00236		6.0×10^{-4}
	H$_2$O	50.0	.015		
IX	H$_2$O	75.0	$<5 \times 10^{-5}$		$<3 \times 10^{-8k}$
	H$_2$O[f]	25.0	1.94 ± 0.02^e	1	
trans-2,3-Dibromo-norbornane[g]	80% EtOH	99.9	0.042[h]		1.0×10^{-3}
exo-2-*syn*-7-Di-bromonor-bornane[i]	80% EtOH	75.0	.029[h]		8×10^{-3}
	80% EtOH	99.9	.16[h]		

[a] Data of E. Clippinger.[10] [b] Reported 0.20 hr.$^{-1}$ at 55.0°.[11] [c] Extrapolated roughly with $E^{\pm} = 25.0$ kcal./mole, based on the value[10] of 24.2 kcal./mole in 80% methanol. [d] 0.0110 M NaOH. [e] Second-order constant, k_2 hr.$^{-1}$ M^{-1}. [f] 0.0548 M NaOH. [g] Sample furnished by H. Kwart[12]; b.p. 74–75° (0.4 mm.), n^{20}D 1.5710. [h] Rough rate constant based on initial rates. [i] Sample furnished by H. Kwart,[12] b.p. 62–63° (0.4 mm.), n^{20}D 1.5618. [j] Approximated on the basis of identical $\Delta S^{\pm}$ for the whole series of compounds. [k] Estimated by comparison with the preceding compound in water.

unsaturated dibromide. The observed solvolysis rate of the unsaturated dibromide was interestingly high for any of these three structures, so that we have followed up this matter by elucidating the structure of the unsaturated dibromide and investigating further the solvolytic behavior of the dibromide and related or derived materials. This work contributes to our knowledge of the anchimeric[6] effects of π-electron-containing substituents[7] in solvolysis.

The first structure proof of the unsaturated dibromide was based on the crystalline dibromoglycol, m.p. 127–128°, which is obtained[4] from the unsaturated dibromide by treatment with dilute potassium permanganate solution. This dibromoglycol yields an acetonide, m.p. 89°, which has been shown in other work[8] to have a dipole moment of 3.64 D. The solvolytic reactivity of the dibromoglycol is shown in Table II, from which it is clear that the dibromoglycol is less reactive in solvolysis than the bromoglycol XII obtained by treatment of *exo*-5-bromonorbornene (XIV) with cold dilute permanganate solution. Thus, the unusually high reactivity associated with the unsaturated dibromide has disappeared on conversion of the olefinic linkage to the glycol grouping.

(6) S. Winstein, C. R. Lindegren, H. Marshall and L. L. Ingraham, THIS JOURNAL, **75**, 147 (1953).

(7) *E.g.*, (a) S. Winstein and R. Adams, *ibid.*, **70**, 838 (1948); (b) S. Winstein, H. M. Walborsky and K. Schreiber, *ibid.*, **72**, 5795 (1950); (c) M. Simonetta and S. Winstein, *ibid.*, **76**, 18 (1954).

(8) M. T. Rogers, unpublished work.

Treatment of the dibromoglycol with zinc in alcohol yielded first a monobromoglycol different from the monobromoglycol XII. This new monobromoglycol was uniquely unreactive in solvolysis as is indicated in Table II. On more extended treatment with zinc and alcohol of either the dibromoglycol or the new monobromoglycol there was obtained a completely debrominated glycol which proved to be identical with *exo-cis*-2,3-dihydroxynorbornane (XI), m.p. 140°, which was prepared from treatment of norbornene XIII with cold dilute permanganate solution and which has been reported recently by Kwart and Vosburgh.[9] On the basis of the conversion of the dibromoglycol to the glycol XI, it was concluded that the bicycloheptene carbon skeleton was preserved in the unsaturated dibromide obtained from bicycloheptadiene I.

Considering the possible structures II, III and IV for the unsaturated dibromide, that of the *cis*-dibromide III can be eliminated on the basis of the available evidence. While the dipole moment of the acetonide of the dibromoglycol is permissive[8] for the glycol acetonide VI, the great decrease in reactivity of the unsaturated dibromide on conversion to the glycol might not be expected on the basis of structure III. Also, the dehalogenation of the dibromoglycol, initially to a monobromoglycol different from XII, is not in line with the *cis*-dibromide structure III for the unsaturated dibromide.

Similarly, the available evidence rules out the *trans*-dibromide structure IV for the unsaturated dibromide. First, the dipole moment of the acetonide of the dibromoglycol is much too high[8] for the acetonide of the dibromoglycol VII. Secondly, the solvolytic reactivity of the dibromoglycol (Table II) is too high for structure VII since it is nearly as reactive as *trans*-2,3-dibromonorbornane. This would correspond to nearly no rate-retarding

(9) H. Kwart and W. G. Vosburgh, THIS JOURNAL, **76**, 5400 (1954).

(10) E. Clippinger, Thesis, U.C.L.A., 1955.

(11) J. D. Roberts, W. Bennett and R. Armstrong, THIS JOURNAL, **72**, 3329 (1950).

(12) H. W. Kwart and L. Kaplan, *ibid.*, **76**, 4072 (1954).

XV   II   V   VIII

XVI   XVII   IX   X   XIII

XVIII   XIX   XI   XII   XIV

effect for the glycol hydroxyl groups, whereas they display a substantial rate-retarding effect in *exo*-5-bromo-*exo-cis*-2,3-bicycloheptanediol.

The available evidence supports only structure II for the unsaturated dibromide, namely, *exo*-5-*anti*-7-dibromonorbornene. Such a structure, together with the *exo* configuration for the 5-bromine atom and the *anti* configuration relative to the olefinic linkage for the 7-bromine atom, can be anticipated on mechanistic grounds.[4] Firstly, the dipole moment of the dibromoglycol acetonide is appropriate for the acetonide of dibromoglycol V. Secondly, structure II for the unsaturated dibromide and therefore V for the dibromoglycol explains the behavior of the dibromoglycol V on zinc debromination. Removal of the *exo*-5-bromine gives the 7-bromoglycol IX, and this, in turn, yields bicycloheptanediol XI on removal of the second less reactive halogen atom. Further, the observations on reactivity receive a satisfactory explanation on the basis of the dibromide structure II for the unsaturated dibromide.

The high reactivity of the unsaturated dibromide II in solvolysis is ascribed to anchimerically assisted ionization of the 7-bromine atom *anti* to the olefinic π-electron cloud. The high reactivity demands the *anti* configuration for the bromine atom since low reactivity is expected for a *syn*-bromine atom. In this connection, Roberts has already mentioned qualitatively that a very low reactivity is associated with a *syn*-chlorine atom in *syn*-7-chloronorbornene.[13] Consistently, we find high reactivity for an *anti*-chlorine atom in the 7-position on the bicycloheptene skeleton in the unsaturated dichloride from bicycloheptadiene I. As is clear from Table III, the unsaturated dichloride exceeds *exo*-5-chloronorbornene in solvolytic reactivity by a factor similar to that which is observed to prevail between the unsaturated dibromide II and *exo*-5-bromonorbornene (XIV) (Table I). Further, it exceeds two other dichlorides[13] in reactivity by at least three to five powers

of ten. On the basis of anchimerically assisted ionization of the 7-bromine atom in the unsaturated dibromide II, it becomes quite clear that the excessively high reactivity should vanish in the absence of the olefinic group. Thus the saturated 2-*exo-syn*-7-dibromonorbornane recently described by Kwart[12] is not more reactive than would be expected from a retarded *exo*-bromide (Table II). Also, the glycol V from the unsaturated dibromide has about the expected reactivity for a dibromide retarded somewhat by the glycol hydroxyl groups (Table II).

The unsaturated dibromide II has been converted to some simpler derivatives which furnish further proof of structure and whose chemistry is also interesting in connection with the homoallylic phenomenon surrounding *anti*-7 derivatives of norbornene. Because of the relatively high reactivity of the 7-bromine relative to the 5-bromine atom in solvolysis, it is possible to solvolyze the unsaturated dibromide II in aqueous acetone to obtain a bromohydrin XV. However, the factor between dibromide II and bromohydrin XV in solvolytic reactivity is approximately only one power of ten[14] (Table I), so successful preparation of the bromohydrin XV depends on careful choice of the stage at which to interrupt the solvolysis of the unsaturated dibromide II. The crystalline bromohydrin XV yields a toluenesulfonate XVII whose reactivity is again

(14) The bromohydrin XV is actually slightly more reactive than the *exo*-5-bromonorbornene instead of slightly less reactive due to the rate-retarding polar effect of an hydroxyl group. At least some of this apparent difference in ionization rates may be due to greater importance of ion pair return[15] in solvolysis of *exo*-5-bromonorbornene than in solvolysis of the bromohydrin XV. However, it seems likely that ionization of bromohydrin XV is facilitated somewhat by hydrogen bonding between the hydroxyl group and the bromine atom.

(13) J. D. Roberts, F. O. Johnson and R. A. Carboni, This Journal, 76, 5692 (1954).

(15) *E.g.*, S. Winstein and K. C. Schreiber, This Journal, 74, 2165 (1952); S. Winstein, E. Clippinger, A. H. Fainberg and G. C. Robinson, *Chemistry and Industry*, 664 (1954).

relatively high. As shown in Table IV, the bromo-hydrin toluenesulfonate XVII is more reactive than *exo*-5-norbornenyl toluenesulfonate in ace-tolysis even before correction for the rate-retarding bromine atom.

TABLE III

COMPARISON OF RATES OF SOLVOLYSIS OF SOME DEHYDRO-NORBORNYL CHLORIDES IN 80% EtOH

Compound	Temp., °C.	k, sec.$^{-1}$	Rel. rate[e] 25°
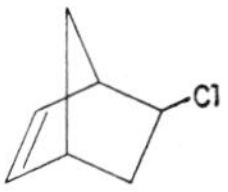	74.6 99.8	6.9×10^{-6a} 6.9×10^{-5a}	1
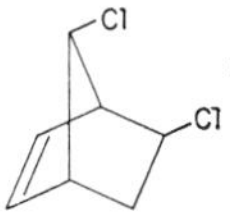	75.0	6.4×10^{-5}	14
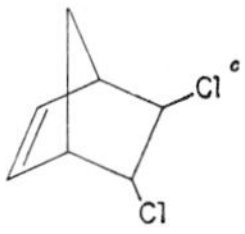	99.9	1.2×10^{-6}	6.3×10^{-3}
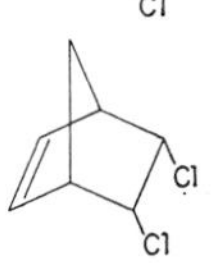	99.9	$<8.3 \times 10^{-8}$	$<2.2 \times 10^{-4}$

[a] Data of M. Shatavsky.[4] [b] Sample, obtained by chlorine addition to bicycloheptadiene and further purification, 59% unsaturated, was furnished by the Shell Development Co., Denver, Colo. [c] Samples supplied by J. D. Roberts.[13] [d] This sample, obtained by Diels–Alder addition of *cis*-1,2-dichloroethene to cyclopentadiene, was probably contaminated with *cis-exo* material. [e] Approximated on the basis of constant $\Delta S^{\pm}$ for the series of compounds.

TABLE IV

COMPARISON OF RATES OF ACETOLYSIS OF SOME DEHYDRO-NORBORNYL *p*-TOLUENESULFONATES AT 25.00°

Compound	k, sec.$^{-1}$	Rel. rate
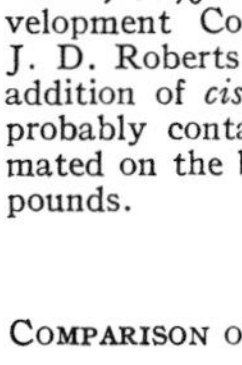	$(1.99 \pm 0.02) \times 10^{-5}$	1×10^4
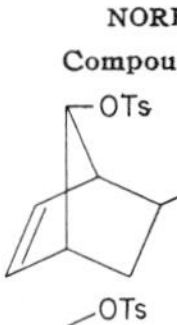	$(3.70 \pm 0.08) \times 10^{-4}$	2×10^5
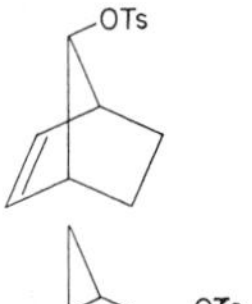	1.5×10^{-5a}	8×10^3
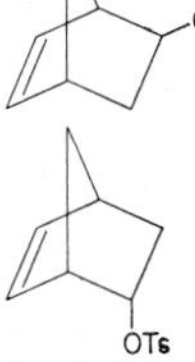	1.9×10^{-9a}	1

[a] One-third of value for the *p*-bromobenzenesulfonate; data of H. J. Schmid and K. C. Schreiber.[7b,16]

(16) H. J. Schmid, unpublished work.

By successive zinc debromination and hydro-genation it was possible to convert the bromo-hydrin XV all the way to the saturated 7-nor-borneol XVIII. This was suggested to us as a further proof of structure by Professor R. B. Woodward since R. B. Woodward and C. Norton at Harvard University had 7-norborneol in hand in an independent study.[1,17] On dehalogenation with zinc and alcohol, bromohydrin XV gave rise to an alcohol XVI *ca*. 90% unsaturated, as shown by quantitative semi-micro hydrogenation. This un-saturated alcohol agreed in m.p. and mixed m.p. with a specimen of 7-hydroxynorbornene which was supplied by R. B. Woodward and C. Norton. The infrared spectra of the two specimens of alcohol agreed well except for some absorption in the 12.4 μ region by the alcohol XVI from zinc debromination of bromohydrin XV due to slight contamination with nortricyclanol. From hydrogenation of the unsaturated alcohol XVI was obtained the alcohol XVIII which proved to be identical in m.p. and in m.p. of the toluenesulfonate derivative with samples supplied by Woodward and Norton.

The toluenesulfonate XIX from the unsaturated alcohol XVI was very reactive in acetolysis. From the data in Table IV, it is clear that the acetolysis rate of the *anti*-7-norbornenyl toluenesulfonate is twenty-five times as reactive as *exo*-5-norborn-enyl toluenesulfonate. On the basis of the high reactivities of the toluenesulfonates, the *anti* configuration with respect to the olefinic group is ascribed to the hydroxyl groups in both the bromo-hydrin XV and the alcohol XVI.

It seems from the present work that the *anti*-7-norbornenyl system should be classed as another homoallylic one along with others such as cholesteryl[7] and 5-norbornenyl.[7] However, the *anti*-7-nor-bornenyl system is geometrically unique as regards the relation of the cationic center at C-7, in a pre-

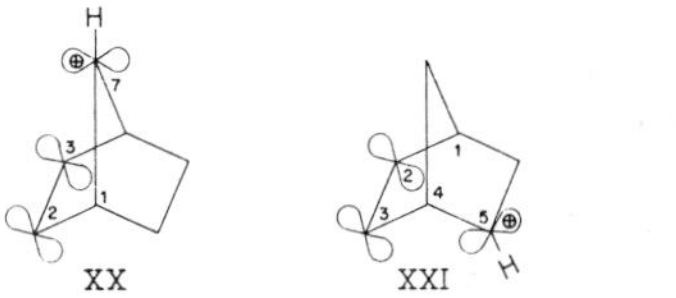

XX   XXI

sumed classical 7-norbornenyl cation XX, to the π-electron cloud of the 2,3-olefinic linkage. In the rate of solvolysis, the *anti*-7-norbornenyl halides and toluenesulfonate exceed very substantially the *exo*-5-norbornenyl derivatives. We regard this result as very instructive. While the cationic center at C-7 in a presumed classical 7-norbornenyl cation XX may interact with both C-2 and C-3, the overlap between the vacant *p*-orbital on C-7 and the atomic *p*-orbital on C-2 or C-3 is somewhat further from σ^{7e} than is the case in the analogous presumed classical 5-norbornenyl cation XXI. However, the 2–7 or 3–7 distance in the 7-norborn-enyl cation XX is less than the 3–5 distance in the 5-norbornenyl cation XXI. Also, it is not obvious how the net balance between strain and further stabilization in going from the presumed classical cation XX to the actual cation XXIII compares

(17) R. B. Woodward and C. Norton, private communication.

with the analogous net balance for the 5-nor-bornenyl case.

The full extent of the anchimeric assistance to ionization of *anti*-7-norbornenyl derivatives XXII may be appreciated only after noting the extremely low reactivity associated with 7-norbornyl or *syn*-7-norbornenyl derivatives. Thus, 7-norbornyl bromide ionizes in 80% ethanol more slowly than *exo*-2-norbornyl bromide by a factor of at least five powers of ten judging by the behavior of the mono-bromoglycols IX and XII summarized in Table II. Also, Roberts[13] has mentioned very low solvolytic reactivity for 7-chloronorbornane as well as *syn*-7-chloronorbornene.

XXII   XXIII   XXIV

The extremely low reactivity toward ionization of the 7-norbornyl system is clearest from the work of Woodward and Norton[1,17] on 7-norbornyl toluenesulfonate (XXV) in the relatively non-nucleophilic acetic acid solvent. Therefore, the extremely large anchimeric assistance provided for ionization of *anti*-7-norbornenyl derivatives XXII becomes clearest by comparison of the rate of acetolysis of *anti*-7-norbornenyl toluenesulfonate (XIX) with Woodward and Norton's value[1,17] for 7-norbornyl toluenesulfonate (XXV). On this basis the comparison is

XIX   >   XXV
$ca \cdot 10^{11}$:   1

The present work was interrupted before much scrutiny was made of the products and stereo-chemistry of solvolysis of *anti*-7-norbornenyl deriv-atives. The indications from the present work suggest at least a very considerable tendency toward over-all retention of configuration in solvolytic substitution at C-7 in solvolysis of *anti*-7-norbornenyl derivatives XXII. Thus, the un-saturated dibromide II gave, at least very pre-dominantly, the bromohydrin XV, whose toluene-sulfonate was very reactive. No other bromohy-drin was detected, although the examination was not quantitative. Also, Woodward and Norton have observed[1,17] essentially quantitative forma-tion of the acetate of the original 7-hydroxy-norbornene (XVI) in acetolysis of 7-norbornenyl toluenesulfonate (XIX). The control of stereo-chemistry of substitution at C-7 in solvolysis of *anti*-7-norbornenyl derivatives XXII by the 2,3-π-electron cloud is analogous to that observed at C-3 with cholesteryl derivatives[7] and C-5 with 5-norbornenyl derivatives.[7,16] The cation XXIII from ionization of an *anti*-7-norbornenyl derivative XXII reacts with a nucleophilic reagent or solvent molecule to yield *anti*-7 product XXIV.

It is interesting, but not surprising, that no product from attack of nucleophilic reagent at C-2 or C-3 of the cation XXIII was observed. Such attack, analogous to the predominant attack at C-6[7,18] in the cholesteryl cation or C-2 in the *exo*-5-norbornenyl cation,[7,16] would need to yield a product having both a 3- and a 4-ring fused into a bicyclo-heptyl skeleton.

Experimental Part

exo-cis-**2,3-Dihydroxynorbornane (XI).**—To 3.5 g. (0.037 mole) of norbornene dissolved in 350 ml. of 95% ethanol at −40 to −60° was slowly added dropwise with stirring a solution made up of 5.5 g. (0.035 mole) of potassium per-manganate, 5.5 g. of magnesium sulfate and 110 ml. of water. The addition required a half-hour. After the addition, the mixture was allowed to stand a half-hour at −40 to −50°. Then it was allowed to warm up to −10°, after which sulfur dioxide was bubbled in. The resulting white mixture was filtered, and the filtrate was evaporated down to *ca.* 50 ml. This solution was now filtered, and the filtrate was extracted with two 50-ml. portions of methyl-ene chloride. The combined methylene chloride extracts were dried over anhydrous magnesium sulfate a few hours, filtered and the solvent evaporated off using a water aspira-tor. There resulted 1.8 g. (40%) of white solid, m.p. 139–140° after recrystallization.

Anal. Calcd. for $C_7H_{12}O_2$: C, 65.59; H, 9.44. Found: C, 65.66; H, 9.46.

exo-cis-**2,3-Dihydroxy-*exo*-5-bromonorbornane (XII).**—A 6.3-g. (0.036 mole) quantity of 70:30 *exo*-dehydronorbornyl, nortricyclyl bromide mixture was treated with perman-ganate solution as in the case of bicycloheptene. The methylene chloride extracts yielded an oily material on evaporation which was extracted with five 20-ml. portions of water at room temperature, leaving a gummy residue. The combined water extracts were filtered and extracted with three 25-ml. portions of methylene chloride. Drying and evaporation of the combined methylene chloride ex-tracts yielded 1.9 g. (36%) of white solid, m.p. 70–71.5° after recrystallization from methylene chloride–petroleum ether and drying for 30 minutes at 1–2 mm.

Anal. Calcd. for $C_7H_{11}O_2Br$: C, 40.60; H, 5.36. Found: C, 40.79; H, 5.65.

Debromination of Bromo-glycols.—*exo-cis*-**2,3-Dihydroxy-*exo*-5-bromonobornane (XII).**—To 3 g. of zinc powder, which was decanted with dilute aqueous cupric sulfate and then washed with two 20-ml. portions of water and one 20-ml. portion of 95% ethanol, was added 25 ml. of 95% eth-anol and 0.5 g. (0.0024 mole) of bromoglycol. The stirred mixture was refluxed for two hours and then cooled, after which 5 ml. of saturated aqueous sodium carbonate was added. The mixture was filtered, and most of the solvent was evaporated from the filtrate using an aspirator. The resulting liquid was decanted with two 25-ml. portions of water. The combined water extracts were then extracted with three 25-ml. portions of methylene chloride. The combined methylene chloride extracts were dried over anhydrous magnesium sulfate for three hours, filtered and the solvent was evaporated off using a water aspirator. There resulted 0.14 g. (45%) of white solid, m.p. 137–138.5° after recrystallization from methylene chloride–petroleum ether, m.p. 138–139° on admixture with the glycol from the permanganate oxidation of norbornene.

Dibromoglycol V.—The dibromoglycol was treated as above with zinc-copper couple using a 40-minute reflux period and omitting the sodium carbonate in the workup. On a 0.2-mole scale there was obtained a 75% yield of *exo-cis*-2,3-dihydroxy-*anti*-7-bromonorbornane (IX), m.p. 100–101° after recrystallization from methylene chloride–petro-leum ether and vacuum drying.

Anal. Calcd. for $C_7H_{11}O_2Br$: C, 40.60; H, 5.36. Found: C, 40.86; H, 5.09.

Treatment of the monobromoglycol IX with zinc-copper couple using a 12-day reflux period (eight hours was insuf-ficient) gave, on a 0.004-mole scale, a 40% yield of glycol,

(18) *E.g.*, S. Winstein and A. H. Schlesinger, This Journal, **70**, 3528 (1948); E. Kosower, unpublished work.

m.p. 139–140°, m.p. 139–140° on admixture with glycol from permanganate oxidation of bicycloheptene.

Glycol Acetonides. Dibromo-glycol V.—To 2.2 g. of anhydrous copper sulfate powder in 20 ml. of dry acetone was added 1.17 g. of the dibromoglycol. The mixture was shaken and allowed to stand in a glass stoppered flask for 69 hours. The resulting mixture was then filtered, the solvent was evaporated off using an aspirator, and the resulting oily solid was taken up in 15 ml. of methylene chloride. The solution was washed with 15 ml. of water, and the water portion was extracted with 15 ml. of methylene chloride. The combined methylene chloride solutions were dried over anhydrous potassium carbonate for 36 hours. The solution was then filtered, and the solvent was evaporated off, using an aspirator, to yield 0.9 g. (67%) of solid, m.p. 88.5–89.2° after recrystallization from pentane and 20 minutes drying at 1–2 mm.

Anal. Calcd. for $C_{10}H_{14}O_2Br_2$: C, 36.84; H, 4.33. Found: C, 37.13; H, 4.52.

exo-cis-2,3-Dihydroxy-*anti*-7-bromonorbornane (**IX**).—A 3.2-g. quantity of the monobromoglycol IX was converted to the acetonide using a 92-hour reaction period. The reaction mixture was filtered, and the solvent was evaporated off using an aspirator. The resulting solid was taken up in 15 ml. of methylene chloride, and the solution was washed with 15 ml. of water, and then dried over anhydrous potassium carbonate. Evaporation of the solvent yielded 1.0 g. (80%) of a white solid, m.p. 80–81° after recrystallization and drying in vacuum.

Anal. Calcd. for $C_{10}H_{15}O_2Br$: C, 48.60; H, 6.12. Found: C, 48.51; H, 5.93.

exo-5-bromo-*anti*-7-Hydroxynorbornene (**XV**).—A 26-g. portion of the dibromide from bromine addition to bicycloheptadiene (23% unsaturated dibromide) was dissolved in 1 l. of 60% acetone, and the solution was kept at 25° for five hours. The reaction mixture was diluted with 2 l. of water and extracted with four 250-ml. portions of methylene chloride. The combined extracts were washed with water and dried over anhydrous magnesium sulfate. Evaporation of the solvent left an oil which was chromatographed on 25 g. of 2:1 silicic acid–Celite.[19]

The chromatographic column was prewashed with 25 ml. of absolute ether, 30 ml. of 1:1 acetone–ether, 25 ml. of absolute ether and 30 ml. of petroleum ether. The oil was put on the column as a solution in petroleum ether, and *ca.* 80 ml. of petroleum ether was passed through to remove dibromide. Elution with *ca.* 75 ml. of 1:1 petroleum ether–absolute ether, and evaporation of the solvent yielded 1.8 g. (54%) of material, m.p. 48–49° on crystallization from petroleum ether after decolorizing the solution with Norite.

The chromatography needed to be performed rapidly since the column becomes discolored if the bromohydrin is left on for an extended period.

Anal. Calcd. for C_7H_9OBr: C, 44.47; H, 4.79. Found: C, 44.07; H, 4.97.

For larger batches, it is more convenient to employ 80% acetone because of the limited solubility of the dibromide in the more aqueous medium. For 25 g. of dibromide mixture, 125 ml. of solvent was employed, and a reaction period of five to six hours at 50° was needed. The final product was not as pure as that from the more aqueous medium.

To a 0.9-g. quantity of the bromohydrin in 10 ml. of pyr-

idine was added 1.3 g. of *p*-toluenesulfonyl chloride with cooling, and the reaction mixture was kept in the refrigerator four days. Working up in the usual way yielded 1.3 g. (quantitative yield) of 2-*exo*-bromo-7-*anti*-tosyloxybicyclo-[2,2,1]heptene-5, m.p. 68–69° on recrystallization from petroleum ether, reacting positively to a permanganate test.

Anal. Calcd. for $C_{14}H_{15}O_3SBr$: C, 48.98; H, 4.40. Found: C, 48.97; H, 4.68.

anti-7-Hydroxynorbornene (**XVI**).—A 12-g. quantity of zinc dust was decanted with 25 ml. of water, dilute cupric sulfate solution, twice with 25-ml. portions of water, and finally twice with 25-ml. portions of 95% ethanol. A solution of 4.0 g. of *exo*-5-bromo-*anti*-7-hydroxynorbornene in 50 ml. of 95% ethanol was refluxed with the zinc–copper couple with stirring. The resulting cooled reaction mixture was diluted with 750 ml. of water and extracted with four 50-ml. portions of methylene chloride. The combined extracts were dried over anhydrous magnesium sulfate and evaporated to yield 1.2 g. (52%) of solid material, m.p. 114–116° on crystallization from pentane. This material gave a positive test to permanganate. Vacuum sublimation at 5 mm. and room temperature raised the melting point of the bicycloheptenol to 118–119°.

Anal. Calcd. for $C_7H_{10}O$: C, 76.32; H, 9.15. Found: C, 76.37; H, 9.21.

A crude sample (m.p. 85–90°) of *anti*-7-hydroxynorbornene, furnished by R. B. Woodward and C. Norton, was recrystallized from pentane to yield material of m.p. 116–117°. This did not depress the melting point of the sample, m.p. 114–116°, from zinc debromination of the bromohydrin. Vacuum sublimation at 5 mm. and room temperature of the material, m.p. 116–117°, raised the melting point to 117–118°.

The infrared spectra of the bicycloheptenols from zinc debromination and from Woodward and Norton agreed well except for absorption in the 12.4 μ region by the bicycloheptenol from zinc debromination due to slight contamination with nortricyclanol.

Conversion of the *anti*-7-hydroxynorbornene to *p*-toluenesulfonate in the usual way in cold pyridine with a reaction time of 24 hours gave a white solid material on crystallization from pentane. This tended to decompose within a few hours on standing at room temperature.

7-Hydroxynorbornane (XVIII).—A solution of 0.2744 g. of crude *anti*-7-hydroxynorbornene from debromination of bromohydrin in 25 ml. of methanol absorbed 90% of the theoretical amount of hydrogen over 0.22 g. of 5% palladium-on-barium carbonate. The hydrogen absorption ceased after ten minutes. Under the same conditions nortricyclanol absorbed no hydrogen.

Dilution of the filtered hydrogenation solution with water, extraction of the aqueous solution with three 50-ml. portions of methylene chloride, drying of the combined extracts with magnesium sulfate, and evaporation of the solvent yielded 0.15 g. (54%) of white needles, m.p. 150–151° on crystallization from pentane, m.p. 147.5–149° on admixture with a sample, m.p. 145–148°, furnished by R. B. Woodward and C. Norton. Conversion of some of the alcohol to *p*-toluenesulfonate in the usual fashion gave rise to material, m.p. 54–55°, m.p. 54.5–56° on admixture with a specimen of the toluenesulfonate, m.p. 55–56°, furnished by R. B. Woodward and C. Norton.

Anal. Calcd. for $C_{14}H_{18}O_3S$: C, 63.13; H, 6.81. Found: C, 63.37; H, 7.00.

Los Angeles 24, California

(19) K. N. Trueblood and E. W. Malmberg, *Anal. Chem.*, **21**, 1055 (1949).

30 | The Series of Cycloalkyl Tosylates

Brown and Ham (Paper No. 30) present a survey of the rate effects in the solvolysis of a number of cycloalkyl tosylates of ring size from 4 to 20. Cyclohexyl is the slowest, cyclodecyl the fastest, covering a range of 380-fold. Effects recognized include the change in angle strain associated with ionization, changes in the torsional or eclipsing strain, and, in the medium-sized rings, important relief of compression strain associated with ionization. From cyclopentyl tosylate up there is a linear correlation of solvolysis rate with the equilibrium constants of *dissociation* (not of formation, as stated in the caption of Figure 3) of the cyanohydrins of the corresponding ketones.

The authors note that cyclobutyl tosylate is out of order in the series, having a solvolysis rate comparable to that of cyclopentyl and over ten times that of cyclohexyl in spite of its bond angle unfavorable for ionization. In view of the later shrinkage in the area of agreement between Brown and Roberts, we note especially a statement in this paper in complete harmony with Roberts' view of cyclobutyl solvolysis:

It may be that the ionization does not proceed to the strained cyclobutyl carbonium ion, but instead proceeds directly to a more stable rearranged structure.

From: *J. Am. Chem. Soc.* **78,** 2735–39 (1956)

[Contribution from the Department of Chemistry of Purdue University]

The Effect of Ring Size on the Rate of Acetolysis of the Cycloalkyl *b*-Toluene and *p*-Bromobenzenesulfonates[1]

By Herbert C. Brown and George Ham[2]

Received November 7, 1955

A number of cycloalkyl tosylates (4-, 5-, 6-, 7-, 8-, 9-, 11-, 12-, 13-, 14-, 15- and 17-ring members) have been synthesized and the rates of acetolysis measured at several temperatures in order to ascertain the effect of ring size on reactivity. The behavior of several brosylates (5-, 6- and 7-) was also examined. In the common rings, the cyclopentyl and cycloheptyl derivatives exhibit an enhanced reactivity attributed to the de-eclipsing of bonds in the ionization stage. On the other hand, the decreased reactivity of the cyclohexyl derivatives is attributed to an increase in bond opposition in the ionization stage. A further increase in reactivity is observed in the medium rings (8- to 12-) followed by a decrease in the large rings (13- to 17-) to rates of reactions similar to those observed in open-chain compounds. The maximum in reactivity in the medium rings is attributed to a relief of strain accompanying the loss of a bond in the ionization stage. For the strained rings (5- to 11-members) a simple relationship exists between the association constants for cyanohydrin formation and the rate constants for acetolysis of the tosylates.

Ring compounds exhibit a remarkable change in chemical reactivity with ring size.[3-6] It has been proposed that the changes in chemical reactivity can be correlated with the changes in internal strain accompanying the formation or breaking of a bond to the ring atom in the rate-determining stage.[5-7]

The available data are too few to permit a rigorous test of the utility of the proposed explanation. In order to obtain data of this kind we are currently examining the effect of ring size on the reactivity of ring derivatives in a few representative reactions. The present paper reports a study of the effect of ring size on the acetolysis of cyclic tosylates[8] and certain selected brosylates.

Results

The *p*-toluenesulfonates of cyclobutanol, cyclopentanol, cyclohexanol, cycloheptanol, cyclooctanol, cyclononanol, cycloundecanol, cyclododecanol, cyclotridecanol, cyclotetradecanol, cyclopentadecanol, cycloheptadecanol and the *p*-bromobenzenesulfonates of cyclopentanol, cyclohexanol and cycloheptanol were prepared by treating the alcohol with *p*-toluenesulfonyl or *p*-bromobenzenesulfonyl chloride in dry pyridine, essentially according to the method described by Tipson.[9]

The *p*-toluenesulfonates of cycloheptanol, cyclooctanol, cyclononanol and cycloundecanol were relatively unstable, the cycloheptyl compound undergoing decomposition after several days at room temperature and the others undergoing decomposition after several days at 0–10°. The product obtained by treatment of cyclodecanol with *p*-toluenesulfonyl chloride in dry pyridine decomposed rapidly at room temperature upon removal of the ether with which it had been extracted. Before the preparation could be repeated, it was learned that the compound had been synthesized in another laboratory and its rate of acetolysis measured.[8] Accordingly no attempt was made to repeat this preparation.

The properties of the cyclanols and the aryl-

(1) Chemical Effects of Steric Strains. XII.

(2) Research assistant on a contract supported by the Office of Naval Research and a grant provided by the National Science Foundation.

(3) V. Prelog, *J. Chem. Soc.*, 420 (1950).

(4) J. D. Roberts and V. C. Chambers, This Journal, **73**, 5034 (1951).

(5) H. C. Brown, R. S. Fletcher and R. B. Johannesen, *ibid.*, **73**, 212 (1951).

(6) H. C. Brown and M. Borkowski, *ibid.*, **74**, 1894 (1952).

(7) P. D. Bartlett, *Bull. soc. chim.*, C100 (1951).

(8) In the course of discussions with Professor V. Prelog during the Fourteenth International Congress of Pure and Applied Chemistry in Zurich, July 21–27, 1955, it was learned that Professor Prelog and Dr. R. Heck had carried out a similar study of the acetolysis of the cycloalkyl tosylates (6-, 7-, 8-, 9-, 10-, 11-, 12- and 20-ring members). These results have since been published: R. Heck and V. Prelog, *Helv. Chim. Acta*, **38**, 1541 (1955). The present study includes data on certain tosylates (4-, 5-, 13-, 14-, 15- and 17- ring members) and brosylates (5- 6- and 7-) not included in the investigation by Heck

and Prelog. Moreover, it should be of interest to compare the agreement realized in a closely similar study in two different laboratories. Consequently, we are reporting all of our results even where these duplicate those obtained by Heck and Prelog.

(9) R. S. Tipson, *J. Org. Chem.*, **9**, 235 (1944).

TABLE I

PHYSICAL PROPERTIES OF CYCLANOLS AND CYCLOALKYL ARYLSULFONATES

n	B.p., °C. (mm.)	M.p., °C.	n^{20}D	B.p., °C. (mm.)	M.p., °C.	n^{20}D	Ref.
	⌐Observed⌐			⌐Literature⌐			

Cyclanols, (CH₂)n-1 CHOH

n	B.p., °C. (mm.)	M.p., °C.	n^{20}D	B.p., °C. (mm.)	M.p., °C.	n^{20}D	Ref.
4	123.0–124.0			125.0			g
5	138.2 (754)		1.4529	139		1.4530	h
6	160.5–161.0		1.4647	158–159		1.4642	i
7	86.0 (20)		1.4770	95 (24)		1.4772²⁵	f
8			1.4835			1.4848²⁵	f
9	115.0–116.0 (16)		1.4901	115 (17)			d
11	118.0–119.0 (7)			128–131 (20)			d
12		75.0–76.0			80		d
13		59.5–60.3			60–60.5		d
14		79.0–80.0			79.0–80.0		d
15		80.5–81.2			81		d
17		80.0–81.0			81		d

Cycloalkyl tosylates, (CH₂)n-1 CHOTs

n	M.p., °C.	n^{20}D	M.p., °C.	Ref.
4	24.0–25.0		24–25	e
5	28.5–29.0		27.0–28.0	e
6	44.5–45.0		43.5–44.0	c
7	19.0–19.6	1.5263	Liq.	k
8		1.5276	Liq.	k
9	43.7–44.5		Liq.	k
11	44.2–45.4		43–44	k
12	87.0–87.6		88–89.5	k
13	36.3–37.2			a
14	77.5–78.8			a
15	47.2–48.0			a
17		1.5092²⁵		a

Cycloalkyl brosylates, (CH₂)n-1 CHOBs

n	M.p., °C.	M.p., °C.	Ref.
5	45.8–46.6	45.5–46.0	j
6	48.5–49.0	48.1–48.6	b
7	32.0–32.5		a

[a] New compound. [b] S. Winstein, E. Grunwald and L. Ingraham, THIS JOURNAL, **70**, 821 (1948). [c] S. Winstein, E Grunwald, R. E. Buckles and C. Hanson, *ibid*, **70**, 816 (1948). [d] M. Kobelt, P. Barman, V. Prelog and L. Ruzicka, *Helv Chim. Acta*, **32**, 256 (1949). [e] Ref. 4. [f] H. H. Zeiss and M. Tsutsui, THIS JOURNAL, **75**, 897 (1953). [g] J. D. Roberts and C. W. Sauer, *ibid*, **71**, 3925 (1949). [h] C. R. Noller and R. Adams, *ibid*, **48**, 1080 (1926). [i] H. E. Ungnade and D. Nightingale, *ibid*, **66**, 1219 (1944). [j] R. B. Loftfield, *ibid*, **73**, 4707 (1951). [k] Ref. 8.

TABLE II

RATE CONSTANTS AND DERIVED DATA FOR THE ACETOLYSIS

OF THE CYCLOALKYL TOSYLATES (CH₂)n-1 CHOTs

n	Temp., °C.	Rate constant k_1, sec.⁻¹	Rel. rate at 70°	$\Delta H^{\ddagger}$, kcal./mole	$\Delta S^{\ddagger}$, e.u.
4	70.0	2.67×10^{-4a}	11.3		
	80.0	7.38×10^{-4}			
	90.0	1.65×10^{-3}			
5	30.0	3.23×10^{-6}	14.0	24.1	−4.2
	50.0	3.82×10^{-5}			
	70.0	3.32×10^{-4}			
6	50.0	1.82×10^{-6}	1.00	27.3	−0.5
	70.0	2.37×10^{-5}			
	90.0	2.22×10^{-4}			
7	50.0	6.45×10^{-5}	25.3	23.3	−5 7
	70.0	6.00×10^{-4}		$(23.5)^b$	$(−5.4)^b$
	90.0	3.95×10^{-3}			
8	25.0	2.82×10^{-5}	191	22.3	−4.5
	50.0	5.68×10^{-4}		$(22.5)^b$	$(−4.1)^b$
	70.0	4.52×10^{-3}			
9	25.0	2.43×10^{-5}	172	22.5	−4.2
	35.0	8.72×10^{-5}		$(23.9)^b$	$(+0.1)^b$
	70.0	4.08×10^{-3}			
10	25.0	$(4.69 \times 10^{-5})^b$	380^c	$(23.0)^b$	$(−1.1)^b$
	50.0	$(1.03 \times 10^{-3})^b$			
11	35.0	2.02×10^{-5}	48.9	23.7	−3.2
	50.0	1.29×10^{-4}		$(24.7)^b$	$(−0.2)^b$
	70.0	1.16×10^{-3}			
12	50.0	5.97×10^{-6}	3.25	27.6	2.8
	70.0	7.70×10^{-5}		$(27.9)^c$	$(3.8)^b$
	90.0	7.63×10^{-4}			
13	50.0	7.27×10^{-6}	3.50	26.2	−1.3
	70.0	8.30×10^{-5}			
	90.0	7.25×10^{-4}			
14	50.0	2.47×10^{-6}	1.32	27.8	1.7
	70.0	3.12×10^{-5}			
	90.0	3.28×10^{-4}			
15	50.0	4.30×10^{-6}	2.19	26.5	−1.3
	70.0	5.18×10^{-5}			
	90.0	4.53×10^{-4}			
17	50.0	4.38×10^{-6}	2.17	26.5	−1.4
	70.0	5.15×10^{-5}			
	90.0	4.60×10^{-4}			
20	50.0	$(3.57 \times 10^{-6})^b$	1.80^c	$(26.6)^b$	$(−1.3)^b$
	75.0	$(7.52 \times 10^{-5})^b$			
(n-C₄H₇)₂- CHOTs	70.0	3.15×10^{-5}	1.33		

[a] Initial rate constant, uncorrected for rearrangement. [b] Ref. 8. [c] Calcd. from extrapolated value of rate constant.

sulfonates used in this investigation are summarized in Table I.

The rates of acetolysis of the cyclic arysulfonates were measured in acetic acid containing 0.046 mole per liter of acetic anhydride essentially according to the procedure described by Winstein and co-workers.[10] In order to have the value for a typical open-chain compound for comparison, 4-heptyl tosylate was synthesized and its rate of acetolysis determined. The results are summarized in Tables II and III.

TABLE III
RATE CONSTANTS AND DERIVED DATA FOR THE ACETOLYSIS
OF THE CYCLOALKYL BROSYLATES $\overline{(CH_2)n\text{-}1}\,CHOBs$

n	Temp., °C.	Rate constant k_1, sec. $^{-1}$	$\Delta H^{\ddagger}$, kcal./mole	$\Delta S^{\ddagger}$, e.u.
5	25.0	6.28×10^{-6}	22.7	-6.3
	50.0	1.29×10^{-4}		
	70.0	1.10×10^{-3}		
6	50.0	6.60×10^{-6}	26.8	0.4
	70.0	8.02×10^{-5}		
	90.0	7.28×10^{-4}		
7	25.0	1.04×10^{-5}	23.0	-4.2
	50.0	2.23×10^{-4}		
	60.0	6.70×10^{-4}		
	70.0	1.98×10^{-3}		

The enthalpies and entropies of activation for the acetolysis of cyclopentyl and cyclohexyl p-toluenesulfonates have been reported previously both by Roberts and Chambers[4] and by Winstein and his co-workers.[11] Unfortunately, their results are not in agreement. Therefore we undertook to measure the rate constants for these two compounds in order to compare our values with those previously reported. The available data are summarized in Table IV.

TABLE IV
ENTHALPIES AND ENTROPIES OF ACTIVATION FOR THE
ACETOLYSIS OF CYCLOPENTYL AND CYCLOHEXYL TOSYLATES

Tosylate	$\Delta H^{\ddagger}$, kcal./mole	$\Delta S^{\ddagger}$, e.u.	Ref.
Cyclopentyl	27.6	6.7	Roberts[4]
	23.7	-6.4	Winstein[11]
	24.1	-4.2	Present study
Cyclohexyl	27.4	0.6	Roberts[4]
	27.0	-1.1	Winstein[11]
	27.3	-0.5	Present study

Roberts and Chambers found no significant difference in the enthalpies of activation for the cyclopentyl and cyclohexyl tosylates and therefore attributed the difference in reactivity to a large entropy factor. On the other hand, Winstein and his co-workers attributed the difference in reactivity of the two compounds primarily to the difference of 3.3 kcal./mole in the enthalpy of activation. Our present results indicate a difference in the enthalpy of activation of 3.2 kcal./mole

(10) S. Winstein, C. Hanson and E. Grunwald, THIS JOURNAL, **70**, 812 (1948).

(11) S. Winstein, E. Grunwald and L. Ingraham, *ibid.*, **70**, 821 (1948); S. Winstein, B. K. Morse, E. Grunwald, H. W. Jones, J. Corse, D. Trifan and H. Marshall, *ibid.*, **74**, 1127 (1952).

and therefore support the conclusion reached by Winstein.

The change in the rate constants with temperature observed in the three studies is shown in Fig. 1.

The solvolysis of the brosylates proceeds at a considerably greater rate than that of the tosylates. However, the effect of ring size on the solvolysis rate is essentially identical in the two systems.

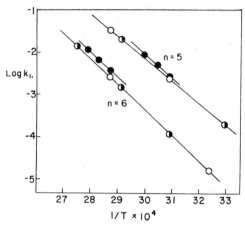

Fig. 1.—Activation energies for the acetolysis of cyclohexyl and cyclopentyl p-toluenesulfonates: O, data reported by Winstein and co-workers[11]; ●, data reported by Roberts and co-workers[4]; ◑, data obtained in this study.

Discussion

At the present time, three sources of steric strains are recognized: (1) the compression of van der Waals radii, (2) the distortion of bond angles, and (3) bond opposition forces. In the case of small rings, the distortion of bond angles appears to be the major source of strain.[5,6] In cyclopentane and cycloheptane it is the bond opposition forces which are primarily responsible for the strains revealed in combustion studies,[12] while the available evidence suggests that both bond oppositions and compressions of van der Waals radii are probably responsible for the strains exhibited by the medium rings.[3]

It was suggested that reactions involving an increase in these internal strains will be hindered, whereas those proceeding with a decrease in internal strains will be assisted.[5] Ideally one should discuss the effect of making or breaking a bond to one of the ring atoms in terms of each of these possible strain factors. Unfortunately, this cannot be done at the present time. These different strains are not mutually independent nor can they be estimated individually with any precision at the present time.

The net change in internal strain accompanying the formation or the breaking of a bond to a ring atom can be estimated with considerable precision from rate, equilibrium and thermochemical data. In view of this circumstance it appears more desirable at the present time to discuss the reactions

(12) K. S. Pitzer, *Science*, **101**, 672 (1945); J. E. Kilpatrick, K. S. Pitzer and R. Spitzer, THIS JOURNAL, **69**, 2483 (1947).

of ring compounds in terms of the net change in internal strain accompanying the reaction (I-strain). It should be recognized that I-strain will be made up of individual contributions from angle deformations, bond oppositions and atomic compressions, the relative magnitudes of which will vary from system to system.

The solvolysis of secondary alkyl p-toluenesulfonates in dry acetic acid is considered to proceed by a mechanism involving a slow rate-determining ionization of the p-toluenesulfonate group.[13]

$$H-\underset{R_2}{\overset{R_1}{\underset{|}{\overset{|}{C}}}}-OTs \xrightarrow{k_1} \underset{H}{\overset{R_2\ \ R_1}{\underset{|}{\overset{|}{C^+}}}} + OTs^-$$

The I-strain theory predicts that such ionization reactions should proceed relatively slowly in the 3- and 4-membered rings primarily because of an increase in angle strain accompanying ionization.[5] Such a slow reaction has been observed in the cyclopropyl tosylate and in 1-chloro-1-methylcyclobutane.[6] However, the rate of solvolysis of cyclobutyl tosylate is relatively fast.[4] The fast rate of this derivative is confirmed in the present study (Table II). Roberts and Chambers noted that the solvolysis of cyclobutyl tosylate is accompanied by extensive rearrangement.[4] It may be that the ionization does not proceed to the strained cyclobutyl carbonium ion, but instead proceeds directly to a more stable rearranged structure. In that event, the I-strain theory would not be applicable.

According to the I-strain interpretation, an ionization reaction should be strongly favored in the strained 5- and 7-ring systems, but not in the stable, unstrained cyclohexyl derivatives. Indeed, in the cyclohexyl carbonium ion there will be introduced two partial oppositions,[14] so that this molecule should tend to resist the ionization reaction in comparison to an open-chain derivative.

Prelog has presented convincing evidence that the medium rings are strongly strained.[3] The strain is presumably the effect of bond opposition forces, with some contribution possible from atom compression. Here also the internal strain should be partially relieved by a decrease in the number of bonds. Finally, the large rings should be essentially strain free and the reactivities should approach those of the open-chain compounds.

The experimental results (Fig. 2) are in complete accord with the predictions of the I-strain interpretation.

According to the I-strain hypothesis the opposite effects should be observed in rate or equilibrium data involving a reaction in which there is an increase in the number of bonds attached to a ring atom. The similarity in the effects of ring size on the rates of acetolysis of the cycloalkyl tosylates (Fig. 2) and on the equilibrium constants for the formation of the cyclic cyanohydrins[15] is noteworthy.

$$(\overline{CH_2})n\text{-}1\ C{=}O + CN^- \rightleftharpoons (\overline{CH_2})n\text{-}1\ C\overset{O^-}{\underset{CN}{\diagdown}}$$

Hammett has demonstrated the existence of linear free energy relationships in *meta* and *para* aromatic systems.[16] In general, aliphatic derivatives do not obey such relationships.[17] However, in the case of the rigid 4-substituted bicyclo[2:2:2]-octane-1-carboxylic acids Roberts and Moreland have demonstrated the existence of similar linear free energy relationships.[18] Presumably, the existence of such free energy relationships in both the benzene and bicyclooctane systems is due to the rigidity of the structures and the fact that the structural changes are far removed from the reaction center.

It was of interest to examine the possible existence of a similar quantitative relationship between the rate constants for the acetolysis of the cycloalkyl tosylates and the equilibrium constants for the formation of the cyclic cyanohydrins (Fig. 3). The rings from 5- to 11-members do appear to obey a simple linear relationship, with the larger rings and the simple open-chain derivatives possibly defining a second line.

It will be important to determine whether this linear relationship is obeyed by other reactions of the cyclic systems. If so, it may be a consequence of the fact that the rings from 5- to 11-members do not possess the free mobility of the larger rings or of the open-chain derivatives.

Experimental Part

Kinetic Measurements.—The solvent was prepared by treating 8.0 l. of reagent grade acetic acid (Baker and

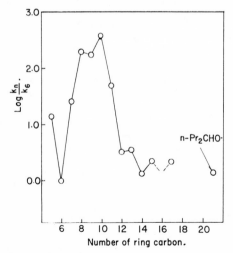

Fig. 2.—The effect of ring size on the rate of acetolysis of the cycloalkyl p-toluenesulfonates at 70°. (The value for cyclodecyl tosylate was provided by Professor V. Prelog, ref. 8.)

(13) E. Grunwald and S. Winstein, THIS JOURNAL, **70**, 846 (1948).

(14) H. C. Brown, J. H. Brewster and H. Shechter, *ibid.*, **76**, 467 (1954).

(15) V. Prelog and M. Kobelt, *Helv. Chim. Acta*, **32**, 1187 (1949).

(16) L. P. Hammett, "Physical Organic Chemistry," McGraw-Hill Book Co., Inc., New York, N. Y., 1940.

(17) In recent years R. Taft has succeeded in developing such linear relationships in a few selected aliphatic systems by introducing a correction term for the steric effect. See R. Taft, THIS JOURNAL, **74**, 2729, 3120 (1952)?; **75**, 4231, 4534, 4538 (1953).

(18) J. D. Roberts and W. T. Moreland, Jr., *ibid.*, **75**, 2167 (1953).

Adamson) with a slight excess of acetic anhydride. The product was fractionated. From a cooling curve on the distillate, the acid was found to be 0.042 M in an impurity assumed to be acetic anhydride. Analysis indicated the solvent to be 0.046 M in acetic anhydride. This product was used for all of the kinetic measurements.

The procedure for determining the rate constants was essentially that of Winstein and co-workers.[10]

Rate measurements were made at three different temperatures for each compound, usually over a range of 40°. The temperatures were controlled to ±0.02°. The values of $\Delta H^{\ddagger}$ and $\Delta S^{\ddagger}$ were obtained by plotting log k_1/T versus $1/T$ and determining $\Delta H^{\ddagger}$ from the slope and $\Delta S^{\ddagger}$ from the intercept of the best straight line through the three points as calculated by the methods of least squares.

Materials.—The cyclanones are all known compounds which were synthesized by methods previously described in the literature.

TABLE V

ANALYTICAL DATA ON THE CYCLANYL ARYLSULFONATES

Compound	Sapon. equiv. Calcd.	Sapon. equiv. Found	Analyses, % Calcd. C	Calcd. H	Found C	Found H
Cycloheptyl tosylate			62.66	7.51	62.78	8.00
Cyclooctyl tosylate	282	287				
Cyclononyl tosylate	296	296				
Cycloundecyl tosylate	324	324				
Cyclododecyl tosylate	339	339	67.41	8.93	67.26	9.05
Cyclotridecyl tosylate	324	324	68.14	9.15	68.37	9.46
Cyclotetradecyl tosylate	367	370	68.81	9.35	69.08	9.33
Cyclopentadecyl tosylate	382	383	69.25	9.51	69.35	9.77
Cycloheptadecyltosylate	409	418	70.54	9.87	70.96	10.34
Cycloheptyl brosylate			46.85	5.12	47.01	5.26

The pure ketones were reduced on a small scale (2.0–3.0 g.) by lithium aluminum hydride in ethyl ether. The yields were from 80 to 95% of the theoretical. The properties of the cyclanols are summarized in Table I.

We were uncertain of the purity of the cycloheptanol and therefore undertook to purify it by the preparation and recrystallization of cycloheptyl 3,5-dinitrobenzoate, followed by hydrolysis of the ester to recover the cycloheptanol. Cycloheptyl 3,5-dinitrobenzoate, recrystallized twice from ethanol and twice from aqueous acetone, melted at 81.0–82.0°. *Anal.* Calcd. for $C_{14}H_{16}N_2O_6$: C, 54.55; H, 5.23. Found: C, 54.84; H, 5.16.

Because of the small amount of materials available, considerable time was devoted to a study of the preparation of the cycloalkyl p-toluenesulfonates and p-bromobenzenesulfonates in good yield on a small scale. The following procedure gave the esters in yields of 70 to 90%.

The alcohol (1.0–2.0 g.) was mixed with cooling with twice the theoretical quantity of the arylsulfonyl chloride and sufficient dry pyridine to make the solution approximately 1.0 molar in alcohol. After 12 to 24 hours at 0°, a small quantity of water was carefully added with cooling to the mixture to hydrolyze the excess sulfonyl chloride. Additional water was then added, until the solution had been diluted to 2 to 5 times its original volume. The aqueous pyridine mixture was extracted with ether. The ether ex-

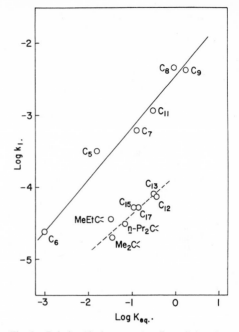

Fig. 3.—Relationship between the effect of ring size on the rate of acetolysis of the cycloalkyl tosylates (70°) and the equilibrium constants (22°) for the formation of the cyclic cyanohydrins. (The equilibrium constants for the aliphatic cyanohydrins at 22° were calculated from the data at 35° of D. D. Evans and J. R. Young, *J. Chem. Soc.*, 1310 (1954).)

tract was washed with cold dilute hydrochloric acid solution, sodium bicarbonate solution, water and then dried over anhydrous sodium sulfate. The ether was then removed under reduced pressure. The product was usually recrystallized from petroleum ether.

Analytical data on the new cyclanyl arylsulfonates are summarized in Table V.

Acknowledgment.—We wish to acknowledge the assistance of Dr. K. Ichikawa in the synthesis of 4-heptyl tosylate and the measurement of its rate of solvolysis.

LAFAYETTE, IND.

31 | Correlation of Solvolysis with Model Reactions

In Paper No. 31 Brown and Ichikawa introduce an interesting method for the partial sorting of the kinetic effects observed in solvolysis. Because the borohydride reduction of a ketone converts a plane-trigonal carbon atom into a tetrahedral one, it should respond in reverse to all three of the effects discussed by Brown and Ham. Table 2 summarizes rate measurements of borohydride reduction for all but two of the cyclic ketones from C-4 to C-17, and compares them with the solvolysis rates of the corresponding secondary tosylates and tertiary chlorides, and with the equilibrium measurements on the corresponding cyanohydrins. For the reason already quoted from Brown and Ham, the C-4 case is left out of the correlation. The borohydride rates correlate well with the cyanohydrin equilibria, roughly with the solvolyses of the secondary tosylates, and not at all with the solvolyses of the tertiary chlorides. With the interesting exception of cyclobutyl, the probability is established that the effect of ring size on solvolysis of secondary tosylates is due primarily to three kinds of steric strain and not to electronic delocalization.

But what about cyclobutyl? If the borohydride reduction is a valuable criterion of normalcy, is this criterion not at its best when it detects something unusual and abnormal? The perceptive comment of Brown and Ham that cyclobutyl tosylate may ionize directly to a "more stable rearranged structure" leads to the next question: What kind of structure is more stable? Not the strained cyclopropylcarbinyl structure, for at equilibrium cyclobutyl chloride is favored by 36/1 over cyclopropylcarbinyl chloride.[1] Indeed, as we go over the possibilities one by one, we recognize in this system the same pattern of a strong *driving force in both*

---

[1] M. C. Caserio, W. H. Graham, and J. D. Roberts, *Tetrahedron* **11**, 175 (1960).

directions which in the cholesteryl and norbornyl cases revealed an ionic inter-mediate more stable than could be accounted for without delocalization of charge. More is said about this point in later papers of the collection.

One of the most striking points brought out in the paper of Brown and Ichikawa is the relatively normal position of 1-methylcyclobutyl chloride in its series, in that it is more than 500 times *less* reactive than 1-methylcyclopentyl chloride. As a tertiary chloride it is still a good deal more reactive than cyclobutyl chloride in the same medium (the tertiary at 25° and the secondary at 97° react at comparable rates). This is probably an example of Winstein's principle of diminution in the driving force from bridging, caused by the presence of a competing mode of ion stabilization.

From: *Tetrahedron* **1**, 221–30 (1957)

CHEMICAL EFFECTS OF STERIC STRAINS—XIV

THE EFFECT OF RING SIZE ON THE RATE OF REACTION OF THE CYCLANONES WITH SODIUM BOROHYDRIDE

HERBERT C. BROWN and K. ICHIKAWA*

Department of Chemistry, Purdue University, Lafayette, Indiana, U.S.A.

Abstract—The rates of reaction of sodium borohydride with a number of cyclanones (4-, 5-, 6-, 7-, 8-, 9-, 10-, 11-, 12-, 13-, 15-, and 17-ring members) were determined at several temperatures in order to ascertain the effect of ring size on the reactivity of the carbonyl group. *Cyclo*butanone is the most reactive of the ketones examined, followed closely by *cyclo*hexanone. *Cyclo*pentanone is considerably less reactive, followed a sharp drop in reactivity in the 7-, 8-, 9-, and 10-ring derivatives. The rate reaches a minimum in the 10-ring and then increases with the larger rings to the value exhibited by the open-chain derivative, di-*n*-hexylketone. The trends in reactivity are very similar to those observed in the equilibrium constants for cyanohydrin formation and in other reactions of ring derivatives. The results agree with the predicted effects of ring size on the magnitude of the internal strains (I-strain).

THE reactivities of ring compounds exhibit a remarkable dependence upon the size of the rings.[1,2] This dependence of the reactivity upon the size of the ring has been attributed to the changes in internal strain accompanying the formation or breaking of a bond to the ring atom in the rate-determining stage.[3–5]

According to this proposal, opposite effects of ring size should be observed in reactions involving the breaking of a bond, such as in the acetolysis of tosylates, and in reactions involving the making of a bond, such as in the reduction of ketones.

Data on the effect of ring size on the rate of solvolysis of cyclanyl tosylates are now available.[6,7] However, rate data for the reactions of ketones are available only for the

---

* Post-doctorate research assistant, 1954–1956, on Contract DA-33-008-ORD-992, supported by the Office of Ordnance Research, U.S. Army.

[1] V. Prelog *J. Chem. Soc.* 420 (1950).
[2] J. D. Roberts and V. C. Chambers *J. Amer. Chem. Soc.* **73**, 5034 (1951).
[3] H. C. Brown, R. S. Fletcher, and R. B. Johannesen *Ibid.* **73**, 212 (1951).
[4] H. C. Brown and M. Borkowski *Ibid.* **74**, 1894 (1952).
[5] P. D. Bartlett *Bull. Soc. Chim.* C100 (1951).
[6] R. Heck and V. Prelog *Helv. Chim. Acta.* **38**, 1541 (1955).
[7] H. C. Brown and G. Ham *J. Amer. Chem. Soc.* **78**, 2735 (1956).

TABLE 1. RATE CONSTANTS AND DERIVED DATA FOR THE REACTION OF THE CYCLANONES WITH SODIUM BOROHYDRIDE IN ISOPROPYL ALCOHOL SOLUTION

$(CH_2)_{n-1}$ C=O	Temp. (°C)	Rate constant $k_2 \times 10^4$ (l. mole^{-1} sec^{-1})	$E_{act.}$ (kcal mole^{-1})	log A	$\Delta H^{\ddagger}$ (kcal mole^{-1})	$\Delta S^{\ddagger}$ (e.u.)
4	−24·1	56·9	8·6	5·4	8·1	−36·4
	−14·5	115				
	0·1	266				
5	0·0	7·01	9·8	4·7	9·3	−38·8
	25·0	31·8				
	35·1	54·1				
6	−23·7	61·7	5·8	2·9	5·1	−48·1
	−9·2	115				
	0·0	161				
7	0·0	1·02	10·2	4·1	9·6	−41·6
	25·0	4·90				
	35·1	8·54				
8	0·0	0·0781	11·9	4·4	11·3	−41·2
	25·0	0·411				
	35·1	0·963				
9	25·0	0·203	12·2	4·3	11·6	−41·4
	35·1	0·381				
	45·0	0·732				
10	25·0	0·103	13·1	4·6	12·6	−43·5
	35·1	0·218				
	45·0	0·416				
11	25·0	0·152	12·0	4·0	11·4	−42·4
	35·1	0·290				
	45·1	0·537				
12	25·0	1·05	11·3	4·3	10·7	−41·0
	35·1	1·98				
	45·1	3·42				
13	0·0	0·194	11·8	4·7	11·1	−39·2
	25·0	1·22				
	35·0	2·22				
15	0·0	0·420	11·5	4·9	10·8	−38·9
	25·0	2·41				
	35·1	4·61				
17	0·0	0·583	10·7	4·4	10·2	−40·5
	25·0	3·07				
	35·0	5·56				
Di-*n*-hexyl ketone	25·0	2·67	11·5	4·9	10·8	−38·8
	35·1	5·05				
	45·0	9·00				

5- and 6-membered rings.[8] The reaction of sodium borohydride with aldehydes and ketones is a kinetically simple reaction which promises to be of considerable utility in examining the reactivity of these compounds.[9] It appeared desirable therefore, to undertake a detailed study of the rates of reaction of sodium borohydride with a wide range of cyclic ketones.

RESULTS

The cyclanones (4-, 5-, 6-, 7-, 8-, 9-, 10-, 11-, 12-, 13-, 15- and 17-ring members) were either commercially available products or were synthesized by recognized literature procedures. In each case the compounds were carefully purified prior to use. The rates of reaction were run in *iso*propyl alcohol solution by the procedure previously described.[9]

For comparison of the rates observed for the large rings with those anticipated for related open-chain structures, di-*n*-hexyl ketone was included in the study.

The results are summarized in Table 1.

DISCUSSION

To facilitate ready comparison, the rate constants at 0° for the borohydride reduction reaction are listed in Table 2. Previously available data for the solvolysis of the 1-chloro-1-methyl*cyclo*alkanes,[4] the cyclanyl tosylates,[6,7] and the dissociation of the cyclic cyanohydrins[10] are also included.

TABLE 2. EFFECT OF RING SIZE ON RATE AND EQUILIBRIUM CONSTANTS OF CYCLIC DERIVATIVES

$(CH_2)_{n-1}$ C	Borohydride[a] reduction $k_2 \times 10^4$ (l. mole^{-1} sec^{-1})	Cyanohydrin[b] dissociation, 22–23° (keq., mole l.$^{-1}$)	Solvolysis[c] of tosylates, 70° ($k_1 \times 10^5$ sec^{-1})	Solvolysis[d] of 1-chloro-1-methyl-*cyclo*alkanes, 25° ($k_1 \times 10^2$ hr^{-1})
n				
4	264		26·7	0·224
5	7·01	0·021	32·2	132
6	161	0·001	2·37	1·06
7	1·02	0·13	60·0	115
8	0·0781	0·86	452	303
9	0·0316[e]	1·70	408	46·5
10	0·0132[e]		891[e]	18·8
11	0·0235[e]	1·12	116	12·7
12	0·182[e]	0·31	7·70	
13	0·194	0·26	8·30	3·02
14		0·06	3·12	
15	0·420	0·11	5·18	1·92
16		0·09		
17	0·593	0·12	5·15	2·01
R$_2$CO	0·454[e],[f]		3·15[h]	4·80[i]

[a] This study. [b] Dissociation of cyanohydrin in 96 per cent ethanol (ref. 11). [c] Acetolysis of cyclanyl tosylates (ref. 7, 8). [d] Solvolysis in 80 per cent aqueous ethanol (ref. 5). [e] Calculated from data at other temperatures. [f] Di-*n*-hexylketone. [g] Di-*n*-octylketone. [h] Di-*n*-propylcarbinyl tosylate. [i] Di-*n*-amylmethylcarbinyl chloride.

[8] F. P. Price, Jr. and L. P. Hammett *Ibid.* **63**, 2387 (1941).
[9] H. C. Brown, O. H. Wheeler, and K. Ichikawa *Tetrahedron* **1**, 214 (1957).
[10] V. Prelog and M. Kobelt *Helv. Chim. Acta* **32**, 1187 (1949).

It was previously suggested that the normal bond angle for a carbon atom with co-ordination number 3, as in carbonyl derivatives ($> C=O$) and carbonium ions ($> C^+\!\!-\!H$), would be expected to be 120°, as compared to the 109·5° for the normal tetrahedral value. Consequently, the deformation of the angle at the carbonyl carbon atom (120° → ∼90°) must be greater than the corresponding deformation for a tetrahedral carbon atom (109·5° → ∼90°). It is reasonable to expect that the larger angular deformation will result in a greater strain. Conversion of the carbonyl carbon to a tetrahedral derivative should relieve this additional strain. On this basis it was predicted that reactions of *cyclo*butanone in which the carbonyl carbon atom undergoes transformation from co-ordination number 3 to 4 in the rate-determining step should be strongly favored.[3] In this discussion it is tacitly assumed that the bond oppositions in the *cyclo*butane system are relatively small and may be ignored in view of the large change in angular strain accompanying the change in the configuration of the ring atom.

The rate constant for the reaction of *cyclo*butanone with sodium borohydride is far larger than that for an open-chain compound, such as acetone, and indeed is larger than that of any other ring compound here examined. This result supports the proposed role of angular strain in controlling the reactivity of 3- and 4-membered ring derivatives.[3]

If the change from co-ordination number 3 to co-ordination number 4 is favored in 4-ring systems, the reverse change should be resisted. This prediction is supported by the low rate of solvolysis of 1-chloro-1-methyl*cyclo*butane.[4] It has been pointed out that the solvolysis of *cyclo*butyl tosylate is far greater than would be anticipated on the basis of the considerations here discussed.[2] However, this compound solvolyzes with rearrangement, and it is probable that the solvolysis proceeds directly to the formation of a carbonium ion more stable than the cyclobutyl cation. The theory cannot be applied to such a case; it should be restricted to cases where the rate-determining stage depends primarily upon a simple change in the number of bonds formed by the ring atom undergoing reaction.

In the 5- and 7-ring compounds the bond angles are presumably near the tetrahedral values and angle strain is not believed to be a major factor. The strains in *cyclo*pentane and *cyclo*heptane, which are indicated by heats of combustion studies,[11] are believed to arise from bond opposition forces. On this basis, a change in co-ordination number from 4 to 3 should reduce the number of bond oppositions and the resulting strain in 5- and 7-ring systems. Such reactions should be favored in these ring systems. Conversely, *cyclo*pentanone and *cyclo*heptanone should resist reactions in which the carbonyl carbon is converted into a tetrahedral derivative in the rate-determining stage.

On the other hand, in *cyclo*hexane all of the carbon-to-hydrogen bonds are nicely staggered and there are no bond opposition effects, whereas in *cyclo*hexanone both the angle is unfavorable and two of the *alpha* carbon-to-hydrogen bonds are in partial opposition to the carbon-to-oxygen bond. These considerations lead to the conclusion that changes in co-ordination number from 4 to 3 should be favored in the 5- and 7-ring and resisted in the 6-ring systems, whereas the converse should be true for reactions involving changes in co-ordination number from 3 to 4. In confirmation of

[11] K. S. Pitzer *Science* **101**, 672 (1945); J. E. Kilpatrick, K. S. Pitzer, and R. Spitzer *J. Amer. Chem. Soc.* **69**, 2483 (1947).

this conclusion, the reduction of *cyclo*hexanone is faster than that of any ring ketone other than *cyclo*butanone, with the rate for *cyclo*pentanone and *cyclo*heptanone being much smaller (Table 2).

The available evidence indicates that the medium rings (8- to 12-members) are highly strained,[1] with the strain reaching a maximum in the 10-ring compounds. These strains are believed to arise from both bond opposition forces and compressions of van der Waals radii. Consequently, these ring systems should favor reactions in which bonds to a ring atom are broken and resist reactions in which additional bonds are made. The low rate of reaction with borohydride ion, with a minimum in rate at *cyclo*decanone, is in agreement with this interpretation.

The large rings exhibit reactivities which are considerably lower than that of acetone (k_2 at $0°$ is $15 \cdot 1 \times 10^{-4}$ l. mol.$^{-1}$ sec^{-1}), but which are comparable to the higher aliphatic ketones, such as di-*n*-hexyl ketone.

In general, the enthalpies of activation parallel the rate constants. Only in the case of *cyclo*hexanone and *cyclo*butanone do the entropies of activation exhibit a wide variation from the average value of approximately -40 e.u. The higher value for *cyclo*butanone, $-36 \cdot 4$, can be accounted for in terms of the relatively high rigidity and order of this ring system.[9] On this basis, the lower value for *cyclo*hexanone might be attributed to a low degree of order in the parent ketone, or to a highly ordered structure in the transition state, or both.

The close similarity in the effects of ring size in the various reactions is indicated in Figs. 1–4. In order to facilitate comparison, the ordinates have been fixed so as to place the points for the 4- and 6-ring systems (either the most reactive, or the least reactive compounds) at the bottom of the diagrams. The remarkable similarity in the effects of ring size on chemical behavior argues for a common factor. This common factor is believed to be the change in internal strain accompanying the change in the co-ordination number of the ring atom undergoing reaction.

The internal strain is made up of several types of interactions: (1) compression of van der Waals radii, (2) the distortion of bond angles, and (3) bond opposition forces.[7] Reactions which proceed with a net decrease in internal strain in the transition state should be favored; those which proceed with a net increase in such strain will be hindered. Ideally, the effect of making or breaking a bond to one of the ring atoms should be analyzed in terms of each of the above strain factors. In actual fact, such an analysis is not possible at the present time. The individual strains are not mutually independent, nor can they be estimated separately with any accuracy at the present time.

On the other hand, the net change in internal strain accompanying the making or breaking of a bond to a ring atom can be estimated with considerable precision. Consequently, it appears desirable to discuss the effect of ring size on chemical behavior in terms of the net change in internal strain accompanying the reaction (I-strain).

It should be recognized that I-strain effects will not be the only factor influencing chemical behavior of ring compounds. It is only claimed that it is an important factor, and in the simple systems here examined it appears to be a dominant factor.

In three of the four reactions considered in Table 2, the maximum or the minimum in the behavior of the system appears at the 10-ring derivative. This behavior is in accord with the evidence that the internal strain is a maximum in the 10-ring compounds.

It is of interest to explore the exception, the solvolysis of the 1-chloro-1-methylcyclanes, where the maximum in rate appears at the 8-ring compound.

Examination of molecular models of the medium rings suggest that compression of van der Waals radii may be involved in the internal strain as well as the bond opposition

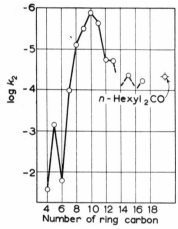

FIG. 1. Effect of ring size on the rate of reaction of sodium borohydride with the cyclanones in isopropyl alcohol at 0°.

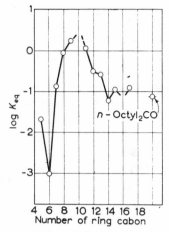

FIG. 2. Effect of ring size on the equilibrium constant for the dissociation of the cyclic cyanohydrins in 96 per cent ethanol at 22–23°.

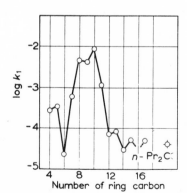

FIG. 3. Effect of ring size on the acetolysis of the cyclanyl tosylates at 70°.

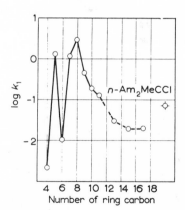

FIG. 4. Effect of ring size on the solvolysis of the 1-chloro-1-methyl-cyclanes in 80 per cent aqueous ethanol at 25°.

forces. On this basis, the introduction of both a methyl group and a chlorine atom on the same carbon atom of a given cyclane molecule may be expected to alter both the internal compressions and the bond opposition forces. There is no reason to expect that both these forces will be equally affected, and the relative magnitude of each effect may vary considerably with the size of the ring and the steric requirements of the substituents.

It would appear that the larger the ring the greater should be its possibilities for modifying its conformation and minimizing the magnitude of the atomic compressions. The maximum observed in the solvolysis of 1-chloro-1-methyl*cyclo*-octane may therefore be attributed to relatively large strains arising from the conflicting steric requirements of the two substituents and the ring hydrogen atoms, superimposed upon the usual bond opposition forces. These atomic compressions are presumably also present in the 10- and 9-ring derivatives, but are reduced to a greater extent than in the smaller ring by modification of the conformation. Conceivably, the maximum in rate could be shifted down as far as the 7-ring, or even further, by a suitable increase of the steric requirements of the substituents.

In general, linear free-energy relationships, such as those pointed out by Hammett for *meta* and *para* aromatic derivatives,[12] are rarely encountered in other than the rigid aromatic systems. The similarity in the structural effects in these ring compounds (Figs. 1–4), encourages an examination of the data from this point of view.

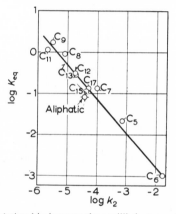

Fig. 5. Free-energy relationship between the equilibrium constants for the dissociation of the cyclic cyanohydrins and the rate constants for the reaction of the cyclanones with sodium borohydride.

Comparison of the equilibrium data for the dissociation of the cyanohydrins with the rate data for the borohydride reaction reveals a reasonably good linear relationship (Fig. 5). The fit is unexpectedly good for systems of this kind and presumably should be attributed to the similarity in the two reactions under comparison.

$$\diagdown C{=}O + HCN \rightleftharpoons \diagdown C \diagup \underset{CN}{\overset{OH}{|}}$$

$$\diagdown C{=}O + H_4B^- \longrightarrow \diagdown C \diagup \underset{OBH_3{}^-}{\overset{H}{|}}$$

Comparison of the rate data for the acetolysis of the cyclic tosylates with the rate data for the borohydride reaction also reveals a rough linear relationship for the 5- to 10-ring derivatives (Fig. 6). Larger rings deviate from this relationship and so do

[12] L. P. Hammett *Physical Organic Chemistry* McGraw-Hill, New York (1940).

related aliphatic compounds. The two reactions under comparison must have significantly different steric requirements, so that the deviations are not unexpected.

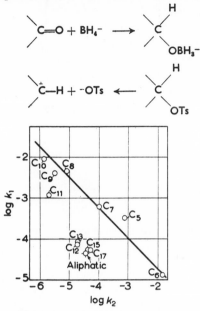

FIG. 6. Free-energy relationship between the rate constants for the acetolysis of the cyclic tosylates and the rate constants for the reaction of the cyclanones with sodium borohydride.

It is the existence of a limited linear relationship for the six consecutive ring systems, 5- through 10-, which must be considered unexpected. The fit, rough as it is, appears to be too good to be considered purely fortuitous. It may be that the fit arises from the fact that the rings from 5- through 10-members are relatively rigid, with comparatively fixed conformations, resembling the aromatic structures in that characteristic, whereas the larger rings possess greater mobility of conformation and more closely resemble aliphatic derivatives.

Carrying the comparison further to the tertiary chlorides, we observe that no linear relationship is indicated (Fig. 7). Presumably this is the result of the much larger steric requirements of the methyl and chlorine substituents in the smaller rings, giving rise to larger strains and enhanced solvolysis rates.

As was pointed out, these effects should be less in the larger rings. Presumably these steric interactions result in the points for the 5-, 6-, 7-, and 8-rings being considerably higher than they would otherwise appear in the plot and thereby destroy the linear relationship which might exist in the absence of this effect.

The existence of a limited linear relationship for the solvolysis of the cyclic tosylates and the reaction of the cyclanones with borohydride may have important consequences. A number of strained substances are known which exhibit enhanced rates of solvolysis. In some cases the enhanced rates have been attributed to relief of steric strain.[13] In others, the enhanced rates have been attributed to the formation of unusually stable "non-classical" ions.[14] A rigorous test of the relative importance of these factors in

[13] H. C. Brown J. Chem. Soc. 1248 (1956).
[14] S. Winstein Bull. Soc. Chim. 18, 55 (1951).

various systems has been rendered difficult by the transient nature of these carbonium ions.

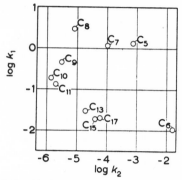

Fig. 7. Free-energy relationship between the rate constants for the solvolysis of the 1-chloro-1-methyl*cyclo*alkanes and the rate constants for the reaction of the cyclanones with sodium borohydride.

Conceivably, the carbonyl derivatives may provide relatively stable models of carbonium ions of related structures.

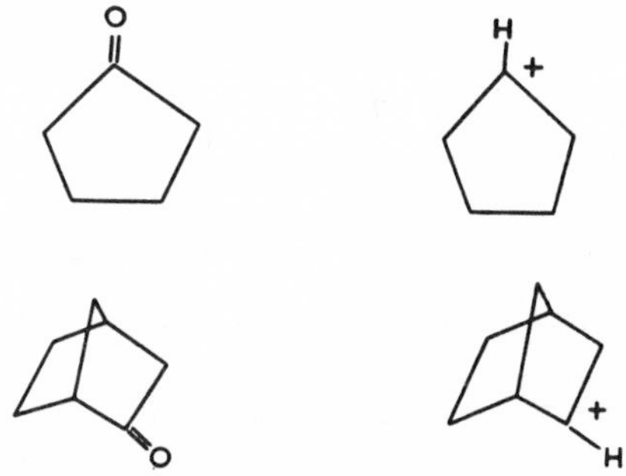

Fig. 23a.

For example, we have attributed the high rate of solvolysis of *cyclo*decyl tosylate to relief of internal strain accompanying the ionization. On the other hand, the alternative possibility that the high rate is due to the formation of a relatively stable "non-classical" *cyclo*decyl cation has been considered.[6]

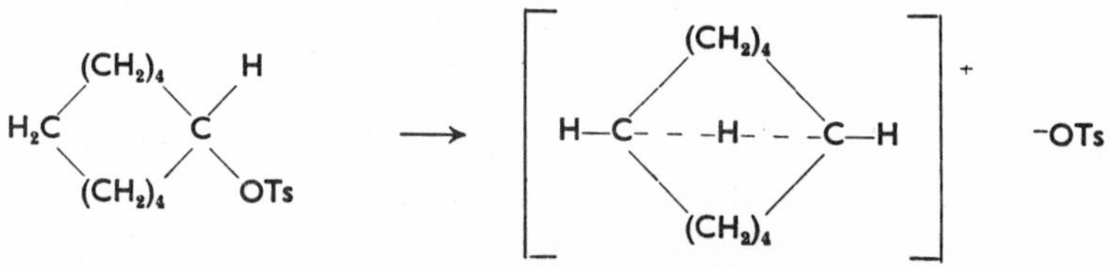

Such a structure would, of course, provide a reasonable explanation for the facile transannular hydride shifts which are observed in this ring system.[15]

However, from Fig. 6 it appears that the high rate of solvolysis of *cyclo*decyl tosylate is not out of line with the low reactivity of *cyclo*decanone. Since "non-classical" structures for this cyclic ketone are of questionable importance, it does not

[15] V. Prelog and K. Schenker *Helv. Chim. Acta* **35**, 2044 (19).52
   V. Prelog, K. Schenker, and W. Kung *Ibid.* **36**, 471 (1953).

appear desirable in the absence of additional evidence to attribute the high reactivity of *cyclo*decyl tosylate to this type of stabilization of the *cyclo*decyl cation.

We are presently investigating this experimental approach, utilizing the carbonyl compounds as models for related carbonium ions, in the hope of attaining a more complete understanding of the factors influencing the rates of formation and the stability of carbonium ions.

EXPERIMENTAL PART

Materials. The purifications of *iso*propyl alcohol and sodium borohydride have been described previously.[9] The carbonyl compounds were either commercial samples, carefully purified, or were synthesized by standard procedures. The physical properties of the cyclic ketones used in the rate measurements are summarized in Table 3.

TABLE 3. PHYSICAL PROPERTIES OF CYCLANONES

$(CH_2)_{n-1}$ C=O	B.p. (°C/mm)		M.p. (°C)		n_D^{20}	
	Obsd.	Lit.	Obsd.	Lit.	Obsd.	Lit.
n						
4	98·2/743	98–100/760[a]			1·4209	1·4189(25°)[a]
5	130·5/744	129·5/761[b]			1·4363	1·4370–1·4373[c]
6	153·8/744	155·7/760[d]			1·4502	1·45066(19·3°)[e]
7	180·0/744	66–70/16[f]			1·4610	1·4608[f]
8			43·5	43·8[g]		
9	97·5/15	92–95/12[h]			1·4475	1·4730(17°)[i]
10			24·5–25	20–22[g]		
11	106/10	108/10[j]			1·4810	1·4786(17°)[j]
12			61–62	60–61[h]		
13			29·5–30·5	30–32[k]		
15			63	63[j]		
17			65	63[j]		

[a] J. D. Roberts and C. W. Sauer *J. Amer. Chem. Soc.* **71,** 3925 (1949). [b] I. Vogel *J. Chem. Soc.* 2030 (1928). [c] E. R. Johnson and W. D. Walters *J. Amer. Chem. Soc.* **76,** 6266 (1954). [d] J. Timmermans and H. Roland *J. Chem. Phys.* **34,** 693 (1937). [e] W. Herz and W. Bloch *Z. physik. Chem.* **104,** 433 (1923). [f] R. H. Cox *J. Amer. Chem. Soc.* **74,** 2924 (1952). [g] E. P. Kohler, M. Tishler, H. Potter, and H. T. Thompson *Ibid.* **61,** 1057 (1939). [h] V. Prelog, L. Frenkiel, M. Kobelt, and P. Barman *Helv. Chim. Acta* **30,** 1741 (1947). [i] L. Ruzicka and W. Brugger *Ibid.* **9,** 399 (1928). [j] L. Ruzicka, M. Stoll, and H. Schinz *Ibid.* **9,** 249 (1928). [k] L. Ruzicka, M. Stoll, H. W. Huyser, and H. A. Bockenoogen *Ibid.* **13,** 1152 (1930).

Kinetic measurements. The experimental procedure was identical with that reported previously.[9] The temperatures were controlled to less than $\pm 0·02°$ except for temperatures below 0°, where the variation was of the order of $\pm 0·1°$. Several individual determinations, with varying initial concentrations of reactants, were carried out for a number of the compounds. In these cases the individual rate constants usually agreed to within 1 per cent. The quality of the agreement realized was similar to that reported in Table 1.[9] Where multiple determinations were available, the mean values of the second-order rate constants are reported in Table 1. For the less accessible ring derivatives, the value of the material made it advisable to restrict our measurements to a single kinetic run at each temperature.

32 | Transannular Hydride Shifts

Prelog's paper (Paper No. 32), delivered before the 16th International Congress of Pure and Applied Chemistry in Paris in 1957, reviews some ingenious and painstaking tracer experiments on transannular hydride shifts attending acetolysis and deamination in the cyclodecane and cycloheptane series. "Transannular" shifts are defined as those which place labeled hydrogen elsewhere in the ring than where it would be found if acetolysis and elimination followed the classical principle of least structure change. For this reason they are also referred to in this paper as "nonclassical" rearrangements, the word "nonclassical" not implying bridged ions in the Roberts sense.

The paper, however, does consider the question of the participation of hydrogen-bridged cations as intermediates in the transannular shifts. Three tosylates (cyclodecyl, cycloheptyl, and cyclododecyl) which were observed by Brown and co-workers (Papers 30, 31) to react with relative rate constants of 891, 60, and 7.7, were here found to undergo transannular shifts to the extents of 36–43, 3.4, and less than 0.2%, respectively, in the course of olefin formation. It would appear that over a range of two orders of magnitude rate of ionization and extent of transannular shift go together. Both could be due to compressional strain independently; or the accelerated rate could be associated with a kind of hydrogen-bridged ion not observed under normal conditions, which would then be a probable intermediate in the rearrangement. The step-by-step degradation of the product alcohol and olefins had shown that the two positions most remote from the tosylate group had provided more rearranging hydrogen than their two next neighbors; yet cyclodecyl-5,6-d_4-tosylate solvolyzed at a rate within about 1% of that of the undeuterated compound. Hence the hydrogen shift is no part of the rate determining step in these solvolyses, but begins after ionization has occurred.

In contrast, compare Winstein and Hansen (Paper No. 47), where in a less symmetrical system, with a driving force of about 1000, $k_H/k_D = 1.24$.

From: *Record Chem. Prog.* **18,** 247–60 (1957)

Investigations on the Transannular Effects in Elimination and Substitution Reactions by Tracer Techniques*

VLADIMIR PRELOG, *Eidgenössische Technische Hochschule, Zürich. Switzerland*

CLASSICAL organic chemistry may be said to be based on the *principle of least structural change* during a reaction; indeed, most chemical-structure proof depends upon that principle. However, it frequently happens that, even in the simplest reactions such as substitutions or eliminations, rearrangements do occur, single atoms or groups of atoms migrate in direct violation of the above principle. Such rearrangements are particularly characteristic of those reactions in which carbonium ions or equivalent particles are considered to be intermediates. In fact, this was recognized relatively early in the history of chemistry in those cases where the rearrangement led to an alteration of the carbon skeleton, as many examples from the realm of the terpenes and related natural products point out so impressively (1). Violations of the principle are more difficult to detect when the carbon-skeleton remains unaltered, as for example in the case of hydrogen shifts. There the structural change could be rationalized either as a direct migration of a hydrogen atom or a sequence of elimination and addition reactions, and only with the advent of isotopic tracers was the frequency of occurrence of direct hydrogen shifts made known (2). Generally these reactions occur via the migration of a hydrogen nucleus with a pair of electrons, from one of two bonded carbon atoms to the second which bears a positive charge, i. e., the so-called *1,2-hydride shift* (Fig. 1). Thus substitution and elimination take place, not on the carbon atom originally substituted, but on a neighboring carbon atom. In only a very few cases can a direct 1,3-hydride shift be identified and shown to not involve a series of two 1,2-shifts (3). It was therefore a surprising discovery that certain reactions of medium ring compounds with 8–11-membered rings could take place in the so-called *transannular* manner. Here the substitution or elimination process proceeds neither at the carbon atom initially substituted nor at one of its neighbors but via a *1,3-, 1,4-, 1,5-, or 1,6-hydride shift* at a more distant and otherwise nonactivated carbon atom.

Transannular substitution was originally observed during performic acid oxidation of certain stereoisomeric cyclic olefins. Treatment of the related cyclic 1,2-epoxides with strong acids leads to the same result. Figure 2

---

* The German original of this lecture, which was given before the XVIth International Congress for Pure and Applied Chemistry in Paris, on July 19, 1957, appeared in Experientia, Supplementum VII.

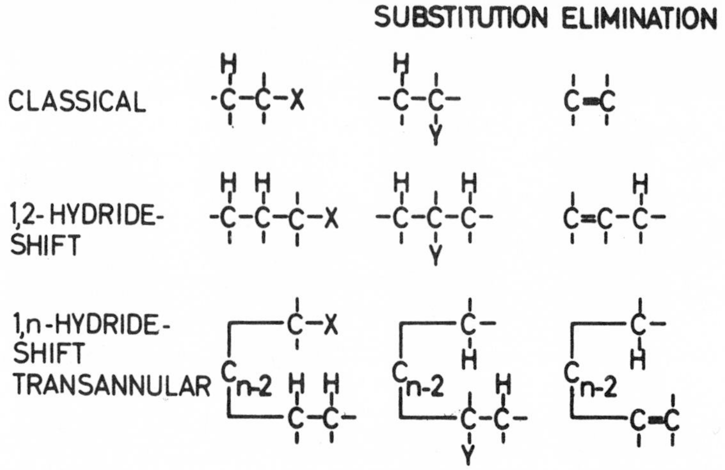

SUBSTITUTION ELIMINATION

FIGURE 1

depicts the relations amongst the stereoisomeric cycloolefins and the diols produced by a variety of oxidizing agents. Osmium (VIII) oxide reacts stereospecifically and always in a 1,2-manner to provide *cis*-diol from *cis*-olefin and *trans*-diol from *trans*-olefin. The action of peracids on *cis*-enes gives *cis*-epoxides. If the original epoxide contains a carbon ring of 5–7 or 12 or more members the major product will be a *trans*-1,2-diol. This contrasts strikingly with the results in the series of *cis*-1,2-epoxides of cyclanes with 8–11 members. Here the situation is as follows: in the eight-membered ring the *trans*-1,2-diol is accompanied by *cis*-cyclo-

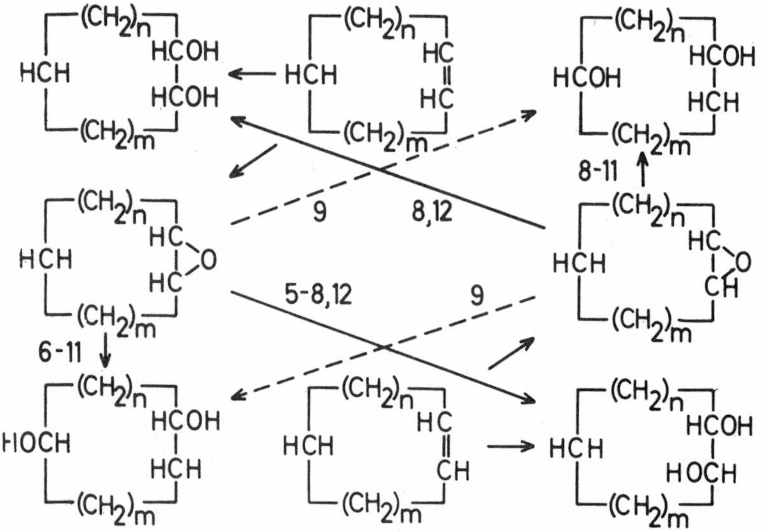

FIGURE 2

octanediol-1,4 (5), the nine ring gives exclusively a mixture of the stereoisomeric 1,5-diols (6), the ten ring, more exclusive yet, gives only one of the stereoisomers of the 1,6-diol (7), and in·the eleven ring system there is found an unidentified diol which differs from both of the known 1,2-diols (8). Analogously the *trans* epoxides give the corresponding stereoisomeric transannular diols. **Cope** and his co-workers (9) have recently isolated small quantities of the corresponding 1,4-diols by acid hydrolysis of 1,2-epoxy-cyclohexane and 1,2-epoxy-cycloheptane. The totality of these results shows that transannular substitution occurring on the opening of 1,2-epoxide rings under acid conditions is a preferential phenomenon of the *medium-ring systems of 8–11-ring members* and is only an occurrence of extremely small magnitude in both ordinary and large-ring systems.

Evidently *carbonium ions* arise when 1,2-epoxides are treated with acids (Fig. 3), which in the case of medium-ring compounds calls forth a transannular hydride shift. Obviously the question as to whether similar transannular reactions are the rule when medium-ring compounds react via carbonium ion intermediates demands investigation. A few of the reactions known to lead to carbonium ion intermediates which we have studied are presented in Fig. 3. These all differ notably from the epoxide reactions, since the position of the final substituent with respect to the initial one is not apparent unless a reference point of some kind is provided. In order to investigate these processes for transannular effects it is necessary to resort to *isotopic labeling* or the use of nonreactive substituents.

Amongst those reactions listed in Fig. 3 as giving rise to carbonium ions, *acetolysis of unsubstituted cyclanyl-p-toluenesulfonates* in dry acetic acid has recently attracted our special attention. I should like to emphasize some results obtained by the use of C^{14} and deuterium which provide some interesting insight into the chemistry of carbonium ions.

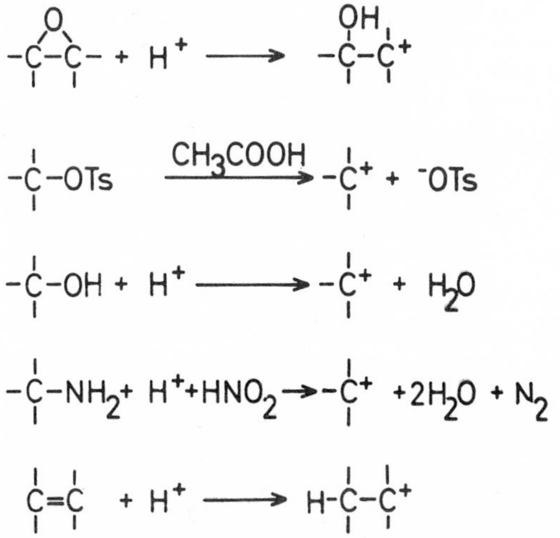

FIGURE 3

The kinetics of the acetolysis of cyclanyl-*p*-toluenesulfonates was investigated first, and the reaction shown to be one of *first order*. Fig. 4, where
log *k* is plotted as a function of ring size, illustrates graphically the notably
greater velocity of this reaction with medium-ring derivatives as compared
with cyclohexyl or cyclododecyl-*p*-toluenesulfonates or large-ring homo-
logues. This is a question of *steric acceleration* which from previous experience is now well known. The acceleration reaches a maximum in the case
of cyclodecyl-*p*-toluenesulfonate, a fact which prompted us to study it
first with the aid of C^{14} as a tracer atom.

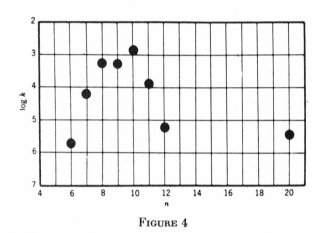

FIGURE 4

The general procedure employed for the synthesis of labeled starting
material is presented in Fig. 5. With an α,ω-dibromoalkane as point of
origin a labeled dinitrile was prepared using radioactive potassium cyanide.
Alkaline hydrolysis produced the corresponding dicarboxylic acid, which
was esterified with diazomethane. Here the invaluable acyloin condensation permitted closure of the medium-size ring to a cyclic acyloin in acceptable yield. Reduction of the acyloin to the cyclic ketone was accomplished with zinc and hydrochloric acid. Three of the carbon atoms of the
ketone are labeled, with half of the activity on the carbon atom 1 and the
remainder divided equally between the two neighboring carbons. The ketone serves as the starting material for preparation of the cyclanol via lithium aluminum hydride reduction, as well as the cyclanylamine obtained in
good yield by catalytic reduction of the corresponding oxime.

If one starts this series with 1,8-dibromooctane one obtains the labeled
cyclodecanol (11) and cyclodecylamine (12). Acetolysis of the *p*-toluene-
sulfonate of the former produces a mixture of the two isomeric cyclodecenes and practically no cyclodecanol, while desamination of the latter
with nitrous acid gives only *cis*-cyclodecene and a small amount of cyclodecanol. Similar differences in the course of these reactions, both assumed

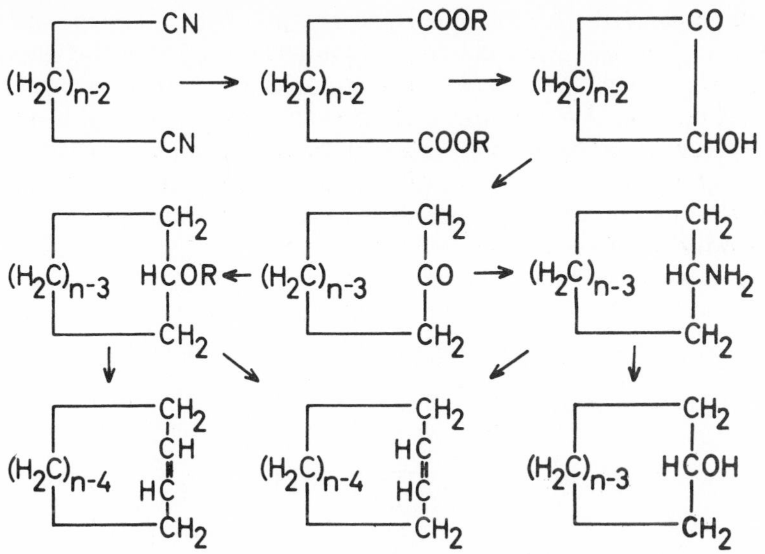

FIGURE 5

to proceed via a carbonium ion intermediate, have frequently been observed and we shall return to this point later.

Figure 6 outlines the reactions which make possible the degradation of either the cyclic olefin or the cyclic alcohol to the same acid—for example in the 10-ring series to sebacic acid. The alcohol is oxidized by means of chromium(VI) oxide to the cyclanone, whose α-hydroxymethylene deriv-

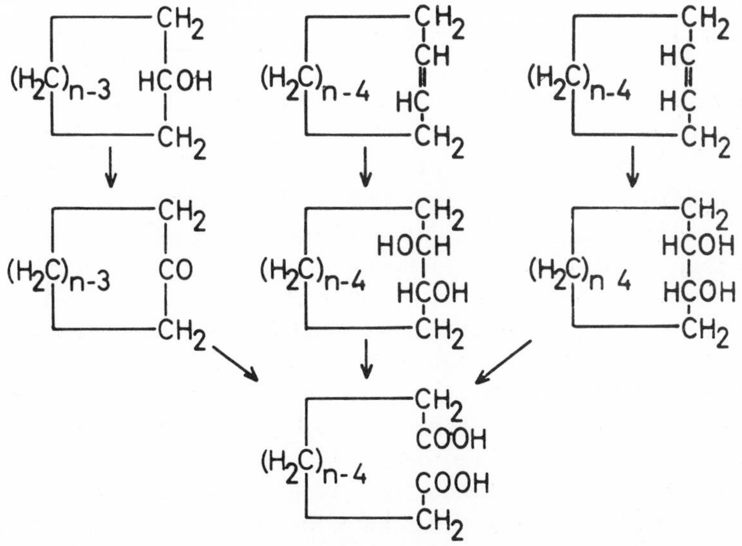

FIGURE 6

ative can be cleaved with alkaline hydrogen peroxide. The stereoisomeric cyclic olefins are first oxidized with osmium(VIII) oxide to the corresponding 1,2-diols, which are in turn further oxidized with concomitant ring cleavage with lead (IV) acetate, and oxygen in the presence of benzoyl peroxide. Thus we arrive in both cases at the open-chain dicarboxylic acid. Had all the reactions carried out up to this point proceeded in the classical manner, the radioactivity present in the acids so obtained would be distributed with $3/_4$ of the activity in the two carboxyl groups and the remaining $1/_4$ on the neighboring carbon atoms. The actual distribution was ascertained by systematic degradation of the dicarboxylic acid as is shown in Fig. 7 (11). First the dicarboxylic acid was decarboxylated according to

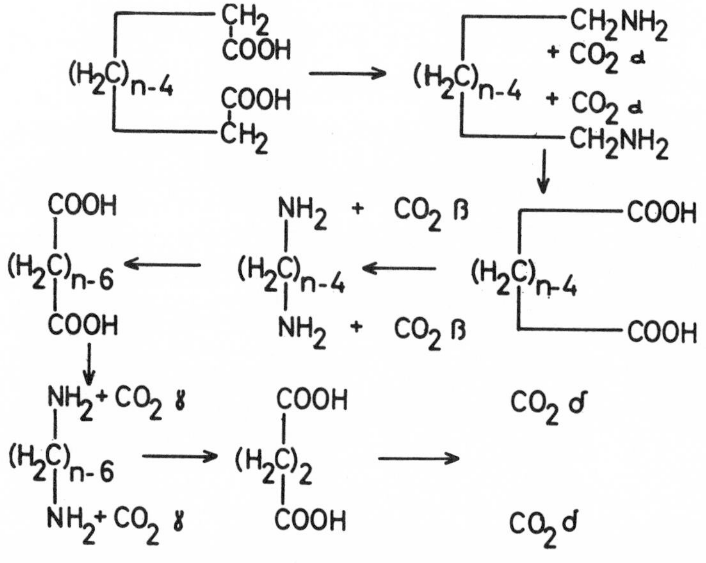

FIGURE 7

the method of **Curtius-Schmidt** to carbon dioxide and a diamine. The latter was oxidized with potassium permanganate to the dicarboxylic acid without loss of carbon. Repetition of this degradative process removed the carbon atoms in sets of two, whose activity was determined. After the loss of the pairs of carbon atoms the diamine thus obtained should no longer be active. As Fig. 8 indicates, however, such was not the case. The actual radioactivity distribution on the carbon atom pairs, designated for convenience as α, β, γ, δ and ϵ, in the cyclodecyl-p-toluenesulfonate acetolysis products shows that a considerable portion of the activity has penetrated the limits expected from classical reactions. Thus a great part of the reaction must have proceeded in a nonclassical direction.

Our conviction that this result is not achieved by a series of addition and elimination steps is the result of treating the two stereoisomeric cyclodec-

10-RING
Acetolysis

α	β	γ	δ	ε
HOOC⊢CH₂⊣CH₂⊣CH₂⊣CH₂			
HOOC⊣ CH₂⊣CH₂⊣CH₂⊣CH₂			
trans 0,420	0,218	0,098	0,105	0,164
cis 0,352	0,223	0,129	0,119	0,177

FIGURE 8

enes under acetolysis conditions with CH_3COOD. A deuterium determination proved that both hydrocarbons remained practically deuterium-free under such treatment (13).

The same synthetic scheme that was used to prepare labeled cyclodecyl-*p*-toluenesulfonate served for the production of the homologous cyclodo-decyl-*p*-toluenesulfonate. Acetolysis of this latter substance resulted in the almost exclusive formation of a mixture of isomeric cyclododecenes, which were degraded according to the aforementioned process to 1,8-diaminooctane.

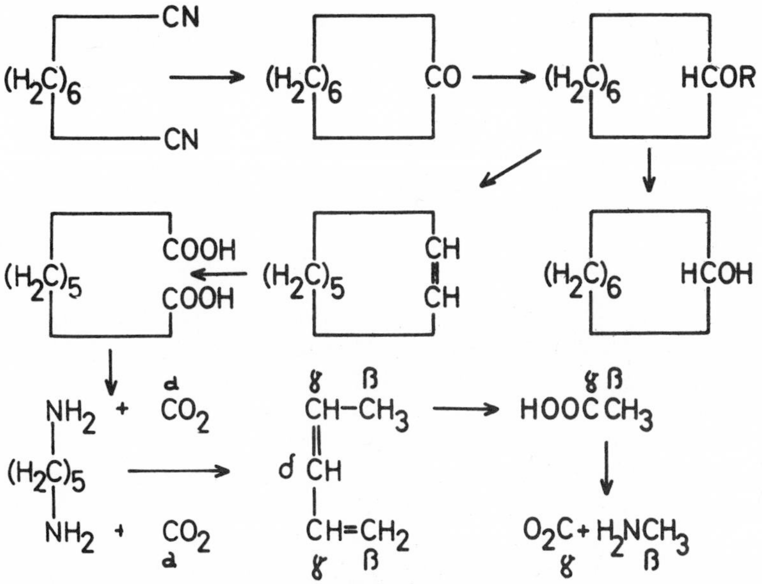

FIGURE 9

A somewhat different procedure was designed for the synthesis of cyclo-heptyl-*p*-toluenesulfonate, and also for the degradation of its acetolysis products, cycloheptanol and cycloheptene (15). As depicted in Fig. 9, we treated 1,6-dibromohexane with radioactive potassium cyanide to obtain 1,6-dicyanohexane. This via **Ziegler's** method gave cycloheptanone singly labeled on the carbonyl carbon. Nitric acid served nicely to transform the cycloheptanol obtained from the acetolysis into pimelic acid. The first step in the degradation of this acid utilized the customary **Curtius-Schmidt** process and produced 1,5-diaminopentane. Exhaustive methylation of this diamine led eventually to piperylene, which was oxidized by a modified **Kuhn-Roth** reaction to acetic acid. The **Curtius-Schmidt** served once again, giving carbon dioxide and methylamine. The latter was oxidized with potassium permanganate to carbon dioxide

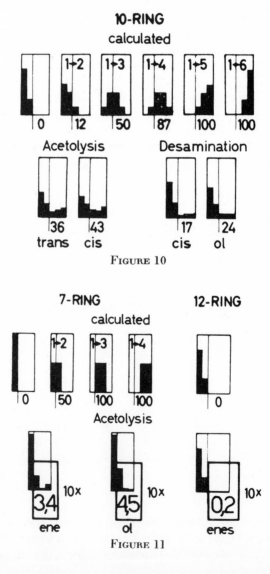

FIGURE 10

FIGURE 11

to complete the degradation process. In its later stages this process has the decided advantage of permitting work on a micro scale.

The next two Figs., 10 and 11, illustrate the distribution of radioactivity found experimentally on the carbon atom pairs α, β, γ, δ, and ϵ and the calculated distributions, assuming in turn a classical process, a 1,2- 1,3-, 1,4-, 1,5- and a 1,6-hydride-shift. The black surfaces represent the fraction of the total activity per carbon atom pair. The following conclusions may be drawn from the results of the 10-ring experiments:

(a) The nature of the reaction products as well as the manner of distribution of activity within them differs in the acetolysis and the desamination. The nonclassical course is more notable in the acetolysis than in the desamination.

(b) The activity distribution in the two stereoisomeric cyclodecenes arising from the acetolysis is only slightly but definitely different.

(c) A notable minimum in the radioactivity at the carbon atom pairs γ and δ is the identifying mark of a 1,5- or as the case may be 1,6-hydride shift, since no such minimum can arise from any combination of classical and 1,2-, 1,3- or 1,4-hydride shifts. Thus the elimination reaction occurring during acetolysis follows a marked transannular course.

Acetolysis in the 12-ring system presents by way of contrast an impressive example of the *classical* reaction pattern. Less than 0.2% of the total activity is found in the reaction product after two pairs of carbon atoms have been removed, and therefore the distribution pattern fits the one calculated theoretically within the limits of experimental error.

Acetolysis in the 7-membered ring constitutes an interesting *limiting case*. Here a small but nevertheless significant deviation from the classical mode is found. It should be noted that the calculated activity distribution patterns differ in this example from those discussed earlier, since the starting material was not labeled in the same manner. In the illustration of the experimentally determined values shown on Fig. 11, the ordinate has in part been magnified 10-fold, in order to provide a clearer picture.

During the course of our investigation of the transannular nature of substitution and elimination we had occasion to utilize a very simple labeling process using deuterium. This consists of reducing the cyclic ketone with lithium aluminum deuteride, thereby introducing on carbon 1 a single atom of deuterium per molecule. Acetolysis of cyclodecyl-p-toluenesulfonate labeled in this manner led to a mixture of deuterated stereoisomeric cyclodecenes. The trans isomer was degraded by the scheme outlined in Fig. 12. It ought to be emphasized here that the single atom of deuterium originally introduced during the preparation of the starting material was still present after the solvolysis in the cyclodecene. Therefore, in accord with expectations, there had occurred no exchange with the solvent during acetolysis. Had the acetolysis proceeded in the classical manner, all the deuterium would have been lost during the oxidation of the cyclodecene to sebacic acid. A considerable amount of deuterium was found beyond

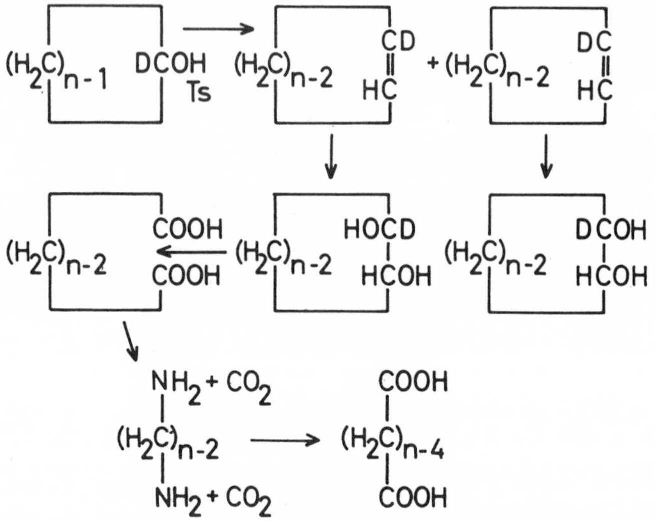

FIGURE 12

the limits expected from classical reactions. Apart from this qualitative agreement between the experiments with C^{14} and those with a deuterium label there is a notable quantitative disagreement. Considerably *less transannular hydride shift* is made apparent by the deuterium label than in the case of the C^{14} label. Before we attempt an interpretation of this interesting isotope effect, which we have come upon only recently, we should prefer to await the results of further experiments. In any case, we know already that the results of experiments with the deuterium-labeled compounds are not always directly comparable with those using a C^{14} label because of isotope effects.

There arose at this point a variety of questions concerning the *mechanism* of transannular hydride shifts. Apparently the decisive factor for such shifts is the compact structure and the resultant *nonclassical strain* in the medium-ring compounds. The axial hydrogen in the transannular position to a carbonium ion in a ring of medium size is ideally situated for a transannular hydride shift. It could thus be supposed that the free energy of activation for such a shift would be small. Moreover, it is possible to ask whether a bridged carbonium ion might not be a labile intermediate in this case. That is to raise the question as to whether any activation energy at all is indeed necessary for a transannular hydride-shift. This question is intimately linked to the question of the physical cause of the steric acceleration of acetolysis in these cases. According to the views of **H. C. Brown** this is mainly a question of relief of strain, i. e., the alteration of nonbonded interactions which in the case of the medium rings are assumed to be larger in the starting material than in the transition state for acetolysis, thereby accounting for the steric acceleration. An

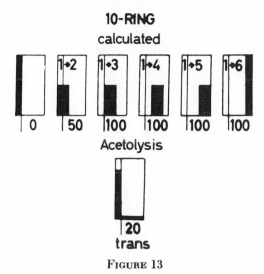

FIGURE 13

alternative possibility is that the carbonium ion, and thus also the transition state for acetolysis, is stabilized by bonded interaction, according to the "neighboring group" concept of **S. Winstein.** This corresponds to the concept of stabilization of the carbonium ion by bridging.

In order to study this question by experimental means, we have prepared (cf. Fig. 14) a cyclodecyl-*p*-toluenesulfonate in which the four hydrogens on carbons 5 and 6 have been replaced by deuterium (16). The symmetrical hexynetetracarboxylic acid was prepared from 1,4-dichlorobutyne-2, deuterated, and then decarboxylated. The tetradeuterosuberic acid so obtained was transformed according to the method of **Arndt-Eistert** into tetradeuterosebacic acid, which gave the desired tetradeuterocyclodecanol *p*-toluene sulfonate via the customary methods. If the steric acceleration of acetolysis was due even in part to a bonded interaction between the positive charged carbon and transannular hydrogen atoms, an isotope effect on the rate-determining step of the acetolysis should become apparent in this tetradeutero compound. As the rates given in Fig. 14 denote, there was *no observable isotope* effect.

In order to make comprehensible the differing behavior of the cyclodecyl cations obtained from different processes, the following points must be kept in mind. The carbonium ions can apparently exist in rings of medium size in several rotational isomers, depending upon the position of the positive carbon in a ring of ellipsoidal shape (17). The free energies of activation for elimination or hydride shift, proceeding from such rotational isomers, are different and of the same order of magnitude as the rotational barriers. The fate of a carbonium ion, and thus the nature of the products obtained from it, will be dependent, therefore, in large measure on the geometry it is forced to assume during its formation process. The exothermic desamina-

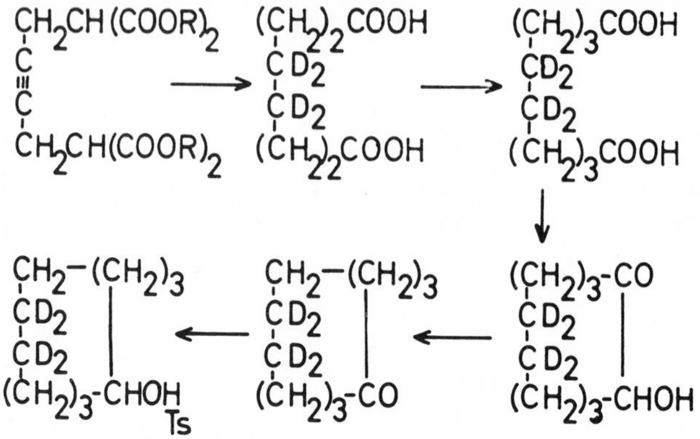

$$k_{25}^{H} = 4{,}60 \times 10^{-5}$$

$$k_{25}^{D} = 4{,}55 \times 10^{-5}$$

FIGURE 14

tion probably produces a different mixture of rotational isomers than the endothermic acetolysis which is dependent upon the steric assistance of the transannular hydrogen atoms. The latter process, therefore, leads directly to rotationally isomeric carbonium ions particularly well suited for trans-annular hydride shifts.

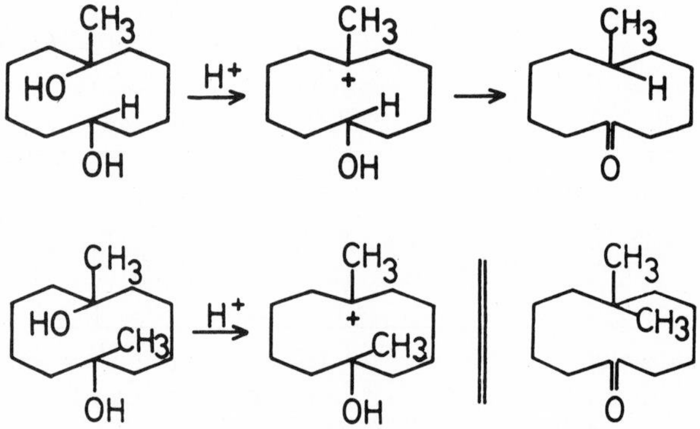

FIGURE 15

In all the experiments mentioned previously the deuterium was utilized as a ring label. In one case, however, we obtained a direct proof of a trans-annular hydride shift by replacing the migratory hydrogen itself with deuterium (18). As Fig. 15 indicates, 1-methylcyclodecanediol-1,6 was found to form upon treatment with phosphoric acid a tertiary carbonium ion which rearranged smoothly into 6-methylcyclodecanone. When we carried out the same reaction with the two isomeric 1,6-dimethyldecane-1,6-diols, which should afford 6,6-dimethylcyclodecanone via a transannular methyl migration, we found no carbonyl-containing compound whatsoever in the product, but only an unsaturated bicyclic hydrocarbon. These results indicate that the large methyl group, unlike the small hydrogen atom, exhibits no tendency toward transannular migration. However, it is also conceivable that the 6-methylcyclodecanone is not formed directly by a 1,6-hydride shift, but arises rather as the enol form by means of a spatially preferable 1,5-hydride shift followed by an elimination.

To test this latter concept we prepared 1-methylcyclodecanediol-1,6 with a deuterium atom at carbon 6 by reducing 6-hydroxy-6-methylcyclodecanone with lithium aluminum deuteride (Fig. 16). Treatment of this deu-

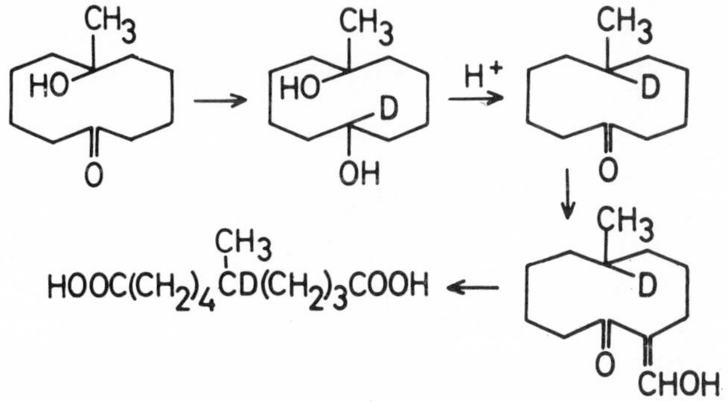

FIGURE 16

terated diol with phosphoric acid gave 6-methylcyclodecanone whose α-hydroxymethylene derivative was degraded to δ-methylsebacic acid. The fact that this acid contained one atom of deuterium points unambiguously to a 1,6-hydride shift, since the 6-methylcyclodecanone arising from a 1,5-hydride shift would have been deuterium free.

These few examples demonstrate the usefulness of isotopes for the investigation of the course and the reaction mechanism of transannular substitutions and eliminations, which represent a new and interesting type of reaction.

The importance of the fact that medium-ring compounds can react in a transannular fashion cannot be overemphasized in interpreting the reactions of these compounds. Recently such compounds have been found in nature or have been obtained in transformations of natural compounds.

Before I conclude, I would like to dwell a moment on some more *general consequences* of transannular substitution and elimination reactions. We are faced here with reactions in which carbon atoms, which on the basis of previous experience should be chemically inert, react rapidly and often stereospecifically because of their special spatial arrangement. Facing such a situation who would not recall such analogous biochemical reactions as the technically important microbiological oxidations of steroids? Do the substrate and the enzyme in that case form a ring-like complex which reacts in a transannular process?

Furthermore, there comes to mind the following provocative question. Can reactions analogous to transannular substitution or elimination be achieved in the aliphatic series or in normal rings by means of proper substitution or choice of reaction conditions? The example of the acetolysis of cycloheptyl-*p*-toluenesulfonate, which reacts even under quite ordinary conditions at least partly in a nonclassical process, indicates that this is not to be considered impossible, and that such reactions need not be limited to the medium-ring field. All of this calls forth new experimentation and new interpretation of old experiments, and I hope that these will prove fruitful in our laboratories as well as in those of many others.

I should like to take this opportunity to thank my younger colleagues: **Stanko Borčić, Axel Bothner-By, Werner Küng, Sara Jane Rhoads, Hans Jakob Urech, Edgar Wunderlich,** and **Joseph Würsch,** who were in many ways influential in bringing these investigations to their present position.

I also wish to extend my thanks to Professor **Elliot Marvell** for the English translation of the German manuscript.

REFERENCES

(1) Cf. L. Ruzicka in A. R. Todd, Perspectives in Organic Chemistry, Interscience Publishers, New York and London, 1956, p. 267.

(2) Cf. A. Streitwieser, Jr., Chem. Revs., *56*, 571 (1956).

(3) Cf. W. von E. Doering and A. P. Wolf, Abstr. of Papers, 12th Internat. Congr., New York, 1951, p. 437.

(4) V. Prelog and Margrit Speck, Helv. Chim. Acta, *38*, 1786 (1955).

(5) A. C. Cope, S. W. Fenton, and C. F. Spencer, J. Am. Chem. Soc., *74*, 5884 (1952); A. C. Cope, Abstracts of Papers, 14th National Organic Chemistry Symposium of the Am. Chem. Soc., Lafayette, Indiana, 1955.

(6) V. Prelog, K. Schenker, and W. Küng, Helv. Chim. Acta, *36*, 471 (1953).

(7) V. Prelog and K. Schenker, Ibid., *35*, 2044 (1952).

(8) V. Prelog and Valerie Boarland, Ibid., *38*, 1776 (1955).

(9) A. C. Cope, H. E. Johnson, and J. S. Stephenson, J. Am. Chem. Soc., *78*, 5599 (1956); A. C. Cope, T. A. Liss, and G. W. Wood, Chemistry & Industry, *1956*, 823.

(10) R. Heck and V. Prelog, Helv. Chim. Acta, *38*, 1541 (1955); cf. H. C. Brown and G. Ham, J. Am. Chem. Soc., *78*, 2735 (1956).

(11) H. J. Urech and V. Prelog, Helv. Chim. Acta, *40*, 477 (1957).

(12) V. Prelog, H. J. Urech, A. A. Bothner-By, and J. Würsch, Ibid., *38*, 1095 (1955).

(13) Unpublished experiments of E. Wunderlich.

(14) Unpublished experiments of W. Küng.

(15) Unpublished experiments of Sara Jane Rhoads.

(16) Unpublished experiments of S. Borčić.

(17) Cf. V. Prelog in A. R. Todd, Perspectives in Organic Chemistry, Interscience Publishers, New York and London, 1956, p. 96.

(18) V. Prelog and W. Küng, Helv. Chim. Acta, *39*, 1394 (1956).

33 | The 7-Oxa- nor-bornyl Chlorides

An oxygen atom, present in a molecule which may form a carbonium ion, has an inductive effect unfavorable to the ionization, but with favorable geometry, a resonance effect stabilizing a carbonium ion at an adjacent carbon atom. The 7-oxa analog of norbornyl chloride is of interest because it shows these two effects one after the other, as the geometry of the ring system changes (Martin and Bartlett, Paper No. 33). Although the *exo* isomer A shows a normal driving force of the norbornyl type, it is very much slower than in norbornyl chloride itself, showing that the 7-oxygen atom can exert only its inductive effect. After

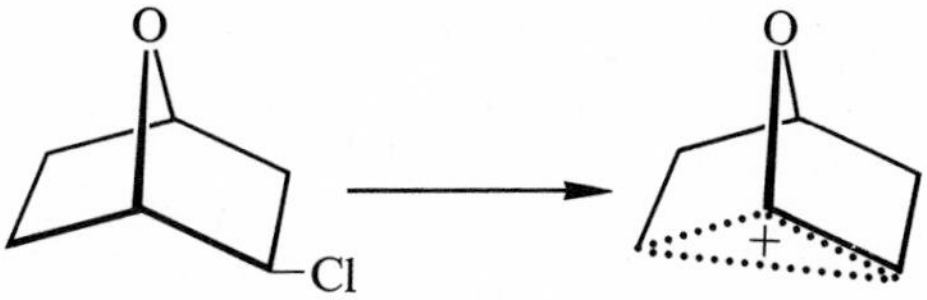

A   B

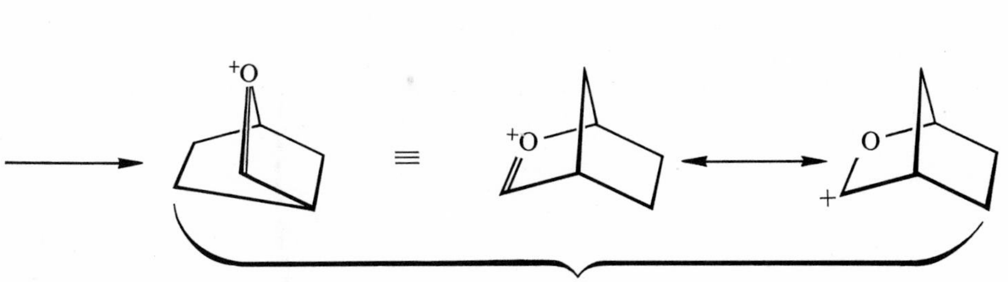

C

ionization, however, to the bridged cation, B, the oxonium isomer C appears to
be the more stable, and the product is the hydroxyaldehyde E via the hemiacetal D.

D   E

From: *J. Am. Chem. Soc.* **79**, 2533–41 (1957)

[CONTRIBUTION FROM THE CONVERSE MEMORIAL LABORATORY OF HARVARD UNIVERSITY]

The Synthesis and Solvolysis of the 2-Halo-1,4-endoxocyclohexanes[1]

BY JAMES C. MARTIN[2] AND PAUL D. BARTLETT

RECEIVED DECEMBER 17, 1956

A kinetic study of the hydrolysis of *exo*-2-chloro-1,4-endoxocyclohexane has shown it to be less reactive than *exo*-norbornyl chloride by a factor of approximately 2000. Its relative inertness is considered to result from the inductive effect of the oxygen bridge, enhanced by its geometric situation. Solvolysis of *endo*-2-chloro-1,4-endoxocyclohexane was slower than that of its *exo* isomer by a factor of 160 (at 140°). This factor is of the same order of magnitude as the corresponding factor in the solvolysis of norbornyl derivatives suggesting that the anchimeric acceleration of ionization of the *exo*-2 substituent is not greatly affected by substitution of an oxygen bridge for the methylene bridge of the norbornyl derivatives. In every case the solvolysis product was that expected to result from rearrangement, 3-formylcyclopentanol. The structures of these chloro ethers, which were obtained from the photochlorination of 1,4-endoxocyclohexane, were confirmed by dipole moment studies. *exo*-2-Bromo-1,4-endoxocyclohexane, isolated from the N-bromosuccinimide bromination of the parent ether, showed a reactivity 30-fold greater than its chloro analog. An interesting side product (16%) isolated from this bromination reaction was β-bromopropionyl isocyanate.

Introduction

A large amount of work of a quantitative nature has been performed on the solvolytic reactions of the various norbornyl derivatives.[3] In the frame of understanding created by this work we have examined the chemical consequences of the replace-

(1) Presented before the Organic Division of the American Chemical Society at its Atlantic City Meeting, September, 1956.

(2) National Science Foundation Fellow, 1953–1954.

(3) (a) J. D. Roberts, W. Bennett and R. Armstrong, THIS JOURNAL, **72**, 3329 (1950); (b) J. D. Roberts and W. Bennett, *ibid.*, **76**, 4623 (1954); (c) S. Winstein and D. Trifan, *ibid.*, **71**, 2953 (1949); (d) S. Winstein and D. Trifan, *ibid.*, **74**, 1147, 1154 (1952); (e) S.

Winstein, B. Morse, E. Grunwald, H. Jones, J. Corse, D. Trifan and H. Marshall, *ibid.*, **74**, 1127 (1952); (f) S. Winstein, E. Clippinger, A. H. Fainberg and G. C. Robinson, *Chem. and Ind.*, 664 (1954); (g) J. D. Roberts and C. C. Lee, THIS JOURNAL, **73**, 5009 (1951); (h) J. D. Roberts, C. C. Lee and W. H. Saunders, Jr., *ibid.*, **76**, 4501 (1954); (i) P. D. Bartlett and L. H. Knox, *ibid.*, **61**, 3184 (1939); (j) W. von E. Doering and E. F. Schoenewaldt, *ibid.*, **73**, 2333 (1951); (k) S. Winstein, M. Shatavsky, C. Norton and R. B. Woodward, *ibid.*, **77**, 4183 (1955); (l) S. Winstein and M. Shatavsky, *ibid.*, **78**, 592 (1956).

ment of the 1,4-endomethylene bridge of the norbornyl system by the oxygen bridge of the 1,4-
endoxocyclohexane system.

Results and Discussion

The photochlorination of 1,4-endoxocyclohex-
ane at −40° led to the isolation of a series of chloro
ethers including *exo*-2-chloro-1,4-endoxocyclohex-
ane and *endo*-2-chloro-1,4-endoxocyclohexane. Infrared analysis showed the *exo* isomer to be formed
in amount 2.2 times that of the *endo* isomer. None
of the α-chloro ether, 1-chloro-1,4-endoxocyclohex-
ane, which would result from bridgehead chlorination, was isolated. This is in accord with previously reported[4] unsuccessful attempts to obtain
bridgehead chlorination in other systems.

The bromination of the parent ether, 1,4-endoxo-
cyclohexane, with N-bromosuccinimide yielded *exo*-
2-bromo-1,4-endoxocyclohexane.

These monohalo ethers were separated and purified by fractional distillation. The more highly
chlorinated ethers resulting from further treatment
with chlorine were separated by means of chromatography on alumina. A summary of the pure
compounds isolated is presented in Table I.

TABLE I

PRODUCTS OF THE HALOGENATION OF 1,4-ENDOXOCYCLO-
HEXANE

Ether	M.p. or b.p. °C.
endo-2-Chloro-1,4-endoxocyclohexane	68.0 (27)[a]
exo-2-Chloro-1,4-endoxocyclohexane	48.0 (4)[a]
exo-2-Bromo-1,4-endoxocyclohexane	68.2 (2)[a]
Dichloro ether	143.2–144.0
Trichloro ether	154.5–145.8
Tetrachloro ether	77.8–78.8
Hexachloro ether	108.6–109.0
Octachloro ether	158.8–159.4

[a] The value in parentheses refers to pressure (mm.).

The constraint afforded by the bicyclic structure
of this series of halo ethers maintains quite constant
the angles between the various bonds and, therefore, the angles between the bond moments. This
greatly facilitates the interpretation of dipole moment data. If one considers the composite electric
moment of the unsubstituted 1,4-endoxocyclohex-
ane to be a vector directed toward the oxygen atom
and perpendicular to the plane of carbon atoms 2,
3, 5 and 6, the effect of superposing moments arising
from replacement of the various hydrogen atoms
by halogen may be computed.

A geometric model for the bicyclic nucleus of this
system was derived using vector analytical procedures.[5] The model chosen for these calculations
used a value for the C–C
bond length of 1.55 Å. and
for the C–O bond length,
1.44 Å. The values of the
angles in this model were:
∠ FAB = 101°, ∠ ABC
= 103°, ∠ AGD = 102°
54′ and ∠ BAG = 101°
14′.

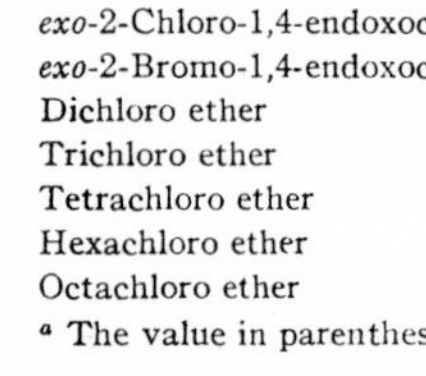

(4) See D. E. Applequist and J. D. Roberts, *Chem. Revs.*, **55**, 1065
(1954).

(5) E. J. Corey and R. A. Sneen, THIS JOURNAL, **77**, 2505 (1955).

The theoretical dipole moments were calculated
as the resultant of the ether dipole moment (the
experimental moment of 1,4-endoxocyclohexane,
1.74 *D*) and the C–Cl bond moment (the experimental moment of cyclopentyl chloride, 2.08 *D*)[6].

TABLE II

RESULTS OF DIPOLE MOMENT STUDIES ON THE MONOHALO-
1,4-ENDOXOCYCLOHEXANES

Compound	Solvent	Moment, *D* Calcd.	Found
1,4-Endoxocyclohexane	Benzene	..	1.70
	CCl₄	..	1.78
1-Chloro-1,4-endoxocyclohexane	.....	3.20	..
exo-2-Chloro-1,4-endoxocyclohex-ane	Benzene	3.17	3.07
	CCl₄	3.17	2.99
endo-2-Chloro-1,4-endoxocyclohex-ane	Benzene	0.82	1.08
exo-2-Bromo-1,4-endoxocyclohexane	CCl₄	3.17	3.03

These data make it clear that the assignment of
structure for *endo*-2-chloro-1,4-endoxocyclohexane
is the correct one. The data for the other chloro
ether are compatible with either *exo*-2-chloro-1,4-
endoxocyclohexane or 1-chloro-1,4-endoxocyclohex-
ane. The isolation of 3-formylcyclopentanol (V)
as the solvolysis product from both of the chloro
ethers confirmed the assignment of the structure
exo-2-chloro-1,4-endoxocyclohexane. The structure
of the bromo ether was similarly shown to be *exo*-
2-bromo-1,4-endoxocyclohexane. The hydroxyaldehyde was formed nearly quantitatively in the
solvolyses of all three of these halo ethers. The
structure 3-formylcyclopentanol was established
by Wolff–Kishner reduction to the known[7] *trans*-3-
methylcyclopentanol.

The assigned structures for these halo ethers were
found to be compatible with the observed infrared
spectra and proton nuclear magnetic resonance
(NMR) spectra. The NMR spectra, obtained using a Varian Associates model V-4300B high resolution spectrograph, are schematically summarized in
Fig. 1.

The parent ether, 1,4-endoxocyclohexane, shows
two resonance peaks, of approximate relative intensities 4 and 1, at positions corresponding to
Gutowsky δ-values[8] of approximately −0.43 and
−0.10 (the methylene and the bridgehead hydrogens, respectively). No evidence of splitting, from
spin-spin interaction, was observed for either of
these peaks.

The spectra of the *exo*-2-halo-1,4-endoxocyclohex-
anes show a total of four main resonance peaks corresponding, presumably (in order of increasingly
negative δ-values), to the bridgehead hydrogens
(intensity 2), the halomethylene hydrogen (1), the
methylene adjacent to halomethylene (2) and the
other two methylene groups (4). The positions of
these peaks are expressed as δ-values: *exo*-chloride,
(−0.10, −0.15, −0.37, −0.43); *exo*-bromide
(−0.10, −0.15, −0.35, −0.43). The peak at 0.10
is a poorly resolved doublet, as might be expected
from the non-equivalence of the bridgehead hydro-

(6) H. Rogers and J. D. Roberts, *ibid.*, **68**, 843 (1946).

(7) M. Godelot, G. Cauquil and R. Calas, *Bull. soc. chim.*, **6**, 1351
(1939).

(8) L. H. Meyer, A. Saika and H. S. Gutowsky, THIS JOURNAL, **75**,
4567 (1953).

TABLE III

ENTHALPIES AND ENTROPIES OF ACTIVATION FOR SOLVOLYSIS

Compound	Solvent	$\Delta H^{\ddagger}$, kcal.	$\Delta S^{\ddagger}$, e.u.
exo-2-Chloro-1,4-endoxocyclohexane	50% dioxane–H₂O	29.43 ± 0.12	-7.47 ± 0.29
endo-2-Chloro-1,4-endoxocyclohexane	50% dioxane–H₂O	30.87 ± 0.15	-14.07 ± 0.34
exo-2-Bromo-1,4-endoxocyclohexane	50% dioxane–H₂O	24.6 ± 0.54	-15.00 ± 1.45
exo-2-Norbornyl p-bromobenzenesulfonate	Acetic acid	23.3^a	7.7^a
endo-2-Norbornyl p-bromobenzenesulfonate	Acetic acid	26.0^b	-1.5^b

[a] This value, calculated from the data of Winstein,[3e] was from two runs at temperatures differing by 8.77°. [b] Calculated from the data of Winstein.[3e]

TABLE IV

SOLVOLYSES OF THE 2-HALO-1,4-ENDOXOCYCLOHEXANES

Run	Compound	Concentration halide, mole/l.	Temp., °C.	Reaction followed, %	Added salt	Salt concn., mole/l.	k, sec.$^{-1a}$
1	exo-Br	0.03967^b	85.0	58.1			$(8.58 \pm 0.06) \times 10^{-7}$
2	exo-Br	$.03988^c$	85.0	52.9			$(4.64 \pm .05) \times 10^{-7}$
3	exo-Br	$.04028^d$	85.0	79.0			$(8.24 \pm .04) \times 10^{-6}$
4	exo-Br	$.04020^d$	100.7	70.6			$(3.77 \pm .03) \times 10^{-5}$
5	exo-Br	$.04344^d$	120.0	90.0			$(1.85 \pm .03) \times 10^{-4}$
6	exo-Br	$.04026^d$	85.0	32.5	KCl	0.10	$(8.41 \pm .04) \times 10^{-6}$
7	exo-Br	$.04193^d$	85.0	52.8	NaClO₄	.10	$(9.07 \pm .03) \times 10^{-6}$
8	exo-Cl	$.04328^d$	100.7	32.8			$(1.17 \pm .03) \times 10^{-6}$
9	exo-Cl	$.04069^d$	120.0	64.1			$(8.81 \pm .37) \times 10^{-6}$
10	exo-Cl	$.04032^d$	140.0	79.1			$(5.66 \pm .04) \times 10^{-5}$
11	endo-Cl	$.03969^d$	140.0	38.7	NaOAc	0.042	$(3.47 \pm .09) \times 10^{-7}$
12	endo-Cl	$.03948^d$	160.0	66.4	NOaAc	.041	$(2.08 \pm .02) \times 10^{-6}$
13	endo-Cl	$.03420^d$	175.0	71.4	NaOAc	.042	$(7.10 \pm .08) \times 10^{-6}$
14	endo-Cl	$.03961^d$	140.0	84.6			Autocatalytic
15	endo-Cl	$.03610^d$	140.0	44.2	HCl	.02	Autocatalytic
16	endo-Cl	$.03312^d$	140.0	19.6	KCl	.02	Autocatalytic

[a] These first-order rate constants were determined by a least squares treatment of the data. The uncertainties which are indicated are standard deviations. [b] In 80% ethanol (vol.). [c] In 80% ethanol (wt.). [d] In 50% dioxane (wt.).

gens because of the halogen at position 2. The halomethylene hydrogen resonance at −0.15 is strongly split into a triplet, presumably from spin–spin interaction with the protons of the neighboring methylene. The resonance of this neighboring methylene, at −0.37 or −0.35, appears as a doublet, as expected from such an interaction.

The endo-chloride shows a similar spectrum with an additional poorly resolved peak, of intensity approximately 1, at −0.32, possibly to be attributed to a transannular interaction of an endo-hydrogen at position 6 with the endo-chlorine. In addition, there is some evidence of splitting in the methylene peak at −0.43. The positions of the resonance peaks for this compound are (−0.05, −0.12, −0.32, −0.37, −0.43).

Results of kinetic studies on the solvolytic reactions of these ethers are outlined in Tables III and IV. The reactions were followed by acidimetric titration of aliquots.

A direct comparison of the rate constants for the exo- and endo-2-chloro-1,4-endoxocyclohexanes at 140° in 50% dioxane–water gives a reactivity ratio of 163 for these isomers, the exo isomer being the more reactive. Table V gives calculated values for this ratio from the present work, the work of Roberts and the work of Winstein. It can be seen that this ratio is not changed greatly in the 1,4-endoxocyclohexane system from its value in the norbornyl system.

The calculated value (from ΔH^* and ΔS^*) of the rate constant for the solvolysis of exo-2-chloro-1,4-endoxocyclohexane in 50% aqueous dioxane at

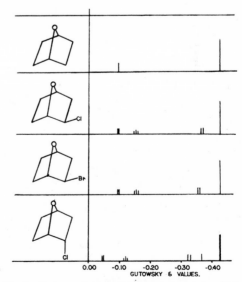

Fig. 1.—Proton nuclear magnetic resonance spectra of 1,4-endoxocyclohexane derivatives.

85.0° is 1.88×10^{-7} sec.$^{-1}$. The value of the rate constant for the solvolysis of the corresponding bromo ether is decreased by a factor of 9.6 when the solvent is changed from 50% dioxane–water to 80% (by vol.) ethanol–water. Assuming a parallel change in the rate constant for the chloro ether in these two solvents, one calculates a rate constant for the *exo*-chloride at 85.0° in 80% (by vol.) ethanol of 1.96×10^{-3} sec.$^{-1}$. Under these same conditions Roberts[3b] found a rate constant of 3.89×10^{-5} sec.$^{-1}$ for *exo*-norbornyl chloride.

Comparison of these values for the two bicyclic systems shows the norbornyl chloride to be more reactive than its oxygen-bridged analog by a factor of 2.0×10^3. A similar calculation for the *endo* isomers gives a factor of 6.0×10^3.

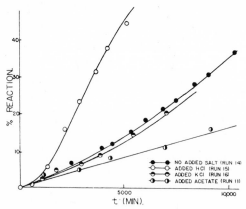

Fig. 2.—Solvolysis of *endo*-2-chloro-1,4-endoxocyclohexane in 50% dioxane-water (by weight) at 140°.

Early kinetic runs on the solvolysis of *endo*-2-chloro-1,4-endoxocyclohexane, with no added salt, proved to be autocatalytic. Several possible mechanisms for this autocatalysis were investigated (see Fig. 2). The possibility that the autocatalytic agent was chloride ion, perhaps operating through an S_N2 inversion to give the reactive *exo*-chloride, was ruled out when the rate with added potassium chloride proved to be almost identical to the rate with no added salt. The addition of hydrochloric acid to the reaction mixture gave, after an induction period, an appreciable acceleration of rate. A direct catalysis, by hydrogen ion, of the ionization of the chloride, such as that observed by Bartlett and Pöckel[9] in the isomerization of camphene hydrochloride, was ruled out by the observation of an induction period in this run. When an equivalent amount of sodium acetate was added to the reaction and the rate of solvolysis followed by titrating aliquots for excess acetate, the reaction was found to follow the first-order rate law very closely.

The catalytic effect of hydrochloric acid may be explained by postulating an ether cleavage to yield a chlorohydrin, which solvolyzes at a rate somewhat faster than the chloro ether. In a related case[3e] the solvolysis of 2-chloro-2-methyl-propanol-1 is slower than that of *t*-butyl chloride by a factor of 6.5×10^{-3}. Since *endo*-2-chloro-1,4-endoxocyclohexane is approximately 10^{-4} as reactive as cyclohexyl chloride in solvolytic reactions, we might expect the chlorohydrin from the ether cleavage to be about 60–70 times as reactive as the

(9) P. D. Bartlett and I. Pöckel, This Journal, 60, 1585 (1938).

chloro ether itself. Such a ratio of reactivities could account for the observed behavior.

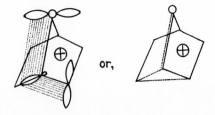

Two different interactions of the unshared electron pairs of the oxygen bridge might be expected to affect the *exo/endo* reactivity ratio in these solvolytic reactions.

With regard to the first of these effects, Woodward and Baer[10] postulated an important contribution from the oxonium form of the positively charged intermediate ion as a driving force in the rearrangement which accompanies the addition of bromine to *exo-cis*-3,6-endoxo-Δ^4-tetrahydrophthalic acid.

In the present work we must consider the possible stabilization, by such an oxonium form, of the transition state leading to the positive ion. Any such stabilization involves an interaction between a lone pair orbital of oxygen, the bonding orbital between C_1 and C_6 and the developing p-orbital at C_2, where the leaving group is *exo*.

Since the observed *exo/endo* ratio is of the same order of magnitude for the endoxo- and endomethylene series, it is unnecessary to postulate an important contribution of this oxonium form in the transition state. Once the ion is formed, however, slight changes in geometry, perhaps over a very small potential energy barrier, might be expected

(10) R. B. Woodward and H. Baer, *ibid.*, 70, 1161 (1948).

TABLE V

exo/endo REACTIVITY RATIOS IN SOLVOLYTIC REACTIONS

Series of compounds	Temp., °C.	k_{exo}/k_{endo}	k_{endo}, sec. $^{-1}$
Norbornyl chlorides[a][b]	85	70	5.6×10^{-7}
Norbornyl brosylates[a][f]	25	350	2.5×10^{-7}
	85	275	4.7×10^{-4}
2-Chloro-1,4-endoxocyclo-	140	163	3.5×10^{-7}
hexanes	85	211	8.9×10^{-10}
	25	318	1.2×10^{-13}

to twist the molecule into a form much more favorable to overlap between oxygen lone pair orbitals and a p-orbital on C_1. The large stabilization so attained would be similar to that in the transition states for the ionizations of α-halo ethers.

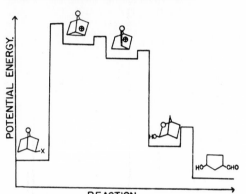

POTENTIAL ENERGY.

REACTION.

A POSSIBLE POTENTIAL ENERGY SCHEME.

Such a scheme is compatible, but of course not uniquely so, with the observed isolation of rearranged product (as aldehyde) in nearly quantitative yield. It is also compatible with results of experiments designed to intercept the cationic intermediate with azide ion. According to Swain[11] the azide ion is a more active nucleophile than water by a factor of 10^4 to 10^5. In his kinetic treatment of interception experiments using azide ion, Swain considered the alkyl azide to be formed irreversibly where the alkyl group was, for example, triphenylmethyl. In the present work solvolyses with 0.6 N added azide (sufficient, using Swain's competition factor, to capture more than 99% of the carbonium ions in competition with water), the product obtained was 3-formylcyclopentanol with less than 3% of an alkyl azide. A possible explanation

(11) C. G. Swain, C. B. Scott and K. H. Lohmann, THIS JOURNAL, **75**, 136 (1953); C. G. Swain and C. B. Scott, *ibid.*, **75**, 141 (1953).

for this unexpected behavior would involve an attack of azide ion either on II or on III, which is formed very rapidly from II, to give the α-azido ether which is then subject to hydrolysis to 3-formylcyclopentanol.

A second effect to be ascribed to the lone pair electrons might be classified as a homoallylic interaction—a direct interaction between the developing p-orbital at the ionizing center and a lone pair orbital. The situation is superficially similar to that which gave rise to a rate acceleration of 10^{11} in the solvolysis of *anti*-7-dehydronorbornyl tosylate.[3k,l] In that system the interaction is between a developing p-orbital at C_7 and the π-electron system of C_2 and C_3. In the present system we might postulate a lesser, but perhaps still substantial, interaction between the developing p-orbital at C_2 and a lone pair orbital on oxygen. The result of such an interaction would be an acceleration of the rate of ionization of an *endo* substituent.

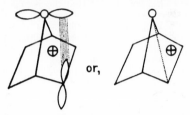

or,

Again, the failure to observe any major difference in the *exo/endo* reactivity ratios for the endoxo and the endomethylene series would seem to rule out any very important contribution from this effect.

It might be argued that the observation of roughly comparable reactivity ratios for the two series of compounds does not, in fact, indicate that these effects are inoperative or of small importance but rather that it represents the result of a fortuitous cancelling of the two effects, which are postulated to affect the *exo/endo* ratio in opposite directions. If such were the case, the reactivity of the entire series of endoxo compounds might be expected to be greater than that observed.

The observed factor of 6×10^3 between the rates of solvolytic reactions of the norbornyl and 1,4-endoxocyclohexyl chlorides is somewhat greater than that to be expected from the consideration of model compounds[12] or that predicted by the dipole interaction calculations of Winstein.[13,14] Winstein concludes that the rate depression in acetolysis reactions to be expected from the purely inductive effect of a neighboring methoxy group is a factor of approximately 100. The observed difference between the solvolysis rates of the endoxo and endomethylene series of compounds is approximately 60 times greater than this.

In the 1,4-endoxo compounds the ether bridge corresponds not only to a β-alkoxy group but also to a γ-alkoxy group relative to substituents at the 2-position. This statement is equivalent to a

(12) S. Winstein and E. Grunwald, *ibid.*, **70**, 828 (1948).

(13) S. Winstein, E. Grunwald and L. L. Ingraham, *ibid.*, **70**, 821 (1948).

(14) E. Grunwald, *ibid.*, **73**, 5458 (1951).

recognition that the orientation of the over-all ether dipole is fixed in such a manner as to increase the effectiveness of its interaction with dipoles at the 2-position.

A somewhat similar situation is discernible in data on the acid dissociation constants of conjugate acids of amines.[15]

Amine	pK_{AH} (25°)
Ethylamine	10.81
β-Methoxyethylamine	9.45
Morpholine	8.70
Piperidine	11.28

The pK_{AH} for ethylamine exceeds that for β-methoxyethylamine by 1.36 units, whereas the difference in the corresponding constants for the two cyclic amines is 2.58.

Another possible explanation for the enhanced inductive effect of the oxygen bridge lies in a consideration of the solubilities of ethers in water. Ferguson[16] has pointed out that the association of liquid water with molecules through hydrogen bonding can apparently be subject to appreciable steric hindrance. The enhanced solubility of cyclic ethers is explained by their greatly reduced steric hindrance to such hydrogen bonding.

An experimental determination of the solubility of 1,4-endoxocyclohexane (10.5 parts per hundred parts water) at 25° showed it to be more soluble than its open-chain analog, diisopropyl ether (0.2 parts per hundred parts water), by a factor of approximately 50.

If this increased solubility may be attributed to increased effectiveness of hydrogen bonding of the ether with water, an individual molecule of the bicyclic ether, in aqueous solution, would be much more likely to be involved in a hydrogen bonded association than an acylic ether. In the rate studies of this work one might expect such hydrogen bonding to deactivate the molecule toward an ionization which would place a positive charge on the bicyclic nucleus.

The most straightforward interpretation of the present results, therefore, would postulate the principal effect of the oxygen bridge on solvolysis rates to be a simple inductive effect. Any resonance effects of this oxygen would seem to be relatively unimportant in the transition states of such reactions.

As a side-product in the photochemical bromination of 1,4-endoxocyclohexane with N-bromosuccinimide (NBS), an appreciable yield (ca. 15%) of β-bromopropionyl isocyanate was isolated. The material, isolated by distillation at reduced pressure (b.p. 53–56° (2 mm.)), showed an infrared absorption peak at 4.45 μ, an absorption characteristic of organic isocyanates. It reacted vigorously with water to evolve one mole of carbon dioxide and yield crystalline β-bromopropionamide. The identity of the material was further established by comparison of its infrared spectrum and reactivity toward water with that of a sample of β-bromopropionyl isocyanate prepared by the reaction of β-bromopropionyl chloride and silver cyanate.

(15) R. J. Bruehlman and F. H. Verhoek, This Journal, **70**, 1401 (1948).

(16) L. N. Ferguson, ibid., **77**, 5288 (1955).

$$AgCNO + RCOCl \longrightarrow R\overset{\overset{\textstyle O}{\|}}{C}-N=C=O + AgCl$$

The formation of isocyanate was also observed in the absence of 1,4-endoxocyclohexane when a boiling suspension of NBS in carbon tetrachloride was strongly irradiated. The yield, followed by observation of the infrared absorption at 4.45 μ, was small but definite, reaching a maximum after about 24 hr., then disappearing as heating and irradiation were continued. This is compatible with the observed instability of β-bromopropionyl isocyanate.

The reaction of N-bromosuccinimide to give the isocyanate was found to proceed only under those conditions generally conceded to be favorable to radical mechanisms. For example, the reaction was observed to proceed when a boiling mixture of NBS and carbon tetrachloride was strongly irradiated or when benzoyl peroxide was added to such a boiling mixture in the dark. No isocyanate was observed when the mixture was boiled in the dark with no added source of radicals.

It would therefore seem that the reaction, formally an isomerization of NBS, either proceeds by a radical mechanism or is catalyzed by products of a radical reaction. A possible mechanism would involve initial homolytic cleavage of the N–Br bond of NBS followed by ring opening of the resulting succinimide radical.

Experimental Section

All melting points and boiling points are uncorrected.

The microanalyses were performed by Dr. S. M. Nagy, Massachusetts Institute of Technology; by Dr. H. Manser, Eidg. Techn. Hochschule, Zurich; and by Schwarzkopf Microanalytical Laboratory, Woodside, N. Y.

Chlorination of 1,4-Endoxocyclohexane: Procedure.—The starting material, 1,4-endoxocyclohexane, was prepared after the manner of Fehnel, Goodyear and Berkowitz.[17] It was purified by distillation through a 100 cm., vacuum jacketed column packed with glass helices. The product showed b.p. 119–119.5° (766 mm.), $n^{20}D$ 1.4480; infrared spectrum (letters refer to intensity—strong, medium or weak; wave length in μ): 3.39s, 3.45m, 3.50m, 6.81m, 6.90m, 7.59m, 7.69m, 7.94s, 8.39s, 8.77w, 9.11w, 9.31m, 10.01s, 10.27m, 10.72s, 11.05m, 11.40s, 12.18s, 12.71m, 13.12w.

The chlorinations were carried out in a reaction vessel fitted with a fritted-glass gas dispersion tube. The reaction vessel was immersed in a cooling bath of Dry Ice in acetone in an unsilvered Dewar flask. This permitted the irradiation of the reaction mixture with a sunlamp at a distance of about 4 in. The chlorine was measured by condensing it into a calibrated Pyrex trap and measuring its volume at the boiling point (where its density is 1.56 g./ml.). As the chlorine evaporated it was carried from this trap in a stream of dry nitrogen (Airco Prepurified Nitrogen), through a phosphorus pentoxide drying tower and into the reaction vessel through a gas dispersion tube. Any unreacted chlorine

(17) E. A. Fehnel, S. Goodyear and J. Berkowitz, ibid., **73**, 4978 (1950).

which was carried through the reaction vessel was condensed in a trap at −78°. This chlorine was distilled back into the first trap in the system and recirculated until all of it was used. A loss of chlorine through the final trap became obvious in some of the longer experiments. Each section of this apparatus was suitably protected from suck-back of liquids by interposition of a reversed trap. All of the traps were of approximately 250-ml. capacity. All of the connections in this apparatus were either of Pyrex glass or Tygon tubing. The lamp was a General Electric sunlamp.

The Monochloro Isomers.—In a typical experiment, 1,4-endoxocyclohexane (190 g., 1.94 moles) was placed in a 250-ml. reaction tube in the chlorination system described above and cooled to −22° in a Dry Ice–carbon tetrachloride-bath. To this solution 137 g. (1.94 moles) of chlorine was added slowly, in a stream of nitrogen, through the gas dispersion tube. The mixture was irradiated during this addition by a sunlamp. The chlorine was added in about 1 hr., and the small amount of chlorine from the exit trap was passed again into the reaction vessel. A moderate flow of nitrogen was maintained throughout the reaction to promote stirring and to remove hydrogen chloride formed in the reaction. After 3 hr. all the chlorine was consumed, as indicated by the loss of color. The reaction was allowed to return to room temperature as the stream of nitrogen was continued for 2 hr. more. The crude reaction mixture (260 g.) was then allowed to stand over moist sodium carbonate overnight to destroy any remaining hydrogen chloride. The mixture was then dried over magnesium sulfate and distilled through a 19-plate column at 1 mm. A large fraction distilled at less than 30° (principally the starting ether, 108.0 g.). A second fraction boiling at 30–37° weighed 15.9 g. (6.2%) and consisted principally of endo-2-chloro-1,4-endoxocyclohexane. A fraction, b.p. 37–40°, weighing 9.29 g. (3.7%) was a mixture of the two isomers. Another fraction, b.p. 40–43°, weighing 73.0 g. (28.4%) was principally exo-2-chloro-1,4-endoxocyclohexane.

The two isomers are easily differentiated and their separation followed by their distinctive C–Cl stretching frequencies in the infrared. The endo isomer absorbs at 14.25 μ and the exo isomer at 14.5 μ. Since the unsubstituted ether is transparent to radiation in the wave length region 14–16 μ and each of the two monochloro isomers has a well-defined absorption peak in a different part of this region, it was possible to estimate the proportion of these isomers formed in the reaction more accurately by infrared analysis. The two absorption maxima were shown to obey Beer's law in carbon tetrachloride solution. The extinction coefficient for the 14.25 μ peak of the endo isomer was found to be larger than that for the 14.50 μ peak of the exo isomer by a factor of 2.1. The analysis was run on the crude product of a chlorination reaction in which the ether was used in sixfold excess to minimize the amount of polychlorination. By comparison of the two (nearly equal) peaks representing the two monochloro ethers, the exo isomer was found to be present in quantity 2.2 times as great as the endo isomer.

The two monochloro isomers were purified by redistillation. The endo isomer boiled at 68° (27 mm.), n^{25}D 1.4780, d_{25} 1.1833; infrared spectrum (wave length in μ): 3.39s, 3.46m, 3.54m, 6.84m, 6.93m, 7.56m, 7.62m, 7.69m, 7.91m, 8.03s, 8.33w, 8.45s, 8.71m, 9.04m, 9.33w, 9.65m, 10.05s, 10.57s, 10.93w, 11.55m, 12.06m, 12.39s, 12.75s, 13.11s, 14.25s.

Anal. Calcd. for C_6H_9OCl: C, 54.32; H, 6.84; Cl, 26.74. Found: C, 54.51; H, 6.81; Cl, 27.4 (Stepanov determination).

The exo isomer boiled at 48.0° (4 mm.), n^{25}D 1.4847, d_{25} 1.1927; infrared spectrum (wave length in μ): 3.39s, 3.52m, 6.84m, 6.95m, 7.61w, 7.75m, 7.81m, 7.91m, 7.97m, 8.04m, 8.24m, 8.33m, 8.40s, 8.70w, 8.86m, 9.30m, 9.55s, 9.76m, 10.00s, 10.18m, 10.63s, 10.95m, 11.03m, 11.29s, 11.84m, 12.25s, 12.53m, 13.03m, 14.50m.

Anal. Calcd. for C_6H_9OCl: C, 54.32; H, 6.84; Cl, 26.74. Found: C, 54.08; H, 6.62; Cl, 27.0 (Stepanov determination).

Dichloro-1,4-endoxocyclohexane.—exo-2-Chloro-1,4-endoxocyclohexane (10 g., 0.075 mole) in a small reaction tube equipped with a gas dispersion tube was placed in a chlorination train similar to the one described above except that smaller traps were used in order to reduce the volume of the system. The ether was treated with one equivalent of chlorine (5.4 g., 3.4 ml.) at −22°, with irradiation. After

reaction was complete (1 hr.), the reaction was warmed to 30° with nitrogen scrubbing for 2 hr. The 11.32 g. of material yielded 2.4 g. (19%) of crystalline material on cooling in a refrigerator, which, after several recrystallizations from benzene and carbon tetrachloride gave small white needles m.p. 143.2–144.0°; infrared spectrum (wave length in μ): 3.32m, 3.38m, 6.90m, 6.95m, 7.59m, 7.80w, 7.90m, 8.05m, 8.16m, 8.27m, 8.40m, 8.55w, 9.80s, 9.95s, 10.20w, 10.55m, 10.85m, 11.03s, 11.40s, 12.42m, 12.51m, 14.02w, 14.81w.

Anal. Calcd. for $C_6H_8OCl_2$: C, 43.10; H, 4.85; Cl, 42.46. Found: C, 43.07, 42.79; H, 4.65, 4.98; Cl, 43.02, 42.28.

More Highly Chlorinated Ethers.—These ethers were formed from the treatment of pure 1,4-endoxocyclohexane with chlorine as described above. Adding more equivalents of chlorine over longer periods of time, it was necessary to raise the temperature of the reaction slowly to prevent formation of solid material. The various crude reaction mixtures were separated by chromatography into crystalline components which were further purified by recrystallization.

A trichloro ether crystallized from benzene as small white needles, m.p. 154.5–154.8°; infrared spectrum (wave length in μ): 3.35w, 6.95w, 7.02m, 7.58m, 7.80w, 7.91m, 8.06m, 8.13m, 8.25m, 8.38m, 8.63m, 9.50w, 9.95s, 10.18m, 10.30w, 10.60m, 10.82m, 11.11s, 11.42s, 12.45s, 14.22m, 14.90m.

Anal. Calcd. for $C_6H_7OCl_3$: C, 35.74; H, 3.50; Cl, 52.75. Found: C, 35.54; H, 3.28; Cl, 52.02.

A tetrachloro ether gave, from pentane solution, chunky rhomboidal crystals, m.p. 77.8–78.8° (softens 77.0°); infrared spectrum (wave length in μ): 3.42w, 6.99m, 7.63w, 7.98m, 8.10m, 8.50m, 8.57m, 8.98m, 9.36m, 9.90m, 10.00m, 10.21s, 10.31m, 10.46m, 10.99m, 12.47s, 13.48m.

Anal. Calcd. for $C_6H_6OCl_4$: C, 30.55; H, 2.57; Cl, 60.12. Found: C, 30.58; H, 2.69; Cl, 60.28.

A hexachloro ether was obtained as white prisms, m.p. 106.8–107.3°, from pentane; infrared spectrum (wave length in μ): 3.30w, 7.73m, 8.08m, 8.23m, 9.67m, 9.74m, 10.25s, 10.55m, 10.69s, 10.90s, 11.62s, 11.73s, 12.76m, 12.90s, 13.43w.

Anal. Calcd. for $C_6H_4OCl_6$: C, 23.65; H, 1.32; Cl, 69.80. Found: C, 23.83; H, 1.49; Cl, 68.78.

An octachloro-1,4-endoxocyclohexane was recrystallized from ligroin to yield long stave-like crystals. m.p. 158.4–159°; infrared spectrum (wave length in μ): 3.28w, 8.25m, 9.57w, 9.90m, 10.28s, 10.66s, 10.74m, 11.06w, 11.58s, 11.96m.

Anal. Calcd. for $C_6H_2OCl_8$: C, 19.28; H, 0.54; Cl, 75.90. Found: C, 19.30; H, 0.61; Cl, 75.83.

Bromination of 1,4-Endoxocyclohexane.—N-Bromosuccinimide (greater than 99% purity) from Arapahoe Chemicals, Inc., was freshly recrystallized from water before use in these experiments. The substitution of NBS from another source (Fisher Scientific Co.) made no apparent difference in the course of the reaction. Merck Reagent carbon tetrachloride was used as solvent.

In a typical experiment 1,4-endoxocyclohexane (196.0 g., 2.0 mole) was dissolved in 500 ml. of carbon tetrachloride in a 1-l. flask fitted with a reflux condenser and a calcium chloride drying tube. NBS (178 g., 1.0 mole) was added to this solution and the suspension heated to boiling while irradiating with a sunlamp. After about 2 hr. the mixture became homogeneous. The heating and irradiation were continued for 5 hr. altogether, and the resulting deep-red solution was cooled overnight in a refrigerator at 0°. The crystals of succinimide (42.0 g., 42.5%) which were deposited during this time were removed by filtration. The solvent and excess 1,4-endoxocyclohexane were removed by distillation at water-pump pressure. The liquid residue was then fractionally distilled through a 50-cm., vacuum-jacketed column packed with glass helices. The following fractions were taken:

Fraction	B.p., °C. (2 mm.)	Weight, g.
I	53.0–56.0	21.40
II	56.0–62.0	7.63
III	62.0–68.0	7.77
IV	68.0–68.5	20.85
V	68.5–75.0	22.30

The various fractions were examined by infrared spectroscopy. The fore-run contained carbon tetrachloride and recovered 1,4-endoxocyclohexane. No part of the fore-run showed an absorption near 4.5 μ which could be attributed to an isocyanate.

Fraction I was essentially pure β-bromopropionyl isocyanate. Fraction II contained a small amount of higher boiling material but was mostly the isocyanate. These first two fractions constitute a yield of 16.3% of β-bromopropionyl isocyanate. Redistillation gave a colorless liquid, b.p. 54.0–55.0° (2 mm.), which had a sharp, characteristic odor and was mildly lachrymatory. A small sample of this material was distilled into a tube and sealed off under high vacuum. It began to acquire a yellow color after one day at room temperature and after two weeks was an extremely viscous, semi-solid material of deep orange color.

Fraction IV was essentially pure *exo*-2-bromo-1,4-endoxocyclohexane (11.8%). The distillation was discontinued during the collection of fraction V when a rapid decomposition occurred in the pot leaving a black tar and evolving much hydrogen bromide.

Reaction of the Isocyanate with Water.—To β-bromopropionyl isocyanate (0.50 g., 0.0028 mole) from the reaction described above, tetrahydrofuran containing 10% water was added dropwise until no further gas evolution was observed on adding another drop of the water solution. The evolved gas was carried in a stream of nitrogen through a trap containing aqueous barium hydroxide. The precipitated barium carbonate was filtered, washed with 100 ml. of water and dried at 100° (0.56 g., 1.13 moles per mole of isocyanate). The tetrahydrofuran and excess water were removed from the reaction mixture by distillation at reduced pressure leaving 0.40 g. of a white crystalline material, m.p. 109.5–111.7°. After two recrystallizations from benzene, the material melted 115.6–116.3°. This was mixed with authentic β-bromopropionamide (m.p. 115.3–116.3°) prepared from β-bromopropionyl chloride and ammonia[18] to give a mixed m.p. 115.3–116.3°.

β-Bromopropionyl Isocyanate from Silver Cyanate.—The method used is a rather general one for the preparation of acyl isocyanates.[19] In a 300-ml. round-bottomed flask fitted with a reflux condenser, addition funnel and calcium chloride drying tube, silver cyanate (Eastman Kodak Co., white label grade, 45.0 g., 0.30 mole) was suspended with magnetic stirring in 100 ml. of dry ether. To this suspension was added, over a 2-hr. period, 34.4 g. (0.20 mole) of β-bromopropionyl chloride in 50 ml. of dry ether. The suspension was then heated to boiling with continued stirring for 6 hr. The silver salts were then filtered from the solution, washed with ether and the washings combined with the reaction mixture. Solvent was removed at reduced pressure and the remaining liquid distilled through a 30-cm. Vigreux column at *ca.* 2 mm. The fraction boiling in the range 52–56° (4.4 g., 12%) exhibited an infrared spectrum identical with that of a sample of the isocyanate from the NBS reaction described above. Infrared spectrum (wave length in μ): 3.43w, 4.45s, 5.77s, 7.19m, 7.50w, 7.95w, 8.25w, 8.50m, 8.72m, 9.87m, 9.77m, 9.95m, 15.20m.

Anal. Calcd. for $C_4H_4O_2NBr$: C, 26.00; H, 2.27. Found: C, 26.35; H, 2.70.

This material also reacted vigorously with water to produce β-bromopropionamide.

N-Bromosuccinimide in Carbon Tetrachloride.—Observation of the very intense absorption of β-bromopropionyl isocyanate at 4.45 μ was used to follow its formation from NBS under a variety of conditions. In these experiments NBS (5.0 g.) was suspended in 50 ml. of carbon tetrachloride in a flask fitted with a reflux condenser and protected from atmospheric moisture by a calcium chloride drying tube. During the reaction 1-ml. aliquots were withdrawn at intervals of 6–8 hr. and examined for absorption at 4.45 μ. In parallel experiments, all conducted at the boiling point of carbon tetrachloride, the mixture was in one case irradiated with a sunlamp, shielded from all light in another case and, in a third case, protected from light after adding 0.10 g. of benzoyl peroxide. After 24 hr. spectra of the crude reaction mixtures taken in sodium chloride cells 0.016 in. in thickness against reference cells containing pure carbon tetrachloride showed 63% absorption at 4.45 μ for the irradiated reaction

ard 85% for the reaction with added benzoyl peroxide. The mixture which was heated in the dark with no added catalyst showed no absorption in this region even after 36 hr. Further heating of the two reaction mixtures which showed absorption at 4.45 μ brought about diminution and eventual loss of this absorption.

exo-2-Bromo-1,4-endoxocyclohexane.—Material from fraction IV of the distillation of the NBS bromination reaction was redistilled (b.p. 68.0–68.2° (2 mm.), $n^{25}D$ 1.5176, d_{24} 1.5410).

Anal. Calcd. for C_6H_9Br: C, 40.7; H, 5.12. Found: C, 40.88; H, 4.89.

This bromo ether (4.4866 g., 0.02534 mole) was dissolved in 20 ml. of 95% ethanol containing 4.748 g. (0.0279 mole) of silver nitrate. The mixture was then allowed to stand in a dark place at room temperature for 24 hr. The precipitated silver bromide was filtered, washed, dried at 95° and weighed (4.7477 g., 0.02528 mole). This corresponds to 45.03% Br in the sample; calcd. for C_6H_9Br, 45.14% Br.

Method of Determining Dielectric Constants.—The heterodyne beat frequency method[20] was used to determine the dielectric constants, at 25.0°, of dilute solutions of the materials being studied, in carbon tetrachloride or benzene. The apparatus used in these determinations is fully described by Osthoff.[21] It consists, in essence, of a fixed frequency crystal oscillator, at 100 kc., coupled with a vacuum-tube oscillator circuit containing the measurement cell and a calibrated precision variable condenser. The frequency of the latter circuit can be very accurately adjusted, by means of the precision condenser, until the beat frequency between the two circuits is zero.

Measurements of Densities.—Densities were measured to an accuracy estimated at one part in 20,000 by means of a single stem pycnometer of 20-ml. volume.

Treatment of Data.—The calculations of the molar polarization at infinite dilution were made by the method of Hedestrand[22] using the convenient notation of Bender, Flowers and Goering.[23] The dipole moments were then calculated from the Debye equation.[20]

Solvolysis of the 2-Halo-1,4-endoxocyclohexanes: Solvents.—Dioxane was purified by the procedure of Hess and Frahm.[24] After this treatment it was distilled through a 100-cm. column packed with glass helices (b.p. 100.6–100.8°). It was then stored under nitrogen in a dark place and used in not more than two weeks.

Absolute ethanol (2 l.) was added to 20 g. of sodium metal and the resulting solution boiled for two days to destroy aldehydes. The ethanol was then distilled and stored under nitrogen until used.

Distilled water from the laboratory source was redistilled from potassium permanganate and stored under nitrogen.

The solvent mixtures used in this work were made up by weighing the required amounts of the pure solvents. The solvent mixture which was made up to volume percentage specifications was weighed out in proportions calculated from the densities of the pure solvents at 25°.

Procedure for the *exo* Isomers.—The kinetic runs were followed by titrating samples individually sealed in glass tubes. These tubes were made by sealing one end of a 12 in. length of 12 mm. Pyrex tubing. Just before use they were carefully flushed with nitrogen and tightly stoppered with a plug of glass wool.

The solutions for kinetic analysis were made up by weighing the halo ether and the added salt into a 250-ml. volumetric flask and making the solution up to volume with the solvent being studied.

A hypodermic needle was used to introduce 16-ml. portions of the solution through the glass wool into the freshly prepared glass tubes. The tubes were then quickly sealed off about 1.5–2 in. above the surface of the liquid, placed in a woven-wire basket and lowered into the constant temperature bath, maintained constant to within ±0.01°.

(18) C. Hamilton and C. Simpson, This Journal, **51**, 3159 (1929).
(19) A. J. Hill and W. M. Degnan, U. S. Patent 2,379,486 (1945).

(20) See C. P. Smyth in A. Weissberger, "Physical Methods of Organic Chemistry," Vol. I, 2nd Ed., Part II, Interscience Publishers. Inc., New York, N. Y., 1949, pp. 1611, et seq.
(21) R. C. Osthoff, Ph.D. Thesis, Harvard University, 1951. We thank Professor E. G. Rochow for the loan of this apparatus.
(22) G. Hedestrand, Z. physik. Chem., **B2**, 428 (1929).
(23) P. Bender, D. Flowers and H. Goering, This Journal, **77**, 3463 (1955).
(24) K. Hess and H. Frahm, Ber., **71B**, 2627 (1938).

At the desired intervals of time samples were withdrawn from the bath, quickly cooled in ice-water and then allowed to come to room temperature. Samples of 15 ml. were then accurately measured out, diluted with 45 ml. of distilled water and titrated with 0.1013 N aqueous sodium hydroxide. All titrations were performed using a Beckman Autotitrator with a 5-ml. microburet.

Procedure for Solvolysis of the *endo* Isomer.—The same procedure was used with *endo*-2-chloro-1,4-endoxocyclo-hexane as with the *exo* isomer with the exception that an amount of sodium acetate approximately equivalent to the halo ether was weighed into the sample. The reaction was then followed by titrating the excess sodium acetate in the aliquots to an end-point at pH 3.6 with 0.121 N hydrochloric acid.

Treatment of Data.—The first-order rate constants were obtained by a least squares treatment of the data as outlined by Youden.[25] The uncertainties are expressed as standard deviations. The values of $\Delta H^{\ddagger}$ and $\Delta S^{\ddagger}$ were calculated from the absolute rate equation with the uncertainties again expressed as standard deviations.

Product Studies.—*exo*-2-Bromo-1,4-endoxocyclohexane (17.7 g., 0.10 mole) was dissolved in 250 ml. of 50% dioxane-water in a 300-ml. flask equipped with openings for an amber-glass electrode, a calomel electrode, a reflux condenser and the addition tip from the Beckman Autotitrator. The mixture was magnetically stirred with a Teflon-covered bar. It was brought to the boiling point by an electric heating mantle and maintained at pH 6.5-7.5 by the Autotitrator for 2000 min. This required 14.55 ml. of 4.89 N sodium hydroxide solution (71% reaction).

The solvent was removed by distillation at water-pump pressure leaving a paste of organic matter and sodium bromide. To this was added 50 ml. of dioxane to dissolve the organic matter, and the inorganic bromide was removed by filtration. The filtrate was then made up to 200 ml. with 50% dioxane–water. Aliquots of 20 ml. were taken for analytical tests.

Using this procedure outlined by Wilds,[26] aldehyde was estimated by titration of the hydrochloric acid released by oximation with hydroxylamine hydrochloride. Two aliquots gave values for aldehyde equivalent to 81.1% and 80.2% of the solvolyzed material.

Other aliquots were used to prepare the 2,4-dinitrophenyl-hydrazone and the *bis*-dimedone condensation product by the directions of Shriner and Fuson.[27]

The solution in which the 2,4-dinitrophenylhydrazone was formed was diluted with 200 ml. of water to make the precipitation complete and then filtered through a sintered-glass crucible. The derivative was washed with 20 ml. of 0.1 N hydrochloric acid, then 200 ml. of water, dried at 100° and weighed. After repeated recrystallization from benzene–pentane mixtures, this derivative gave m.p. 118.6–119.8°. The same derivative was isolated from the sealed tube solvolysis of the *endo*- and *exo*-chlorides; infrared spectrum (wave length in μ): 3.41s, 3.52m, 6.85m, 6.92m, 6.98m, 7.60w, 7.68w, 7.79m, 7.94m, 8.17m, 8.40s, 8.75m, 8.89m, 9.60m, 9.80m, 9.98s, 10.21m, 10.41w, 10.68s, 11.00w, 11.10w, 11.35s, 11.90m, 15.15w, 15.39w.

Anal. Calcd. for $C_{12}H_{14}O_6N_4$: C, 48.98; H, 4.80; N, 19.04. Found: C, 49.15; H, 4.59; N, 18.74.

The dimedone derivative was recrystallized from benzene–pentane mixtures to a constant melting point of 163.3–164.2°; infrared spectrum (wave length in μ): 2.79m, 2.95m, 3.42s, 3.70m, 5.80s, 6.97m, 7.25m, 7.50m, 8.10m, 8.55m, 9.30m, 9.89s, 10.53m.

Anal. Calcd. for $C_{22}H_{32}O_5$: C, 70.18; H, 8.56. Found: C, 70.47; H, 8.61.

Runs protected from oxygen by the use of the sealed tube technique showed substantially higher yields of aldehyde. In these experiments two tubes from a kinetic run were opened simultaneously. One 15-ml. aliquot was titrated directly. The other was mixed with 15 ml. of 0.5 N hydroxylamine hydrochloride solution, allowed to stand overnight, then titrated to the same pH as shown by a parallel blank run. The difference in the two titers represents aldehyde present.

In run 1, in 80% (by vol.) ethanol at 85.0°, such duplicate points were taken at 5212, 12470 and 16820 min. The percentage of aldehyde in the solvolysis product at each of these points was determined by the above outlined method. These percentages were found to be 100.8, 98.2 and 103.2%, respectively, at these three times.

In a special run at 120.0°, the *exo*-chloride, in 50% dioxane, was shown to yield 97.3 and 99.6% aldehyde at 653 and 1213 min.

The solvolysis product of the *endo*-chloride was analyzed at 160°, using points of run 12, in 50% dioxane with added sodium acetate. In these analyses the customary 15-ml. aliquot was diluted with 30 ml. of water and titrated with standard acid to pH 3.4 to learn the extent of solvolysis. The 15 ml. of 0.5 N hydroxylamine hydrochloride was added and the solution allowed to stand at room temperature overnight. It was then titrated back to pH 3.4 with standard base. At 2245 min. this method indicated 91.7% of the solvolysis product to be aldehyde and at 5110 min., 85.4%. (In these runs at the higher temperature a considerable darkening of the solution was observed in samples withdrawn after about 3000 min.)

Identification of 3-Formylcyclopentanol.—A sample (1.5 g.) of the crude product from a solvolysis of *exo*-2-bromo-1,4-endoxocyclohexane in boiling 50% dioxane was dissolved in 10 ml. of hydrazine (Eastman Kodak Co., 95%) and heated on a steam-bath for 24 hr. The solution was then concentrated to 4–5 ml. by distilling excess hydrazine at reduced pressure. This solution was added to an ethanolic solution of sodium ethoxide prepared by dissolving 1.0 g. of sodium in 10 ml. of absolute ethanol. The solution was sealed in a Carius tube and heated at 190–200° for 36 hr. The resulting solution was acidified with concd. hydrochloric acid and distilled. After removal of the ethanol two colorless liquid phases co-distilled at 55° (60 mm.). The non-aqueous phase was taken up in ether and dried over magnesium sulfate. Removal of the solvent left a colorless oil (0.3 g.), $n^{28}D$ 1.4446; *trans*-3-methylcyclopentanol,[7] $n^{28}D$ 1.4450. To this was added 0.24 g. of phenyl isocyanate, the mixture heated on a steam-bath for 10 min. and then diluted with 30 ml. of pentane. On chilling the material the phenylurethan (0.26 g.) was deposited from the solution as white needles (after recrystallization from pentane, m.p. 81.4–82.0°; phenylurethan derivative of *trans*-3-methyl-cyclopentanol,[7] m.p. 82°).

Solvolysis with Added Azide.—*exo*-2-Bromo-1,4-endoxocyclohexane (15.0 g., 0.0847 mole) was dissolved in a solution of 250 ml. of 50% dioxane containing 20 g. of sodium azide (0.308 mole, 1.23 molar). The solution was treated as in the previously described product studies, being boiled for 1600 min. at pH 6.0–7.0. Removal of the solvent and inorganic bromide left 8.45 g. of a viscous oil which showed an infrared spectrum nearly identical with that of 3-formyl-cyclopentanol with an added absorption peak of medium intensity at 4.74 μ. Chromatography on alumina of 1.60 g. of the crude product gave 29 mg. of an oil (eluted with 100% ether) which showed a very intense absorption at 4.74 μ. This was dissolved in 5 ml. of methanol and 10 mg. of platinum oxide added. The suspension was stirred under one atm. of hydrogen for 12 hr. The supernatant liquid was then saturated with hydrogen chloride and the crystalline amine hydrochloride (18 mg.) collected and dried, m.p. *ca.* 240°.

Acknowledgment.—The expenses of this research were met in part by a grant from the Mallinckrodt Chemical Works.

CAMBRIDGE, MASSACHUSETTS

(25) W. J. Youden, "Statistical Methods for Chemists," John Wiley and Sons, Inc., New York, N. Y., 1951, pp. 40–44.

(26) R. Wilds, "Estimation of Organic Compounds," University Press, Cambridge, 1953, pp. 144–150.

(27) R. L. Shriner and R. C. Fuson, "The Systematic Identification of Organic Compounds," by John Wiley and Sons, Inc., New York, N. Y., 1948, pp. 171–172.

34 | The Special Salt Effect

An important byproduct of the study of nonclassical ions has been the discovery of ways of distinguishing between the different kinds of ionic intermediates in solvolyses and rearrangements. The first internal ion-pair return phenomena to be discovered[1] were impervious to any competition from added reagents. In the "special salt effect,"[2] observable in certain solvolyzing compounds, lithium perchlorate was found to have the power to eliminate some of the ion pair return at rather low concentrations. Paper No. 34 gives a detailed discussion of the phenomenon in the case of *threo*-3-anisyl-2-butyl arenesulfonates and the conclusions to be drawn from it. In the many cases in which the noninterceptible reaction (detected by racemization) responds to the ionizing power of the solvent in the same way as the solvolysis itself it is concluded that this is return from the intimate ion pair, while the return which can be intercepted by lithium perchlorate is attributed to the solvent-separated ion pair. Borderline cases are discussed. The analogy between internal return in ion pairs and the cage effect in free radical pairs is pointed out. Ion pair return is much more complicated because of the superposition of electrostatic and ion-atmosphere effects upon those of simple diffusion. The opinion is expressed here that there may be residual covalent forces holding the intimate ion pair together.

This paper is one of a large number on this topic from Winstein's laboratory. It reviews the evidence for the existence of the eight rate constants shown in the solvolysis scheme on page 229, and gives many pertinent references.

---

[1] W. G. Young, S. Winstein, and H. L. Goering, *J. Am. Chem. Soc.* **73**, 1958 (1951).
[2] S. Winstein, E. Clippinger, A. H. Fainberg, and G. C. Robinson, *ibid.*, **76**, 2597 (1954); *Chem. and Ind.* (*London*) 1954, 664.

From: *J. Am. Chem. Soc.* **80**, 169–81 (1958)

[Contribution from the Chemistry Department of the University of California, Los Angeles]

Salt Effects and Ion Pairs in Solvolysis and Related Reactions. IX. The *threo-3-p-*Anisyl-2-butyl System[1-3]

By S. Winstein and G. C. Robinson

Received August 7, 1957

The rates and stereochemical results of solvolysis of *threo*-3-*p*-anisyl-2-butyl arenesulfonates show that ionization is essentially exclusively anchimerically assisted. Such ionization gives rise to the internally compensated *cis*-anisyl-bridged cation, from which racemic *threo*-acetate results in acetolysis. Polarimetric rate constants (k_α) represent ionization rate constants (k_1), while titrimetric solvolysis rate constants (k_t) can be considerably smaller because of ion pair return accompanying solvolysis. With the *threo*-3-anisyl-2-butyl bromobenzenesulfonate, (k_α/k_t) is 4.1 in acetic acid and *ca.* 16 in 10% HCOOH–dioxane. Lithium perchlorate salt effects on k_α in acetolysis of *threo*-3-anisyl-2-butyl bromobenzenesulfonate show only the normal linear pattern. On the other hand, salt effects on k_t show the combination of the steep special and the more shallow normal linear pattern. It is very clear that special salt effects are not concerned with ionization, but with reduction of ion pair return. The most striking aspect of the present results is that the special salt effect only partly closes the gap between polarimetric and titrimetric rate constants for acetolysis. On re-examination of the question of identity of polarimetric and ionization rate constants, it is concluded that these are identical for systems such as the present one in the common solvolyzing solvents. Therefore, ion pair return is only partially eliminated by the special salt effect. Regarding the mode of action of the salt in the special salt effect, the indications are strong that it is not by way of a sort of ion atmosphere effect on the relative rate constants determining the importance of ion pair return. The best working hypothesis is that two kinds of carbonium ion pairs, intimate (II) and solvent-separated (III) are distinguishable as discrete intermediates in solvolysis, and that they respond differently to the special salt. The solvent-separated ion pair III is presumed to be much more reactive than the intimate ion pair II toward added lithium perchlorate. The latter is presumed to trap III while still permitting internal return from II. On this basis, it is possible to dissect ion pair return accompanying acetolysis of *threo*-3-anisyl-2-butyl arenesulfonates into internal return from II and return from solvent-separated ion pair III. Comparison of the 3-anisyl-2-butyl and 3-phenyl-2-butyl systems shows that the substitution of the *p*-methoxyl group into the 3-phenyl-2-butyl system has a negligible effect on the over-all importance of ion pair return accompanying acetolysis. On the other hand, it has a major effect on the distribution of ion pair return between internal return from II and return from the solvent-separated ion pair III. The former is decreased, while the latter is introduced strongly. The structure of the two varieties of ion pair is discussed somewhat, and the question of merging of intimate ion pair and cyclic rearrangement mechanisms is touched on. The use of isotopic criteria for the occurrence of ion pairs as intermediates in rearrangements is discussed.

In acetolysis a number of systems[3] have displayed special salt effects[4] clearly to be ascribed to the elimination of a definite and substantial fraction of ion pair return by salts such as lithium perchlorate. With none of the systems displaying special salt effects so far discussed in papers V,[4] VI[5] and VIII[6] of this series, was total ionization rate easily measured. Therefore, it was not clear in those cases whether all or only part of ion pair return was eliminated by the special salt effect.

It was anticipated that the *threo*-3-*p*-anisyl-2-butyl arenesulfonate system I would be useful in this connection, since it was already clear that the *erythro* isomer displayed special salt effects.[5] With *threo*-3-anisyl-2-butyl arenesulfonate I, ionization could be expected to be very predominantly anchimerically assisted, the internally compensated bridged cation II being the intermediate. The rate constant for ionization, k_1, is given by the polarimetric[7] rate constant, k_α, for the change in optical rotation. The fraction of ion pair return eliminated in the special salt effect would be disclosed by the effect of lithium perchlorate on the gap between polarimetric and titrimetric rate constants, k_α and k_t, respectively. The preparation

and solvolysis of active *threo*-3-anisyl-2-butyl *p*-bromobenzenesulfonate and *p*-toluenesulfonate I are described in the present paper. The implica-

tions of the present results for the nature and behavior of carbonium ion pairs are discussed.

Results

3-Anisyl-2-butanols and their Derivatives.—The 3-anisyl-2-butanol[8,9] was derived from treatment of 2-anisylpropanal with the methyl Grignard re-

(1) Sponsored by the Office of Ordnance Research, U. S. Army.

(2) (a) Presented at Kansas City Meeting of the American Chemical Society, March, 1954, page 21-N of Abstracts; (b) presented in summary at VIth Reaction Mechanism Conference, Swarthmore, Pa., Sept. 12, 1956.

(3) S. Winstein, E. Clippinger, A. H. Fainberg and G. C. Robinson: (a) This Journal, **76**, 2597 (1954); (b) *Chemistry & Industry*, 664 (1954).

(4) A. H. Fainberg and S. Winstein, This Journal, **78**, 2767 (1956).

(5) A. H. Fainberg, G. C. Robinson and S. Winstein, *ibid.*, **78**, 2777 (1956).

(6) S. Winstein and E. Clippinger, *ibid.*, **78**, 2784 (1956).

(7) S. Winstein and K. C. Schreiber, *ibid.*, **74**, 2165 (1952).

(8) A. Sosa, *Ann. chim.*, [11] **14**, 5 (1940).

(9) S. Winstein, M. Brown, K. C. Schreiber and A. H. Schlesinger, This Journal, **74**, 1140 (1952).

TABLE I
SUMMARY OF PROPERTIES OF 3-*p*-ANISYL-2-BUTYL DERIVATIVES

Derivative		Erythro		Threo	
		dl	Active	*dl*	Active
Alcohol, m.p., °C.		60[a]	80–81.5	1.5161[b]	
Acid phthalate $\begin{cases} \text{m.p., °C.} \\ [\alpha]\text{D (CHCl}_3\text{), °} \end{cases}$		137–138[c]	109–112 / −29.0	123–124.5	121–122[d]
p-Toluenesulfonate $\begin{cases} \text{m.p., °C.} \\ [\alpha]\text{D (CHCl}_3\text{), °} \end{cases}$			70–72 / −8.25	49–50[10]	69–70 / −11.3
p-Bromobenzenesulfonate $\begin{cases} \text{m.p., °C.} \\ [\alpha]\text{D (CHCl}_3\text{), °} \end{cases}$		67–69[5]		97.5–98.5[10]	84–86 / +11.3
p-Nitrobenzoate, m.p., °C.		102.5–103.5		84–85	

[a] M.p. of 60° previously reported by Sosa[8] for the solid racemate. [b] n^{25}D. [c] Previously reported[9] 136.5°. [d] Brucine sal.

agent as in previous work.[9] From the crude mixture, roughly 3:1, of solid and liquid diastereomeric 3-anisyl-2-butanols, respectively, considerable solid diastereomer crystallized directly on standing. The residual mixture was separated by repeated crystallization of the acid phthalate[9] into the acid phthalates of the solid and liquid carbinols. By use of a large excess of *p*-nitrobenzoyl chloride the solid and liquid carbinols could be converted essentially quantitatively to *p*-nitrobenzoates, these derivatives being especially useful for characterization of the carbinols.

As indicated in Table I, which summarizes the physical properties of the 3-*p*-anisyl-2-butanols and their derivatives, the *erythro* designation is assigned to the solid racemate and the *threo* designation to the liquid. Such an assignment is suggested by analogy with the diastereomeric 3-phenyl-2-butanols,[11] and it is borne out by the behavior of the arenesulfonates of the optically active 3-anisyl-2-butanols described below.

Optically active specimens of both the *erythro*- and *threo*-3-anisyl-2-butanols were obtained by crystallization from a 1:1 mixture of brucine and acid phthalate of mainly *threo*-carbinol. The solution first deposited the brucine salt of active *erythro*-acid phthalate. Dilution with petroleum ether and cooling deposited the brucine salt of active *threo*-acid phthalate. The physical properties of the various derivatives of the optically active *erythro*- and *threo*-carbinols are summarized in Table I.

Anisyl Participation.—The pronounced tendency for neighboring anisyl participation in the rate-determining ionization of 3-anisyl-2-butyl arenesulfonate I was indicated in our earlier kinetic work by the substantial rate factor between 3-anisyl-2-butyl and 3-phenyl-2-butyl-*p*-toluenesulfonates.[9] The present work supplies stereochemical evidence for essentially complete control of the solvolysis of 3-anisyl-2-butyl derivatives by neighboring anisyl.

Acetolysis of *dl-threo*-3-anisyl-2-butyl *p*-bromobenzenesulfonate (I) and subsequent treatment of the solvolysis product with lithium aluminum hydride gave rise to carbinol containing a small proportion of olefin. The carbinol product was completely *threo* as indicated by formation of very pure *threo-p*-nitrobenzoate. Furthermore, when active *threo*-3-anisyl-2-butyl bromobenzenesulfonate (I)

(10) S. Winstein, E. Clippinger, A. H. Fainberg, R. Heck and G. C. Robinson, THIS JOURNAL, **78**, 328 (1956).
(11) D. J. Cram, *ibid.*, **71**, 3863, 3883 (1949).

was solvolyzed, the solvolysis product was completely racemic *threo*. These stereochemical results obviously are due to the formation of the *cis*, and therefore internally compensated, bridged cation II, which gives rise to *dl-threo*-acetate V.[9,11]

The above interpretation is confirmed by the behavior in acetolysis of the active *erythro*-3-anisyl-2-butyl *p*-toluenesulfonate. With this diastereomer, optical activity does not disappear during acetolysis. Instead, optical rotation rises as acetolysis proceeds. Optically active *erythro*-acetate results from *erythro*-arenesulfonate which solvolyzes by way of a *trans*, and therefore optically active, intermediate bridged cation.

Polarimetric–Titrimetric Rate Comparisons.—As noted previously,[10] acetolysis of *threo*-3-*p*-anisyl-2-butyl *p*-bromobenzenesulfonate and *p*-toluenesulfonate I, followed titrimetrically, obeyed good first order kinetics. Satisfactory first-order behavior also was observed for the *p*-bromobenzenesulfonate in a series of other solvents, namely, ethanol, 25% formic acid–acetic acid, and 10% formic acid–dioxane. The observed rate constants, k_t, at 25° are summarized in Table II.

Polarimetric rate constants, k_α, were measured for comparison with the corresponding titrimetric values. Decrease of optical activity associated with solvolysis of the active *threo*-3-anisyl-2-butyl arenesulfonates obeyed good first-order kinetics, this being illustrated graphically in Fig. 1 in the case of acetolysis of the *p*-bromobenzenesulfonate. The observed polarimetric rate constants also are summarized in Table II.

As the summary in Table III shows, the polarimetric rate constants exceeded the titrimetric values. The k_α/k_t ratio in acetolysis at 25° was 4.07 for *threo*-3-anisyl-2-butyl *p*-bromobenzenesulfonate and 4.65 for the corresponding toluenesulfonate. The latter value is analogous to the figure 4.59 observed in acetolysis of *threo*-3-phenyl-2-butyl *p*-toluenesulfonate[7] at 50°. The change of solvent from acetic acid to 10% formic acid–dioxane as a solvent in the case of *threo*-3-anisyl-2-butyl *p*-bromobenzenesulfonate has the effect of increasing substantially the k_α/k_t ratio to a value of *ca.* 16. On the other hand, the k_α/k_t values are very small in 25% formic–acetic acid (1.08) and ethanol (1.27) as solvents.

Salt Effects on k_α.—In the presence of 0.01, 0.03, 0.06 and 0.10 *M* lithium perchlorate, the active *threo*-3-anisyl-2-butyl *p*-bromobenzenesulfonate (I) displayed good first-order polarimetric rate constants in acetolysis. These are summarized in

TABLE II

SUMMARY OF RATE CONSTANTS FOR TITRIMETRIC AND POLARIMETRIC SOLVOLYSIS OF *threo*-3-*p*-ANISYL-2-BUTYL BENZENE-SULFONATES AT 25.00°

Compound	Solvent	[RX], M	Other solute, M LiClO₄	Method	Initial α, °	10^5k, sec.⁻¹
ROBs	AcOH	0.0100		Tit.		19.6 ± 0.3
ROBs	AcOH	.0300		Tit.		19.5 ± 0.4
ROBs	AcOH	.0262		Pol.	+0.57	80.6 ± 8.4ᵃ
ROBs	AcOH	.0248		Pol.	+ .76	79.0
ROBs	AcOH	.0100	0.00100	Tit.		26.8 ± 0.8
ROBs	AcOH	.0100	.00500	Tit.		46.9 ± 1.6
ROBs	AcOH	.00992	.0100	Tit.		57.0 ± 0.7
ROBs	AcOH	.0270	.0100	Pol.	+ .85	87.3 ± 3.4
ROBs	AcOH	.00995	.0300	Tit.		84.0 ± 2.4
ROBs	AcOH	.0242	.0300	Pol.	+ .63	111ᵇ
ROBs	AcOH	.00997	.0600	Tit.		115 ± 4
ROBs	AcOH	.0259	.0600	Pol.	+ .65	156 ± 12ᶜ
ROBs	AcOH	.00994	.100	Tit.		161 ± 10
ROBs	AcOH	.0321	.100	Pol.	+ .98	198 ± 7
ROBs	12.5% AcOH–dioxane	.0271		Pol.	+ .83	*ca.* 0.34
ROBs	10% AcOH–C₆H₆	.0266		Pol.	+ .91	*ca.* 0.55
ROBs	10% HCOOH–dioxane	.0100		Tit.ᵈ		2.84 ± 0.09
ROBs	10% HCOOH–dioxane	.0100		Tit.		*ca.* 0.15
ROBs	10% HCOOH–dioxane	.0289		Pol.	+ .91	2.45 ± 0.09
ROBs	EtOH	.00884		Tit.		21.3 ± 0.6
ROBs	EtOH	.0278		Pol.	+ .74	27.1 ± 1.4ᵉ
ROBs	25% HCOOH–AcOH			Tit.		608 ± 20
ROBs	25% HCOOH–AcOH	.0270		Pol.	+ .65	656 ± 42ᶠ
ROTs	AcOH	.0105		Tit.		5.77 ± 0.10
ROTs	AcOH	.0287		Pol.	− .86	27.0 ± 1.2
ROTs	AcOH	.0102	.0300	Tit.		30.8 ± 0.6
ROTs	AcOH	.0101	.0600	Tit.		45.6 ± 1.8
ROTs	AcOH	.0102	.0800	Tit.		54.5 ± 1.4
ROTs	AcOH	.0287	.0500	Pol.	− .89	52.4 ± 2.4
ROTs	AcOH	.0266	.100	Pol.	− .82	69.9 ± 3.7

ᵃ 81.0 graphically. ᵇ Graphically. ᶜ 150 graphically. ᵈ 50.0°. ᵉ 27.0 graphically. ᶠ 670 graphically.

TABLE III

SUMMARY OF POLARIMETRIC–TITRIMETRIC COMPARISONS IN VARIOUS SOLVENTS

Solvent	*threo*-3-An-2-BuOBs, 25° Rel. k_α^0	k_α^0/k_t^0	*threo*-3-Ph-2-Bu OTs, k_α^0/k_t^0, 50°
HCOOH	44,000ᵃ		1.18ᶜ
25% HCOOH–AcOH	1930	1.08	
AcOH	235	4.07, 4.65ᵇ	4.59
EtOH	80	1.27	2.05ᵈ
10% HCOOH–dioxane	7.2	*ca.* 16	
10% AcOH–C₆H₆	1.6		
12.5% AcOH–dioxane	1.0		

ᵃ Based on a k_α of 1.49 × 10⁻³ sec.⁻¹ in formic acid estimated from the values in acetic acid and 25% HCOOH–AcOH with the aid of the mY correlation of solvolysis rates.[14] The m-value given by the AcOH and 25% HCOOH–AcOH points is 0.609. ᵇ *p*-Toluenesulfonate. ᶜ At 25°. ᵈ At 75°.

Table II and shown graphically in Fig. 2. Within essentially the experimental error of the polarimetric kinetic measurements, the polarimetric rate constants vary linearly with lithium perchlorate concentration. In other words, the salt effects follow the normal,[4,12] rather than the special[4] pattern. The data may be expressed in the form of equation 1, in the fashion employed previ-

(12) A. Fainberg and S. Winstein, THIS JOURNAL, **78**, 2763 (1956).

ously[3,4–6,12,13] for linear salt effects, the subscript α being used to designate polarimetric data. The

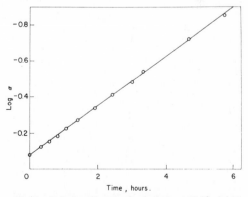

Fig. 1.—Polarimetric rate of solvolysis at 25.0° of (+)-*threo*-3-*p*-anisyl-2-butyl *p*-bromobenzenesulfonate in AcOH, 0.0100 M LiClO₄.

value of b_α, 16.2, recorded in Table IV is similar in magnitude to other b-values observed previously for linear salt effects.[12]

(13) A. Fainberg and S. Winstein, *ibid.*, **78**, 2780 (1956).
(14) (a) E. Grunwald and S. Winstein, *ibid.*, **70**, 846 (1948); (b) S. Winstein, E. Grunwald and H. W. Jones, *ibid.*, **73**, 2700 (1951); (c) A. Fainberg and S. Winstein, *ibid.*, **78**, 2770 (1956).

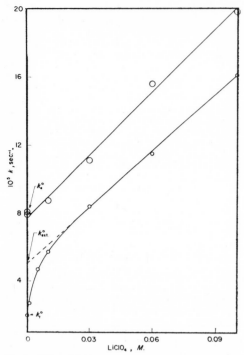

·Fig. 2.—Effect of lithium perchlorate on acetolysis of *threo*-3-*p*-anisyl-2-butyl *p*-bromobenzenesulfonate at 25.0°.

$$k_\alpha = k_\alpha^\circ \left[1 + b_\alpha(\text{LiClO}_4)\right] \qquad (1)$$

$$k_t = k_{\text{ext}}^\circ \left[1 + b_t(\text{LiClO}_4)\right] \qquad (2)$$

With the active *threo*-3-anisyl-2-butyl toluenesulfonate (I), the effect of two concentrations of lithium perchlorate on polarimetric acetolysis rate was studied. These data lead to a b_α value, listed in Table IV, similar to the one for the bromobenzenesulfonate.

TABLE IV

SUMMARY OF LITHIUM PERCHLORATE SALT EFFECTS IN ACETOLYSIS AT 25°

	threo-ROBs	*threo*-ROTs	*erythro*-ROBs[5]
$10^5\,k_{\text{ext}}^\circ$, sec. $^{-1}$	5.05	1.67	10.6[a]
$k_{\text{ext}}^\circ / k_t^\circ$	2.58	2.88	3.14
$(\text{LiClO}_4)_{1/2}$, M	0.0022		0.0040
b_α	16.2	17.4	
b_t	21.6	28.4	18.5

[a] Previously[5] listed erroneously as 1.06 due to typographical error.

Special Salt Effects on k_t.—

Titrimetric rate constants were nicely first order for acetolysis of the *threo*-3-anisyl-2-butyl *p*-bromobenzenesulfonate (I) in the presence of added lithium perchlorate. These rate constants at six concentrations of lithium perchlorate up to 0.1 M are summarized in Table II and plotted *vs.* lithium perchlorate concentration in Fig. 2. From the plot, it is evident that the salt effect has the steep special[4-6] pattern at lower concentrations and develops the normal[4,12] linear pattern at the higher concentrations of salt.

While the special and normal salt effects are not as sharply differentiated as in the cholesteryl,[6] 2,4-dimethoxyphenylethyl[6] or 2-anisyl-1-ethyl[4] cases, the separation is not difficult. In Fig. 2 is shown the extrapolation[4] of the linear k_t *vs.* (LiClO$_4$) plot to the intercept, k_{ext}°, the rate constant which includes the special but excludes the normal salt effect. The fit of the normal part of the salt effect to the linear relation 2 is summarized in Table IV, b_t being 21.6, larger than the b_α. The magnitude of the special salt effect, measured by the $k_{\text{ext}}^\circ / k_t^\circ$ ratio of 2.58, turns out to be comparable to that displayed by the *erythro*-3-anisyl-2-butyl *p*-bromobenzenesulfonate,[5] for which the $k_{\text{ext}}^\circ / k_t$ ratio is 3.14. Also, the value of $(\text{LiClO}_4)_{1/2}$, 2.2×10^{-3} M, for the *threo*-3-anisyl-2-butyl *p*-bromobenzenesulfonate is similar to the value observed with the *erythro* diastereomer.[5]

For the *threo*-3-anisyl-2-butyl *p*-toluenesulfonate (I), the effects of 0.03, 0.06 and 0.08 M lithium perchlorate were examined, the behavior here being analogous to that observed with the *p*-bromobenzenesulfonate. Table IV summarizes the values of $k_{\text{ext}}^\circ / k_t^\circ$ and b_t, these being slightly larger for the toluenesulfonate than· for the bromobenzenesulfonate.

Discussion

Special Salt Effects and Ion Pair Return.—For the other compounds whose behavior in acetolysis was reported in detail in previous papers of this series, it was reasoned that the special salt effects on titrimetric acetolysis rates must be concerned, not with effects on ionization rate, but with reduction of ion pair return.[4-6] The argument was based on the failure to observe special salt effects on ionization rate of closely similar substances. For example, special salt effects were observed on the acetolysis rate of *p*-anisylethyl[4] but not the *p*-methoxyneophyl[12] derivative. For the *threo*-3-anisyl-2-butyl derivatives in the present paper, salt effects are now available for both polarimetric and titrimetric acetolysis rates on the same substances. Thus, it is even clearer that special salt effects are concerned with reduction of ion pair return.

The most striking aspect of the present results is that the special salt effect only partly closes the gap between the polarimetric and titrimetric rates. The value of k_{ext}° is well below k_α° and the k_t points on the normal salt effect line are well below the k_α line, as is clear from Fig. 2. Before we conclude that the special salt effect only partly eliminates ion pair return, we should re-examine our assumption that k_α should be identified with k_1, the ionization rate constant.[7] If k_α were to include an important contribution from an independent cyclic rearrangement reaction[7,15,16] not involving ionization, this might explain simply the failure of the special salt·effect to close the gap between k_α and k_t. In discussing the present results with the 3-anisyl-2-butyl system, it will nevertheless be helpful to keep in mind the behavior of other systems in acetolysis, both those displaying and those not displaying special salt effects.

(15) W. G. Young, S. Winstein and H. L. Goering, THIS JOURNAL, **73**, 1958 (1951).

(16) C. A. Grob and S. Winstein, *Helv. Chim. Acta*, **35**, 782 (1952).

Identity of Polarimetric and Ionization Rate Constants.—If k_α receives a contribution from an independent cyclic rearrangement reaction,[7,15,16] we can express k_α analytically, as in equation 3, as the sum of k_r, the rate constant for racemization by such a cyclic rearrangement process, and k_1, the rate constant for ionization. As regards salt effects, one would expect k_r to be relatively insensitive to salt and k_1 to show a linear salt effect. The right-hand side of equation 3 is expressed on this basis. Actually, equation 3 for k_α has the observed form of equation 1 as can be seen by rewriting 3 in the form of equation 4. The term $(k_r + k_1^\circ)$ would be the k_α°, and the term $\left(\dfrac{k_1^\circ b_1}{k_r + k_1^\circ}\right)$ would be the b_α of equation 1.

$$k_\alpha = k_r + k_1 = k_r + k_1^\circ[1 + b_1(\text{LiClO}_4)] \quad (3)$$

$$k_\alpha = (k_r + k_1^\circ)\left[1 + \left(\frac{k_1^\circ b_1}{k_r + k_1^\circ}\right)(\text{LiClO}_4)\right] \quad (4)$$

$$k_t = Fk_1 = Fk_1^\circ[1 + b_1(\text{LiClO}_4)] \quad (5)$$

$$k_r = k_\alpha - k_{\text{ext}} = k_{\text{ext}}^\circ\left[\frac{k_\alpha^\circ}{k_{\text{ext}}^\circ} - 1 + \left(\frac{k_\alpha^\circ}{k_{\text{ext}}^\circ}b_\alpha - b_t\right)(\text{LiClO}_4)\right] \quad (6)$$

$$k_r = k_{\text{ext}}^\circ\,[0.58 + 4.0(\text{LiClO}_4)] \quad (7)$$

If the special salt effect were concerned with complete elimination of ion pair return, k_r for a system displaying the special salt effect would be $k_\alpha - k_{\text{ext}}$, where k_{ext} refers to points on the k_{ext}°, k_t normal salt effect line. For a system displaying only the normal salt effect pattern, such as 3-phenyl-2-butyl[2b,7,14] or norbornyl,[2b,7,17] the simplest assumption would be that k_r is equal to $k_\alpha - k_t$. The major objection to an appreciable contribution of an independent cyclic rearrangement process to the solvolyses we are dealing with is based on the behavior of the derived k_r-values toward variation of solvent and the structure of the substrate.

Of the solvent properties, the most relevant in discriminating between ionization and an independent cyclic rearrangement is ionizing power. Thus it already has been emphasized[7] that the derived k_r-values for solvolysis of 3-phenyl-2-butyl *p*-toluenesulfonate[7] are essentially as sensitive to solvent ionizing power as is solvolysis rate. This is also true in the case of norbornyl bromobenzenesulfonate[2b,7,17,18] and norbornyl bromide.[2b,17] To quote fragments of the data available in the case of the latter two substances, solvolysis rate of norbornyl bromobenzenesulfonate varies by some 4 powers of ten in carboxylic acid–dioxane mixtures while k_α/k_t varies by a factor of *ca.* 4. Similarly, for norbornyl bromide in propionic, acetic and formic acid solvents, solvolysis rate varies by nearly 5 powers of ten while k_α/k_t varies from 28 to 4. Nearly equal sensitivity to ionizing power for both the alleged k_r and the solvolysis rate may be seen also in the solvolysis of *cis*- and *trans*-5-methyl-2-cyclohexenyl[19] and *trans*-α,γ-dimethylallyl[20] acid phthalates and α,α-di-methylallyl chloride[21] and *p*-nitrobenzoate[21] in water–acetone mixtures.

The similarity of solvent requirements for the supposedly independent cyclic rearrangement and solvolysis process may be treated more quantitatively with the aid of *m*Y correlations.[14] For example, in the case of solvolysis of *cis*-5-methyl-2-cyclohexenyl[14c,19] and *trans*-α,γ-dimethylallyl[20] acid phthalates and α,α-dimethylallyl chloride[21] and *p*-nitrobenzoate[21] in water–acetone mixtures, both solvolysis rate and total rate of solvolysis plus rearrangement are well correlated by the *m*Y rate correlation[14] with similar *m*-values. The fact that both solvolysis rate and total rate of solvolysis plus rearrangement are correlated with the same **Y** values suggests that the rate of the extra rearrangement is sensitive to essentially the same blend of specific and general solvent functions[22] applicable to solvolysis. As emphasized previously,[7] the dependence of rates on solvent suggests strongly that there is a common rate-determining step for solvolysis and the extra racemization or rearrangement.

Another solvent property useful in discriminating between ionization and an independent cyclic rearrangement is nucleophilicity. For example, in solvolysis of α,α-dimethylallyl chloride,[15] rearrangement accompanies solvolysis in acetic acid but not ethanol. The disappearance of the accompanying rearrangement in the more nucleophilic solvent is not explicable on the basis of an independent cyclic process for the rearrangement. However, it is understandable on the basis of a common ion pair intermediate for both solvolysis and rearrangement, this intermediate being diverted essentially completely into solvolysis in the more nucleophilic solvent.[2b,15]

Further evidence against competing cyclic processes in acetolysis is the dependence of the derived k_r values on substrate structure. For example, k_r turns out to be zero with *trans*-2-acetoxycyclohexyl *p*-toluenesulfonate,[23] in contrast with a number of other systems. Such contrast is not understandable on the basis of cyclic processes.[23] Further, there are many cases where k_r varies with change in R or X of the substrate RX molecule almost exactly as does acetolysis rate. For example, this is true for X = Cl, Br, I and OBs in the norbornyl system.[2b,17] This is true for X = OBs and OTs in the present work on the 3-anisyl-2-butyl system. Comparing the 3-phenyl-2-butyl[7] and 3-anisyl-2-butyl toluenesulfonates, it is clear that the *p*-methoxyl group[9] increases k_r and k_t by nearly the same large factor.[24,25] Such effects of substrate structure suggest a common rate-determining ionization step for both solvolysis and racemization.

The pattern of observed salt effects in acetolysis also does not support an interpretation of the gap between k_α and k_{ext} or k_t in terms of a k_r for a cyclic rearrangement process insensitive to salt effects. Formulating k_t as a fraction[13] F of the ionization rate constant k_1, as in equation 5, F would be equal to 1 for norbornyl *p*-bromobenzenesulfonate and

(17) E. Clippinger, unpublished work.
(18) S. Winstein and D. Trifan, THIS JOURNAL, **74**, 1154 (1952).
(19) H. L. Goering and E. F. Silversmith, *ibid.*, **77**, 1129 (1955).
(20) H. L. Goering and R. W. Greiner, *ibid.*, **79**, 3464 (1957).
(21) C. Wilcox, Thesis, U.C.L.A., 1957.

(22) (a) A. H. Fainberg and S. Winstein, THIS JOURNAL, **79**, 1597 (1957); (b) **79**, 1602 (1957); (c) **79**, 1608 (1957); (d) S. Winstein, A. H. Fainberg and E. Grunwald, *ibid.*, **79**, 4146 (1957); (e) S. Winstein and A. H. Fainberg, *ibid.*, **79**, 5937 (1957).
(23) S. Winstein and R. Heck, *ibid.*, **74**, 5584 (1952).
(24) S. Winstein and R. Heck, *ibid.*, **78**, 4801 (1956).
(25) R. Heck and S. Winstein, *ibid.*, **79**, 3432 (1957).

for the 3-anisyl-2-butyl ester along the $k_{ext}^°$, k_t line. On this basis, the k_α vs. (LiClO$_4$) line should be parallel to the k_t vs. (LiClO$_4$) line for a system such as norbornyl and parallel to the $k_{ext}^°$, k_t line for 3-anisyl-2-butyl or analogous ones.

For the 3-anisyl-2-butyl p-bromobenzenesulfonate system, the gap between the k_α line and the $k_{ext}^°$, k_t line is not constant. Instead, it actually widens as (LiClO$_4$) increases. This can be seen in Fig. 2. Also, the variation of the presumed k_r with (LiClO$_4$) is shown in equation 6, which is derived from equations 1 and 2. Equation 6 is expressed numerically for the 3-anisyl-2-butyl p-bromobenzenesulfonate acetolysis in equation 7.

Whereas the presumed k_r in the case of the 3-anisyl-2-butyl system rises as lithium perchlorate is added, the same treatment applied to the 2-anisyl-1-propyl[2b,3,26,27] system leads to a negative salt effect on k_r. On the other hand, for norbornyl bromobenzenesulfonate in 60% acetic acid–dioxane, k_r rises about twice as steeply as does k_t with addition of lithium perchlorate.[2b,28] Similarly, the presumed k_r is more sensitive to lithium perchlorate than is k_t in acetolysis of cis-5-methyl-2-cyclohexenyl chloride.[13,29] Thus, instead of being insensitive to salt effects, k_r shows variations even in the sign of the salt effect and often rises even more steeply than k_t with increase in salt concentration. Such behavior of k_r is not anticipated for a cyclic rearrangement process.

All of the above considerations reconfirm that the polarimetric rate constant k_α in acetolysis of a system such as 3-anisyl-2-butyl p-bromobenzenesulfonate (I) should indeed be identified with the ionization rate constant k_1. On this basis, the relative ionization rates for 3-anisyl-2-butyl p-bromobenzenesulfonate, based on relative k_α values, in the different solvents employed in the present work are summarized in Table III. From this table, it is clear that ionization rates increase by nearly 5 powers of ten over the range of solvents from 12.5% AcOH–dioxane to formic acid.

Interpretation of Special Salt Effects.—The discussion in the previous section has forced us to the conclusion that ion pair return is only partially eliminated by the special salt effect.

It remains to inquire to what extent the apparent special salt effect receives a contribution from the fact that addition of lithium perchlorate introduces salt-promoted[13] ionization which may give rise to less ion pair return than the ionization in the absence of salt. This matter may be discussed analytically by expressing k_1, as in equations 8 and 9, as the sum of two terms, one for salt-unassisted and the other for salt-promoted ionization. It may be useful to associate the one term with ionization to an ion pair, and the other with formation of an ion quadruplet from the substrate molecule and a salt ion pair.[13] In equation 9, F_0 and F_{salt} are the fractions of each of the ionizations, respectively, which result in solvolysis product. Equation 9 may be rewritten in the form of equation 10, di-

vision of which by equation 8 leads to equation 11 for F, the apparent fraction of ionization leading to solvolysis product.

Examination of equation 11 shows that neither the magnitude nor the shape of the special salt effects are accounted for in this manner. Even if F_{salt} were 1.00, salt-promoted ionization is introduced too slowly as lithium perchlorate is added to account for much of the apparent reduction in ion pair return. This is especially true in cases such as cholesteryl,[6] 2,4-dimethoxyphenylethyl[6] and 2-p-anisylethyl,[4,30] where the special salt effect is introduced at concentrations of lithium perchlorate where salt-promoted ionization is still negligible.

$$k_1 = k_1^° + k_1^° b_1(\text{LiClO}_4) \tag{8}$$

$$k_t = F_0 k_1^° + F_{salt} k_1^° b_1(\text{LiClO}_4) \tag{9}$$

$$k_t = F_0 k_1^° \left[1 + \frac{F_{salt}}{F_0} b_1(\text{LiClO}_4) \right] \tag{10}$$

$$F = F_0 \frac{\left[1 + \frac{F_{salt}}{F_0} b_1(\text{LiClO}_4) \right]}{[1 + b_1(\text{LiClO}_4)]} \tag{11}$$

We can see that the typical cases of special salt effects in acetolysis do not involve primarily the presence of lithium perchlorate already in the rate-determining ionization step. The action of lithium perchlorate is in some later step. Regarding the mode of action of the salt in the special salt effect, the indications are strong that it is not by way of a sort of ion atmosphere effect, or ion pair or ion clump versions of such an effect, on the relative rate constants determining the importance of ion pair return.

One indication against an ion atmosphere description for the special salt effect is the high specificity with regard to the structure of the substrate system. Thus, (LiClO$_4$)$_{1/2}$ varies widely from system to system,[3-6] being very sensitive to structure. On the other hand, the normal salt effects[3-6,12] vary much less with structure.

The worst difficulty encountered by an ion atmosphere type of explanation of the special salt effect is the unique specificity of the effect as regards the common-ion salt, lithium toluenesulfonate or bromobenzenesulfonate, in the case of an alkyl toluenesulfonate or bromobenzenesulfonate, respectively. The common ion salt is able to exercise a normal salt effect[12,13] on ionization rate, but is peculiarly incapable of exercising a special salt effect. For such reasons we have been led to an explanation of the special salt effect which depends on specific reactions between the added salt and ion pair intermediates in acetolysis of the solvolyzing system.

Any formulation of the special salt effect in acetolysis must account for the absence of such effects in acetolysis of certain systems such as norbornyl[17] and 3-phenyl-2-butyl[7,13] where, nevertheless, ion pair return is important. Also, it must account for the elimination of only a discrete fraction of such ion pair return even when special salt effects are displayed, as in the present case. Our best working hypothesis[3] has been that two kinds of carbonium ion pairs, intimate and solvent-separated ion pairs II and III, respectively, may be

(26) S. Winstein and K. C. Schreiber, THIS JOURNAL, 2171 (1952).

(27) A. Fainberg, unpublished work.

(28) A. Colter, unpublished work.

(29) H. L. Goering, T. D. Nevitt and E. F. Silversmith, THIS JOURNAL, **77**, 5026 (1955).

(30) P. Klinedinst, unpublished work.

distinguished as discrete intermediates in solvolysis, and that these respond differently to the addition of salt to the acetolysis medium. Of the two varieties of ion pair, discussed more fully later in this manuscript, the solvent-separated ion pair III is presumed to be much more reactive than the intimate ion pair II toward added lithium perchlorate. The latter is presumed to trap III while still permitting return from the intimate ion pair, namely internal return.[7,10,14b,15] Thus the special salt effect in the present case and some similar ones is concerned with elimination of external ion pair return.[10] The present work does not supply any definite evidence on the mechanism of the action of the salt in the special salt effect. However, as mentioned already in summary form,[2b,3] the available evidence points to a major mechanism for the action of lithium perchlorate in acetolysis involving diversion of ion pair III to a carbonium perchlorate ion pair by exchange of III with a lithium perchlorate ion pair.

Solvolysis Scheme in Acetolysis.—Invoking two types of carbonium ion pairs as well as dissociated carbonium ions means that, in general, three varieties of the carbonium ion need to be considered in interpreting acetolysis. This is shown in the following solvolysis scheme, the three varieties of carbonium ion, II, III and IV, representing progressively further stages of ionization–dissociation of RX.

$$\text{I} \xrightarrow{\text{ionization}} \text{II} \qquad \text{III} \xrightarrow{\text{dissociation}} \text{IV}$$

$$\begin{array}{ccc} & \text{solvent-} & \\ \text{intimate} & \text{separated} & \text{dissociated} \\ \text{ion pair} & \text{ion pair} & \text{ions} \end{array}$$

$$\text{RX} \underset{k_{-1}}{\overset{k_1}{\rightleftarrows}} \text{R}\oplus\text{X}\ominus \underset{k_{-2}}{\overset{k_2}{\rightleftarrows}} \text{R}\oplus \parallel \text{X}\ominus \underset{k_{-3}}{\overset{k_3}{\rightleftarrows}} \text{R}\oplus + \text{X}\ominus$$

$$\downarrow k_s^{\text{III}} \qquad\qquad \downarrow k_s^{\text{IV}}$$

$$\text{ROS} \qquad\qquad \text{ROS}$$

Return to covalent RX accompanying acetolysis may be from any one of the ionic stages, II, III or IV, as the furthest stage of ionization–dissociation.[2,3,10] From the absence of common ion rate depression[10] of acetolysis of *threo*-3-anisyl-2-butyl bromobenzenesulfonate or toluenesulfonate, it was concluded previously that return from dissociated carbonium ion IV ("external ion return")[10] did not accompany acetolysis in the case of the 3-anisyl-2-butyl system. In fact, a comparison of the behavior of the 3-anisyl-2-butyl system with that of other systems led to the conclusion[10] that dissociation of ion pairs to dissociated ions IV was unimportant in acetolysis of the 3-anisyl-2-butyl system, rate of dissociation being much slower than the rate of other reactions of the ion pairs.

The above conclusion that the dissociated carbonium ion stage was not attained in acetolysis applied to other systems besides the 3-anisyl-2-butyl arenesulfonates.[10] An example of such a system is norbornyl bromobenzenesulfonate.[10] On the basis of the present explanation of special salt effects in acetolysis, we can go further in defining what return accompanies acetolysis of norbornyl bromobenzenesulfonate. The absence of special salt effects in acetolysis suggests that return from the solvent-separated ion pair III ("external ion pair return")[10] is unimportant. Thus only internal return is important in acetolysis of norbornyl bromobenzenesulfonate, and the same conclusion may be drawn for 2-phenyl-1-propyl[26] and 3-phenyl-2-butyl[7,13] arenesulfonates.

Solvolysis product may arise from more than one of the varieties of carbonium ion. In general, all three varieties of carbonium ion, II, III and IV, may lead to solvolysis product ROS with rate constants k_s^{II}, k_s^{III} and k_s^{IV}, respectively. However, the solvolysis scheme shown is designed for a case where ROS arises from solvent-separated ion pair III and dissociated ion IV.[31] Where dissociation is negligible, as in acetolysis of 3-anisyl-2-butyl, norbornyl and 3-phenyl-2-butyl arenesulfonates, the route to ROS from dissociated ion IV may be omitted.

The solvolysis scheme for acetolysis which includes product formation from solvent-separated ion pair III, but omits it from the intimate ion pair II, is intended for systems leading to bridged carbonium ions such as norbornyl and 3-anisyl-2-butyl. It is quite clear that solvent-separated ion pair III has all it needs to enable it to yield solvolysis product ROS. For 3-anisyl-2-butyl arenesulfonate, k_s^{III}/k_{-2} is not large and external ion pair return is important in acetolysis in the absence of added salt. On the other hand, for a system such as norbornyl bromobenzenesulfonate, k_s^{III}/k_{-2} is presumed to be very large, the inevitable result of attaining the solvent-separated ion pair stage of ionization–dissociation being formation of solvolysis product.

The omission of an ROS-forming reaction of intimate ion pair II (rate constant k_s^{II}) for cases such as norbornyl and 3-anisyl-2-butyl arenesulfonates is based on the supposition that the anion portion of the intimate ion pair II effectively shields the bridged cation from covalent solvent attack until solvent intrudes on the intimate ion pair II to the point that the ion pair may be labeled solvent-separated. In qualitative accord with such a description is the relatively low sensitivity of the polarimetric–titrimetric rate ratio in solvolysis of norbornyl bromobenzenesulfonate to solvent nucleophilicity. For example, the change in k_α/k_t is not drastic from acetic acid to absolute ethanol[7,18] as solvent, contrary to what one might expect if covalent solvent attack took place on intimate pair II. Previously,[7] the discussion of formation of solvolysis product in acetolysis of norbornyl bromobenzenesulfonate was in terms of "further separation of the (intimate) ion pair with formation of solvolysis product." While the present description is more definite, it remains to be seen whether it will become necessary to complicate the scheme

(31) We emphasized previously[10] that this should not be misunderstood[32] as an indication that we believe the intimate ion pair II does not ever give rise to ROS. Also, we mentioned several cases where the intimate ion pair II is believed able to yield solvolysis product.

(32) *E.g.*, B. Bensley and C. Kohnstam, *J. Chem. Soc.*, 3408 (1955).

by inclusion of a k_s^{II} path involving attack of solvent on ion pair II.[33,34]

The conversion of solvent-separated ion pair III to solvolysis product may proceed in a number of ways. While one can visualize a carbonium acetate ion pair intermediate along the lines

$$\underset{Ac}{R \overset{\oplus}{O}H} \; \overset{\ominus}{OTs} \longrightarrow \underset{Ac}{R \overset{\oplus}{O}O} \; H\text{-}OTs$$

such an intermediate is certainly not necessary. For example, the product formation may be visualized as

$$\underset{Ac}{R \overset{\oplus}{O}H} \; \overset{\ominus}{OTs} \longrightarrow \underset{Ac}{R\text{---}\overset{\oplus}{O}H} \; \overset{\ominus}{OTs}$$

We have no definitive information in this connection. There is one set of circumstances where it seems relatively certain that acetate formation will involve carbonium acetate ion pairs. This is for acetolysis in the presence of added alkali acetate of a system subject to special salt effects. Under these conditions, carbonium acetate ion pairs, both solvent-separated and intimate, are probably formed.

$$R\overset{\oplus}{} \overset{\ominus}{\|OTs} \longrightarrow R\overset{\ominus}{} \overset{\ominus}{\|OAc} \longrightarrow R\overset{\oplus}{}OAc \longrightarrow ROAc$$

Dissection of Ion Pair Return.—We can now proceed to perform the arithmetic relating to internal and external ion pair return during acetolysis of the *threo*-3-anisyl-2-butyl arenesulfonates. Since the k_{ext} values for rate constants on the k_{ext}°, k_t line include the full special salt effect, they are rate constants for formation of solvent-separated ion pair III. Thus k_{ext} is given by equation 12 as a function of k_1 (or k_α) and the (k_{-1}/k_2) ratio relating to internal return.

$$k_{ext} = \frac{k_1}{1 + (k_{-1}/k_2)} = k_{ext}^{\circ}\,[1 + b_t(LiClO_4)] \quad (12)$$

$$(k_{-1}/k_2) = (k_\alpha/k_{ext}) - 1 \quad (13)$$

$$k_t = \frac{\dfrac{k_1}{1 + (k_{-1}/k_2)}}{k_s^{III}/(k_{-2} + k_s^{III})} \quad (14)$$

$$\frac{k_s^{III}}{(k_{-2} + k_s^{III})} = \frac{(k_\alpha/k_{ext}) - 1}{(k_\alpha/k_t) - 1} \quad (15)$$

The latter ratio is given explicitly by equation 13 as a function of k_α and k_{ext}. According to a previous derivation,[3b,10] k_t is given by equation 14 which takes into account both internal and external ion pair return.[35] Substituting for (k_{-1}/k_2) its equivalent from equation 13 allows one to solve for $k_s^{III}/(k_{-2} + k_s^{III})$ as in equation 15.

As summarized in Table V, the k_α°, k_{ext}° and k_t° values lead to values of 0.627 for $k_2/(k_{-1} + k_2)$ and 0.193 for $k_s^{III}/(k_{-2} + k_s^{III})$ in acetolysis of *threo*-3-anisyl-2-butyl bromobenzenesulfonate with no

(33) See E. Grunwald, A. Heller and F. S. Klein, *J. Chem. Soc.*, 2604 (1957), for a discussion of possible attack of solvent on the α-phenylethyl chloride intimate ion pair from the chloride ion side.

(34) There are many other possible variations of the solvolysis scheme. For example, the first intimate ion pair II could rearrange to a still intimate ion pair, but with the anion near some other portion of the cation, thus leaving the reactive spot on the cation exposed to solvent.

(35) A more convenient form of equation 14 for some purposes is

$$\frac{1}{k_t} = \frac{1}{k_1} + \frac{1}{k_1}\frac{k_{-1}}{k_2} + \frac{1}{k_1}\frac{k_{-1}}{k_2}\frac{k_{-2}}{k_s^{III}}$$

added lithium perchlorate. In other words, 37% of intimate ion pair II formed from covalent bromobenzenesulfonate I returns to the covalent state, while 80.7% of solvent-separated ion pair III formed from II returns to II instead of yielding solvolysis product. As summarized in Table VI, the situation with the toluenesulfonate is quite similar to that for the bromobenzenesulfonate.

TABLE V

ANALYSIS OF EFFECT OF VARIOUS CONCENTRATIONS OF LITHIUM PERCHLORATE

[LiClO₄], M	0	0.003	0.01	0.03
$10^5\,k_{ext}$	5.05	5.40	6.15	8.32
k_α/k_t	4.07	2.02	1.54	1.35
k_{ext}/k_t	2.58	1.39	1.08	1.00
$k_s^{III}/(k_{-2} + k_s^{III})$	0.193	0.452	0.783	1.00
$k_2/(k_{-1} + k_2)$	0.627	0.679	0.702	0.740
$[(k_{ext}/k_\alpha^{\circ}) - b_\alpha(LiClO_4)]^a$	0.668	0.666	0.653	0.62

 ^{a} F_0 values from equation 16 assuming $F_{salt} = 1.00$.

As lithium perchlorate is added in acetolysis of the *threo*-3-anisyl-2-butyl bromobenzenesulfonate, the apparent $k_s^{III}/(k_{-2} + k_s^{III})$ values rise relatively rapidly to 1.00 as external ion pair return is eliminated. This is shown in Table V. On the other hand, the $k_2/(k_{-1} + k_2)$ values show only a small increase, reflecting the relative insensitivity of internal return to the added salt.

The small increase in $k_2/(k_{-1} + k_2)$ values as lithium perchlorate is added does indicate that some change in internal return is included within the normal salt effect pattern.[13] At least some of this effect must be due to the fact that appreciable fractions of ionization of substrate I are salt-assisted as lithium perchlorate is added, and that internal return is less serious for the salt-promoted ionization than for the salt-unassisted ionization.

It is useful here to refer again to equation 10, putting in k_{ext} instead of k_t, k_α° instead of k_1° and b_α instead of b_1. Rearrangement of the resulting equation leads to equation 16 for F_0, the fraction of

$$F_0 = (k_{ext}/k_\alpha^{\circ}) - F_{salt}\,b_\alpha(LiClO_4) \quad (16)$$

unpromoted ionization escaping internal return. Assuming an extreme value of 1.00 for F_{salt} in equation 16, F_0 values listed in Table V are obtained for comparison with the $k_2/(k_{-1} + k_2)$ values. These actually drift down slightly, showing that the extreme assumption of no internal return in salt-promoted ionization over-corrects for the upward trend in $k_2/(k_{-1} + k_2)$ values.

Comparison of 3-Anisyl-2-butyl and 3-Phenyl-2-butyl Systems.—It is interesting to contrast the behavior of the 3-anisyl-2-butyl system in acetolysis with that of 3-phenyl-2-butyl.[7] In acetolysis of 3-phenyl-2-butyl *p*-toluenesulfonate, previous observations[7] and the previous[7] and present discussion show that internal return is important, but external ion pair return is not, k_s^{III} exceeding k_{-2} by a substantial factor.

The summary in Table VI makes it clear that total ion pair return is of comparable importance in acetolysis of the 3-anisyl-2-butyl and 3-phenyl-2-butyl systems. Where the two systems differ markedly is in the distribution of ion pair return between internal return and external ion pair return. The structural change from 3-phenyl-2-butyl to 3-anisyl-2-butyl which stabilizes the intermediate carbonium ion species does not increase total ion pair return. It decreases k_{-1}/k_2 and thus the efficiency of internal return from II and increases k_{-2}/k_s^{III} and thus the efficiency of return from III.

TABLE VI

COMPARISON OF ION PAIR RETURN IN SOLVOLYSIS OF *threo*-3-PHENYL-2-BUTYL (3-Ph-2-Bu) AND *threo*-3-ANISYL-2-BUTYL (3-An-2-Bu) ARENESULFONATES

Solvent	Compound	Temp., °C.	Ion pair return,[a] % From II[b]	From III[c]	Total[d]
10% HCOOH–dioxane	3-An-2-BuOBs	25			94
AcOH	3-Ph-2-BuOTs[7]	50	78	*ca.* 0	78
	3-An-2-BuOBs	25	37	81	75
	3-An-2-BuOTs	25	38	83	78
EtOH	3-Ph-2-BuOTs[7]	75	51	0	51
	3-An-2-BuOBs	25	21	0	21
25% HCOOH–AcOH	3-An-2-BuOBs	25			7
HCOOH	3-Ph-2-BuOTs[7]	25	15	0	15

[a] At zero LiClO$_4$ concentration. [b] $100k_{-1}/(k_{-1} + k_2)$. [c] $100k_{-2}/(k_{-2} + k_s^{III})$. [d] $100[1 - (k_t^o/k_\alpha^o)]$.

Other Solvents.—The change from acetic acid to ethanol as solvent causes a very pronounced drop in total ion pair return accompanying solvolysis of 3-anisyl-2-butyl derivatives, the polarimetric-titrimetric rate ratio, k_α/k_t, being only 1.27 in ethanol. For norbornyl bromobenzenesulfonate[7,18] or 3-phenyl-2-butyl toluenesulfonate,[7] the corresponding solvent change produces much less response in the k_α/k_t ratio. Thus, systems whose solvolysis is accompanied by return from solvent-separated ion pair III contrast with those which do not, not only with respect to salt effects, but with respect to behavior toward solvent variation.

A sharp reduction in return from solvent-separated ion pair III accompanying solvolysis as solvent nucleophilicity is increased can be anticipated, since k_s^{III}/k_{-2} should be relatively sensitive to solvent nucleophilicity. It seems likely, therefore, that in ethanol essentially all ion pair return accompanying solvolysis of 3-anisyl-2-butyl bromobenzenesulfonate is the residual internal return from intimate ion pair II. This is the way the data are treated in Table VI.

The contrast between the 3-anisyl-2-butyl and 3-phenyl-2-butyl systems in their response to the AcOH → EtOH solvent change is much reduced if we restrict our attention to internal return alone (Table VI). Also, the contrast between acetic acid and ethanol as solvents for the 3-anisyl-2-butyl system is much less if we consider only internal return, instead of total ion pair return in acetic acid and what is only internal return in ethanol. Thus $(k_{-1} + k_2)/k_2$ is 1.59 in acetic acid and 1.27 in ethanol for 3-anisyl-2-butyl bromobenzenesulfonate.

It is obvious from Tables III and VI that ion pair return accompanying solvolysis of *threo*-3-anisyl-2-butyl bromobenzenesulfonate is increased substantially in 10% HCOOH–dioxane over that occurring in acetic acid. On the other hand, addition of even 25% formic acid to acetic acid nearly completely eliminates ion pair return. The pattern of ion pair return, its possible dissection into internal and external return, and even variation of the solvolysis scheme as solvent varies is being further examined with the 3-anisyl-2-butyl as well as other systems. The results will be reported and discussed elsewhere.

Two Varieties of Ion Pair, Structure and Merging of Ion Pair and Cyclic Mechanisms.—We first visualized two varieties of ion pair in the solvolysis scheme on the basis of *a priori* considerations. In the solvation of ions the inner shell of solvent molecules determines most of the energy of solvation.[36] The first product of ionization of covalent R–X, the intimate ion pair II, is peripherally solvated, but no solvent is yet between the two ions. The solvation shells of the two ions are thus very incomplete and powerful electrostatic, polarization and even other bonding forces are important in stabilizing the intermediate.

Because the medium is not a continuum but composed of discrete molecules of definite size, further separation of the intimate ion pair can be expected to be associated with an energy barrier. In the ascent to the top of the barrier more energy is required to oppose the attractive forces than is compensated for by increased solvation. However, past a certain separation, which permits solvent to enter between the ions, increased solvation more than compensates for energy input required for further separation of the ions. Thus a definite energy barrier is visualized between intimate and solvent-separated ion pairs, these being discrete species. Another way to describe the intimate and solvent-separated ion pairs II and III is as a pair of ions in the same or different solvent cages,[37] respectively.

When only partial elimination of ion pair return by lithium perchlorate was observed in our study of acetolysis of certain arenesulfonates, it was immediately obvious that this was explicable on the basis of two discrete varieties of carbonium ion pairs. Thus, the behavior of arenesulfonates in acetolysis can be taken as support for the idea of discriminating between intimate and solvent-separated ion pairs generally.

At about the same time as intimate and solvent-separated ion pairs were invoked in solvolysis of arenesulfonates,[3] Grunwald[38] furnished an excellent discussion pointing to the probable usefulness of the concept of two distinct chemically different intimate and solvent-separated ion pair species even in the case of ordinary stable ions. Also, Sadek and Fuoss[39] found that, in treating conductivity data on solutions of tetrabutylammonium bromide, a constant interionic distance instead of values dependent on solvent composition was obtained when they assumed a conventional model to describe cation–anion approach up to a separation of one layer of solvent molecules and that the ex-

(36) (a) J. D. Bernal and R. H. Fowler, *J. Chem. Phys.*, **1**, 515 (1933); (b) D. D. Eley and M. G. Evans, *Trans. Faraday Soc.*, **34**, 1093 (1938).
(37) S. Winstein, *Experientia*, Suppl., II, 137 (1955).
(38) E. Grunwald, *Anal. Chem.*, **26**, 1696 (1954).
(39) H. Sadek and R. M. Fuoss, THIS JOURNAL, **76**, 5905 (1954).

pulsion of the last layer of solvent molecules from between the ions is a discrete stepwise process. Their treatment then involves equilibrium between intimate and solvent-separated ion pairs and dissociated ions corresponding to II, III and IV in our solvolysis scheme.

It seems probable that the fullest understanding of the behavior of various salts in both normal[12] and special[4−6] salt effects will require information on the distribution of the salt ion pairs between intimate and solvent-separated species.

While the cation and anion of the solvent-separated ion pair tend to have little or no definite geometric or structural relationship, the situation can be expected to be different in the intimate ion pair. Here the attraction between the ions is sufficiently strong, that certain structures could well be favored over others. Even on the basis of only electrostatic forces between ions in contact, some structures will correspond to greater stability than others. Further, some covalent character may be visualized for the cation–anion interaction in an intimate ion pair. This is certainly true of ion pairs such as the trimethylcarbonium chloride ion pair VI in solvolysis of t-butyl chloride.[14b] Depending on the

VI   VII

exact hybridization of orbitals in the $C_7C_1C_2C_3$ framework of a bridged carbonium ion such as norbornyl (VII), there may be some covalent character to the cation–anion interaction in the intimate ion pair even in such cases.[7]

Because of the character of intimate ion pairs, there is no sharp distinction between such an ion pair and a covalently bound intermediate in a so-called cyclic rearrangement. These are not qualitatively distinct, but form extremes in a graded series.[40] Thus, there is no sharp distinction between formation of an intimate ion pair followed by internal return and a cyclic rearrangement, and marginal cases can be anticipated.

Actually, change of solvent may convert one phenomenon to the other and a probable example of this has already been given by Grob and Winstein[16] in the case of mutarotation of Δ^5-cholestene dibromide. Thus the mutarotation–solvolysis could be best described by way of a bromonium bromide ion pair VIII in relatively good ionizing solvents such as acetic acid or ethanol. On the other hand, mutarotation was best described by way of a transition state or intermediate like IX in very poorly ionizing solvents such as heptane.

VIII   IX

An analogy has been pointed out recently by Kosower[41] between our solvolysis scheme in acetol-

(40) Discussion, "Symposium on Molecular Rearrangements," Queen Mary College, Univ. of London, April 6, 1954; see *Chem. Eng. News*, **32**, 1898 (1954); *Nature*, **173**, 898 (1954).

(41) E. Kosower, THIS JOURNAL, **78**, 5700 (1956).

ysis and the following set of equilibria[42] in ionization–dissociation of N-methylpyridinium iodide

Each of the species in the solvolysis scheme has its counterpart in the N-methylpyridinium case. Specifically, the counterpart of the intimate ion pair II is an intimate ion pair termed a charge-transfer complex[43,44] by Kosower because it displays a charge-transfer absorption band.

The spectral transition energy[45] ΔE^* for the charge-transfer band of the N-methylpyridinium iodide is sensitive to solvent change, and Kosower[41] has observed linear relations between ΔE^* and the solvent **Y** values[14c] which correlate solvolysis rates of alkyl halides, etc., in the Grunwald–Winstein m**Y** relation.[14] On the basis of the parallelism between ΔE^* and **Y**, as well as the similarity between the ionization–dissociation schemes for RX and for N-methylpyridinium iodide, Kosower[41] has suggested that the intimate ion pair intermediate in solvolysis may derive a portion of its binding energy from charge-transfer forces and that charge transfer may contribute to the stabilization of the transition state for its formation.

The implications of the linear relation between ΔE^* and **Y** may be best understood as follows. The ΔE^* quantity represents the change in energy from the charged ground state pyridinium iodide to the "neutral" excited state in light absorption. Let $\Delta F^\pm$ be the free energy change from t-butyl chloride to the transition state in solvolysis. Let $\Delta\Delta E^*$ and $\Delta\Delta F^\pm$ represent the changes in ΔE^* and $\Delta F^\pm$, respectively, associated with a solvent change.[22] From the definition of **Y**, $\Delta\Delta F^\pm$ is proportional to Δ**Y**.

As water is added to ethanol, for example, the pyridinium iodide ground state is stabilized and the "neutral" excited state is destabilized; $\Delta\Delta E^*$ is positive. On the other hand, addition of water to ethanol, raises the free energy of the ground state[46] t-BuCl molecules and lowers that of the transition state[14,22]; $\Delta\Delta F^\pm$ is negative. What the linear relation between ΔE^* and **Y** for a series of solvents means is that relation 17 is obeyed, c being a proportionality constant.

$$\Delta\Delta E^* = c\Delta\Delta F^\pm \qquad (17)$$

Actually, the response of two phenomena to solvent change can be sufficiently similar for a linear

(42) (a) E. M. Kosower, *ibid.*, **77**, 3883 (1955); (b) E. M. Kosower and J. C. Burbach, *ibid.*, **78**, 5838 (1956).

(43) (a) R. S. Mulliken, *ibid.*, **74**, 811 (1952); (b) R. S. Mulliken, *J. Phys. Chem.*, **56**, 801 (1952).

(44) Unless charge-transfer forces are shown to account for the major part of the energy of interaction between the two ions, we would prefer the term intimate ion pair. Actually, there are intimate ion pairs of various configurations, many of them presumably unfavorable for the charge-transfer interaction.

(45) The symbol E_T was employed by Kosower,[41] but our discussion is made clearer by the use of ΔE^* to parallel the symbol $\Delta F^\pm$ in solvolysis.

(46) **Y** values do not measure the effect of solvent merely on the transition state, as has been stated.[41]

relation such as 17 to be quite successful for each binary solvent set, and yet the structural changes associated with the two phenomena are not strictly analogous. For example, solvolysis rates of substances RX requiring covalent solvent participation give linear log k vs. Y plots for aqueous alcohols or aqueous acetones.[14,22] In other words, $\Delta\Delta F^{\pm}_{RX}$ is proportional to $\Delta\Delta F^{\pm}_{BuCl}$ in spite of considerable difference in the structural changes associated with the change from ground state to transition state for RX and *t*-BuCl.

Thus, the proportionality between $\Delta\Delta E^*$ and $\Delta\Delta F^{\pm}_{BuCl}$ does not indicate strict analogy between the structural changes associated with the ΔE^* and the $\Delta F^{\pm}_{BuCl}$. It doesn't indicate sufficient structural analogy between the pyridinium iodide charge-transfer complex and the intimate ion pair II in solvolysis to label the latter a charge-transfer complex because the former is so designated. In spite of the fact that relation 17 should not be offered as support, the suggestion that intimate ion pairs such as VI and II be expressed as charge-transfer complexes is interesting.

For cationic acceptor and anionic donor components like the ions in the intimate ion pair VI there is no big distinction between charge-transfer character and covalent character to the interaction between the ions. Actually, for an interaction to be designated as a charge-transfer interaction between the components of an intimate ion pair II containing a bridged cation such as the one in the present 3-anisyl-2-butyl case, the structure of the first intimate ion pair produced by ionization of I may be unfavorable relative to a structure which has the anion situated near the aromatic ring.

Since intimate ion pairs may well have considerable structure, care needs to be exercised in the use of isotopic criteria for the occurrence of ion pairs as intermediates in rearrangements. For example, for an anionotropic rearrangement and a peroxide rearrangement involving acylate group shifts, it has been stated[47] or implied[48, 48a] that the two acylate oxygen atoms must necessarily attain equivalence in an intermediate ion pair. Therefore, O^{18}-scrambling has been employed as a criterion for ion pair formation. Our feeling is that an O^{18}-scrambling result could be support for an ion pair interpretation, but that a unique isotopic result doesn't disprove it. It may merely supply evidence regarding the structure of the intermediate ion pair or ion pairs. In our view, the best criterion for ionization is sensitivity of the reaction to ionizing power of medium.

In the case of thermal isomerization of α-phenylallyl *p*-nitrobenzoate (X) to the γ-phenylallyl isomer XI in chlorobenzene solvent, Braude and Turner[47] have observed that exclusively the acyl oxygen atom of the starting material becomes the alkyl oxygen atom in the rearranged product. A similar result apparently has been obtained by Doering[49] in isomerization of α-phenyl-γ-methyl-allyl *p*-nitrobenzoate. While Braude and Turner[47] prefer a synchronous cyclic rearrangement mechanism, the facts in the case do not preclude an ion pair intermediate.

It seems certain that an ion pair intermediate in isomerization of the α-phenylallyl ester X in a solvent like chlorobenzene would tend to remain intimate. Having in mind the distribution of charge in the allylic cation and the acylate anion, it would not be surprising if the intimate ion pair preferred the geometry shown in XII. Thus the O^{18} result

constitutes no evidence against an ion pair interpretation.[50] While the rearrangement in question shows considerable sensitivity to salt effects and solvent ionizing power in non-solvolyzing solvents,[51] as well as solvolyzing solvents referred to earlier in this report, it is still not clear whether the rearrangement in chlorobenzene is best described by way of an ion pair intermediate.

In isomerization of 9-decalyl perbenzoate (XIII) to the acylal XIV in both methanol and acetic acid solvents, Denney[48] observed that the O^{18} remained

essentially exclusively as carbonyl oxygen. On this basis he regarded the most attractive explanation of the rearrangement to involve a concerted shift of the benzoate group by way of a transition state or short-lived intermediate such as XV. Such a formulation is essentially identical to the one used earlier by Grob and Winstein[16] for the mutarotation of Δ^5-cholestene dibromide in the very poorest ionizing solvents.

(47) E. A. Braude and D. W. Turner, *Chemistry & Industry*, 1223 (1955).

(48) D. B. Denney, THIS JOURNAL, **77**, 1706 (1955).

(48a) NOTE ADDED IN PROOF.—D. B. Denney and D. G. Denney have now employed an ion pair interpretation for the rearrangement of 9-decalyl perbenzoate [*ibid.*, **79**, 4806 (1957)].

(49) W. E. Doering, quoted by H. L. Goering and R. W. Greiner.[30]

(50) As one of us (S.W.) has already pointed out elsewhere,[40] the same can be said of the isomerization of X in chlorobenzene without isotopic exchange with labeled *p*-nitrobenzoic acid, as reported by E. A. Braude, D. W. Turner and E. S. Waight, *Nature*, **173**, 863 (1954).

(51) (a) J. Meisenheimer, W. Schmidt and G. Schäfer, *Ann.*, **501**, 131 (1933); (b) A. G. Catchpole and E. D. Hughes, *J. Chem. Soc.*, 1 (1948).

There are strong indications that the peroxide rearrangement in question involves ionization[52] and Bartlett[53] and Goering[54] both formulated the rearrangement of 9-decalyl perbenzoate by way of ionization and internal return. The rearrangement reaction is extremely sensitive to solvent ionizing power.[52,55] Also, the addition of water to methanol as solvent raises rate substantially, but it does not affect markedly the proportion of solvolysis and rearrangement.[54] Substituents in the benzoate part of 9-decalyl perbenzoate lead to a Hammett ρ-value of 1.34.[53] Further, substitution in the migrating phenyl group of cumyl per-p-nitrobenzoate (XIX) leads to a ρ-value of -5.1 in acetic acid[55] compared to -3.7 for acetolysis of neophyl bromobenzenesulfonates XX.[25]

All of the observations support ionization to an ion pair such as XVII as the rate-determining step in rearrangement of 9-decalyl perbenzoate in methanol or acetic acid solvent. Therefore, we regard the O^{18}-result as an indication of preferred structure of the ion pair intermediate or intermediates. Even without covalent character to the cation–anion interaction it seems possible on electrostatic grounds that the greatest stability of intermediates is achieved when only one of the two negative oxygen atoms remains close to both the positive oxygen and positive carbon atoms throughout the sequence of events from starting material XVI to acylal XVIII.

It is interesting that in isomerization of 2-phenyl-1-propyl bromobenzenesulfonate[26] (XXI) and 2-anisyl-1-propyl toluenesulfonate[2b,3,26,27] (XXIII) during acetolysis, Denney[56] has observed quite different O^{18}-results. In the former case, the alkyl oxygen atom in the rearranged ester XXII is 57% the original alkyl oxygen in the 2-phenyl-1-propanol, and 43% one of the other oxygen atoms. With the 2-anisyl-1-propyl ester XXIII, the three oxygen atoms of the toluenesulfonate group have become equivalent in the rearranged ester XXIV.

(52) R. Criegee and R. Kaspar, *Ann.*, **560**, 127 (1948).
(53) P. D. Bartlett and J. L. Kice, THIS JOURNAL, **75**, 5591 (1953).
(54) H. L. Goering and A. C. Olson, *ibid.*, **75**, 5853 (1953).
(55) K. Nelson, unpublished work.
(56) (a) D. B. Denney, VIth Reaction Mechanism Conference, Swarthmore, Pa., Sept. 12, 1956; (b) D. B. Denney and B. Goldstein, THIS JOURNAL, **79**, 4948 (1957).

The arenesulfonate reactions are no more sensitive than the peroxide reactions to ionizing power of solvent. Therefore, the differences in O^{18}-results in the two kinds of reactions cannot be ascribed to a difference in the ionization character of the rate-determining step in the two cases. Rather, the preferred description in both the peroxide and arenesulfonate cases involves ionization to an ion pair. The differences in O^{18}-results should be discussed on the basis of the nature and behavior of the ion pairs in the several cases.

It is an important feature of the O^{18}-results with the arenesulfonates[56] that essentially complete equivalence of the three oxygen atoms is attained in isomerization of the 2-anisyl-1-propyl ester XXIII, but not in isomerization of the 2-phenyl-1-propyl analog XXI. This difference is in line with our interpretation,[3] based on kinetic evidence, that essentially only internal return occurs with the 2-phenyl-1-propyl ester XXI, but nearly all return with the 2-anisyl-1-propyl analog XXIII involves ion pairs which have attained the degree of interionic separation of the solvent-separated ion pair.

Experimental Part

3-p-Anisyl-2-butanols.—2-p-Anisylpropanal, b.p. 83–86° (0.4 mm.), was prepared in 67% yield essentially by the method of Sosa.[8] To the Grignard reagent from 64 g. (0.45 mole) of methyl iodide and 10.8 g. (0.45 gram atom) of magnesium, prepared in 400 ml. of ether, was added, as rapidly as possible, a solution of 50.5 g. (0.307 mole) of 2-p-anisylpropanal in 200 ml. of ether. The reaction mixture was decomposed with a saturated ammonium chloride solution. On distillation, the crude product yielded 47.0 g. (84%) of a mixture of *erythro*- and *threo*-3-p-anisyl-2-butanol, b.p. 85–90 (0.3 mm.). This mixture partially crystallized on standing; 47.0 g. of mixture deposited 21.4 g. of solid *erythro*-alcohol, m.p. 56–60°.

The liquid mother liquors were converted to the acid phthalate in the usual way with phthalic anhydride in pyridine at 90°. The resulting mixture of acid phthalates was subjected to repeated crystallization, first from benzene-Skellysolve F and finally from benzene. The *erythro*-acid phthalate (m.p. 137–138°) was the least soluble component and separated, when pure, as long needles. The *threo*-acid phthalate, when pure, crystallized from benzene as thick prisms, m.p. 123–124.5°. The separation of the last of the *erythro* material from the *threo*-acid phthalate was difficult and was greatly aided by a mechanical separation of the two kinds of crystals. The total recovery of 3-p-anisyl-2-butanol in the separation was 67%, and the results indicated that the *erythro/threo* ratio in the crude product was ca. 3.

Saponification of 1.0 g. (0.00305 mole) of *threo*-3-p-anisyl-2-butanol acid phthalate, m.p. 123–124.5°, by refluxing for 2 hours with 2.0 g. of sodium hydroxide in 20 ml. of 50% ethanol, yielded 0.55 g. (quantitative yield) of crude *threo*-

3-*p*-anisyl-2-butanol. Micro distillation at 20 mm., with the bath at 155°, gave material, n^{25}D 1.5161.

A solution of 54.6 mg. (0.302 millimole) of *threo*-3-*p*-anisyl-2-butanol and 59.1 mg. (0.318 millimole) of *p*-nitrobenzoyl chloride in 2 ml. of pyridine was heated at 100° for two minutes and diluted with water on cooling. The solid formed was separated by filtration and washed with water, 3 N hydrochloric acid, water, 10% potassium carbonate solution and again with water. After drying, there was obtained 72.1 mg. (72%) of crude *p*-nitrobenzoate, m.p. 82–84°, m.p. 84–85°, after one recrystallization from absolute ethanol.

Anal. Calcd. for $C_{18}H_{19}NO_5$: C, 65.64; H, 5.82. Found: C, 65.78; H, 5.75.

erythro-3-*p*-Anisyl-2-butanol was converted to *p*-nitrobenzoate exactly as was the *threo* isomer except that a large excess of *p*-nitrobenzoyl chloride was employed. From 50.6 mg. (0.281 mmole) of *erythro*-3-*p*-anisyl-2-butanol, m.p. 58–60°, 111.0 mg. (0.598 mmole) of *p*-nitrobenzoyl chloride and 2 ml. of pyridine was obtained 90.2 mg. (97%) of crude *p*-nitrobenzoate, m.p. 101–103°, m.p. 102.5–103.5° after one recrystallization from absolute alcohol.

Anal. Calcd. for $C_{18}H_{19}NO_5$: C, 65.64; H, 5.82. Found: C, 65.45; H, 5.85.

Optically Active 3-*p*-Anisyl-2-butyl Derivatives.—A solution of 45 g. (0.137 mole) of acid phthalate, m.p. *ca.* 118°, mostly *threo*, but containing some *erythro* diastereomer, and 61.8 g. (0.132 mole) of brucine in methyl ethyl ketone was prepared. On standing, this solution deposited a very insoluble white powder, m.p. 140° after one recrystallization from methyl ethyl ketone. Regeneration of the acid phthalate from this brucine salt gave rise to active *erythro*-3-*p*-anisyl-2-butyl acid phthalate, m.p. 109–112°, $[\alpha]^{22}$D −29.0° (CHCl₃, *c* 2.6).

The filtrate after separation of the insoluble white powder was diluted with a small amount of Skellysolve F and allowed to stand in the ice-box. Fine needle-like crystals slowly separated. Three recrystallizations from methyl ethyl ketone–Skellysolve F yielded 16.1 g. of material, m.p. 121–122°, the brucine salt of the acid phthalate of active *threo*-3-*p*-anisyl-2-butanol.

The saponification of 1.00 g. (0.00305 mole) of the (−)-*erythro*-3-*p*-anisyl-2-butyl acid phthalate, m.p. 109–112°, gave rise to 0.51 g. (93%) of active *erythro*-3-*p*-anisyl-2-butanol, m.p. 74–78° for crude material, m.p. 80–81.5° after one crystallization from Skellysolve F. The crude active *erythro*-alcohol was converted in 55% yield to (−)-*erythro*-3-*p*-anisyl-2-butyl *p*-toluenesulfonate, m.p. 70–72°, $[\alpha]^{25}$D −8.25° (CHCl₃, *c* 1.96). In acetolysis of this material, the rotation of the solvolysis solution increases in magnitude.

Regeneration of active *threo*-3-*p*-anisyl-2-butanol acid phthalate from 8.0 g. of the brucine salt, m.p. 121–122°, led to 4.0 g. of crude product which didn't crystallize. This acid phthalate was saponified to yield 1.61 g. (73% over-all) of crude liquid alcohol. This crude alcohol, on conversion to the *p*-bromobenzenesulfonate in the usual way, yielded (after recrystallization from Skellysolve F–benzene) 2.43 g. (66%) of (+)-*threo*-3-*p*-anisyl-2-butyl *p*-bromobenzenesulfonate, m.p. 84–86°, $[\alpha]^{25}$D +11.3° (CHCl₃, *c* 2.3). In

solvolysis in both acetic acid and ethanol the observed rotation (*ca.* 0.7°) tended to zero.

In another experiment, 2.0 g. of the brucine salt of the *threo*-3-*p*-anisyl-2-butyl acid phthalate gave rise to 0.44 g. (88%) of active *threo*-3-*p*-anisyl-2-butanol. This alcohol gave 0.51 g. (62%) of (−)-*threo*-3-*p*-anisyl-2-butyl *p*-toluenesulfonate, m.p. 69–70°, $[\alpha]^{25}$D −11.3° (CHCl₃, *c* 2.0).

Acetolysis of *dl*-*threo*-3-*p*-Anisyl-2-butyl *p*-Bromobenzenesulfonate.—A solution of 0.3968 g. (0.994 mmole) of *p*-bromobenzenesulfonate in 100 ml. of 0.01 M lithium acetate was kept at 25.0° for 118 hours (*ca.* 12 half-lives). The solvolysis mixture was then diluted with 1800 ml. of water and extracted twice with 500-ml. portions of ether. The ether extract was washed with 800 ml. of water, dried over potassium carbonate, concentrated to *ca.* 75 ml., and reduced with 1.0 g. of lithium aluminum hydride. The reduction mixture was worked up with water and aqueous sodium hydroxide solution. The ether solution was separated from basic salts by filtration. Subsequent distillation of the ether and micro-distillation of the residual material at 25 mm. with a pot temperature *ca.* 165° gave 0.1194 g. (66% as *threo*-3-*p*-anisyl-2-butanol) of crude product, n^{25}D 1.5198. The *p*-nitrobenzoate, from this material, prepared in 97% yield assuming the crude alcohol was 12% olefin,[57] had a crude m.p. 79–82°, m.p. 83–85° after simple washing with ethanol, undepressed on admixture of pure *threo*-3-*p*-anisyl-2-butyl *p*-nitrobenzoate.

An analogous acetolysis employing acetic acid without added lithium acetate gave 0.27 g. (75% as alcohol) of product, n^{25}D 1.5200, from 0.8017 g. (2.005 mmoles) of *p*-bromobenzenesulfonate in 200 ml. of acetic acid. This product gave rise to a *p*-nitrobenzoate (97% yield assuming 12% olefin in alcohol), crude m.p. 75–82°, m.p. 81–84° after one crystallization from ethanol.

Kinetics.—Anhydrous solvents were prepared and solvolyses were followed by the usual methods.[10]

For the polarimetric rate measurements,[7,16,18] solutions were prepared by dissolving a weighed sample of active material in 5.6 ml. of total solution. The solution was then filtered through a coarse sintered glass funnel into a jacketed 4-dm. side-filling polarimeter tube. The jacket of the polarimeter tube was maintained at 25.0° by circulation of oil from a constant temperature bath. The time required for thermal equilibrium in the polarimeter tube was minimized by keeping the solvents in the 25.0° bath until they were to be used. The initial polarimetric readings were taken from 3–20 minutes after preparation of the final kinetic solution.

With some solvents, the solutions tended to become colored and opaque, so experimental infinity readings could not be obtained. A zero infinity rotation was assumed in these cases, since the infinity polarimeter reading agreed exactly with the instrument zero point reading in solvents, such as 25% HCOOH–AcOH and formic acid, where infinity polarimeter readings were not interfered with.

LOS ANGELES 24, CALIFORNIA

---

(57) Rough estimate based on refractive index, using n^{25}D 1.5478 for the olefin, b.p. 120–135° (25 mm.), obtained by refluxing a mixture of acetic anhydride and the 2-*p*-anisyl-2-butanol from the action of *p*-anisylmagnesium bromide on 2-butanone.

35 | The Acet-
oxonium Ion

In Paper No. 35 Winstein and co-workers return to an old favorite problem and add evidence on the acetoxonium ion from preparative work and a survey of chemical behavior concerning the ketene acetal of *cis*-1,2-cyclohexanediol. References are given to the previous work on the acetoxonium ion. Though an excellent example of a symmetrical, mesomeric cationic intermedicate, we are not including it otherwise in this collection.

From: *J. Am. Chem. Soc.* **80**, 1247–54 (1958)

[Contribution from the Department of Chemistry of the University of California, Los Angeles]

The Role of Neighboring Groups in Replacement Reactions. XXIV.[1] The Acetoxy Group. Preparation and Reactions of the Ketene Acetal of cis-1,2-Cyclohexanediol (2-Methylene-cis-4,5-tetramethylenedioxolane)[2,3]

By R. M. Roberts, J. Corse, R. Boschan, D. Seymour and S. Winstein

Received September 10, 1957

As previously anticipated, the ketene acetal of *cis*-1,2-cyclohexanediol (2-methylene-*cis*-4,5-tetramethylenedioxolane) is a source of the *cis*-cyclohexeneacetoxonium ion. Therefore, knowledge about the behavior of this ketene acetal in solvolytic media contributes to the understanding of the mechanisms of transformations involving neighboring acetoxy group participation. In ethanol the ketene acetal is transformed smoothly to *cis*-cyclohexene ethyl orthoacetate, while in moist acetic acid the product is the monoacetate of *cis*-1,2-cyclohexanediol. In hot anhydrous acetic acid the ketene acetal is converted to *trans*-1,2-diacetoxycyclohexane. This is true whether the acetic acid is rendered anhydrous by drying with triacetyl borate, or whether it contains excess acetic anhydride. Also, the stereochemical outcome is the same whether or not the acetic acid solvent contains potassium acetate. In anhydrous acetic acid containing toluenesulfonic acid the ketene acetal is converted partly to *cis*-1,2-diacetoxycyclohexane and partly to *trans*-2-acetoxycyclohexyl *p*-toluenesulfonate. The latter substance has been isolated in *ca.* 70% yield. It seems likely that the reactions of the ketene acetal in acetic acid solvent commence with proton addition. The cyclohexene acetoxonium ion intermediate is presumed to react with nucleophilic agents uniformly more rapidly at C-3 than at C-1 or C-2. Thus, an orthodiacetate is the product of kinetic control of the reaction of the acetoxonium ion intermediate in neutral or basic anhydrous acetic acid solution. Under these conditions the orthodiacetate is converted to *trans*-1,2-diacetoxycyclohexane by ionization and eventual attack of acetate ion on C-1 or C-2. An acid-catalyzed path from orthodiacetate to *cis*-1,2-diacetoxycyclohexane is available, and possible mechanisms involving glycol oxygen ionization are suggested. The orthodiacetate reacts with toluenesulfonic acid to give *trans*-2-acetoxycyclohexyl *p*-toluenesulfonate, this product arising from attack of toluenesulfonate ion on C-1 or C-2 of the cyclohexene acetoxonium ion. The formation of acetoxy-toluenesulfonate in the present work fits in with the previously observed downward drift in the first-order rate constant for acetolysis of the acetoxy-toluenesulfonate as toluenesulfonic acid accumulates. Ion pair considerations explain the decrease of acetolysis rate by toluenesulfonic acid and not by diphenylguanidinium toluenesulfonate.

Previous work[2,4-8] on participation of the neighboring acetoxy group in nucleophilic substitution has shown that solvolysis of *trans*-2-acetoxycyclohexyl *p*-toluenesulfonate (I) proceeds by way of the *cis*-cyclohexeneacetoxonium ion V in solvents such as acetic acid or ethanol. As mentioned in connection with the previous work,[6] another likely source of the bridged ion V appears to be II, the ketene acetal of *cis*-1,2-cyclohexanediol (2-methylene-*cis* - 4,5 - tetramethylenedioxolane). Therefore, knowledge about the behavior of this ketene acetal in solvolytic media can contribute to our understanding of the mechanisms of transformations involving neighboring acetoxy group participation. In this paper are reported the results of a study of the preparation and behavior of the ketene acetal II. Preliminary results of the study of the analogous acetal of dichloroketene are also reported.

Ketene Acetal of cis-1,2-Cyclohexanediol.—The bromoacetal of *cis*-1,2-cyclohexanediol (X) was prepared by acid-catalyzed exchange between the *cis*-glycol and diethyl bromoacetal, the reaction

being driven to completion by distillation of the ethanol produced. Incidentally, the bromoacetal of *trans*-1,2-cyclohexanediol also was prepared, but no further work was carried out with it.

Elimination of hydrogen bromide from the *cis*-bromoacetal X was achieved readily by the use of potassium *t*-butoxide in McElvain's customary method of preparation of ketene acetals.[9] Like other ketene acetals,[9] the ketene acetal II proved to be an extremely reactive substance, difficult to work with. It polymerized readily at room temperature to a white solid, the polymerization being considerably accelerated by minute traces of acid. Distillation at reduced pressure caused spontaneous polymerization unless the entire distillation apparatus was previously treated to ensure a dry, neutral surface.

Behavior of Ketene Acetal in Ethanol and Moist Acetic Acid.—In absolute ethanol at room temperature the ketene acetal II was converted smoothly to *cis*-cyclohexene ethyl orthoacetate (III), while in moist acetic acid the product was a mixture of predominantly monoacetate IX with some diacetate VII of pure *cis*-1,2-cyclohexanediol. These results parallel the observation that the cyclohexeneacetoxonium ion V is diverted to isolable orthoester III by ethanol[6] and to the partially hydrolyzed orthoester VI by water in moist acetic acid during solvolysis of *trans*-2-acetoxycyclohexyl toluenesulfonate[5] (I) or in analogous reactions.[4] Tautomerization[4-6] of the partially hydrolyzed orthoester VI gives rise to *cis*-monoacetate IX, which is in turn partially acetylated to yield diacetate VII.

The diversion of cyclic acetoxonium ions such as V by even small amounts of water in acetic acid has been observed generally, and brief reviews of available examples were included in previous

(1) Paper XXIII, F. L. Scott, R. E. Glick and S. Winstein, *Experientia*, **13**, 183 (1957).

(2) Most of the material of this paper was reported in summary: (a) before the Organic Division of the American Chemical Society, St. Louis, Mo., Sept., 1948; (b) at the Eleventh National Organic Symposium, Madison, Wis., June 21, 1949, p. 65 of Abstracts; (c) at Montpellier, France, April 26, 1950 [*Bull. soc. chim.*, [5] **18**, 55C (1951)].

(3) The research reported in this manuscript was kindly supported by the Research Corporation and by the Eli Lilly Co.

(4) (a) S. Winstein and R. E. Buckles, This Journal, **64**, 2780, 2787 (1942); (b) S. Winstein and D. Seymour, *ibid.*, **68**, 119 (1946); (c) S. Winstein and R. M. Roberts, *ibid.*, **75**, 2297 (1953).

(5) S. Winstein, H. V. Hess and R. E. Buckles, *ibid.*, **64**, 2796 (1942).

(6) S. Winstein and R. E. Buckles, *ibid.*, **65**, 613 (1943).

(7) (a) S. Winstein, C. Hanson and E. Grunwald, *ibid.*, **70**, 812 (1948); (b) S. Winstein and R. Heck, *ibid.*, **74**, 5584 (1952).

(8) (a) S. Winstein, E. Grunwald and L. L. Ingraham, *ibid.*, **70**, 821 (1948); (b) S. Winstein, E. Grunwald, R. E. Buckles and C. Hanson, *ibid.*, **70**, 816 (1948).

(9) F. Beyerstedt and S. M. McElvain, *ibid.*, **58**, 529 (1936).

papers.[4a,c] An interesting example recently reported by Brutcher and Vara[10] involves the cyclopentadieneacetoxonium ion produced by the action of lead tetraacetate on cyclopentadiene in acetic acid solvent.

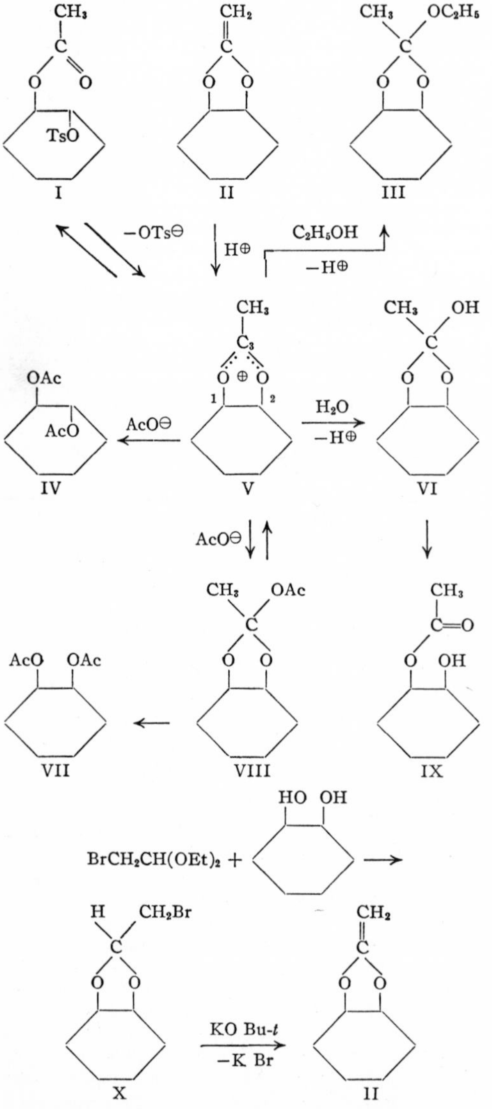

I   II   III

IV   V   VI

VII   VIII   IX

$$BrCH_2CH(OEt)_2 +$$

X   II

Behavior of Ketene Acetal in Anhydrous Acetic Acid.—The reaction of ketene acetal with anhydrous acetic acid was complicated by formation of higher molecular weight products unless the ketene acetal was added dropwise slowly to hot stirred acetic acid. A plausible explanation of the formation of higher molecular weight products involves electrophilic attack of the cyclohexene acetox-

(10) F. V. Brutcher, Jr., and F. J. Vara, THIS JOURNAL. **78**, 5695 (1956).

onium ion intermediate V on ketene acetal II as

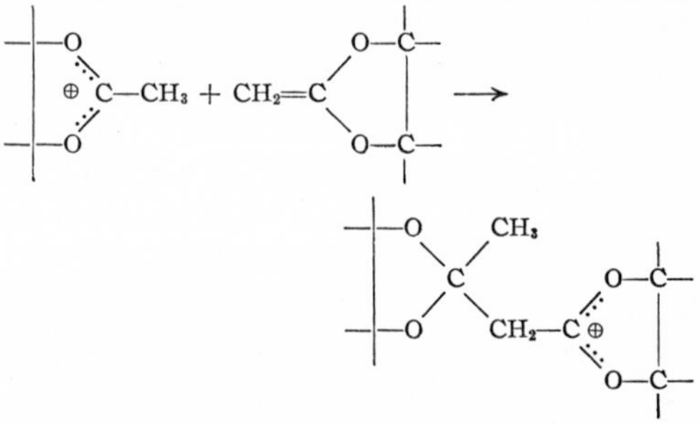

The proportion of such reaction is minimized by the slow addition of ketene acetal to hot acetic acid, each increment of ketene acetal tending to proceed to final stable product before the next increment is added.

The diacetoxycyclohexane product, whether obtained in poor yield or in high yield under the different reaction conditions employed, was quite pure trans-IV. This was true whether the acetic acid was rendered anhydrous by treatment with triacetyl borate, or whether it contained excess acetic anhydride. Also, the stereochemical outcome was the same whether the acetic acid solvent contained potassium acetate or not.

Anhydrous Acetic Acid Containing Toluenesulfonic Acid.—A somewhat surprising observation was that the addition of ketene acetal II to hot anhydrous acetic acid containing 0.1 of an equivalent of toluenesulfonic acid (0.1 N) gave rise to a diacetate product in 71% yield, evidently a cis–trans mixture, but quite predominantly trans-IV. Diacetate, again predominantly trans-IV, was obtained in lower yield, along with higher molecular weight material, when the ketene acetal was added to 0.1 equivalent of toluenesulfonic acid in anhydrous acetic acid at room temperature, and then the reaction mixture was heated.

When the ketene acetal II was added over a period of 45 minutes to hot anhydrous acetic acid containing ca. 0.5 equivalent of toluenesulfonic acid (ca. 0.45 N), and then the reaction mixture was held at 100° three hours longer, the diacetate produced was now predominantly cis-VII rather than trans-IV.

An important feature of the reactions of ketene acetal II with anhydrous acetic acid containing toluenesulfonic acid is that considerable ketene acetal II may be first converted to trans-2-acetoxycyclohexyl p-toluenesulfonate (I). Then this material solvolyzes under the conditions employed. The formation of the trans-acetoxy-toluenesulfonate I was proved by its isolation in 69% yield from an aliquot of the reaction mixture from addition of ketene acetal II to 0.5 equivalent of toluenesulfonic acid just after the addition was complete.

At 100°, the formation of acetoxy-toluenesulfonate I from ketene acetal II is rapid. According to titrations of the toluenesulfonic acid, this reaction is complete within several minutes. On the other hand, the solvolysis of the acetoxy-toluenesulfonate I is relatively slow.[7] Therefore, it was possible to determine by titration how much toluenesulfonic acid was consumed by ketene acetal II in the initial phase of the reaction. Also, it was possible to isolate the diacetate which was formed simultaneously with the acetoxy-toluenesulfonate before it became intermingled with diacetate produced in solvolysis of acetoxy-toluenesulfonate. In this way it was determined that 60% of the toluenesulfonic acid was consumed by the addition of ketene acetal II at 100° to 1 equivalent of 0.15 *N* toluenesulfonic acid. Also, the diacetate formed simultaneously with the acetoxy-toluenesulfonate was relatively pure *cis*-VII. When ketene acetal II was added at 100° to half an equivalent of 0.075 *N* toluenesulfonic acid, nearly quantitative consumption of the acid occurred.

Since the final *cis-* and *trans*-1,2-diacetoxycyclohexanes were stable toward toluenesulfonic acid at 100°, the ability of ketene acetal or derived intermediates to consume toluenesulfonic acid could be put to use in following reaction progress during treatment of ketene acetal in anhydrous acetic acid. In this way it was ascertained that no ketene acetal or toluenesulfonic acid-consuming intermediate survived by the end of the addition of ketene acetal at 100° to anhydrous acetic acid over a 3-minute period.

When ketene acetal II was added at room temperature over a 6-minute period to 0.07 equivalent of 0.01 *N* toluenesulfonic acid, there was visible evidence of reaction, the mixture tending to warm up. Treatment of aliquots of this solution kept at room temperature with aliquots of standard 0.1 *N* toluenesulfonic acid for a few minutes at 100° and back titration showed that the reaction solution contained more than 46% of toluenesulfonic acid-consuming material initially. Further, the concentration of acid-consuming material decreased with time, being negligible after *ca.* 800 minutes.

cis-Cyclohexene Ethyl Orthoacetate in Anhydrous Acetic Acid Containing Toluenesulfonic Acid.—The behavior of *cis*-cyclohexene ethyl orthoacetate (III) toward toluenesulfonic acid in anhydrous acetic acid also was examined for comparison with that of the ketene acetal II. Thus, from addition of orthoester III at 110° to 0.4 equivalent of 0.35 *N* toluenesulfonic acid was isolated a 56% yield of *trans*-2-acetoxycyclohexyl *p*-toluenesulfonate (I).

The orthoester III was added at room temperature to 1 equivalent of 0.098 *N* toluenesulfonic acid in acetic acid containing excess acetic anhydride, and the consumption of toluenesulfonic acid was followed by titration. There was consumed 63% of the equivalent amount of toluenesulfonic acid, this reaction being half complete after *ca.* 300 minutes.

Mechanistic Interpretation of the Reactions in Anhydrous Acetic Acid.—It seems likely that the reactions of the ketene acetal II in anhydrous acetic acid commence with proton addition. This gives rise to the cyclohexeneacetoxonium ion V. This intermediate may react with nucleophilic species at C-3 or at C-1 and C-2; the assumption that the rate of reaction is uniformly much greater at C–3 than at C-1 or C-2 leads to the most satisfactory interpretation of all of the various observations.

By reaction with either acetate ion or acetic acid, cyclohexeneacetoxonium ion V leads to orthodiacetate[5,7a] VIII. While this is the product from kinetic control of reaction product in dry, neutral or basic, acetic acid solution, the orthodiacetate VIII has only a short life at 100°. Under such conditions, the orthodiacetate VIII is quickly converted to *trans*-diacetate IV. For the mechanism of this conversion one may visualize reionization to the cyclohexeneacetoxonium ion V, which eventually undergoes nucleophilic attack at C-1 or C-2 to yield the *trans*-diacetate IV. Thus thermodynamic control of reaction product involves reaction at C-1 or C-2, in contrast with kinetic control which involves C-3.

According to the present interpretation, the orthodiacetate VIII is involved also in the acetolysis of *trans*-2-acetoxycyclohexyl toluenesulfonate[5,7,8] (I) and in the treatments of the corresponding bromide[4a] with silver acetate in glacial acetic acid. It is now clear that no extra acetate salt need be added in order to achieve an over-all stereochemical result leading to *trans*-diacetate IV since orthodiacetate VIII gives rise to *trans*-diacetate IV even in neutral anhydrous glacial acetic acid solution. Thus, it is not necessary to comment, as we did previously,[5] on the unusual effectiveness of acetate ion in the reaction mixtures using silver acetate and a bromide compared to that of acetate ion in reaction mixtures employing potassium acetate and the acetoxy-toluenesulfonate I.

The present results have a bearing on the interpretation of the reaction of orthoester III in acetic acid containing acetic anhydride.[6] It was previously[6] reported that *trans*-diacetate IV was obtained in the absence or presence of added potassium acetate. A possible role of acetic anhydride in causing the inversion reaction leading to *trans*-diacetate IV was visualized,[6] but this is no longer necessary. The results are explicable now on the basis of formation of orthodiacetate VIII from the orthoester III followed by its conversion to *trans*-diacetate IV.

Since *cis*-diacetate VII is obtained under acidic conditions in glacial acetic acid from reactions proceeding by way of the cyclohexeneacetoxonium ion V[5], it seems clear that there exists[5] an acid-catalyzed route from orthodiacetate VIII to *cis*-diacetate VII. The acid-catalyzed conversion of orthodiacetate VIII to *cis*-diacetate VII may be depicted as follows. Whereas ionization of the neutral orthodiacetate species XI involves essentially only the acetate group at C-3, ionization of the conjugate acid of XI may be visualized to involve also ionization of a glycol oxygen atom. This would give rise to the ionic species XIII. The latter may be expected to be a powerful acetylating agent, and *cis*-diacetate XIV may conceivably be formed by intramolecular acetylation of the free hydroxyl group

An alternative route from the ionic species XIII to *cis*-diacetate XIV may involve formation of acetic anhydride and the monoacetate of the *cis*-glycol XV, followed by acetylation of the monoacetate by the acetic anhydride to give *cis*-diacetate XIV. The envisioned possible reaction of XIII giving rise to acetic anhydride recalls the formation of acetic anhydride observed by Arens and Modderman[11] in the treatment of ethoxyacetylene with acetic acid. This reaction may be visualized to involve the addition product XVI and later the ion XVII, an analog of ion XIII.

$$CH_3 \quad OCOCH_3$$
$$\underset{\substack{| \\ O \quad O \\ >C_1 \!\!-\!\! C_2< \\ XI}}{C_3} \quad \overset{H\oplus}{\rightleftarrows}$$

$$\underset{\substack{C \\ \oplus \\ O \quad OH \\ >C\!\!-\!\!C< \\ XII}}{CH_3 \quad OCOCH_3} \quad \rightleftarrows \quad \underset{\substack{C \\ O \quad OH \\ >C\!\!-\!\!C< \\ XIII}}{CH_3\oplus \quad OCOCH_3}$$

$$\downarrow AcOH \quad\quad \downarrow -H\oplus$$
$$-H\oplus$$

$$Ac_2O + \underset{\substack{O\!\!-\!\!C=O \\ OH \\ >C\!\!-\!\!C< \\ XV}}{CH_3} \Big\} \rightarrow \underset{\substack{O\!\!-\!\!C=O \\ OCOCH_3 \\ >C\!\!-\!\!C< \\ XIV}}{CH_3}$$

It is apparent, when toluenesulfonic acid is the acid with which the glacial acetic acid is acidified, that the orthodiacetate VIII produces substantial amounts of trans-2-acetoxycyclohexyl toluenesulfonate (I). This product may be visualized to arise from attack of toluenesulfonate ion on C-1 or C-2 of the acetoxonium ion V, akin to the attack of chloride ion[6] or acetate ion.[4,5] Because this reaction competes with the acid-catalyzed conversion of orthodiacetate VIII to cis-diacetate VII, it is clear why treatment of ketene acetal II with glacial acetic acid containing toluenesulfonic acid gives rise to a mixture of cis-diacetate VII and trans-2-acetoxycyclohexyl toluenesulfonate (I). In runs in which the latter material is allowed to solvolyze subsequent to its formation, the final diacetate includes the diacetate from solvolysis of the initially formed acetoxy-toluenesulfonate I.

The peculiar results obtained when ketene acetal II is added to 0.1 equivalent of toluenesulfonic acid in anhydrous acetic acid now become understandable. Because of the large excess of ketene acetal, the toluenesulfonic acid concentration is reduced to such a low figure while the bulk of the ketene acetal is being added, that it is proceeding to trans-diacetate IV by the mechanism which does not involve strong acid catalysis. Eventually, the acetoxy-toluenesulfonate I does solvolyze to give mainly cis-diacetate VII, and a mixed diacetate which is mainly trans is finally obtained.

The situation that prevails in the treatment of orthoester III with toluenesulfonic acid in anhydrous acetic acid is similar to that which obtains for the ketene acetal II. Considerable acetoxy-toluenesulfonate I is obtained, presumably by way

(11) Proc. Koninklijke Nederlandse Akademie van Wetenschappen, **53**, No. 8, 1 (1950).

of the orthodiacetate VIII. In the previous work in which orthoester III was treated with toluenesulfonic acid in acetic acid, the acetoxy-toluenesulfonate I was allowed to solvolyze.[6]

$$HC\equiv COC_2H_5 \xrightarrow{AcOH} \underset{\substack{| \\ OCOCH_3 \\ XVI}}{H_2C=C}\overset{OC_2H_5}{} \xrightarrow{H\oplus}$$

$$\left[\underset{\substack{| \\ OCOCH_3 \\ }}{CH_3\!\!-\!\!C}\overset{OC_2H_5}{\underset{\oplus}{}}\right] \rightarrow CH_3C\overset{OC_2H_5}{\underset{O}{}} + Ac_2O$$
$$XVII$$

The observed formation of acetoxy-toluenesulfonate I in the present work fits in with the previous kinetic work[7a] on the acetolysis of the acetoxy-toluenesulfonate I. In solvolysis of this material in the absence of potassium acetate, first-order acetolysis rate constants drifted down to approximately one-third the initial value as toluenesulfonic acid accumulated.[7a] This was visualized as due to a reaction between some intermediate and toluenesulfonic acid which regenerated acetoxy-toluenesulfonate I. While we have now actually observed this reaction which regenerates the acetoxy-toluenesulfonate I, one feature of the observed kinetics still requires explanation. This feature is that diphenylguanidinium toluenesulfonate was not effective in reducing the first-order rate of solvolysis of the acetoxy-toluenesulfonate I, while toluenesulfonic acid was. If trans-diacetate formation involves the acetoxonium ion V, which also gives rise to the acetoxy-toluenesulfonate I, it is still not clear why toluenesulfonate ion is more effective in competition for the acetoxonium ion V when it is supplied as toluenesulfonic acid rather than as a toluenesulfonate salt. It seems likely that the difficulty here is that the reactions being observed are chiefly those of ion pairs rather than dissociated ions.[12]

Even though the matter needs actual study, we can sketch the manner in which the competition between toluenesulfonate ion and acetate ion (or acetic acid) for the acetoxonium ion V may be controlled by ion pair considerations. In view of the evidence[12] on the nature of the intermediates in acetolysis of other systems, it seems logical that most of the conversion of orthodiacetate XI to trans-diacetate XIX occurs by way of an acetoxonium acetate ion pair XVIII. Such an intermediate can return to orthodiacetate XI or, after some reorientation of the two component ions, it can also give rise to trans-diacetate XIX.

In the reaction between orthodiacetate XI with toluenesulfonic acid, the ionic species XIII produced by glycol oxygen ionization is better described as the ion pair XX, while the acetoxonium ion V produced by acetate ionization is better described as the acetoxonium toluenesulfonate ion pair XXI. The latter, after attaining the proper

(12) See, e.g., (a) S. Winstein, E. Clippinger, A. H. Fainberg and G. C. Robinson, This Journal, **76**, 2597 (1954); Chemistry & Industry, 664 (1954); (b) S. Winstein, E. Clippinger, A. H. Fainberg, R. Heck and G. C. Robinson, This Journal, **78**, 328 (1956); (c) S. Winstein and G. C. Robinson, ibid., **80**, 169 (1958).

orientation of the component ions, can give rise to *trans*-acetoxy-toluenesulfonate XXII.

On the above basis, the acetoxonium ion V is produced from orthodiacetate XI as the acetate ion pair XVIII in neutral or basic acetic acid solution, but as a toluenesulfonate ion pair XXI under conditions where toluenesulfonic acid-promoted reactions of orthodiacetate XI have become predominant. If conversion of acetate ion pair XVIII to toluenesulfonate ion pair XXI by exchange,[12] followed by its conversion to acetoxy-toluenesulfonate XXII, does not compete with formation of *trans*-diacetate XIX from acetate ion pair XVIII, the ineffectiveness of added toluenesulfonate salt compared to acid in producing kinetic disturbances[7a] in acetolysis of acetoxy-toluenesulfonate I is understandable.

Dichloroketene Acetal of *cis*-1,2-Cyclohexanediol.—The dichloroketene acetal of cyclohexanediol (2-dichloromethylene-*cis*-4,5-tetramethylene-1,3-dioxolane, XXIV) was anticipated to be more favorable for actual isolation of derivatives akin to the orthodiacetate VIII. Therefore, the dichloroketene acetal XXIV was prepared. Preliminary work with this material was promising, but the work has remained interrupted for some time.

Acid-catalyzed reaction of chloral with *cis*-1,2-cyclohexanediol gave rise to the chloral acetal XXIII, just as in the analogous reaction between chloral and ethylene glycol.[13] Dehydrochlorination of the chloral acetal XXIII with potassium *t*-butoxide yielded the desired dichloroketene acetal[14] XXIV. This material, a crystalline solid, was sensitive to acids, but in carefully treated glassware it kept better than the unchlorinated ketene acetal II. For the ethylene glycol derivatives, McElvain

(13) S. M. McElvain and M. J. Curry, This Journal, **70**, 3781 (1948).

(14) This material has also been prepared by A. Scattergood and W. Marcy (private communication from A. Scattergood, Sept., 1949).

and Curry[13] have reported greater stability of the dichloroketene acetal.

Experimental

trans-**2-Hydroxycyclohexyl *p*-toluenesulfonate** was prepared from cyclohexene by a modification of the method previously used by Criegee and Stanger.[15] A 90-g. (0.88 mole) quantity of acetic anhydride was added to a solution of 40 g. (0.21 mole) of *p*-toluenesulfonic acid monohydrate in 24.0 g. of 30% hydrogen peroxide solution. During the addition of the acetic anhydride the temperature was kept below 40° with the aid of an ice-bath. After addition of the acetic anhydride, 16.8 g. (0.205 mole) of cyclohexene was added, the temperature still being kept under 40°. After the addition of cyclohexene was complete, the reaction mixture was stirred for three hours at room temperature, and then it was poured into *ca.* 300 ml. of cold water. The oil which originally formed crystallized readily. The crystals were filtered to yield 33 g. (57%) of product, m.p. 93–95°.

trans-**2-Acetoxycyclohexyl-*p*-toluenesulfonate** was prepared by acetylation of *trans*-2-hydroxycyclohexyl toluenesulfonate.[5]

cis- **and *trans*-1,2-Cyclohexanediols.**—Some of the *cis*-glycol was prepared by solvolysis of *trans*-2-acetoxycyclohexyl *p*-toluenesulfonate in moist acetic acid containing potassium acetate.[5] Some of the *trans*-glycol was prepared by acid-catalyzed opening of cyclohexene oxide with water.[16] Large amounts of the glycols were prepared by separation of the glycol mixture obtained by hydrogenation of catechol over Raney nickel catalyst at 1800 lb. pressure and 175°. The separation of the glycols was achieved by a procedure very similar to that of Derx,[17] the *cis*-glycol being converted to the acetonide. Steam distillation of the ketal and subsequent hydrolysis gave rise to *cis*-glycol, m.p. 97°. From the residue remaining after steam distillation of the ketal was obtained the *trans*-glycol by chloroform extraction, m.p. 104° after recrystallization.

2-Bromomethyl-*cis*-4,5-tetramethylene-1,3-dioxolane.— A 32.8-g. (0.282 mole) quantity of *cis*-1,2-cyclohexanediol, 60.0 g. (0.305 mole) of diethyl bromoacetal and a crystal of *p*-toluenesulfonic acid monohydrate were heated in a bath at 100–110° (173 mm.) with two Dry Ice–ethanol traps to collect the distillate. During 2.5 hours, 32.5 cc. (99%) of ethanol was collected in the first trap. The reaction mix-

(15) R. Criegee and H. Stanger, *Ber.*, **69B**, 2753 (1936).

(16) S. Winstein, This Journal, **64**, 2792 (1942).

(17) H. G. Derx, *Rec. trav. chim.*, **41**, 312 (1922).

ture was allowed to cool; then it was shaken with *ca.* 0.5 g. of calcium carbonate for 20–30 minutes and allowed to stand overnight. The calcium carbonate was filtered off, and the filtrate was fractionally distilled. Besides 2.7 g. of forerun, b.p. 25–90° (7 mm.), there was collected 61.1 g. (98%) of main fraction, b.p. 93° (3.2 mm.) −87° (2.0 mm.), n^{25}D 1.5012, n^{20}D 1.5032, d^{25}_4 1.4343, d^{20}_4 1.4405, MRD 45.80 (calcd.), 45.43 (25°), 45.41 (20°).

Anal. Calcd. for $C_8H_{13}O_2Br$: C, 43.46; H, 5.92. Found: C, 43.55; H, 5.92.

2-Bromomethyl-*trans*-4,5-tetramethylene-1,3-dioxolane. —A solution of 38.5 g. (0.33 mole) of *trans*-1,2-cyclohexanediol and 67 g. of bromoacetal was heated with a small crystal of *p*-toluenesulfonic acid at 172 mm. in an oil-bath at 108° for 2.5 hours. There was recovered 29 ml. of ethanol in a Dry Ice trap (theory 38 ml.). The residue in the reaction flask was poured into cold potassium carbonate solution and extracted with ether. There was obtained 48.6 g. of product, b.p. 108–113° (3–5 mm.). Redistillation gave rise to 45.6 g. (61.9%) of material, b.p. 107–108° (6 mm.), d^{25}_4 1.434, n^{25}D 1.5056, MRD 45.78 (calcd. 45.80).

***cis*-2-Methylene-4,5-tetramethylenedioxolane.**—In a 200-cc. round-bottomed flask was placed 105 g. (133 cc.) of dry *t*-butyl alcohol and 6 g. (0.154 g. atom) of clean potassium metal. The mixture was refluxed for two hours to dissolve the potassium and allowed to stand overnight. To this solution was added 27.8 g. (0.126 mole) of the bromoacetal of *cis*-1,2-cyclohexanediol and several boiling chips. An 8-cm. Vigreux column, insulated with glass wool, was connected, and the reaction mixture was heated in an oil-bath at 120°. Potassium bromide began to precipitate in *ca.* 3 minutes, and after 10 minutes the solvent began to distil at 82–85°. After 50 minutes the bulk of the *t*-butyl alcohol had distilled, and the distillation rate was very slow. The pressure was gradually lowered to 29.5 mm. and the main fraction of ketene acetal, 15.6 g. (88.5%), was collected, b.p. 99° (29.5 mm.), d^{25}_4 1.0226, n^{25}D 1.4720, MRD 38.39 (calcd. 37.57). The material polymerized rapidly on the refractometer plates, the index increasing. The above n^{25}D is the lowest of several observed.

Anal. Calcd. for $C_8H_{12}O_2$: C, 68.54; H, 8.63. Found: C, 67.99; H, 8.95.

In order to prevent polymerization of the ketene acetal during its isolation, all the apparatus used in this preparation was soaked in ammonium hydroxide solution for an hour or more, rinsed with water, and dried thoroughly before use. The ketene acetal tended to polymerize on standing, but it could be kept for periods of several weeks at Dry Ice temperatures in carefully treated glassware. Usually, the material was prepared immediately before use.

Reaction of Ketene Acetal with Anhydrous Ethanol.—In test-tube experiments on the addition of ketene acetal to absolute ethanol, a white precipitate, presumably polymeric material, was observed. Therefore, the ketene acetal was added dropwise to a large volume of stirred ethanol in order to minimize polymerization.

To 200 cc. of high-grade absolute ethanol in a 500-cc. round-bottomed flask at room temperature was added 13.8 g. (0.099 mole) of ketene acetal dropwise with stirring over a period of 25 minutes. Stirring was continued for an hour more, and the mixture was distilled through an efficient column. After the ethanol was removed at atmospheric pressure, the residue was distilled at 10 mm. to yield 15.2 g. (83%) of a colorless liquid; b.p. 94° (10 mm.), n^{25}D 1.4470 (reported[5] for cyclohexene ethyl orthoacetate, b.p. 92–93° (10 mm.), n^{25}D 1.4479–1.4489).

Reaction of Ketene Acetal with Moist Acetic Acid.—A 15.7-g. (0.112 mole) quantity of ketene acetal was added dropwise with stirring over a period of 22 minutes to 100 ml. of acetic acid, m.p. 16.1°, to which 3.1 ml. of water had been added (1.5 moles of water per mole of ketene acetal). The solution became quite warm during the addition of the ketene acetal. After the addition was complete, the solution was allowed to stand at room temperature for 2 hours. Then the reaction mixture was filtered from a small amount of polymer and distilled through a 20-cm. Vigreux column until 85 cc. of acetic acid had been collected. The concentrated reaction mixture was then neutralized with 32 cc. of nearly saturated potassium carbonate solution. An oily layer separated which was extracted with three portions of ether (total 250 cc.). The ether extract was dried over potassium carbonate overnight, and the ether was removed

through a Vigreux column on a steam-bath. The residue was transferred to a small flask and distilled through a 40-cm. glass-sleeve column, 13.4 g. of distillate, b.p. 116–118° (12.5 mm.), n^{25}D 1.4624, being obtained. On the basis of reported refractive indices of the pure and mixed diacetate and monoacetate of *cis*-1,2-cyclohexanediol,[4a,6] the above product corresponds to more than 84 mole % monoacetate. On this basis, the calculated yield is 72.5%.

Saponification of 1 cc. of the ester product yielded 0.67 g. (*ca.* 95%) of *cis*-cyclohexanediol, m.p. 94–98°, m.p. after recrystallization from carbon tetrachloride 94–96.5°, m.p. 94.5–97° after a second recrystallization. The mixed m.p. taken with an authentic sample of *cis*-1,2-cyclohexanediol was 94–97°; the mixed m.p. taken with a sample of *trans*-1,2-cyclohexanediol was 69–75°.

Reaction of Ketene Acetal with Anhydrous Acetic Acid.— The addition of a few drops of ketene acetal to dry acetic acid at room temperature caused formation of some white precipitate, presumably polymeric material. The addition of ketene acetal dropwise to hot acetic acid gave much less of undesired side reaction. At 100°, the over-all reaction of ketene acetal with dry acetic acid to yield diacetate was quite rapid. An 0.0148-mole quantity of ketene acetal was added over a period of 3 minutes at 100° to 100 ml. of acetic acid dried with triacetyl borate[18] or containing excess acetic anhydride. Then the mixture was cooled and aliquots were added to standard toluenesulfonic acid in glacial acetic acid and heated 5 minutes at 100°. Back titration of the toluenesulfonic acid showed no consumption of acid by the ketene acetal reaction mixture.

In a 500-cc. 3-necked round-bottomed flask equipped with a stirrer and reflux condenser was placed 100 cc. of anhydrous acetic acid which was dried over triacetyl borate. The acetic acid was heated to 100° by an oil-bath kept at 105–110°, and 14.4 g. (0.103 mole) of ketene acetal was added dropwise to the stirred solution so that the drops fell freely into the stirred acetic acid. After the addition of ketene acetal, which required 40 minutes, the mixture was kept at 105–110° in the oil-bath for 2.5 hours and allowed to stand overnight. Distillation through a 40-cm. glass-sleeve column gave rise to 14.4 g. (70%) of diacetate, b.p. 120–121° (12 mm.), n^{25}D 1.4456 (reported[4a] for *trans*-1,2-diacetoxycyclohexane, b.p. 120° (12 mm.), n^{25}D 1.4457).

A one-ml. sample of the diacetate was saponified to yield 0.7 g. of crude glycol, m.p. 84–94°, m.p. 90–99° when mixed with *trans*-glycol, m.p. 62–78° when mixed with *cis*-glycol. One recrystallization from carbon tetrachloride yielded 0.50 g. of white crystals, m.p. 102–104°, m.p. 101–104° when mixed with *trans*-glycol, m.p. 71–79° when mixed with *cis*-glycol.

Similar results were obtained when acetic acid dried with excess acetic anhydride was employed instead of the material dried with triacetyl borate.

When the addition of ketene acetal to anhydrous acetic acid was performed in 10 minutes at room temperature, and then the reaction mixture was refluxed for 2 hours, only an 18.5% yield of *trans*-diacetate was obtained. A large nonvolatile residue remained after the distillation. When the ketene acetal was added in 25 minutes at room temperature to the anhydrous acetic acid *ca.* 1.5 *M* in potassium acetate, and then the reaction mixture was refluxed 2 hours, a 26% yield of *trans*-diacetate was obtained.

Reaction of Ketene Acetal with Anhydrous Acetic Acid Containing Toluenesulfonic Acid.—To anhydrous acetic acid (m.p. 16.2°) was added 1.9 g. (0.01 mole) of *p*-toluenesulfonic acid monohydrate and 6 cc. of acetic anhydride (calcd. 2.0 cc. required), and the solution was refluxed for 2 hours and allowed to cool. The solution was heated in an oil-bath at 110° with stirring while 14.7 g. (0.105 mole) of ketene acetal was added dropwise over a period of 45 minutes. The solution was kept at 100° for 5 hours after the addition and allowed to stand overnight. Then 1.96 g. (0.02 mole) of anhydrous potassium acetate was added and the mixture was refluxed for 2 hours and allowed to cool. The solution was added to 500 cc. of water and worked up in the usual way. Distillation gave rise to 14.8 g. (71%) of diacetate, b.p. 118° (12.2 mm.), n^{25}D 1.4460.

Saponification of 1 cc. of the ester product yielded 0.55 g. of crude glycol, m.p. 70–90°, mixed m.p. with *cis*-glycol 62–73°, mixed m.p. with *trans*-glycol 75–97°. One recrys-

(18) W. C. Eichelberger and V. K. LaMer, THIS JOURNAL, **55**, 3633 (1933).

tallization from carbon tetrachloride yielded 0.43 g. of white crystals, m.p. 92–100°, mixed m.p. with *cis*-glycol 73–76°, mixed m.p. with *trans*-glycol 92–102°.

When the above addition of ketene acetal to 0.1 equivalent of toluenesulfonic acid in anhydrous acetic acid was repeated with initially 0.045 *N* toluenesulfonic acid instead of 0.1 *N*, and with the addition carried out at room temperature, after which the mixture was held 3 hours at *ca.* 105°, a 42% yield of diacetate was obtained. Considerable non-volatile residue also was observed. The diacetate was again predominantly *trans*.

A 9.5-g. (0.05 mole) quantity of toluenesulfonic acid monohydrate was added to 100 cc. of acetic acid (m.p. 16.2°). To this solution was added 10.0 ml. of acetic anhydride, and the mixture was refluxed for 2 hours. A 15.6-g. (0.11 mole) quantity of ketene acetal was added dropwise to the acetic acid solution at 100° over a period of 45 minutes. A 10-ml. sample of the mixture was removed and added to 100 cc. of water. The remainder of the reaction mixture was kept at 100° for *ca.* 3 hours longer; then it was poured into 500 cc. of water and worked up in the usual way. Distillation through a 40-cm. glass-sleeve column gave 0.5 g. of forerun, 6.3 g. of diacetate, b.p. 118–119° (12 mm.), n^{25}D 1.4480, and 3.3 g. more, n^{25}D 1.4450, collected after some decomposition of pot residue set in. The combined yield of diacetate, 9.6 g., was 48%.

Saponification of 1 cc. of the main fraction of diacetate gave rise to an oil which crystallized slowly when seeded with a tiny crystal of *cis*-1,2-cyclohexanediol. This yielded 0.65 g. of crystals, m.p. 50–68°. After one recrystallization from 10 cc. of carbon tetrachloride, there was obtained 0.3 g. of white crystals, m.p. 83–87°, mixed m.p. with *cis*-glycol 86–93°, mixed m.p. with *trans*-glycol 71–74°. One more recrystallization from 8 cc. of carbon tetrachloride yielded *ca.* 0.2 g. of crystals, m.p. 90–92°, mixed m.p. with *cis*-glycol 93–96°, mixed m.p. with *trans*-glycol 70–74°.

The 10-ml. sample which was removed after the ketene acetal was added to the acetic acid and poured into 100 cc. of water was extracted with ether. The ether extract was washed with potassium carbonate solution, then with water, and dried over anhydrous potassium carbonate. The ether was removed and 15 cc. of petroleum ether (b.p. 30–60°) was added. This gave rise to 0.80 g. (69%) of yellow crystals, m.p. 69–74°. One recrystallization yielded 0.6 g. of light yellow crystals, m.p. 76–77.5°, mixed m.p. (with authentic *trans*-2-acetoxycyclohexyl *p*-toluenesulfonate) 76–78.5°.

In a run similar to the one described above, 0.126 mole of ketene acetal was added over 65 minutes at 80° to a solution of 0.06 mole of toluenesulfonic acid in 132 ml. of anhydrous acetic acid (*ca.* 0.45 *N* acid). This solution was maintained 20 more minutes at 80°, and then it was worked up to yield 8.66 g. (46%) of *trans*-2-acetoxycyclohexyl *p*-toluenesulfonate and 5.36 g. (21%) of predominantly *cis*-diacetate.

A 0.0148-mole quantity of ketene acetal was added to 100 ml. of 0.149 *N* toluenesulfonic acid in dry acetic acid at 100° over a period of 5 minutes. The reaction mixture was heated and stirred an additional 3 minutes and cooled. Titration of 5-ml. aliquots of this solution with 0.1000 *N* sodium acetate in acetic acid showed that 0.0090 equivalent (60%) of *p*-toluenesulfonic acid was consumed.

The rest of the above reaction mixture was poured into excess potassium bicarbonate solution and extracted with ether. Evaporation of the ether from the dried ether extract and addition of petroleum ether gave a crystalline product. After recrystallization there was obtained 2.65 g. (31%) of *trans*-2-acetoxycyclohexyl *p*-toluenesulfonate, m.p. 76–78°, mixed m.p. 76–77°.

By distillation of the mother liquors from the crystallization of the acetoxycyclohexyl toluenesulfonate there was obtained 0.53 g. of diacetate, b.p. 97–107° (5–6 mm.), as well as an 0.85 g. of non-volatile residue (probably acetoxycyclohexyl toluenesulfonate). Saponification of the diacetate gave rise to 0.21 g. of sublimed glycol, recrystallization of which yielded 0.14 g. of *cis*-glycol, m.p. 92.5–93°, mixed m.p. with *cis*-glycol 94.8–95.2°, mixed m.p. with *trans*-glycol 74.5–75.8°.

An 0.0148-mole quantity of ketene acetal was added over a 3.3-minute period to 100 ml. of 0.0752 *N* *p*-toluenesulfonic acid in dry acetic acid at 100°. Titration of 5-ml. aliquots of the reaction mixture indicated that at least 98% of the toluenesulfonic acid had been consumed. When the ketene acetal was added to 0.297 *N* toluenesulfonic acid solution over a period of 4.5 minutes at 100°, 22% of the acid was consumed, 44% of the ketene acetal reacting with acid.

A 0.0148 mole quantity of ketene acetal was added at room temperature over a 6-minute period to 100 ml. of anhydrous acetic acid 0.01 *N* in toluenesulfonic acid. The reaction mixture warmed up perceptibly during the addition. From time to time, 5-ml. aliquots were added to 5 ml. of 0.1 *N* toluenesulfonic acid and heated 6–7 minutes at 100° to allow toluenesulfonic acid to be consumed. Back titration with standard diphenylguanidinium acetate solution showed that 46% of the equivalent amount of acid was consumed by an aliquot 3 minutes after the addition of ketene acetal was completed. However, less and less acid was consumed by aliquots of the ketene acetal solution as it stood at room temperature. The half-life of reactive species was roughly 150 minutes. The concentration of reactive species was inappreciable at 829 minutes.

Reaction of *cis*-Cyclohexene Ethyl Orthoacetate with Anhydrous Acetic Acid Containing Toluenesulfonic Acid.—To 25 cc. of acetic acid (m.p. 16.2°) was added 5 cc. of acetic anhydride and 2.0 g. (0.0105 mole) of *p*-toluenesulfonic acid monohydrate. The mixture was refluxed for two hours and allowed to stand overnight. To this solution, heated in an oil-bath at 110°, was added 4.65 g. (0.0250 mole) of cyclohexene ethyl orthoacetate in several portions with swirling. The solution was kept in the bath at 110° for 20 minutes, then cooled and poured into 250 cc. of water. This aqueous solution was extracted with two 200-cc. portions of ether. The ether solution was washed with potassium carbonate solution and dried over anhydrous potassium carbonate. The ether was removed on the steam-bath and 50 cc. of petroleum ether, b.p. 60–72°, was added. From this mixture there was obtained 1.83 g. (56%) of crystals, m.p. 75–77°, m.p. 75–78° when mixed with an authentic sample of *trans*-2-acetoxycyclohexyl *p*-toluenesulfonate.

A 1.81-g. (0.00971 mole) quantity of orthoester was added at room temperature to 100 ml. of 0.0978 *N* toluenesulfonic acid in anhydrous acetic acid. Aliquots (5 ml.) of this solution were titrated with 0.0996 *N* diphenylguanidinium acetate. The titration data showed that 63% of the equivalent amount of toluenesulfonic acid was consumed, the half-time for the reaction being roughly 300 minutes.

Stability of Diacetoxycyclohexanes.—Samples of *cis*- and *trans*-1,2-diacetoxycyclohexane were held at 100–105° for 100 hours in solution with 0.5 *N* toluenesulfonic acid in dry acetic acid. The diacetates were then recovered in 91–97% yields. Saponification of the diacetates gave rise to essentially pure glycols. Solutions of the diacetates with 0.1 *N* toluenesulfonic acid in dry acetic acid at 75° were followed for acid consumption up to elapsed times of 147 hours. No detectable acid consumption was observed.

2-Trichloromethyl-*cis*-4,5-tetramethylene-1,3-dioxolane. —To a solution of 10.0 g. (0.0863 mole) of *cis*-1,2-cyclohexanediol and 25.0 g. (0.170 mole) of freshly distilled chloral in 75 cc. of anhydrous benzene was added three drops of concd. sulfuric acid. The mixture was refluxed for four days with an attached water trap, 3.33 g. of an aqueous fraction being collected. The benzene solution was poured into 300 cc. of saturated sodium bicarbonate solution and extracted with four portions of ether (*ca.* 300 cc.). The dried ether extract was distilled, the last traces of solvent being removed on an aspirator. There remained 19.14 g. of a yellow liquid, to which 10 cc. of petroleum ether, b.p. 30–60°, was added, and the solution was cooled in Dry Ice. A 3.91-g. quantity of white crystals, m.p. 33.5–35.0°, was filtered off. An additional 5.20 g. of crystals were obtained in a similar fashion from the mother liquor to bring the total yield of acetal to 43%. After another recrystallization the analytical sample melted at 34.5–35.0°.

Anal. Calcd. for $C_8H_{11}O_2Cl_3$: C, 39.12; H, 4.52. Found: C, 38.94; H, 4.65.

A liquid remained after evaporation of solvent from the filtrate, which yielded 3.7 g. of colorless liquid, b.p. 95° (2 mm.), on distillation.

Anal. Calcd. for $C_8H_{11}O_2Cl_3$: C, 39.12; H, 4.52. Found: C, 41.57; H, 5.05.

The liquid is probably acetal contaminated with *cis*-cyclohexanediol, so, including this liquid, the total yield of acetal is 60%.

2-Dichloromethylene-*cis*-4,5-tetramethylene-1,3-dioxolane.—To a solution of 1.2 g. (0.031 g. atom) of freshly trimmed potassium metal in *ca.* 40 cc. of anhydrous *t*-butyl alcohol was added 2.96 g. (0.012 mole) of the acetal described above, and the mixture was refluxed for 80 minutes. Part of the *t*-butyl alcohol was removed by reduced pressure distillation, but the brown suspension bumped badly. The solution was diluted with anhydrous ether, but it could not be filtered through a sintered glass funnel. After the solution was distilled to dryness at reduced pressure and more ether was added, the brown suspension could be filtered through a fine sintered glass filter. The ether was removed from the clear filtrate by distillation, and *ca.* 10 cc. of petroleum ether was added to the residue. The mixture was cooled in Dry Ice and filtered to yield 1.20 g. (48%) of white crystals, m.p. 55.5–56.0°, m.p. 56.5–57.0° after two recrystallizations from petroleum ether. The sample was dried in a vacuum desiccator over paraffin and 85% potassium hydroxide.

Anal. Calcd. for $C_8H_{10}O_2Cl_2$: C, 45.96; H, 4.82. Found: C, 45.95; H, 4.87.

Los Angeles 24, Calif.

36 | Tertiary Cyclopropyl-carbinols

Hart and Sandri find that the effects of cyclopropyl groups in promoting ionization at adjacent carbon are cumulative and that the kinetically determined product of solvolysis of isopropyldicyclopropylcarbinyl *p*-nitrobenzoate is unrearranged. They discuss the multiple activation by the cyclopropyl groups in terms of a delocalization less specific than that of Roberts' bicyclobutonium ion. It was subsequently found[1] that the third cyclopropyl group in tricyclopropylmethyl benzoate contributes further great activation in solvolysis, this ester undergoing alkyl-oxygen fission in 95% aqueous dioxane at 25° to unrearranged tricyclopropylcarbinol, which in turn can be hydrogenolyzed to tricyclopropylmethane.

[1] H. Hart and P. A. Law, *J. Am. Chem. Soc.* **84**, 2462 (1962).

From: *J. Am. Chem. Soc.* **81**, 320–26 (1959)

[Contribution from the Kedzie Chemical Laboratory, Michigan State University]

The Solvolysis of *p*-Nitrobenzoates of Certain Cyclopropylcarbinols[1,2]

By Harold Hart and Joseph M. Sandri[3]

Received June 26, 1958

The *p*-nitrobenzoates of carbinols Ia–Va were prepared and solvolyzed in various concentrations of aqueous or methanolic dioxane at several temperatures. The relative first-order rates (Vb = 1) in 80% aqueous dioxane at 60° were: IVb, 60.7; IIIb, 246; Ib, 23,500; IIb, 124,000. Alkyl–oxygen fission was demonstrated, and a second cyclopropyl group on the carbonium carbon atom was nearly as effective as the first in enhancing the solvolysis rate. The solvolysis products were the original carbinols (or their methyl ethers); no elimination or rearrangement to cyclobutanols or allylcarbinols was observed. In several instances, "internal return" to a non-solvolyzing *p*-nitrobenzoate (shown to be the isomeric allylcarbinyl ester VII in the case of IIIb) occurred, the ratio of rearrangement to solvolysis increasing with decreasing ionizing power of the solvent. But rearrangement of IIIb → VII was not thermal, nor was the extent of rearrangement a direct function of the solvolysis rate. Rates, products and energetics can be interpreted in terms of an ion-pair mechanism which includes stabilizing the positive charge in the carbonium ion by *each* cyclopropyl group. Attempts to prepare tricyclopropylcarbinyl *p*-nitrobenzoate lead to 1,1-dicyclopropyl-4-chloro-1-butene (VIII) which, with aqueous potassium carbonate, was reconverted to tricyclopropylcarbinol.

Studies of physical properties, particularly spectra, place the cyclopropyl group between a vinyl and a saturated group with regard to ability to conjugate with adjacent unsaturation.[4] But the solvolysis of cyclopropylcarbinyl derivatives is exceptional,[5] proceeding at a greater rate than the corresponding allyl compounds

$$\triangleright\!\!-CH_2X > CH_2\!\!=\!\!CHCH_2X \gg CH_3CH_2CH_2X$$

This acceleration is particularly striking in rigid systems, such as the i-steroids.[6] The positive charge which remains on carbon when X⁻ ionizes from the above systems is apparently better accommodated by the cyclopropyl than by the vinyl group. The rates cannot be explained by considering cyclopropyl as a less polarizable analog of the vinyl group (as has been done in interpretations of spectra). Special features have been ascribed to the carbonium ion intermediate which, in the extreme case of the reaction of cyclopropylcarbinyl-amine with nitrous acid,[7] is pictured with the three

$$\left[\begin{array}{c} CH \\ CH_2\text{---}\!\!\mid\!\!\text{---}CH_2 \\ CH_2 \end{array}\right]^+$$

methylene carbons equivalent. Often,[6,8–10] but not always,[10,11] rearrangement to allylcarbinyl or cyclobutyl derivatives occurs during solvolysis of cyclopropylcarbinyl compounds under ionizing conditions.

It was our purpose to examine some tertiary systems of this type (heretofore only primary and secondary systems had been studied) with regard both to rates and products. Compounds with more than one cyclopropyl group on the carbonium carbon atom were thought to be of particular interest for several reasons. If the driving force in these rapid solvolyses is release of strain in the three-membered ring, then one such ring should be sufficient to ensure rate enhancement, and one might predict no large effect from additional cyclopropyl substitution. Indeed, the electron-withdrawing inductive effect of the cyclopropyl group compared with other alkyl groups[1d] might decrease the rate of an SN1[5] process. Alternatively, if resonance structures were possible which would allow distribution of the positive charge over several cyclopropane rings, a considerable rate increase might be observed, much as in the benzyl, benzhydryl, triphenylmethyl series. Certain similarities between phenyl and cyclopropyl groups[12] lend plausibility to this view.

To determine which of these alternatives prevailed, the *p*-nitrobenzoates of dicyclopropyliso-propylcarbinol (Ia), di-(2-methylcyclopropyl)-iso-propylcarbinol (IIa), diisopropylcyclopropylcarbinol (IIIa) and dicyclopropylcarbinol (IVa) were

$$\begin{array}{cccc} \triangledown & \triangledown & \triangledown & \triangledown \\ \!\mid & \!\mid & \!\mid & \!\mid \\ >\!\!-C\!\!-X & >\!\!-C\!\!-X & >\!\!-C\!\!-X & HC\!\!-X \\ \!\mid & \!\mid & \!\mid & \!\mid \\ \triangle & \triangle & \wedge & \triangle \\ & \!\mid & & \\ I & II & III & IV \end{array}$$

a, X = OH; b, X = –OCC₆H₄-*p*-NO₂; c, X = OCH₃

prepared, and the solvolysis rates and products in aqueous dioxane determined. The products were also determined in methanolic dioxane. For com-

(1) Part V of a series on Cyclopropane Chemistry. For previous papers see (a) H. Hart and O. E. Curtis, Jr., This Journal, **78**, 112 (1956); (b) H. Hart and J. M. Sandri, *Chemistry & Industry*, 1014 (1956); (c) H. Hart and O. E. Curtis, Jr., This Journal, **79**, 931 (1957); (d) T. L. Brown, J. M. Sandri and H. Hart, *J. Phys. Chem.*, **61**, 698 (1957).

(2) Presented in part at a Symposium on the Chemistry of Three-membered Rings, American Chemical Society Meeting, Miami, Fla., April, 1957.

(3) From the Ph.D. thesis of Joseph Mario Sandri, Michigan State University, 1956; American Viscose Corporation Fellow, 1954–1955.

(4) For a review, see E. Vogel, *Fortschr. Chem. Forsch.*, **3**, 431 (1955). We refer especially to electron-donating ability, as in cyclopropyl ketones, esters, aromatics, etc.

(5) See A. Streitwieser, Jr., *Chem. Revs.*, **56**, 571 (1956), for a discussion and review.

(6) For a recent case, see E. M. Kosower and S. Winstein, This Journal, **76**, 4347, 4354 (1956).

(7) J. D. Roberts and R. H. Mazur, *ibid.*, **73**, 3542 (1951).

(8) J. D. Roberts and R. H. Mazur, *ibid.*, **73**, 2509 (1951).

(9) J. D. Roberts and V. C. Chambers, *ibid.*, **73**, 5034 (1951).

(10) C. G. Bergstrom and S. Siegel, *ibid.*, **74**, 145 (1952).

(11) R. G. Pearson and S. H. Langer, *ibid.*, **75**, 1065 (1953).

(12) See ref. 8 with regard to solvolysis rates. But similarities do not appear to be restricted to ionic reactions. Hydrogen *atoms* are nearly as difficult to remove from cyclopropane as from benzene (A. F. Trotman-Dickenson and E. W. R. Steacie, *J. Chem. Phys.*, **19**, 329 (1951); J. R. McNesby and A. S. Gordon, This Journal, **79**, 825 (1957)). Other evidence with regard to peroxide decompositions reinforces this analogy (H. Hart and D. P. Wyman, unpublished results).

parison, triisopropylcarbinyl *p*-nitrobenzoate (Vb) also was studied.[13] Attempts to prepare the *p*-

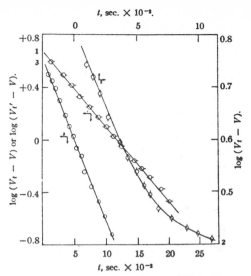

nitrobenzoate of tricyclopropylcarbinol[1b] (VI) were unsuccessful, but some of the chemistry of this alcohol is described.

Results

The Reaction Rates.—The solvolysis rates were determined in aqueous dioxane by titrating the liberated *p*-nitrobenzoic acid (PNBA). The rate constants and derived thermodynamic functions[14] are listed in Table I. In most instances, the ester was quantitatively solvolyzed to PNBA, but in certain cases less than the theoretical amount of acid was produced, due to a competing rearrangement discussed more fully below. The rate constants in Table I were calculated by two different methods for these two alternatives.

When solvolysis was complete, strict first-order kinetics were observed; plots of log $(V_t - V)$ *vs.* time (where V_t was the volume of standard sodium hydroxide required to neutralize the theoretical quantity of PNBA in a 5-ml. aliquot and V was the volume of the base required at time t) were linear, the reactions being followed nearly to completion. For those cases where no other rate constant is given in Table I, the values of k were determined from the slopes of these lines[15] (see Fig. 1).

Rearrangement was first detected during the solvolysis of diisopropylcyclopropylcarbinyl *p*-nitrobenzoate (IIIb) in 80% aqueous dioxane at 80°, when a plot of log $(V_t - V)$ *vs.* t started out nearly linear, but soon curved rather sharply and leveled off after 64.4% of the theoretical amount of PNBA had been produced (see Fig. 1). If the observed value for volume of base required to titrate the total PNBA *actually produced* in a 5-ml. aliquot was designated V_t', then a plot of log $(V_t' - V)$ *vs.* t was linear (Fig. 1). This implied that the original ester reacted by two paths, both kinetically first order, but only one of which produced PNBA. For these cases k, the over-all rate constant for reaction of ester, was calculated from the slopes of these lines. The fraction of original ester which rearranged to isomeric ester, $f_r = 1 - V_t'/V_t$, is also listed in Table I. That these kinetically determined values were valid was verified by product isolation.

The Products.—The alcohol produced from each ester was unrearranged (*i.e.*, a cyclopropylcarbinol), as shown by identity of its infrared spectrum

(13) *Cf.* P. D. Bartlett and M. Stiles, THIS JOURNAL, **77**, 2806 (1955).

(14) The heat of activation was determined from the usual linear Arrhenius plot, by subtracting RT from the energy of activation. The activation entropy was calculated from the Eyring equation $\Delta S^{\ddagger} = 2.303\ R \log (kh/k'T) + \Delta H^{\ddagger}/T$, where k is the rate constant, h is Planck's constant and k' is the Boltzmann constant.

(15) Since, in those instances where rearrangement was unimportant, the points fell beautifully on straight lines for the entire course of the reaction, it was felt unnecessary to go beyond the differential form of the rate equation to calculate k's.

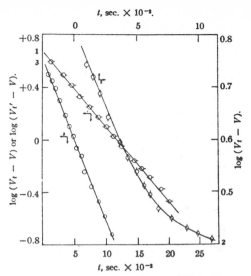

Fig. 1.—Plots of log $(V_t - V)$ or log $(V_t' - V)$ *vs.* t: curve 1, Ib in 80% aqueous dioxane at 25° (solvolysis was complete); curve 2, IIIb in 80% aqueous dioxane at 80°, plotted as log $(V_t - V)$ *vs.* t (35.6% rearrangement, 64.4% solvolysis); curve 3, the same data as curve 2, plotted as log $(V_t' - V)$ *vs.* t.

with that of authentic carbinol. This was true regardless of the extent of solvolysis (*vs.* rearrangement). For example, from Ib in 80% aqueous dioxane at 25° there was isolated a 95% yield of Ia; no evidence for olefin or isomeric alcohol was obtained. A high yield (81%) of the corresponding methyl ether Ic was isolated from methanolic dioxane under the same conditions; the infrared spectrum was indistinguishable from that of authentic ether prepared by reaction of methyl iodide with the corresponding potassium alcoholate.

$$\text{Ib} \xrightarrow[\text{dioxane, 25°}]{80\% \text{ methanolic}} \text{Ic} \xleftarrow[\text{2, CH}_3\text{I}]{\text{1, K}} \text{Ia}$$

The other product obtained when less than the theoretical amount of PNBA was formed was examined in detail with IIIb, and shown to be the isomeric ester, 4-isopropyl-5-methyl-3-hexenyl *p*-nitrobenzoate (VII). Its structure was proved by reduction with lithium borohydride to 4-isopropyl-5-methyl-3-hexenol (74%) and *p*-nitrobenzyl

$$\text{IIIb} \xrightarrow{\substack{\text{aqueous} \\ \text{dioxane}}} \text{IIIa} + \underset{(\text{CH}_3)_2\text{CH}}{\overset{(\text{CH}_3)_2\text{CH}}{\diagdown}}\!\!\!\text{C}=\text{CHCH}_2\text{CH}_2\text{OC}-\!\!\!\diagdown\!\!\!\diagup\!\!\!-\text{NO}_2$$

VII

alcohol (81%). The unsaturated alcohol gave a good yield of diisopropyl ketone on permanganate oxidation. This fixed the position of the double bond, but the ester function might have been at C_1 or C_2. Rearrangements from cyclopropylcarbinyl to allylcarbinyl systems are well known; furthermore, if the ester function were at C_2 it would be allylic; VII did not produce any PNBA even after boiling for 26 hours in 70% aqueous dioxane;

TABLE I
SOLVOLYSIS RESULTS

Ester	Wt. % dioxane	Temp., °C.	$k \times 10^4$, sec.$^{-1}$	$fr \times 100^a$	$\Delta H^{\ddagger a}$	$\Delta S^{\ddagger a}$
Ib	95	60	5.84	8.4		
			5.53	7.4		
	90	25	1.61			
			1.59			
		40	6.60		17.3	−17.8
			6.77			
		50	16.7			
			16.8			
	85	25	5.44			
			5.47			
	80	7	1.52			
			1.54			
		16	5.01			
			4.78			
			4.55^b		19.3	−7.1
			4.73^c			
		25	13.2			
			13.0			
			13.5			
			13.5			
IIb	90	16	2.71	7.4		
			2.88	8.0		
		25	7.02	7.8	16.9	−16.3
			7.16	8.2		
		35	17.8	9.4		
			18.4	10.5		
			18.6	10.3		
	80	7	8.01			
			8.09			
IIIb	90	60	0.73	71.8		
			0.74	72.1		
	85	60	2.12	59.9		
			2.05	60.0		
		70	5.69	59.2	22.2	−9.1
			5.79	59.8		
		80	14.6	62.6		
			14.9	60.8		
	80	60	5.00	35.2		
			4.65	35.5		
			4.47^d	32.2		
			4.65^e	37.4		
			5.09	36.1		
			4.27	34.4		
			4.49^f	34.7		
			4.90^f	36.3		
		70	12.0	35.0	20.8	−11.6
			11.7	35.3		
		80	30.2	35.8		
			28.9	35.6		
	70	40	1.64	4.4		
			1.57	3.8		
		50	5.21	4.4	20.7	−9.7
			5.02	4.6		
			4.58^g			
			4.66^h			
		60	14.5	5.7		
			14.8	5.5		
IVb	85	80	2.62			
			2.73			
	80	60	1.10			
			1.21			
		70	2.86		20.5	−15.4
			2.98			
		80	7.06			
			7.04			
Vb	80	60	0.020			
			.018			
		70	.068		30.4	+6.2
			.068			
		80	.277			
			.265			
	70	60	.076			
			.075			
		70	.250		27.2	−0.6
			.259			
		80	.832			
			.798			

^{a} For the method of calculating these quantities, see the section on Results. ^{b} The solvolysis solution (0.009368 M in ester) was also 0.009525 M in sodium hydroxide initially. The rate was followed by titration with standard hydrochloric acid. ^{c} Initially 0.008845 M in ester and 0.009525 M in sodium hydroxide; see note b. ^{d} The ester was dissolved in anhydrous dioxane and maintained at 60° for 3 days after which sufficient water was added to make the solution 80% dioxane, and rate measurements were begun immediately. ^{e} Same as note d, except sample was stored 5 days at 60°. ^{f} Rates determined by the inverse procedure (see Experimental). ^{g} 0.009296 M ester and 0.009410 M NaOH initially; see note b. ^{h} 0.009068 M ester and 0.009410 M NaOH initially; see note b.

the structure is therefore most certainly as shown.

The isomeric p-nitrobenzoates from Ib and IIb were not isolated, but the rearrangement probably followed the same pattern; IIb may give two isomeric homoallylic p-nitrobenzoates, depending upon the direction of ring opening.

Discussion

The cyclopropylcarbinyl p-nitrobenzoates studied must have solvolyzed with unimolecular alkyl–oxygen fission, supported by the following evidence. The kinetics were cleanly first order, independent of added hydroxide ion (see experiments with Ib at 16° and with IIIb at 60° in 80% dioxane, Table I), and unaffected by PNBA produced during the reaction (see Fig. 1). For a given ester, the rate was increased greatly by increasing the ionizing power of the solvent (compare Ib at 25° in 90, 85 and 80% dioxane, Table I). Finally, methanolysis gave the methyl ether and PNBA, rather than alcohol and methyl ester.[16]

The reactions were followed in only one manner, that is, titrimetrically. For this reason, it is not possible to assess quantitatively the importance of "internal return" from ion-pairs separated to varying degrees by solvent molecules,[17] but it is clear from the gross aspects of the reaction that this phenomenon is involved. The results are best interpreted in terms of ionization to an R+PNB− ion-pair which may return either to the original or rearranged ester, or solvolyze. As the separation of ion-pair counterparts increases, return to ester becomes less important, and reaction with solvent molecules to produce solvolysis products (alcohol or ether) predominates. The degree to which ion-

(16) See C. K. Ingold "Structure and Mechanism in Organic Chemistry," Cornell University Press, Ithaca, N. Y., 1953, pp. 763, 764 and 780, for a discussion of this criterion applied to alkyl–oxygen fission.

(17) For a detailed discussion and leading references, see S. Winstein and G. C. Robinson, THIS JOURNAL, **80**, 169 (1958), and S. Winstein and A. H. Fainberg, *ibid.*, **80**, 459 (1958).

pair counterparts become separated will be a function of the solvent polarity and of the structure of the R group. All the data presented in this paper are consistent with, and best explained in terms of, this mechanism.

The dependence of the rearrangement/solvolysis ratio (f_r) on solvent is shown in Table II. The percentage of. rearrangement fell rapidly with increasing water content of the solvent until, in 70% dioxane, the reaction was almost entirely solvolysis (94.4%). But in the same percentage of *methanolic* dioxane, 66% of the original ester rearranged to the isomeric ester VII, demonstrating the considerably weaker ionizing power of methanol *vs.* water. In absolute methanol, however, the product resulted exclusively from solvolysis.

TABLE II

PERCENTAGE REARRANGEMENT OF DIISOPROPYLCYCLO-
PROPYLCARBINYL *p*-NITROBENZOATE (IIIb) IN SEVERAL
SOLVENTS AT 60°

Solvent	r^a × 100
90% aq. dioxane	72.0
85%	60.0
80%	35.2
70%	5.6
70% meth. dioxane^b	66.0
100% methanol^c	0.0
100% dioxane	^{d}

^{a} Defined in section on Results. ^{b} Complete in 16 hours. ^{c} Product was solely the methyl ether IIIc; complete in 12 hours reflux. ^{d} No rearrangement (or solvolysis) after 3 days.

That the isomerization was not thermal but required some ionization is shown by the results in absolute dioxane. Even after five days at 60°, no isomerization occurred; when such a solution was diluted to 80% aqueous dioxane, solvolysis and isomerization proceeded smoothly, the same values of f_r being obtained as with fresh solutions (see Table I).

Before discussing the structural influences of *R* on the fraction of rearrangement, it will be instructive to consider briefly their effect on the over-all rates. The relative rates, for the limited number of structural changes studied thus far, are indicated in Table III. Those tertiary esters with two cyclopropyl groups are the fastest solvolyzing aliphatic *p*-nitrobenzoates yet reported. Indeed the secondary ester IVb solvolyzed as rapidly as tri-*t*-butylcarbinyl *p*-nitrobenzoate.[18] From the series Vb, IIIb, Ib it is apparent that as isopropyl groups were successively replaced by cyclopropyl, the rate increased, *with the second cyclopropyl group causing a rate enhancement nearly equal to that of the first*.

But the steric requirements of cyclopropyl are very likely less than isopropyl, because the methyls are pinned back. Inductive electron release (which would stabilize a carbonium ion) is also considerably less for cyclopropyl than for isopropyl. Quantitative data to this effect were obtained from the integrated O–H absorption intensities for the cyclopropylcarbinols reported in this paper, together with several reference compounds. The σ^*-value[18]

(18) See R. W. Taft, Jr.,in M. S. Newman, "Steric Effects in Organic Chemistry," John Wiley and Sons, Inc., New York, N. Y., 1956, pp. 605 ff.

TABLE III

RELATIVE SOLVOLYSIS RATES OF SEVERAL *p*-NITROBENZO-
ATES IN 80% AQUEOUS DIOXANE, 60°

$$R_1R_2R_3COC\!\!-\!\!\underset{O}{\overset{\displaystyle \|}{}}\!\!\!\!-\!\!\!\left\langle\!\!\!\!\!\!\right\rangle\!\!-\!\!NO_2,$$

Ester	R_1	$R_3 = R_3$	Rel. rate
Vb	*i*-Pr	*i*-Pr	1^a
IVb	H	Cyclo-Pr	60.7
IIIb	Cyclo-Pr	*i*-Pr	246^b
Ib	*i*-Pr ·	Cyclo-Pr	23,500^c
IIb	*i*-Pr	2-Me-cyclo-Pr	124,000^d

^{a} The referee raised some doubt about the suitability of Vb as a reference standard, arguing that this ester may undergo very rapid internal rearrangement on being dissolved in a part aqueous medium, and that the ester whose solvolysis rate was measured solvolyzes more slowly than authentic Vb (see ref. 13), or that indeed what is claimed to be Vb is actually a rearranged ester, rearrangement possibly having occurred during the preparation or workup. That neither of these is correct was demonstrated by two additional experiments. Partial solvolysis (50%) of Vb in 80% aqueous dioxane, followed by recovery of unsolvolyzed ester gave Vb, identical (m.p., mixed m.p., infrared spectrum) with the original ester, demonstrating no rearrangement during solvolysis. Reduction of this recovered ester with lithium aluminum hydride (the reaction is slow, and lithium borohydride was without effect on the ester) gave triisopropylcarbinol (Va), infrared spectrum identical in every detail with that of authentic Va. We feel, therefore, that the reference standard is valid. ^{b} This is the only example involving solvolysis *and* rearrangement, in this solvent. The figure given is for the total rate of ester disappearance, by both processes. A value of 195 is obtained from data in 70% dioxane at 60°, where rearrangement of IIIb is negligible. ^{c} Calculated for 60° from measurements at 7, 16 and 25°. ^{d} Obtained from the ratio of k_{IIb}/k_{Ib} at 7°, which was 5.26.

for the cyclopropyl group is +0.11 ± 0.03,[19] intermediate between H (+0.49) and CH$_3$ (0.00), and strongly electron-withdrawing when compared with isopropyl ($\sigma^* = -0.19$). If, then, the relative rates in Table III were corrected for steric and inductive changes, both of which should decrease the solvolysis rates, the rate increase per cyclopropyl group would be even greater than observed.

It seems reasonable to attribute the rate enhancement to stabilization of the carbonium ion by some mechanism of electron-release from each cyclopropyl group attached to the carbonium carbon. This may be expressed in terms of the hyperconjugative resonance structures

or some alternative, less clearly defined release mechanism.[20]

It is significant that the ester solvolysis products corresponded structurally in every case to the original alcohol from which the ester had been prepared, indicating that the positive charge in the in-

(19) T. L. Brown, *Spectrochim. Acta*, in press.

(20) H. C. Brown, O. H. Wheeler and K. Ichikawa, *Tetrahedron*, 1, 214 (1957), and H. C. Brown and K. Ichikawa, *ibid.*, 1, 221 (1957), have recently used the carbonyl group as a model for a carbonium ion and found an excellent correlation of sodium borohydride reduction rates with what might have been predicted on this model. Professor Brown also found (private communication) a large and successive decrement in reduction rates as methyl groups were replaced by cyclopropyl groups in the series acetone, methyl cyclopropyl ketone, dicyclopropyl ketone. A common factor appears to be operative in the solvolyses and reductions.

termediate was concentrated on the tertiary (or with IV, the secondary) carbon atom.

Two methyl substituents on the cyclopropyl groups increased the solvolysis rates fivefold; this would be rather large for an inductive effect transmitted through saturated bonds to the tertiary carbon in IIb, and suggests the possibility of hyperconjugative release transmitted through the three-membered ring.

Alternatively, the methyls may increase the rate due to relief of steric crowding.

There is no direct correlation between over-all solvolysis rates of the esters, and their tendency to rearrange; Ib, for example, which solvolyzes at a rate intermediate between IIIb and IIb (see Tables III and IV) shows the least rearrangement of the three esters in comparable solvents.

TABLE IV
PERCENTAGE REARRANGEMENT AS A FUNCTION OF STRUCTURE AND SOLVENT

Ester	Dioxane, %		
	95	90	80
Ib	8	0	0
IIb		9	0
IIIb		72	35

Rearrangement appears to be favored by bulky groups which might hinder the approach of solvent molecules to the ion-pair.

In a given solvent, the rate seems controlled more by entropy than by energy changes (compare Ib, IIIb and IVb in 80% dioxane, Table I). The effects are consistent with the ion-pair mechanism. The important structural change in going from the di-cyclopropylcarbinyl (IVb) to the dicyclopropylisopropylcarbinyl (Ib) ester is from a secondary to a tertiary carbinyl group. In the latter, because of steric requirements, the number of degrees of freedom is less than in the secondary ester. But in the ion-pairs derived from each ester, charge would be about equally dispersed (each ester has two cyclopropyl groups), requiring similar orientations of solvent molecules. Therefore, in going from reactant to transition state, the tertiary ester would experience less of a change in degrees of freedom than the secondary ester, and would have the more positive $\Delta S^{\ddagger}$.

On the other hand, dicyclopropylisopropylcarbinyl (Ib) and diisopropylcyclopropylcarbinyl (IIIb) p-nitrobenzoates have roughly equivalent steric requirements restricting atomic motions in the ester. But in the former, the two cyclopropyl groups permit greater charge dispersion in the transition state than in the latter (only one cyclopropyl group). This will result not only in a lower $\Delta H^{\ddagger}$ (about 1.5 kcal.) but will also require less restriction in orientation of solvent molecules; hence $\Delta S^{\ddagger}$ would be expected to be, and is, more positive for the ester with two cyclopropyl groups.

The energetics of Vb are worthy of further investigation. There is a large solvent effect on both

the enthalpy and entropy of activation; both decreased ($\Delta H^{\ddagger}$ from 30.4 to 27.2 kcal., $\Delta S^{\ddagger}$ from +6.2 to −0.6 e.u.) when the water content was raised from 20 to 30%. This is apparently a trend, for Bartlett and Stiles[13] reported $\Delta H^{\ddagger} = 23.5$ kcal., $\Delta S^{\ddagger} = -9.0$ e.u., for this ester in 60% aqueous dioxane.

It would have been instructive to include a case with three cyclopropyl groups in this series, to determine whether the cumulative rate effect obtains. Several attempts to prepare VIb from tricyclopropylcarbinol failed, possibly due to the anticipated sensitivity of the product to moisture, and to side reactions. The lithium alcoholate, with p-nitrobenzoyl chloride, gave a homoallylic chloride VIII, which also was produced from the alcohol and hydrochloric acid.

Its structure was proved by oxidation to dicyclopropyl ketone and β-chloropropionic acid, and by reconversion to VI.

Acknowledgment.—We wish to express appreciation to the American Viscose Corporation (J.M.S.) and the John Simon Guggenheim Memorial Foundation (H.H.) for fellowships which facilitated this work.

Experimental[20a]

Di-(2-methylcyclopropyl) Ketone.—The procedure was essentially the same as that used by Hart and Curtis[1a] to prepare dicyclopropyl ketone, γ-valerolactone being used in place of γ-butyrolactone. From 600 g. (6 moles) of γ-valerolactone there was obtained 207 g. (50%) of di-(2-methylcyclopropyl) ketone, b.p. 66° at 7 mm., $n^{25}D$ 1.4602.

Anal. Calcd. for $C_9H_{14}O$: C, 78.21; H, 10.21. Found: C, 78.11; H, 10.39.

The 2,4-dinitrophenylhydrazone, after recrystallization from 95% ethanol, melted at 101–102°.

Anal. Calcd. for $C_{15}H_{18}N_4O_4$: C, 56.59; H, 5.70; N, 17.60 Found: C, 56.88; H, 5.56; N, 17.53.

Cyclopropyllithium.—The procedure for the preparation and use of this organometallic has already been described.[1b] Initiation of the reaction with ethyl bromide is often helpful.

Preparation of the Alcohols.—The tertiary alcohols were all prepared from appropriate organometallics and ketones in the usual fashion. The reagents, yields, physical constants and analyses are given in Table V.

Preparation of the p-Nitrobenzoates.—The p-nitrobenzoates of the tertiary alcohols were prepared according to a single procedure, of which the following for dicyclopropylisopropylcarbinyl p-nitrobenzoate (Ib) is typical. The lithium salt of Ia was prepared in pentane solvent from 28 g. (4 g. atoms) of lithium, 157 g. (2 moles) of isopropyl chloride and 220 g. (2 moles) of dicyclopropyl ketone. The flask was cooled in an ice–salt-bath and a solution of 223 g. (1.2 moles) of p-nitrobenzoyl chloride in 1800 ml. of dry ether was added slowly, the temperature being kept between −5 and 0°. The mixture was stirred at 0° for 8 hours, then filtered and the solid extracted with hot ligroin (b.p. 66–75°). The extracts were combined with the filtrate and the solvent evaporated *in vacuo*. The residue (which contained unchanged ketone and tertiary carbinol as well as the desired ester) was taken up in a little ligroin and crystallization induced

---

(20a) Analyses were performed by Clark Microanalytical Laboratory, Urbana, Illinois; Micro-Tech Laboratories, Skokie, Illinois, and Spang Microanalytical Laboratory, Ann Arbor, Michigan.

TABLE V

PREPARATION AND PROPERTIES OF CERTAIN TERTIARY ALCOHOLS

Alcohol	Organo-metallic[a]	Yield, %	Boiling point °C.	Mm.	n^{25}D	Carbon, % Calcd.	Found	Hydrogen, % Calcd.	Found
VI	C-Li	94	88.5	10	1.4802	78.89	78.60	10.59	10.65
Ia	I-Li	69	81	10	1.4648	77.87	77.72	11.76	11.56
	I-MgCl	67							
IIa	I-Li	83	67	3	1.4570	79.06	79.12	12.17	12.22
Dicyclopropylmethylcarbinol	M-MgI	70	45	4	1.4618	76.14	75.93	11.18	10.89
IIIa	C-Li	75	75	10	1.4518	76.86	77.08	12.90	13.12

[a] C = cyclopropyl; I = isopropyl; M = methyl. The other reagent in each instance was the appropriate ketone.

TABLE VI

MELTING POINTS, YIELDS AND ANALYSES OF SEVERAL *p*-NITROBENZOATES

p-Nitrobenzoate	Yield, %	M.p., °C.	Carbon, % Calcd.	Found	Hydrogen, % Calcd.	Found	Nitrogen, % Calcd.	Found
Ib	22	114–115 d.	67.30	67.27	6.98	6.81	4.62	4.49
IIb	20	73–74 d.	68.86	68.81	7.60	7.57	4.23	4.22
IIIb	22	91–92	66.86	66.84	7.59	7.63	4.59	4.65
IVb	15	74–75	64.35	64.59	5.79	5.79	5.36	5.48
Vb[a]	20	74–75	66.42	66.58	8.20	8.11	4.56	4.56

[a] This ester was described recently by P. D. Bartlett and M. Stiles,[13] and is included here for comparison purposes and for completeness.

(Dry Ice). The crude ester (80 g., 22%) was freed of *p*-nitrobenzoic acid by stirring a warm ligroin solution of the ester with activated alumina. After several recrystallizations from ligroin, there was obtained 66 g. of pure Ib. Yields and physical constants are given in Table VI.

Dicyclopropylcarbinyl *p*-nitrobenzoate (IVb) was prepared by the general method recently described by Brewster and Ciotti.[21] *p*-Nitrobenzoic acid (16.7 g., 0.1 mole) was dissolved in 800 ml. of warm pyridine. To the cooled (room temperature) solution 17.7 g. (0.1 mole) of benzenesulfonyl chloride was added, the whole cooled in an ice-bath and 11.2 g. (0.1 mole) of dicyclopropylcarbinol (IVa)[1a] was added in one portion. After two hours with occasional shaking at 0° the mixture was poured into 1500 ml. of ice-water and filtered immediately, yielding 4 g. (15%) of IVb which was recrystallized several times from low-boiling petroleum ether. Physical constants are listed in Table VI.

Kinetic Measurements. (a) Solvents.—The dioxane was purified by the method of Fieser.[22] CO₂-free distilled water was used for making up solvent mixtures and reagents. Methanol was distilled over magnesium methoxide. All solutions are in weight per cent.

(b) Standardization of Reagents.—Sodium hydroxide was made up approximately 0.01 N in aqueous dioxane of the same composition as the solvent for the particular kinetic experiment. It was standardized immediately before each run against Bureau of Standards benzoic acid using phenolphthalein. If a run required more than one day, the base was standardized each day.

(c) Procedure.—Approximately 0.01 M solutions of ester were employed and the reaction was followed by titrating the liberated *p*-nitrobenzoic acid with standard sodium hydroxide. Reactions were conducted in a constant temperature bath maintained at ±0.1° of the desired temperature.

The aqueous dioxane solvent was equilibrated in the constant temperature bath before each run was started. Approximately 0.001 mole of the ester was weighed accurately into a dry 100-ml. volumetric flask. At zero time, 100 ml. of the equilibrated solvent was pipetted into the flask containing the ester and the solution was thoroughly mixed. At various time intervals, 5-ml. aliquots were withdrawn, quenched by cooling (ice–salt-bath) and titrated immediately with standard base using phenolphthalein. Usually 10 to 15 points were taken for each run, at least two runs were made for each set of conditions, and solvolyses were followed nearly to completion.

An alternative procedure involved addition of excess base in small increments and recording the time at which the phenolphthalein lost its color. This method was only used in

(21) J. H. Brewster and C. J. Ciotti, Jr., THIS JOURNAL, **77**, 6214 (1955).

(22) L. F. Fieser, "Experiments in Organic Chemistry," second edition, D. C. Heath and Co., Boston, Mass., 1941, p. 368.

a few runs and was abandoned in favor of the aliquot procedure, because the end-points were easier to observe. The two methods agreed well, when applied to the same ester under the same conditions. The rate data are summarized in Table I.[23]

Product Analysis. (a) Dicyclopropylisopropylcarbinyl *p*-Nitrobenzoate (Ib).—The products of solvolysis in 80% aqueous and 80% methanolic dioxane were determined. A solution of Ib (12.4 g., 0.041 mole) in 300 ml. of 80% aqueous dioxane was maintained at 25° for 48 hours, then poured into 700 ml. of water, made slightly alkaline with sodium hydroxide and extracted with eight 100-ml. portions of petroleum ether. The combined extracts were washed with several portions of water to remove the dioxane, dried over Drierite, and the solvent removed. Distillation of the residue gave 6.0 g. (95%) of Ia, b.p. 64° at 4 mm., n^{25}D 1.4645, infrared spectrum identical with that of an authentic sample. Similar results were obtained in a duplicate experiment altered only by scaling down the amounts used, and shortening the time to six hours.

In a preliminary experiment, methanolysis of the ester in 80% methanolic dioxane at 25° gave the theoretical amount of *p*-nitrobenzoic acid (titration) in 17 hours. A solution of 10 g. (0.033 mole) of Ib in 100 ml. of 80% methanolic dioxane was maintained at 25° for 18 hours, then worked up as for the hydrolysis just described. There was obtained 4.5 g. (81%) of Ic, b.p. 61° at 4 mm., n^{25}D 1.4566.

Anal. Calcd. for $C_{11}H_{20}O$: C, 78.51; H, 11.98. Found: C, 78.55; H, 11.98.

The infrared spectrum, which showed an intense ether band at 9.2 μ and no absorption in the 2.7–3.0 or 5.9–6.3 μ regions, was identical with that of an authentic sample prepared as follows. A mixture of 11.1 g. (0.072 mole) of Ia, 150 ml. of anhydrous benzene and 2.81 g. (0.072 g. atom) of potassium was refluxed (protected from moisture of the air) for 72 hours. A solution of 23.4 g. (0.172 mole) of methyl iodide in 50 ml. of benzene was added, and the mixture refluxed for 20 hours, then filtered and the residue (potassium iodide) rinsed with several portions of benzene. Removal of the solvent and distillation gave 10.5 g. (87%) of the desired methyl ether.

(b) Diisopropylcyclopropylcarbinyl *p*-Nitrobenzoate (IIIb).—The nature and relative amounts of products depended on the solvent used. (1) **70% aqueous dioxane:** Refluxing a solution of 0.2971 g. of IIIb in 100 ml. of solvent for 26 hours gave only 93.6% of the theoretical acid titer. In an isolation experiment, a solution of 6.42 g. of IIIb in 200 ml. of solvent was heated at 60° for 12 hours, and worked up as above. The residue (3.0 g.) showed both hydroxyl (2.85 μ) and carbonyl (5.8 μ) in the infrared. Petroleum ether (5

(23) For more complete details, consult the doctoral thesis of J. M. S. (ref. 3), especially the appendix which gives the concentrations of ester, titrant, etc.

ml.) was added and the solution was placed on crushed Dry Ice, whereupon some crystals were formed (75 mg.), m.p. 46–48°. This was subsequently shown to be 4-isopropyl-5-methyl-3-hexenyl p-nitrobenzoate (VII) (*vide infra*). The filtrate from these crystals yielded 2.3 g. (70%) of IIIa, b.p. 60–61° at 4 mm., n^{25}D 1.4516, infrared identical with an authentic sample. (2) 90% aqueous dioxane: The ester (10.43 g., 0.0341 mole) in 250 ml. of solvent was maintained at 60° for 48 hours, then worked up as above. There was obtained 6.4 g. (63%) of VII, m.p. 46–48°.

Anal. Calcd. for $C_{17}H_{23}NO_4$: C, 66.86; H, 7.59; N, 4.58. Found: C, 66.91; H, 7.30; N, 4.49.

From the filtrate, 0.7 g. (13%) of IIIa was isolated. (3) Absolute methanol: A preliminary experiment showed that the theoretical PNBA titer was obtained from a solution which had been refluxed 12 hours. In an isolation experiment, 6.57 g. (0.0215 mole) of ester in 300 ml. of absolute methanol was refluxed for 12 hours, then worked up as usual. There was obtained 3.2 g. (81%) of ether, presumably 3-cyclopropyl-3-methoxy-2,4-dimethylpentane (IIIc), b.p. 56° at 4 mm., n^{25}D 1.4338, intense band at 8.93 μ (ether), none at 2.7–3.0 or 5.9–6.3 μ.

Anal. Calcd. for $C_{11}H_{22}O$: C, 77.58; H, 13.02. Found: C, 78.29; H, 13.03.

(4) 70% methanolic dioxane: A preliminary experiment showed that after 16.25 hours at 60°, only 34% of the theoretical PNBA titer was obtained, and no additional acid was liberated after 37.5 hours. In an isolation experiment, 5.71 g. (0.0187 mole) of ester in 100 ml. of solvent was maintained at 60° for 36 hours, then worked up as usual. The petroleum ether extracts were concentrated to 50 ml. and cooled in Dry Ice. There was obtained 3.5 g. (61%) of VII, m.p. 46–48° and, from the filtrate, 0.7 g. (22%) of IIIc, infrared identical with that obtained from solvolysis in absolute methanol.

Structure Proof of 4-Isopropyl-5-methyl-3-hexenyl p-Nitrobenzoate (VII). (a) Reduction with Lithium Borohydride.—A solution of 8.0 g. (0.026 mole) of the ester in 50 ml. of tetrahydrofuran was added slowly (no noticeable heat evolved) to 2.2 g. (0.1 mole) of lithium borohydride in 100 ml. of tetrahydrofuran, and the mixture stirred at room temperature for 12 hours, cooled in an ice-bath, 300 ml. of water slowly added and the resulting mixture extracted with several portions of ether. The ether extracts, after drying (Drierite) and removal of the solvent *in vacuo* left a residue which was taken up in a little petroleum ether and filtered, yielding 3.2 g. (81%) of p-nitrobenzyl alcohol, m.p. 91–93° (lit.[24] value 93°). The filtrate was distilled, from which was obtained 3.0 g. (74%) of presumably 4-isopropyl-5-methyl-3-hexenol, b.p. 83° at 5 mm., n^{25}D 1.4505 with infrared bands at 3.0 μ (broad, –OH) and 6.0 μ (weak).

Anal. Calcd. for $C_{10}H_{20}O$: C, 76.86; H, 12.90. Found: C, 76.91; H, 12.87.

(24) I. Heilbron, "Dictionary of Organic Compounds," Oxford University Press, London, 1953, Vol. 3, p. 645.

(b) Oxidation of 4-Isopropyl-5-methyl-3-hexenol.—Oxidation of the lithium borohydride reduction product (1 g.) with neutral permanganate (4 g. in 100 ml. of water) at room temperature for four hours gave diisopropyl ketone (0.65 g.) identified by its infrared spectrum and vapor chromatogram.

Attempted Preparation of Tricyclopropylcarbinyl p-Nitrobenzoate (VIb).—Several attempts to prepare this ester from the lithium alcoholate and p-nitrobenzoyl chloride according to the general procedure which was successful for the other esters (*vide supra*) failed over a temperature range from −70° to refluxing pentane. Identifiable products were p-nitrobenzoic acid and its anhydride, unchanged alcohol, and a chlorine-containing liquid, b.p. 82° at 3 mm., n^{25}D 1.4998, shown to be 1,1-dicyclopropyl-4-chloro-1-butene (VIII). The infrared showed a carbon–carbon double bond (6.06 μ). The structure follows from the oxidation products.

Anal. Calcd. for $C_{10}H_{15}Cl$: C, 70.37; H, 8.86; Cl, 20.77. Found: C, 70.31; H, 8.90; Cl, 20.79.

Other attempts to prepare the desired ester from the potassium alcoholate and p-nitrobenzoyl chloride, from the lithium alcoholate and p-nitrobenzoic anhydride, and *via* the method of Brewster and Ciotti[21] all failed.[23]

Oxidation of VIII.—A mixture of 17 g. (0.1 mole) of VIII, 31.6 g. (0.2 mole) of potassium permanganate and 400 ml. of water was stirred for two hours at 0° and 28 hours at room temperature, then filtered and the filtrate extracted with five 70-ml. portions of ether. After drying (magnesium sulfate) and removal of the solvent, there remained 4 g. (40%) of dicyclopropyl ketone, b.p. 65° at 18 mm., infrared spectrum identical with an authentic sample.[18]

The aqueous solution (after ether extraction) was acidified (hydrochloric acid) and again extracted as above. From the residue there was isolated 3 g. (30%) of β-chloropropionic acid, m.p. 38–39° (lit.[25] value 39°). Its infrared spectrum was identical with that of an authentic sample.

Reaction of Tricyclopropylcarbinol (VIa) with Hydrochloric Acid.—To a test-tube containing 10 ml. of ice-cold concentrated hydrochloric acid there was added 5 g. (0.033 mole) of VIa and the mixture was shaken frequently for 30 minutes at 0°. The organic layer and ether extracts of the aqueous layer were combined, dried (potassium carbonate) and distilled, yielding 4.5 g. (80%) of VIII, identical with that obtained from the lithium alcoholate and p-nitrobenzoyl chloride.

Hydrolysis of 1,1-Dicyclopropyl-4-chloro-1-butene (VIII).—A mixture of 34 g. (0.2 mole) of VIII and 200 ml. of 10% aqueous potassium carbonate was refluxed with stirring for 24 hours. The organic layer and ether extracts of the aqueous layer were combined, dried (magnesium sulfate) and, after removal of the solvent, gave 27 g. (89%) of VIa, b.p. 71° at 4 mm., infrared spectrum identical with that of an authentic sample.

(25) Reference 24, Vol. 1, p. 556.

East Lansing, Mich.

37 | The 1,2,2-Triphenylethyl Cation

In Paper No. 37 Collins, Bonner, and Lester examine the stereochemical course of the solvolysis of 1,2,2-triphenylethyl tosylate and the deamination of the corresponding amine. Their previous conclusion that bridged ions are not involved in any way in these reactions is reinforced by showing that the partial retention of configuration is not associated with phenyl migration in the proportion that should be observed if the reaction proceeded through phenonium ions of *cis* or of *trans* configuration, or a mixture of the two forms. Since there is more retention than rearrangement, instead of less, as demanded by an hypothesis of direct formation of a symmetrical phenonium ion, it is clear that the carbonium ion intermediate is not symmetrical. The authors propose that the only charge delocalization is of the benzylic type, and advocate physical shielding as a cause for the retention of configuration. A believer in continuous change from one extreme bonding type to another might argue for a major benzylic and a minor, unsymmetrical phenonium delocalization, which would provide asymmetry, a mild chemical mechanism for shielding against inversion, and at the same time an easy channel for Wagner-Meerwein rearrangement.

From: *J. Am. Chem. Soc.* **81**, 466–75 (1959)

[Contribution from the Chemistry Division, Oak Ridge National Laboratory, and the Department of Chemistry and Chemical Engineering, Stanford University]

Molecular Rearrangements. XV. The Stereochemistry of the Solvolytic and Deamination Reactions of 1,2,2-Triphenylethyl Derivatives[1]

By Clair J. Collins, William A. Bonner and Charles T. Lester

Received July 3, 1958

The solvolytic and deamination reactions of 1,2,2-triphenylethanol and its derivatives, previously reported with respect to radiochemistry, have now been studied stereochemically. It has been found that (1) the products of hydrolysis and acetolysis of 1,2,2-triphenylethyl tosylate and (2) the deamination product from the reaction of 1,2,2-triphenylethylamine with nitrous acid are formed with some racemization plus *retention of configuration*. The products from the deamination of labeled (−)-amine at 36.9° and of labeled (+)-amine at 25° were separated into olefin, acetate and carbinol fractions. Each carbinol fraction was further separated into retained and racemic material, then all fractions were subjected to oxidative degradation, and the carbon-14 distribution of each was determined. From these data it can be shown that there is more rearrangement of the carbon-14 label in carbinol of *inverted* configuration than in carbinol of *retained* configuration, thus completely excluding bridged ions as the cause of configuration retention. These results, however, are compatible with our previously proposed[4-6] mechanism involving equilibrating, classical carbonium ion intermediates. Retention of configuration is explained by (1) a rate of rotation (k_x, equation 4) about the central carbon–carbon bond which is not extremely rapid with respect to the rate of phenyl migration (k_y, equation 4), and (2) a preferential frontside attack by the entering group owing to steric shielding from back-side attack (Fig. 1) by an *o*-hydrogen of one of the adjacent phenyls.

Introduction

The radiochemistry of the Wagner–Meerwein rearrangement of several carbon-14 labeled 1,2,2-triphenylethyl compounds has been the subject of previous papers.[2-6] It was shown that the reactions studied could be explained most simply if it is assumed that open or classical carbonium ions, capable of phenyl migration, are the intermediates. In particular reactions of the 1,2,2-triphenylethyl system neither the chain nor the ring labels achieved their statistical values; for example, if equation 1 represents the reactions of the chain-labeled reactants, and equation 2 represents the reactions of the ring-labeled reactants, then the mole fractions x and y, respectively, of rearranged products, were less than the statistical values of 0.500 and 0.667. For a given reaction, however, y was al-

ways greater than x by an amount generally[6] predictable on the basis of the equilibrating classical carbonium ion mechanism. Certain other reactions of 1,2,2-triphenylethyl derivatives, notably

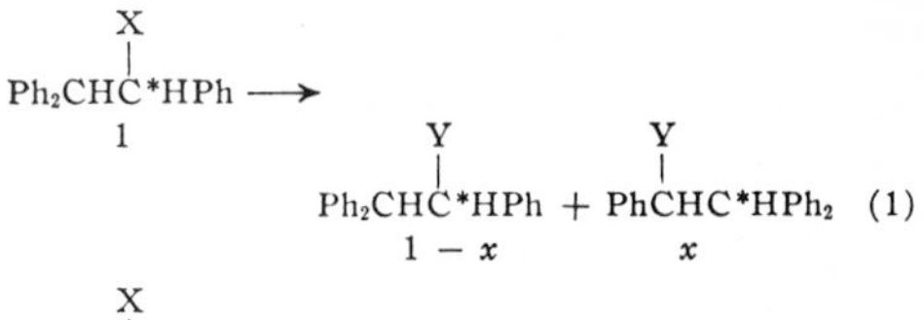

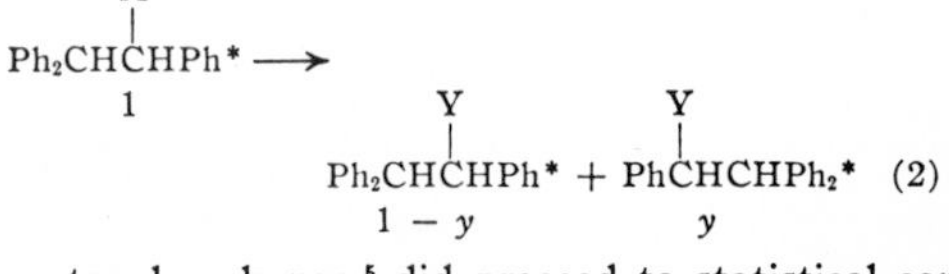

$$\underset{1}{Ph_2CH\overset{X}{\overset{|}{C}^*HPh}} \longrightarrow$$

$$\underset{1-x}{Ph_2CH\overset{Y}{\overset{|}{C}^*HPh}} + \underset{x}{PhCH\overset{Y}{\overset{|}{C}^*HPh_2}} \quad (1)$$

$$\underset{1}{Ph_2CH\overset{X}{\overset{|}{C}HPh^*}} \longrightarrow$$

$$\underset{1-y}{Ph_2CH\overset{Y}{\overset{|}{C}HPh^*}} + \underset{y}{PhCH\overset{Y}{\overset{|}{C}HPh_2^*}} \quad (2)$$

acetoxyl exchange,[5] did proceed to statistical conclusions (that is, $x = 0.500$ and $y = 0.667$), and were explained on the basis of the same general mechanism.

The idea of a bridged "bromonium" ion was invented by Roberts and Kimball[7] and was subse-

(1) This paper is based in part upon work performed for the Atomic Energy Commission at Oak Ridge National Laboratory, operated by Union Carbide Corporation. Paper XIV, C. J. Collins, W. T. Rainey, W. B. Smith and I. A. Kaye, This Journal, **81**, 460 (1959).

(2) W. A. Bonner and C. J. Collins, *ibid.*, **75**, 5372 (1953).

(3) C. J. Collins and W. A. Bonner, *ibid.*, **75**, 5379 (1953).

(4) C. J. Collins and W. A. Bonner, *ibid.*, **77**, 92 (1955).

(5) W. A. Bonner and C. J. Collins, *ibid.*, **77**, 99, 6725 (1955).

(6) W. A. Bonner and C. J. Collins, *ibid.*, **78**, 5587 (1956).

(7) I. Roberts and G. E. Kimball, *ibid.*, **59**, 947 (1937).

quently employed[8] by Winstein and Lucas to explain the stereochemistry of the reaction of optically active 3-bromobutanol-2 with hydrobromic acid. The bridged-ion hypothesis was extended[9] to include a carbon bridge, and the phenonium ion concept was developed by Cram and his co-workers[10] to rationalize the stereochemistry of a great number of solvolytic and elimination reactions. The concept of a symmetrical phenonium ion in which the phenyl bridge was equidistant between the migration origin and the migration terminus was later expanded to include the idea of an "unsymmetrical" phenonium ion.[11,12]

Although stereospecificity is required during concerted migrations and also during those reactions which require phenonium ion intermediates,[10] the converse is not necessarily true. Stereospecificity can, in theory at least, be involved in reactions which are not concerted, and in which bridged ions do not intervene, even though the sole cationic intermediates are classical or open carbonium ions[13,14]; it is only necessary that the rate of rotation (k_x, equation 3) about the carbon–carbon bond is not very fast compared with the rate of migration (k_y).

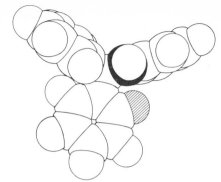

Fig. 1.

(3)

In nitromethane, in acetaldehyde and in difluoromethylborane, whose geometries probably approach that of an open carbonium ion, the rotational energy barriers are 6, 14 and 1,150 cal., respectively, per mole.[15] In the simple ethane molecule it has been calculated that the barrier to rotation is about 2800 cal. per mole,[16a] and Pitzer[16b] has assumed that in more complicated molecules this value is no less than 3600 cal. per mole. Bondi[16c] has shown that barriers to free rotation can be much greater.

(8) S. Winstein and H. J. Lucas, THIS JOURNAL, **61**, 1576 (1939).

(9) T. P. Nevell, E. DeSalas and C. L. Wilson, *J. Chem. Soc.*, 1188 (1939).

(10) D. J. Cram, *et al.*, THIS JOURNAL, **71**, 3863, 3871, 3875 (1949); **74**, 2129, 2137, 2159 (1952); **75**, 3189 (1953).

(11) J. D. Roberts and C. M. Regan, *ibid.*, **75**, 2069 (1953).

(12) D. J. Cram and F. A. Abd Elhafez, *ibid.*, **75**, 3189 (1953).

(13) This fact has been stated previously; see, for example, S. Winstein and E. Grunwald, *ibid.*, **70**, 835 (1948); S. Winstein and B. K. Morse, *ibid.*, **74**, 1134 (1952); S. Winstein and L. L. Ingraham, *ibid.*, **77**, 1739 (1955).

(14) This statement is meant to exclude those cases in which the leaving group shields the front side of the carbonium ion being formed, thus favoring inversion. See C. K. Ingold, "Structure and Mechanism in Organic Chemistry," Cornell University Press, Ithaca, N. Y., 1953, pp. 381–386.

(15) E. B. Wilson, *Proc. Nat. Acad. Sci.*, **43**, 816 (1957).

(16) (a) D. H. R. Barton and R. C. Cookson, *Quart. Revs.*, **10**, 44 (1956); (b) K. S. Pitzer, *Chem. Revs.*, **27**, 39 (1940); (c) A. Bondi, *J. Phys. Chem.*, **58**, 929 (1954); (d) see also the discussion by W. G. Dauben and K. S. Pitzer in "Steric Effects in Organic Chemistry," John Wiley and Sons, Inc., New York, 1956, Chapter 1.

Since the activation energies for migration processes such as A → B are unknown there is no reason to assume, therefore, that they are necessarily always greater than the rotational (A → C) energy barriers.

From our previous work[2-6] it appears that the sole cationic intermediates in the several reactions of 1,2,2-triphenylethanol and its derivatives are equilibrating, open, "classical" carbonium ions. A stereochemical study of these same reactions should be enlightening with respect to the relative rates of processes A → B and A → C. Since these reactions are presumed not to involve those intermediates which are normally associated with stereospecificity, it is important to determine whether stereospecificity, in fact, can be associated with the "classical" or open carbonium ion. We report in this paper the results of these stereochemical studies.

Results

Given in Table I is a summary of the stereochemical results for (a) the deamination of optically active 1,2,2-triphenylethylamine, (b) the hydrolysis and (c) the acetolysis of optically active 1,2,2-triphenylethyl tosylate. Included also are the radiochemical results for these same reactions. That the hydrolysis and acetolysis of optically active 1,2,2-triphenylethyl tosylate proceed with a net retention of configuration follows from the sign of rotation of the products so obtained, for in the preparation of the tosylate the carbon–oxygen bond of the asymmetric center is never broken. For example, (+)-carbinol on conversion to tosylate followed by either hydrolysis or acetolysis affords (+)-carbinol and (+)-1,2,2-triphenylethyl acetate, respectively, the latter compound yielding (+)-carbinol on reduction with lithium aluminum hydride. The deamination of optically active 1,2,2-triphenylethylamine has been shown also to proceed with retention of configuration to yield carbinol of the same sign of rotation as the amine from which it was produced. The assignment of like configuration to 1,2,2-triphenylethylamine and 1,2,2-triphenylethanol of like sign of rotation is based upon data obtained through well-established[17] methods of configurational relationship.

(17) (a) D. J. Cram and John E. McCarty, THIS JOURNAL, **76**, 5740 (1954); (b) A. McKenzie and G. O. Wills, *J. Chem. Soc.*, **127**, 290 (1925); (c) A. McKenzie and A. C. Richardson, *ibid.*, 79 (1923);

Although some of these methods, such as (1) the ammonolysis[17a] of the tosylate of (−)-1,2,2-triphenylethanol, (2) an attempted interrelation through mandelic acid and phenylglycine[17b,c,d] and (3) an application of Freudenberg's "Displacement Rule"[17e] were unsuccessful, our assignment of configuration is based on the following facts: (1) Double-labeling experiments upon the solvolytic and deamination reactions of 1,2,2-tri-

TABLE I

Summary of Stereochemical and Radiochemical Results for Solvolytic and Deamination Reactions of 1,2,2-Triphenylethyl-1-C¹⁴ Derivatives

Reaction	Conditions	C¹⁴, % rearr.[a]	Retention, %	Inversion, %
Deamination	−2°	23	72	28
Deamination	−2°	..	75	25
Deamination	−2°	22	77	23
Deamination	12.5°	..	69	31
Deamination	25°[b]	27	64	36
Deamination	36.9°[b]	24	67	33
Deamination	36.9°[b]	..	64	36
Deamination	36.9°[b]	22	70	30
Tosylate hydrolysis	Acetone-H₂O	22[c]	64	36
Tosylate hydrolysis	reflux	..	69	31
Tosylate hydrolysis	Acetone–H₂O	..	64	36
Tosylate hydrolysis	reflux	..	62	38
Tosylate acetolysis	HOAc, NaOAc, 85°	40[c]	54	46
Tosylate acetolysis	HOAc, NaOAc, 85°	..	58	42
Tosylate acetolysis	HOAc, NaOAc, 85°	..	54	46
Tosylate acetolysis	HOAc, NaOAc, 85°	..	53	47

[a] Of the chain label in 1,2,2-triphenylethyl-1-C¹⁴ derivative. [b] In the runs at 25° and 36.9°, in addition to 2–4% olefin, there was produced 5–8% of triphenylethyl acetate (see Tables II and III). When the product was separated from olefin, the $[\alpha]^{25}$D of the mixed carbinol and acetate was not appreciably different from the carbinol obtained upon reduction of this mixture with LiAlH₄. [c] Taken from ref. 6.

phenylethyl derivatives have demonstrated that both types of reaction proceed through the same open carbonium ion intermediates, and whereas the solvolytic reactions have been shown to take place with retention of configuration, then, with a very high probability the deamination reaction can also be said to proceed with retention of configuration; (2) in an application of the Fredga[17f] method of solid–liquid phase relationships of enantiomers of derivatives of carbinol and amine, although there was no evidence of the formation of quasi-racemates or eutectics, the *solidi* were characteristically different in the case of (+)-1,2,2-triphenylethyl acetate with (+)- and (−)-N-acetyl-1,2,2-triphenylethylamine, sufficient to allow a tentative conclusion that the two compounds of like sign possess like configuration; (3) the optical rotatory dispersion curves of (+)-1,2,2-triphenylethyl acetate and of (+)-N-acetyl-1,2,2-triphenylethylamine (kindly determined by Professor Carl Djerassi) are very similar,

(d) C. K. Ingold, "Structure and Mechanism in Organic Chemistry," Cornell University Press, Ithaca, N. Y., 1953, pp. 386 and 397; (e) K. Freudenberg, "Stereochemie," Franz Deuticke, Leipzig and Vienna, 1933, p. 699 ff.; (f) A. Fredga in "The Svedberg," Almqvist and Wiksells, Uppsala (Sweden), 1944, pp. 261 ff.; A. Fredga, *Arkiv för Kemi*, **11**, 23 (1957); K. Mislow and M. Heffler, This Journal, **74**, 3668 (1952); K. Mislow and W. C. Meluch, *ibid.*, **78**, 5920 (1956); (g) R. Huisgen and C. Rüchardt, *Ann.*, **601**, 21 (1956); (h) E. H. White, This Journal, **77**, 6014 (1955).

and although both dispersion curves are simple they offer presumptive evidence of like configuration; and finally, (4) the thermal decomposition, in a non-polar solvent, of the N-nitroso derivative of (+)-N-acetyl-1,2,2-triphenylethylamine yielded (+)-1,2,2-triphenylethyl acetate.[18] Since the work of Huisgen[17g] and of White[17h] demonstrates that under these conditions such thermal decompositions take place with configurational *retention*, (+)-1,2,2-triphenylethylamine, (+)-1,2,2-triphenylethyl acetate and (+)-1,2,2-triphenylethanol can now be said to possess the same configuration.

Given in Tables II and III are summaries of experiments which were performed with (−)- and (+)-1,2,2-triphenylethyl-1-C¹⁴-amine, respectively.

TABLE II

Summary of Radiochemical Data for Various Fractions Obtained on Deamination of (−)-1,2,2-Triphenyl-ethyl-1-C¹⁴-amine at 36.9°

Product	Yield, %	$[\alpha]^{25}$D	C¹⁴ rearrangement, %
Ph₂*C=*CHPh	4	...	37
(−)-Ph₂*CHC*HPh OCOCH₃	8	−23°[a]	13[b]
(−)-Ph₂*CHC*HPh[d] OH	88[d] { Fract. 1[c] Fract. 2 Fract. 3 Fract. 4	0 − 5.4 − 91 −119	24.5 24.6 20.7 20.6

[a] This value is calculated from $[\alpha]^{25}$D determinations of three different fractions. [b] This value was obtained by oxidation of a fraction whose $[\alpha]^{25}$D was −3°. [c] In addition to fractions 1–4 there were several intermediate fractions. [d] The crude carbinol had an $[\alpha]^{24.7}$D of −47.9°, corresponding to 70% net retention.

TABLE III

Summary of Radiochemical Data for Various Fractions Obtained on Deamination of (+)-1,2,2-Triphenyl-ethyl-1-C¹⁴-amine at 25.0°

Product	Yield, %	$[\alpha]^{25}$D	C¹⁴ rearrangement, %
Ph₂*C=*CHPh	2.5	....	25.5
(+)-Ph₂*CH*CHPh OAc	5.5		24.0[a]
(+)-Ph₂*CH*CHPh[b] OH	92 { Fract. 1 Fract. 2	0° +121°	28.1 26.5

[a] Of total acetate fraction. [b] The crude carbinol had an $[\alpha]^{24.7}$D of +34.9°, corresponding to 64% net retention.

The deamination products from each of these reactants—one reaction carried out at 36.9°, the other at 25.0°—were separated into olefin, acetate and carbinol fractions. The carbinol fractions were then resolved into samples of completely retained configuration and into racemic material. The percentages of rearrangement of the carbon-14 label were determined for each of the foregoing fractions.

(18) Mrs. Joan B. Christie, unpublished work. When (+)-N-acetyl-1,2,2-triphenylethylamine, $[\alpha]^{25}$D +110° (dioxane), obtained from (+)-1,2,2-triphenylethylamine, $[\alpha]^{25}$D +74.6° (ethanol) was converted[17g] to the N-nitroso derivative and subjected to thermal decomposition in carbon tetrachloride, the 1,2,2-triphenylethyl acetate so obtained had a positive rotation, $[\alpha]^{25}$D +26°, corresponding to 70% of the (+)-enantiomer and 30% of the (−)-isomer.

Discussion

The data of Tables I, II and III clearly indicate that although hydrolysis and acetolysis of 1,2,2-triphenylethyl tosylate and deamination of 1,2,2-triphenylethylamine proceed with considerable racemization, each product is formed with a net retention of configuration. We must now answer the question of how retention of configuration is possible in view of our postulation[2-6] that open, equilibrating carbonium ions (equations 4 and 5)

$$Ph_2CH\overset{\oplus}{C}{}^*HPh \underset{k}{\overset{k}{\rightleftharpoons}} Ph\overset{\oplus}{C}H\overset{*}{C}HPh_2 \quad (4)$$

$$Ph_2\overset{\oplus}{C}H\overset{*}{C}HPh \underset{k}{\overset{k}{\underset{2}{\rightleftharpoons}}} Ph\overset{\oplus}{C}H\overset{*}{C}HPh_2 \quad (5)$$

are the only intermediates necessary to explain our previous[2-6] radiochemical data.[19]

In Fig. 1 is a drawing of a Fisher–Hirshfelder model of the benzhydryl phenyl carbonium ion in conformation II, and in a position of maximum steric shielding. It can be seen from Fig. 1 that

the *o*-hydrogen (shaded in the drawing) of the phenyl (Ph[a]) below the plane of the carbonium center completely shields the positively-charged carbon (solid in the drawing) from rearward attack (that is, from below ion II). Attack from the front-side (top) of the ion, however, is sterically favorable. Conformational considerations[16] suggest that I is the most probable rotational isomer for 1,2,2-tri-

(19) An examination of equation 5 discloses that because of our choice of the position of the ring label, carbonium ion II (which represents a particular conformation of the unrearranged ions of equation 5) initially formed from the ring-labeled reactant I could rearrange to ion IV with exclusive migration of only one (Ph[a]) of the two possible migrating phenyls, and still fulfill the requirements imposed upon equation 4 and 5 by our choice of specific rate constants for these reactions. It is only after ion IV has been formed that these rate constants require the two phenyls (Ph* and Ph[a]) to possess equal opportunities for migration. This would not be true if the ring-labeled reactants were labeled as in IA. In this case it would be

possible to identify which of the phenyls on carbon 2 migrates initially. Only in the event that the labeled and unlabeled phenyls of IA should migrate equally (that is, the concentrations of IIA and IIIA are equal) would the specific rate constants of equations 4 and 5 be applicable to the reactions of IA.

phenylethylamine, the corresponding carbinol and derivatives of each, and also that II (*cf.* Fig. 1) should be the preferred conformation of the ions derived therefrom. Conformation II which is shielded by Ph[a] (*cf.* Fig. 1) from attack below the plane of the ion, may follow any one of three paths: (1) It may undergo migration of Ph[a] to produce rearranged ion IV; (2) it may rotate about the central carbon atoms to produce its rotational isomer III, which, if it then reacts from below the plane of the positively charged carbon, produces *inverted* product; or (3) it may react to produce unrearranged product VI whose configuration is the same as that of reactant I. Ion III, of course, may rearrange to produce ion V; then III, IV and V may undergo similar fates. If rotation of II to produce III is slow with respect to the migration of Ph[a] and conversion to product, then predominant retention of configuration will result. It is interesting that the relation of the fraction of chain label to the fraction of ring label rearrangement from previous double-labeling experiments[4,6] is not exactly as predicted by the classical carbonium ion mechanism in the absence of internal return but always slightly higher. At least in the case of the deamination reaction, this may be ascribed to the as yet incomplete equilibration of the rotational isomers of the initially rearranged carbonium ions of equations 4 and 5.

The foregoing hypothesis is thus compatible with previous[2-6] double-labeling data and with the present (Table I) stereochemical results. The question arises, however, as to whether the intermediates in the reactions studied might be mixtures of bridged ions and open ions, the *trans*-bridged ions (VIII) accounting for the retention of configuration in the product as well as for the scrambling of the carbon-14 labels, and the open ions leading to racemization. The data of Tables II and III allow us to state with complete assurance that bridged ions are not the cause, in the present instance, of configurational retention. Consider, for example (equation 6), the radiochemical consequences of the deamination of 1,2,2-triphenylethyl-1-C[14]-amine (I, X = NH₂) to the carbinol (VI and VII, Y = OH) through the *trans*-phenonium ion VIII. Any portion of the reaction proceeding by this path would be expected to produce unrearranged

$$(3)$$

(VI) and rearranged (VII) product in equal proportions. Further, the product (VI and VII) should possess the same configuration as reactant (I); *i.e.*, configuration should be *retained*. (To the extent that the *trans*-phenonium ions are not "symmetrical" but might be considered "unsymmetrical,"[11,12] the retained product should fail to have an equal carbon-14 distribution between the two central carbons.) Similar reasoning demonstrates that *cis*-phenonium ions should yield configurationally retained, unrearranged product, plus inverted product which has undergone complete

(100%) isotope position isomerization. Thus, compound I reacting through the *cis*-ion should yield inverted product whose carbon-14 is contained only in the 2-position. Accordingly, we separated the olefin, acetate and carbinol fractions from the deamination of (−)-1,2,2-triphenylethyl-1-C^{14}-amine at 36.9°, and from the deamination of the (+)-amine at 25°. Each carbinol fraction, as shown in Tables II and III, was further resolved into a racemic carbinol and into a (−)- or (+)-carbinol. In each deamination the carbinol of *inverted* configuration had undergone more rearrangement of its carbon-14 label than had the product of *retained* configuration. From these data we can now draw the following conclusions: (1) the mechanism of the deamination of I cannot involve the direct formation of bridged ions alone which go directly to product, for whether or not such bridged ions are "symmetrical"[10] or "unsymmetrical"[11,12] with varying proportions of *cis* and *trans* character such a mechanism would require the inverted product to contain *all* of its carbon-14 in the 2-position; the data of Tables II and III therefore refute such a mechanism. (2) The direct formation of bridged ions (of any type) and open ions, in which the open ions do not rearrange, and in which both types of ion go directly to product can also be ruled out, for such a scheme would not allow more rearrangement of the ring-label than of the chain-label during deamination; since we have demonstrated[6] adequately that the phenyl label undergoes considerably more rearrangement than does the chain label, the foregoing mechanism is also refuted. (3) The formation of bridged ion of the *trans* variety either symmetrically[10] or unsymmetrically[11,12] bridged plus open ions, all of which are interconvertible, is also not possible, for such a mechanism could never provide more rearrangement of the inverted than of the retained product. (4) Finally, we may rule out a mechanism in which the intermediates are mixtures of *cis* and *trans* bridged ions, symmetrical[10] or unsymmetrical,[11,12] plus open ions, all of which may interconvert to some degree before going to product, since the data of Table II alone, or the data of Table III, when combined with prior radiochemical results,[6] are stoichiometrically incompatible with any such scheme. Since experiments of the type reported in Tables II and III were not performed for the hydrolyses and acetolyses (Table I), we can only state by analogy with the deamination reaction that we believe the mechanisms of all three reactions to be similar. However, when one considers the incredible degree of coincidence required for any mixture of bridged and open ions to relate the rearrangements of chain and ring label[6] one to the other by the two limiting equations derived solely on the basis of our equilibrating, classical carbonium ion mechanism, the hydrolyses and acetolyses can be said also, with a high degree of assurance, not to owe their configurational retention to bridged ions.

It is clear, therefore, that retention of configuration during the deamination of 1,2,2-triphenylethylamine cannot be ascribed to bridged ions. Given in Chart I is the mechanism previously employed[6] by us to explain the results of double-labeling experiments upon deamination of 1,2,2-triphenylethylamine, but so expanded to account for the stereochemical results reported in this paper. An examination of Chart I discloses that the extent of carbon-14 rearrangement exhibited by the (+)- or (−)-carbinol is a function of the specific rate constants k_1, k_2, k_ϕ and k_r. Lacking knowledge concerning the relative values of these specific rate constants, it is not possible to predict whether the fraction of rearrangement of the (−)-carbinol should be equal to, greater or less than the fraction of rearrangement exhibited by the (+)-carbinol. The mechanism of Chart I allows any of these three possibilities.

Chart I

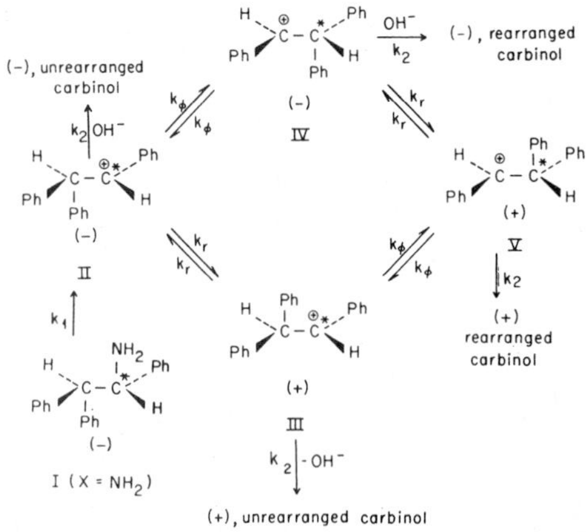

The reasons for the rather large differences in amounts of rearrangement undergone by the olefin, carbinol and acetate fractions during deamination at 36.5° (Table II) are not clear. Although the olefin is known[4] to rearrange under acid catalysis at higher temperatures, it is particularly difficult to understand why the acetate fractions from both deaminations (Tables II and III) should exhibit *less* rearrangement than the carbinol fractions. It may be that the mechanism proposed by Huisgen[17g] for the thermal decomposition of N-acyl nitroso derivatives is also applicable to that portion of the deamination reaction which yields acetate. These questions will be the subject of future papers.

The greater extent of racemization during hydrolysis and acetolysis of 1,2,2-triphenylethyl tosylate than during deamination of 1,2,2-triphenylethylamine is possibly due to internal return between the triphenylethyl carbonium-ion and the tosylate anion.

In summary, the present data, combined with previous radiochemical experiments[2−6] upon the solvolytic, elimination, and deamination reactions of 1,2,2-triphenylethyl derivatives, are best explained on the basis of equilibrating, classical carbonium ions which predominantly retain their configurations because of (1) steric shielding from rear-ward attack by the entering group and (2) rates of phenyl migration (k_x, equation 4) and rotation (k_y, equation 4) about the central carbon–carbon bond which do not differ greatly in magnitude.

Further, the possibility that bridged ions can be the cause of retention of configuration or rearrangement of the label during deamination of 1,2,2-triphenylethylamine is excluded.[20,21]

Experimental

(+)- and (-)-1,2,2,-Triphenylethylamine.—Racemic 1,2,2-triphenylethylamine[6] (115.4 g.) was dissolved in ethanol (426 ml.) and the solution was treated with a warm solution of (+)-camphor-10-sulfonic acid (98.0 g.) in water (426 ml.). The mixture was seeded with (−)-1,2,2-triphenylethylammonium (+)-camphor-10-sulfonate from a previous resolution and allowed to crystallize. The solid was filtered, pressed well, air-dried and weighed, 135.3 g., $[\alpha]^{25}$D +15.6° (c, 2.6, ethanol). It was then crystallized repeatedly from dilute ethanol, 2 ml. of 95% ethanol and 2 ml. of water being employed per gram of salt. After the fourth crystallization the 62.8 g. of salt had $[\alpha]^{25}$D + 10.1° (c 2.3, ethanol), a rotatory value which did not change sensibly on further crystallization. The salt was treated with excess aqueous sodium hydroxide, and the liberated amine was extracted thoroughly with ether. The extract was washed with water, dried over anhydrous sodium sulfate and was decolorized by being filtered through a bed of Norit. After removal of the solvent from the filtrate—last traces in vacuo—there remained 35.2 g. (61% of the (−)-amine) of clear sirup, $[\alpha]^{25}$D −64.5° (c 2.6, ethanol). The amine, after crystallization from hexane in Dry Ice, had a m.p. of 67° and an $[\alpha]^{25}$D −69.5° (c 3.7, ethanol) or $[\alpha]^{25}$D −89.5° (c 0.9, dioxane).

Anal. Calcd. for $C_{20}H_{19}N$: C, 87.86; H, 7.01; N, 5.16. Found: C, 87.50, 87.58; H, 7.00, 6.97; N, 5.21, 5.06.

All mother liquors from the crystallizations in the above resolution were combined and concentrated to a small volume by evaporation in an air stream on the steam-bath. The residue was treated with excess sodium hydroxide and the amine was isolated as before; 67.3 g. (89% total amine recovery), $[\alpha]^{26}$D + 30.4° (c 2.2, ethanol). The recovered amine (67.1 g.) was dissolved in ethanol (100 ml.) and treated with a hot solution of (+)-tartaric acid (36.9 g.) in water (100 ml.). The resulting tartrate salt was collected and repeatedly recrystallized from a mixture of ethanol and water (1.2 ml. of each solvent per gram of salt). After six crystallizations the 46.8 g. of tartrate had $[\alpha]^{25}$D + 47.5° (c 1.5, pyridine). Two further crystallizations gave 41.5 g. of salt of identical rotation. Decomposition of the latter salt and that in its mother liquors (44.4 g. total) with excess sodium hydroxide, followed by usual extraction of the amine gave 26.0 g. (91%) of (+)-1,2,2-triphenylethylamine, $[\alpha]^{25}$D + 65.4° (c 3.2, ethanol). After two crystallizations from hexane the (+)-amine had a m.p. of 67–68°, and an $[\alpha]^{25}$D +74.6°. The unresolved amine in the combined mother liquors was recovered as usual, 39.2 g. (total amine recovery, 97.5%), $[\alpha]^{25}$D +5.7° (c 5.2, ethanol).

(+)- and (−)-1,2,2-Triphenylethanol.—(−)-1,2,2-Triphenylethylamine, $[\alpha]^{25}$D −69.5° (ethanol), was obtained by fractional crystallization of the (+)-camphor-10-sulfonic acid salt. The dextrorotatory enantiomer was obtained in slightly higher purity, $[\alpha]^{26}$D +74.6° (ethanol), by recrystallization of the tartaric acid salt of the amine recovered from the mother liquors of the first resolution. When either enantiomeric amine was deaminated with nitrous acid under the conditions previously employed,[6] the 1,2,2-triphenylethanol resulting was found to be optically active and to have the same sign of rotation as its amine precursor. Early attempts to resolve the dl-carbinol with alkaloids *via* its half-succinate, half-phthalate, etc., were unsuccessful, so the carbinol obtained from deamination of the optically active amine and the acetate derived therefrom were subjected to fractional crystallization in a variety of solvents. It was found that samples of 1,2,2-triphenylethyl acetate, enriched in one optical isomer, could be further enriched to a constant optical rotatory power by fractional crystallization from ethyl alcohol, the racemic form of the acetate being considerably less soluble than either enantiomorph. In this way (−)-1,2,2-triphenylethyl acetate of $[\alpha]^{25}$D −60°, (+)-1,2,2-triphenylethyl acetate of $[\alpha]^{25}$D +61.4°, (−)-1,2,2-triphenylethanol of $[\alpha]^{25}$D −119° (m.p. 82–83°) and (+)-1,2,2-triphenylethanol of $[\alpha]^{25}$D +122° (m.p. 82–83°) were obtained.[22]

Anal. Calcd. for $C_{20}H_{18}O$: C, 87.54; H, 6.62. Found (+)-isomer: C, 87.51, 87.47; H, 6.58, 6.64. Found (−)-isomer: C, 87.30; H, 6.65.

Enantiomeric 1,2,2-Triphenylethylammonium Chlorides.—A sample of (+)-1,2,2-triphenylethylamine (9.9 g.) having $[\alpha]^{25}$D + 59.3° (c 3.5, ethanol) (80% optically pure) was dissolved in ethanol (20 ml.) containing water (15 ml.). The solution was treated with excess concentrated hydrochloric acid, and the resulting solid was filtered, washed and air-dried; 10.3 g. (92%). Purification was accomplished by vacuum sublimation at 210° (0.1 mm.). The sublimate was exposed to hydrogen chloride fumes,[6a] then dried in vacuo prior to analysis, when it had a m.p. of approximately 270° (w. subl.) (Fisher block) and $[\alpha]^{26}$D + 8.2° (c 0.7, ethanol).

Anal. Calcd. for $C_{20}H_{20}NCl$: C, 77.59; H, 6.51. Found: C, 77.90; H, 6.61.

A sample of (−)-1,2,2-triphenylethylamine $[\alpha]^{25}$D −67.1° (c 3.8, ethanol) (90% optically pure) was converted to its hydrochloride and purified in a similar fashion, m.p. *ca.* 270° (subl.), $[\alpha]^{25}$D −7.9° (c 1.4; ethanol).

Anal. Calcd. for $C_{20}H_{20}NCl$: C, 77.59; H, 6.51. Found: C, 77.46; H, 6.51.

Given in Table IV are the physical constants and carbon and hydrogen analyses for several N-derivatives of (+)- or (−)-1,2,2-triphenylethylamine.

Deamination of Enantiomeric 1,2,2-Triphenylethylamines.—(−)-1,2,2-Triphenylammonium chloride (5.86 g.) was dissolved in hot water (290 ml.). The solution was cooled, filtered (Celite), treated with acetic acid (8.3 ml.) and chilled to 5–8°. A solution of sodium nitrite (12.5 g.) in water (125 ml.) was added dropwise with stirring to the amine solution over a period of five minutes. After being allowed to stand for 20 minutes at room temperature, the mixture was made alkaline with sodium hydroxide solution, and the insoluble carbinol product was recovered by four extractions with ether. The extract was dried over anhydrous sodium sulfate, decolorized by filtration through Norit and freed of solvent, leaving 5.30 g. (102%) of crude 1,2,2-triphenylethanol, $[\alpha]^{25}$D −41.3° (c 3.2, ethanol). After seven crystallizations the 0.45 g. of product (dried in vacuo over phosphoric anhydride) had $[\alpha]^{25}$D −64.5° (c 0.7-ethanol). As with the racemic carbinol, the partially resolved samples retained solvent of crystallization when taken from acetic acid. The above sample of carbinol, when merely air-dried, was analyzed.

Anal. Calcd. for $C_{20}H_{18}O \cdot C_2H_4O_2$: C, 79.10; H, 6.64. Found: C, 79.41, H, 6.60.

When desiccated to constant weight in vacuo over sulfuric acid, the weight loss was 15.10% (calcd. for 1 mole CH_3-COOH of solvation, 17.95%), and the sample was analyzed.

Anal. Calcd. for $C_{20}H_{18}O$: C, 87.56; H, 6.61. Found: C, 86.92; H, 6.56.

(+)-1,2,2-Triphenylethylammonium chloride (10.5 g.) was deaminated as described in the previous section, proportional quantities of reagents being used. The crude carbinol obtained weighed 10.0 g. (107%) and had $[\alpha]^{25}$D +39.3° (c 1.8, ethanol). On successive crystallization from acetic acid the rotation rose to +59.3° after desiccation.

(20) Other experimental evidence has been explained by the intervention of carbonium ions which react to yield product more rapidly than they achieve rotational equilibrium; see, for example, B. M. Benjamin, H. J. Schaeffer and C. J. Collins, THIS JOURNAL, 79, 6160 (1957); V. F. Raaen and C. J. Collins, *ibid.*, 80, 1409 (1958). The work of P. Ballinger and P. B. D. de la Mare, *J. Chem. Soc.*, 1481 (1957), is also pertinent.

(21) We would like to emphasize the point made in an earlier paper (ref. 6, footnote 4) that although our present and past[2-6] data clearly rule out the possibility that bridged ions are the cause of retention of configuration in the 1,2,2-triphenylethyl system, these data should not be taken as evidence contrary to bridged ions in other systems. The well-known studies of Winstein[8,13] and of Cram,[10,12,17a] in our opinion, offer evidence as conclusive as is possible for the soundness of the bridged ion concept.

(22) Since the completion of this work, dl-1,2,2-triphenylethyl hydrogen succinate has been resolved in two ways (Mrs. Joan B. Christie, unpublished work): (a) through the cinchonidine salts and (b) through the salts of (+)- and (−)-1,1-diphenyl-2-aminopropanol. The (+)-1,2,2-triphenylethanol obtained therefrom had $[\alpha]^{25}$D +123°, and the (−)-isomer an $[\alpha]^{25}$D −123°. Both enantiomers had m.p. 82–83°

TABLE IV

PHYSICAL PROPERTIES AND ANALYSES OF DERIVATIVES OF (+)- AND (−)-1,2,2-TRIPHENYLETHYLAMINE

N-Acyl deriv. of 1,2,2-triphenylethylamine	M.p. °C.	$[\alpha]^{24-25.5}{}_D$	Formula	Carbon, % Calcd.	Found	Hydrogen, % Calcd.	Found	Nitrogen, % Calcd.	Found
(+)-Acetyl[a]	235.5	+109°[c]	$C_{22}H_{21}ON$	83.78	83.70	6.71	6.47	4.44	4.44
(−)-Acetyl[b]	231.5-232	−104.2°[c]	$C_{22}H_{21}ON$	83.78	83.53	6.71	6.34	4.44	4.31
(−)-Propionyl[b]	164-165	− 78.1°[c]	$C_{23}H_{23}ON$	83.85	83.22	7.04	7.12		
		− 62.5°[c]			83.39		7.11		
(−)-Benzoyl[b]	231-232	−135.9°[c]	$C_{27}H_{23}ON$	85.91	86.35	6.14	6.20		
(−)-3,5-Dinitrobenzoyl[b]	186-187	− 54.1°[c]	$C_{27}H_{21}O_5N_3$	69.37	68.78	4.53	4.72		
(−)-Acid succinoyl[b]	184.5-185	− 81.9°[c]	$C_{24}H_{23}O_3N$	75.70	75.49	6.52	6.35		
		− 62.5°[d]	$+ \frac{1}{2}C_2H_5OH$		75.28		6.15		
					75.38		6.26		
(−)-p-Toluenesulfonyl[b]	196-196.5	−107°[c]	$C_{27}H_{25}O_2NS$	75.90	76.03	5.90	5.96		

[a] From (+)-1,2,2-triphenylethylamine. [b] From (−)-1,2,2-triphenylethylamine. [c] In dioxane. [d] In dilute ethanol containing 3% NaOH. [e] In acetone.

Anal. Calcd. for $C_{20}H_{18}O$: C, 87.56; H, 6.61. Found: C, 86.93; H, 6.37.

(+)- and (−)-1,2,2-Triphenylethyl-p-toluenesulfonates. —Owing to the difficulty, during the early stages of this work, of obtaining large amounts of completely resolved (+)- and (−)-1,2,2-triphenylethanol, the tosylates for the solvolytic reactions were prepared from partially racemic carbinol fractions. Three such samples were prepared, tosylates A, B and C, from carbinol samples whose $[\alpha]^{25}{}_D$ were −52.0°; +58.2° and +51.6°, respectively (ethanol). The tosylate samples were prepared as described previously[2] for racemic tosylate and possessed melting points of 83–84°.

Anal. Calcd. for $C_{27}H_{24}O_3S$: C, 75.70; H, 5.65. Tosylate A: Found: C, 75.44, 75.47; H, 5.36, 5.40; $[\alpha]^{25}{}_D$ + 8.0° (acetone). Tosylate B: Found: C, 75.28, 75.30; H, 5.45, 5.60. Tosylate C: Found: C, 75.28, 75.30; H, 5.45, 5.60; $[\alpha]^{25}{}_D$ −6.7° (acetone).

Upon crystallization of these tosylates from acetone–hexane mixture, there was no change in optical rotation nor melting point of the samples. Finally, 5.0 g. of optically pure (−) carbinol[22] of $[\alpha]^{25}{}_D$ − 123° (ethanol) and m.p. 82–83°, was similarly converted[2] to 2.91 g. (48%) of (+)-1,2,2-triphenylethyl tosylate (m.p. 88–88.5° dec. and $[\alpha]^{25}{}_D$ + 16.2° (c 1.47, acetone).

Anal. Calcd. for $C_{27}H_{24}O_3S$: C, 75.70; H, 5.65. Found: C, 75.53, 75.65; H, 5.66, 5.59.

Hydrolysis of (+)-1,2,2-Triphenylethyl Tosylate. —One gram of the optically pure tosylate, $[\alpha]^{25}{}_D$ +16.2°, was dissolved in a mixture of acetone (30 ml.) and water (10 ml.). The solution was refluxed for 3.5 hours, diluted with water, and freed of acetone by warming in an air stream. The oily 1,2,2-triphenylethanol product was isolated by three extractions with ether. Vacuum rotary evaporation of the solvent yielded 0.66 g. (103%) of sirupy product, $[\alpha]^{25}{}_D$ − 28.8° (c 1.11, ethanol). This specific rotation corresponds to a mixture of 62% (−)- and 38% (+)-1,2,2-triphenylethanol.

Non-racemization of 1,2,2-Triphenylethanol under Hydrolysis Conditions. —To be certain that the above product was not further racemized under the reaction conditions producing it, the following experiment was performed. The above carbinol (0.64 g.) from the tosylate hydrolysis was dissolved in acetone (30 ml.) and water (10 ml.) and the solution was refluxed for 3.5 hours. Product isolation was accomplished as above, yielding 0.57 g. (89%) of sirupy carbinol having essentially identical rotation, $[\alpha]^{25}{}_D$ −28.5° (c 3.02, ethanol). This was crystallized from 2.5 ml. of acetic acid, drying the product for several days *in vacuo*, m.p. 82.5–84°.

Acetolysis of (+)-1,2,2-Triphenylethyl Tosylate. —Acetolysis was conducted under conditions previously described[2] for the acetolysis of 1,2,2-triphenylethyl-1-C[14] tosylate. A mixture of 1.10 g. of (+)-tosylate of $[\alpha]^{25}{}_D$ + 16.2°, in acetic acid (10 ml.) containing acetic anhydride (0.1 ml.) and anhydrous sodium acetate (0.25 g.) was heated on the steam-bath during 45 minutes. The mixture was treated with water until turbid and allowed to crystallize. The filtered product weighed 0.66 g. (82%) and had m.p. 152–153° and $[\alpha]^{25}{}_D$ −6.3° (c 1.577, dioxane). When this product was resubmitted to an identical reaction environment for a 45-minute period the 1,2,2-triphenylethyl acetate reisolated had m.p. 153–154° and $[\alpha]^{25}{}_D$ −3.7° (c 1.627, dioxane), agreeing within experimental error to the initially obtained acetate. The average of the above rotations corresponds to

that of a mixture containing 54% (−)- and 46% (+)-1,2,2-triphenylethyl acetate.

This product was added to an ethereal suspension of lithium aluminum hydride in the manner previously described[2] to accomplish its deacetylation. The crude sirupy 1,2,2-triphenylethanol obtained (97%) had $[\alpha]^{25}{}_D$ −6.3° (c 3.973, ethanol), corresponding to a mixture of 53% (−)- and 47% (+)-enantiomer. Crystallization of the sirup from 2.5 ml. of acetic acid afforded a solid product having m.p. 83–84.5° after extensive drying *in vacuo*.

Non-racemization of 1,2,2-Triphenylethyl Acetate under Acetolysis Conditions. —A mixture of (−)-1,2,2-triphenyl acetate (0.50 g., $[\alpha]^{25}{}_D$ −58.3°, m.p. 129–130°), sodium acetate (0.16 g.), p-toluenesulfonic acid hydrate (0.30 g.), acetic anhydride (0.23 ml.) and acetic acid (6.2 ml.), corresponding approximately to that prevailing after the above acetolysis, was heated on the steam-bath. After 45 minutes an aliquot of the solution was removed and added to excess water containing sodium sulfate. The precipitated acetate was filtered, washed and air-dried, m.p. 129–131.5°, $[\alpha]^{25}{}_D$ −54.4° (c 1.543, dioxane). The reaction mixture was heated for an additional 90 minutes, and the acetate was recovered as before, $[\alpha]^{25}{}_D$ −54.4° (c 2.377, dioxane).

The above experiment was duplicated exactly except that 2.4 g. (*ca.* 1400% excess) of sodium acetate and 12.4 ml. of acetic acid were employed instead of the previously indicated quantities. The acetate isolated after 45 minutes had m.p. 129–131.5° and $[\alpha]^{25}{}_D$ −54.4° (c 1.787, dioxane), while the acetate isolated after 135 minutes showed $[\alpha]^{25}{}_D$ −54.6° (c 1.793, dioxane). Thus no detectable racemization of 1,2,2-triphenylethyl acetate occurred under the acetolysis conditions which produced it from 1,2,2-triphenylethyl tosylate. Given in Table V is a summary of the data obtained upon hydrolysis and acetolysis of tosylates A, B and C (optically impure) and upon the tosylate of $[\alpha]^{25}{}_D$ + 16.2°, obtained from optically pure carbinol of $[\alpha]^{25}{}_D$ −123°. The data obtained with tosylates which were not optically pure are listed in order to demonstrate the duplicability of the results.

Effect of Temperature on the Extent of Racemization During Deamination of (−)-1,2,2,-Triphenylethylamine. —(−)-Amine of 98% optical purity (9.00 g.) was dissolved in warm acetic acid (16 ml.), giving 24 ml. of solution. Aliquots (8.00 ml.) of this solution were pipetted into three flasks containing concentrated hydrochloric acid (1.00 ml.) in water (170 ml.). Three solutions each containing sodium nitrite (7.3 g.) in water (73 ml.) were prepared. Each amine solution and nitrite solution was brought to the desired temperature, when the nitrite solution was added dropwise to the amine solution with magnetic stirring over a 5-minute period. Temperature prevailing during the three additions were −2°, 12.5° and 35–38°. Immediately after each addition was complete, excess sodium bicarbonate (13 g.) was stirred cautiously into the mixture, and the product was extracted twice into two 100 ml. portions of C.P. ether. The extracts were dried over anhydrous sodium sulfate (10 g.), filtered, and the solvent evaporated from each. Product yields were: 35–38°, 3.19 g.; 12.5°, 3.03 g.; −2°, 1.29 g. In the −2° experiment, a portion (1.56 g.) of the amine hydrochloride crystallized out at the low temperature, and was removed mechanically during processing of the reaction mixture. Each crude product was dissolved in 50 ml. of 55–85° ligroin, and the solutions were passed through 1 × 7-inch alumina columns in order to separate any hydrocarbon

TABLE V
SUMMARY OF TOSYLATE SOLVOLYSIS DATA

| Run | Rotation of starting carbinol | Rotation of tosylate | Hydrolysis carbinol | | Acetolysis products | | | |
| | | | Rotation | Inverted, % | Acetate | | Carbinol | |
					Rotation	Inverted, %	Rotation	Inverted, %
1	+ 51.6[ob]	− 6.72[oa]	+14.7[ob]	36	+2.16[oc]	..	+5.72[ob]	46
2	+ 58.2[b]	.....	+22.6[b]	31	.....	..	+9.7[b]	42
3	− 52.0[b]	+ 8.0[a]	−14.7[b]	36	.....	..	−4.6[b]	46
4	−123.0[b]	+16.2[a]	−28.8[b]	38	−5.0	46	−6.3[b]	47

[a] Rotation observed in acetone.   [b] Rotation observed in ethanol.   [c] Rotation observed in glacial acetic acid.

by-products. Each column was then washed with three 75-ml. portions of ligroin, and the ligroin fractions were evaporated to dryness. The yields of non-adsorbed by-products for the three experiments were: 35–38°, 0.11 g.; 12.5°, 0.10 g.; −2°, 0.04 g. A blank evaporation of 100 ml. of the ligroin used gave no residue. Each alumina column was next eluted with three 75-ml. portions of ethanol, and the ethanol washings in each experiment were evaporated to dryness, last traces at 100° *in vacuo*. Yields and $[\alpha]^{25}$D in ethanol of the recovered carbinol products corresponding to each temperature were: (1) 35–38°, 3.03 g., −32.8° (c 3.1); 12.5°, 2.99 g., −44.5° (c 4.1); −2°, 1.28 g., −60.0° (c 3.0). In similar experiments we obtained the results listed in Table I.

Deamination of (+)- and (−)-1,2,2-Triphenylethyl-1-C¹⁴-amine.—Racemic 1,2,2-triphenylethyl-1-C¹⁴-amine[6] was resolved into (−)-amine of $[\alpha]^{25}$D −69.5° and (+)-amine whose $[\alpha]^{25}$D +74.6° (m.p. 67–68°) as described earlier in the Experimental section. The molar radioactivity of the free (−)-amine was 1.625 ± 0.023 mc./mole. The (−)-acetate derived therefrom had a molar radioactivity of 1.636 ± 0.013 mc./mole, and $[\alpha]^{25}$D −116°. In a typical experiment 6.0 g. of (−)-1,2,2-triphenylethylamine-1-C¹⁴ was dissolved in 10.7 cc. of glacial acetic acid, and to it was added 2 cc. of concentrated hydrochloric acid in 340 cc. of water. The flask containing the solution was placed in a water-bath at 36.6–37.2° for 90 minutes, then to it was added dropwise with stirring a solution of 14.6 g. of sodium nitrite in 146 cc. of water. The addition required 40 minutes. After the addition was complete, the mixture was stirred for 35 minutes, then removed from the bath and treated with 26 g. of sodium bicarbonate. The ether extract, washed well with water, was concentrated to dryness, and dissolved in hexane so that the total volume was 150 cc. A 12.5-cc. aliquot of this solution was concentrated and desiccated, yielding 547 mg. of crude, dry material, $[\alpha]^{24.5}$D −47.0° (ethanol). The solution was allowed to stand overnight and from it crystallized a small amount of nearly racemic 1,2,2-triphenylethyl acetate, m.p. 158°. The entire sample from the 12.5-cc. aliquot was hereupon combined, deacetylated with lithium aluminum hydride and the carbinol product recovered. The $[\alpha]^{25.5}$D of the recovered carbinol was −47.9°. The carbinol product (446 mg.) was dissolved in hexane and placed on a column of alumina. The column was washed with hexane until no more 1,1-triphenylethylene remained, then the carbinol (428 mg.) was removed with ethanol. The 428 mg. of 1,2,2-triphenylethanol was oxidized in 11 cc. of glacial acetic acid by adding to it 430 mg. of CrO₃ in 4 cc. of glacial acetic acid and 2.5 cc. of water. Both solutions had been chilled prior to mixing. After one hour the benzhydryl phenyl ketone was isolated; 407 mg., m.p. 138°. This ketone was oxidized to benzophenone as described previously.[6] The yield of 2,4-dinitrophenylhydrazone obtained therefrom was 369 mg. (68%). After being crystallized 3 times the derivative (m.p. 240–242°) had a radioactivity assay of 0.3220 ± 0.002 mc./mole, corresponding to 19.7% rearrangement of the carbon-14 label. This value is too low to be compatible with the percentages scrambling (Table II and *vide infra*) of the racemic and of the resolved carbinols isolated from the same mixture. This anomaly was subsequently shown to be due to two causes: (a) the presence of varying but small percentages of unreacted amine in the non-crystalline deamination product and (b) fractionation of the racemic carbinol during chromatography. Our inability to remove the last traces of unreacted amine from the crude product undoubtedly contributes to the variability of the observed rotations of the deamination products. These same considerations do not apply to the data of Tables II and III, or to our prior[2−6] radiochemical results, which were obtained upon rigorously purified products.

The remaining 137.5 cc. of hexane solution of the original deamination product was concentrated to dryness, dissolved in 110 cc. of 95% ethanol, and allowed to stand overnight, yielding 422 mg. of tan crystals, m.p. 150°. After one crystallization from ethanol, 298 mg. of 1,2,2-triphenylethyl acetate was obtained whose m.p. and mixed m.p. with authentic racemic material was 158°, $[\alpha]^{25}$D −2.6°. After conversion to 1,2,2-triphenylethanol by deacetylation with lithium aluminum hydride, the recovered carbinol (257 mg.) had $[\alpha]^{25}$D −10.7°. This carbinol was oxidized to ketone (244 mg.) thence to benzophenone which was converted to 222 mg. (71%) of 2,4-dinitrophenylhydrazone. After three crystallizations from dioxane, the 2,4-dinitrophenylhydrazone had m.p. 240° and a radioactivity assay of 0.2109 ± 0.0005 mc./mole, corresponding to 12.9% rearrangement of the carbon-14 label.

The filtrate from which the 422 mg. of 1,2,2-triphenylethyl acetate was obtained was concentrated, then diluted to 10 cc. in a volumetric flask with hexane. A 25-cc. sample was placed on a column of alumina then washed with hexane until no more 1,1,2-triphenylethylene could be obtained. On concentration of the hexane solution there was obtained 48 mg. of olefin (3.5%) which crystallized when scratched with a spatula. The olefin fraction was dissolved in 4 cc. of glacial acetic acid, then oxidized with 50 mg. of CrO₃. The benzophenone isolated therefrom was converted to 40.0 mg. of 2,4-dinitrophenylhydrazone which, after one crystallization from dioxane–ethanol, had a radioactivity assay of 0.6007 ± 0.0007 mc./mole, corresponding to 36.8% carbon-14 rearrangement.

The remaining 75 cc. of hexane solution mentioned in the preceding paragraph was subjected to chromatography on alumina. After the olefin had been removed with hexane, the column was eluted with benzene–hexane and finally with benzene, yielding an additional 200 mg. of 1,2,2-triphenylethyl acetate. (From the weight of this sample of acetate, plus the 422 mg. obtained previously, it can be estimated that the total yield of 1,2,2-triphenylethyl acetate obtained in the deamination of 1,2,2-triphenylethylamine represents about 8% of the product.) After the acetate had been removed, there was obtained in the benzene eluent 431 mg. of 1,2,2-triphenylethanol of $[\alpha]^{25}$D −83°; the sample was dissolved in hexane, placed on a column of alumina. The column was washed with benzene to yield an initial fraction of 97.5 mg. of carbinol whose $[\alpha]^{25}$D −91.8°, and whose benzophenone oxidation fragment (102 mg. of 2,4-dinitrophenylhydrazone) had a radioactivity assay of 0.3375 ± 0.0015 mc./mole, corresponding to 20.68% rearrangement of the carbon-14 label.

The two alumina columns above were washed thoroughly with ethanol, and the resultant carbinol fractions therefrom were combined with all remaining carbinol fractions from the deamination. The 3.62 g. of carbinol so obtained was converted to 1,2,2-triphenylethyl acetate, and crystallized fractionally from ethanol. In this way there was obtained 603 mg. of acetate of $[\alpha]^{25}$D −59°, m.p. 122° (hot-bank), m.p.128–129° (capillary). This was deacetylated with lithium aluminum hydride to yield 446 mg. of 1,2,2-triphenylethanol, $[\alpha]^{24.7}$D −118°. The 446 mg. of carbinol was oxidized as usual, and the purified benzophenone 2,4-dinitrophenylhydrazone had a radioactivity assay of 0.3367 ± 0.0015 mc./mole, corresponding to 20.62% rearrangement of the carbon-14 label. Another fraction of 1,2,2-triphenylethylacetate (383 mg., $[\alpha]^{25}$D −1.72°) was converted to 1,2,2-triphenylethanol (322 mg., $[\alpha]^{25}$D −5.4°). Oxidation[6] of this material yielded benzophenone whose 2,4-dinitrophenylhydrazone, when purified, had a radioactivity assay of 0.4008 ± 0.0008 mc./mole, corresponding to 24.52% carbon-14 rearrangement. Finally there was obtained 957 mg. of essentially racemic 1,2,2-triphenylethyl acetate, $[\alpha]^{25}$D −0.24°, which was converted to 800 mg. of carbinol by

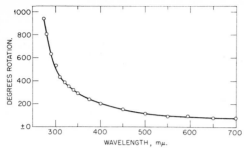

Fig. 2.—Optical rotary dispersion curve, (+)-N-acetyl-1,2,2-triphenylethylamine in methanol at 26° (c 0.0885)

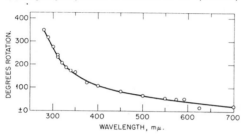

Fig. 3.—Optical rotary dispersion curve, (+)-1,2,2-triphenylethyl acetate in methanol at 26° (c 0.0845).

treatment with lithium aluminum hydride. After two crystallizations from acetic acid there was obtained 477 mg. of 1,2,2-triphenylethanol, m.p. 86°, whose benzophenone oxidation fragment, as the purified 2,4-dinitrophenylhydrazone, had a radioactivity assay of 0.3975 ± 0.0050 mc./mole, which corresponds to a rearrangement of the carbon-14 label of 24.5%.

Stability of 1,2,2-Triphenylethanol-1-C^{14} Under Conditions of the Deamination.—A sample of 1,2,2-triphenylethanol-1-C^{14} (2.12 mc./mole, 300 mg.) was dissolved in 5 cc. of acetic acid, then treated with 10 cc. of water containing 0.04 cc. of concentrated HCl. The solution was cooled to −2° and 0.2 g. of NaNO$_2$ in 4 cc. of H$_2$O was added. The mixture was stirred at −2° for 30 minutes, and then worked up as a normal deamination product. Oxidation of the carbinol with CrO$_3$ to benzhydryl phenyl ketone was followed by degradation[6] of this ketone to benzophenone. The 2,4-dinitrophenylhydrazone obtained therefrom was non-radioactive.

Non-racemization of (−)-1,2,2-Triphenylethanol under Conditions of the Deamination.—A 505-mg. sample of (−)-1,2,2-triphenylethanol, [α]^{25}D −122° (ethanol), m.p. 82-83°, was treated with 1 cc. of glacial acetic acid, 28 cc. of water and 0.2 cc. of concd. HCl. The mixture was heated to 80° and to it was added 1.2 g. of NaNO$_2$ in 12 cc. of water. After 40 minutes the carbinol was reisolated as a yellow sirup, which crystallized on standing; yield 488 mg., [α]^{25}D −121°.

Configurational Relationship of (+)-1,2,2-Triphenylethyl amine and (+)-1,2,2-Triphenylethanol.—Presumptive evidence of like configuration of (+)-1,2,2-triphenylethyl amine and of (+)-1,2,2-triphenylethanol is to be found in the optical rotary dispersion curves[23] (Figs. 2 and 3). Additional presumptive evidence is given in Figs. 4 and 5, respectively, representing the solid–liquid phase relationships[17e] of (+)-1,2,2-triphenylethyl acetate with (+)- and (−)-N-acetyl-1,2,2-triphenylethylamine. Although there is no evidence of eutectic or *quasi*-racemate formation, the *solidi* are characteristically different, sufficient to allow the tentative conclusion that the two derivatives of positive sign possess the same configuration. Finally, 1.3 g. of N-acetyl-1,2,2-triphenylethylamine (m.p. 230°, [α]^{25}D +108°) was added with stirring at 0° to 500 cc. of carbon tetrachlo-

(23) The optical rotary dispersion data were kindly furnished by Professor Carl Djerassi.

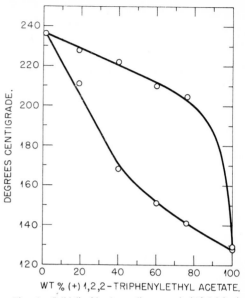

Fig. 4.—Solid–liquid phase diagram of (+)-1,2,2-triphenylethyl acetate with (+)-N-acetyl-1,2,2-triphenylethylamine.

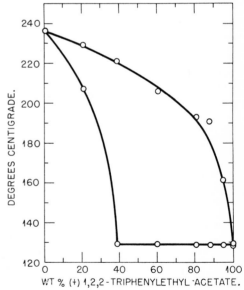

Fig. 5.—Solid–liquid phase diagram of (+)-1,2,2-triphenylethyl acetate with (−)-N-acetyl-1,2,2-triphenylethylamine.

ride containing 8 g. of N$_2$O$_4$[17g,h] and 12 g. of anhydrous sodium acetate. After 2 hours the mixture was poured over ice, after which the organic layer was separated, washed with sodium carbonate, water and then dried over magnesium sulfate. Unreacted N-acetyl-12,2-triphenylethylamine (0.7 g.) was recovered during the work-up. The dried carbon tetrachloride solution was heated under gentle reflux overnight, cooled and shaken with 5% sodium hydroxide solution, water, and finally dried over magnesium sulfate and evaporated. The solid material was taken up in hot 95% ethanol once the solution was treated with Norit and filtered. In this way 160 mg. of (+)-1,2,2-triphenyl-ethyl acetate was isolated, m.p. 140°, $[\alpha]^{25}D$ +26° (dioxane). Still more N-acetyl-1,2,2-triphenylethylamine remained in the alcoholic mother liquors. The identity of the (+)-1,2,2-triphenylethyl acetate was established by deacetylation to (+)-1,2,2-triphenylethanol, followed by oxidation of the carbinol to benzhydryl phenyl ketone. The ketone was oxidized[6] with nitric–acetic acid to α-phenyl-benzoin which was oxidized with chromic acid to benzophenone and benzoic acid.[24]

---

(24) The preparation of the N-nitrosoacyl-1,2,2-triphenylethylamine and its subsequent thermal decomposition were carried out by Mrs. Joan B. Christie. Further details will be published at a later date.

Oak Ridge, Tenn.
Stanford, Calif.

38 | Migration Aptitudes

The paper by Stiles and Mayer makes it clear why there should have been so much confusion in the earlier literature concerning the relative migration aptitudes of the aliphatic groups in the pinacol or Wagner-Meerwein rearrangement. The authors place methyl, ethyl, and tertiary butyl groups in turn in an environment which is otherwise constant. By a combination of rate, product, and tracer analysis they find out how fast the group is migrating in each case. To reconcile the results with previous knowledge of the dependence of the rate of the pinacol rearrangement upon acidity, and of oxygen isotope exchange, the authors propose an intermediate which is like an intimate ion pair, except that the anion is replaced by the uncharged H_2O ionically bound to carbon. In the cationic partner of this pair, neighboring alkyl groups compete for migration to the positively charged carbon atom.

None of the simple, one-piece conceptions of the pinacol rearrangement can handle the facts as developed in this paper. In Stiles and Mayer's compound IIb the migration of methyl from the less to the more crowded center, from the more to the less crowded center, and the migration of ethyl are 3.9, 5.1, and 17 times as rapid, respectively, as that of a single methyl in pinacol under corresponding conditions. The fastest process does not correspond to the greatest relief of strain, but to that transition state in which the "best" cationic group is on its way between adjacent carbons.

From: *J. Am. Chem. Soc.* **81**, 1497–1503 (1959)

[CONTRIBUTION FROM THE DEPARTMENT OF CHEMISTRY OF THE UNIVERSITY OF MICHIGAN]

Rearrangement of Alkyl Groups. Kinetic and Tracer Studies in the Pinacol Rearrangement[1]

BY MARTIN STILES AND RAYMOND P. MAYER[2]

RECEIVED SEPTEMBER 4, 1958

The rearrangement of 2,3-dimethyl-2,3-pentanediol (IIb) in aqueous sulfuric acid yielded 83% methyl *t*-amyl ketone and 17% ethyl *t*-butyl ketone. Isotopic labeling showed that the methyl ketone arose both by ethyl migration (69%) and methyl migration (31%). Similar rearrangement of 2,3,4,4-tetramethyl-2,3-pentanediol (IIc) led to 98.6% methyl triptyl ketone and 1.4% hexamethylacetone. In this case the methyl ketone was shown to result entirely from *t*-butyl migration. The relative rates of rearrangement of pinacol (IIa), IIb and IIc were $1.0 : 7.2 : >10^3$. The tendencies of alkyl groups to migrate in this rearrangement are expressed in terms of partial rates, which are in the ratio $>4000 : 17 : 1$ for *t*-butyl, ethyl and methyl, respectively. A reaction mechanism is discussed in the light of these and other recent results.

Rearrangements which involve the 1,2-shift of an aryl group to an electrophilic carbon atom are generally believed to pass through an intermediate or transition state of the phenonium ion[3] type (I). In this process the C-1 of the aromatic ring has increased its coördination number from 3 to 4 and has altered its hybridization in the direction of the tetrahedral arrangement. So far as the migrating group is concerned the process is analogous to

normal aromatic substitution, the similarity of the intermediates[4] and substituent effects for the two processes being generally recognized.

The nature of the transition state for the 1,2-shift of a saturated alkyl group is much more obscure. Although such rearrangements are very common, a detailed description of the process has not been attempted. Particularly interesting is the nature of the valence state of the carbon atom undergoing migration, which appears to have a coördination number of 5. If considered as a displacement reaction upon the alkyl group the process involves a charge type (electrophilic) and stereochemistry (retention of configuration) which are uncommon in the chemistry of saturated aliphatic compounds. Only with organometallic derivatives[5] does an analogous process seem likely, and at present the chemistry of this class of compounds is not sufficiently understood to aid in the interpretation of alkyl migration.

Furthermore, no systematic information is available concerning the effect of structural variation upon the migration tendencies of alkyl groups. The results of Meerwein,[6] Nybergh,[7] and Reeve and Karickhoff[8] indicated that ethyl migration predominates over methyl in the pinacol rearrangement,

but Cram and Knight[9] found a large preference for methyl migration in the rearrangement which accompanies the solvolysis of 3,4-dimethyl-4-phenyl-3-hexyl *p*-bromobenzenesulfonate.

More precise reactivity data would be a logical starting point in attempting a detailed description of alkyl group rearrangements. The aim of the present work was to evaluate the performance of some simple alkyl groups in the pinacol rearrangement. The system chosen for study was the family of glycols II. Locquin[10] studied the rearrangement of this series

a, R = CH$_3$; b, R = C$_2$H$_5$; c, R = *t*-C$_4$H$_9$

where the dissimilar group R was ethyl, *n*-propyl, isopropyl, *n*-butyl, isobutyl and *t*-butyl, and reported that the chief product in each case was the methyl ketone III. This result was not useful in comparing the migration of methyl and the other alkyl groups, however, since III could arise by either R migration or methyl migration. We have separated the products (III and IV) of the rearrangement of glycols IIb and IIc by vapor-phase chromatography, and have used isotopic labeling to determine the extent to which the methyl ketone III arose by R migration.[11] This information, coupled with the results of a kinetic study of the rearrangement of IIa, IIb and IIc, has allowed a com-

(1) Presented before the Division of Organic Chemistry, American Chemical Society, Chicago, Ill., September, 1958; Abstracts, p. 9P.

(2) Based upon the Ph. D. thesis of Raymond P. Mayer, University of Michigan, 1958.

(3) D. J. Cram, THIS JOURNAL, **71**, 3863 (1949).

(4) L. Melander, *Arkiv Kemi*, **2**, 211 (1950).

(5) S. Winstein and T. G. Traylor, THIS JOURNAL, **78**, 2597 (1956), and earlier papers.

(6) H. Meerwein, *Ann.*, **419**, 121 (1919).

(7) B. Nybergh, *Ber.*, **55**, 1960 (1922).

(8) W. Reeve and M. Karickhoff, THIS JOURNAL, **78**, 6053 (1956).

(9) D. J. Cram and J. D. Knight, *ibid.*, **74**, 5839 (1952).

(10) R. Locquin and W. Sung, *Bull. soc. chim.*, [4] **35**, 753 (1924); *Compt. rend.*, **178**, 1179 (1924); R. Locquin and L. Leers, *Bull. soc. chim.*, [4] **39**, 426, 433 (1926).

(11) Kinetic isotope effects were neglected in interpreting the tracer results. Duncan and Lynn [*Austral. J. Chem.*, **10**, 7 (1957)] have reported an extraordinarily large rate difference (more than a factor of two) between pinacol and pinacol containing C^{14} in rearrangements carried out in aqueous acid at 78°, 100° and 113.5°, although no rate difference was detected. We have found (M. Stiles and R. B. Bernstein, unpublished results) the ratio k_{12}/k_{13} to be less than 1.007 at 100°, where k_{12} is the rate constant for rearrangement of molecules containing only C^{12}, and k_{13} that for molecules containing one C^{13} atom. Since the C^{13} was randomly distributed in the molecule, this isotope effect must be multiplied by a factor of 6, yielding a value of *ca.* 4% for the *maximum* C^{13}-isotope effect for a single carbon atom. This suggests that the C^{12}/C^{14} isotope effect would be only as large as 8–9% even if it were confined to a single carbon atom. NOTE ADDED OCTOBER 6, 1958: V. F. Raaen and C. J. Collins, THIS JOURNAL, **80**, 4432 (1958), have now reinvestigated the C^{14}-isotope effect and have shown that it is less than 1%.

plete evaluation of methyl, ethyl and *t*-butyl as migrating groups in this system.

Results

Tracer Study.—The two labeled glycols IIb and IIc were prepared as indicated in the flow diagrams. Each step in the synthesis of both compounds was based on published procedures except the reaction of pivalyl chloride with dimethylcadmium, which gave disappointing yields (*ca.* 10%). The low yield is particularly puzzling in view of the fact that methyl *t*-amyl ketone could be prepared in 61% yield by the same method. The use of methyllithium instead of methyl Grignard reagent in the final step allowed isolation of the glycols without acidification.

$$CH_3CH_2\overset{\overset{O}{\|}}{C}CH_3 \xrightarrow[\text{2, H}_3\text{O}^+]{\text{1, NaC*N}} CH_3CH_2\overset{\overset{OH}{|}}{\underset{\underset{CH_3}{|}}{C}}C^*O_2H \xrightarrow[\text{2, CH}_3\text{Li}]{\text{1, CH}_2\text{N}_2}$$

$$CH_3CH_2\overset{\overset{OH\ \ \ OH}{|\ \ \ \ \ |}}{\underset{\underset{CH_3\ \ CH_3}{|\ \ \ \ \ |}}{C\text{—}C^*CH_3}}$$
IIb

$$CH_3\overset{\overset{CH_3}{|}}{\underset{\underset{CH_3}{|}}{C}}Cl \xrightarrow[\text{2, C*O}_2]{\text{1, Li}} CH_3\overset{\overset{CH_3}{|}}{\underset{\underset{CH_3}{|}}{C}}C^*O_2H \xrightarrow[\text{2, (CH}_3)_2\text{Cd}]{\text{1, SOCl}_2}$$

$$CH_3\overset{\overset{CH_3}{|}}{\underset{\underset{CH_3}{|}}{C}}\overset{\overset{O}{\|}}{C^*}\text{—}CH_3 \xrightarrow[\text{2, CH}_2\text{N}_2]{\text{1, KMnO}_4}$$

$$CH_3\overset{\overset{CH_3}{|}}{\underset{\underset{CH_3}{|}}{C}}\overset{\overset{O}{\|}}{C^*}\text{—CO}_2CH_3 \xrightarrow{\text{CH}_3\text{Li}} CH_3\overset{\overset{CH_3}{|}}{\underset{\underset{CH_3}{|}}{C}}\overset{\overset{OH}{|}}{\underset{\underset{CH_3}{|}}{C^*}}\overset{\overset{OH}{|}}{\underset{\underset{CH_3}{|}}{C}}CH_3$$
IIc

The glycol IIb rearranged at room temperature in 50% aqueous sulfuric acid, conditions under which the ketones IIIb and IVb are stable,[12] to give a mixture of ketones in 78% yield. The composition of the mixture was revealed to be 83% methyl *t*-amyl ketone (IIIb) and 17% ethyl *t*-butyl ketone (IVb) by vapor-phase chromatographic separation.

The glycol IIc rearranged completely in a few minutes with 50% sulfuric acid, which does not cause any measurable change[13] in IIIc and IVc, to give a 78% yield of a liquid product whose infrared spectrum was essentially that of IIIc. The product was separated by vapor-phase chromatography into a small fraction (5%) which was probably unsaturated hydrocarbon, and the two ketones IIIc and IVc in a ratio of 72 to 1.

The methyl ketones IIIb and IIIc were degraded by hypochlorite oxidation to the carboxylic acids Vb and Vc, respectively, which were converted to the amides and thence *via* the Hofmann rearrangement to the carbamate esters, which were hydrolyzed and decarboxylated to the amine hydrochlorides VIb and VIc. Since hexamethylacetone (IVc) is inert to hypohalite it did not give rise to any degradation products to contaminate those from the methyl ketone IIIc. Ethyl *t*-alkyl ketones are attacked by hypochlorite,[14] however, and the acid Vb obtained in the oxidation was presumed to be contaminated with a small quantity of pivalic acid (Va). Nevertheless Vb gave a crystalline amide which appeared to be pure dimethyl-*t*-butylacetamide, and the amine hydrochloride obtained in the final degradation was shown to contain only 2.4% *t*-butylamine hydrochloride (VIa) as a contaminant in VIb. The composition was determined by vapor-phase chromatographic separation of the pure amines, using authentic samples for comparison. A correction was applied to the radiochemical assay data to allow for the presence of 2.4% VIa.

$$R\overset{\overset{CH_3}{|}}{\underset{\underset{CH_3}{|}}{C}}\overset{\overset{O}{\|}}{C}CH_2 \xrightarrow{\text{KOCl}} R\overset{\overset{CH_3}{|}}{\underset{\underset{CH_3}{|}}{C}}CO_2H \xrightarrow[\substack{\text{3, NaOH}\\\text{4, HCl}}]{\substack{\text{1, SOCl}_2;\ \text{NH}_3\\\text{2, Br}_2 + \text{NaOCH}_3}}$$

III V

$$R\overset{\overset{CH_3}{|}}{\underset{\underset{CH_3}{|}}{\overset{+}{C}}}NH_3Cl^- + CO_2$$
VI

a, R = CH₃; b, R = C₂H₅; c, R = *t*-C₄H₉

The counting data are given in Table I and the results of the tracer study are expressed in equations 1 and 2. The carbon dioxide was counted as barium carbonate and the amines as the solid hydrochlorides. Various plate thicknesses were used and the results tabulated were obtained by extrapolation to zero thickness.

TABLE I

RADIOCHEMICAL ASSAY OF DEGRADATION PRODUCTS

Starting ketone	Degradation product	Counts/min./mmole
IIIb	Acid Vb	4380[a]
	Amine VIb	2870
	BaCO₃	1300
IIIc	Acid Vc	2080
	Amine VIc	0
	BaCO₃	2010

[a] Counted as the solid amide.

IIb →

$$CH_3\overset{\overset{O}{\|}}{C}\text{—}\overset{\overset{CH_3}{|}}{\underset{\underset{CH_3}{|}}{C^*}}\text{-CH}_2CH_3 \quad CH_3CH_2\overset{\overset{H_2C\ \ \ O}{|\ \ \ \ \|}}{\underset{\underset{CH_3}{|}}{C^*}}\text{-CH}_3 \quad CH_3CH_2\overset{\overset{O}{\|}}{C}\text{—}\overset{\overset{CH_3}{|}}{\underset{\underset{CH_3}{|}}{C}}CH_3$$
57%   26%   17%   (1)

IIc →

$$CH_3\overset{\overset{O}{\|}}{C^*}\text{—}\overset{\overset{CH_3\ \ CH_3}{|\ \ \ \ \ |}}{\underset{\underset{CH_3\ \ CH_3}{|\ \ \ \ \ |}}{C}}\text{-CCH}_3 \quad CH_3\overset{\overset{CH_3\ \ CH_3\ \ O}{|\ \ \ \ \ |\ \ \ \ \|}}{\underset{\underset{CH_3\ \ CH_3}{|\ \ \ \ \ |}}{C}}\text{-}C^*\text{-CCH}_3$$
98.6%   0%

$$CH_3\overset{\overset{CH_3\ \ O\ \ \ CH_3}{|\ \ \ \ \|\ \ \ \ \ |}}{\underset{\underset{CH_3\ \ \ \ \ CH_3}{|\ \ \ \ \ \ \ \ \ |}}{C}}\text{-}\overset{}{C}\text{-CCH}_3 \quad (2)$$
1.4%

Kinetic Study.—The rates of rearrangement of IIa-IIc are summarized in Table II. The reactions were followed by infrared analysis of carbon tetrachloride solutions of the quenched reaction

(12) H. D. Zook, W. E. Smith and J. L. Greene, THIS JOURNAL, **79**, 4436 (1957).

(13) M. Stiles and R. P. Mayer, *Chemistry & Industry*, 1357 (1957).

(14) H. Meerwein, *Ann.*, **396**, 253 (1913).

mixtures. The rates of IIa and IIb were followed to 70–75% completion. Glycol IIc was completely rearranged in 5 minutes at 25° in 49.22% sulfuric acid and accurate rate data could not be obtained. The use of lower acidities or lower temperatures, where the reaction would be slower, was not feasible because of reduced solubility. The figure for the first order rate constant for this compound is a minimum value, calculated from the fact that reaction was at least 99% complete in 5 minutes.

TABLE II
FIRST-ORDER RATE CONSTANTS FOR REARRANGEMENT IN AQUEOUS SULFURIC ACID

| | 10^5k_{obs}, sec.$^{-1}$ at 25.0° | |
	49.22% H_2SO_4	59.16% H_2SO_4
IIa	0.0150	0.145[a]
	.0145[a]	
IIb	.108	0.952
IIc	>15	

[a] Interpolated from data of Deno and Perizzolo, ref. (22).

Discussion

Migration Tendencies.—The pattern of rearrangement of pinacols has usually been correlated in terms of migration aptitudes,[15] which expressed the rate of rearrangement of a substituent relative to some standard substituent in the same molecule, such as a phenyl group. This *intramolecular* comparison, when applied to symmetrical aromatic pinacols, yields information useful in predicting the course of some untried rearrangement. However, it does not constitute a theoretically valid description of any property of the migrating group which is independent of other substituents on the pinacol molecule. In the present series, for example, the migration aptitude of the group R would be expressed in terms of its superiority over methyl, by comparing the rate of the processes symbolized by VII and VIII.[16] By this method the migration

	a, R = CH_3
	b, R = C_2H_5
	c, R = t-C_4H_9

aptitudes of the ethyl and t-butyl groups are determined from the product ratios (eq. 1 and 2) to be 3.4 and 72, respectively. These two processes differ by factors other than those inherent in the migrating group, however, the importance of β-substitution having been amply demonstrated[17] in rearrangements of the Wagner–Meerwein type.

We propose therefore to utilize *intermolecular* comparisons in describing the migration tendencies of substituents. A comparison of the rates of the process symbolized by VII for a series of pinacols should constitute a valid comparison of the differ-

(15) M. Tiffeneau and A. Orekhoff, *Bull. soc. chim.*, **35**, 1639 (1924).

(16) Structures VII and VIII are intended only as symbols for R– and CH$_3$–migration and do not attempt to describe the transition state. It should be emphasized that the partial rates, k_p, described in this paper are not dependent upon any assumptions concerning the reaction mechanism except the acidity dependence described by equation 4.

(17) S. Winstein, C. R. Lindegren, H. Marshall and L. L. Ingraham, THIS JOURNAL, **75**, 117 (1953).

ent R groups.[18] In order to make these intermolecular comparisons one has to know the over-all rate of rearrangement of each pinacol, and the fraction (α) of the over-all process which involves migration of the dissimilar group. It is convenient to define a partial rate, k_p

$$k_p = \alpha k \qquad (3)$$

where k is the acidity-independent first-order rate constant,[19] k_{obs} is the observed first-order rate constant at a particular value of the Hammett acidity

$$k = k_{obs} K_A / h_0 \qquad (4)$$

function h_0, and K_A is the acid dissociation constant of protonated pinacol. The migration tendency, M_{CH_3}, of any group R compared to methyl may then be expressed as the ratio of partial rates as in equation 5 where the superscripts identify

$$M_{CH_3} = \frac{k_p^R}{k_p^{CH_3}} = \frac{\alpha^R k_{obs}^R K_A^R h_0^{CH_3}}{\alpha^{CH_3} k_{obs}^{CH_3} K_A^{CH_3} h_0^R} \qquad (5)$$

the migrating group. All of the quantities necessary to determine M_{CH_3} are readily measured except K_A. If it is assumed that K_A does not vary appreciably for a series of pinacols such as II, the migration tendency M_{CH_3} for the ethyl and t-butyl groups may be calculated to have the values shown in Table III. If values for individual dissociation constants, K_A, become available, a refinement in the calculation of M_{CH_3} will be possible.

TABLE III
MIGRATION TENDENCIES OF ALKYL GROUPS

Group	α	10^6k_p, sec.$^{-1}$	M_{CH_3}
CH_3	0.25	0.19 K_A^{Me}	1.0
C_2H_5	0.57	3.2 K_A^{Et}	17
t-C_4H_9	0.99	>700 K_A^{tBu}	>4000

The inapplicability of the older migration aptitude formulation to aliphatic pinacols is illustrated by comparison of the rates of the processes symbolized by VIII. In the present series the relative values of the partial rates, k_p, for pinacols where R is methyl, ethyl and t-butyl are 1:4.7:54. Thus a non-migrating ethyl group in the β-position increases the rate of methyl migration by almost 5 times and a β-t-butyl group increases it more than 50-fold.

Reaction Mechanism.—The striking rate differences in the series IIa–IIc provide a strong argument for a mechanism in which bond formation between C_α and the migrating group occurs in a

(18) It should be pointed out that while this comparison is a much better measure of the migration tendency than the earlier one, it still neglects possible second-order differences between VIIa, b, and c due to variation in the extent of positive character of Cβ as R is varied; this variation would result in different degrees of interaction between Cβ and the non-migrating group.

(19) This acidity dependence has been demonstrated rigorously only in the rearrangement of pinacol[20–23] in aqueous acids, and benzopinacol in acetic–perchloric acid mixtures.[24] We made no effort to establish this acidity dependence in the present work, but it may be noted that the data for glycol IIb are reasonably consistent ($-\Delta$ log $k/\Delta H_0 = 0.86$) with this formulation and not with other likely dependences.

(20) J. F. Duncan and K. R. Lynn, *J. Chem. Soc.*, 3512 (1956).

(21) J. B. Ley and C. A. Vernon, *ibid.*, 2987 (1957).

(22) N. C. Deno and C. Perizzolo, *J. Org. Chem.*, **22**, 836 (1957).

(23) C. A. Bunton, T. Hadwick, D. R. Llewellyn and Y. Pocker, *J. Chem. Soc.*, 403 (1958).

(24) H. J. Gebhart, Jr., and K. H. Adams, THIS JOURNAL, **76**, 3925 (1954).

slow step. This conclusion, when considered in the light of the acidity dependence for the rearrangement, indicates that the carbonium ion mechanism (eq. 6) frequently proposed[21,23,25] is inadequate.

$$
\underset{\substack{\text{OH} \ \oplus\text{OH}_2 \\ [\text{ROH}_2{}^+]}}{\text{RC}---\text{CR}} \underset{k_2}{\overset{k_1}{\rightleftharpoons}} \underset{\substack{\text{OH} \quad \text{R} \\ [\text{R}^+]}}{\text{RC}-\oplus\text{C}} \overset{k_3}{\rightarrow} \underset{\text{R} \ \oplus\text{OH}_2}{\text{RC}---\text{CR}} \quad (6)
$$

If one assumes a "steady state" concentration of the carbonium ion, the observed rate of rearrangement can be expressed as in equation 7 where the brackets denote concentration, f_i is the activity co-

$$
v = \frac{k_1 k_3 [\text{ROH}_2{}^+](f_{\text{ROH}_2{}^+} f_{\text{R}^+}/f_{\text{X}_1} f_{\text{X}_2})}{k_2 [\text{H}_2\text{O}](f_{\text{R}^+} f_{\text{H}_2\text{O}}/f_{\text{X}_1}) + k_3 (f_{\text{R}^+}/f_{\text{X}_2})} \quad (7)
$$

efficient of species i, referred to dilute aqueous solution, and X_1 and X_2 refer to the transition states for the formation and decomposition of R^+. The limiting case where $k_2[\text{H}_2\text{O}](f_{\text{R}^+} f_{\text{H}_2\text{O}}/f_{\text{X}_1}) << k_3(f_{\text{R}^+}/f_{\text{X}_2})$ is eliminated since the rate equation then reduces to 8, which, though consistent with the de-

$$
v = k_1 [\text{ROH}_2{}^+](f_{\text{ROH}_2{}^+}/f_{\text{X}_1}) \quad (8)
$$

pendence on H_0, predicts no dependence on the rearrangement step k_3.[26] The other limiting case, where $k_2[\text{H}_2\text{O}](f_{\text{R}^+} f_{\text{H}_2\text{O}}/f_{\text{X}_1}) >> k_3(f_{\text{R}^+}/f_{\text{X}_2})$ leads to 9, which predicts[27]

$$
v = (k_1 k_3/k_2)[\text{ROH}_2{}^+](f_{\text{ROH}_2{}^+}/a_{\text{H}_2\text{O}} f_{\text{X}_2}) \quad (9)
$$

a dependence of the rate upon C_0 rather than H_0. If the two terms in the denominator of eq. 7 are comparable then the dependence should be intermediate between the two acidity functions. All kinetic results so far reported[20-24] indicate a strict H_0 dependence.[28] It would thus appear that equation 6 fails to account for the data at hand regardless of the relative rates of the various steps.

The large rate enhancement provided by groups which are demonstrably more prone to migrate than methyl groups, and the dependence of the the rearrangement upon the stereochemistry of the pinacol,[8,20,21] both point to a mechanism in which the removal of water from the protonated pinacol is anchimerically assisted by the migrating alkyl

group.[32] The acidity dependence is consistent with the idea that this process (eq. 10) is the kinetically measurable one.

$$
\underset{\substack{\text{OH} \ \bullet\text{OH}_2}}{\overset{\substack{\text{R} \quad \text{R} \\ \frown}}{\text{R}-\text{C}-\text{C}-\text{R}}} \longrightarrow \underset{\substack{\bullet\text{OH} \quad \text{R}}}{\overset{\text{R}}{\text{R}-\text{C}-\text{C}-\text{R}}} \quad (10)
$$

However this picture needs modification in view of recent experiments by Bunton, Hadwick, Llewellyn and Pocker.[23] These investigators found that pinacol which was recovered from an interrupted rearrangement reaction had partially exchanged its oxygen with that of the solvent, O^{18}-enriched water. Except for the seemingly remote possibility that the exchange reaction is a bimolecular attack of a water molecule upon the conjugate acid,[34] it would involve intermediates which need to be considered in any mechanism for the rearrangement. The simple carbonium ion, for example, would be expected to rearrange at least as readily as the conjugate acid, and therefore cannot be excluded from the rearrangement mechanism without exclusion from the exchange reaction also.

It is possible that pinacol (IIa) rearranges both by a carbonium ion path (eq. 6) and a concerted path (eq. 10), the former being responsible for the oxygen exchange. The enhanced rates of IIb and IIc would indicate complete dominance by the latter mechanism in these cases. However the importance of anchimeric assistance in ionizations at a tertiary carbon atom remains in doubt at present, and for this reason the mechanism represented by eq. 11 is favored. In this mechanism both rearrangement and oxygen exchange are preceded by the formation of a "carbonium hydrate." This intermediate is pictured as containing the original H_2O bound by a p-orbital to C_α, and is essentially

$$
\underset{\substack{\text{OH} \ \oplus\text{OH}_2}}{\overset{\substack{\text{R} \quad \text{R}}}{\text{RC}---\text{CR}}} \underset{k''}{\overset{k'}{\rightleftharpoons}} \left[\underset{\substack{\text{OH} \quad \text{OH}_2}}{\overset{\substack{\text{R} \\ \text{RC}_\beta-\alpha\text{C} \overset{\cdot\cdot}{\underset{\text{R}}{\cdot\cdot}} \text{R}}}{}} \right]^+ \quad (11)
$$

$$
\text{exchange of water} \quad \updownarrow \quad \downarrow k_{\text{R}} \quad \text{pinacolone} \times \text{H}^+
$$

that proposed by Doering and Zeiss[34] for solvolytic reactions. It is structurally analogous to an "intimate ion pair."[35] The rearrangement process (k_{R}) involves a backside displacement of the water molecule by a neighboring R group, similar to the process of eq. 10, except that the attack is upon a carbon atom whose geometry and hybridization make it considerably more vulnerable to such displacement than the conjugate acid of pinacol would be.

(25) F. A. Long and M. A. Paul, Chem. Revs., 57, 975 (1957).

(26) A referee has pointed out the possibility that k_1 is highly sensitive to steric acceleration, which would increase in the series IIa-IIc, and that equation 8 is the correct rate equation. Steric strain would appear to be more effectively alleviated by the loss of the hydroxyl group from the carbon atom bearing the largest groups, however, and since this path is not observed with IIc and makes a minor (26%) contribution in the case of IIb, we think it unlikely that the observed rate differences are due to steric acceleration in carbonium ion formation. It should be kept in mind, however, that the relief of steric strain may be an important factor in the large migration tendency of the t-butyl group.

(27) N. C. Deno, J. J. Jaruzelski and A. Schriesheim, THIS JOURNAL, 77, 3044 (1955).

(28) Evidence has recently been presented[1b,29] to suggest that the applicability of the H_0 and C_0 functions to kinetic data depends on the structure of the intermediate ions and the transition state (X) in rather subtle ways, and that equality of empirical formula between X and $\text{ROH}_2{}^+$ or R^+ may be only one of several factors. However there seems to be general agreement[28,29] that a reaction such as eq. 7 (where $k_7 > k_2$) should follow C_0 more closely than H_0.

(29) N. C. Deno and A. C. Perizzolo, THIS JOURNAL, 79, 1345 (1957).

(30) P. D. Bartlett and R. F. Brown, ibid., 62, 2927 (1940).

(31) E. R. Alexander and D. C. Dittmer, ibid., 73, 1665 (1951).

(32) S. Winstein and L. L. Ingraham, ibid., 77, 1738 (1955), have discussed the various possibilities for anchimeric assistance in the pinacol rearrangement.

(33) Such a mechanism was proposed [N. C. Deno, T. Edwards, and C. Perizzolo, ibid., 79, 2108 (1957)] for the exchange between tertiary butyl and secondary butyl alcohols and water. In the pinacol case, however, it seems highly unlikely in view of the "neopentyl" character of the carbon undergoing substitution.

(34) W. E. Doering and H. Zeiss, ibid., 75, 4733 (1953); see also the discussion by A. Streitwieser, Chem. Revs., 56, 571 (1956).

(35) S. Winstein, E. Clippinger, A. H. Fainberg and G. C. Robinson, THIS JOURNAL, 76, 2597 (1954).

The dissociation–rearrangement mechanism represented by eq. 11 is analogous to the Wagner Meerwein rearrangements which accompany many solvolytic reactions, but at least one important difference should be mentioned. The driving force for rearrangement is normally much greater in the pinacol case, due to the stabilization provided by the incipient carbonyl group. Thus, even though the dissociation takes place at a tertiary carbon atom, rearrangement occurs at a relatively early stage, while the water molecule is still weakly bonded to C_α.

If one assumes a "steady-state" approximation for the mechanism of eq. 11, the rate is given by

$$v = \frac{k_R k'[ROH_2^+]}{k' + k_R} \quad (12)$$

provided the Hammett–Zucker hypothesis is assumed to apply to both steps. In order to explain the observed variation of the rate in the series IIa–IIc, k' must be much larger than k_R, at least for the first two compounds in the series.

The exchange of water between the carbonium hydrate and the solvent might occur either by a direct displacement reaction between a solvent water molecule and the intermediate, which would invert the configuration of C_α, or by participation of the neighboring hydroxyl group to give an intermediate similar to the protonated epoxide. No data are at hand to distinguish between these two possibilities although clarifying stereochemical experiments can be envisaged.

The intervention of carbonium hydrate intermediates similar to the one in eq. 11 serves also to explain several recently investigated reactions which otherwise exhibit contradictory kinetic and stereochemical features. Noteworthy are the exchange of O^{18} between 2-butanol and aqueous acid,[36] which exhibits complete stereochemical inversion, apparently without kinetic dependence upon water, and the acid-catalyzed opening of substituted ethylene oxides[37] which also occurs by inversion without kinetic dependence on the nucleophile. In these two cases the carbonium hydrate must be attacked by a solvent molecule more rapidly than it collapses to form the conjugate acid of the substrate. The ratio of the two processes is thus essentially the inverse of that postulated for the pinacol intermediate. This difference follows from the much greater steric hindrance to backside attack upon the more highly branched intermediate from pinacol.

Experimental

Pivalic Acid-carboxyl-C[14] was prepared in 63% yield by the carbonation of t-butyllithium[38a] (prepared from 0.75 mole of t-butyl chloride and 1.64 g. atom of lithium[38b]) with carbon dioxide generated from 2.6 g. (0.0132 mole, 15 microcuries) of labeled barium carbonate-C[14]. The radioactive carbon dioxide was swept into the reaction flask with ordinary carbon dioxide, and sufficient of the latter was then added until

the t-butyllithium had reacted completely. The acid distilled at 160–161° and solidified at room temperature (reported[39] b.p. 162–165°, m.p. 34–35°).

Pivalyl Chloride-carbonyl-C[14].—Treatment of 10.5 g. (0.103 mole) of labeled pivalic acid with 15 ml. of thionyl chloride under reflux for 3 hr., followed by distillation through a 35-cm. tantalum-spiral column, yielded 6.9 g. (53%) of the acid chloride, b.p. 100–103° (reported[40] b.p. 103–104°).

Pinacolone-Carbonyl-C[14].—A solution of dimethylcadmium was prepared by the addition of 20.0 g. (0.11 mole) of cadmium chloride to methylmagnesium iodide prepared from 0.20 mole of magnesium and 0.20 mole of methyl iodide. The solvent ether was replaced by benzene and 6.9 g. (0.057 mole) of labeled pivalyl chloride in 50 ml. of benzene was added during 5 min. After a further 20 min. at reflux the solution was hydrolyzed with dilute hydrochloric acid. The organic layer was washed with 5% sodium hydroxide and dried over sodium sulfate. Removal of most of the solvent yielded a product which was shown by its infrared spectrum to be essentially pure pinacolone. Since the yield was low (ca. 10%) and separation from the benzene rather difficult on this small scale, the crude labeled ketone was diluted with 5.0 g. of unlabeled pinacolone and the diluted material was carefully fractionated through a 35-cm. tantalum-spiral column. The purified material weighed 3.0 g., b.p. 100–103° (reported[41] b.p. 105° (746 mm.)).

Methyl Trimethylpyruvate-carbonyl-C[14].—Labeled pinacolone (3.0 g., 0.030 mole) was oxidized with alkaline permanganate as described by Glucksmann.[42] The crude labeled trimethylpyruvic acid was treated with an etheereal solution of diazomethane, prepared from 8.0 g. (0.078 mole) of nitrosomethylurea.[43] Distillation through a short column gave 2.35 g. (54% based on ketone) of the labeled ester, b.p. 60–64° (16 mm.); ν_{CCl_4} 1740, 1720 (reported[44] b.p. 160–162° (atm.), 69–70° (20 mm.)).

In a larger unlabeled preparation the intermediate trimethylpyruvic acid was purified to give a 50% yield of material, b.p. 70–74° (10 mm.); ν_{CCl_4} 2980 (broad), 1785 and 1715 (reported[45] b.p. 85° (20 mm.)).

2,3,4,4-Tetramethyl-2,3-pentanediol-3-C[14] (IIc).—An etheereal solution of methyllithium, prepared from 4.5 g. (0.65 mole) of lithium and 62.0 g. (0.43 mole) of methyl iodide, was cooled in an ice-bath and 2.35 g. (0.0162 mole) of labeled methyl trimethylpyruvate in 25 ml. of anhydrous ether was added over a 10-min. period. The solution was refluxed for 2.5 hr. and then hydrolyzed by the slow careful addition of 150 ml. of water. In order to avoid rearrangement, the solution was not acidified. The ether layer was extracted with 100 ml. of water, the combined water layer was extracted with 50 ml. of ether, and the combined ether layer was dried over sodium sulfate. Removal of solvent and distillation of the residue through a short column gave 1.95 g. (75%) of the labeled glycol, b.p. 100–104° (17 mm.); ν_{CCl_4} 3600, 3520, 3440, 2980, 1485, 1385, 1350, 1220, 1180, 1105, 1075, 1015, 960, 910 and 840 cm.$^{-1}$, which solidified in the refrigerator (reported b.p. 98–100° (17 mm.),[45] m.p. 22°,[45] 27°[46]).

Rearrangement of the Labeled Glycol IIc.—A sample of 2,3,4,4-tetramethyl-2,3-pentanediol-3-C[14] (1.95 g., 0.0121 mole) was added to 20 ml. of 50% sulfuric acid in a separatory funnel and the mixture was shaken intermittently for 10 min. at room temperature. The ketone layer which separated weighed 1.35 g. (78%). The infrared spectrum of the product of rearrangement of an unlabeled sample of the glycol was nearly identical with that of 3,3,4,4-tetramethyl-pentan-2-one (IIIc) prepared as described previously.[47] However the former sample was shown by vapor-phase chro-

(36) C. A. Bunton and D. R. Llewellyn, *J. Chem. Soc.*, 3402 (1957).

(37) J. G. Pritchard and F. A. Long, THIS JOURNAL, **78**, 2667 (1956); see the discussion by F. A. Long and M. A. Paul, *Chem. Revs.*, **57**, 961 (1957).

(38) (a) P. D. Bartlett and E. B. Lefferts, THIS JOURNAL, **77**, 2804 (1955). (b) The lithium contained 1–2% sodium, which had been added to the melt in preparing lithium sand. Several attempts to prepare t-butyllithium from "sodium-free" lithium failed.

(39) S. V. Puntambeker and E. A. Zoellner. "Organic Syntheses," Coll. Vol. I, John Wiley and Sons, Inc., New York, N. Y., 1941, p. 524.

(40) H. C. Brown, *ibid.*, **60**, 1325 (1938).

(41) F. C. Whitmore, C. I. Noll and V. C. Meunier, *ibid.*, **61**, 683 (1939).

(42) C. Glucksmann, *Monatsh.*, **10**, 770 (1889).

(43) F. Arndt, "Organic Syntheses," Coll. Vol. II, John Wiley and Sons, Inc., New York, N. Y., 1943, p. 461.

(44) A. Richard, *Ann. chim.*, [8] **21**, 360 (1910).

(45) W. J. Hickinbottom, A. A. Hyatt and M. B. Sparke, *J. Chem. Soc.*, 2533 (1954).

(46) R. Locquin and W. Sung, *Compt. rend.*, **176**, 682 (1923).

(47) P. D. Bartlett and R. B. Stiles, THIS JOURNAL, **77**, 2806 (1955).

matographic separation[48] at 106° to contain IIIc and hexamethylacetone (IVc) in a ratio of (73 ± 5) to 1. In addition a small fraction (5%, assuming comparable thermal conductivity), which was assumed to be unsaturated hydrocarbon, was eluted before the ketones.

Oxidation of the Methyl Ketone IIIc.—The crude methyl ketone IIIc (1.35 g.) was added to a potassium hypochlorite solution, prepared from 20.0 g. of calcium hypochlorite, 14.0 g. of potassium carbonate and 4.0 g. of potassium hydroxide. The mixture was stirred and heated at 75° for 38 hr. Ten grams of potassium hydroxide was added and stirring and heating at reflux was continued for 10 hr. more. The aqueous solution was cooled, extracted twice with 25 ml. of ether, and acidified with concentrated hydrochloric acid. The precipitated acid was collected by filtration, dissolved in hot 40–60° petroleum ether, filtered from inorganic salts, and concentrated. Upon cooling there was obtained 0.60 g. (44%) of t-butyldimethylacetic acid (Vc), m.p. 194–196° (reported m.p. 198–199°,[d] m.p. 200°[10]). A 6.2-mg. sample of this acid spread over an area of 2 cm.[3] gave 90 counts per minute above background (14.5 c./min./mg. or 2080 c./min/mmole) measured in a windowless, gas-flow Geiger-Muller counter.

Hofmann Degradation of the Labeled Acid.—A sample (0.55 g.) of the t-butyldimethylacetic acid (Vc) obtained in the foregoing experiment was converted to the acid chloride[47] and thence to the amide by treatment of an ethereal solution with anhydrous ammonia. The over-all yield was 0.40 g. (73%) of t-butyldimethylacetamide, m.p. 197–199°; ν_{Nujol} (of an unlabeled sample) 3400, 3180, 1675 cm.$^{-1}$ (reported[10] m.p. 200°).

A solution of sodium methoxide (prepared from 0.5 g. of sodium metal) was cooled in ice and 0.40 g. (0.0027 mole) of t-butyldimethylacetamide was added, followed by 0.4 ml. of bromine. After standing 5 min. in the ice-bath, the solution was refluxed 15 min. on the steam-bath. The solution was cooled, 25 ml. of water was added, and the mixture was extracted three times with 25-ml. portions of ether. The ether was evaporated, leaving the crude carbamate which solidified upon cooling. It was dissolved in 40–60° petroleum ether and dried, and the solution was concentrated to 1 ml., cooled and filtered, giving 0.38 g. (82%) of labeled methyl N-(2,3,3-trimethyl-2-butyl)-carbamate, m.p. 63–65°; ν_{Nujol} (of an unlabeled sample) 3350, 2920, 1735, 1530, 1460, 1405, 1375, 1260, 1220, 1190, 1160, 1090, 970 and 770 cm.$^{-1}$.

Anal. Calcd. for $C_9H_{19}NO_2$: C, 62.39; H, 11.06; N, 8.09. Found (for an unlabeled sample): C, 62.52; H, 11.25; N, 8.17.[d]

A 100-ml. 3-necked flask was swept with nitrogen, 0.38 g. (0.0022 mole) of the labeled carbamate in 10 ml. of methyl alcohol was added, followed by 10 ml. of 50% carbonate-free sodium hydroxide, and the solution was refluxed for 8 hr., while protected from atmospheric carbon dioxide. The solution was cooled in an ice-bath and the top of the reflux condenser was connected to a fritted glass sparger immersed in a 100-ml. solution of N carbonate-free sodium hydroxide. Concentrated hydrochloric acid, 35 ml., was added slowly from a dropping funnel to the hydrolysis solution and carbon dioxide-free air was sucked through the system to sweep the liberated carbon dioxide into the alkali. The acidified hydrolysis solution was boiled and flushed in this way for 10 min. The sodium hydroxide solution was then treated with 5.35 g. (0.1 mole) of ammonium chloride followed by 25 ml. of a 30% solution of barium chloride (0.0375 mole). After standing 5 min., the solution was filtered through a dry, weighed, sintered-glass funnel and the precipitate was washed 3 times with distilled water and dried 3 hr. at 115°, to give 0.435 g. (100%) of labeled barium carbonate. A 7.6-mg. sample spread over approximately 2 sq. cm., gave 77 c./min. above background or 10.1 c./min./mg. of barium carbonate (2,010 c./min./mmole) (96% of the C^{14} labeling).

The acidified hydrolysis solution was covered with a 50-ml. layer of ether and neutralized with 25% sodium hydroxide. The ether layer was separated and the aqueous solution was extracted twice more with 25-ml. portions of ether. The amine was purified by extraction into aqueous acid, followed by neutralization and re-extraction with ether. The ether solution of the purified material was dried over potassium hydroxide and then treated with hydrogen chloride to precipitate the labeled 2-amino-2,3,3-trimethylbutane hydrochloride (VIc). The amine salt was collected and dried at room temperature to give 0.30 g. (90% yield) of material which sublimed at 320°: ν_{Nujol} 2900, 2100, 1630, 1530, 1480, 1425, 1405, 1395, 1295, 1210 and 1170 cm.$^{-1}$.

Anal. Calcd. for $C_7H_{18}NCl$: C, 55.42; H, 11.96; N, 9.24; Cl, 23.38. Found (for an unlabeled sample): C, 55.14; H, 11.86; N, 9.17; Cl, 23.24.[d]

A 21.7-mg. portion spread over approximately 2 sq. cm. gave a total of 74 c./min. compared with the background of 76 c./min., counting both for a 30-min. interval. With a standard deviation of 2 c./min. or 0.09 c./min./mg. of amine hydrochloride (14 c./min./mmole), the C^{14}-labeling of the acid precursor was 0.0 ± 0.7% in the amine hydrochloride.

2-Methyl-2-hydroxybutanoic acid-1-C^{14} was prepared by the procedure of Young, Dillon and Lucas.[50] An unlabeled batch distilled at 125–128° (17 mm.), m.p. 70–72° (reported b.p. 133–134° (16 mm.),[14] m.p. 72.5°[50]). The labeled material was not distilled but was converted directly to the ester.

Methyl 2-Methyl-2-hydroxybutanoate-1-C^{14}.—The unlabeled acid reacted with ethereal diazomethane to produce the ester, b.p. 146–150° (reported[14] b.p. 151–152°), in 80% yield; ν_{CCl_4} 3520, 2980, 1735, 1470, 1440, 1385, 1250, 1180, 1050, 990 and 940 cm.$^{-1}$. The ether solution of the labeled ester was dried and used directly in the next step.

2,3-Dimethyl-2,3-butanediol-2-C^{14} (IIb).—An ether solution of methyl 2-methyl-2-hydroxybutanoate-1-C^{14}, prepared from 8 g. (0.0678 mole) of the acid, was treated with an ether solution of methyllithium, prepared from 8.5 g. (1.21 g.-atoms) of lithium and 91 g. (0.65 mole) of methyl iodide, for 3 hr. at reflux. The mixture was worked up without acidification and the product distilled through a 10-cm. Vigreux column to yield 7.1 g. (79%) of the glycol, b.p. 88–91° (16 mm.) (reported[14] 94–95° (21 mm.)); ν_{CCl_4} (of an unlabeled sample) 3440, 2980, 1470, 1390, 1375, 1275, 1150, 1105, 1045, 1005, 955, 920 and 680 cm.$^{-1}$.

Rearrangement of the Glycol IIb.—The labeled glycol, 7.1 g., was added to 100 ml. of 50% sulfuric acid which had been cooled to 5°. The mixture was stirred for 6 hr. at room temperature, added to approximately 100 g. of ice and extracted three times with 50-ml. portions of ether. The organic layer was washed with 50 ml. of 5% sodium carbonate, dried over sodium sulfate, and evaporated to yield 4.8 g. of crude labeled ketones.

Distillation of an unlabeled batch through a 10-cm. Vigreux column gave a fraction, b.p. 125–132°, whose infrared spectrum was nearly identical with that of authentic methyl t-amyl ketone (IIIb) containing 15% ethyl t-butyl ketone (IVb). Gas chromatographic separation[48] of an unlabeled batch indicated the ratio of IIIb to IVb to be (4.9 ± 0.3) to 1.0. No other compound was found in significant quantity.

Oxidation of the Mixture of Labeled Ketones IIIb and IVb.—The undistilled, labeled ketones, 4.8 g., from the glycol rearrangement were placed in 240 ml. of hypochlorite solution prepared from 40 g. of calcium hypochlorite. The mixture was heated at 75° in a water-bath and stirred for a 12-hr. period. Ten grams of potassium hydroxide was added and the solution was refluxed for 4 hr. The solution was cooled and worked up in the usual manner to yield 3.6 g. of crude labeled ethyldimethylacetic acid (Vb). The small amount of pivalic acid present as a contaminant was not detected in the infrared spectrum.

Hofmann Degradation of the Acid Vb.—The crude labeled ethyldimethylacetic acid was added to 10 ml. of thionyl chloride and the mixture was refluxed for 4 hr. under a cold finger condenser. The mixture was cooled in an ice-bath, 100 ml. of anhydrous ether was added, ammonia gas was bubbled in until the solution was saturated and the mixture was allowed to stand for 2 hr. Ammonium salts and unreacted acid were removed by extraction and the crude amide

(48) The apparatus used for the separations in this paper is described by K. Burgess, Thesis, University of Michigan, 1957. The ketone mixtures were separated on a column of 30–60 mesh firebrick coated with silicone grease. The amine mixtures were separated on a column of 30–60 mesh Celite which had been coated first with potassium hydroxide, then with mineral oil [cf. A. T. James, A. J. Martin and G. H. Smith, *Biochem. J.*, **52**, 238 (1952)]. Helium was used as a carrier and the exit gas was analyzed by thermal conductivity measurements. In every case mixtures of known composition were analyzed to establish retention times and relative thermal conductivities.

(49) Spang Microanalytical Laboratory, Ann Arbor, Mich.

(50) W. G. Young, R. T. Dillon and H. J. Lucas, THIS JOURNAL, **51**, 2528 (1929).

was recrystallized from petroleum ether to yield 0.80 g. of labeled **ethyldimethylacetamide**, m.p. 103–104° (reported[51] m.p. 103–104°).

Plates of varying thickness, spread over a uniform area, were made so that the specific activity could be evaluated for an infinitely thin plate. The amide gave 38.0 c./min./ mg. (4380 c./min./mmole) above background of 70 c./ min., extrapolated to zero thickness.

The labeled ethyldimethylacetamide, 0.7 g., was rearranged to the carbamate ester using the procedure described for the amide from Vc. In this case the carbamate ester did not crystallize. It was hydrolyzed and decarboxylated as described above to give 0.25 g. (33%) of *l*-amylamine hydrochloride (VIb), m.p. 229–231°, and 0.76 g. (63%) of barium carbonate (yields based on the amide).

Anal. Calcd. for C₅H₁₄NCl: C, 48.57; H, 11.42; N, 11.33; Cl, 28.68. Found (unlabeled duplicate sample): C, 48.42; H, 11.57; N, 11.44; Cl, 28.58.[48]

The picrate melted at 180–182° (reported[52] 182–183°).

Anal. Calcd. for C₁₁H₁₆N₄O₇: C, 41.77; H, 5.10; N, 17.72. Found (unlabeled duplicate sample): C, 41.76; H, 5.11; N, 17.81.[48]

Both the *l*-amylamine hydrochloride and the barium carbonate were radioactive. Plates of varying thickness were made from portions spread over a uniform area so that the specific activity could be evaluated for an infinitely thin plate. The amine salt gave 23.5 c./min./mg. (2900 c./ min./mmole) and the carbonate gave 6.45 c./min./mg. (1270 c./min./mmole) above background of 70 c./min., extrapolated to zero thickness. The results were corrected for the 2.4% *l*-butylamine hydrochloride (*vide infra*), which had all the activity of the ethyl *l*-butyl ketone, and the 2.4% barium carbonate, which had none of the activity of the ethyl *l*-butyl ketone, to give 2870 c./min./mmole for *l*-amylamine hydrochloride and 1300 c./min./mmole for barium carbonate from the methyl *l*-amyl ketone.

Liberation of the labeled *l*-amylamine from its hydrochloride and subjection to vapor-phase chromatography[48]

(51) A. Haller and E. Bauer, *Ann. chim.*, [9] 1, 5 (1914).
(52) R. Brown and W. E. Jones, *J. Chem. Soc.*, 781 (1946).

detected the presence of 2.4% *l*-butylamine as a contaminant.

Reference Compounds.—**Hexamethylacetone** (IVc) was prepared as described earlier.[47] **Methyl *l*-amyl ketone** (IIIb) was prepared in 61% yield by the reaction of ethyldimethyl-acetyl chloride[53] with dimethylcadmium according to the procedure described above for making pinacolone-carbonyl-C¹⁴. The material distilled at 128–130°, n_D^{20} 1.4087 (reported b.p. 131.5–132.5°,[53] n_D^{20} 1.4100[54]); 2,4–dinitro-phenylhydrazone, m.p. 111–112° (reported[54] 112°). **Ethyl-*l*-butyl ketone** (IVb) was prepared by the method of Whitmore, Noll and Meunier.[41] The product contained some unsaturated material, as indicated by its infrared spectrum. Treatment with dilute permanganate in acetone solution followed by redistillation gave a sample which was homogeneous as determined by vapor-phase chromatography, b.p. 120°, n_D^{20} 1.4025 (reported[41] b.p. 124.5°, n_D^{20} 1.4049– 1.4052); 2,4–dinitrophenylhydrazone, m.p. 144–145° (reported[41] m.p. 143.5–144.5°). Pure samples of *l*-butylamine and *l*-amylamine were generated from the hydrochlorides which had been prepared by Hofmann degradation of the corresponding amides. The picrates melted at 196–198° (reported[52] 197–198°) and 178–181° (reported[58] 182–183°), respectively.

Kinetic Measurements.—Solutions of the glycols (0.03– 0.1 molar) in aqueous sulfuric acid were prepared and stored at 25.0 ± 0.1°. Five-ml. samples were quenched periodically with 5 g. of ice, and extracted with 1.00 ml. of carbon tetrachloride. The carbon tetrachloride solutions were analyzed for total ketone content by infrared analysis, using the carbonyl absorption peak. Known mixtures could be analyzed in this way with an error of less than 5%. The first-order rate constants were determined graphically.

Acknowledgment.—The advice and coöperation of Professor W. W. Meinke in the radiochemical work is gratefully acknowledged.

(53) A. Wischnegradsky, *Ann.*, 178, 103 (1875).
(54) F. C. Whitmore and C. E. Lewis, This Journal, 64, 2964 (1942).

Ann Arbor, Mich.

39 | The Bicyclo-butonium Ion

Among nonclassical ions the ratio of conceptual difficulty to molecular weight reaches a maximum with the cyclopropylcarbinyl-cyclobutyl system. Roberts and co-workers in Paper No. 39 show that the equivalence of the three CH_2 groups in the deamination of cyclopropylcarbinylamine is incompletely established, ruling out the previously proposed tricyclobutonium ion of C_{3v} symmetry as an all-purpose intermediate. They further show that in the reaction of cyclopropylcarbinol with hydrogen chloride and zinc chloride, which yields the thermodynamically determined product allylcarbinyl chloride, and therefore presumably allows equilibration of the kinetically determined products, the three CH_2 groups do attain equivalence. The authors are thus faced with the problem of choosing the most economical representation which will account for the rapid equilibrations observed, and also for the bidirectionally accelerated ionization of the equilibrating cyclobutyl and cyclopropylcarbinyl compounds. The result—ions XVIIIa–c of the paper —taxes the three-dimensional imagination of most organic chemists.

Actually there are not three, but twelve, formally distinguishable bicyclobutonium ions of the type of XVIIIa–c, derivable from any cyclopropylcarbinol derivative with separately identified methylene carbon atoms. These are shown on pages 274 and 275 (duplicated at the end of the book). To use these to best advantage the reader should cut them out (duplicate set) and fold each one back along the dotted diagonal until it best approximates a regular tetrahedron. The four carbon atoms then appear at the vertices of the tetrahedron. The atom shown in solid black is in each case the one bearing a single hydrogen, the carbon which *does not* become equivalent to the others. The other three carbon atoms are identified by one, two, and three bands, respectively, in the models.

For purposes of representation in the models it has been assumed that in the three-center bond the C–C bond whose order is between zero and one (i.e., which, on reacting, either becomes a single bond or disappears) is 1.12 times as long as a normal covalent C—C bond, and that the bond whose order is between one and two has a length like that of an ordinary C=C double bond. The ratio 1.12 is obtained by analogy to B–B and B–H distances in the boron hydrides B_6H_{10} and B_2H_6.[1] On the face of the model which contains the three-center bond, this fact is schematically indicated by mutual overlap of three orbitals of unspecified type, one from each participating carbon atom. These orbitals are made to look alike for simplicity although we do not disagree with the conclusion expressed in Figure 6 that the overlap of the orbitals along the short side of the triangle is more π-like than along the other two sides. The three permanent σ orbitals in the ion are shown similarly.

The fact that the bent bicyclobutane-like structure of the bicyclobutonium ion approximates a tetrahedron much more closely than it does any planar structure divides the twelve possible permutation isomers of this species into six DL pairs. Since one ion can undergo conversion into another with small changes in the bond distances, it may be easier for any of the ions of the D series to interconvert than for any of them to turn into one of the L series. The D and L series can undergo mutual interconversion by processes which might amount to the intervention of a planar classical cyclobutyl cation (not a favored species because of the preferred 120° bond angle of the sp^2 hybridized carbon atom) or of the likewise unfavored primary allylmethyl cation, or of allylcarbinol itself. The ions shown on page 274 belong to one stereochemical series, those on page 275 to the other. (When viewed from the *methine* apex of the tetrahedron, methylenes 1, 2, and 3 appear in clockwise order in one series, counterclockwise in the other.)

In examining the models it is helpful to place all six of the same enantiomeric series so that they rest on the same face of the tetrahedron—say, the methine carbon and methylenes 1 and 3—regardless of where the bonding happens to be. It will then become evident that for any one of these forms to be converted to any other all that is required is an electronic reallocation involving changes in bond distances which are mostly small, 0.17 to 0.20 Å. The interconversion of 1 with 2, 3 with 4, and 5 with 6 is especially easy, since the "nonbonded" pair of carbon atoms remains nonbonded. For the other interconversions the establishment of the bond between the formerly unbonded atoms must be the most important source of an energy barrier. From the amount of label found at the 3 position in cyclobutanol, this energy requirement must be surprisingly small.

Equally interesting is the almost negligible amount of hydride shift in the course of this rearrangement, a shift which would have caused the methine carbon to become equivalent to the methylene carbons. Can any reason be seen from the models why this hydride shift, which is extremely fast in the analogous case of the norbornonium ion, should be relatively very slow here?

[1] W. N. Lipscomb, Chapter 3 in *Advances in Inorganic and Radiochemistry,* Vol. 1 (Academic Press, New York, 1959) pp. 119, 120.

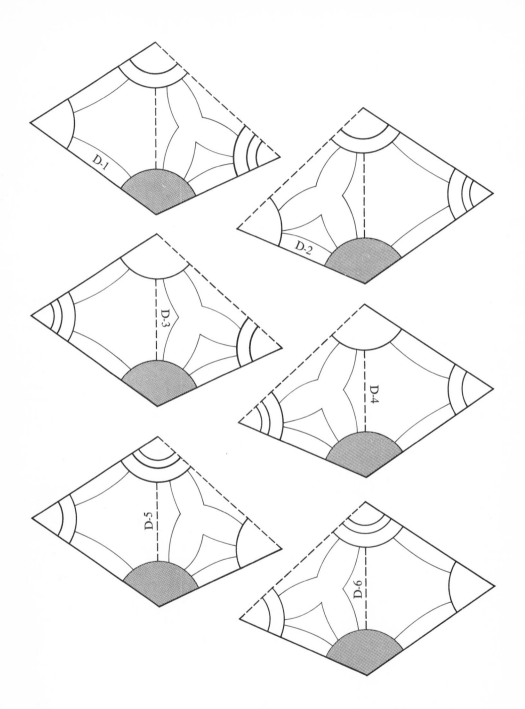

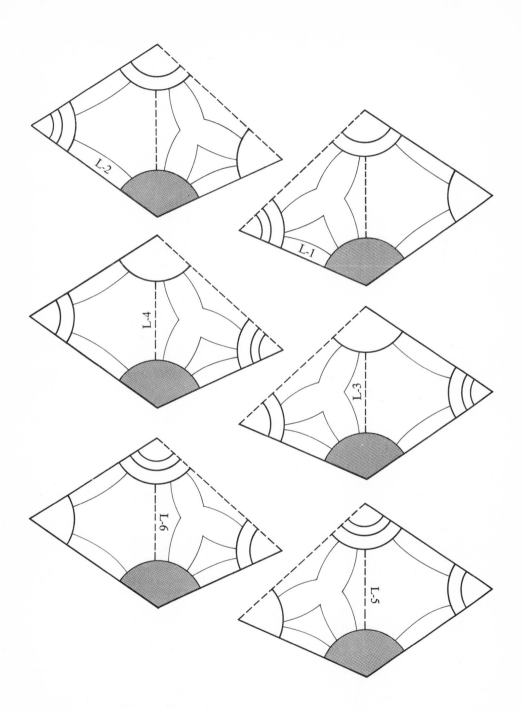

From: *J. Am. Chem. Soc.* **81**, 4390–98 (1959)

[Contribution No. 2369 from the Gates and Crellin Laboratories of Chemistry, California Institute of Technology, and the Department of Chemistry and Laboratory for Nuclear Science and Engineering, Massachusetts Institute of Technology]

Small-ring Compounds. XXIII. The Nature of the Intermediates in Carbonium Ion-type Interconversion Reactions of Cyclopropylcarbinyl, Cyclobutyl and Allylcarbinyl Derivatives[1a]

By Robert H. Mazur, William N. White,[1b] Dorothy A. Semenow, C. C. Lee, Marc S. Silver[1c] and John D. Roberts[1d]

Received September 4, 1958

Investigation of the extent of isotope-position rearrangement in carbonium ion-type reactions of ^{14}C-labeled cyclopropylcarbinyl derivatives has revealed that the three methylene groups of the starting material achieve a striking degree of equivalence between reactants and products. These results, taken in conjunction with the abnormally large solvolytic reactivities of cyclopropylcarbinyl and cyclobutyl halides and sulfonate esters, can best be accounted for by assuming rapid but not instantaneous equilibration of three isomeric non-classical unsymmetrical "bicyclobutonium" ion intermediates.

Considerable interest attends the question of how best to formulate the intermediate or intermediates involved in carbonium ion-type interconversion reactions of cyclopropylcarbinyl, cyclobutyl and allylcarbinyl derivatives.[2] The abnormally large solvolytic reactivities of cyclopropylcarbinyl and cyclobutyl halides[2] and sulfonate esters[3–5] are characteristic of reactions for which we believe that

non-classical cationic intermediates have been well established.[6] Detailed information as to the structures of the intermediates was sought in the present research by measurement of the extent of isotope-position rearrangement in the reactions of cyclopropylcarbinylamine-α-^{14}C with nitrous acid[7] and cyclopropylcarbinol-α-^{14}C with Lucas reagent.

Synthetic and Degradative Methods

Cyclopropylcarbinylamine-α-^{14}C was obtained by lithium aluminum hydride reduction of the amide from cyclopropanecarboxylic-1-^{14}C acid. This acid was prepared by carbonation of the Gri-

(1) (a) Supported in part by the Petroleum Research Fund of the American Chemical Society and the U. S. Atomic Energy Commission. Grateful acknowledgment is hereby made to the Donors of the Petroleum Research Fund. Presented in part at the 75th Anniversary Meeting of the American Chemical Society, September 7. 1951; (b) National Research Council Postdoctoral Fellow, 1953–1954; (c) National Science Foundation Predoctoral Fellow, 1955–1958; (d) Gates and Crellin Laboratories, California Institute of Technology, Pasadena, Calif.

(2) J. D. Roberts and R. H. Mazur, This Journal, **73**, 2509 (1951).

(3) J. D. Roberts and V. C. Chambers, *ibid.*, **73**, 5034 (1951).

(4) C. G. Bergstrom and S. Siegel, *ibid.*, **74**, 145 (1952).

(5) R. G. Pearson and S. H. Langer, *ibid.*, **75**, 1065 (1953).

(6) As leading references see (a) S. Winstein, B. K. Morse, E. Grunwald, H. W. Jones, J. Corse, D. Trifan and H. Marshall, *ibid.*, **74**, 1127 (1952); (b) J. D. Roberts, C. C. Lee and W. H. Saunders, Jr., *ibid.*, **76**, 4501 (1954).

(7) For a preliminary communication concerning this work, see J. D. Roberts and R. H. Mazur, *ibid.*, **73**, 3542 (1951).

gnard reagent from cyclopropyl bromide[8] with radioactive carbon dioxide.[9] A control degradation of the cyclopropanecarboxylic acid by the Schmidt reaction (see Fig. 1) showed that it contained $\leq 0.7\%$ of the total radioactivity in the ring carbon atoms.

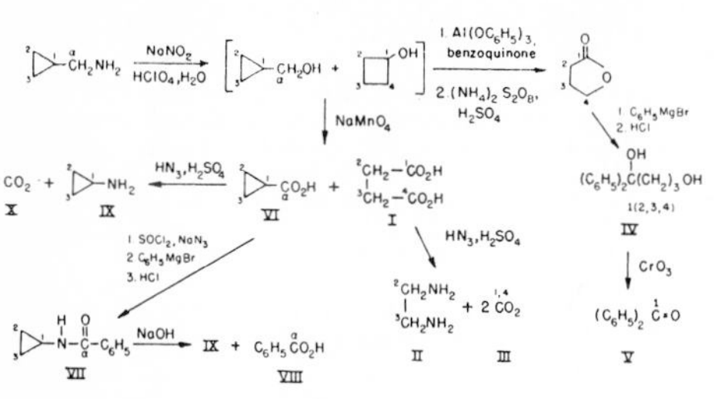

Fig. 1.

Treatment of cyclopropylcarbinylamine-α-^{14}C with sodium nitrite in aqueous perchloric acid solution gave a 60% yield of an alcohol mixture containing 48% cyclopropylcarbinol, 47% cyclobutanol and 5% allylcarbinol.[2] The small amount of allylcarbinol was removed by fractional distillation and the cyclopropylcarbinol and cyclobutanol were oxidized with permanganate to a mixture of cyclopropanecarboxylic and succinic acids. The acids were separated quantitatively by steam distillation and then further degraded as shown in Fig. 1.

Degradation of cyclobutanol-^{14}C (obtained by lithium aluminum hydride reduction of radioactive cyclobutanone[10] prepared from ketene and diazomethane-^{14}C) by the scheme shown in Fig. 1 gave a ^{14}C-distribution ($C_1 = 0.0\%$, $C_2 = C_4 = 37.1\%$, $C_3 = 25.4\%$, total activity = 99.6%) which was in good agreement with that obtained by a second degradative scheme[10] ($C_1 = 0.0\%$, $C_2 = C_4 = 37.1\%$, $C_3 = 25.8\%$, total activity = 100.0%) in which the activity of C_3 was measured directly. These results indicate the degree of reliability of the two methods of degradation.[11]

Degradation of cyclopropylcarbinol-α-^{14}C (obtained by lithium aluminum hydride reduction of cyclopropanecarboxylic-1-^{14}C acid) as per Fig. 1 gave cyclopropylamine (IX, $C_{1,2,3}$) containing 2.1% of the total radioactivity of the cyclopropanecarboxylic acid (VI, $C_{\alpha,1,2,3}$). The low activity of IX establishes that no extensive rearrangement occurs in the lithium aluminum hydride reduction of cyclopropanecarboxylic-1-^{14}C acid[12] nor during the degradation of cyclopropylcarbinol. It was further shown that cyclopropylcarbinol-α-^{14}C does not rearrange appreciably under the reaction and isolation conditions. We believe it safe to conclude

by analogy that no extensive ^{14}C-rearrangement occurs in the preparation of cyclopropylcarbinylamine by lithium aluminum hydride reduction of cyclopropanecarboxamide-1-^{14}C.

Allylcarbinyl-^{14}C chloride, the only monochloride isolated from treatment of cyclopropylcarbinol-α-^{14}C with Lucas reagent,[2] was degraded by two procedures as outlined in Fig. 2. The results obtained by the two procedures were in good agreement.

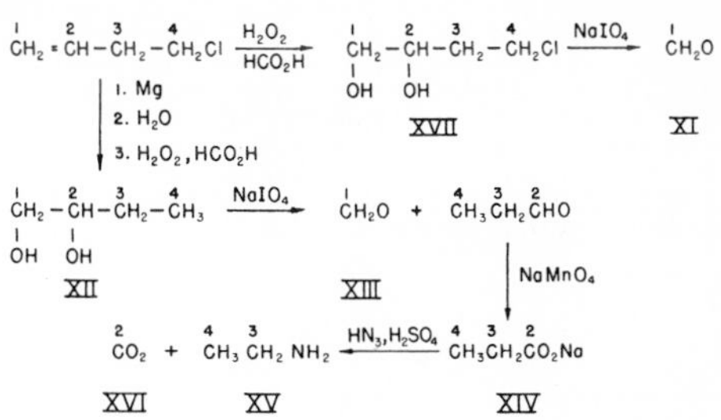

Fig. 2.

The ^{14}C-analyses for the various degradations are given in Tables I–III.

Discussion

A striking feature of most carbonium ion-type reactions of cyclopropylcarbinyl and cyclobutyl derivatives is that they give similar product mixtures and the compositions are essentially independent of whether one starts with a cyclopropylcarbinyl or a cyclobutyl compound. Thus, the reaction of cyclopropylcarbinylamine and cyclobutylamine with nitrous acid,[2] the solvolysis of cyclopropylcarbinyl and cyclobutyl derivatives,[2,3] the reactions of cyclopropylcarbinol and cyclobutanol with thionyl chloride, and cyclopropylcarbinol with hydrogen bromide or phosphorus tribromide[2] all give mixtures having closely similar relative amounts of products with the cyclopropylcarbinyl, cyclobutyl and allylcarbinyl structures.[12] This suggests that such reactions of cyclopropylcarbinyl and cyclobutyl compounds go through common cationic intermediates, and that the small observed variations in product composition are due to specific influences and not to drastic changes in mechanism.

A simple explanation of the product compositions is that classical cyclopropylcarbinyl and cyclobutyl cations are the intermediates and that they are very rapidly equilibrated. A possible test of such equilibration was provided by the reaction of cyclopropylcarbinol-α-^{14}C with Lucas reagent[2] since, under the reaction conditions, the small-

(8) J. D. Roberts and V. C. Chambers, THIS JOURNAL. **73**, 3176 (1951).

(9) The carbon dioxide was prepared from barium carbonate-^{14}C supplied by the Oak Ridge National Laboratory on allocation from the U. S. Atomic Energy Commission.

(10) D. A. Semenow, E. F. Cox and J. D. Roberts, THIS JOURNAL, **78**, 3221 (1956).

(11) Since the error in the C_3 activity due to ^{14}C–^{12}C isotope effects in the previously described scheme[10] is estimated to be approximately ±0.25%, the error introduced by such isotope effects in the scheme of Fig. 1 is inferred to be negligible; for the general method of the isotope effect calculations, see E. F. Cox, Ph.D. thesis, California Institute of Technology, 1955.

(12) Professor H. C. Brown (Purdue) has questioned the validity of our earlier conclusions[2] regarding the ease of rearrangement of cyclopropylcarbinyl derivatives in carbonium ion-type reactions other than the deaminations with nitrous acid and the preparations of chlorides from alcohols with Lucas reagent. In particular, he has repeatedly alleged that there is no convincing evidence for the reported[2] formation of rearrangement products in the solvolysis of cyclopropylcarbinyl chloride in ethanol–water mixtures [see also H. C. Brown and M. Borkowski, THIS JOURNAL, **74**, 1894 (1952)]. These allegations will be discussed in detail in later papers—it should suffice for the present to report that they are not supported by the results of either the previous[2] or current experiments.

TABLE I

RADIOACTIVITY ANALYSES OF DEGRADATION PRODUCTS OF ALLYLCARBINYL-x-^{14}C CHLORIDE

Allylcarbinyl-x-^{14}C chloride		4-Chloro-1,2-butanediol (XVII)	Formaldehyde (XI)	1,2-Butanediol (XIII)	Formaldehyde (XIII)	Sodium propionate (XIV)	Ethylamine (XV)	CO$_2$ (XVI)
From cyclopropylcarbinol-	Meas. act.[b]	1926	150[d]	2704	214[d]	620[e]	700[f,g]	10.3[h]
α-^{14}C[a] with Lucas re-	Cor. act.[c]	2660	881	3735	1258	2354	1936	3.6
agent, 0°, 1 hr.	% total act.	(100.0)	33.1	(100.0)	33.7	63.0	51.8	0.1
							(66)[g]	

[a] This material was prepared by the method employed for cyclopropylcarbinol (B) in Table III and therefore contains ≲2.1% of the radioactivity in the ring atoms. [b] Measured ^{14}C-activities in counts/min., determined with a windowless methane-filled counter (Nucleometer), of "infinitely thick" barium carbonate samples of cross-sectional area equal to 2.90 cm.^{2} and prepared as described by J. D. Roberts, W. Bennett, E. W. Holroyd, Jr., and C. H. Fugitt, *Anal. Chem.*, **20**, 904 (1948). The activities are corrected for background and have standard deviations of less than 2.2%. [c] ^{14}C-Activities in dis./min./mg. of barium carbonate, corrected for self-absorption and dilution by non-labeled carbon atoms as described by J. D. Roberts, R. E. McMahon and J. S. Hine, THIS JOURNAL, **72**, 4237 (1950). [d] Formaldehyde as dimethone. [e] Sodium propionate as *p*-bromophenacyl ester. [f] Ethylamine as *p*-bromobenzenesulfonamide. [g] Infrared spectra indicated that this material contained 76% N-ethyl- and 24% N-methyl-*p*-bromobenzenesulfonamide; the activity of the product *assuming pure XV* is 51.8% of XII and recalculation assuming 24% inactive N-methyl-*p*-bromobenzenesulfonamide corrects this value to 66%. [h] CO$_2$ as barium carbonate.

TABLE II

RADIOACTIVITY ANALYSES OF DEGRADATION PRODUCTS OF CYCLOBUTANOL-x-^{14}C

Cyclobutanol-x-^{14}C	Run		Succinic acid (I)	1,2-Diaminoethane (II)	2CO$_2$ (III)	1,1-Diphenylbutane-1,4-diol (IV)	Benzophenone (V)
From cyclobutanone	1	Meas. act.[a]	0.1236	0.07733[d]	0.04590[f]	....	....
from ketene and		% total act.	(100.0)	62.56 ± 0.11	37.14 ± 0.29	....	....
diazomethane-^{14}C	2	Meas. act.[a]	0.710	....	....	0.712	0.0000[i]
		% total act.	(100.0)	....	....	(100.0)	0.0
From cyclopropyl-	1	Meas. act.[a]	0.05665	0.03607[d]	0.02024[f]	....	....
carbinylamine-α-		% total act.	(100.00)	63.67 ± 0.22	35.73 ± 0.26	....	....
^{14}C with HONO,	2	Meas. act.[b]	936, 981[e]	1200,[f] 1238[r,j]	670,[g] 668[g,h]	....	....
100°, 1 hr.		Cor. act.[c]	1292, 1356	828, 854	462, 462	....	....
		% total act.	(100.0), (100.0)	64.1, 63.0	35.8, 34.1	....	....
	3	Meas. act.[a]	0.543	....	....	0.553	0.0036[j]
		% total act.	(100.0)	....	....	(100.0)	0.66 ± 0.03

[a] Activities in microcuries per millimole (μc./mmole); determined using the vibrating-reed electrometer method as described by O. K. Neville, THIS JOURNAL, **70**, 3499 (1948). [b,c] See corresponding footnotes for Table I. [d] 1,2-Diaminoethane as dibenzamide. [e] Repurified and recounted. [f] 1,2-Diaminoethane as dihydrobromide. [g] CO$_2$ as barium carbonate; activities are per 2 moles of barium carbonate. [h] Recounted. [i] Benzophenone as 2,4-dinitrophenylhydrazone. [j] Benzophenone as phenylhydrazone.

TABLE III

RADIOACTIVITY ANALYSES OF DEGRADATION PRODUCTS OF CYCLOPROPYLCARBINYL-x-^{14}C COMPOUNDS

Cyclopropylcarbinyl-x-^{14}C compound		Cyclopropanecarboxylic acid (VI)	N-Cyclopropylbenzamide (VII)	Benzoic acid (VIII)	Cyclopropylamine (IX)	CO$_2$ (X)
Cyclopropanecarboxylic acid (A) from	Meas. act.[b]	1313	......	....	3.9[e]	4338[g]
cyclopropylmagnesium bromide and	Cor. act.[c]	1812	......	....	13	1498
^{14}CO$_2$	% total act.	(100.0)	......	....	0.7	83[g]
Cyclopropylcarbinol (B) from LiAlH$_4$	Meas. act.[a]	0.693[d]	0.694	....	0.0145[e]	...
reduction of cyclopropanecarboxylic acid (A)	% total act.	(100.0)	(100.0)	....	2.09	...
Cyclopropylcarbinol from treatment of	Meas. act.[a]	0.688[d]	0.688	0.679	0.0131[e]	...
cyclopropylcarbinol (B) with ethyl- amine and HONO, 60°, 20 min.	% total act.	(100.0)	(100.0)	98.7	1.90	...
Cyclopropylcarbinol from cyclopropyl-	Meas. act.[a]	0.548[d]	0.550	0.292	0.265[e]	...
carbinylamine-α-^{14}C with HONO, 60°, 20 min.	% total act.	(100.0)	(100.0)	53.2	48.3[f]	...

[a] See corresponding footnote for Table II. [b,c] See corresponding footnotes for Table I. [d] Cyclopropanecarboxylic acid as anilide. [e] Cyclopropylamine as benzamide. [f] Degradation of the ring gave values of 6.3 and 20.9% of the total radioactivity for C$_1$ and C$_2$ = C$_3$, respectively; *however*, the ring degradation method employed was shown to be unreliable. Related experiments indicated that C$_1$ probably had <1% of the total activity of the cyclopropylcarbinol. [g] CO$_2$ as barium carbonate; activity probably low because of contamination with atmospheric CO$_2$.

ring chlorides appear to be in equilibrium with cationic intermediates but the final reaction product, allylcarbinyl chloride, is not. If equilibrium of the small-ring cations is complete before allylcarbinyl chloride is formed, then treatment of cyclopropylcarbinol-α-^{14}C with Lucas reagent should give allylcarbinyl chloride with the ^{14}C distributed equally between the three methylene groups, as Fig. 3 shows. The experimental results are entirely in accord with this prediction and elimi-

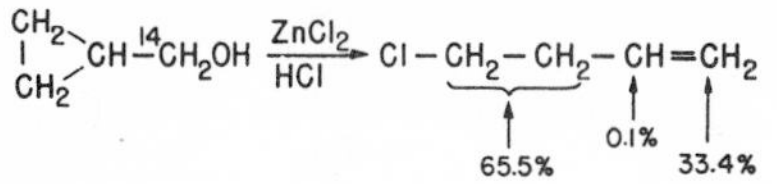

$$CH_2 \underset{CH_2}{\overset{CH_2}{<}}CH-^{14}CH_2OH \xrightarrow{ZnCl_2 / HCl} Cl-CH_2-CH_2-CH=CH_2$$

65.5%   0.1%   33.4%

nate direct "push–pull" formation of allylcarbinyl chloride from cyclopropylcarbinol, since this would give a predominance of C_4-labeled chloride.

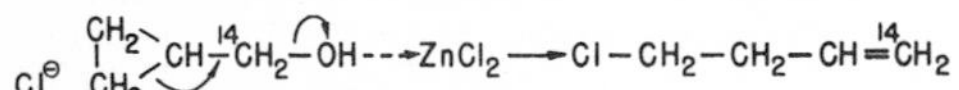

$$Cl^{\ominus} \overset{CH_2}{\underset{CH_2}{<}}CH-^{14}CH_2-OH \text{---} ZnCl_2 \longrightarrow Cl-CH_2-CH_2-CH=^{14}CH_2$$

Although equilibrating classical cations can account for the course of the above rearrangement, the unusual solvolytic reactivity of both cyclopropylcarbinyl and cyclobutyl derivatives is hardly explicable on the basis of formation of such intermediates.[2,3] To be sure, the reactivity of the three-membered ring compounds might be explained by assuming relief of strain in the solvolysis transition state through direct formation of the cyclobutyl cation, but it seems impossible to use the same explanation for the reactivity of the four-membered ring compounds unless they directly

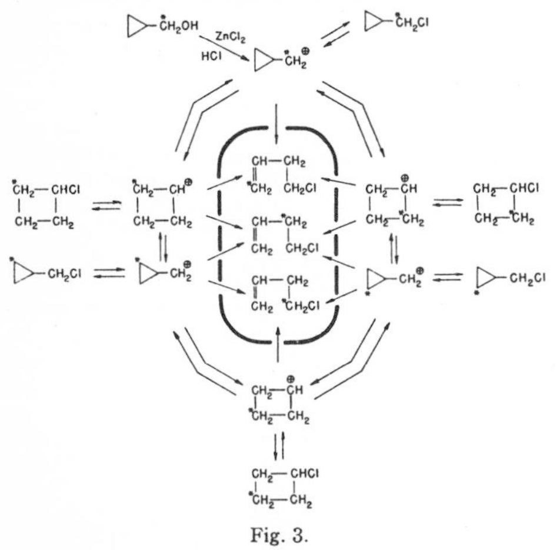

Fig. 3.

form allylcarbinyl cations. This latter possibility is ruled out by the failure to observe large amounts of allylcarbinyl derivatives as products in non-reversible reactions[2] and the great difficulty which attends efforts to obtain the allylcarbinyl cation in other ways.[2] While, presumably, separate explanations could be offered for the reactivities of three- and four-membered ring derivatives, all of the experimental data seem better accommodated by the assumption of a single common non-classical intermediate, or a rapidly equilibrating mixture of several such intermediates.[13] Indeed, the experi-

(13) In a recent paper, H. Hart and J. M. Sandri, THIS JOURNAL, 81, 320 (1959), imply that non-classical ion formation with cyclopropylcarbinyl derivatives must lead to rearrangement products if associated with enhanced solvolytic reactivity. However, as will be shown later with cyclopropylcarbinyl and cyclobutyl derivatives (and as is already well known with such substances as camphene hydrochloride or cyclocholesteryl compounds), overall rearrangement need not arise from non-classical intermediates formed in processes showing enhanced reactivities provided that the starting materials have certain predictably favorable structures.

mental observations are highly reminiscent of those obtained with the norbornyl system, a system which features enhanced reactivity and scrambling of ^{14}C that can only be reasonably accounted for by non-classical intermediates.[6] We proceed, therefore, to consider the kinds of non-classical intermediates which could be involved in carbonium ion-type interconversions of cyclopropylcarbinyl and cyclobutyl compounds. It should be realized that, although the discussion is detailed for the sake of clarity, the conclusions reached are tentative.

Pyramidal structures may be written as possible conformations for the cations derived from the cyclopropylcarbinyl system, and these might

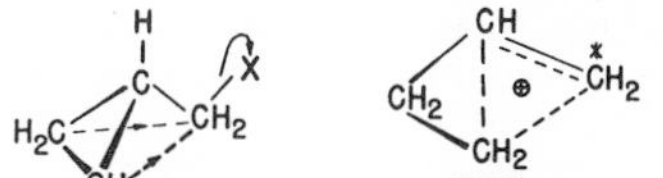

XVIIIa

have either unsymmetric or symmetric shapes. A single unsymmetric cation (XVIIIa) is not a satisfactory representation because it would lead to allylcarbinyl chloride with ^{14}C located only in the methylene group of the double bond (cf. Fig. 4).

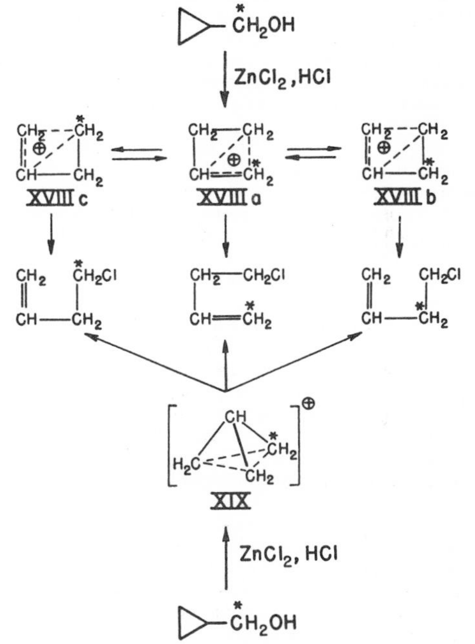

Fig. 4.

But, as Fig. 4 demonstrates, rapid equilibration of *three* unsymmetrical pyramidal cations, XVIIIa-c (each of which is a d,l pair), could account for the ^{14}C distribution in the allylcarbinyl chloride from cyclopropylcarbinol-α-^{14}C and Lucas reagent. Establishment of equilibrium between the ions XVIIIa-c is not hard to imagine, since they are so closely related that rather minor vibrations might suffice to interconvert them. If no barrier to interconversion exists, a symmetric "tricyclobuto-nium" ion[4,7] (XIX) results, in which the three methylene groups are entirely equivalent.

The isotopic distribution of the allylcarbinyl ^{14}C chloride from cyclopropylcarbinol-α-^{14}C and Lucas reagent does not permit differentiation between equilibrating ions XVIIIa-c and XIX since each pathway would lead to the same results for a re-action involving reversible intermediate stages. The only hope for differentiation between the two pathways appears to lie in a determination of the degree of equivalence achieved by the methylene groups during an irreversible process in a highly nucleophilic solvent. If cations XVIIIa-c are involved and they do not equilibrate much faster than they react with solvent to give the final prod-ucts, then the degree of equivalence achieved by the methylene groups would be less than if the more symmetrical ion XIX were the sole intermediate. In the event that equilibration is essentially com-plete before reaction with solvent (implying a potential barrier of substantially less than 5 kcal. between the isotope-position isomers), the two formulations essentially merge for all practical purposes and it is almost a matter of taste to decide which to use.[14]

As a possible choice for an irreversible carbo-nium ion-type reaction, the deamination of cyclo-propylcarbinylamine-α-^{14}C seemed most satisfac-tory. Loss of nitrogen from alkyldiazonium ions is amost certainly irreversible and the reaction is conveniently carried out in water, a solvent with excellent nucleophilic properties. Furthermore, the deamination conditions are customarily suf-ficiently mild to preclude undesirable rearrange-ments of the reaction products. However, these advantages have to be balanced against the con-siderable doubt which exists as to the exact nature of the carbonium ion formed by the loss of nitrogen from the diazonium ion.[15] Nonetheless, the prod-uct composition from the reaction of cyclopropyl-carbinylamine with nitrous acid (48% cyclopropyl-carbinol, 47% cyclobutanol, 5% allylcarbinol)[2] is rather typical for the carbonium ion reactions of this family of compounds, and, consequently, it was believed that the deamination of cyclopropyl-carbinylamine-α-^{14}C might, in fact, contribute to an understanding of the normal carbonium ion reactions of cyclopropylcarbinyl and cyclobutyl derivatives.

The ^{14}C-distributions in the alcohols formed from cyclopropylcarbinylamine-α-^{14}C and nitrous acid provide strong evidence for behavior similar to that observed for the reaction of cyclopropylcarbinol-

α-^{14}C with Lucas reagent. Although the methylene groups do not attain complete equivalence, the ex-tent of isotope-position rearrangement is truly striking. The points made earlier are still valid, and certainly the single unsymmetrical non-classical ion XVIIIa insufficiently accounts for the results for, as Fig. 5 shows, it could not be expected to give rise to ^{14}C in the 3-position of cyclobutanol or the ring positions of cyclopropylcarbinol. However, formation and partial conversion of XVIIIa to XVIIIb and XVIIIc (84% of the equi-librium value) can account for the ^{14}C distribution in cyclobutanol but for only part of the excess ^{14}C in the α-position of cyclopropylcarbinol. The latter might arise from a non-rearranging S_N2-type displacement at the α-carbon of the diazonium ion before XVIIIa is formed. Another possibility is that a "hot" classical cyclopropylcarbinyl cation is the first intermediate and it gives some non-rearranged alcohol by reaction with water before going over to XVIIIa.

Since symmetrical intermediate XIX would lead to complete equilibration of the methylene groups in the cyclobutanol at least, this intermediate seems to be ruled out unless some subordinate re-action path which gives a smaller degree of rear-rangement also prevails. This is hardly the most economical explanation and it seems better to regard XIX not as the most stable non-classical intermediate but rather as a possible way point in the interconversion of XVIIIa-c (*vide infra*).

The most geometrically favorable conformation for the unsymmetrical "bicyclobutonium" ions XVIIIa-c would seem to be as in Fig. 6. For this arrangement, the degree of overlap of the three $2p$-orbitals in which the two unsaturation electrons are delocalized could be very nearly the same as for the geometrically comparable and highly stabilized 7-dehydronorbornyl cation.[16,17] Reaction of a cation such as is shown in Fig. 6 with nucleophilic agents at positions 1, 2 and 4 would lead to cyclo-propylcarbinyl, cyclobutyl or allylcarbinyl deriva-tives, respectively. The charge on the cation must be fairly evenly distributed between the 1-, 2- and 4-positions as judged by the fact that the propor-tions of the products corresponding to attack on

(14) A somewhat analogous situation has been encountered with respect to the intermediates involved in hydride ion migrations in nor-bornyl derivatives.[6b]

(15) See, for instance, A. Streitwieser, Jr., *J. Org. Chem.*, **22**, 861 (1957); D. J. Cram and J. E. McCarty, THIS JOURNAL, **79**, 2866 (1957), the discussion of ref. 6b, and also B. M. Benjamin, H. J. Schaeffer and C. J. Collins, *ibid.*, **79**, 6160 (1957).

(16) W. G. Woods, R. A. Carboni and J. D. Roberts, *ibid.*, **78**, 5653 (1956).

(17) The geometry here predicted for the cation formed from cyclo-propylcarbinyl derivatives is not greatly different from our earliest proposal (J. D. Roberts, W. Bennett and R. Armstrong, *ibid.*, **72**, 3329 (1950)) except that the present formulation suggests that the nortri-cyclyl cation would be more favorable electronically than implied before. The earlier theorizing was based too heavily on π-type over-lap of p-orbitals. The essential point of difference between the elec-tronic stabilization envisioned for XVIII and a "hyperconjugated" cyclopropylcarbinyl cation (Roberts, Bennett and Armstrong, above) is that, for XVIII, substantial bonding is postulated between the car-binyl carbon and one of the ring methylene carbons. This bonding is particularly helpful in accounting for the ready formation of cyclo-butyl derivatives which are not obviously expected to arise from a more or less highly hyperconjugated cyclopropylcarbinyl cation, irrespec-tive of whether one or both of the C–C bonds of the ring were involved.

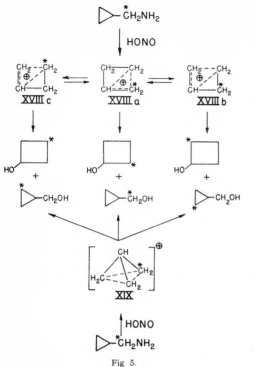

Fig 5.

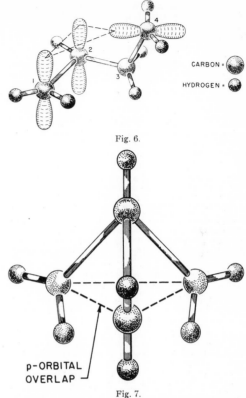

Fig. 6.

p-ORBITAL OVERLAP

Fig. 7.

these positions are about 10:10:1. Since a very delicate balance between electrical and steric factors must be necessary to give such small differences in energy barriers for formation of the three products, it is to be expected that substitution of even a single methyl group on one of the carbons might alter the charge distribution sufficiently to change the product ratios drastically. Large effects of this type have been observed and will be discussed in detail in later papers. It suffices for the present to point out that these results substantiate the general correctness of the formulation presented above.

The mode of interconversion of the cations XVIIIa-c has only been briefly mentioned. If it is true that this interconversion takes place by way of XIX, the model for XVIIIa-c shown in Fig. 6 suggests that this may possibly be achieved with the least movement of atoms by passing through a conformation of XIX such as is shown in Fig. 7. It should be noted that in Fig. 7 the plane determined by the carbon and two hydrogens of each methylene group is *perpendicular* to the plane of the three methylene carbon atoms.

The atomic arrangement shown in Fig. 6 suggests another interesting possibility, namely that the barrier to the interconversion of XVIIIa and XVIIIb may be lower than the barrier for the conversion of either of these species to XVIIIc. If we now view the numbers of Fig. 6 as labeling specific carbon atoms, the models show that the transfer of carbon atom 4 from atom 3 to atom 1, with the resultant interchange in the roles of atoms

3 and 1, corresponds to the conversion XVIIIa to XVIIIb. This transfer might occur with a relatively slight movement of atoms. However, the change from either XVIIIa or XVIIIb to XVIIIc necessitates the formation of a bond between atoms 1 and 3, and might very well involve a pyramidal-type intermediate similar to XIX (which, of course, can open to any of the three unsymmetrical forms). Rearrangement of XVIIIc in correspondence to the interconversion of XVIIIa and XVIIIb results in no ^{14}C rearrangement but rather in the formation of the mirror image of XVIIIc.

As shown in Fig. 5, interconversion of XVIIIa and b would result in movement of ^{14}C into the cyclopropyl ring without introducing it into the 3-position of the cyclobutyl ring. If there is indeed an easier path than XIX for the XVIIIa-XVIIIb interconversion, a reaction may exist in which such a cyclopropylcarbinyl-α-^{14}C derivative may give ^{14}C rearrangement into the cyclopropyl ring but not to the 3-position of the cyclobutyl ring. The deamination of 1-methylcyclopropylcarbinyl-amine-α-^{14}C might well be expected to show such an effect, but unfortunately 1-methylcyclobutanol was the only product isolated.[11,18] However, the observation that only 2.6% of the total ^{14}C migrated to the 3-position of the cyclobutyl product is in accord with the above suggestions.[11,18]

(18) E. F. Cox, M. S. Silver and J. D. Roberts. This Journal, unpublished.

Acknowledgment.—We are indebted to Miss Winifred Bennett for help with some of the radioactivity determinations.

Experimental

Starting Materials. Cyclopropylcarbinol-α-^{14}C.—Illustrative procedures are given. Cyclopropyl bromide[3] (0.60 g., 0.005 mole) was converted to the Grignard reagent and carbonated in an evacuated system at $-20°$ with carbon dioxide generated from 0.7932 g. (0.00403 mole) of radioactive barium carbonate. The product was hydrolyzed with 2.0 g. of sulfuric acid in 12 ml. of water, about 10 g. of nonradioactive cyclopropanecarboxylic acid was added, and the mixture was continuously extracted with ether overnight. The ether was distilled, 10 ml. of benzene added, and the product dried by azeotropic distillation. Fractionation of the residue gave 9.43 g. (54% based on ^{14}C utilization) of cyclopropanecarboxylic-1-^{14}C acid, b.p. 100° (38 mm.). The acid was reduced with lithium aluminum hydride by the procedure previously described[19] to give cyclopropylcarbinol-α-^{14}C, b.p. 123°, n^{25}D 1.4300, in 78% yield.

Cyclopropylcarbinylamine-α-^{14}C.—A solution of 25.8 g. (0.30 mole) of cyclopropanecarboxylic-1-^{14}C acid in 44.1 g. (0.37 mole) of thionyl chloride was warmed to 30° over 0.5 hr., maintained at reflux for an additional hr., then fractionated through a 30-cm. column packed with a coil of tantalum wire to give 29.5 g. (94%) of cyclopropanecarbonyl-1-^{14}C chloride, b.p. 116.5–117.5° (lit.[20] b.p. 118–119° (739 mm.)).

The acid chloride (29.5 g., 0.282 mole), in 250 ml. of anhydrous ether, was cooled by an ice-bath and stirred vigorously while a rapid stream of dry ammonia was passed over it for 30 min. The ether was evaporated and the residue extracted with eight 75-ml. portions of boiling chloroform. The chloroform was evaporated to give 21.9 g. (91%) of colorless crystals of cyclopropanecarboxamide-1-^{14}C, m.p. 123.6–124.5° (lit.[21] m.p. 124.5–126.0°).

A mixture of the amide (3.74 g., 0.044 mole) (which is insoluble in solvents commonly used for lithium aluminum hydride reductions), 3.34 g. (0.088 mole) of lithium aluminum hydride and 100 ml. of anhydrous benzene was maintained at reflux and stirred under an atmosphere of nitrogen for 24 hr. The excess lithium aluminum hydride was decomposed by the addition of 25 ml. of 10 N sodium hydroxide. Most of the benzene was decanted, and the residue was boiled twice under reflux with 50 ml. of ether. The ether extracts and the benzene portion were combined and extracted with 2 N hydrochloric acid. The acidic extracts were evaporated to dryness to give cyclopropylcarbinylamine-α-^{14}C hydrochloride which, after recrystallization from ethanol–ether, had m.p. 201.5–203.5°. The hydrochloride, diluted with 6.00 g. (0.056 mole) of unlabeled cyclopropylcarbinylamine hydrochloride, was dissolved in 25 ml. of water and the solution made strongly basic by addition of ice-cold aqueous sodium hydroxide. The solution was steam distilled to give cyclopropylcarbinylamine-α-^{14}C, 0.090 mole (77%), as determined by titration with perchloric acid.

Reaction of Cyclopropylcarbinol-α-^{14}C with Lucas Reagent.—The procedure was as described previously.[2] From 6.6 g. (0.092 mole) of cyclopropylcarbinol-α-^{14}C and 66.0 g. of Lucas reagent was obtained 6.9 g. (84%) of crude allylcarbinyl-x-^{14}C chloride.

Degradation of Allylcarbinyl-x-^{14}C Chloride. Procedure 1.—To 6.9 g. (0.077 mole) of the crude chloride was added 50 ml. of 87% formic acid and 17.0 g. (0.15 mole) of 30% hydrogen peroxide. The temperature of the stirred mixture was maintained below 50° by intermittent cooling until a clear solution resulted (30 min.). Stirring was continued for 2 hr. and the formic acid was removed under reduced pressure. Methanolic hydrogen chloride (50 ml.) was added to the residue, the resulting solution was maintained at reflux for 1 hr., and the methyl formate and methanol were removed by distillation to give 6.1 g. (64%) of 4-chloro-1,2-butanediol (XVII), n^{25}D 1.4760. 4-Chloro-1,2-butanediol was found to be unstable to heat, some 3-hydroxytetrahydrofuran probably being formed through elimination of hydrogen chloride. Distillation of the crude

chloroglycol gave material with b.p. 117° (0.8 mm.), n^{25}D 1.4735.

Anal. Calcd. for $C_4H_9O_2Cl$: C, 38.56; H, 7.28; Cl, 28.46. Found: C, 39.30; H, 7.34; Cl, 26.56.

Hydrolysis of the intermediate formate with aqueous potassium hydroxide in the usual manner[22] gave only 3-hydroxytetrahydrofuran, b.p. 61–62° (7 mm.), n^{25}D 1.4396 (lit.[23] b.p. 84–86° (13 mm.), n^{19}D 1.4431). The N-phenyl-carbamate of 3-hydroxytetrahydrofuran, after crystallization from ethanol–water and recrystallization from hexane–benzene, had m.p. 117.2–117.6° (lit.[23] m.p. 120°).

Distilled 4-chloro-1,2-butanediol-x-^{14}C (0.66 g., 0.0053 mole) was mixed with a solution of 1.13 g. (0.0053 mole) of sodium metaperiodate in 50 ml. of water and allowed to stand for 2 hr. at room temperature. The solution was extracted with ether and the aqueous layer added to a filtered solution of 0.74 g. (0.0053 mole) of methone in 200 ml. of water. The mixture was allowed to stand for 1 hr., the product removed by filtration and recrystallized from 95% ethanol to give 0.38 g. of formaldehyde-^{14}C (XI) dimethone, m.p. 191.6–192.6° (lit.[24] m.p. 191–191.5°), which was analyzed for ^{14}C.

Degradation of Allylcarbinyl-x-^{14}C Chloride. Procedure 2.—Allylcarbinyl-x^{14}C chloride (4.66 g., 0.0521 mole) was converted to the Grignard reagent with 1.44 g. (0.06 mole) of magnesium turnings in 20 ml. of anhydrous di-n-butyl ether and the mixture was treated with 6.0 g. of sulfuric acid in 20 ml. of water. The evolved 1-butene was passed into a flask fitted with a Dry Ice condenser and containing 30 ml. of 87% formic acid and 11.3 g. (0.10 mole) of 30% hydrogen peroxide. The formic acid mixture was stirred for 4 hr. while the sulfuric acid–di-n-butyl ether mixture was heated to 110°, and then worked up as described above for 4-chloro-1,2-butanediol-x-^{14}C except that the crude glycol was dried by azeotropic distillation of the water present with benzene. The product was distilled through a semi-micro column packed with a platinum spiral to give 1.05 g. (23%) of 1,2-butanediol-x-^{14}C (XII), b.p. 90° (12 mm.), n^{25}D 1.4396; (lit. *levo*, b.p. 94–96° (12 mm.)[25]; *dextro*, b.p. 91–91.5° (13 mm.)[24] n^{20}D 1.435[26]).

The di-(N-phenylcarbamate), after recrystallization from hexane–benzene, had m.p. 116–117° (lit.[25] *levo*, m.p. 121–123°, *dextro*, m.p. 125–127°).

Anal. Calcd. for $C_{18}H_{20}O_4N_2$: C, 65.84; H, 6.14. Found: C, 65.92; H, 6.21.

Oxidation of 1,2-butanediol-x-^{14}C was carried out as described for 4-chloro-1,2-butanediol-x-^{14}C except that the reaction mixture was continuously extracted with ether for 2 hr. after the completion of the oxidation. The ether extract, containing propionaldehyde-x-^{14}C, was reserved for further degradation. From 0.516 g. (0.0056 mole) of 1,2-butanediol-x-^{14}C, 1.20 g. (0.0056 mole) of sodium metaperiodate and 1.57 g. (0.0112 mole) of methone was obtained 1.37 g. (84%) of formaldehyde (XIII) dimethone, m.p. 187–190°. After recrystallization from absolute ethanol, the dimethone had m.p. 190.2–191.0°; this material was analyzed for ^{14}C.

The ether extract containing propionaldehyde-x-^{14}C was stirred for 30 min. at 0° with a solution of 0.98 g. (0.005 mole) of sodium permanganate trihydrate and 0.12 g. (0.003 mole) of sodium hydroxide in 25 ml. of water. The manganese dioxide was removed by filtration, washed with 25 ml. of water, the combined filtrates decolorized with sodium bisulfite, and the ether separated. To the aqueous layer was added 30 g. of sodium sulfate and 3 g. of sulfuric acid, and the mixture was steam distilled until 300 ml. of distillate had been collected. The distillate was neutralized with carbonate-free sodium hydroxide and evaporated to dryness to give 0.87 g. of salt which probably contained some sodium bisulfite.

A portion of the salt XIV was converted to p-bromophenacyl propionate-x-^{14}C which, after recrystallization

(19) R. F. Nystrom and W. G. Brown, THIS JOURNAL, **69**, 2548 (1947).

(20) N. Kishner, *Chem. Zentr.*, **76**, I, 1703 (1905).

(21) N. J. Demjanow and M. Dojarenko, *Ber.*, **56**, 2200 (1923).

(22) D. Swern, G. N. Billen and J. T. Scanlan, THIS JOURNAL, **68**, 1504 (1946).

(23) S. Olsen, *Acta Chem. Scand.*, **4**, 462 (1950).

(24) E. C. Horning and M. G. Horning, *J. Org. Chem.*, **11**, 95 (1946).

(25) P. A. Levene and H. L. Haller, *J. Biol. Chem.*, **74**, 343 (1927).

(26) D. V. Tischenko, *J. Gen. Chem. (U.S.S.R.)*, **7**, 658 (1937).

from ethanol–water, had m.p. 62.4–62.8° (lit.[27] m.p. 63°) and was analyzed for [14]C.

The remainder of the sodium propionate-x-^{14}C was mixed with 0.6 ml. of concentrated sulfuric acid and treated with 0.0028 mole of hydrazoic acid in chloroform at 50°. The evolved gases were bubbled through carbonate-free sodium hydroxide and the system flushed with carbon dioxide-free nitrogen after completion of the reaction. To the sodium hydroxide was added a solution of 0.3 g. of barium chloride dihydrate in 5 ml. of boiled distilled water, the resulting precipitate was washed with boiled distilled water and acetone by centrifugation, and dried at 70° to give 0.194 g. of barium carbonate (XVI) which was analyzed for [14]C.[28]

The sulfuric acid–chloroform mixture was cooled to 0°, basified with cold dilute sodium hydroxide, and treated with a solution of 0.3 g. of p-bromobenzenesulfonyl chloride in 5 ml. of chloroform. The mixture was stirred for 15 min., the aqueous layer separated and heated to 100° to remove traces of chloroform, acidified with concentrated hydrochloric acid, and allowed to stand in the ice-box overnight to give, after 2 recrystallizations from hexane–benzene, a mixture of p-bromobenzenesulfonamides which had m.p. 74.5–75.0°. This material (XV), which was shown by infrared analysis to be a mixture containing 76% N-ethyl- and 24% N-methyl-p-bromobenzenesulfonamide, was analyzed for [14]C. Mixed melting points taken on authentic mixtures were slightly lower than the melting points of the pure components (N-methyl-p-bromobenzenesulfonamide, m.p. 77.2–77.8°, lit.[29] m.p. 77°; N-ethyl-p-bromobenzenesulfonamide, m.p. 80.6–81.2°, lit.[30] m.p. 81°) and the radioactivity analyses (Table I) checked if it was assumed that the mixture was 76% active N-ethyl- and 24% inactive N-methyl derivative. The N-methyl compound was probably derived from ethanol used as a preservative in chloroform.

Deamination of Cyclopropylcarbinylamine-α-[14]C.—The cyclobutanol-x-^{14}C which was degraded was obtained from a deamination procedure similar to that previously described for crotylamine[2] except that the steam distillate was continuously extracted with ether for 10 hr. From 0.090 mole of cyclopropylcarbinylamine-α-^{14}C perchlorate and 20.7 g. (0.30 mole) of sodium nitrite heated at 100° for 1 hr. there was obtained, after fractionation through a center-tube column,[31] 0.32 g. of alcohols containing some allylcarbinol-x-^{14}C, b.p. 116–125°, and 3.60 g. of material containing no allylcarbinol, b.p. 125–126.5°, yield 3.92 g. (60%). The cyclopropylcarbinol-x-^{14}C which was degraded was obtained from a similar deamination procedure except that the reaction mixture was heated only to 55–60° for 20 min.

Degradation of Deamination Products. Oxidation of Mixture of Alicyclic-x-[14]C Alcohols.—A warm solution of 36.5 g. (0.231 mole) of potassium permanganate in 300 ml. of water was added over a 15-min. period to a solution of 5.50 g. (0.0764 mole) of cyclic alcohol-x-^{14}C mixture and 1 pellet of potassium hydroxide in 10 ml. of water. The oxidation was quite exothermic. The reaction mixture was then heated on a steam-bath for 30 min., cooled, and treated with sodium formate solution to discharge the excess permanganate. The manganese dioxide was removed by filtration, and the filter cake was washed with 100 ml. of 2% sodium hydroxide. The filtrate was acidified with 120 ml. of 6 N sulfuric acid and distilled until 400 ml. of distillate (A) had been collected in a flask containing 25 ml. of 15% sodium hydroxide solution.

The acidic residue (75 ml.) from this distillation was continuously extracted with ether for 24 hr. The ether was removed by evaporation and the solid residue crystallized from water to give 2.23 g. (25%) of succinic-x-^{14}C acid (I), m.p. 184.0–185.0° (lit.[32] m.p. 184.5–185°). Four recrys-

tallizations from water gave material of m.p. 186.5–187.0°, which was analyzed for [14]C.

The alkaline solution of steam distillate A was concentrated to 50 ml. and acidified with a solution of 7.5 ml. of concentrated sulfuric acid in 25 ml. of water. The resulting solution was continuously extracted with ether for 12 hr. The ether extract was dried over magnesium sulfate and the ether removed by evaporation. The high-boiling residue was distilled to give 2.92 g. (44%) of cyclopropanecarboxylic-x-^{14}C acid (VI), b.p. 160–180° (mainly 173–178°)(lit.[2] b.p. 97–98° (40 mm.)).

Cyclopropanecarboxylic-x-^{14}C acid (0.200 g., 0.00232 mole) was heated with 0.50 g. (0.0042 mole) of thionyl chloride for 5 min. at 50° and 10 ml. of anhydrous ether was added followed by 2.00 g. (0.0215 mole) of aniline in 10 ml. of anhydrous ether. The ethereal solution was washed with 50 ml. of 10% hydrochloric acid and the ether removed by evaporation. The solid residue was crystallized once from 80 ml. of water and twice from cyclohexane to give 0.163 g. (44%) of cyclopropanecarboxanilide-x-^{14}C, colorless needles, m.p. 108.8–109.7° (lit.[20] m.p. 110°), which was analyzed for ^{14}C to give the activity of VI.

Degradation of Cyclobutanol-x-[14]C. Procedure 1.—Succinic-x-^{14}C acid (I) (prepared from the mixture of alicyclic alcohols as described above) was degraded by the Schmidt reaction as described previously for glutaric acid.[33,28] From 2.5 g. (0.21 mole) of succinic-x-^{14}C acid, 9.7 ml. of concentrated sulfuric acid and 0.049 mole of hydrazoic acid (1.61 M solution in chloroform which had been washed with sulfuric acid to remove any ethanol) there was obtained barium carbonate-[14]C (from III) and 3.30 g. (60%) of crude ethylenediamine-[14]C (II) dibenzamide. A small portion of the dibenzamide was recrystallized three times from absolute ethanol to give white needles, m.p. 250.9–251.3° (lit.[34] m.p. 249°). The pure dibenzamide and the barium carbonate were analyzed for [14]C.

Degradation of Cyclobutanol-x-[14]C. Procedure 2.—The mixture of alicyclic alcohols (2.00 g., 0.0278 mole) from the cyclopropylcarbinylamine-α-^{14}C-nitrous acid reaction was combined with 1.0 g. of aluminum phenoxide, 6.48 g. (0.060 mole) of benzoquinone and 50 ml. of anhydrous toluene, heated on a steam-bath for 5 hr., and then distilled until 45 ml. of distillate had been collected. The distillate was shaken with a solution of 2 g. of sodium hydroxide and 3 g. of sodium sulfite in 20 ml. of water until the yellow color in the organic layer had disappeared, and this two-phase system was then distilled until 50 ml. of distillate was obtained. The aqueous layer of the distillate was saturated with sodium bisulfite and separated. The organic layer was washed five times with 10-ml. portions of saturated sodium bisulfite solution. The combined bisulfite solutions were made alkaline with solid potassium carbonate, diluted to 90 ml. with water and distilled until 45 ml. of distillate was collected. Ammonium persulfate (13 g., 0.057 mole) was dissolved in the distillate, and 20 ml. of concentrated sulfuric acid was added to the swirled solution while the temperature was kept below 10°. The solution was kept at 2° for 43 hr., and then continuously extracted with ether for 20 hr. during which time the solution being extracted was kept below 5°. The ethereal extract was dried over magnesium sulfate and the ether removed by evaporation. The residue was distilled to give 0.84 g. (35%) of slightly yellowish liquid, which was shown by its infrared spectrum to contain 75% γ-butyrolactone-x-^{14}C, b.p. 160–200° (lit.[35] γ-butyrolactone, b.p. 204° (756 mm.)). This material, in 30 ml. of anhydrous ether, was added during 10 min. to a stirred solution of phenylmagnesium bromide (prepared from 7.85 g. (0.050 mole) of bromobenzene, 1.25 g. (0.0514 g. atom) of magnesium and 75 ml. of anhydrous ether), the stirring was continued for 20 min. more and then 40 ml. of 10% hydrochloric acid was added cautiously. The ether layer was separated and the aqueous layer washed twice with 25-ml. portions of ether. The combined ether solutions were dried over potassium carbonate and the ether removed by evaporation. The solid residue was recrystallized three times from benzene to give 0.588 g. (9%) of 1,1-diphenylbutane-

(27) R. L. Shriner and R. C. Fuson, "The Systematic Identification of Organic Compounds," John Wiley and Sons, Inc., New York, N. Y., 3rd ed., 1948, p. 222.

(28) Since this work was completed an improved procedure for isolation of carbon dioxide from Schmidt reactions has been developed; J. D. Roberts, D. A. Semenow, H. E. Simmons, Jr., and L. A. Carlsmith, THIS JOURNAL, **78**, 601 (1956).

(29) C. S. Marvel and F. E. Smith, ibid., **45**, 2696 (1923).

(30) W. Ssolonina, J. Russ. Phys. Chem. Soc., **31**, 640 (1899); Chem. Zentr., **70**, II, 867 (1899).

(31) E. A. Naragon and C. J. Lewis, Ind. Eng. Chem., Anal Ed., **18**, 1448 (1946).

(32) M. T. Leffler and R. Adams, THIS JOURNAL, **58**, 1551 (1936).

(33) R. B. Loftfield, ibid., **73**, 4713 (1951).

(34) N. D. Cheronis and J. B. Entriken, "Semimicro Qualitative Organic Analysis," T. Y. Crowell Co., New York, N. Y., 1947, p. 402.

(35) P. Henry, Z. physik. Chem., **10**, 96 (1892).

1,4-diol-x-[14]C (IV), m.p. 105.5–106.4° (lit.[36] m.p. 108°), which was analyzed for [14]C.

To a solution of 0.26 g. (0.00107 mole) of 1,1-diphenylbutane-1,4-diol-x-[14]C (IV) in 10 ml. of hot glacial acetic acid was added during 15 min. 1.50 g. (0.015 mole) of chromium trioxide. The reaction was vigorous. The mixture was heated on a steam-bath for 1 hr., then poured into 75 ml. of water. The aqueous solution was extracted five times with 10-ml. portions of ether. The combined ethereal solutions were washed with 30 ml. of water and twice with 30-ml. portions of 10% sodium bicarbonate solution, then dried over potassium carbonate. The ether was removed by evaporation and the residue heated with a solution of 1.50 g. (0.0104 mole) of phenylhydrazine hydrochloride in 6.0 ml. of ethanol and 3.0 ml. of water for 1 hr. on a steam-bath. The benzophenone-[14]C (V) phenylhydrazone obtained upon cooling was filtered, washed twice with 3-ml. portions of ethanol, and recrystallized three times from ethanol to give 0.194 g. (67%) of slightly tan prisms, m.p. 135.4–136.0° (lit.[37] m.p. 137–138°), which were analyzed for [14]C.

Degradation of Cyclopropylcarbinol-x-[14]C. Procedure 1.—The cyclopropylcarbinol-x-^{14}C was oxidized to cyclopropanecarboxylic-x-^{14}C acid (VI) by the method described above. The sodium salt was degraded by the Schmidt reaction as described for sodium propionate-x-[14]C. From 0.581 g. (0.00539 mole) of cyclopropanecarboxylic-x-^{14}C acid (VI) was obtained 0.473 g. (45%) of barium carbonate-[14]C (X) and 30% of cyclopropylamine-x-[14]C (IX) isolated as the benzamide (0.255 g.) which, after two recrystallizations from hexane–benzene, had m.p. 97.6–98.0° (lit.[20] m.p. 98.5°) and was analyzed for [14]C.

Degradation of Cyclopropylcarbinol-x-[14]C. Procedure 2.—To 0.80 g. (0.0093 mole) of cyclopropanecarboxylic-x-^{14}C acid (VI) (obtained as before) was added 1.30 g. (0.0109 mole) of thionyl chloride. The solution was heated at reflux for 45 min. and then cooled and dissolved in 15 ml. of cold tetrahydrofuran. To this solution was added an ice-cold solution of 3.25 g. (0.050 mole) of sodium azide in 15 ml. of water. The mixture, cooled in an ice-bath, was shaken for 15 min., then poured into 50 ml. of cold saturated sodium chloride solution, and extracted five times with 10-ml. portions of toluene. The combined extracts were dried over magnesium sulfate, then over Drierite, heated at reflux for 2 hr., cooled and added during 10 min. to a solution of phenylmagnesium bromide (prepared from 6.28 g. (0.040 mole) of bromobenzene, 1.00 g. (0.041 g. atom) of magnesium and 50 ml. of anhydrous ether). The reaction mixture was heated at reflux for 30 min., cooled, and cautiously treated with 40 ml. of 10% hydrochloric acid. The organic layer was separated and the aqueous layer washed twice with 20-ml. portions of ether. The combined

organic phases were dried over potassium carbonate, and the solvents removed by evaporation, finally at reduced pressure. The residue was recrystallized three times from benzene–cyclohexane to give 0.886 g. (58%) of N-cyclopropylbenzamide-x-[14]C (VII), slightly tan needles, m.p. 94.1–95.3°. Recrystallization of a portion of the benzamide once from water and once from cyclohexane gave colorless plates, m.p. 96.1–96.5°, which was analyzed for [14]C.

A mixture of 0.35 g. (0.0022 mole) of N-cyclopropylbenzamide-x-[14]C (VII) and 20 ml. of 10% sodium hydroxide was heated at reflux for 15 hr. during which time the cyclopropylamine-x-[14]C (IX) evolved was collected in a receiver cooled in a Dry Ice-bath. At the end of this time, a single phase was present and 15 ml. of water was added. The solution was distilled until 25 ml. of distillate had been collected in an ice-cooled flask containing 5.0 ml. of 10% hydrochloric acid. The contents of the Dry Ice-cooled receiver were washed into the distillate, and the solution washed three times with 10-ml. portions of ether (the washings were discarded). To the aqueous layer was added 1.00 g. (0.00715 mole) of benzoyl chloride and a solution of 2.00 g. (0.050 mole) of sodium hydroxide in 6.0 ml. of water. The N-cyclopropylbenzamide-x-[14]C (from IX) was washed twice with 3-ml. portions of water and crystallized twice from water to give 0.226 g. (65%) of colorless plates, m.p. 96.0–96.5°, which was analyzed for [14]C.

The basic residue from the aqueous distillation was diluted to 25 ml. with water and washed three times with 10-ml. portions of ether (the ether washings were discarded). The basic solution was acidified with 40 ml. of 10% hydrochloric acid, and the liberated benzoic-^{14}C acid (VIII) extracted with four 10-ml. portions of ether. The ethereal extracts were combined, the ether removed by gentle evaporation, and the residue crystallized twice from water to give 0.200 g. (75%) of fine white needles, m.p. 120.6–121.2° (lit.[38] m.p. 122.38°), which were analyzed for [14]C.

Control Reaction of Cyclopropylcarbinol-α-^{14}C under Deamination Conditions.—To a solution of 2.30 g. (0.032 mole) cyclopropylcarbinol-α-^{14}C and 3.64 g. (0.081 mole) of ethylamine in 13.5 ml. of water were added, rapidly and consecutively, 85 ml. of 1.0 N perchloric acid and 15.53 g. (0.225 mole) of sodium nitrite in 50 ml. of water. The solution was maintained at 55–60° for 20 min., and then the excess acid was removed by the addition of 60 g. of potassium carbonate. The reaction mixture was worked up as before to give 1.80 g. (78%) of crude cyclopropylcarbinol, b.p. 118–124°. The product was degraded by the second procedure above and afforded an 84% yield of cyclopropanecarboxylic acid in the initial oxidation step. No significant rearrangement of ^{14}C was noted in the cyclopropylcarbinol (cf. Table III).

(36) Ch. Weizmann and F. Bergmann, THIS JOURNAL, **60**, 2647 (1938).

(37) E. Fischer, Ber., **17**, I, 576 (1884).

(38) F. W. Schwab and E. Wichers, J. Research Natl. Bur. Standards, **34**, 333 (1945).

PASADENA, CALIF.

40 | The Reversible Cholesteryl Rearrangement

Winstein and Kosower return to the homoallylic behavior of cholesteryl derivatives with a study of the reverse reaction of *i*-cholesteryl (3,5-cyclocholestan-6-yl) trichloroacetates and chlorides under solvolytic conditions. The cyclocholesteryl β-derivatives, despite having an axial-axial interaction between their functional groups and the angular methyl group of the sterol ring system, are the kinetically controlled products of solvolysis of cholesteryl arenesulfonates.[1] This strain might be enough to account for the observed β/α ratio of solvolysis rates of these epimers. However, the strain cannot account for the preferential *formation* of the *more* strained isomer from the intermediate ion. The combination of facts presented and discussed in this paper forces the authors to conclude that there are at least two intermediate homoallylic cations in the cholesteryl rearrangement: a wholly unsymmetrical ion XII, previously recognized, with reactivity at C-3 and C-6, and a more nearly symmetrical ion XX, with reactivity, at least formally, at C-4 also. Because the structure of XX implies delocalization from both the 3,5- and 4,5-bonds of the cyclopropane ring, its formation affords a potential driving force for the ionization not only of the β derivatives (25,000,000 times as fast as cholesteryl) but also of the α derivatives, which are only 1 to 2 powers of ten less accelerated. The stereospecificity of the solvolytic formation of the β-cyclocholestanol derivatives means that either these products are not formed from the symmetrical cation, or else there is a cation which is symmetrical enough to provide driving force from two epimers but unsymmetrical enough to exert a selectivity in favor of the nonthermodynamic product. The latter is a reasonable

---

[1] E. M. Kosower and S. Winstein, *J. Am. Chem. Soc.* **78,** 4347, 4354 (1956); see also Papers 5 and 6 of this collection.

possibility, since preparative observations like that of the formation of the β epimer may mean anything from a product ratio of 5–10 up; and such a small factor would still be compatible with an ion delocalized in the sense of XX, but *unequally* at the 3,5- and 4,5-bonds. It does not seem easy to separate entirely the functions of anchimeric assistance to ionization and stereochemical control in reaction with a nucleophile.

Since there is some evidence for delocalization in the direction of XX even in the sterol series where there are restraints against it in the fused ring system, it is significant that the norbornenyl-nortricyclyl and the cyclopropylcarbinyl-cyclobutyl systems both show an amount of isotopic rearrangement which points to at least an increased accessibility of transition states such as XXXI (the vinyl counterpart of the phenonium ion), if not the actual stable existence of such an ion (see Papers 25 and 51).

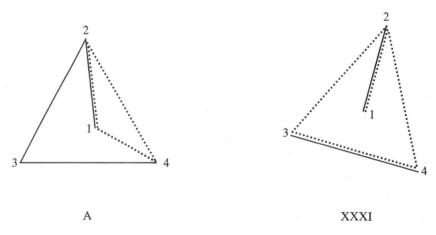

A   XXXI

The type of delocalization in XXXI implies a rather different geometry from that of the bicyclobutonium ion A. In A the CH_2 group including C-1 should lie almost in the plane of C1–C2–C3 (or bent somewhat away from C-4, if the orbital contributed by C-1 to the three-center bond is not purely *p*). In XXXI the methylene group in question should lie in the plane which includes C-2 and is perpendicular to the C3–C4 bond, so that this methylene group must rotate in the conversion of A into XXXI. The C1–C2 bond should also make an angle of 115° or more with the plane of the remaining three carbon atoms, probably larger than exists in A.

Later work gives increased reason for thinking that a nonclassical ion will often find its energy minimum with the use of orbital hybridizations and geometries which represent unequal compromises between the demands of familiar limiting structures, and that the compromise may lie anywhere along the scale.

In any equilibrating system with an unstable intermediate,

$$A \underset{k_{\mathrm{A}}}{\overset{k_{-\mathrm{A}}}{\rightleftharpoons}} (\mathrm{I}) \underset{k_{-\mathrm{B}}}{\overset{k_{\mathrm{B}}}{\rightleftharpoons}} B,$$

the kinetically determined product ratio p is equal to $k_{\mathrm{A}}/k_{\mathrm{B}}$ and the ratio of reaction rates r is $k_{-\mathrm{A}}/k_{-\mathrm{B}}$, so that the equilibrium constant is

$$K = \frac{k_{-\mathrm{A}}k_{\mathrm{B}}}{k_{\mathrm{A}}k_{-\mathrm{B}}} = \frac{r}{p}.$$

In these solvolytic reactions the relation still holds if one determines p from ether or acetate ratios and r from tosylates. In the case of interconversion of cyclobutyl and cyclopropylcarbinyl compounds (Paper No. 42) p is near unity, giving the unusually simple result that $K \cong r$.

From: *J. Am. Chem. Soc.* **81**, 4399–4408 (1959)

[CONTRIBUTION FROM THE DEPARTMENT OF CHEMISTRY OF THE UNIVERSITY OF CALIFORNIA AT LOS ANGELES]

Neighboring Carbon and Hydrogen. XXXIII.[1] Reactivities of 3,5-Cyclocholestan-6-yl Derivatives. Strain and Reactivity in Homoallylic Systems[2]

BY S. WINSTEIN AND EDWARD M. KOSOWER[3]

RECEIVED OCTOBER 1, 1958

The kinetics of solvolysis of the relatively reactive 3,5-cyclocholestan-6-yl trichloroacetates and chlorides have been studied. In addition, the rates of acid-catalyzed isomerization of the 3,5-cyclocholestan-6-ols and the corresponding acetates to cholesterol or cholesteryl acetate have been measured. A striking feature of the present results is the very high reactivity of the 3,5-cyclocholestan-6β-yl derivatives in solvolysis. In acetic acid or 90% dioxane at 25°, 3,5-cyclocholestan-6β-yl chloride is more reactive than cholesteryl chloride by a factor of $10^{7.4}$. The ratio of 3,5-cyclocholestan-6β-yl chloride to cholesteryl chloride at equilibrium may be estimated from the kinetic data, since the equilibrium constant, K_e, is the product of a reactivity ratio and a partition factor for reaction of the intermediate cation at the two reaction centers. On this basis, K_e is *ca.* $10^{-6.4}$, the difference in molar standard ground state free energies of the two isomers being *ca.* 9000 calories. The important role of ground state free energies in determining the relative reactivity pattern in homoallylic systems is discussed, the 5-norbornenyl system being contrasted with cholesteryl. As we go from one system to the other, ground state free energy factors are responsible for a 10^8 change in relative reactivity of the two isomers. A connection is drawn between the ground state free energy pattern and the magnitude of strain and electron delocalization effects on reactivity of homoallylic isomers. 3,5-Cholestan-6β-yl derivatives are more reactive than the 6α-isomers in the various reactions by factors of 10^1–10^2. The bearing of these results on the question of the nature of the non-classical cation first produced by ionization is discussed. Further consideration is given the general question of plurality of homoallylic cations and the relation between homoallylic and bicyclobutonium cations.

In two previous articles we reported the preparation and solvolysis of trichloroacetates[4] and chlorides[5] derived from the epimeric 3,5-cyclocholestan-6-ols. Because the results were of interest in furthering our understanding of reactivity in homoallylic systems[2,6–9] and the nature of homoallylic cations,[2,6–10] we studied the kinetics of solvolysis of the trichloroacetates and chlorides. Also, the rate of solvolysis of cholesteryl chloride was studied briefly. In addition, the kinetics of the acid-catalyzed isomerization of the 3,5-cyclocholestan-6α- and 6β-ols to cholesterol and that of the corresponding acetates to cholesteryl acetate were examined. The results of this investigation are presented and discussed · in the present article.

Results

Trichloroacetates.—The rates of hydrolysis of the epimeric 3,5-cyclocholestan-6-yl trichloroacetates[4] I and II were measured in 90% dioxane. Due to ion pair return[4,11] accompanying the hydrolysis of the trichloroacetates, the amount of acid generated in hydrolysis fell below one equivalent.

(1)(a) Paper XXX, R. Baird and S. Winstein, THIS JOURNAL, **79**, 4238 (1957); (b) Paper XXXI, S. Winstein and J. Takahashi, *Tetrahedron*, **2**, 316 (1958); (c) Paper XXXII, S. Winstein, E. Gadient, E. T. Stafford and P. E. Klinedinst, Jr., THIS JOURNAL, **80**, 5895 (1958).

(2) Part of the material of this manuscript was presented at the 15th National Organic Chemistry Symposium of the American Chemical Society, Rochester, N. Y., June 17–20, 1957, p. 29 of Abstracts.

(3) Research Fellow of the National Institutes of Health, 1949–1952.

(4) E. M. Kosower and S. Winstein, THIS JOURNAL, **78**, 4347 (1956).

(5) E. M. Kosower and S. Winstein, *ibid.*, **78**, 4354 (1956).

(6) (a) S. Winstein and R. Adams, *ibid.*, **70**, 838 (1948); (b) S. Winstein and A. H. Schlesinger, *ibid.*, **70**, 3528 (1948).

(7) (a) S. Winstein, *Bull. soc. chim. France*, **18**, 55 (1951); (b) S. Winstein, *Experientia Suppl. II*, 137 (1955).

(8) S. Winstein, H. M. Walborsky and K. C. Schreiber, THIS JOURNAL, **72**, 5795 (1950).

(9) (a) S. Winstein, M. Shatavsky, C. Norton and R. B. Woodward, *ibid.*, **77**, 4183 (1955); (b) S. Winstein and M. Shatavsky, *ibid.*, **78**, 592 (1956).

(10) (a) S. Winstein, M. Brown, K. C. Schreiber and A. H. Schlesinger, *ibid.*, **74**, 1140 (1952); (b) M. Simonetta and S. Winstein, *ibid.*, **76**, 18 (1954).

(11) S. Winstein, E. Clippinger, A. H. Fainberg, R. Heck and G. C. Robinson, *ibid.*, **76**, 328 (1956).

lent. For example, the infinity acid titer was 83% of theoretical in the hydrolysis of the 3,5-cyclocholestan-6β-yl trichloroacetate I in the absence of any added salts. Good first-order behavior in the solvolysis was observed by treating the disap-

I, X = OCOCCl₃
III, X = Cl
V, X = OH
VII, X = OAc

II, X = OCOCCl₃
IV, X = Cl
VI, X = OH
VIII, X = OAc

pearance of the trichloroacetates in terms of a first-order solvolysis with a specific reaction rate constant k_{solv} and a first-order rearrangement to inert cholesteryl derivative with a rate constant k_r, according to the scheme

$$3,5\text{-cyclocholestan-6-yl X} \xrightarrow{k_{solv}} \text{products} + H^{\oplus}$$
$$\downarrow k_r$$
$$\text{cholesteryl X}$$

On this basis the integrated kinetic expression to be employed is the one in equation 1, where H_0, H and H_∞ are acid titers at zero time, time t,

$$2.303 \log \left(\frac{H_\infty - H_0}{H_\infty - H} \right) = (k_s + k_r) t = kt \quad (1)$$

and infinity, respectively. The first-order reaction rate constant k which is evaluated in this way is actually the sum of k_{solv} and k_r.

A representative run, illustrating the first-order kinetics of hydrolysis of 3,5-cyclocholestan-6β-yl trichloroacetate (I) in 90% dioxane is shown in Table I. All the results of the study of the kinetics of hydrolysis of the epimeric 3,5-cyclocholestan-6-yl trichloroacetates are summarized in Table II.

A difficulty in the rate measurements was the tendency for the infinity acid titers to drift downward due to disappearance of trichloroacetic acid. One possible cause of this disappearance is decarboxylation by way of trichloroacetate ion.[12] However, the rate of decomposition of trichloro-

(12) F. H. Verhoek, *ibid.*, **56**, 571 (1951).

TABLE I

RATE OF SOLVOLYSIS OF 0.029 M 3,5-CYCLOCHOLESTAN-6β-YL TRICHLOROACETATE IN 90% DIOXANE AT 24.9°

Time, sec.	Base,[a] ml.	10^5k, sec.$^{-1}$
. . .	0.138	
3120	.387	(4.26)
6000	.552	3.85
8100	.643	3.58
11100	.786	3.51
14310	.937	3.55
17580	1.060	3.50
22080	1.256	3.69
27100	1.390	3.61
31090	1.516	3.73
∞	2.146[b]	

Mean 3.63 ± 0.10

[a] Vol. of 0.0559 N sodium hydroxide per 5.019-ml. aliquot. [b] 83.2% of theoretical.

TABLE II

RATE CONSTANTS FOR HYDROLYSIS OF 3,5-CYCLOCHOLESTAN-6-YL TRICHLOROACETATES IN 90% DIOXANE

Isomer	Concn. $10^2 M$	Other solute	Concn. $10^2 M$	Temp., °C.	% ∞	$10^5 k$, sec.$^{-1}$
β	2.9	. . . . .	. .	24.9	84	36.3
β	3.1	. . . . .	. .	24.9	83	33.6
β	3.1	LiOAc	4.2	24.9	83[a]	25.4
β	2.9	LiClO₄	3.0	24.9	89	52.3
β	3.0	LiTCA[b]	3.1	24.9	82	36.8
β	2.9	. . . . .	. .	50.0	81	654
α	2.8	. . . . .	. .	24.9	82[c]	3.86
α	3.1	. . . . .	. .	24.9	84[c]	3.80
α	2.8	LiClO₄	3.0	24.9	82[c]	4.38
α	2.0	. . . . .	. .	75.0	81[c]	899

[a] Estimated graphically from plot of titration data. [b] Lithium trichloroacetate. [c] Estimated roughly from decrease of apparent ∞ titer with time.

acetic acid decreases[13] rapidly in dioxane–water solutions with dioxane content greater than 62%, and it is relatively negligible in 90% dioxane. In the presence of added salts, ionization of trichloroacetic acid is increased and loss of acidity from this cause is more serious. Loss of acidity was the most serious when the added salt was lithium trichloroacetate. Another reason for disappearance of trichloroacetic acid is the slow consumption of trichloroacetic acid by the hydrolysis product[4] 3,5-cyclocholestan-6β-ol V with resultant formation of cholesteryl trichloroacetate.

Where the drift in the infinity acid titer warranted it, corrected values of $H_∞$, estimated empirically, were employed in evaluating rate constants with the aid of equation 1. Thus, some of the infinity titers listed in Table II and the corresponding rate constants are relatively inaccurate. Nevertheless, the rate constants show that common ion rate effects[11] from added lithium trichloroacetate are negligible, for the added common-ion salt neither depresses rate nor increases the formation of cholesteryl trichloroacetate which accompanies hydrolysis.

Chlorides.—The rates of solvolysis of the various chlorides were studied in acetic acid and 90% dioxane as solvents. Since solvolysis of cholesteryl chloride is relatively slow, it was studied at 100°.

(13) E. J. Salmi and R. Korte, *Annales Acad. Scient. Fennicae (Finland)*, **A54**, No. 10 (1940).

In acetic acid, even with lithium acetate included, and in aqueous dioxane, first-order solvolysis rate constants drifted down badly. This is illustrated in Table III. A similar behavior has been noted by Shoppee and his co-workers[14] in acetolysis of

TABLE III

RATE OF SOLVOLYSIS OF 0.0247 M CHOLESTERYL CHLORIDE WITH 0.0380 M LITHIUM ACETATE IN ACETIC ACID AT 99.8°

Time, min.	KCNS, ml.	10^4k, min.$^{-1}$
. . .	5.052	
212	4.793	2.48
725	4.317	2.19
1016	4.012	2.28
1730	3.636	1.91
1994	3.504	1.84
2622	3.381	1.54
3385	3.160	1.39
4722	2.807	1.25
6105	2.476	1.17
8380	2.270	0.96
15772	1.270	0.91
∞	0.093 (Calcd.)	

cholesteryl bromide. The downward drift is evidently due to the fact that solvolysis of cholesteryl chloride gives rise to 3,5-cyclocholestanyl derivatives which are not stable under the reaction conditions. In acetic acid containing lithium chloride, or in aqueous dioxane containing hydrogen chloride, the 3,5-cyclocholestanyl derivatives re-ionize and yield a certain proportion of cholesteryl chloride. This reconversion to cholesteryl chloride becomes more and more serious as the reaction progresses, so that first-order rate constants drift down in a run. The rate constants listed for cholesteryl chloride in Table V, which summarizes the data for the several chlorides, are estimated initial values.

TABLE IV

SOLVOLYSIS OF 0.019 M 3,5-CYCLOCHOLESTAN-6β-YL CHLORIDE (83.6% "ACTIVE") IN 90% DIOXANE AT 25.0°

Time, sec.	Base, ml.	10^3k, sec.$^{-1}$
. . .	0.371	
95	1.085	1.45
195	1.689	1.39
285	2.297	1.49
360	2.670	1.48
480	3.383	1.63
645	3.834	1.51
885	4.636	1.65
5805	5.427[a]	
10945	4.945	
49800	3.198	

Mean 1.51 ± 0.07

[a] Correction of this figure by +0.5 ml. leads to 68% infinity acid titer.

Solvolysis of 3,5-cyclocholestan-6β-yl chlorides III followed first-order kinetics quite satisfactorily in 90% dioxane or 50% acetic acid–dioxane at 25°, a sample run in 90% dioxane being shown in Table IV. However, the infinity hydrogen chloride titer in 90% dioxane tended to drift down due to con-

(14) R. H. Davies, S. Meecham and C. W. Shoppee, *J. Chem. Soc.*, 679 (1955).

TABLE V

RATE CONSTANTS OF SOLVOLYSIS OF CHOLESTERYL AND 3,5-CYCLOCHOLESTAN-6-YL CHLORIDES

Isomer	Solvent	Concn. $10^2 M$	Other solute	Concn. $10^2 M$	Temp. °C.	% ∞^{a}	$10^3 k$, sec. $^{-1}$
3β	AcOH^b	2.5	LiOAc	3.8	99.8		0.0042^c
3β	90% dioxane	4.0	....	..	99.7		.0002^c
6β	90% dioxane	1.2^d	....	..	25.0	69	1.64^e
6β	90% dioxane	1.9^f	....	..	25.0	68	1.51
6β	90% dioxane	1.3^f	LiCl	1.9	25.0	80	1.44
6β	90% dioxane	1.1^f	LiBr	1.4	24.9	71	1.79^g
6β	90% dioxane	1.1^f	LiClO$_4$	1.2	24.9	77	2.30
6β	90% dioxane	2.7^f	LiOAc	3.9	24.9	76	1.47
6β	50% AcOH–dioxane^h	4.4^f	LiOAc	3.4	24.9	20	0.61

^{a} % of "active chloride" appearing as chloride ion. ^{b} 0.01 M in Ac$_2$O. ^{c} Estimated initial rate constants. ^{d} Molarity of RCl, 72.4% of which was "active chloride"; sample prepared with pyridine. ^{e} Less accurate procedure employed in this run. ^{f} Molarity of RCl, 83.6% of which was "active chloride." ^{g} Rate constant drifted upward in run from 1.55 to 1.96. ^{h} Run carried out by Dr. Arnold Fainberg.

version of 3,5-cyclocholestan-6β-ol (V) to cholesteryl chloride. For this reason, it was necessary to make a small correction for the drift in choosing an H_∞-value to be employed in calculating the first-order rate constant by means of equation 1.

Ion pair return accompanied the solvolysis of 3,5-cyclocholestan-6β-yl chloride to a very considerable extent.[5] This was most serious in 50% acetic acid–dioxane containing lithium acetate. In this case the titratable chloride ion which was produced was only 20% of the theoretical value. Ion pair return was less serious in 90% dioxane, 68% of the theoretical acid titer being obtained. Added salts tended to decrease ion pair return, this being reflected in somewhat higher infinity acid titers listed in Table V. Added lithium bromide had a more complicated action, since the rate constant rose during the run, suggesting that 3,5-cyclocholestan-6β-yl bromide was being formed.

As reported previously,[5] the product from the action of thionyl chloride on 3,5-cyclocholestan-6α-ol (VI) contained an "active chloride," presumably 3,5-cyclocholestan-6α-yl chloride (IV), somewhat less reactive than 3,5-cyclocholestan-6β-yl chloride (III). Therefore, the chloride mixture displayed a drifting first-order rate constant of hydrolysis in 90% dioxane. From an analysis of the data described in the Experimental section, a value of 1.6 ± 0.3 was obtained for $10^4 k$ for hydrolysis of the less reactive chloride in 90% dioxane at 25°.

Acid-catalyzed Rearrangements of 3,5-Cyclo-cholestan-6-yl Derivatives.—The acid-catalyzed isomerization of 3,5-cyclocholestan-6-β-ol (V) to cholesterol and analogous isomerizations of various derivatives of the alcohol are well known. Also, Wallis[15] has reported virtually quantitative conversion of 3,5-cyclocholestan-6α-ol[16] (VI) into cholesterol by treatment with sulfuric acid in acetic acid and subsequent hydrolysis. The kinetics of the sulfuric acid-catalyzed rearrangement of the 6α-alcohol[16] VI in dry dioxane have been reported by Wolff and Wallis.[17]

The rates of acid-catalyzed isomerization of the epimeric 3,5-cyclocholestan-6-ols V and VI to cholesterol in 90% dioxane, and also that of the

(15) A. F. Wagner, N. E. Wolff and E. S. Wallis, J. Org. Chem., **17**, 529 (1952).
(16) This epimer was designated β by Wallis; see ref. 4.
(17) N. E. Wolff and E. S. Wallis, J. Org. Chem., **17**, 1361 (1952).

corresponding acetates VII and VIII to cholesteryl acetate in acetic acid solvent, were measured. For comparison, one measurement was made of the rate of the somewhat related acid-catalyzed conversion of 3,5-cyclocholestan-6-one (IX) to the 3β-acetoxycholestan-6-one[18] (X) in acetic acid solvent. Rates of acid-catalyzed isomerizations were followed polarimetrically, the data being treated by means of equation 2, where α_0, α and α_∞ represent optical rotations at zero time, time t and infinity, respectively. Fairly satisfactory

$$2.303 \log \left[\frac{\alpha_\infty - \alpha_0}{\alpha_\infty - \alpha} \right] = kt \qquad (2)$$

first-order kinetics were observed, sample runs for 3,5-cyclocholestan-6β-ol (V) and the α-epimer VI with perchloric acid as catalyst being summarized in Tables VI and VII. An over-all summary of the rates of the acid-catalyzed rearrangements is given in Table VIII.

TABLE VI

REARRANGEMENT OF 0.038 M 3,5-CYCLOCHOLESTAN-6β-OL WITH 0.0301 N PERCHLORIC ACID IN 90% DIOXANE AT 24.5°

Time, sec.	Obsd. α, °	$10^5 k$, sec. $^{-1}$
...	+0.652	
810	.568	9.27
1980	.502	6.97
3150	.378	8.55
4380	.274	8.99
5700	.178	9.20
7185	.090	9.22
9390	−0.037	9.57
11610	.120	9.39
48510^a	.510	

Mean   9.17 ± 0.23

^{a} 6.4 Reaction half-lives.

In the perchloric acid-catalyzed isomerization of 3,5-cyclocholestan-6β-ol (V), the isomerization rate was nearly linear in perchloric acid over a 10-fold

(18) K. Ladenburg, P. N. Chakravorty and E. S. Wallis, THIS JOURNAL, **61**, 3483 (1939).

TABLE VII

REARRANGEMENT OF 0.036 M 3,5-CYCLOCHOLESTAN-6α-OL WITH 0.0301 N PERCHLORIC ACID IN 90% DIOXANE AT 75.2°

Time, min.	Obsd. α, °	$10^3 k$, min.$^{-1}$
..	+0.843	
15	.682	9.03
30	.565	8.27
47	.446	7.98
87	.220	7.76
110	.082	8.31
149	−0.070	8.54
200	.190	8.40
1200(∞)	.426	

Mean 8.33 ± 0.28

in solvolysis. A comparison of reactivities of 3,5-cyclocholestan-6β-yl chloride (III) and cholesteryl chloride (XI) in acetic acid, summarized in Table IX, may be made by extrapolating the observed rate of cholesteryl chloride at 100° down to 25°. While the necessary activation energy was not directly observed, there is available the activation energy for acetolysis of cholesteryl bromide from the work of Shoppee and his co-workers.[14] These authors studied the acetolysis of the bromide in lieu of the chloride, which they noted was too slow for convenient measurement. From the reported activation energy of 26.5 kcal./mole for acetolysis of the bromide, a value of 27.4 kcal./mole may be estimated for cholesteryl chloride, since 0.9 kcal./

TABLE VIII

RATES OF ACID-CATALYZED REARRANGEMENTS OF 3,5-CYCLOCHOLESTAN-6-YL DERIVATIVES

Compound	Solvent	Concn. $10^2 M$	Acid	Concn. $10^2 M$	Temp., °C.	$10^5 k$, sec.$^{-1}$	$10^3 k/(HX)$
6β-OH	90% dioxane	6.2	HClO₄	0.32	25.0	0.67	2.1
6β-OH	90% dioxane	3.8	HClO₄	3.01	24.5	9.2	3.1
6β-OH	90% dioxane	4.1	HClO₄ / LiClO₄	3.01 / 3.4	24.5	10.3	3.4
6β-OH	90% dioxane	4.1	HTCA[a]	2.35	24.4	0.032	0.014
6β-OH	90% dioxane	4.2	HTCA / LiClO₄	2.35 / 2.4	25.0	0.46	0.20
6α-OH	90% dioxane	5.6	HClO₄	0.32	25.0	0.001	0.0031
6α-OH	90% dioxane	3.6	HClO₄	3.01	75.2	14	4 7
6α-OH	90% dioxane	3.6	HClO₄	3.01	99.7	190	63
6β-OAc	AcOH	3.9	HClO₄	0.0464	24.8	45	970
6α-OAc	AcOH	3.9	HClO₄	0.0464	24.8	10	220
6-Ketone	AcOH	5.3	HClO₄	4.66	20.0	12	2.6

[a] Trichloroacetic acid.

change in perchloric acid concentration, this being evident from the second-order rate constant, $[10^3 k/(HX)]$, in Table VIII. Further, inclusion of lithium perchlorate produced only a very small rise in isomerization rate. Trichloroacetic acid produced much lower rates of isomerization than did perchloric acid, and this rate was increased by a factor of approximately 15 by the inclusion of 0.024 M lithium perchlorate.[19] Trichloroacetic acid is a weak acid in 90% dioxane, and ionization is obviously very much facilitated by inclusion of salt. While these effects are of some interest in themselves, the main interest of the present investigation was in relative reactivity of isomeric materials, and these observations were not pursued further

From comparison of rates of reaction given in Table VIII, allowing for the difference in concentrations of perchloric acid catalyst employed, the conversion of 3,5-cyclocholestan-6-one (IX) to 3β-acetoxycholestan-6-one (X) appears to be slower than the acid-catalyzed rearrangement of 3,5-cyclocholestan-6β-yl acetate (VII) in acetic acid by approximately two powers of ten.

Discussion

3,5-Cyclocholestan-6β-yl Reactivity.—A striking feature of the present results is the very high reactivity of the 3,5-cyclocholestan-6β-yl derivatives

mole is the average difference in energies of activation between chloride and bromide in several systems[20], namely, t-Bu, α-phenylethyl, neophyl and benzhydryl.

The derived factor between the 3,5-cyclocholestan-6β-yl and cholesteryl chlorides in acetic acid is $10^{7.4}$. A similar factor may be estimated in 90% dioxane (Table IX). The derived reactivity ratio between the 3,5-cyclocholestan-6β-yl and cholesteryl chlorides is on the conservative side as an estimate of relative rates of ionization. This is because the measured rate constants for both chlorides are lower than ionization rate constants due to ion pair return. Judging by the relative reactivities[4,5] of the intermediate cation XII at carbon atoms C₃ and C₆, correction for ion pair return would revise the measured rate constant upwards

(19) Qualitative indication of this effect of lithium perchlorate was observed previously.[4] Whereas the product of hydrolysis of 3,5-cyclocholestan-6β-yl trichloroacetate (I) in 90% dioxane contains a large proportion of the 6β-alcohol V, it contains predominantly cholesterol when lithium perchlorate is included in the hydrolysis medium.

(20) (a) S. Winstein and A. H. Fainberg, THIS JOURNAL, **79**, 5937 (1957); (b) A. H. Fainberg and S. Winstein, *ibid.*, **79**, 1597 (1957); (c) A. H. Fainberg and S. Winstein, *ibid.*, **79**, 1602 (1957); (d) A. H. Fainberg and S. Winstein, *ibid.*, **79**, 1608 (1957); (e) S. Winstein, A. H. Fainberg and E. Grunwald, *ibid.*, **79**, 4146 (1957).

Comparison of Solvolytic Reactivities of 3,5-Cyclo-
cholestan-6β-yl and Cholest-5-en-3β-yl Chlorides at
25°

Solvent	AcOH	90% dioxane
6β-Cl; $10^3 k$, sec.$^{-1}$	9.2^a	1.5
3β-Cl; $10^{10} k$, sec.$^{-1}$	3.8^b	0.60^c
6β/3β ratio	$10^{7.4}$	$10^{7.4}$

^{a} Observed k in 50% AcOH–dioxane multiplied by 15, the factor observed for norbornyl p-bromobenzenesulfonate between AcOH and 50% AcOH–dioxane.[21] ^{b} Extrapolated from 100° with an activation energy of 27.4 kcal./mole. ^{c} Extrapolated from 100° with an activation energy of 23.9 kcal./mole, lower than the 27.4 kcal./mole figure for acetic acid solvent by 3.5 kcal./mole. The latter figure is the average difference between activation energies for solvolysis in acetic acid and 90% dioxane observed[20] with t-butyl, α-phenylethyl and benzhydryl chlorides.

by more in the case of the 3,5-cyclocholestan-6β-yl chloride than for cholesteryl chloride.

As large as the derived reactivity factor is, it still does not fully represent the high reactivity of the 3,5-cyclocholestan-6β-yl chloride, since solvolysis of cholesteryl derivatives are anchimerically accelerated[6a] by a factor of the order of 10^2.

Free Energy, Strain and Reactivity.—It is very instructive for our understanding of reactivities in homoallylic systems to consider first the equilibrium between two homoallylic isomers. In the present instance, the equilibrium is between cholesteryl and 3,5-cyclocholestan-6β-yl chlorides, XI and III, respectively, and it may be visualized by way of the unsymmetrical homoallylic cation XII. For our present purposes, it will be sufficient to employ only one homoallylic cation and to formulate the equilibrium by way of a dissociated cation rather than ion pairs. The corresponding equilibrium constant K_e may be expressed in the form of equation 3 as the product of two ratios, a reactivity ratio, (k_3/k_6), and a partition factor (k_{-6}/k_{-3}). The latter, symbolized P_6, is the ratio of reactivities of the cation XII toward chloride ion at its two reaction centers, C_6 and C_3.

$$K_e = \frac{[6\beta\text{-Cl}]}{[3\beta\text{-Cl}]} = \left(\frac{k_3}{k_6}\right)\left(\frac{k_{-6}}{k_{-3}}\right) = \left(\frac{k_3}{k_6}\right) P_6 \quad (3)$$

$$\underset{\text{Reactivity ratio}}{\qquad} \underset{\text{Partition factor}}{\qquad}$$

$$(k_6/k_3) = (1/K_e)P_6 \quad (4)$$

Equation 3 may be rewritten in the form of expression 5 for $\Delta F°$, the difference in molar standard free energies of the two homoallylic isomers. This is given as the difference between two quantities, $(\Delta F^*_{-3} - \Delta F^*_6)$, the difference in free energies of activation for ionization of the two homoallylic isomers, and $(\Delta F^*_{-3} - \Delta F^*_{-6})$, the difference

$$\Delta F° = -RT \ln K_e = (\Delta F^*_3 - \Delta F^*_6) - (\Delta F^*_{-3} - \Delta F^*_{-6}) \quad (5)$$

$$(\Delta F^*_3 - \Delta F^*_6) = \Delta F° + (\Delta F^*_{-3} - \Delta F^*_{-6}) \quad (6)$$

in free energies of activation for reaction of the homoallylic cation at the two reaction centers. The various quantities are indicated in Fig. 1 which presents a free energy diagram helpful in visualizing the thermodynamic situation.

(21) E. Clippinger, unpublished work.

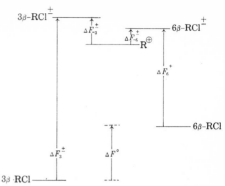

Fig. 1.—Free energy diagram for equilibrium between cholesteryl and 3,5-cyclocholestan-6β-yl chlorides.

Applying equation 3, we see that K_e is equal to $10^{-7.4}P_6$. The partition factor, P_6, for chloride ion as nucleophile is at least 5, and more probably higher than this.[5] The value is more nearly 10 for methanol and water as nucleophiles.[4,5] In any case, a value of 10^1 for P_6 to be employed in equation 3 is sufficiently accurate for our purposes. On this basis, K_e is estimated as $10^{-6.4}$, $\Delta F°$, the difference in molar standard free energies of the two homoallylic isomers, being ca. 9,000 cal./mole. Obviously, cholesteryl chloride is very much more stable than its homoallylic isomer.

For a discussion of relative reactivity of the homoallylic isomers, it is convenient to rewrite equations 3 and 5 in the form of equations 4 and 6. From these, it is clear that the (k_6/k_3) ratio of $10^{7.4}$ for the relative reactivity of the two homoallylic isomers is mainly due to the large ground state free energy difference, $\Delta F°$. Making up ca. 10,000 cal./mole difference in free energies of activation for ionization of the two homoallylic chlorides is ca. 9,000 cal./mole ground state free energy difference and ca. 1,000 cal./mole difference in free energies of activation for reaction of the homoallylic cation at its two reaction centers. That the latter quantity is so small is not surprising, in view of the fact that the intermediate cation is a very reactive species, and the transition states for its reactions at one or the other of its reaction centers may be expected to resemble the cation closely.[22] Thus, the difference between ΔF^*_{-3} and ΔF^*_{-6} is inevitably small. To a first approximation, therefore, $(\Delta F^*_3 - \Delta F^*_6)$, the difference in free energies of activation for ionization of the two homoallylic isomers, may be taken equal to $\Delta F°$, the difference in ground state free energies.

To appreciate further the role of ground state free energy in controlling reactivity of homoallylic isomers, it is instructive to consider the system of dehydronorbornyl and nortricyclyl bromobenzene-

(22) G. S. Hammond, This Journal, **77**, 334 (1955).

sulfonates[2,7,8,23] XIII and XV. Using the indicated numbering system, the analogs of equations 3 and 4 are 7 and 8, respectively.

$$K_e = \frac{[\text{nortricyclyl OBs}]}{[\text{norbornenyl OBs}]} = \left(\frac{k_2}{k_5}\right)\left(\frac{k_{-5}}{k_{-2}}\right) = \left(\frac{k_2}{k_5}\right)P_5 \quad (7)$$

$$(k_5/k_2) = (1/K_e)P_5 \quad (8)$$

Applying equation 7 to the dehydronorbornyl and nortricyclyl bromobenzenesulfonates XIII and XV, (k_2/k_5) is ca. 5 for acetolysis[8,23] and 2–3 for hydrolysis[23] in 75% acetone at 25°. The partition factor, P_5, is ca. 15 in acetolysis[8,23] and ca. 6 in hydrolysis[23]; if these values are used as approximations to P_5 for bromobenzenesulfonate ion, the estimated K_e is in the range of 12–75. In actual fact, while side reactions preclude an accurate determination of K_e by direct equilibration, attempts to equilibrate the two isomers in nitrobenzene at 75° do show[23] that the equilibrium proportion of dehydronorbornyl bromobenzenesulfonate XIII is less than 10%. In this homoallylic system, the isomer containing the cyclopropane ring is the more stable one,[2,24] in contrast with the relationship which exists between cholesteryl and 3,5-cyclocholestanyl isomers.

Using equations 4 and 8 to contrast the relative reactivities of the homoallylic isomers in the norbornenyl and cholesteryl systems, we have already seen that (k_5/k_2) in the norbornenyl system is less than unity, whereas (k_6/k_3) in the cholesteryl system is $10^{7.4}$. The partition factors P_5 and P_6 are approximately equal in the two systems. Therefore, the difference between (k_5/k_2) and (k_6/k_3) is to be sought in the $(1/K_e)$ factor. In other words, ground state free energy factors are responsible for a 10^8 change in relative reactivity of the homoallylic isomers from one system to another. Since there is no reason to expect the above two systems to be extremes, there may arise even more extreme examples.

Strain and Electron Delocalization.—Without regard for the role of ground state free energies in controlling reactivity of homoallylic derivatives, one can be misled regarding the importance of electron delocalization in stabilizing homoallylic cations. To make this point clear, it may be helpful to consider the cholesteryl–cyclocholestanyl chloride system further, focusing attention on the homoallylic cation rather than on transition states, since we have already seen that the latter resemble the intermediate cation quite closely. As portrayed in Fig. 2, ionization of cholesteryl chloride is assisted by electron delocalization, which more than compensates for strain introduced in the cation.[10b] Equation 9 expresses the standard free energy of ionization of cholesteryl chloride, ΔF^0_3, as ΔF^0_{in}, the value in the absence of strain and electron delocalization, modified by a positive strain free energy, ΔF°_{s3} and a negative term due to electron delocalization, ΔF°_{e3}.

$$\Delta F^0_3 = \Delta F^0_{in} + \Delta F^0_{s3} + \Delta F^0_{e3} \quad (9)$$
$$\Delta F^0_6 = \Delta F^0_{in} + \Delta F^0_{s6} + \Delta F^0_{e6} \quad (10)$$
$$\Delta F^0 = \Delta F^0_{s3} - \Delta F^0_{s6} \quad (11)$$

Equation 10, analogous to equation 9, expresses the standard free energy of ionization of cyclocholestanyl chloride, ΔF^0_6, as ΔF^0_{in}, the value in the absence of strain and electron delocalization effects, modified by strain and electron delocalization free energies, ΔF^0_{s6} and ΔF^0_{e6}, respectively. Since the situation is idealized, the same ΔF^0_{in} is used in equations 9 and 10, differences due to inductive effects, repulsions between non-bonded atoms, etc., being neglected.

Both bond energies and strain energies are logically involved in a discussion of the thermochemistry of an equilibrium between olefinic chloride XI and cyclocholestanyl chloride III. However, we can choose to have the term "strain" include changes in both bond and strain energies. On this basis, ΔF° may be called the strain free energy difference between the homoallylic isomers XI and III. Since ΔF° is the difference between the strain free energies of ionization of the two isomers, ΔF^0_{s3} and ΔF^0_{s6}, repectively, we can write equation 11. From this, it is clear that ΔF^0_{s6} has a negative value, ionization of cyclocholestanyl chloride III being attended by relief of strain. This conclusion may be reached from structural considerations, also.

As brought out above and illustrated in Fig. 2, the high reactivity of cyclocholestanyl chloride III is to be ascribed partly to strain relief and partly to electron delocalization. If strain relief on ionization were ignored, and the whole rate enhancement of this homoallylic derivative were taken as an indication of stabilization of a cationic intermediate by electron delocalization, this might appear so high as to call for a unique explanation. For example, cyclocholestanyl chloride III is more reactive in solvolysis than the classically allylic compounds, cyclohexenyl chloride XVI, studied by Goering,[25] and 6β-chlorocholest-4-ene (XVII) and 4β-chlorocholest-5-ene (XVIII), studied by W. G. Young and his co-workers[26] in these laboratories.

XVI   XVII   XVIII

Depending on the case, insufficient consideration of the role of ground state free energies in solvolysis of α-cyclopropylalkyl derivatives may lead one either to overestimate or underestimate the conjugative accelerative effect of the cyclopropane ring. For example, cyclopropylcarbinyl derivatives are more reactive in solvolysis than the allyl analogs,[27] and this was part of the basis for the suggestion of the "tricyclobutonium" structure[27b,28] XIX for the cationic intermediate. The apparently greater conjugative acceleration of rate by α-cyclopropyl compared to α-vinyl was thus accounted for by the increased resonance energy[27b] due to the threefold

(23) H. J. Schmid, unpublished work.

(24) P. Schleyer, THIS JOURNAL, **80**, 1700 (1958), has reported equilibration of the parent hydrocarbons, norbornene and nortricyclene; nortricyclene is favored over norbornene at equilibrium by a factor of ca. 3 at reflux temperature.

(25) H. L. Goering, T. D. Nevitt and E. F. Silversmith, THIS JOURNAL, **77**, 5026 (1955).

(26) R. E. Ireland, T. I. Wrigley and W. G. Young, ibid., **80**, 4604 (1958).

(27) (a) J. D. Roberts and R. H. Mazur, ibid., **73**, 2509 (1951); (b) C. G. Bergstrom and S. Siegel, ibid., **74**, 145 (1952).

(28) J. D. Roberts and R. H. Mazur, ibid., **73**, 3542 (1951).

symmetry of XIX. Actually, such a structure was not required to explain the rate, nor was it demanded by any of the other facts.[27-29] Instead of XIX, bicyclobutonium ions, discussed in a later section of this article, are now being invoked by Roberts and co-workers.[30]

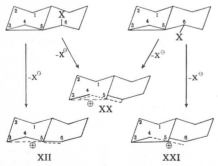

XIX

In the norbornenyl–nortricyclyl homoallylic system (XIII and XV), the relatively low rate of the nortricyclyl isomer, already commented on, has been taken as an indication of relatively poor electron release by the cyclopropane ring and ascribed[31] to "steric inhibition of hyperconjugation." Actually, we believe it is the ground state free energy picture which accounts mainly for the relatively low rate of the nortricyclyl derivative, and not steric inhibition of conjugation.

$6\beta : 6\alpha$-**Comparison.**—Solvolysis product studies[4,5] have shown that the intermediates which give rise to products are the same, whether the derivative being solvolyzed is cholesteryl, 3,5-cyclo-cholestan-6β-yl or 3,5-cyclocholestan-6α-yl. Further information on the nature of the first cationic intermediates produced by ionization of the 3,5-cyclo-6β- and 6α-steroids could conceivably come from a comparison of reactivities of 6β- and 6α-derivatives. A study of crude models suggests that, if ionization of the 6β- and 6α-derivatives proceeds stereospecifically to unsymmetrical homoallylic ions[4] XII and XXI, respectively, that geometry is much more favorable for participation of the 3,5-bonding electron pair in the 6β-derivative than the 4,5-bonding pair in the 6α-derivative. Since we might expect,[4] further, that XII is more stable than XXI, a large 6β:6α rate factor would be anticipated on this basis.

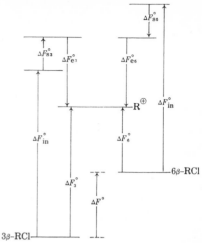

Fig. 2.—Free energy diagram representing strain and electron delocalization effects in ionization of cholesteryl and 3,5-cyclocholestan-6-yl chlorides.

ion XX. In a chair B ring, the plane of a cationic C_6 center is only slightly away from perpendicular to the plane of the cyclopropane ring, which wavemechanical considerations[32] suggest is the best arrangement for conjugation. If ionization of both 6β- and 6α- derivatives were to a symmetrical homoallylic ion XX, and the transition states corresponded to a high degree of ionization, the reactivity ratio between 6β- and 6α-derivatives would not be expected to be large.

A comparison of relative reactivities of the 6β- and 6α-derivatives in the various reactions studied is summarized in Table X. From the table, it

TABLE X

RELATIVE REACTIVITIES OF 3,5-CYCLOCHOLESTAN-6-YL DERIVATIVES AT 25°

Reaction	$6\beta/6\alpha$ rate ratio
ROCOCCl₃, 90% dioxane	8.7
ROCOCCl₃, 90% dioxane, 0.03 M LiClO₄	11.9
RCl, 90% dioxane	10
ROH, 90% dioxane, HClO₄	670ᵃ
ROAc, AcOH, HClO₄	4.5

ᵃ This figure, for 0.32×10^{-2} M HClO₄, is relatively rough because of the low rate of the 6α-alcohol at 25°. Extrapolation of the 99.7° and 75.2° values for the 6α-alcohol at 3.01×10^{-2} M HClO₄ down to 24.5° and comparison with the value for the 6β-alcohol leads to a value of 540.

is clear that the 6β:6α-ratio is of the order of only 10^1 or 10^2, a small factor compared to 10^9 or 10^{10}, the factor by which 3,5-cyclocholestan-6β-yl derivatives are accelerated over cholestan-3β-yl analogs. The variation in the 6β:6α-ratios for the various reactions is considerable, and this feature is being studied further. One of the disturbances which affects the apparent 6β:6α-ratio is due to ion pair return. For this reason, the rate constants evaluated by means of equation 1 for the 6β-derivatives are lower than ionization rate

XII   XXI

Models suggest that the stereoelectronic situation is quite favorable in a symmetrical[4,7,10] homoallylic

(29) (a) A. Streitwieser, Jr., *Chem. Revs.*, **56**, 710 (1956); (b) H. Hart, J. M. Sandri and D. P. Wyman, American Chemical Society, Miami, Florida, April 7–12, 1957, Abstracts, p. 65-O.

(30) R. H. Mazur, W. N. White, D. A. Semenow, C. C. Lee, M. S. Silver and J. D. Roberts, THIS JOURNAL, **81**, 4390 (1959).

(31) J. D. Roberts, W. Bennett and R. Armstrong, *ibid.*, **72**, 3329 (1950); see also J. D. Roberts and W. Bennett, *ibid.*, **76**, 4623 (1954), and ref 30.

(32) (a) A. D. Walsh, *Trans. Faraday Soc.*, **45**, 179 (1949); (b) C. A. Coulson and W. E. Moffitt, *Phil. Mag.*, [7] **40**, 1 (1949).

constants. Similarly, the rates of the acid-catalyzed reactions of the 6β-derivatives are lower than ionization rate constants by a factor of *ca.* 10^1 due to the tendency for the cationic intermediate to return to 6β-derivative instead of yielding the cholesteryl product. The same kinds of return must occur in the reactions of the 6α-derivatives, so a certain steady-state proportion of more reactive 6β-derivative must appear relatively early in a run and then be reacting along with the 6α-derivative during the main part of the rate run. However, the kinetic studies were not sufficiently thorough to disclose this disturbance.

The important point established by the 6β:6α-comparison is that there is actually not a very large difference in reactivities of the 6β- and 6α-derivatives. This is especially noteworthy when we allow further for the fact that ionization of the 6β-derivatives might be expected to be sterically accelerated compared to the 6α-analogs due to the 6β-X,10-CH₃ interaction in the 6β-derivative. All the facts are probably best accommodated by supposing that ionization of the 3,5-cyclocholestan-6α-yl derivatives first yields the symmetrical homoallylic cation XX. This would allow us to understand, not only rate, but the indication that some 6α-chloride is formed along with 6β- by the action of thionyl chloride on 3,5-cyclocholestan-6α-ol. In the case of ionization of the 3,5-cyclocholestan-6β-yl derivatives, the rate data could be accommodated by formation of either the symmetrical cation XX or unsymmetrical XII, as far as our present information goes. We hope to study this matter further.

Homoallylic and Bicyclobutonium Ions.—With certain systems, homoallylic rearrangements become intertwined with Wagner–Meerwein rearrangements involving 3 → 4 ring expansion or 4 → 3 ring contraction. For example, cyclopropyl-carbinyl derivatives XXV are related, not only to

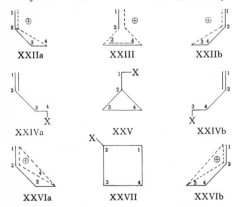

XXIIa   XXIII   XXIIb

XXIVa   XXV   XXIVb

XXVIa   XXVII   XXVIb

allylcarbinyl XXIV, but to cyclobutyl analogs XXVII as well. This is clearest from the elegant work of J. D. Roberts and co-workers[27a,28,30] in recent years. The number and the structures of electron-deficient cationic intermediates involved in homoallylic and Wagner–Meerwein rearrangements of the sort being considered represent difficult questions, the answers to which are still

in a state of flux. Either explicitly, or from the kind of resonance structures envisioned, the cation from a cyclopropylcarbinyl derivative XXV has at various times been formulated as an unsymmetrical homoallylic ion[27a,29a] XXII, symmetrical homoallylic ion[27b] XXIII, symmetrical tricyclobutonium ion[27b,28] XIX, or unsymmetrical bicyclobutonium ion[30] XXVI. It is necessary to note the differences between these formulations.

In connection with participation of a β-olefinic group in solvolysis, an unsymmetrical homoallylic cation XII was first proposed for the cholesteryl system by Winstein and Adams[6a] and almost simultaneously by Dodson and Riegel.[33] This formation of the unsymmetrical homoallylic cation may be symbolized in the general case by XXIVa→ XXIIa. The cation from cyclopropylcarbinyl derivatives XXV subsequently was formulated in this fashion.[27a,29a]

Further electron delocalization and change in geometry of XXIIa may be visualized[7,10] to give rise to the symmetrical homoallylic ion XXIII and finally the second unsymmetrical homoallylic ion XXIIb. These may be considered[7,10] as possible discrete species which accommodate homoallylic rearrangement, as well as Wagner–Meerwein rearrangement of the vinyl group between atoms 3 and 4. The symmetrical homoallylic ion XXIII, considered as a possible discrete intermediate in the conversion of one unsymmetrical homoallylic ion to the other, is presumed to involve conjugation of the cyclopropane ring with a cationic center at C_1, the plane of the cationic carbon atom being perpendicular to the plane of the cyclopropane ring. Species XXIII can be visualized to give rise to homoallyl derivative XXIVa, cyclopropane derivative XXV, and homoallyl derivative XXIVb, species XXIIa to the first two of these products, and species XXIIb to the latter two. However, the actual products and their proportions from reaction of X⊖ with each species are related by the principle of microscopic reversibility to the nature and the relative timing of formation of the various cationic species involved in equilibrating homoallylic and cyclopropane-ring-containing isomers XXIVa, XXIVb and XXV.

The norbornenyl system XIII is one for which both unsymmetrical[31,34] and symmetrical[7b,35] homoallylic cations were visualized early.[36] The highly accelerated rate[8] of solvolysis of the *exo*-norbornenyl ester XIII and the results of Roberts and his co-workers[35] on ¹⁴C-scrambling in the norbornenyl product of solvolysis of ¹⁴C-labeled norbornenyl bromobenzenesulfonate show that (i) an unsymmetrical homoallylic cation XIV, leading to some unrearranged norbornenyl solvolysis product, is formed first by ionization of norbornenyl bromobenzenesulfonate, and (ii) at least one additional intermediate cation is required. The investigation

(33) R. M. Dodson and B. M. Riegel, *J. Org. Chem.*, **13**, 424 (1948).

(34) J. D. Roberts, Symposium on Organic Reaction Mechanisms, 75th Anniversary Meeting of the American Chemical Society, Sept. 7, 1951.

(35) J. D. Roberts, C. C. Lee and W. H. Saunders, Jr., THIS JOURNAL, **77**, 3034 (1955).

(36) S. Winstein, Symposium on Organic Reaction Mechanisms, 75th Anniversary Meeting of the American Chemical Society, Sept. 7, 1951.

of Schmid[7b,23] has shown that the percentage of unsaturated component in the solvolysis product is definitely lower from nortricyclyl than from the norbornenyl bromobenzenesulfonate. This suggests that solvolysis product does not arise from only unsymmetrical homoallylic cations, otherwise nortricyclyl and norbornenyl starting materials would give solvolysis products with the same proportion of unsaturated component. Although a stereochemical study would be desirable, the available facts suggest that all three unsymmetrical and symmetrical homoallylic cations are involved in solvolysis of the bromobenzenesulfonates, the norbornenyl ester first ionizing to an unsymmetrical ion, the nortricyclyl ester to a symmetrical one.[7b,37] For the symmetrical cation, the geometry of the nortricyclyl skeleton is perfect, the plane of a cationic center at C_5 being exactly perpendicular to the plane of the cyclopropane ring.

In the cholesteryl system there are no clear indications of the occurrence of all three conceivable homoallylic cations XII, XX and XXI. However, with 4,4-dimethylcholesteryl toluenesulfonate, the rate of solvolysis is similar to that of cholesteryl toluenesulfonate, but the predominant products are ring-contracted.[38] The 4,4-dimethylcholesteryl cation, with the 4,4-methyl groups favoring the change, apparently does pass through the structure of the second unsymmetrical homoallylic cation analogous to XXI.

In carbonium ion reactions of the simplest α-cyclopropylalkyl derivatives, namely, cyclopropylcarbinyl XXV, the products contain[27a] cyclobutyl materials XXVII and display a considerable degree of approach to equivalence[28,30] of carbon atoms C_1, C_3 and C_4. J. D. Roberts and co-workers[30] now explain this behavior with the aid of bicyclobutonium ions of the type of XXVI, which tend to equilibrate C_1, C_3 and C_4 possibly by way of XIX.[39] The bicyclobutonium ion XXVI presumably is formed by ionization of either cyclopropylcarbinyl or cyclobutyl derivatives XXV or XXVII, and it reacts with nucleophiles to yield the allylcarbinyl, cyclopropylcarbinyl and cyclobutyl products XXIV, XXV and XXVII, respectively.

The geometry and orbital description which have been suggested[30] for the unsymmetrical bicyclobutonium ion XXVI are very similar to those visualized by Simonetta and Winstein[10b] in their treatment of the unsymmetrical homoallylic ion

XXII. However, in the unsymmetrical bicyclobutonium ion XXVI, a C_4–C_1 interaction is explicitly considered along with C_4–C_2, and some rotation of the C_4-methylene group about the C_3–C_4 bond is visualized[30] for improved overlap of the p-orbital on C_4 with the p-orbital on C_1.

In principle, it can be argued that the 1,4-interaction should never be omitted and that all homoallylic cations have some "bicyclobutonium" character. For example, the unsymmetrical homoallylic norbornenyl cation XIV could be rewritten as XXVIII. However, it is common practice to limit any treatment to the more important interactions and omit a generally less important one until the latter becomes necessary to understand a specific situation. The usual treatment of an allyl cation includes 1,2- and omits 1,3-interactions, while the treatment of Simonetta and Winstein[10b] of the unsymmetrical homoallylic cation includes 1,3- and omits 1,4-interactions.

In systems such as cholesteryl (XII) and norbornenyl (XIV), the constraints of the ring systems favor 1,3-interactions more than 1,4-interactions and "bicyclobutonium" character in the cations. For ion XIV, this can be illustrated with the results of calculations[40] which have been carried out for bicycloheptadiene XXIX. In this hydrocarbon, the 2,6-overlap integral, S_{26}, is greater than S_{25} by a factor of 2.2. Depending on the treatment[40] the exchange integral, β_{26}, is greater than β_{25} by factors of 2–9. Inspection of crude models suggests further that deformation of ions XII and XIV to increase 1,4-bonding would be attended by unusually large strain energies. There is one noteworthy cation where the distinction between 1,3- and 1,4-interactions has vanished, namely, the 7-norbornenyl cation XXX, discovered by Winstein, Shatavsky, Norton and Woodward.[9a] The equivalent overlap of the C_7-p orbital with C_2- and C_3-p orbitals in XXX has been emphasized[9,41] and the cation has been called both homoallylic[9] and "bis-homocyclopropenyl."[41]

Where homoallylic rearrangements do become intertwined with 3→4 and 4→3 ring changes, it seems to us not yet clear[10b] how many non-classical cations are actually involved. It proved[30] impossible to maintain economy of non-classical intermediates at one symmetrical tricyclobutonium ion[27,28] XIX in the interpretation of reactions of cyclopropylcarbinyl derivatives XXV, and the question still remains whether bicyclobutonium ions

(37) If this is correct, the principle of microscopic reversibility leads to the conclusion that reaction of bromobenzenesulfonate ion with the symmetrical cation yields only nortricyclyl ester, while reaction with the unsymmetrical ion yields only norbornenyl ester. By analogy, reaction with solvent would be formulated similarly. On this basis, the behavior of the homoallylic cations toward nucleophiles differs from that visualized previously.[7b,35]

Since, on this basis, two homoallylic cations are involved in equilibration of norbornenyl and nortricyclyl bromobenzenesulfonates, equation 7 for the equilibrium constant, K_e, becomes $K_e = (k_2/k_1)$ $(k_{-1}/k_{-2})(k^{\mathrm{u}}/k^{\mathrm{s}})$. A third ratio, $(k^{\mathrm{u}}/k^{\mathrm{s}})$, the relative rate constants for conversion of unsymmetrical and symmetrical cations into each other, is thus added to the right-hand side of equation 7. The counterpart of this change is necessary in free energy diagrams of the type in Figs. 1 and 2. Two cations at similar free energy levels need to be introduced in place of the one intermediate.

(38) G. Just and R. Sneen, unpublished work.

(39) The orbital hybridization and geometry about each of the three methylene groups are quite different from those in the original[28] XIX.

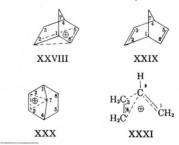

XXVIII   XXIX

XXX   XXXI

(40) C. Wilcox, unpublished work.

(41) W. G. Woods, R. A. Carboni and J. D. Roberts, THIS JOURNAL, **78**, 5653 (1956).

of the XXVI type are sufficient. For example, one could inquire whether the symmetrical homoallylic ion XXIII (or XXXI) is involved.

The question raised is essentially one of distinction between homoallylic and bicyclobutonium cations. It would seem that bicyclobutonium ions suffice if no energy barrier occurs between classical cyclobutyl and unsymmetrical homoallylic cations, and between classical cyclobutyl and symmetrical homoallylic cations.[42] Models suggest that this state of affairs may not be equally probable in the two cases.

Experimental

Materials and Solvents.—The 3,5-cyclocholestan-6β- and 6α-trichloroacetates and the corresponding alcohols were those described previously.[4] The 3,5-cyclocholestan-6-yl chloride specimens were also those described previously.[5]

Cholesteryl chloride was prepared by an improved procedure. Cholesterol (200 g.) was mixed with 148 ml. of thionyl chloride (240 g.), and the mixture was allowed to stand for 24 hours. The partially solid reaction mixture was poured onto ice and potassium carbonate, and the chloride was filtered off and washed with water. The wet solid was transferred to a beaker and warmed with 2 liters of redistilled petr. ether, b.p. 36–41°. The water layer was removed with a pipet, and the solution was poured through an alumina column (10 × 33 cm., *ca.* 1.6 kg.). Petroleum ether was added until the total volume of eluate had reached 3 liters. The solvent was distilled off on the steam-bath, and 800 ml. of acetone was added to the very light yellow oil. The chloride crystallized almost immediately, and it was filtered off to yield a material, m.p. 96–97°. Concentration of the filtrate yielded an additional amount of product, m.p. 95.5–96.5°. The total yield was 201.5 g. (95.6%).

Dioxane, b.p. 100.5–101.0°, was tested frequently for peroxide, and it was usually refluxed over sodium and distilled prior to use. The 90% dioxane solvent was prepared by mixing nine volumes of dioxane with one volume of water. Acetic acid solvent, approximately 0.03 M in acetic anhydride, was prepared in the usual way.[43]

Lithium trichloroacetate, in the form of a white powder, rather soluble in polar solvents, and decomposing on heating at about 270°, was prepared by addition of trichloroacetic acid to an equivalent amount of lithium carbonate suspended in ether. The solid was filtered off, washed with cold ether, dissolved in boiling ether and precipitated by cooling. The final product was obtained by filtration and drying under vacuum. Lithium perchlorate trihydrate, m.p. 94–95°, was kindly supplied by Dr. K. C. Schreiber.

Rate Measurements.—Acid-catalyzed isomerization of the 3,5-cyclocholestan-6α- and 6β-ols and acetates was followed polarimetrically.[44] Fast rates were measured in a jacketed polarimeter tube with temperature maintained by oil pumped from a constant temperature bath through the tube. At intervals, a reading was made as rapidly as possible and the time recorded immediately afterwards. Slow rates were followed by withdrawing samples from solutions maintained at constant temperature, placing the solution in a 1-dcm. polarimeter tube, measuring the rotation, and recording the time immediately after reading the rotation. For runs at 75 and 100°, 1.2–1.5 ml. aliquots were sealed into small ampoules, times taken as the instant of quenching in ice, and the rotations measured as usual.

In following solvolysis of the trichloroacetates, aliquots were removed with a calibrated automatic pipet and quenched in 25 ml. of water. The time used was the instant of opening the pipet to release the sample, except for runs at higher temperatures where the time used was that of cooling the ampoule in ice. The ampoule was warmed to room temperature and sampled as before. The aqueous solution was titrated with standard sodium hydroxide using phenolphthalein as indicator, the solutions showing no drift in end-point. Especially in the case of solvolysis in the presence of added lithium acetate, it was not possible to obtain a reliable infinity titer, and this was estimated graphically.

In following solvolysis of the chlorides, samples were quenched in 50-ml. glass-stoppered flasks containing 25 ml. of pentane and 10 ml. of water. A well-greased stopper was placed in the mouth of the flask, and the whole was shaken vigorously 25 times.[43] The water layer was separated, a boiling chip was added, and the solution was boiled on a hot-plate for 2–3 minutes. Then it was allowed to cool, protected from the atmosphere by an ascarite tube, and the acid was titrated with standard base, using the green color of brom thymol blue as end-point. The aqueous solutions derived from the run with lithium acetate were titrated for chloride by the usual Volhard procedure, nitrobenzene being used to protect the silver chloride.

In solvolysis of the chloride prepared from 6α-alcohol and thionyl chloride,[5] a 211-mg. quantity of material (78.6% "active") was dissolved in 63 ml. of pure dioxane and mixed with 7 ml. of water. The solution was thermostatted at 25.0°, and 5.049-ml. aliquots were removed and analyzed for acid. The results obtained are

Time, sec.	Base,[a] ml.	10^3k, sec.$^{-1}$	Time, sec.	Base,[a] ml.	10^3f, sec.$^{-1}$
..	0.142		780	1.211	1.07
90	.339	1.22	4080	1.770	0.48
180	.535	1.29	7920	1.927	.36
285	.684	1.19	15180	2.036	
360	.780	1.14	22380	2.000	
450	.916	1.17		2.072[b]	
540	1.007	1.13			

[a] Ml. 0.00959 N base per aliquot. [b] Corrected infinity titer; 67% of theoretical value.

From the measured rate constant for the 6β-chloride and the development of acidity during the first 7 minutes, due essentially entirely to solvolysis of 6β-chloride, the initial concentration of 6β-chloride was estimated. The remainder of the "active" chloride was a slower reacting material. From the initial amount of this chloride and the remaining "active" chloride at 7920 sec. a rate constant of 1.3×10^{-4} sec.$^{-1}$ may be estimated for this chloride. From a plot of log $(a - x)$ *vs.* time, a rate constant of 1.9×10^{-4} sec.$^{-1}$ is estimated for the slower "active" chloride from the straight line through the late points. Correcting the residual "active" chloride concentrations at each of the earlier points for the amount of slower "active" chloride, a good straight line plot is obtained for log $(a - x)$ of the 6β-chloride *vs.* time. From this plot, 1.7×10^{-3} sec.$^{-1}$ is obtained as the rate constant of the 6β-chloride.

Los Angeles 24, Calif.

---

(42) Some analogy exists for the occurrence of only one potential energy minimum in carbonium ion conversions involving 3 ⇄ 4 ring changes. For example, a non-classical tricycloheptonium ion intervenes for the 4 ⇄ 5 ring changes in reactions of the highly strained 2-bicyclo[3.2.0]heptyl and 7-bicyclo[2.2.1]heptyl arenesulfonates.[1c]

(43) A. H. Fainberg and S. Winstein, This Journal, **78**, 2770 (1956).

(44) S. Winstein and D. Trifan, *ibid.*, **74**, 1147 (1952).

41 | 3-Bicyclo-(3.1.0)hexyl Tosylate

In the communication of Winstein, Sonnenberg, and deVries it is shown that the solvolysis of the conformationally rigid 3-bicyclo(3.1.0)hexyl tosylate exhibits four properties suggesting a nonclassical intermediate: formation of only *cis* product from either geometrical isomer, *cis/trans* rate ratio of about 35, special salt effect, and isotopically detected equivalence of positions 1, 3, and 5. On purely conformational grounds, without neighboring group participation in the ionization, the *trans* isomer should have solvolyzed a few times faster than the *cis,* as is common for rigid axial-equatorial pairs.[1] The rather mild driving force indicates that this type of nonclassical ion is not likely to be found except where a conformationally rigid ring produces ideal geometry for it.

[1] S. Winstein and N. J. Holness, *J. Am. Chem. Soc.* **77**, 5562 (1955).

From: *J. Am. Chem. Soc.* **81,** 6523 (1959)

THE TRIS-HOMOCYCLOPROPENYL CATION[1]

Sir:

Examination of models of the 3-bicyclo[3.1.0]-hexyl cation I suggests that little reorganization and rehybridization are required to make carbon atoms 1, 3 and 5 equivalent. On this basis it becomes conceivable that the cation I would possess the symmetrical non-classical structure II. We now report the results of experiments with the *cis*- and *trans*-3-bicyclo[3.1.0]hexyl toluenesulfonates which bear out this expectation.

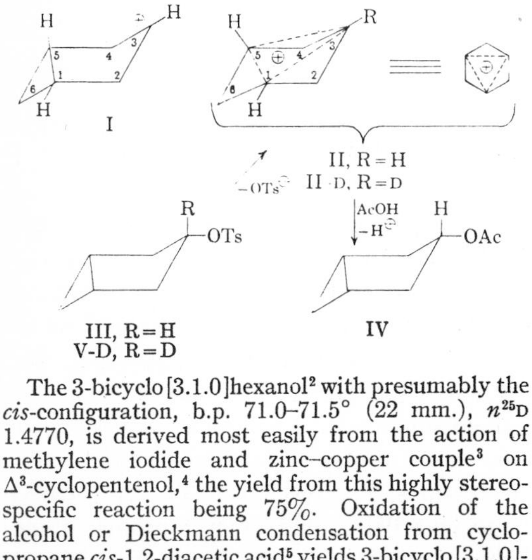

III, R=H
V-D, R=D

IV

The 3-bicyclo[3.1.0]hexanol[2] with presumably the *cis*-configuration, b.p. 71.0–71.5° (22 mm.), n^{25}D 1.4770, is derived most easily from the action of methylene iodide and zinc–copper couple[3] on Δ³-cyclopentenol,[4] the yield from this highly stereospecific reaction being 75%. Oxidation of the alcohol or Dieckmann condensation from cyclopropane *cis*-1,2-diacetic acid[5] yields 3-bicyclo[3.1.0]-hexanone, b.p. 54–55° (25 mm.), n^{25}D 1.4590, 2,4-dinitrophenylhydrazone, m.p. 149–150°. Reduction of the bicyclohexanone with lithium aluminum hydride leads to an 89:11 mixture, while aluminum isopropylate gives a 40:60 mixture of the *cis*- and *trans*-alcohols, respectively. Acetolysis of 0.08 M *cis*-toluenesulfonate III, m.p. 51.6–51.8°, in the presence of 0.10 M sodium acetate at 50° leads exclusively to *cis*-acetate IV with no accompanying olefin. The *trans*-toluenesulfonate, m.p. 70.5–

71.5°, gives rise to the same *cis*-acetate with considerable accompanying olefin (*ca.* 33%).

In acetolysis the *cis*-toluenesulfonate III is substantially more reactive than the *trans*-epimer. With the *cis*-toluenesulfonate III the addition of lithium perchlorate in the acetolysis at 50° gives rise to a special salt effect,[6] the magnitude being measured by a (k^0_{ext}/k^0_t) value of 3.2. A special salt effect does not occur in acetolysis of analogous toluenesulfonates, such as Δ³-cyclopentenyl, cyclopentyl and cyclohexyl.

The factor of *ca.* 35 between the rates of acetolysis of the *cis*- and *trans*-toluenesulfonates suggests that ionization of the *cis*-toluenesulfonate III is somewhat anchimerically accelerated. The occurrence of the special salt effect in acetolysis of the *cis*-toluenesulfonate is diagnostic[6b] for the occurrence of an ion pair with a special structure for the cation, which evidently reacts stereospecifically with solvent.

That the cation from toluenesulfonate III does indeed have the non-classical structure II is suggested by the behavior of 3-deuterated bicyclohexyl toluenesulfonate V-D, m.p. 51.5–52.0°, prepared from deuterated alcohol from lithium aluminum deuteride reduction of the bicyclohexanone. The infrared spectrum of the alcohol from acetolysis of V-D shows that the product alcohol now has deuterium on the cyclopropane ring, the corresponding C-D stretching vibration occurring at 2266 cm.$^{-1}$. Analogously, the intensity of the C-D stretching absorption at 2155 cm.$^{-1}$, the major absorption band for the deuterium on the carbinol carbon atom, is much decreased, the absorption in the product alcohol being 33 ± 1% as large as that in the parent deuterated alcohol. Although the analysis is less accurate, proton magnetic resonance spectra are consistent with the 2:1 ratio of cyclopropane ring deuterium to carbinol carbon deuterium in the product. It is quite clear that the deuterium scrambling during acetolysis of the labelled toluenesulfonate V-D corresponds exactly to expectations based on the non-classical cation II.

Because of an analogy with the cyclopropenyl action, II may be named the "tris-homocyclopropenyl" cation.

(1) This research was supported by a grant from The Petroleum Research Fund administered by the American Chemical Society. Grateful acknowledgment is hereby made to the donors of this fund.

(2) Satisfactory carbon and hydrogen analyses were obtained for all the new compounds here mentioned.

(3) H. E. Simmons and R. D. Smith, THIS JOURNAL, **81,** 4256 (1959).

(4) S. Winstein, E. L. Allred and J. Sonnenberg, *ibid.,* **81,** 5833 (1959).

(5) K. Hofmann, *et al., ibid.,* **81,** 992 (1959).

(6) (a) S. Winstein, *et al.,* THIS JOURNAL, **76,** 2597 (1954); *Chemistry and Industry,* 664 (1954); (b) S. Winstein, *Experientia Supplementum,* **II,** 137 (1955).

DEPARTMENT OF CHEMISTRY   S. WINSTEIN
UNIVERSITY OF CALIFORNIA   JOSEPH SONNENBERG
LOS ANGELES 24, CALIFORNIA   LOUIS DEVRIES
RECEIVED NOVEMBER 16, 1959

42 | Cyclobutyl Solvolysis Reinvestigated

During the period of interest in nonclassical ions there have been two experimental advances—VPC and NMR—so great that one would like to repeat all the earlier work with the later technique. In the case of Paper No. 42, Caserio, Graham, and Roberts found this necessary in part in order to test some alternative proposals of H. C. Brown (Paper No. 42, references 5 and 8). Brown and Ham (Paper No. 30) had recognized that cyclobutyl solvolysis was anomalously fast in comparison with cyclopentyl and cyclohexyl and that this fact could be explained if cyclobutyl tosylate or chloride were ionizing directly to something other than a "classical" cyclobutyl cation. Although this ground had been gone over by others, it had seemed to Brown a legitimate simplification to replace the postulated bicyclobutonium ion intermediate with a single cyclopropylcarbinyl cation unique in its stability among saturated primary cations. For this ion to be "classical" in the desired sense it should react only to give derivatives of cyclopropylcarbinol. The tertiary di- and tricyclopropylcarbinyl esters of Hart (Paper No. 36, and commentary, reference 1) do react without rearrangement. When Brown suggested that the observation of Roberts and Mazur, made before VPC and NMR, was the result of impure starting material, the Roberts group reinvestigated as here reported. The earlier work was fully confirmed: In 80% ethanol cyclopropylcarbinyl chloride and cyclobutyl chloride are both converted into the same mixture of six components, namely, cyclobutanol, cyclopropylcarbinol, allylcarbinol, and their ethyl ethers. The results at 97° are consistent with the following scheme[1] of

---

[1] Our assignment differs slightly from that of the authors, who made an estimate ignoring the effect of solvent and of a temperature change from 25° to 97°. We are assuming instead that in the kinetically determined product the relative amounts of cyclobutyl and cyclopropyl-

relative rate constants:

$$\text{CH}_2\text{-CH}_2 \quad | \quad | \quad \xrightleftharpoons[k]{1} \quad \text{Ion} \quad \xrightleftharpoons[30]{2k} \quad \underset{\text{CH}_2}{\overset{\text{CH}_2}{\diagdown}} \text{CH-CH}_2\text{Cl}$$
$$\text{CH}_2\text{-CH-Cl}$$

Caserio, Graham, and Roberts point out two confirmatory facts: Zinc chloride at 25° equilibrates cyclobutyl and cyclopropylcarbinyl chlorides to an equilibrium in favor of the former by 36/1; and dilute aqueous acid converts cyclopropyl-carbinol into cyclobutanol in a useful preparative procedure. A change in the equilibrium constant from 36 to 15 in going from 25° to 97° would be right in direction and reasonable in magnitude.

Any natural interatomic movement to relieve angle strain in the bicyclobu-tonium ion (see commentary on Paper No. 38) would make the two single dotted bonds of unequal length, and this would be a factor favoring the kinetic prefer-ence for reaction to yield a cyclopropylcarbinyl derivative. In the case of the tertiary ions with two and three cyclopropyl groups, one can see another reason for highest reactivity at the central carbon atom. Strain in this ion would appear to be at a minimum with all cyclopropyl groups bisected by a symmetry plane running through the carbonium carbon atom and the three atoms attached to it. This is the proper arrangement for the type of delocalization shown in XXXI, Paper No. 40, with respect to each cyclopropyl ring. From this conformation, no other product can be formed with as little atomic reordering as can the un-rearranged tertiary carbinol or its derivatives.

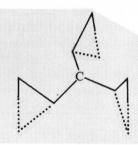

_____

carbinyl ethyl ethers reflect a similar partition in reaction of the intermediate ion with chloride ion, all at 97° in 80% ethanol.

From: *Tetrahedron* **11**, 171–82 (1960)

SMALL-RING COMPOUNDS—XXIX

A REINVESTIGATION OF THE SOLVOLYSIS OF CYCLOPROPYL-CARBINYL CHLORIDE IN AQUEOUS ETHANOL. ISOMERIZATION OF CYCLOPROPYLCARBINOL*†

Marjorie C. Caserio, William H. Graham‡ and John D. Roberts
Gates and Crellin Laboratories of Chemistry, California Institute of Technology,
Pasadena, California

(*Received 7 March* 1960; *in revised form* 30 *April* 1960)

Abstract—The solvolysis of cyclopropylcarbinyl chloride in 80% ethanol is attended by substantial rearrangement—not only do the solvolysis products include cyclobutyl and allylcarbinyl alcohols and ethyl ethers but cyclopropylcarbinyl chloride undergoes partial rearrangement by "internal return" to cyclobutyl and allylcarbinyl chlorides. Nuclear magnetic resonance spectroscopy has been used to demonstrate that considerable isotope-position rearrangement takes place under quite mild conditions in the reactions of deuterium-labeled cyclopropylcarbinol and cyclobutanol with thionyl chloride. Isotope-position changes have been studied in the acid-induced isomerization of cyclopropylcarbinol.

INTRODUCTION

Studies of the solvolysis of cyclopropylcarbinyl chloride (I) in aqueous ethanol by two groups of workers have given somewhat different results. Chloride (I) was first obtained pure§ by Mazur[1] via vapor-phase photochlorination of methylcyclopropane, and he made a rather extensive investigation of its solvolysis reactions. The behavior of I in acetic acid was most unusual when viewed in the light of the knowledge of the time. In the first place, chloride I in this and other solvents was most uncommonly reactive for a saturated primary chloride; and, second, by the time 30 per cent of the theoretical amount of chloride ion was liberated, I essentially was completely converted to a mixture of substantially less reactive cyclobutyl and allylcarbinyl chlorides in a ratio of about 1·7 to 1. The acetolysis products arising from I were cyclopropylcarbinyl and cyclobutyl acetates in the ratio of about 2·6:1 with perhaps a few percent of allylcarbinyl acetate as well.

Similar, but much less extreme, behavior was noted in 50 per cent aqueous ethanol. In this solvent, rearrangement was found to occur at only about one-third the rate of

---

* This research was supported in part by a grant from the Petroleum Research Fund administered by the American Chemical Society. Grateful acknowledgement is hereby made to the donors of said fund. This research was also supported in part by the Office of Naval Research, to whom our appreciation is extended. Presented in part at the *National Organic Chemistry Symposium of the Amer. Chem. Soc.* June 15, Seattle (1959).

† Contribution No. 2554 from the Gates and Crellin Laboratories of Chemistry, California Institute of Technology, Pasadena, California

‡ Arthur Amos Noyes Research Fellow.

§ As judged by the absence of infrared absorption corresponding to cyclobutyl and allylcarbinyl chlorides.

[1] J. D. Roberts and R. H. Mazur, *J. Amer. Chem. Soc.* **73**, 2509 (1951).

liberation of chloride ion. Although the reaction products were not determined in 50 per cent ethanol, the neutral heterogeneous reaction with water was found to give rearranged chlorides and a mixture of cyclopropylcarbinol cyclobutanol, and allyl-carbinol in about the same proportions as formed from the treatment of either cyclopropylcarbinylamine or cyclobutylamine with nitrous acid.

The rearrangement of chloride I to cyclobutyl and allylcarbinyl chlorides in solvolytic reactions is now well understood as an example of "internal return" from an "intimate" carbocation-chloride ion pair, which phenomenon was first clearly demonstrated by Young, Winstein and Goering[2] for α,α-dimethylallyl chloride and subsequently scrutinized with great care by Winstein et al.[3] The abnormally high solvolytic reactivity of I and its tendency both to rearrange to isomeric chlorides and to form rearranged solvolysis products speak strongly for the intermediacy of a bridged, rather substantially stabilized carbonium ion embodying structural elements of the cyclopropylcarbinyl, cyclobutyl, and allylcarbinyl cations—the "non-classica" bicyclobutonium cation (II).[4]

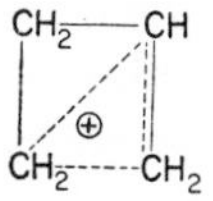

II

Chloride I has also been prepared by Brown and Borkowski[5] by liquid-phase chlorination of methylcyclopropane. The carefully purified product was judged to be 94 mole per cent I by analysis of its cooling curve. Solvolysis rate studies in 80 per cent ethanol showed the reactivity to be about 1/15 as large as t-butyl chloride, whereas a normal saturated primary chloride might be expected to form carbonium ions about 10^{-10} times slower than t-butyl chloride.[6] No evidence for internal-return isomerization of chloride I can be deduced from the reported solvolysis rate measurements,[5] which were stated to be in accord with simple, first-order kinetics throughout. The solvolysis products were not investigated.

While the discrepancies between the above investigations may seem trivial, the finding of simple, first-order kinetics for the solvolysis of I[5] in aqueous ethanol, buttressed by the reported[7] formation of substantially pure cyclopropylcarbinyl ethyl ether from the solvolysis of cyclopropylcarbinyl benzenesulfonate in absolute ethanol,* has been taken as evidence for the conclusion that cyclopropylcarbinyl

---

* The significance of the particular experiment as a *solvolysis* is open to question. To be sure, Bergstrom and Siegel report an apparently insignificant increase in the first-order solvolysis rate constant of the benzene-sulfonate in the presence of sodium ethoxide (from $6\cdot3 \times 10^{-5}$ to $7\cdot2 \times 10^{-5}$ sec^{-1} with 0·0266 M ethoxide) so that one might well infer a negligible contribution of non-rearranging S$_N$2 type substitution between the ester and ethoxide ion. However, a simple calculation shows that [benzenesulfonate] . [ethoxide] was $2\cdot1 \times 10^3$ *times greater* under the conditions where the reaction products were determined than under the conditions used for the kinetic runs. It should be clear that the seemingly small increase in the ethanolysis rate constant with a small amount of added ethoxide might well mean essentially exclusive S$_N$2 reaction where the arithmetic product of ester and ethoxide concentrations is so very high.

[2] W. G. Young, S. Winstein and H. L. Goering, *J. Amer. Chem. Soc.* **73**, 1958 (1951).

[3] S. Winstein and A. H. Fainberg, *J. Amer. Chem. Soc.* **80**, 459 (1958) and earlier papers.

[4] R. H. Mazur, W. N. White, D. A. Semenow, C. C. Lee, M. S. Silver and J. D. Roberts, *J. Amer. Chem. Soc.* **81**, 4390 (1959).

[5] H. C. Brown and M. Borkowski, *J. Amer. Chem. Soc.* **74**, 1894 (1952).

[6] L. C. Bateman, K. A. Cooper, E. D. Hughes and C. K. Ingold, *J. Chem. Soc.* 925 (1940); E. Grunwald and S. Winstein, *J. Amer. Chem. Soc.* **70**, 841 (1948); S. Winstein, E. Grunwald and H. W. Jones, *Ibid.* **73**, 2700 (1951).

[7] C. G. Bergstrom and S. Siegel, *J. Amer. Chem. Soc.* **74**, 145 (1952).

derivatives may solvolyze by way of a cationic intermediate without formation of rearrangement products and that the enhanced rate of solvolysis may not be due to any driving force for formation of a non-classical cation.[8] It has been further maintained that the extraordinary facile interconversions of cyclopropylcarbinyl, cyclobutyl, and allylcarbinyl derivatives observed in amine-nitrous acid and many other carbonium ion type reactions[1,4] need not be typical of solvolysis or other reactions occurring under very mild conditions. The results obtained in the solvolysis of chloride I by Mazur[1] have been attributed to impurities[8] on the grounds that material of 94 per cent purity, prepared by Brown and Borkowski[5] gave a first-order rate of hydrogen chloride production.

The above criticisms of Mazur's work are important since they clearly strike at the very heart of the argument[4] for intervention of non-classical ions such as II in carbonium ion-type interconversion reactions of cyclopropylcarbinyl, cyclobutyl, and allylcarbinyl derivatives. Although, as indicated, the factual basis for the criticisms leaves much to be desired, the importance of the points in question has prompted us to repeat and extend much of the earlier work. The investigation has been greatly facilitated by the use of vapor-phase chromatography (v-p-c) which technique was not available at the time of the previous investigation. Fortunately, samples of I prepared by Mazur in 1950 were still available for analysis.

EXPERIMENTAL RESULTS

Vapor-phase chromatography is well suited for the analysis of cyclopropylcarbinyl cyclobutyl, and allylcarbinyl chlorides. Fig. 1A shows a chromatogram* for a typical chloride mixture resulting from the reaction of cyclopropylcarbinol with thionyl chloride. The composition of the mixture (69 per cent cyclopropylcarbinyl chloride, 27 per cent cyclobutyl chloride and 4 per cent allylcarbinyl chloride) agrees well with Mazur's infrared analysis of a mixture prepared in the same way (67 per cent cyclopropylcarbinyl chloride, 30 per cent cyclobutyl chloride, and 3 per cent allylcarbinyl chloride). The sample of chloride I used in Mazur's kinetic measurements[1] was found to be 99+ per cent cyclopropylcarbinyl chloride. Only a faint indication of allylcarbinyl chloride was noted in the v-p-c analysis. Consequently, there seems to be no question that the internal-return mechanism must be invoked to account for the isomerization of the chloride during the solvolysis reaction because the chloride does not rearrange at the solvolysis temperature in the absence of an ionizing solvent or ionizing agent such as zinc chloride.

The internal consistency and clarity of the data reported by Mazur[1] for chloride I in acetic acid leave no room for doubt that, in acetic acid, solvolysis and rearrangement are very intimately related. The results in all respects are consistent with the formation of II (or its intimate ion-pair with chloride ion). We have seen no need to repeat this work nor the measurements of the kinetics of the solvolysis of I in 50 per cent aqueous ethanol since the essential point in question as to whether internal-return isomerization actually occurred has been answered in the affirmative by the finding that the starting chloride was even purer than advertised and by verification of the validity of the

---

* All vapor-phase chromatographic analyses reported herein were obtained with Perkin–Elmer Vapor Fractometer using"A"-type packing (diisodecyl phthalate on crushed firebrick).

[8] H. C. Brown, *Falk-Plaut Lecture*, Columbia University, March 6 (1957) and seminar at Harvard University, October 10 (1958).

infrared analysis used to establish the presence of rearranged chloride in the unreacted halide isolated from the reaction mixture.

We turn next to consideration of the solvolysis of I in 80 per cent ethanol for which clean, first-order kinetics are reported[5] and for which it has been inferred that no rearrangement products are formed.[8] The following technique was used in studying

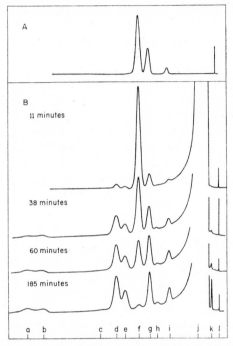

FIG. 1. A, v-p-c of chloride mixture from reaction of thionyl chloride with cyclopropyl-carbinol; B, v-p-c of mixtures from solvolysis of cyclopropylcarbinyl chloride in 80% ethanol at 97° showing the change of composition with time. Peaks were identified as: a, cyclobutanol; b, cyclopropylcarbinol; c, allylcarbinol; d, cyclopropylcarbinyl ethyl ether; e, cyclobutyl ethyl ether; f, cyclopropylcarbinyl chloride; g, cyclobutyl chloride; h, allylcarbinyl ethyl ether; i, allylcarbinyl chloride; j, solvent; k, hydrogen chloride; l, air.

this reaction and the solvolysis of cyclobutyl chloride. A few microliters of standard solutions of the chlorides in 80 per cent aqueous ethanol were sealed into melting point capillaries, heated to 97° for various periods, and then small samples of the intact reaction mixtures analyzed by v-p-c. The accuracy of the analyses was at first somewhat limited by lack of reproducibility of the size of the sample injected into the v-p-c apparatus, but this difficulty was surmounted by incorporating a few per cent of cyclohexane in the reaction mixture to act as an internal standard. The added cyclohexane made no discernible change in the results except to permit considerably greater analytical precision. Since the supply of Mazur's high-purity chloride was limited, we used a somewhat less pure material (96 per cent cyclopropylcarbinyl, 2 per cent cyclobutyl, and 2 per cent allylcarbinyl chlorides) prepared from cyclopropylcarbinol and thionyl chloride in ether in the presence of tri-n-butylamine.[9,*]

* This reaction, when carried out with crotyl alcohol, gives no allylic rearrangement.

[9] R. H. DeWolfe and W. G. Young, *Chem. Rev.* **56**, 815 (1956); F. F. Caserio, Jr., Ph.D. Thesis, U.C.L.A. (1954).

The v-p-c tracings for typical solvolysis mixtures of I in 80 per cent ethanol are shown in Fig. 1B. The substances responsible for the various v-p-c peaks were assigned, by comparison of retention times, with those established for known samples. It is clear that solvolysis under these circumstances yields a variety of rearrangement products as chlorides, alcohols, and ethyl ethers. Fig. 2 shows the progress of the reaction as measured by the proportions of the various products formed. Again we conclude that solvolysis and rearrangement are intimately related.

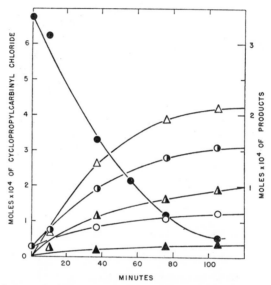

Fig. 2. Rate of change in composition of the mixture from the solvolysis of cyclopropyl-carbinyl chloride in 80% ethanol at 97°: ● cyclopropylcarbinyl chloride, ◑ cyclobutyl chloride, ○ allylcarbinyl chloride, △ cyclopropylcarbinyl ethyl ether, ▲ cyclobutyl ethyl ether, ▲ allylcarbinyl ethyl ether. Cyclopropylcarbinol, cyclobutanol and allylcarbinol are also formed in small amounts but their formation is not shown.

Weight has been added to the argument[4] for intervention of a common inter-mediate(s) in solvolysis reactions of cyclopropylcarbinyl and cyclobutyl chlorides by evidence for close similarity (in energy, at least) of the solvolysis transition states for these chlorides with the aid of the procedure discussed by Winstein and Kosower[10]. Thus, isomerization of cyclopropylcarbinyl chloride with zinc chloride at 25° gives a mixture of cyclobutyl-cyclopropylcarbinyl chlorides, the approximate equilibrium composition of which was determined by v-p-c as about 36/1 in favor of cyclobutyl chloride. The ratio of the total rates of disappearance of the chlorides (solvolysis plus internal-return isomerization) in 80 per cent ethanol at 97° is $1 \cdot 37 \times 10^{-5}$ sec^{-1}/$4 \cdot 17 \times 10^{-4}$ sec^{-1} equal to 1/30. Assuming that the equilibrium and relative rate data are not subject to large changes with change of media and temperature, the conclusion follows that the difference in rates between the two chlorides is not due to differences in transition-state stabilities but to differences in ground-state stabilities.*

* This possibility was suggested previously[1] but not given appropriate emphasis partly because no adequate data for the equilibrium composition was available.

[10] S. Winstein and E. M. Kosower, *J. Amer. Chem. Soc.* **81**, 4399 (1959); see also, E. F. Cox, Ph.D. Thesis, California Institute of Technology (1955).

The isomerization of cyclopropylcarbinyl chloride to cyclobutyl and allylcarbinyl chlorides induced by ionizing solvents is an excellent example of an interconversion reaction occurring under exceptionally mild conditions. Considerable interest is therefore attached to the degree of isotope-position rearrangement which accompanies this process. Some information bearing on this point has been obtained by deuterium-labeled chloride as follows.

First of all, the synthesis of cyclopropylcarbinyl chloride labeled with deuterium in the α-position presented a considerable problem. It was known from Mazur's[1] work that the reaction of cyclopropylcarbinol with thionyl chloride, with or without pyridine, gives a mixture of isomeric chlorides which cannot be separated conveniently. Allylic alcohols behave similarly under these conditions. However, chlorides may be prepared from primary allylic alcohols and thionyl chloride without rearrangement[9] if the reaction is carried out under carefully controlled conditions in the presence of an equivalent amount of tri-n-butylamine in ether or pentane solution. Using these conditions, a typical product obtained from cyclopropylcarbinol was found to consist of 91 per cent cyclopropylcarbinyl chloride, 8 per cent cyclobutyl chloride, and 1 per cent allylcarbinyl chloride. Clearly, the propensity for rearrangement in this system is high even under mild conditions known to give no rearrangement with allyl derivatives. Despite this, the method was used reasonably successfully for the preparation of deuterium-labeled cyclopropylcarbinyl chloride as shown in the following scheme:

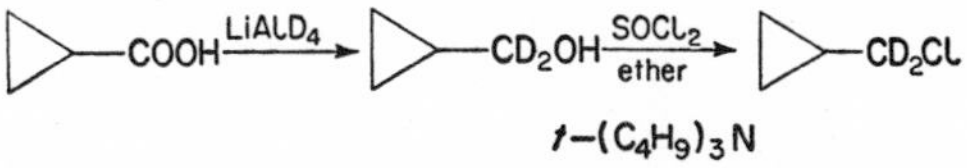

$$\triangleright\!\!-\!COOH \xrightarrow{LiAlD_4} \triangleright\!\!-\!CD_2OH \xrightarrow[\text{ether}]{SOCl_2} \triangleright\!\!-\!CD_2Cl$$
$$t\text{--}(C_4H_9)_3N$$

The nuclear magnetic resonance (NMR) spectra of cyclopropylcarbinyl and cyclopropylcarbinyl-α-$^2H_2$ chlorides are shown in Figs. 3A and 3B, respectively. The characteristic doublet of the carbinyl protons is barely evident in the labeled chloride, and it is estimated that less than 4 per cent isotopic rearrangement occurred during its formation. This estimate was made from the peak area of the carbinyl protons relative to the tertiary ring proton which, of course, is assumed to be 2:1 in the unlabeled chloride.

In an attempt to observe isotope-position rearrangement during hydrolysis, a sample of cyclopropylcarbinyl-α-$^2H_2$ chloride (containing 6 per cent cyclobutyl chloride) was shaken with water in a sealed tube at 97°. After 140 minutes, the unreacted chloride was separated from the aqueous layer and analyzed by v-p-c. The ratio of chlorides, cyclopropylcarbinyl:cyclobutyl:allylcarbinyl, was found to be 7·5:3·2:1·0, respectively. The hydrolysis products remained largely in aqueous solution, but small amounts of alcohols (and water) were also present in the chloride mixture. The NMR spectra of this mixture and that obtained from unlabeled chloride under the same conditions are shown in Figs. 3C and 3D, respectively. The incidence of isotopic rearrangement is evident from Fig. 3C, which shows a sharp doublet due to the carbinyl protons of cyclopropylcarbinyl chloride, the spectrum of which was barely evident initially (cf. Fig. 3B). Unfortunately, the complexity of the spectrum precluded a *precise* measurement of how much rearrangement of the deuterium label had occurred. However, it is estimated from the ratio of peak areas of the carbinyl and tertiary cyclopropylcarbinyl protons that some 24 per cent of isotopically

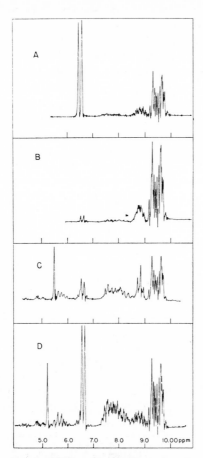

Fig. 3. NMR spectra at 60 mc in ppm relative to tetramethylsilane as internal standard (equal to 10 ppm). A, cyclopropylcarbinyl chloride from photochlorination of methylcyclopropane;[1] B, cyclopropylcarbinyl-α-$^2H_2$ chloride from cyclopropylcarbinol-α-$^2H_2$ and thionyl chloride in ether and tri-n-butylamine; C, chloride mixture from hydrolysis of cyclopropylcarbinyl-α-$^2H_2$ chloride; D, chloride mixture from hydrolysis of cyclopropylcarbinyl chloride.

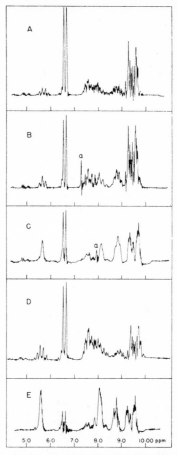

Fig. 4. NMR spectra at 60 mc in ppm relative to tetramethylsilane as internal standard (equal to 10 ppm) of chloride mixtures obtained from reaction of thionyl chloride with: A, cyclopropylcarbinol or cyclobutanol; B, cyclopropylcarbinol-α-$^2H_2$, peak marked *a* is impurity; C, cyclobutanol-2,4-$^2H_4$, peaked marked *a* is impurity; D, cyclobutanol in presence of tri-n-butylamine and ether; E, cyclobutanol-2,4-$^2H_4$, conditions as in C.

rearranged cyclopropylcarbinyl chloride is present in the mixture. Further evidence for isotope-position rearrangement was obtained from other related reactions which we now describe.

It was originally observed by Mazur that chloride mixtures of the *same* composition were obtained from the reaction of cyclopropylcarbinol and cyclobutanol with thionyl chloride (no solvent). We have repeated these reactions with deuterium-labeled alcohols, using the conditions defined by Mazur, in order to observe the extent of isotope-position rearrangement in the chloride mixtures by means of NMR. The labeled alcohols required for these experiments were prepared as follows. Cyclopropylcarbinol-α-$^2H_2$ was prepared by the reduction of cyclopropanecarboxylic acid with lithium aluminum deuteride. To obtain deuterium-labeled cyclobutanol, cyclobutanone-2,4-^{2}H$_4$ was prepared to about 95 per cent isotopic purity by base-catalyzed exchange of cyclobutanone in deuterium oxide and the product was subsequently reduced to the alcohol with lithium aluminum hydride. The NMR spectrum of the crude labeled ketone is shown in Fig. 6C and may be compared to the

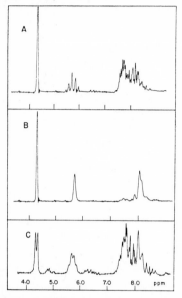

Fig. 5. NMR spectra at 60 mc in ppm relative to tetramethylsilane as internal standard (equal to 10 ppm). A, cyclobutanol from acid-catalyzed rearrangement of cyclopropylcarbinol; B, cyclobutanol-2,4-^{2}H$_4$; C, deuterium-labeled cyclobutanol from acid-catalyzed rearrangement of cyclopropylcarbinol-α-^{2}H$_2$(allylcarbinol is also present in small amounts).

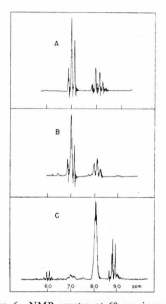

Fig. 6. NMR spectra at 60 mc in ppm relative to tetramethylsilane as internal standard (equal to 10 ppm). A, cyclobutanone; B, deuterium-labeled cyclobutanone from oxidation of labeled cyclobutanol (minor peaks are due to impurities); C, cyclobutanone-2,4-^{2}H$_4$ (impure).

spectrum of unlabeled cyclobutanone in Fig. 6A. The spectrum of the labeled ketone was run at high gain in order to detect any residual protonation of the 2 and 4 positions. The presence of significant amounts of impurities is apparent, but it is also evident that there remains only 4–5 per cent of ketone with protons in the 2 or 4 positions. The spectra of cyclobutanol and cyclobutanol-2,4-^{2}H$_4$ are shown in Figs. 5A and 5B, respectively. The 3-methylene protons of the labeled alcohol appear as a rather indistinct quartet since these two protons are non-equivalent; the 4–5 per cent of 2- or 4-protonated material appears on the low field side of this quartet.

The composition of the chloride mixtures from the thionyl chloride reaction was determined by v-p-c. The results are shown in Table 1 and, clearly, they confirm that the *same* mixture of chlorides is obtained from either alcohol. The NMR spectra corresponding to the chloride mixtures obtained from cyclopropylcarbinol (or cyclobutanol), cyclopropylcarbinol-α-^{2}H$_2$, and cyclobutanol-2,4-^{2}H$_4$ are shown respectively in Figs. 4A, 4B and 4C. They are exceedingly complex, and it was not possible to determine the distribution of the deuterium label within the cyclobutyl ring with certainty. However, by focusing attention on the sharp doublet of the carbinyl protons

M. C. Caserio, W. A. Graham, and J. D. Roberts

TABLE 1. PERCENT COMPOSITION OF CHLORIDE MIXTURES FROM REACTION OF THIONYL CHLORIDE WITH
CYCLOPROPYLCARBINOL AND CYCLOBUTANOL

Alcohol	Cyclopropylcarbinyl	Cyclobutyl	Allylcarbinyl
▷—CH$_2$OH[a]	% 69	% 27	% 4
▷—CD$_2$OH[a]	67	28	5
☐—OH[a]	69	25	6
D$_2$ ☐—OH[a] D$_2$	67	29	4
▷—CH$_2$OH[b]	~67	~30	~3
☐—OH[b]	~67	~30	~3

[a] Analyzed by v-p-c.
[b] Analyzed by infrared spectrometry.[1]

of cyclopropylcarbinyl chloride, one thing becomes immediately apparent—in order
for this doublet to appear at all, extensive isotope-position rearrangement must have
occurred during the formation of cyclopropylcarbinyl chloride from both deuterium-
labeled alcohols. Moreover, the area of this doublet relative to the area of the tertiary
ring hydrogen of cyclopropylcarbinyl chloride permits a rough estimate of the percent
isotopic rearrangement to be made. Such measurements reveal that 66 ± 5 per cent
of the cyclopropylcarbinyl chloride obtained from cyclopropylcarbinol-α-^{2}H$_2$ has a
—CH$_2$— group in the α-position, while 33 ± 2 per cent of the chloride from cyclo-
butanol-2,4-^{2}H$_4$ has a —CH$_2$— group in the α-position. These figures closely approach
the values of 67 per cent and 33 per cent, respectively, for a statistical distribution of
the deuterium label in cyclopropylcarbinyl chloride derived from both labeled alcohols.
Thus, the three methylene groups of cyclopropylcarbinol and cyclobutanol achieve
near equivalence during reaction—a result which, in conjunction with the identity of
product composition, argues for formation of the same cationic intermediates from
either alcohol. As a check on the validity of area measurements, the ratio of cyclopropylcarbinyl chloride to the cyclobutyl chloride present was estimated from the
ratio of peak areas of the tertiary proton of each chloride. The results gave a ratio
of cyclopropylcarbinyl to cyclobutyl of $2 \cdot 28 \pm 0 \cdot 12$ and $2 \cdot 26 \pm 0 \cdot 19$ for the chlorides
from labeled cyclopropylcarbinol and cyclobutanol, respectively (cf. Figs. 3B and 3C),
while analysis by v-p-c gave the ratio as $2 \cdot 3$ (cf. Table 1). The agreement is satisfactory.

On treating these same alcohols with thionyl chloride in the presence of tri-n-butylamine in a non-ionizing solvent (ether or pentane) somewhat different results were
obtained as already discussed in the case of cyclopropylcarbinol. Under these
conditions, cyclobutanol reacted with extensive rearrangement to give 45 per cent
cyclopropylcarbinyl, 50 per cent cyclobutyl, and 5 per cent allylcarbinyl chlorides.

The NMR spectrum of the mixture is shown in Fig. 4D. If one assumes that the product distribution arising from carbonium ion intermediates is the same as that obtained in the absence of added base and solvent (cf. Table 1), then it may be estimated that 66 per cent of reaction takes an ionic path with rearrangement and 34 per cent proceeds without rearrangement probably by an S_N2 displacement.[9] The NMR spectrum of the chloride mixture from cyclobutanol-2,4-$^2H_4$ (Fig. 4E) is especially interesting since it shows that only $16 \cdot 5 \pm 1$ per cent of the —CH_2— group turns up in the α-position of cyclopropylcarbinyl chloride. Again, the area measurements were judged to be significant since the ratio of cyclopropylcarbinyl chloride to cyclobutyl chloride was determined as $1 \cdot 03 \pm 0 \cdot 10$ by NMR and $0 \cdot 9$ by v-p-c. In this case then, the extent of isotopic rearrangement is about one half that expected for complete equilibration of the three methylene groups. This result is highly significant in that it rules out the possibility of a symmetrical ion such as III as the sole intermediate in these interconversion reactions. The methylene groups are completely equivalent in III, which inevitably would lead to products with a random isotope distribution under any set of reaction conditions. A similar conclusion was reached from the results of nitrous-acid deamination of cyclopropylcarbinylamine-α-$^{14}C^4$. The ^{14}C-distribution in the products, cyclopropylcarbinol and cyclobutanol, showed that extensive but not random ^{14}C-rearrangement had taken place. It was suggested that these results could

III

best be explained by the intermediacy of the unsymmetrical bicyclobutonium ions IIa, IIb, and IIc, which equilibrate rapidly but not instantaneously. Clearly, the present results can be rationalized by these same intermediates. The advent of less isotopic

IIa   IIb   IIc

rearrangement in the reaction of cyclobutanol with thionyl chloride when carried out in the presence of tri-n-butylamine in ether solution is indicative that equilibration of IIa–c is not fully attained in this medium. Under the best ionizing conditions, when the alcohol acts as its own solvent, equilibration is attained more rapidly and results in a more nearly random isotope distribution.

Cyclopropylcarbinol has been found to undergo a facile rearrangement in dilute aqueous acid to give cyclobutanol and small amounts of allylcarbinol.* The rearrangement, which provides an excellent synthetic route to cyclobutanol, has been studied with the aid of cyclopropylcarbinol-α-$^2H_2$, and it was hoped that the position of the deuterium label in the resulting cylcobutanol could be observed from its NMR

* This rearrangement was first observed by Mr. David I. Schuster in these Laboratories.

spectrum. Unfortunately, the spectrum of the product turned out to be too complex to interpret (Fig. 5C). To overcome this, the labeled cyclobutanol was oxidized to cyclobutanone with chromic oxide in pyridine, and the distribution of deuterium was observed from the NMR spectrum of the cyclobutanone which is relatively simple. The spectra obtained for both labeled and unlabeled cyclobutanones are shown in Figs. 6A and 6B, respectively. The presence of 2-labeled cyclobutanone in the rearrangement product is clearly evident from Fig. 6B since the five-line spectrum of the 3-methylene protons in the unlabeled ketone is reduced to a broad triplet in the labeled material. Equally clear is the presence of 3-labeled cyclobutanone since the triplet due to the 2-methylene protons has a central peak of far greater intensity than in the unlabeled ketone. Thus, the deuterium label is found in all three methylene groups of the ring. The relative amounts of 2- and 3-labeled cyclobutanones may be roughly calculated from relative peak areas. The area of the 2- and 4-protons relative to the 3-protons was measured as $2 \cdot 1 \pm 0 \cdot 1$, which gives the composition of the mixture as 67 per cent cyclobutanone-2-$^2H_2$ and 33 per cent cyclobutanone-3-$^2H_2$. Consequently, it is inferred that cyclobutanol derived from cyclopropylcarbinol-α-$^2H_2$ has the deuterium-labeled methylene group statistically distributed between the 2,3- and 4-ring positions.

EXPERIMENTAL

Cyclopropylcarbinol-α-$^2H_2$. (b.p. 121–122·5°, 746 mm) was prepared in 75% yield by the reduction of cyclopropanecarboxylic acid with lithium aluminum deuteride.

Cyclobutanol-2,4-$^2H_4$. A mixture of three parts of cyclobutanone to four parts of deuterium oxide, 0·1 M in sodium acetate, was heated in a sealed tube at 97° for 37 hr. The ketone was recovered from solution and similarly treated with fresh deuterium oxide, 0·1 M in sodium acetate. The crude, recovered cyclobutanone gave an NMR spectrum showing 95% deuterium in the 2- and 4-positions (Fig. 6C). This material was reduced with lithium aluminum hydride, and the crude product was fractionally distilled. The purest fraction of labeled cyclobutanol obtained which was used in subsequent experiments had b.p. 122·5–123·0° at 745 mm, $n_D^{25} = 1·4315$, and gave a single peak in the v-p-c. The NMR spectrum of this material is shown in Fig. 5B.

Cyclobutanol from cyclopropylcarbinol. A solution of cyclopropylcarbinol (30·0 g) in 280 ml water and 25 ml conc hydrochloric acid was heated on a steam bath for 100 min. Most of the acid was neutralized by the addition of 11·0 g sodium hydroxide pellets to the cooled mixture. Neutralization was completed with potassium carbonate. The mixture was continuously extracted with ether and the ether extracts were dried over magnesium sulfate, filtered, and the ether removed by distillation. The residue was distilled through a small wire spiral-packed column to give 21·6 g (72%) material, b.p. 121–124°, which analyzed by v-p-c as 97% cyclobutanol and 3% allylcarbinol.

By the above procedure, 5·33 g of cyclopropylcarbinol-α-$^2H_2$ gave 3·73 g (70%) deuterium-labeled material, b.p. 121·5–125°, which analysed by v-p-c as 93% cyclobutanol and 7% allylcarbinol.

Oxidation of deuterium-labeled cyclobutanol to cyclobutanone. The oxidizing agent employed was chromic oxide in pyridine, and the procedure was essentially that described by Poos et al.[11] To a stirred suspension of chromic oxide-pyridine complex in pyridine (5·0 g chromic oxide to 48 g pyridine) at 17° was added 3·53 g deuterium-labeled cyclobutanol (containing 7% allylcarbinol) in 32 g pyridine. The mixture was allowed to stand at room temp for about 18 hr. The pyridine was converted to the hydrochloride by the addition of 98 g conc hydrochloric acid in 100 g ice water to the ice-cooled mixture. The resulting solution was evaporated immediately *in vacuo* at room temp and the vapors condensed in a series of dry ice traps. The aqueous distillate was continuously extracted with ether and the ether extracts were dried over sodium sulfate and distilled. The crude product obtained was shown by v-p-c to consist of unreacted cyclobutanol, cyclobutanone, and small amounts of allylcarbinol. The cyclobutanone was separated from the alcohols by v.p.c. using a preparative column.

Thionyl chloride reactions. Thionyl chloride (1·65 g) was added dropwise to 1·0 g cyclopropylcarbinol at 0° with stirring. Evolution of sulfur dioxide immediately took place. The mixture was

[11] G. I. Poos, G. E. Ayth, R. E. Beyler and L. H. Sarett, *J. Amer. Chem. Soc.* **75**, 422 (1953).

allowed to stand at room temp for 3·5 hr. Dissolved hydrogen chloride was neutralized by the addition of a few drops of water and solid potassium carbonate. The chloride mixture was analyzed by v-p-c and then distilled. The product composition was found not to vary with reaction time; however, on working up the mixture immediately upon addition of thionyl chloride, some unrearranged cyclopropylcarbinol was recovered. Cyclopropylcarbinol-α-^{2}H$_2$, cyclobutanol, and cyclobutanol-2,4-^{2}H$_4$ were treated with thionyl chloride exactly as described for cyclopropylcarbinol.

To a well-stirred, ice-cooled mixture of 10·0 g (0·139 mole) of cyclopropylcarbinol, 25·4 g (0·139 mole) of tri-n-butylamine (b.p. 123° at 51 mm) in 200 ml ether was added 16·5 g (0·139 mole) of thionyl chloride at such a rate that the temp did not exceed 6°. The addition took about 80 min and the precipitate which formed during the addition eventually re-dissolved to give two liquid phases, one of which was orange-yellow in color. The volatile components were flash-distilled *in vacuo* and trapped at $-78°$. The ether was evaporated from the distillate and the residue, after analysis by v-p-c, was fractionally distilled. There was obtained overall 10·8 g (86%) material, b.p. 82·5–85·5° at 748 mm, of which 2·9 g had b.p. 85·5° and which analyzed for 97% cyclopropylcarbinyl chloride and 3% cyclobutyl chloride.

Cyclopropylcarbinyl-α-^{2}H$_2$ chloride was prepared by this method. On treating cyclobutanol and cyclobutanol-2,4-^{2}H$_2$ with thionyl chloride as described above, the reaction was found to be appreciably slower; it was necessary to leave the reaction mixture at room temp for 3 hr before flash-distilling the products. Shorter reaction times gave poor yields, yet the product composition remained unchanged.

43 | Benzo-norbornenyl Sulfonates

Bartlett and Giddings (Paper No. 43) compare the effect of a fused benzene ring with that of a double bond on the reactivity of sulfonate groups in solvolysis at positions 2 and 7 in the norbornene ring. In *exo*-2-norbornenyl bromobenzene-sulfonate the intermediate ion has been described (Papers 22 and 25) as an unsymmetrical homoallylic structure. The substitution of a benzo ring for the double bond would cause the benzene ring to be involved in the ionization in the same manner as if an aromatic substitution were taking place at that atom which constitutes position 6 of the norbornene ring. The type of activation seen in *anti*-7-norbornenyl derivatives would, in the benzo analog, require some localization of the aromatic electrons for the formation of the required three-center bond between C-5, C-6, and C-7. It is intelligible on this basis that the fused benzene ring is a perfect substitute for the double bond in activation at the 2-position, but provides only 6 powers of ten acceleration at the 7-position, compared to 11 powers of ten for the double bond.

It has been discovered more recently[1] that the solvolysis of *exo*-2-benzonorbornenyl *p*-bromobenzenesulfonate is attended by complete racemization. Pending a fuller investigation, this seems to imply that the plane of the benzene ring becomes a plane of symmetry either of the intermediate ion or of a low-lying transition state connecting a pair of enantiomeric ions. Compare dePuy, Ogawa, and McDaniel, Paper No. 51.

---

[1] W. P. Giddings and J. Dirlam, *J. Am. Chem. Soc.* **85**, 3900 (1963).

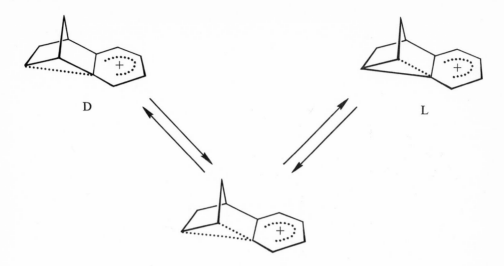

D   L

Symmetrical ion or transition state

From: *J. Am. Chem. Soc.* **82**, 1240–46 (1960)

[Contribution from the Converse Memorial Laboratory of Harvard University]

Some 2- and 7-Derivatives of Benznorbornene

By Paul D. Bartlett and William P. Giddings

Received July 23, 1959

exo- and *endo* 2-benznorbornenol, *anti*-7-benznorbornenol and *anti*-7-benznorbornadienol (II, IV, VII and IX, respectively) have been prepared and the rates of acetolysis of their *p*-bromobenzenesulfonates have been measured for comparison with the esters of the corresponding norborneols and norbornenols. All four esters undergo acetolysis without rearrangement. The results are shown in Tables I and II. Compared with the C–C double bond, the fused benzene ring has a similar effect on the 2-bromobenzenesulfonates, but it provides only about half (on an energy scale) of the large assistance to ionization at C_7 which the double bond offers. The additional double bond in the *p*-bromobenzenesulfonate of IX favors ionization by a factor of 100.

Introduction

Wittig's elegant procedure[1] for the addition of dehydrobenzene (benzyne) to dienes has made readily available benznorbornadiene (I) from which the benzo analogs of *endo*-, *exo*- and 7-norbornenol can be prepared. These compounds are of special interest in view of the extraordinary spread of reactivities observed in the solvolysis of the sulfonate esters of 2- and 7-norborneol and norbornenol. Figure 1 summarizes the reported rate constants relative to the corresponding cyclohexyl ester at 25°. The high driving force for ionization of *exo*-2-norbornenyl *p*-bromobenzenesulfonate is associated with homoallylic delocalization of the π-electron pair in the double bond and leads to a rearranged product. The much greater driving force observed in *anti*-7-norbornenyl *p*-bromobenzenesulfonate has been attributed to delocalization of the same electron pair among the three centers represented by carbon atoms 5, 6 and 7, but this ionization leads to a product in which both structure and configuration have been fully retained.

In the S_N1 reactions of allylic and benzylic compounds, the benzene ring affords a driving

force between those of the vinyl and 1-propenyl groups. For example, from rate constants in the literature, α-phenylethyl chloride undergoes ethanolysis at 25° in absolute alcohol at a first-order rate about 3.5 times that of α-methylallyl chloride,[2–4] but a thousand times more slowly than α, γ-dimethylallyl chloride.[5]

Since allylic delocalization is entirely by π-interactions, while homoallylic delocalization depends strongly upon oriented σ-overlap of orbitals,[6,7] it was of special interest to compare the effects of the benzene ring fused at 5,6 with those of the double bond in the same position.

Preparation of Compounds.—The flow sheet summarizes the preparations starting with benznorbornadiene prepared by the method of Wittig and Knauss. As expected, direct hydration of the double bond led to *exo*-2-benznorbornenol, m.p. 74.1–75.4°, which could be oxidized to the corre-

(1) G. Wittig and E. Knauss, *Ber.*, **91**, 895 (1958).

(2) E. D. Hughes, C. K. Ingold and A. D. Scott, *J. Chem. Soc.*, 1201 (1937).

(3) W. G. Young and L. J. Andrews, This Journal, **66**, 421 (1944).

(4) E. Grunwald and S. Winstein, *ibid.*, **70**, 846 (1948).

(5) H. L. Goering, T. D. Nevitt and E. P. Silversmith, *ibid.*, **77**, 5026 (1955).

(6) M. Simonetta and S. Winstein, *ibid.*, **76**, 19 (1954).

(7) W. G. Woods, R. A. Carboni and J. D. Roberts, *ibid.*, **78**, 5653 (1956).

sponding ketone (yellow 2,4-dinitrophenylhydra-zone, m.p. 175.4–177.0°). Lithium aluminum hydride reduction of this ketone yielded *endo*-2-benznorbornenol. The *endo*-benznorbornenol melted at 74.5–75.4°, but was readily distinguished from the *exo* isomer by its *p*-bromobenzenesulfonate, m.p. 135.1–136.1°, in contrast to that of the *exo*-alcohol, m.p. 82.2–84.4°, as well as by the infrared spectra. Benznorbornadiene is readily oxidized by monoperphthalic acid to a single epoxide, m.p. 26–29°, whose behavior on reaction with hydrogen bromide is parallel to that of epoxynorbornane. Addition of HBr occurs with rearrangement producing *exo*-2-bromo-*anti*-7-benznorbornenol, m.p. 135.3–136.8°, which can be

FIG. 1. Reported solvolytic reactivities (Relative to cyclohexyl) of 2- and 7-*p*-bromobenzenesulfonates of norbornane and norborene.

[a] S. Winstein, M. Shatavsky, C. J. Norton and R. B. Woodward, THIS JOURNAL, 77, 4183 (1955). [b] S. Winstein and M. Shatavsky, *ibid.*, 78, 592 (1956). [c] S. Winstein and E. T. Stafford, *ibid.*, 79, 505 (1957). [d] S. Winstein and D. Trifan, *ibid.*, 74, 1154 (1952). [e] S. Winstein, B. K. Morse, E. Grunwald, H. W. Jones, J. Corse, D. Trifan and H. Marshall, *ibid.*, 74, 1127 (1952).

FLOW SHEET

![flow sheet diagram]

convert this into *syn*-7-benznorbornenol. In the case of *anti*-7-benznorbornadienol, attempts to produce a ketone by even the mildest procedures led only to the formation of naphthalene with loss of the 7-carbon atom.

Rearrangement of the epoxide occurred not only on addition of hydrogen bromide but also on heating under reflux with lithium aluminum hydride in ether. The product isolated by crystallization and chromatography melted at 103.0–104.6° and was identified by its infrared spectrum as *anti*-7-benznorbornenol. This reaction has also been observed by Meinwald and Lewis.[8]

Solvolysis of *p*-Bromobenzenesulfonates.—Solvolysis of the brosylates of *endo*- and *exo*-2-benznorbornenols in glacial acetic acid containing equivalent sodium acetate yielded the same acetate in each case, which was reduced by lithium aluminum hydride to *exo*-2-benznorbornenol. Solvolysis of *anti*-7-benznorbornenyl brosylate yielded *anti*-7-benznorbornenyl acetate while *anti*-7-benznorbornadienyl brosylate yielded *anti*-7-benznorbornadienyl acetate. Both of these acetates were reduced by lithium aluminum hydride to *anti*-7-benznorbornenol. *anti*-Benznorbornadienyl acetate also was prepared by acetylation of the alcohol and reconverted to the latter by methylmagnesium iodide.

The solvolysis rates of the four *p*-bromobenzenesulfonates are summarized in Table I together with the derived activation parameters. For purposes of comparison with related compounds, the rate constants at 25° have been calculated in each case using extrapolation in those cases where the rate was not measured directly at that temperature. Table I shows a comparison of the rates here determined with those for related compounds measured by others. In the *endo*-2-brosylate the rate is slower than that of *endo*-norborneol by a factor of about 250 and is about five times slower than in *endo*-2-norbornenyl brosylate. The ratio of solvolysis rate constants for the *exo* and *endo* isomers is 5000, in the same range as the corresponding ratio in the 2-norborneneyl brosylates.

In the 7 series the disparity is much greater between the effect of the fused benzene ring and that of the double bond. *anti*-7-Benznorbornenyl brosylate undergoes solvolysis at a rate more than

converted into *anti*-7-benznorbornenol, m.p. 105.6–107.1° by reduction with hydrogen-on-palladium or into *anti*-7-benznorbornadienol, m.p. 106.3–108.2°, by treatment of the dihydropyran derivative with potassium *t*-butoxide. 7-Benznorbornenol can be oxidized by the Oppenauer method to 7-benznorbornenone (principal carbonyl absorption at 5.58 mμ; 2,4-dinitrophenylhydrazone, m.p. 143.6–146.4°), but no way has been found to

(8) J. Meinwald, private communication.

TABLE I

KINETIC DATA FOR BENZNORBORNENYL p-BROMOBENZENESULFONATE ACETOLYSIS IN GLACIAL ACETIC ACID CONTAINING SODIUM ACETATE

Compound	Temp., °C.	$k_1 \times 10^6$, sec.$^{-1}$	$\Delta H^{\ddagger}$, kcal.	$\Delta S^{\ddagger}$, cal./deg.	Extrapolated k_1, (25°) sec.$^{-1} \times 10^9$	k_1 (25°) relative to		
						Cyclohexyl	Norbornyl analog (CH₂—CH₂ in place of benzo)	Norbornenyl analog (CH=CH in place of benzo)
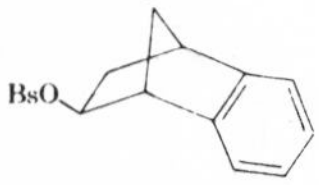 BsO⟨	50.03 ± 0.01 25.03 ± .02	188 ± 18 7.47 ± 0.20	24.1 ± 0.9	−1.2 ± 3.1	7470	43	0.06	0.16
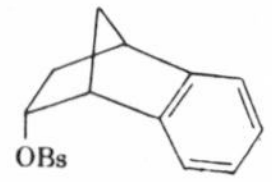 ⟩OBs	114.8 ± .2 95.75 ± .05	54.9 ± .7 7.60 ± .14	27.85 ± 1.45	−7.0 ± 3.9	1×10^{-4}	0.006	0.004	0.2
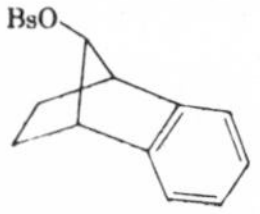 BsO⟨	95.75 ± .05 74.79 ± .05	105.8 ± 3.3 10.22 ± 0.58	27.6 ± 1.1	−2.3 ± 3.0	10	0.06	6×10^5	6×10^{-4}
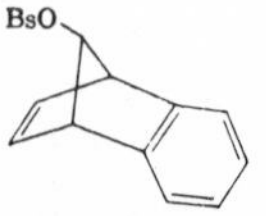 BsO⟨	60.00 ± .05 35.00 ± .05	161.5 ± 1.5 5.57 ± 0.16	26.85 ± 0.35	4.45 ± 0.95	1200	7.0	1.4×10^6	

five powers of ten less than that reported for *anti*-7-norbornenyl brosylate[9] or for the similarly constituted brosylate derived from dicyclopentadiene.[10] At the same time, if we compare the 7-brosylate having a fused benzene ring with the saturated 7-norbornyl brosylate, the benzene fusion is seen to provide a net driving force amounting to a factor of about 6×10^5. The further introduction of the double bond in *anti*-7-benznorbornadienyl brosylate increases the rate of solvolysis by a factor of over 100.

Discussion

In both norbornenyl and benznorbornenyl compounds there is a pair of bond moments (at C_1–C_6 and C_4–C_5) unfavorable to a positive charge at C_2 or C_7. The depression of ionization rate by factors of 44 and 250 in the respective *endo*-2-p-bromobenzenesulfonates measures the effect of this sp^2-sp^3 polarization. In correcting for the effect of β-phenyl groups on ionization rate, Winstein and co-workers[11] used a rough factor of 10 per phenyl group. This is consistent with the effects in the bicyclic compounds, where two such moments are present instead of one, and where the aromatic ring resists the strain imposed by the bicycloheptenyl system and keeps the shared carbons using more truly sp^2 orbitals than the simple double bond can do. If this opposition to ionization is cancelled by looking at the *exo/endo* ratio, the aromatic ring is seen to be almost identical to the double bond in its ability to assist ionization at the 2-position. The charge delocalization in the structure X would appear as favorable in the benzene ring as in any phenonium ion or any aromatic substitution intermediate.

(9) S. Winstein, M. Shatavsky, C. J. Norton and R. B. Woodward, THIS JOURNAL, 77, 4183 (1955).
(10) R. B. Woodward and T. J. Katz, *Tetrahedron*, 5, 70 (1959).
(11) S. Winstein, B. K. Morse, E. Grunwald, K. Schreiber and J. Corse, THIS JOURNAL, 74, 1117 (1952).

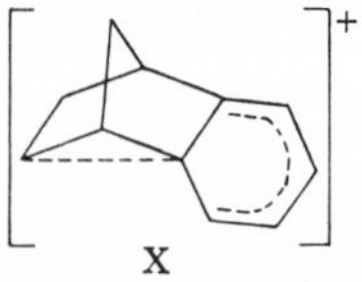

X

On the other hand, the fused benzene ring is vastly inferior to the double bond in assisting ionization at C_7, providing about 7 instead of 14 kcal. of free energy of activation to the ionization process. Unlike the situation in X, the stabilization in the ion XI develops a realignment of

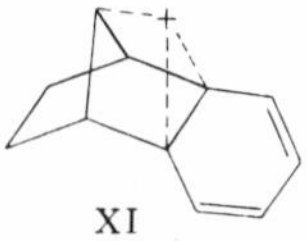

XI

atomic orbitals which can absorb a double bond completely but which, in benzene, can occur only at the expense of some of the aromatic stabilization energy. This difference is reflected in the results of a simple MO calculation for the 7-benznorbornadienyl cation using the same treatment which Roberts and co-workers applied to the 7-norbornenyl.[7,12]

The hundredfold increase in ionization rate brought about by the double bond in *anti*-7-benznorbornadienyl p-bromobenzenesulfonate occurs despite dipole effects which might tend to produce up to a hundredfold retardation instead. There is accordingly a driving force of the order of 10^4 arising from this structure. The possibility might be considered that some incipient stabilization of the cation occurs at the transition state from the side of the departing group as well as from the opposite side. However, *syn*-7-nor-

(12) W. P. Giddings, Thesis, Harvard University, 1959.

bornenyl tosylate,[13] which is accelerated in acetolysis by a factor of 10^4 over the saturated tosylate (and hence has a driving force of about 10^6), does not form the 7-norbornenyl cation. There is no evidence at present to indicate that the frontside assistance in question can be of any importance. One of the suggested explanations for the slow solvolysis of 7-norbornyl esters is the bond angle C_1–C_7–C_4 of probably less than 100°, especially unfavorable for the formation of a trigonal carbonium ion.[7] Because the net effect of the 2,3-double bond is to push C_1 and C_4 farther apart (because of increased C_1–C_2–C_3–C_4 bond angles and in spite of a shortened C_2–C_3 bond distance) it may relieve the constriction of the C_1–C_7–C_4 angle enough to be of real importance.

The rearrangement attending reduction of benznorbornadiene oxide was unexpected in view of cases in which the AlH_4^- ion appears to give normal displacement by an S_N2 mechanism. Its occurrence must be connected both with hindrance to attack at the *endo* side (the epoxide being assumed to be *exo*) and with first attachment of the lithium ion to the epoxy oxygen, permitting an electronic delocalization which is the basis of attack of the hydride at C_1 as in the case of HBr addition.

Still another mechanism of lithium reduction is seen in the ready conversion of 1-bromotriptycene into 1-triptycyllithium by lithium aluminum hydride[14] and by *n*-butyllithium.[15]

Experimental[16]

Benznorbornadiene (I) was prepared by the procedure of Wittig and Knauss,[17] b.p. 88–89° (19 mm.) (reported[1] 82.5–83.0° (12 mm.)).

exo-Benznorbornenol (II).—Benznorbornadiene was heated under reflux for five hours with rapid stirring with four times its weight of 25% sulfuric acid.[18] After cooling, the brown upper layer was dissolved in ether, separated; the aqueous layer extracted three times with ether; the combined organic layers washed with water and with dilute sodium carbonate solution, dried over sodium sulfate, and evaporated. The residue was dissolved in petroleum ether and chromatographed over Merck alumina with petroleum ether until all unreacted benznorbornadiene and a product thought to be

di-*exo*-benznorbornadienyl ether were eluted. *exo*-Benznorbornenol was eluted slowly with anhydrous ether and rapidly with 20% absolute ethanol in anhydrous ether, along with a yellow gum which was removed by treatment of the solution with charcoal. Recrystallization from petroleum ether yielded from 10 to 50% of white crystalline product, m.p. 74.1–75.4°. Subsequently, addition of acetic acid to the double bond[19] was found to be a preferable procedure for the preparation of *exo*-norborneol. Standard procedures were used for this sequence. Infrared spectrum of II: 2.79, 3.00, *3.40*, *6.85*, 6.91, 7.00, 7.29, 7.67, 7.78, 7.97, 8.17, 8.44, 8.64, 8.26, 9.19, *9.31*, *9.59*, 9.80, *10.29*, 10.86, 11.07, 11.37, 12.14, 12.84, 13.36, 13.78.

Anal. Calcd. for $C_{11}H_{12}O$: C, 82.50; H, 7.50. Found: C, 82.25; H, 7.69.

exo-Benznorbornenyl p-bromobenzenesulfonate was prepared in the usual manner,[20] with anhydrous pyridine. Crystals formed directly upon addition of the pyridine solution after two days at room temperature to ice and water. The brosylate was collected by suction filtration and washed repeatedly with water, then dissolved in ether; the solution was washed 3 times with ice-cold dilute hydrochloric acid and twice with cold dilute sodium carbonate solution, and dried over sodium sulfate. The solution was decanted and evaporated to about one-fifth of its volume; then four times the remaining volume of petroleum ether was added and the solution cooled at −25° in a freezer. After several recrystallizations in this manner the brosylate melted at 82.2–84.4°. Pumping in a drying pistol with phosphorus pentoxide caused the brosylate to darken and become infusible; pumping with potassium hydroxide pellets and paraffin shavings gave a white product.

Anal. Calcd. for $C_{17}H_{15}O_3SBr$: C, 53.83; H, 3.96. Found: C, 53.91; H, 4.11.

Structure of Acetolysis Product.—The product from the acetic acid solvolysis for 10 half-lives of *exo*-benznorbornenyl brosylate was diluted with ether and aqueous sodium carbonate solution was added. Solid sodium carbonate was added in small portions until no further bubbling occurred. After washing twice with aqueous sodium carbonate and drying over sodium sulfate, the ether solution was evaporated on the steam-bath and the residue pumped for several hours in a vacuum desiccator. The residue was added dropwise to excess lithium aluminum hydride in ether, causing gentle boiling with each drop, and allowed to stand at room temperature overnight. Water was added cautiously until no further reaction occurred; then 10% sulfuric acid was added until all precipitate had dissolved. The ether layer was separated, washed with sodium carbonate solution and dried over sodium sulfate. Evaporation of the ether left white crystals which had an infrared spectrum identical with that of *exo*-benznorbornenol.

2-Benznorbornenone (III) was prepared in 70% yield by oxidation of *exo*-benznorbornenol with chromium trioxide in pyridine.[21] A more convenient preparation was the following: A solution of 12.70 g. of *exo*-benznorbornenol, 10.0 g. of quinone and 38.3 g. of aluminum *t*-butoxide in 1000 ml. of benzene was heated under reflux for two days. The black solution was extracted twice with dilute sulfuric acid and 5 times with dilute sodium hydroxide solution until the extract was colorless. The benzene solution was dried over sodium sulfate and evaporated and the residue chromatographed over Merck alumina in petroleum ether. With petroleum ether and absolute ether 11.7 g. (90%) of ketone was eluted with the principal carbonyl absorption in the infrared at 5.69 μ with no alcohol detected. Ultraviolet maxima in ethanol were at 210 mμ (log ε 4.03), 264 (2.76), 273 (2.78) and 300 (mμ 2.92); infrared spectrum of III: 3.38, 5.55, *5.69*, 5.83, *6.81*, 7.08, 7.68, 7.87, 8.30, 8.47, 8.72, *8.92*, 9.23, 9.42, 9.88, *10.22*, 10.75, 11.12, 12.28, 12.58, *13.25*, 13.48.

Anal. Calcd. for $C_{11}H_{10}O$: C, 83.54; H, 6.33. Found: C, 83.47; H, 6.33.

(13) S. Winstein and E. T. Stafford, THIS JOURNAL, **79**, 505 (1957).

(14) R. P. Anderson, unpublished work in this Laboratory, 1954.

(15) G. Wittig and U. Schöllkopf, *Tetrahedron*, **3**, 91 (1958).

(16) All melting points were taken with uncalibrated Anschütz thermometers; boiling points are uncorrected. Microanalyses were performed by Dr. S. M. Nagy, Microchemical Laboratory, Massachusetts Institute of Technology. Infrared spectra were taken with a Perkin–Elmer model 21 and ultraviolet spectra with an Applied Physics Corporation Cary recording spectrophotometer.

(17) G. Wittig and E. Knauss, ref. 1. We thank Professor Wittig for kindly supplying the details of this procedure before publication.

(18) H. A. Bruson and T. W. Riener, THIS JOURNAL, **67**, 723 (1945).

(19) J. Bertram and H. Walbaum, *J. prakt. Chem., N. F.,* **49**, 1 (1894); H. A. Bruson and T. W. Riener, THIS JOURNAL, **67**, 1178 (1945); P. von R. Schleyer, Ph.D. Thesis, Harvard University, 1956.

(20) R. S. Tipson, *J. Org. Chem.,* **9**, 235 (1944).

(21) G. I. Poos, G. E. Arth, R. E. Beyler and L. H. Sarett, THIS JOURNAL, **75**, 427 (1953).

The 2,4-dinitrophenylhydrazone was prepared in the usual manner.[21] After 3 recrystallizations from 95% ethanol, the yellow derivative melted at 175.4–177.0°. The ultraviolet spectrum in ethanol showed maxima at 232 mμ (log ϵ 4.51) and at 361 mμ (log ϵ 4.64).

Anal. Calcd. for $C_{17}H_{13}O_4N_4$: C,6 0.35; H, 4.14. Found: C, 60.81; H, 4.46.

endo-**Benznorbornenol (IV).**—To 1.2 g. of lithium aluminum hydride in 40 ml. of ether was added cautiously dropwise 10.10 g. of 2-benznorbornenone. Each drop produced a violent audible momentary reaction. The mixture was refluxed for three hours, cooled and worked up as described above for the acetolysis product of *exo*-benznorbornenyl brosylate. The crude product, 9.41 g. (93%) of white crystals, melted at 61–66° and its infrared spectrum showed the presence of no *exo*-benznorbornenol. After repeated recrystallization from ether–petroleum ether the m.p. was 74.5–75.4°; infrared spectrum of IV: 2.80, *3.37*, 6.85, 6.90, 6.97, *7.20*, 7.48, 7.66, 7.84, 8.08, 8.22, 8.73, 8.85, *8.93*, *9.05*, 9.38, *9.61*, 9.93, 10.27, 10.57, 10.77, 11.20, 12.54, 12.84, *13.33*, 14.13, 14.57.

Anal. Calcd. for $C_{11}H_{12}O$: C, 82.50; H, 7.50. Found: C, 82.17; H, 7.35.

endo-**Benznorbornenyl *p*-bromobenzenesulfonate** melted at 135.1–136.1° after repeated recrystallization from ether–petroleum ether. *Anal.* Calcd. for $C_{17}H_{15}O_3SBr$: C, 53.83; H, 3.96. Found: C, 53.85; H, 3.94. Treatment of the solvolysis product as described above for the *exo* isomer yielded an acetate with an infrared spectrum identical with that of the *exo* product.

Benznorbornadiene Oxide (V).—A solution of 22.2 g. of benznorbornadiene in 375 ml. of 0.437 *N* monoperphthalic acid in ether, prepared by the method of Royals and Harrell,[22] was kept in the refrigerator at about 6° for 7 days, then extracted three times with 20% sodium hydroxide solution, washed twice with water, dried over sodium sulfate, the ether evaporated and 15.5 g. (63%) of benznorbornadiene oxide, m.p. 26–29°, distilled at 97–97.5° (7 mm.); infrared spectrum of V: *3.38*, 5.17, 5.28, *6.83*, 6.91, 7.09, *7.32*, *7.79*, *8.10*, 8.36, 8.40, 8.73, 9.16, 9.21, 9.93, *9.99*, 10.20, 10.50, 10.80, *11.04*, 11.18, 11.52, *11.81*, 12.45, *13.28*, *13.53*, 14.37.

Anal. Calcd. for $C_{11}H_{10}O$: C, 83.53; H, 6.33. Found: C, 83.42; H, 6.38.

exo-**2-Bromo-*anti*-7-benznorbornenol[24] (VI).**—A solution of 15.5 g. of benznorbornadiene oxide in 90 ml. of petroleum ether was cooled to 10° and poured slowly in portions into 20 ml. of 48% hydrobromic acid with shaking and cooling in an ice-bath. The liquid phases were frequently decanted from the copious bluish sticky precipitate and shaken further in a clean flask. The solid was filtered off and dissolved in 400 ml. of ether; the aqueous phase was extracted three times with ether and the combined ethereal solution washed with dilute aqueous sodium carbonate solution and dried over sodium sulfate. The ether solution was then evaporated down to about 50 ml. and 300 ml. of petroleum ether added. After cooling to −25° in the freezer 12.0 g. (51.2%) of bromohydrin, m.p. 127–134°, was collected. After several recrystallizations from ether–petroleum ether the pure product melted at 135.3–136.6°; infrared spectrum of VI: 2.80, 3.38, *6.83*, 6.95, 7.17, 7.78, 7.89, *8.07*, 8.30, 8.39, 8.51, 8.70, 8.80, 8.95, 9.37, 9.88, 10.39, 11.32, 12.66, 13.15, 13.43, 14.03, 15.40.

Anal. Calcd. for $C_{11}H_{11}OBr$: C, 55.23; H, 4.60. Found: C, 55.63; H, 4.77.

anti-**7-Benznorbornenol (VII).**—The above bromohydrin was treated with hydrogen in the presence of Baker and Co. 10% palladium-on-charcoal catalyst in absolute ethanol solution. Evaporation of the filtered solution left a black residue which was dissolved in ether, decolorized with charcoal, and evaporated to yield 96% of an alcohol, m.p. 87.6–100° after one recrystallization from ether–petroleum ether, the infrared spectrum of which showed the presence of no *exo* or *endo* isomers. Pure material, m.p. 105.6–

(22) R. L. Shriner and R. C. Fuson, "The Systematic Identification of Organic Compounds," 3rd edition, John Wiley and Sons, Inc., New York, N. Y., 1955, p. 619.

(23) E. E. Royals and L. L. Harrell, Jr., THIS JOURNAL, **77**, 3405 (1955).

(24) H. M. Walborsky and D. F. Loncrini, *J. Org. Chem.*, **22**, 1117 (1957).

107.1°, could be obtained only by chromatography in anhydrous ether over Merck alumina, in the first fraction containing any product.

A solution of benznorbornadiene oxide in ether was heated under reflux for 2 hr. with excess lithium aluminum hydride and worked up in the usual manner. After separation from unreacted epoxide by two recrystallizations from petroleum ether and by chromatography over Merck alumina in ether, *anti*-7-benznorbornenol, m.p. 103.0–104.6°, was identified by the infrared spectrum. To 1.7 g. of lithium aluminum hydride in 40 ml. of ether was added from a dropping funnel 14.9 g. (0.0943 mole) of epoxide, resulting in gentle boiling, and heated on the steam-bath for 5 hr. Workup in the usual manner yielded 14.0 g. of liquid containing a few crystals; the infrared spectrum showed mostly recovered epoxide. This residue was added dropwise with stirring to a refluxing mixture of 2 g. of lithium aluminum hydride in 100 ml. of ether. By the time 21 hr. of refluxing and stirring had elapsed, the ether had evaporated and a gray paste remained. Ether was added and the mixture worked up as usual to yield 13.3 g. (0.0832 mole, 88.2%) of *anti*-7-benznorbornenol, m.p. 91–102°, infrared spectrum identical with pure material. Chromatography as above yielded 5.0 g., m.p. 104.1–105.7°, and subsequent fractions of lower melting point which could be purified by further chromatography but not by recrystallization alone; infrared spectrum of VII: 2.80, 3.00, *3.41*, 6.83, 6.88, 7.27, 7.77, 8.07, 8.42, 8.68, *9.00*, *9.33*, 9.87, 10.14. 10.76, 10.96, 11.48, 11.95, *13.38*.

Anal. Calcd. for C H $_2$O: C, 82.50; H, 7.50. Found: C, 82.71; H, 7.47.

anti-**7-Benznorbornenyl *p*-bromobenzenesulfonate** melted at 132.5–135.0° after recrystallization.

Anal. Calcd. for $C_{17}H_{15}O_3SBr$: C, 53.83; H, 3.96. Found: C, 53.91; H, 4.11.

Treatment of the acetolysis product as described above for the *exo* isomer yielded an acetate with an infrared spectrum different from that of the *exo* product; reduction with lithium aluminum hydride in the same manner yielded a white crystalline product with an infrared spectrum identical with that of *anti*-7-benznorbornenol.

7-Benznorbornenone (VIII) was prepared by Oppenauer oxidation as described for 2-benznorbornenone. The principal carbonyl absorption in the infrared spectrum was at 5.58 μ; the ultraviolet spectrum in ethanol showed maxima at 211 mμ (log ϵ 3.8; the solvent *vs.* air had an absorption of 0.6 at this wave length, but the baseline of solvent *vs.* solvent remained at zero), at 257 (2.74), at 263 (2.92) and at 271 (2.95); infrared spectrum of VIII: 3.44, *5.55*, *5.58*, 5.70, 6.85, 7.12, 8.85, 8.95, 9.32, 9.43, 9.86, 11.30, 12.94, *13.43*, 1375, 14.35.

Anal. Calcd. for $C_{11}H_{10}O$: C, 83.54; H, 6.33. Found: C, 83.35; H, 6.45.

The 2,4-dinitrophenylhydrazone, from ethanol, melted at 143.6–146.4°. The ultraviolet spectrum showed maxima at 267 mμ (log ϵ 4.01) and at 358 (4.29).

Anal. Calcd. for $C_{17}H_{13}O_4N_4$: C, 60.35; H, 4.14. Found: C, 60.28; H, 4.38.

To 0.20 g. of 7-benznorbornenone in 20 ml. of ether was added lithium aluminum hydride in excess and the mixture was refluxed for four hours, then worked up in the usual manner. The product had an infrared spectrum identical with that of pure *anti*-7-benznorbornenol: recrystallized once from petroleum ether, m.p. 103.8–105.2°, mixed m.p. 103.8–106.2°.

anti-**7-Benznorbornadienol (IX).**—To a mixture of several grams of *exo*-2-bromo *anti*-7-benznorbornenol in 22 g. of dihydropyran freshly distilled from potassium hydroxide was added a small drop of concd. sulfuric acid. A vigorous momentary reaction ensued; the reaction mixture turned dark and small amounts of black tar formed; the temperature rose above 40°. The remainder of 27.4 g. of bromohydrin was added and it all dissolved when the temperature remained above 30°. The sides of the flask were washed down with a small amount of ether and the mixture allowed to stand overnight. About 50 ml. of ether was added and the solution was shaken over sodium hydroxide pellets and left standing over sodium hydroxide for 3 hr. The cloudy solution was chromatographed over 3 ml. of Merck alumina in anhydrous ether. The combined residues from evaporation of the first four 500-ml. fractions were pumped in a vacuum desiccator for several hr. This product was dissolved in benzene and heated with the potassium *t*-butoxide prepared under nitrogen from 5.0 g. of potassium metal.[25] After a total of 17 hours of heating at 80°, the dark brown benzene solution was decanted from the solid residue, which was refluxed for 0.5 hr. with more benzene and dissolved entirely in water. The combined benzene solution was washed 3 times with water and twice with saturated sodium chloride solution, then concentrated by evaporation. The residue was chromatographed over 300 ml. of Merck alumina in benzene. The residues of the first 1900 ml. of eluent were dissolved in 150 ml. of 95% ethanol, a solution of 15 ml. of 36% hydrochloric acid in 200 ml. of 95% ethanol added and heated to 75° on the steam-bath, then allowed to stand at room temperature overnight. Solid sodium carbonate was added until effervescence ceased; then the solution was filtered, evaporated under reduced pressure from a warm water-bath, and pumped with an oil-pump for 1 hr. after it was dry. The crude *anti*-7-benznorbornadienol was dissolved in 1 l. of boiling petroleum ether and chromatographed over 200 ml. of Davison activated silica gel, since alumina had been found to discolor this product. With 20% anhydrous ether in petroleum ether was eluted a total of 12.83 g. (71%) of white, crystalline product melting above 104°; recrystallized twice from petroleum ether, m.p. 106.3–108.2°; infrared spectrum of IX: 2.80, 3.24, 3.33, 6.87, *7.19*, 7.66, 8.00, *8.23, 8.56*, 8.80, 9.03, *9.26, 9.40*, 9.93, 10.81, 10.93, 11.57, 11.82, *12 34*, 12.58, 12.79, *13.51, 14.29*.

Anal. Calcd. for $C_{11}H_{10}O$: C, 83.54; H, 6.33. Found: C, 83.57; H, 6.71.

anti-7-Benznorbornadienyl *p*-bromobenzenesulfonate, m.p. 126.8–128.5°.

Anal. Calcd. for $C_{17}H_{13}O_3SBr$: C, 54.11; H, 3.45. Found: C, 54.54; H, 3.52.

anti-7-Benznorbornadienyl Acetate.—To 0.20 g. of *anti*-benznorbornadienol in 1 ml. of pyridine was added 1 ml. of acetic anhydride and allowed to stand overnight, then pumped for 5 hr. with an oil-pump and allowed to stand overnight, in a vacuum desiccator over potassium hydroxide pellets. The residue was dissolved in ether, washed 3 times with cold dilute hydrochloric acid and twice with sodium carbonate solution and dried over anhydrous potassium carbonate. The residue after evaporation of the ether had an infrared spectrum identical with that of acetolysis product of *anti*-7-benznorbornadienyl brosylate.

When refluxed with lithium aluminum hydride in excess in ether overnight, this acetate yielded *anti*-7-benznorbornenol with an infrared spectrum identical with that of the authentic material described above and with that of the product of hydrogenation of *anti*-7-benznorbornadienol in ethanol over platinum catalyst. Reaction of *anti*-7-benznorbornadienyl acetate with methylmagnesium iodide regenerated *anti*-7-benznorbornadienol, identified by its infrared spectrum.

Oxidation of *anti*-7-Benznorbornadienol.—Oppenauer oxidation as described for 2-benznorbornenone yielded mostly naphthalene, identified by odor and by comparison of the infrared spectrum with that of an authentic sample; some unchanged *anti*-7-benznorbornadienol was recovered. Similar results were found using ether as solvent and refluxing for 5 days, and also using benzene as solvent and stirring for 9 days at room temperature. In the latter case the solvent was evaporated under reduced pressure and naphthalene was found in the Dry Ice trap after overnight pumping with an oil-pump.

Attempted Epimerization of *anti*-Benznorbornadienol.—When equimolar aluminum isopropoxide and *anti*-7-benznorbornadienol in about 3 ml. of xylene with a small amount of acetone according to the procedure of Doering and Aschner[26] was heated in a sealed tube at 100° for 5 days, most of the starting alcohol was recovered unchanged and a small amount of naphthalene was detected in the infrared spectrum. With sodium, fluorene and fluorenol by the procedure of Doering and Aschner[26] on similar heating at 100° for 5 days, the crude product showed no infrared absorption at 14.4 μ characteristic of the benznorbornadienyl double bond. Heating *anti*-7-benznorbornadienyl brosylate simi-

larly with a tenfold excess of potassium acetate in acetone for 5 days at 100° produced a yellow varnish-like product which was eluted from Merck alumina only with 5% or more absolute ethanol in anhydrous ether. Refluxing a similar mixture in acetone for 40 hours brought about no reaction; after 7 days in a sealed tube at 76–78° mostly brosylate was recovered, but dissolving the residue in 3 ml. of petroleum ether and cooling to −25°, filtering, evaporating the mother liquor to half its volume and cooling and filtering again, the residue from the mother liquor showed strong peaks in the infrared spectrum at 2.70, at 5.90, and the peaks corresponding to the unsaturation were shifted to higher wave length than those in the spectrum of the brosylate. The 2,4-dinitrophenylhydrazone was red, showing maxima in its ultraviolet spectrum in ethanol at 263 mμ (log ε 4.40) and at 382 mμ (ε 4.50, calcd. for mol. wt. of 388), indicating a highly conjugated aldehyde.[27a]

The 2,4-dinitrophenylhydrazone of 1-naphthaldehyde[27b] prepared by the procedure of Brown and Subba Rao[28] showed maxima in its ultraviolet spectrum in ethanol at 310 mμ (log ε 3.3) and at 388 (3.9).

exo-Norborneol.—Norbornylene was prepared from dicyclopentadiene and ethylene by the procedure of Thomas[29] and was hydrated by the procedure described above for *exo*-benznorborneol. The method of Bertram and Walbaum[19] was found to be far preferable: To 25 ml. of glacial acetic acid was added 4.9 g. of norbornylene and about 0.5 ml. of 50% sulfuric acid. The solution was heated under reflux for 1 hr. and it quickly turned dark gray. The reaction mixture was poured into 400 ml. of water, extracted twice with ether, and left overnight over solid sodium carbonate. The ether solution was washed twice with aqueous sodium carbonate solution and dried over magnesium sulfate. Charcoal was added and the solution filtered, then refluxed overnight in ether with excess lithium aluminum hydride.

When norbornylene oxide,[30] prepared as described above for benznorbornylene oxide, was left in refluxing ether with excess lithium aluminum hydride overnight and the ether all evaporated, working up in the usual manner yielded a mixture of *exo*-norborneol, identified by comparison of the infrared spectrum of the product with that of an authentic sample, and of 7-norborneol identified from the infrared spectrum of authentic material prepared by Norton.[31] When care was taken that the ether did not evaporate, after refluxing for 72 hr. the infrared spectrum of the product still showed some norbornylene oxide along with *exo*-norborneol; no 7-norborneol was detected.

exo-Norbornyl tosylate was prepared in the same manner as the brosylates described above; m.p. after several recrystallizations from petroleum ether, 53.0–54.5°.

Kinetic Procedures.—Acetolysis conditions and procedures were chosen to be similar to those of Norton and Woodward, which in turn had been chosen to be similar to those of Winstein, *et al.*,[32] and of Roberts, *et al.*[33] Samples of sulfonate ester were weighed into 50-ml. volumetric flasks so that solutions approximately 0.1 molar in ester would be obtained, then filled to 50 ml. with 0.100 molar sodium acetate from anhydrous sodium carbonate, glacial acetic acid, and refluxed for 5 hr. with sufficient acetic anhydride to leave 1% excess after removing the water of neutralization. Rate constants were determined by the infinity titer method, the first aliquot after thermal equilibrium had been reached was called zero time. Aliquots, usually 3 ml., were pipetted either from individual sealed ampoules which had been quenched in an ice-bath and then warmed to 25° or directly from the volumetric flask in the constant temperature bath and drained into 20 ml. of purified[34] dioxane. Two drops of a saturated solution of brom phenol blue in acetic acid was added, and the residual sodium acetate titrated with 0.020 molar perchloric acid in glacial

(25) A. I. Vogel, "Practical Organic Chemistry," 3rd edition, Longmans, Green and Co., London, 1956, p. 920.

(26) W. von E. Doering and T. C. Aschner, THIS JOURNAL, **71**, 838 (1949).

(27) (a) E. A. Braude and E. R. H. Jones, *J. Chem. Soc.*, 498 (1945); (b) H. W. Coles and M. L. Dodds, THIS JOURNAL, **60**, 853 (1938).

(28) H. C. Brown and B. C. Subba Rao, *ibid.*, **80**, 5379 (1958).

(29) C. L. Thomas, *Ind. Eng. Chem.*, **36**, 310 (1944).

(30) H. M. Walborsky and D. F. Loncrini, THIS JOURNAL, **76**, 5396 (1954); H. Kwart and W. G. Vosburgh, *ibid.*, **76**, 5400 (1954).

(31) C. J. Norton, Ph.D. Thesis, Harvard University, 1955.

(32) S. Winstein, C. Hanson and E. Grunwald, THIS JOURNAL, **70**, 812 (1948); S. Winstein, E. Grunwald and L. L. Ingraham, *ibid.*, **70**, 821 (1948).

(33) J. D. Roberts and V. C. Chambers, *ibid.*, **73**, 5034 (1951).

(34) L. F. Fieser, "Experiments in Organic Chemistry," 2nd edition, D. C. Heath and Co., Boston, Mass., 1941, p. 369.

acetic acid which had been refluxed with 1% excess acetic anhydride. The disappearance of the yellow indicator color was taken as the end-point. Least squares slopes and their probable errors were calculated for plots of ln (% unreacted) against time; in all cases good straight lines were obtained for every run and at least one run for each compound was followed for three or more half-lives.

Acknowledgment.—We thank the National Science Foundation for a research grant, and the National Institutes of Health for a Fellowship to the junior author.

CAMBRIDGE 38, MASS.

44 | 4-Cycloheptenyl-methyl Bromo-benzenesulfonate

To Mme. G. LeNy, a co-worker of H. Felkin in Paris, belongs the credit for introducing a new approach to the study of nonclassical ions. Removing a neighboring double bond from the allylic and homoallylic positions all the way to the 5,6-position and then giving it forced proximity by means of a 7-membered ring, she showed that the double bond of 4-cycloheptenylmethyl bromo-benzenesulfonate provides an acceleration of at least 30-fold over the saturated compound, and the product of acetolysis is at least 90% *endo*-2-bicyclo(3.2.1)-octyl acetate. This appears to be a particularly straightforward way of forming a three-center nonclassical ion, and the product in this case is formed with the stereospecificity to be expected from the manner in which the ion is formed. On the limits of the stereospecificity, see Note 2 in the commentary on Paper No. 50.

From: *Compt. rend.* **251**, 1526–28 (1960)

CHIMIE ORGANIQUE. — *Participation transannulaire de la double liaison lors de l'acétolyse du p-bromobenzènesulfonate de cycloheptène-4 yle.* Note (*) de Mme **Geneviève Le Ny**, présentée par M. Marcel Delépine.

L'acétolyse à 80° du *p*-bromobenzènesulfonate de cycloheptène-4 yle est nettement plus rapide que celle du composé saturé correspondant, et le produit obtenu est l'acétate de cis-bicyclo [3 : 2 : 1] octyle-2, la réaction s'effectuant avec participation transannulaire de la double liaison.

Nous avons poursuivi l'étude entreprise sur la réactivité de composés cyclaniques à fonction juxtacyclique (¹), (²) en étudiant l'acétolyse de deux *p*-bromobenzènesulfonates (I à cycle hexagonal et II à cycle heptagonal) possédant une double liaison dans le cycle. Ces composés nous semblaient susceptibles de réagir avec participation transannulaire de la double liaison, et de conduire ainsi aux acétates bicycliques (III) et (IV).

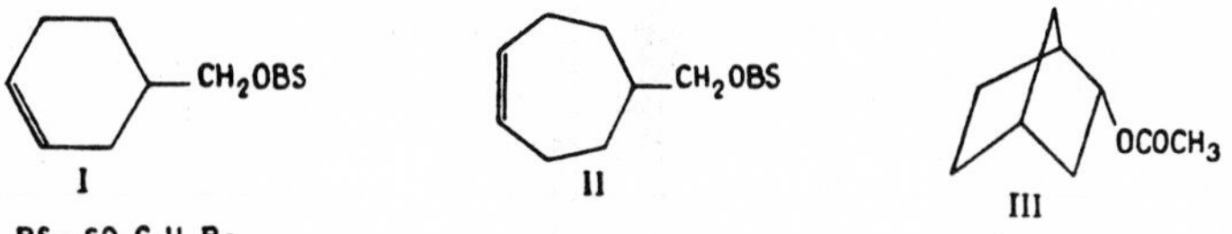

BS = $SO_2C_6H_4Br$

Fig. 1.

Nous avons effectivement observé que l'acétolyse du *p*-bromobenzène-sulfonate (II) donne, avec un rendement supérieur à 95 %, un mélange d'acétates *saturés* contenant au moins 90 % d'acétate de cis-bicyclo[3 : 2 : 1] octyle-2 (IV). De plus une étude cinétique préliminaire a montré que la vitesse de solvolyse de ce composé est plus de trente fois supérieure à celle du *p*-bromobenzènesulfonate saturé correspondant.

La formation presque exclusive d'acétate bicyclique cis (IV) et l'augmentation de vitesse de réaction par rapport à celle du composé saturé correspondant sont compatibles avec la formation intermédiaire de l'ion (A) :

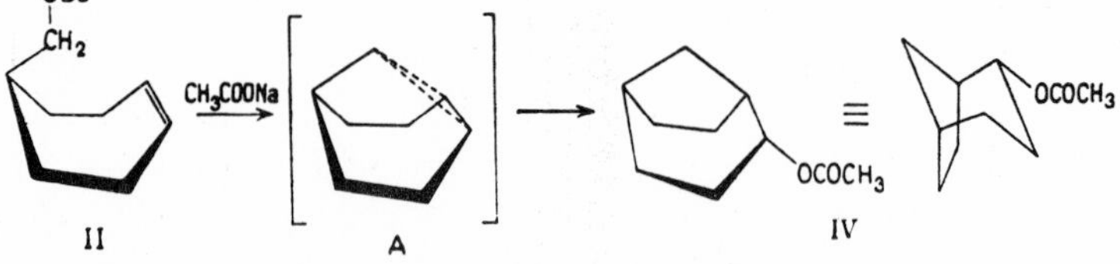

Fig. 2.

Par contre, le composé formé de façon presque exclusive lors de l'acétolyse du composé (I) est l'acétate de cyclohexène-3 yl méthyle, et si des produits bicycliques (qui résulteraient d'une réaction avec participation transannulaire de la double liaison : acétate de norbonyle (III) et norbornylène) se sont formés, leur rendement n'excède pas 0,5 % (³). D'autre part, la vitesse de solvolyse de ce composé est proche de celle du composé saturé correspondant. Il n'y a donc pas, dans ce cas, participation transannulaire de la double liaison.

La distance entre le groupement CH_2 juxtacyclique et la double liaison peut être beaucoup plus courte dans le composé cyclohepténique (II) (1,75 Å environ) que dans le composé cyclohexénique (I) (2,9 Å environ), de plus l'orientation de ce groupement par rapport à la double liaison est beaucoup plus favorable. C'est ce qui explique sans doute le comportement différent de ces deux composés.

Il est intéressant de constater qu'une participation transannulaire de la double liaison peut s'effectuer en direction d'un carbone juxtacyclique et qu'elle provoque un accroissement de vitesse appréciable. Nous étudions actuellement la solvolyse d'autres composés cycliques insaturés pour voir à quel point la réaction que nous décrivons est généralisable et par là susceptible de rendre accessibles différents composés bicycliques.

PARTIE EXPÉRIMENTALE. — *p-bromobenzènesulfonate de cycloheptène-4 yl méthyle.* — Le cycloheptène-4 yl méthanol ($C_8H_{14}O$, É_{19} 116,5-117°) a été obtenu par réduction, par LiALH_4, de l'acide cycloheptène-4 carboxylique préparé à partir de la cyclopentanone par la méthode de Stork et Landesman ([4]). Le *p*-bromobenzènesulfonate ($C_{14}H_{17}O_3SBr$, F 53,5-55°) a été préparé par la méthode habituelle avec un rendement de 83 %.

La solvolyse a été effectuée en ampoule scellée à 80°, la solution dans l'acide acétique étant 3,7 M en *p*-bromobenzènesulfonate et 4,07 M en acétate de sodium. Après chauffage pendant 5 h (10 demi-temps de réaction environ) la solution acétique a été neutralisée par la lessive de soude puis épuisée par l'éther.

Après distillation de l'éther la solution, contenant exclusivement des acétates saturés, a été hydrogénolysée par LiALH_4. Le rendement, calculé à partir du *p*-bromobenzènesulfonate, est de 95 %. L'alcool obtenu [après sublimation : F 178-180° (tube scellé)] a été oxydé ([5]) en cétone saturée correspondante [après sublimation : F 118-121° (tube scellé)].

M. Walborsky a accepté de comparer (par spectres infrarouges et points de fusion) l'alcool et son *p*-nitrobenzoate (F 79-81°), la cétone et sa semicarbazone (F 176-178°) avec ses échantillons authentiques ([6]). Il nous a confirmé que l'alcool est constitué par plus de 90 % de cis-bicyclo (3 : 2 : 1) octanol-2 et que la cétone est la bicyclo [3 : 2 : 1] octanone-2.

p-bromobenzènesulfonate de cyclohexène-3 yl méthyle. — L'acide cyclohexène-3 carboxylique, qui nous a été fourni par M. Rumpf, a été réduit par LiALH_4 en cyclohexène-3 yl méthanol.

Le *p*-bromobenzènesulfonate ($C_{13}H_{15}O_3SBr$, F 34-35,5°) a été préparé avec un rendement de 75 %.

La solvolyse a été effectuée en ampoule scellée à 100°, la solution dans l'acide acétique étant 0,138 M en *p*-bromobenzènesulfonate et 0,156 M en acétate de sodium. Après chauffage pendant 48 h (10 demi-temps de réaction environ) la solution acétique a été neutralisée par la lessive de soude et épuisée à l'éther. Le mélange obtenu a été étudié par comparaison avec des échantillons authentiques de norbornylène et d'acétate de norbornyle fournis par M. Rassat.

Il a été vérifié que l'acétate de norbornyle est stable dans les conditions de l'expérience; dans les mêmes conditions le norbornylène se transforme en grande partie en acétate de norbornyle.

(*) Séance du 3 octobre 1960.

(1) H. FELKIN et G. LE NY, *Bull. Soc. Chim.*, 1957, p. 1169.

(2) G. LE NY, *Comptes rendus*, 250, 1960, p. 368.

(3) R. S. BLY et H. L. DRYDEN (*Chemistry and Industry*, 1959, p. 1287) avaient obtenu des résultats comparables lors de l'acétolyse du méthanesulfonate.

(4) G. STORK et H. K. LANDESMAN, *J. Amer. Chem. Soc.*, 78, 1956, p. 5129.

(5) A. GAGNEUX et C. A. GROB, *Helv. Chim. Acta.*, 42, 1959, p. 1753.

(6) A. A. YOUSSEF, M. E. BAUM et H. M. WALBORSKY, *J. Amer. Chem. Soc.*, 81, 1959, p. 4709.

(*C. N. R. S., 25, boulevard Saint-Jacques, Paris, 14e.*)

45 | 7-Norbornadienyl Chloride

Winstein and Ordronneau (Paper No. 45) find that 7-norbornadienyl chloride is 10^3 times as reactive in solvolysis as *anti*-7-norbornenyl and 10^{14} times as reactive as 7-norbornyl. There is some imaginative speculation as to the cause of the extra driving force from the second double bond, but the geometrical explanation involving relaxation of the narrow angle at C-7 (Paper No. 43) is not one of those considered. At present there appear to be three reasons for favoring the unsymmetrical over the symmetrical structures of the postulated ion. (1) The idea of front-side participation in the transition state is avoided. (2) The long-lived ion of Story and Saunders (Paper No. 62) is unsymmetrical. (3) Of the forms of VIII shown, VIIIb, suitable for direct transition from starting material, encounters difficulties of quantum mechanical formulation because if the dotted bonds from C-7 are *p* in character, as they must be, there will be an antibonding node between some pair of bridges.

From: *J. Am. Chem. Soc.* **82,** 2084–85 (1960)

THE 7-NORBORNADIENYL NON-CLASSICAL CATION[1]

Sir:

The *anti-* and *syn-*7-norbornenyl systems V[2] and VI[3] represent interesting and instructive examples of neighboring carbon participation in solvolysis. *anti-*7-Norbornenyl *p*-toluenesulfonate[2] (V) is more reactive than the related 7-norbornyl derivative VII in acetolysis by a factor of 10^{11}, the anchimerically assisted ionization leading to cation IX. The isomeric *syn*-isomer[3] VI is more reactive than the 7-norbornyl analog by a factor of 10^4, the allylic cation X being formed. In this connection, 7-norbornadienyl derivatives IV with both *syn-* and *anti-*olefinic groups were obviously of interest, and we have now prepared 7-norbornadienol (III) and have observed the behavior of its derivatives in solvolysis.

The norbornadienol III was prepared from bromohydrin[2] I, m.p. 48°, previously employed in the synthesis of *anti-*7-norbornenol. Treatment of the crude tetrahydropyranyl ether of bromohydrin I with potassium *t*-butoxide in refluxing toluene led to 7-norbornadienyl tetrahydropyranyl ether[4] (II), b.p. 89–90° (1.5 mm.), in high yield. Careful hydrolysis of this material gave rise to 7-norborna-

I II III

dienol (III), b.p. 76° (52 mm.), n^{25}D 1.5060, homogeneous in vapor phase chromatographic analysis. On hydrogenation the tetrahydropyranyl ether II consumed 1.99 moles, and the 7-norbornadienol (III) 2.00 moles, of hydrogen. This led to a homogeneous alcohol, m.p. 144–145°, identified as 7-norborneol by melting point, vapor phase chromatographic analysis and infrared spectrum.

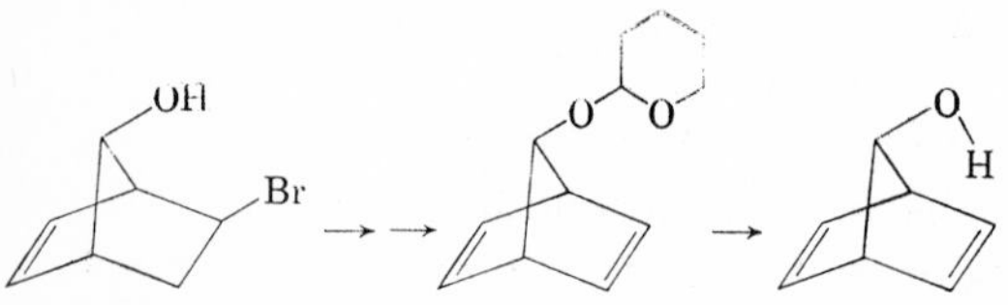

By standard methods, the 7-norbornadienol was converted to the *p*-nitrobenzoate, m.p. 101–102°, the trichloroacetate, b.p. 112° (3.5 mm.), n^{25}D 1.5087, and the trifluoroacetate, b.p. 85° (66 mm.), n^{25}D 1.4095. The 7-norbornadienyl chloride, b.p. 77.5° (63 mm.), n^{25}D 1.5050, was obtained from treatment of the dienol with thionyl chloride in

ether. The infrared spectra of all the 7-norbornadienyl derivatives confirmed the fact that they possessed the IV-structure.

In dilute solution in carbon tetrachloride, 7-norbornadienol (III) displays doublet monomeric O–H absorption in the first overtone region,[5] the two bands[6] being at 1.4110 and 1.4434 μ. The band at longer wave length is probably to be associated with π-hydrogen bonding,[7] and it is

noteworthy that the frequency shift is the largest observed in these Laboratories for any analogous cases.

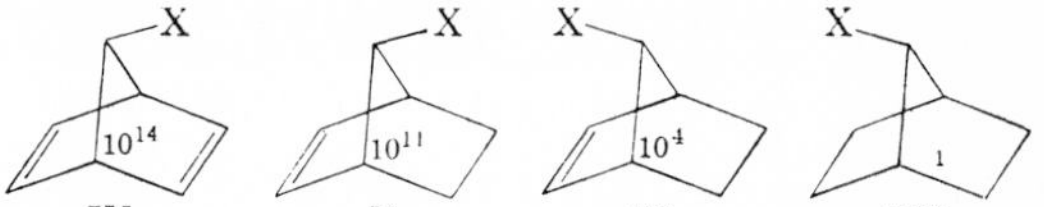

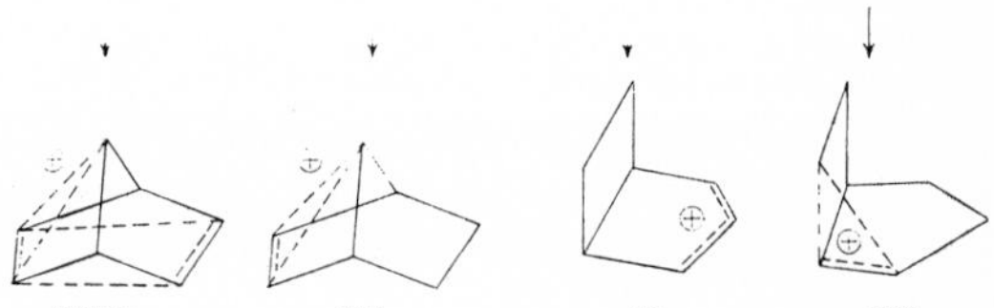

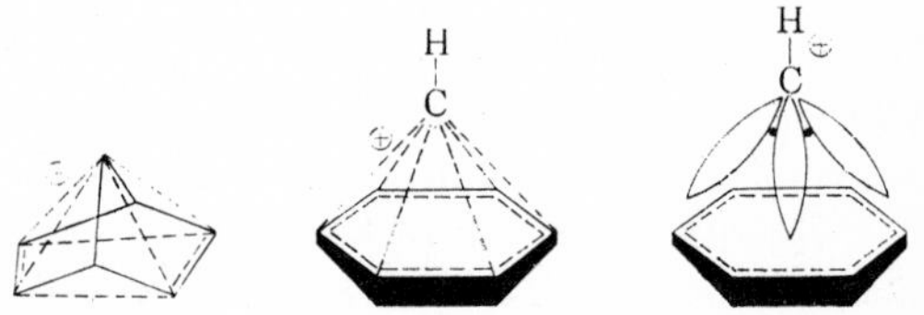

In solvolytic reactivity, the 7-norbornadienyl derivatives have proven to be *ca.* 10^3 times as reactive as the *anti-*7-norbornenyl analogs.[2,8] Thus, the first order rate constant for hydrolysis of 7-norbornadienyl chloride in 80% aqueous acetone at 25.0° is $(6.12 \pm 0.08) \times 10^{-4}$ sec.$^{-1}$, compared to a value of $(8.1 \pm 0.2) \times 10^{-7}$ for a sample of *anti-*7-norbornenyl chloride[8] kindly supplied by Robert Hansen. On this basis, the 7-norbornadienyl system is *ca.* 10^{14} times as reactive as the 7-norbornyl analog! As regards products of solvolysis of 7-norbornadienyl derivatives, only unrearranged 7-norbornadienol (III) in *ca.* 90% yield has been observed as the product from hydrolysis of 7-norbornadienyl chloride or trifluoro-

(1) This research was supported by a grant from The Petroleum Research Fund administered by the American Chemical Society. Grateful acknowledgment is hereby made to the donors of this fund.

(2) (a) S. Winstein, M. Shatavsky, C. Norton and R. B. Woodward, THIS JOURNAL, **77,** 4183 (1955); (b) S. Winstein and M. Shatavsky, *ibid.,* **78,** 592 (1956).

(3) S. Winstein and E. T. Stafford, *ibid.,* **79,** 505 (1957).

(4) Satisfactory carbon and hydrogen analyses were obtained for the new compounds here mentioned.

(5) R. Piccolini and S. Winstein, *Tetrahedron Letters,* **13,** 4 (1959).

(6) R. Piccolini, unpublished work.

(7) *E.g.,* P. Schleyer, D. S. Trifan and R. Bacskai, THIS JOURNAL, **80,** 6691 (1958).

(8) W. G. Woods, R. A. Carboni and J. D. Roberts, THIS JOURNAL, **78,** 5653 (1956).

acetate in 80% aqueous acetone in the presence of sodium bicarbonate at 50°.

It is obvious that the 7-norbornadienyl cation is highly stabilized by non-classical electron delocalization, but it is not yet clear whether it should be depicted as VIIIa, somewhat unsymmetrical and analogous to the *anti*-7-norbornenyl cation[2,8] (IX) except for some electron delocalization from the second olefinic group, or as a symmetrical cation VIIIb. Further, it is not yet clear to what extent the 1,7- and 4,7-bonding electrons are delocalized, with the 7-norbornadienyl cation partaking of the character of VIIIc. In the extreme, the cation could be regarded as a delocalized eight-electron system resulting from the interaction of an approximately tetrahedrally hybridized HC^+: group with a benzene ring (see VIIId). In this extreme, there are six equivalent carbon atoms.[9]

In 96% sulfuric acid, 7-norbornadienol (III) gives a yellow solution, with an ultraviolet absorption band at 350 mμ ($\epsilon = ca.$ 5 × 10^3), most probably[10] due to the non-classical cation VIII.

(9) The possibility of this type of geometry, but with different atomic orbital hybridization at the HC:group, was independently suggested by Dr. A. Streitwieser.

(10) *E.g.*, (a) J. A. Grace and M. C. R. Symons, *J. Chem. Soc.*, 958 (1959); (b) G. Leal and R. Pettit, THIS JOURNAL, **81**, 3160 (1959).

DEPARTMENT OF CHEMISTRY   S. WINSTEIN
UNIVERSITY OF CALIFORNIA   C. ORDRONNEAU
LOS ANGELES 24, CALIFORNIA

RECEIVED MARCH 7, 1960

46-48 | Some Special Transannular Effects

The next three papers (Papers 46, 47, and 48) concern anchimeric effects upon the rate and products of solvolysis in some unusual tetracyclic compounds containing two norbornyl ring systems and a forced proximity between two sites in the 1,5-relation. Evidence of anchimeric assistance by double bonds includes reaction with complete ring closure and some of the highest known driving forces toward ionization. Compound A (as the trichloroacetate, since the bromobenzene-

| A | B | C | D |

sulfonate was too unstable to be isolated) underwent solvolysis a million times as fast as a comparable model with an *endo*-2-ester group. In Paper No. 48, compound B-OBs is reported to solvolyze, again with total rearrangement, at a rate only 4-fold less than *anti*-7-norbornenyl ester (C), which is 10^{11} times the rate of the saturated analog (see Paper No. 26). In Paper No. 47 a transannular participation of a saturated hydrogen atom is reported (in D-OBs) which produces a driving force of about 1000-fold and, unlike the 5-hydrogen atom of Paper No. 32, shows a deuterium kinetic isotope effect and yields no unrearranged product.

From: *Chem. Ind. (London)* **1960,** 590–91

as (G), (F) and (J). Among the saturated products are the bird-cage hydrocarbon[1,2] (II) and the half-cage alcohol[1,2] (III–OH). Besides the latter, three other saturated alcohols occur in the saturated product, one of them, for example, having the "twisted" structure (VI). The same saturated products, the bird-cage hydrocarbon in larger amount and (VI–OH) in lesser amount, are obtained in solvolysis of the half-cage bromobenzenesulphonate[1,2] (III–OBs).

In the solvolysis of bromobenzenesulphonate (I–OBs) none of the unsaturated alcohol (IV–OH) with the *endo-endo*-fusion was observed in the product.[1,2] The reaction of the intermediate ion (A) with solvent to produce (IV–OH) fails to compete appreciably with the one leading to (I–OH) with the *endo-exo*-fusion of the bicycloheptane nuclei. However, we have recently prepared[3] the unsaturated (IV–OH), and this substance has a unique geometry which is very favourable for anchimeric acceleration of alkyl-oxygen ionisation in solvolysis of its esters.

NEW CARBONIUM ION ROUTES TO THE BIRD-CAGE HYDROCARBON AND RELATED COMPOUNDS*

By P. Bruck,†, D. Thompson and S. Winstein

Department of Chemistry, University of California, Los Angeles 24, California, U.S.A.

As reported elsewhere,[1,2] solvolysis of bromo-benzenesulphonate (I–OBs) gives rise not only to unsaturated solvolysis product (I–OH) but to major amounts of saturated products as a result of interesting, complex rearrangements of the initial bridged ion (A) involving other non-classical structures such

* (*a*) This research was supported in part by a grant from The Petroleum Research Fund administered by the American Chemical Society. Grateful acknowledgment is hereby made to the donors of this fund. (*b*) Research sponsored by the Office of Ordnance Research, U.S. Army

† Recipient of a Wellcome Trust Travel Grant, 1959–1960.

(*a*) *p*-Nitrobenzoates in 70% aqueous acetone.

(*b*) Toluene-*p*-sulphonates or *p*-bromobenzenesulphonates in acetic acid solvent.

These provide an interesting route to the same non-classical carbonium ions ((G), (F), (J)) involved in solvolysis of (I–OBs) and (III–OBs). An alternative route is the acid-catalysed hydration of the *endo-endo*-diene (V), which has also become available recently.[3]

Derivatives of (IV–OH) have proved to be so reactive that we were unable to prepare the bromo-benzenesulphonate (IV–OBs). The material isolated from the attempted preparation of (IV–OBs) was the corresponding half-cage derivative,[1,2] namely (III–OBs), m.p. 77°. This substance was identified by its melting point, elemental analysis, and first order acetolysis rate constant.[1,2] It was possible to prepare less reactive derivatives of the unsaturated (IV–OH), namely the p-nitrobenzoate‡ (IV)-OCOC$_6$H$_4$NO$_2$), m.p. 128°, and the trifluoroacetate (IV–OCOCF$_3$).

In solvolysis, the unsaturated (IV–system) is even more reactive than the *anti*-7-norbornenyl-(VII) one.[4] The rate of ionisation with the (IV–system) is *ca.* 10^2 times that of the half-cage analogue[2] (III), *ca.* 10^4 times that of the unsaturated (I)[2] and *ca.* 10^6 times that of (VIII), the *endo*-isomer[2] of (I). This is shown by the following comparison of relative solvolysis rates at 25°C.:

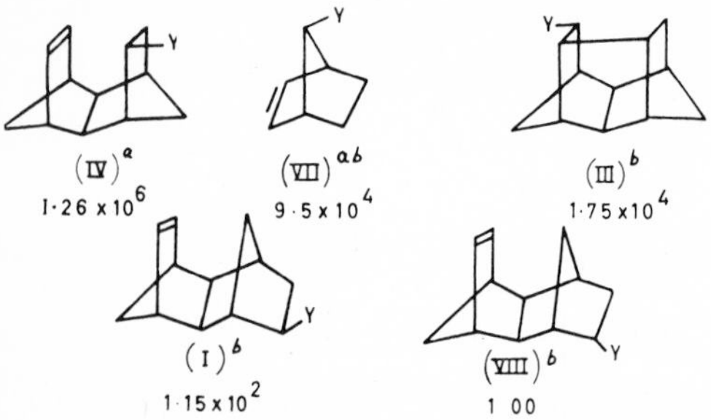

[4] (a) Winstein, S., Shatavsky, M., Norton, C. & Woodward, R. B., *J. Amer. chem. Soc.*, 1955, **77**, 4183; (b) Winstein, S. & Shatavsky, M., *ibid.*, 1956, **78**, 592
[5] Winstein, S. & Shatavsky, M., *Chem. & Ind.*, 1956, 56

$(IV)^a$ $(VII)^{a,b}$ $(III)^b$
$1·26 \times 10^6$ $9·5 \times 10^4$ $1·75 \times 10^4$

$(I)^b$ $(VIII)^b$
$1·15 \times 10^2$ $1·00$

The product of solvolysis of (IV–OCOCF$_3$), in 70% aqueous acetone heated under reflux, in the presence of calcium carbonate, is totally saturated. By chromatography there can be isolated substantial amounts of bird-cage hydrocarbon (II) (14%), half-cage alcohol (III–OH) (34%) and "twisted" alcohol (VI–OH) (43%). The remainder of the product (9%) is a syrupy mixture of saturated alcohols. Treatment of the *endo-endo*-diene (V) with a boiling 0·02 M solution of toluene-p-sulphonic acid in 75% aqueous dioxan gave rise to a similar saturated product, from which the same bird-cage hydrocarbon (II), half-cage alcohol (III–OH) and alcohol (VI–OH) were isolated. The homoconjugative hydration of the *endo-endo*-diene (V) with formation of half-cage (III–OH) is quite analogous to the 2,6-homoconjugative electrophilic additions to bicycloheptadiene.[1b,5]

The compositions of the saturated products from (IV–OCOCF$_3$) and the *endo-endo*-diene (V) resemble much more that of the product from unsaturated (I–OBs) than that from half-cage (III–OBs). However, more quantitative analysis of products from solvolyses under identical conditions will be necessary to ascertain whether the saturated products from the (I–), (IV–) and (V-systems) are really identical or differ somewhat.

Received March 7, 1960

References
[1] (a) Winstein, S., Symposium on "Dynamic Stereochemistry," Manchester, England, March 31, 1954: see *Chem. & Ind.*, 1954, 562–563; (b) Winstein, S., *Experientia Supplementum II*, 1955, 137
[2] de Vries, L. & Winstein, S., *J. Amer. chem. Soc.*, in the press
[3] Bruck, P., Thompson, D. & Winstein, S., *Chem. & Ind.*, 1960, in the press

‡ This and other new substances here reported gave satisfactory analyses.

From: *J. Am. Chem. Soc.* **82**, 6206–07 (1960)

1,5-HYDROGEN SHIFT IN A DECAHYDRODIMETHANONAPHTHALENE SYSTEM[1]

Sir:

Since the unsaturated alcohol I was available from the study of the octahydrodimethanonaphthyl non-classical homocyclopropenyl cation[2] II also, this made available the saturated alcohol III-OH, m.p. 124–126°, by hydrogenation over palladium on charcoal. Since the simple 7-norbornyl system[3] is exceedingly slow to ionize and structures such as III possess unique hydrogen congestion,[4] system III is an instructive one for the study of anchimeric effects of 5-hydrogen in carbonium ion reactions.

While bromobenzenesulfonate[5] III-OBs, m.p.

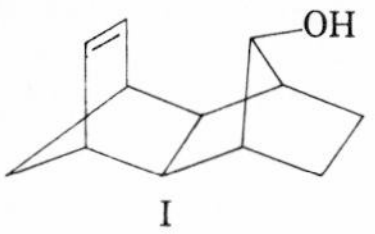

I 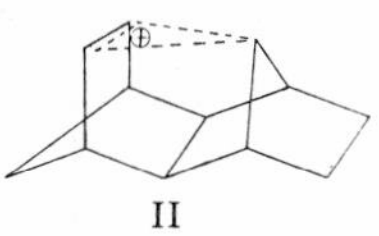 II

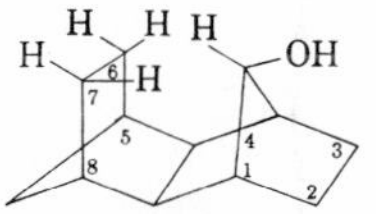

III-OH

109–110°, acetolyzes quite slowly by absolute standards, it is nevertheless very much more reactive than is the 7-norbornyl analog. The observed first order rate constant for acetolysis of III-OBs in 0.01 M sodium acetate in acetic acid solvent is $(4.27 \pm 0.12) \times 10^{-5}$ sec.$^{-1}$ at 127.6° and $(1.94 \pm 0.05) \times 10^{-6}$ sec.$^{-1}$ at 100.0°, leading to an extrapolated value of 2.42×10^{-11} sec.$^{-1}$ at 25.0°. Thus, rate of ionization of III-OBs exceeds that of the 7-norbornyl system[3] by a factor of slightly more than 10^{3}.

The product of acetolysis of III-OBs, analyzed by vapor phase chromatography and confirmed by infrared spectrum, is an 83:17 mixture of the *exo-exo*-fused and *endo-exo*-fused acetates VII-OAc and VIII-OAc, respectively (Table I). The *exo-exo*-fused alcohol VII–OH, m.p. 74–76°, has been described previously by Soloway,[6] while the *endo-exo*-fused isomer[5] VIII–OH, m.p. 95.5–97.5°, was available[7] from hydroboration–oxidation of the corresponding *endo-exo*-fused monoene described earlier.[8] Analogously, the product of hydrolysis of III-OBs is an 80:20 mixture of VII–OH and VIII–OH, respectively (Table I). Only the hydrogen-shifted products were observed, there being no evidence of the ring contraction which occurs

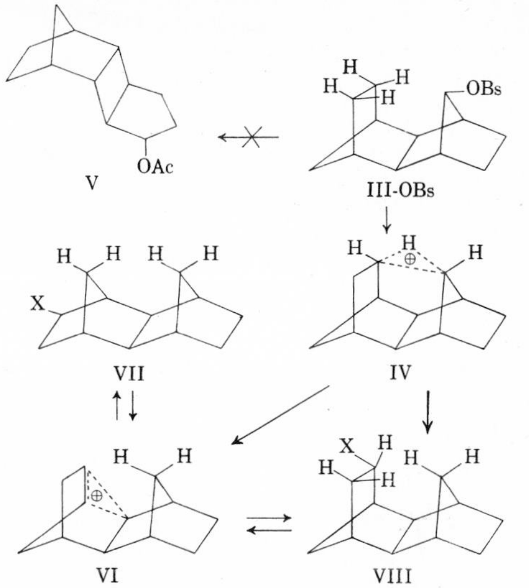

(1) Research sponsored by the Office of Ordnance Research, U. S. Army.

(2) S. Winstein and R. L. Hansen, *Tetrahedron Letters*, in press.

(3) (a) S. Winstein, M. Shatavsky, C. Norton and R. B. Woodward, This Journal, **77**, 4183 (1955); (b) C. J. Norton, Thesis, Harvard University, 1955.

(4) L. de Vries and S. Winstein, This Journal, **82**, 5363 (1960).

(5) This compound, as well as the other indicated materials, had a satisfactory C,H analysis.

(6) S. B. Soloway, This Journal, **74**, 1027 (1952).

(7) D. Thompson and R. L. Hansen, unpublished work.

(8) P. Bruck, D. Thompson and S. Winstein, *Chemistry and Industry* 405, (1960).

V

III-OBs

X

VII IV

VI VIII

with 7-norbornyl[9] and which would give rise to V in the present instance.

When the shifting hydrogen atom in III-OBs is replaced by deuterium, an appreciable kinetic isotope factor is observed. Deuterated III-OH containing 86% of the theoretical 8 deuterium atoms per molecule was prepared through the Diels–Alder reaction between hexachlorocyclopentadiene and *anti*-7-norbornenol, dechlorination with lithium and *t*-BuOD in tetrahydrofuran,[8] and hydrogenation with deuterium over palladium on charcoal. The (k_H/k_D) isotope factor in acetolysis at 100°, obtained with the deuterated III-OBs, was 1.24. The composition of the acetolysis product from the deuterated material was the same as that from ordinary III-OBs (Table I).

TABLE I
PRODUCTS OF SOLVOLYSIS

ROBs	Temp., °C.	Product, % ±0.3 VII	VIII
AcOH; 0.01 M NaOAc			
VII	50	96.1	3.9
VIII	50	96.3	3.7
VII	100	92.7	7.3
III	100	82.5	17.5
III-D$_8$	100	82.5	17.5
90% Me$_2$CO			
VII	50	94.1	5.9
VIII	50	94.1	5 9
70% Me$_2$CO; 0.02 M NaOAc			
III	100	80.5	19.5

The two solvolysis products, VII-OAc and VIII-OAc, or VII–OH and VIII–OH, are also obtained from the related bromobenzenesulfonates,[5] VII-OBs and VIII-OBs. However, these derivatives give rise to a much smaller proportion of the *endo-exo*-fused[10] VIII-product, only several per cent. of this

(9) S. Winstein, F. Gadient, E. T. Stafford and P. E. Klinedinst, Jr., This Journal, **80**, 5805 (1958).

(10) See also S. Cristol, W. Seifert and S. B. Soloway, *ibid.*, **82**,

being formed from the norbornyl-type[11] non-classical carbonium ion VI (Table I).

Inspection of models, as well as the occurrence of an anomalously high C–H stretching frequency[4] in the infrared spectrum of III-OH, makes it evident that non-bonded H-H distances between the methano-carbon atom and C-6 or C-7 of the decahydrodimethanonaphthalene system III-OH are much below ordinary van der Waals distances. Thus, great steric acceleration of ionization of III-OBs could be expected. The observed rate factor between III-OBs and 7-norbornyl is larger than that observed in the accelerated solvolysis of cyclodecyl toluenesulfonate[12] and smaller than the one observed for the tri-t-butylcarbinyl system.[13] For completely rearranging cases, it is not easy to distinguish[13,14] between steric acceleration without neighboring group participation in the rate-determining step, and that which involves neighboring group participation and which we include, therefore,

under anchimeric acceleration. In the present case, neither the large rate factor, nor even the isotope factor,[15] are as convincing as the absence of products like V that hydrogen participation is occurring in the ionization step for III-OBs. Also, the geometry of III-OBs is such that it seems difficult for ionization to occur at Cα without some C–H electron delocalization in the transition state.

The solvolysis products from III-OBs apparently arise mostly from the rearranged norbornyl-type ion VI. However, the distinctly higher proportion of the VIII-structure in the products from III-OBs than from VII-OBs and VIII-OBs, suggests that some of the product arises at a stage earlier than ion VI. One of the simplest possibilities is that a hydrogen-bridged species such as IV intervenes between III-OBs and VI, and this intermediate can either lead to VIII-product or rearrange to VI, this in turn leading to its characteristic mixture of VII plus a little VIII.

235 (1960), and P. Schleyer and M. M. Donaldson, *ibid.*, **82**, 4645 (1960).

(11) S. Winstein and D. S. Trifan, *ibid.*, **71**, 2953 (1949); **74**, 1154 (1952).

(12) R. Heck and V. Prelog, *Helv. Chim. Acta*, **38**, 1541 (1955).

(13) (a) P. D. Bartlett and E. B. Lefferts, THIS JOURNAL, **77**, 2804 (1955); (b) P. D. Bartlett and M. Stiles, *ibid.*, **77**, 2806 (1955).

(14) S. Winstein, *et al.*, *ibid.*, **74**, 1113 (1952).

(15) (a) V. Prelog, *Chimia*, **11**, 257 (1957); (b) L. S. Bartell, *Tetrahedron Letters*, **6**, 13 (1960); (c) K. T. Leffek, J. A. Llewelyn and R. E Robertson, *Chemistry and Industry*, 588 (1960).

DEPARTMENT OF CHEMISTRY   S. WINSTEIN
UNIVERSITY OF CALIFORNIA   ROBERT L. HANSEN
LOS ANGELES 24, CALIFORNIA
RECEIVED OCTOBER 27, 1960

From: *Tetrahedron Letters* **1960,** No. 25, 4–8

An Octahydrodimethanonaphthyl Non-Classical

Homocyclopropenyl Cation[1]

S. Winstein and Robert L. Hansen

Dept. of Chemistry, University of California, Los Angeles, Calif.
(Received 31 October 1960)

In connection with non-classical carbonium ions, system II was of
interest for comparison with the anti-7-norbornenyl[2] analog I and the
unsaturated endo-endo system[3] III. One could anticipate great anchimeric
acceleration of ionization of suitable II-derivatives, with formation of
a relatively unique homocyclopropenyl variety of carbonium ion IV.

Alcohol II-OH has now been prepared through the Diels-Alder condensation of cyclopentadiene with anti-7-norbornenol[2] tetrahydropyranyl
ether[4], b.p. 89-93° (2.5 mm.), n^{25}D 1.4865, under nitrogen at 215° in
the presence of diphenyl amine. Careful hydrolysis of the fraction of
the product with b.p. 105-130° (2.5 mm.), followed by recrystallization
and sublimation, leads to alcohol[4] II-OH, m.p. 108-109°; p-nitrobenzoate[4],
m.p. 131-132°; p-toluenesulfonate[4], m.p. 102.5-103°; p-bromobenzenesulfonate[4] II-OBs, m.p. 96-97° (dec.).

---

[1] Research sponsored by the Office of Ordnance Research, U.S. Army.

[2] (a) S. Winstein, M. Shatavsky, C. Norton and R. B. Woodward, J.
Am. Chem. Soc. 77, 4183 (1955); (b) S. Winstein and M. Shatavsky,
ibid. 78, 592 (1956).

[3] P. Bruck, D. Thompson and S. Winstein, Chemistry and Industry 590
(1960).

[4] A satisfactory C,H-analysis was obtained for this and the other
indicated new compounds here reported.

I   II   III

V-OBs   IV   V-OAc

IVa   IVb

Bromobenzenesulfonate II-OBs is very reactive in acetolysis, the first order rate constant being $(2.38 \pm 0.02) \times 10^{-4}$ sec.$^{-1}$ at 25.0°. Ion pair return accompanies the acetolysis, 12% of a less reactive bromobenzenesulfonate being formed. The acetolysis rate constant of this latter isomer, measured after the solvolysis of II-OBs was complete, was $(8.9 \pm 0.3) \times 10^{-5}$ sec.$^{-1}$ at 75.0°.

The solvolysis product from II-OBs is saturated and consists of a single compound as indicated by vapor phase chromatographic examination

of the acetate (A-OAc) and the derived alcohol[4] (A-OH), m.p. 80.0-81.5°.
The acetolysis rate constant of the bromobenzenesulfonate[4] (A-OBs) of
this latter alcohol, m.p. 112.5-113.8°, is identical with that of the
isomer formed from II-OBs during its acetolysis, being $(9.12 \pm 0.08) \times 10^{-5}$ sec.[5] at 75.0° and $(3.85 \pm 0.04) \times 10^{-6}$ sec.[-1] at 50.4°. Further,
no visible rearrangement occurs in acetolysis of A-OBs, only A-OAc being
regenerated.

It is quite clear that A-OAc and A-OBs, the saturated isomers of
II-OAc and II-OBs formed during acetolysis of II-OBs, have the V-struc-
ture. Thus, bromobenzenesulfonate A-OBs is recovered unchanged from an
18 hour treatment with potassium t-butoxide in refluxing benzene, no
elimination being observed. Under these conditions, the olefinic group
is introduced smoothly into other bicycloheptyl derivatives[5]. Further,
the A-ketone from oxidation of A-OH showed no detectable deuterium exchange on treatment with 0.05 M sodium methoxide in 95% tetrahydrofuran-
deuterium oxide for 51 hours at 50°. Under these conditions, ketone VI,
obtained by oxidation of the corresponding alcohol[6], exchanges rapidly.
The behavior of A-OBs and A-ketone is in accord with the position of the
OBs and ketone groups in structures V-OBs and VII, since these would require a double bond or the enolate ion to be formed at a bridgehead. Finally, the carbon skeleton of V is confirmed by conversion of ketone VII
to hydrocarbon VIII. Treatment of ketone VII with ethylene dithiol under
forcing conditions converts it to an ethylene dithioketal. By Raney
nickel desulfurization the latter is reduced to a saturated hydrocarbon
whose infrared spectrum and vapor phase chromatographic behavior are

---

[5] (a) S. Winstein and E. T. Stafford, J. Am. Chem. Soc. 79, 505 (1957);
(b) S. Winstein and C. Ordronneau, ibid. 82, 2084 (1960); (c) E. T.
Stafford, F. Gadient and R. Hansen, unpublished work.

[6] S. B. Soloway, J. Am. Chem. Soc. 74, 1027 (1952).

VI   VII   VIII

IX   X   XI

identical with those of hydrocarbon[4] VIII obtained by hydrogenation of olefin[7] XI. The latter olefin is the one related to the "twisted" alcohol[3,7]
X, one of the important rearranged saturated products of solvolysis of
system[3] III or bromobenzenesulfonate[7] IX.

While rate of ionization in the II-system is not up to that observed[3]
with III, it is nearly the same as that for anti-7-norbornenyl[2] (I). The
rate constants observed with II-OTs or II-OBs are lower than those for the
anti-7-norbornenyl analogs by a factor of only ca. 4. Thus, II-OBs ionizes more rapidly than 7-norbornyl[2,5c] bromobenzenesulfonate by the very
large factor of 10^{11}.

The anchimerically accelerated ionization of II-OBs presumably leads
to the non-classical cationic structure IV, which may be regarded as a
cyclopropenyl cation in which 3-carbon segments have been inserted in each
of two sides. The homoconjugation in ion IV, involving electron delocali-

[7] L. de Vries and S. Winstein, *ibid*. in press.

zation across intervening carbon atoms[8], is wave-mechanically analogous to that in cyclopropenyl[9], except that 1,3- as well as 1,2-overlap and exchange integrals are involved. As illustrated in IVa, the axes of the p-orbitals on the three cationic carbon atoms are each turned ca. 90° from their orientation in cyclopropenyl. The situation is quite analogous in the non-classical cation described by Leal and Pettit[10].

The simplest mechanism of formation of the single solvolysis product from II-OBs and V-OBs involves solvent attack on carbon atoms C-6 and C-7 of ion IV, rather than on a further rearranged species such as IVb. This point is subject to stereochemical check, so the stereochemistry of solvolysis of V-OBs is being examined.

---

[8] (a) M. Simonetta and S. Winstein, ibid. 76, 18 (1954); (b) S. Winstein, ibid. 81, 6524 (1959).

[9] (a) E. Hückel, Z. Physik 70, 204 (1931); (b) J. D. Roberts, A. Streitwieser, Jr., and C. M. Regan, J. Am. Chem. Soc. 74, 4579 (1952); (c) W. G. Woods, R. A. Carboni and J. D. Roberts, ibid. 78, 5653 (1956).

[10] G. Leal and R. Pettit, ibid. 81, 3160 (1959).

49, 50 | Bicyclooctyl Derivatives

Papers 49 and 50 supplement the work on the norbornyl cation in an important way. A stable "classical" norbornyl cation from optically active *exo*-2-norbornyl bromobenzenesulfonate would retain its optical activity, whereas the actual product is fully racemized. On the other hand, a "classical" ion (G) from optically active 2-bicyclo(2.2.2)octyl bromobenzenesulfonate would have a plane of symmetry and should lead to racemized product or, if it behaved like most open-chained reactive carbonium ions, to some preponderance of inversion of configuration. In fact, as found by Walborsky, Baum, and Youssef (Paper No. 49), there is a preponderance of retention over inversion. The bridged ion which explains the stereochemical result also predicts that nucleophilic attack at the non-equivalent charged positions should lead to a mixture of bicyclo(2.2.2)octyl and *exo*(*"trans"*)-2-bicyclo(3.2.1)octyl product, a fact also verified in Papers 49 and 50.

In the 2-bicyclo(3.2.1)octyl bromobenzenesulfonates we have a pair of epimers (A and B) related to the same "classical" ion, C. If such an ion as C were intermediate in solvolysis these two esters should undergo easy interconversion and should both lead to mixtures of *endo*- and *exo*-alcohols or acetates. Instead of this, the *exo*-sulfonate is rapidly interconverted with the 2-bicyclo(2.2.2) isomer (F) but yields less than 1% of *endo* product in acetic acid and none in aqueous acetone.[1,2] More recent careful studies of this system as generated by direct solvolysis[1,2] and by the ring-enlargement route from deamination of *endo*- and *exo*-2-

[1] H. M. Walborsky, J. Webb, and C. G. Pitt, *J. Org. Chem.* **28**, 3214 (1963).
[2] G. N. Fickes, Ph.D. Thesis, University of Wisconsin, 1965.

A   D   D   F

C   G

B (dextro)   E   B (levo)

aminomethylnorbornane[3,4,5] have shown that there is competition between the processes to be expected of classical and of nonclassical intermediates. The solvolysis of optically active *endo*-2-sulfonate B, unlike that of the *exo,* leads to totally racemic *endo*-acetate as demanded by the plane-symmetrical ion E,[2] but with extensive crossing over into *exo* and bicyclo(2.2.2)octyl products A and F as if the classical species C were readily accessible from E. Optically active F sulfonate leads to more racemization than does A sulfonate, while the F acetate is always more racemized than the A acetate from a common active source. These facts are interpreted[2,4] as indicating that the occurrence of the symmetrical classical ion G provides additional racemization beyond that which Paper No. 23 leads us to expect from a 7,2-hydride shift:

[3] J. A. Berson and P. Reynolds-Warnhoff, *J. Am. Chem. Soc.* **86**, 595 (1964).

[4] J. A. Berson and D. Willner, *ibid.,* **86**, 609 (1964).

[5] J. A. Berson in deMayo, *Molecular Rearrangements* (Interscience, New York, 1963), Chapter 3.

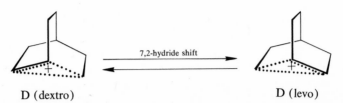

D (dextro)   D (levo)

The disparity between the amounts of racemization in F and A acetates appears to be much greater (3-fold or more)[4] in the ring enlargement route than in solvolysis (about 10%).[2]

From: *J. Am. Chem. Soc.* **83**, 988–93 (1961)

[CONTRIBUTION FROM THE CHEMISTRY DEPARTMENT, THE FLORIDA STATE UNIVERSITY, TALLAHASSEE, FLA.]

Acetolysis of Bicyclo[2.2.2]octyl-2 p-Bromobenzenesulfonate and the Absolute Configurations of Bicyclo[2.2.2]octanol-2 and cis- and trans-Bicyclo[3.2.1]octanol-2

BY H. M. WALBORSKY, M. E. BAUM AND A. A. YOUSSEF

RECEIVED OCTOBER 7, 1960

The titrimetric and polarimetric acetolysis rates of bicyclo[2.2.2]octyl-2 p-bromobenzenesulfonate have been measured at 25° and found to be 9.07×10^{-6} and 9.4×10^{-6} sec.$^{-1}$, respectively. The acetolysis product was shown to contain, besides bicyclo[2.2.2]octyl-2 acetate, $35 \pm 3\%$ of the rearranged bicyclo[3.2.1]octyl-2 acetate. The residual activity found in the acetolysis product of the optically active bicyclo[2.2.2]octyl-2 p-bromobenzenesulfonate was shown to reside in both the rearranged and unrearranged alcohols. Retention of activity and configuration in the unrearranged alcohol is discussed in terms of non-classical ion formation. On the basis of the negative Cotton effect exhibited by (−)-bicyclo-[3.2.1]octanone-2 and by the application of the Octant rule, absolute configurations have been assigned to (2S)-(+)-bicyclo-[2.2.2]octanol-2,(1R:2S:5R)-(−)-cis-bicyclo[3.2.1]octanol-2 and (1R:2R:5R)-(−)-trans-bicyclo[3.2.1]octanol-2.

Introduction

The bridged-ion intermediate was originally postulated by Wilson[1] for the transformation of camphene hydrochloride to isobornyl chloride. Subsequent work on the norbornane derivatives gave support to this hypothesis. It was shown that in the acetolysis of optically active *exo-*[2] and *endo*-norbornyl p-bromobenzenesulfonate (I)[3] both compounds produced racemic *exo*-norbornyl acetate (IV). This result coupled with the observation that the *exo* isomer solvolyzed 350 times faster than the *endo* was interpreted as evidence for the briged-ion intermediate II.

The skeletal rearrangement (I→IV) implied in the above solvolysis was investigated[4] by tagging the carbon atoms at positions 2 and 3. The results of this experiment demonstrated that rearrangement did occur but that it was more extensive than expected from a bridged-ion such as II. These results could be rationalized by assuming that 55% of the reaction proceeded by II, and 45% by III. The bridged ion III can lead to a 1,3-hydride shift.

The above work prompted the investigation of the analogous bicyclo(2.2.2)octane derivative (V). This system has a number of unique features. In

the first place, if a bridged-ion comparable to II is formed, this ion (VI), in contrast to II, does not possess a plane of symmetry. The bridged ion VII which is analogous to the one proposed by Roberts does, however, possess a plane of symmetry. Secondly, any skeletal rearrangement leads to the formation of an entirely different ring system: a bicyclo(3.2.1)octane derivative (VIII). Finally, this system is essentially free of angle strain, whereas the norbornane system is not.[5] A study of the solvolysis of racemic and optically active V was undertaken to determine the effect of this bridged bicyclic system on the rates as well as on the products of this reaction.

Results

Titrimetric Rates.—Bicyclo(2.2.2)octanol-2 and the p-bromobenzenesulfonate ester were prepared as previously described.[6] The solvolysis was conducted in acetic acid, freed of water by reaction with acetic anhydride, and containing sufficient sodium acetate to neutralize the p-bromobenzene-

(1) T. P. Nevell, E. de Salas and C. L. Wilson, *J. Chem. Soc.*, 1188 (1939).

(2) S. Winstein and D. Trifan, *J. Am. Chem. Soc.*, **71**, 2953 (1949).

(3) S. Winstein and D. Trifan, *ibid.*, **74**, 1147, 1154 (1952).

(4) J. D. Roberts, C. C. Lee and W. H. Saunders, Jr., *ibid.*, **76**, 4501 (1954).

(5) R. B. Turner, W. R. Meador and R. G. Winkler, *ibid.*, **79**, 4116 (1957).

(6) H. M. Walborsky and D. F. Loncrini, *ibid.*, **76**, 5396 (1954).

sulfonic acid which is liberated during the reaction. The unreacted sodium acetate was titrated with perchloric acid at appropriate time intervals, and the data plotted. The first-order rate constants for the solvolysis of bicyclo(2.2.2)octyl-2 *p*-bromobenzenesulfonate as well as for the comparison compounds are collected in Table I, which lists also the derived values of the thermodynamic quantities of activation, $\Delta H^{\ddagger}$ and $\Delta S^{\ddagger}$. The relative rates at 25° are also shown, taking that of cyclohexyl *p*-bromobenzenesulfonate as unity.

TABLE I

SPECIFIC RATE CONSTANTS[a] AND ACTIVATION PARAMETERS

p-Bromoben- zenesulfonate	Temp., °C.	k_1 sec.$^{-1}$	$\Delta H^{\ddagger}$, kcal./ mole	$\Delta S^{\ddagger}$, e.u.	Relative rate
Bicyclo(2.2.2)- octyl-2	25.00	9.07×10^{-6}	24.6	1.2	53.0
Bicyclo(2.2.2)- octyl-2	50.97	2.61×10^{-4}			
endo-Bicyclo- (2.2.1)hep- tyl-2[b]	25.00	2.52×10^{-7}	26.0	−1.5	1.5
exo-Bicyclo- (2.2.1)hep- tyl-2[b]	24.96	8.79×10^{-6}			514.0
Cyclohexyl[b]	25.00	1.71×10^{-7}	26.8	0.4	1.0
Cyclopentyl[c]	25.00	6.28×10^{-6}	22.7	−6.3	37.0

[a] All solvolyses were conducted in acetic acid. [b] Ref. 3. [c] H. C. Brown and G. Ham, *J. Am. Chem. Soc.*, **78**, 2735 (1956).

Product Analysis.—Infrared analysis and vapor phase chromatography techniques were used to determine the product composition. The acetate mixture did not lend itself to analysis by either of these methods and was therefore reduced by lithium aluminum hydride to the corresponding alcohols.

The infrared analysis of the alcohol mixture provided only limited information. The analysis showed that the product did not contain any *cis*-bicyclo(3.2.1)octanol-2[7] as evidenced by the absence of a characteristic absorption band[8] at 1065 cm.$^{-1}$. This method could not be used, with certainty, to distinguish between *trans*-bicyclo-(3.2.1)octanol-2[7] and bicyclo(2.2.2)octanol-2.

After much trial and error it was found that a 30% glycerol-on-chromosorb column was effective in separating the mixture of alcohols by vapor phase chromatography. Analysis by this procedure showed the mixture to consist of 35 ± 3% of *trans*-bicyclo(3.2.1)octanol-2 and 65 ± 3% of bicyclo(2.2.2)octanol-2. No *cis*-bicyclo(3.2.1)octanol-2 could be detected.

Polarimetric Rate.—For the work with active *p*-bromobenzenesulfonate esters, bicyclo(2.2.2)octanol-2 was converted to the acid phthalate and resolved *via* its brucine salt to yield upon saponification optically active bicyclo(2.2.2)octanol-2, $(\alpha)^{25}$D − 7.45 and (+)6.8°, respectively. The (−)-alcohol was converted to the *p*-bromobenzenesulfonate ester, $[\alpha]^{25}$D +1.2°.

(7) *cis* and *trans* refers to the position of the substituent with respect to the *ethylene* bridge.

(8) A. A. Youssef, M. E. Baum and H. M. Walborsky, *J. Am. Chem. Soc.*, **81**, 4709 (1959).

The polarimetric rate of solvolysis was determined under comparable conditions to that of the titrimetric rate at 25°. When (−)-bicyclo-(2.2.2)-octyl-2 *p*-bromobenzenesulfonate was used the "infinity" reading showed some residual activity (α = +0.09°) (*vide infra*). The data were plotted (see Experimental) and the polarimetric rate constant was calculated to be 9.4 ± 1.4 × 10^{-6} sec.$^{-1}$, which is similar to the titrimetric rate constant, 9.07 ± 0.25 × 10^{-6} sec.$^{-1}$.

Product Analysis.—As noted above the infinity titer showed some residual activity. The solvolysis was run on a larger scale and the mixture of acetates was isolated in 84% yield. The infrared spectrum of the product was identical to that obtained from the solvolysis of the racemic *p*-bromobenzenesulfonate ester. The solvolysis product showed a rotation of $[\alpha]^{25}$D +0.215° (neat). The question arises as to where this activity resides: is it in the bicyclo(2.2.2)octyl-2 acetate or in the *trans*-bicyclo(3.2.1)octyl-2 acetate, or in both? In order to gain some insight into this question it was decided to reduce the solvolysis mixture to the corresponding alcohol by lithium aluminum hydride and then oxidize the alcohol mixture to the corresponding ketones. The mixture of semicarbazones obtained from the oxidation product mixture had a rotation of $[\alpha]^{25}$D +0.97° (chloroform, *c* 4.0) after two crystallizations from acetonitrile. This optical activity can only reside in the semicarbazone of bicyclo(3.2.1)octanone-2 since the bicyclo(2.2.2)octanone-2 has a plane of symmetry.

When the enantiomorph of the above *p*-bromobenzenesulfonate ester was solvolyzed, reduced and oxidized, the semicarbazone obtained had a rotation equivalent in magnitude but opposite in sign, $[\alpha]^{25}$D −0.92° chloroform, (*c* 3.4).

In order to determine whether the bicyclo-(2.2.2)octanol-2 retained any activity it was necessary to separate this mixture by v.p.c. on a preparative scale. The retention times of the alcohols in this mixture are only 1.7 minutes apart and the peaks overlapped considerably. A mixture (750 mg., $[\alpha]^{25}$D +3.41°) was chromatographed, to yield 6 mg. of 96% pure bicyclo(2.2.2)octanol-2, which was dextrorotatory. The observed rotation corresponds to 82 ± 15% retention of activity and configuration (see Experimental).

The other component of the mixture, *trans*-bicyclo(3.2.1)octanol-2, was isolated (4 mg.) in 98% purity and was levorotatory.

Discussion

In the bicyclo(2.2.1)heptyl systems rate enhancement has been observed in the solvolysis of the *exo* and *endo* isomers. That the *exo* isomer solvolyzed faster than the *endo* has been interpreted in terms of carbon participation[9] and/or relief of steric strain.[9,10] The general topic has been discussed in a recent review.[11]

(9) S. Winstein, B. K. Morse, E. Grunwald, H. W. Jones, J. Corse, D. Trifan and H. Marshall, *ibid.*, **74**, 1127 (1952).

(10) See H. C. Brown, *Science*, **103**, 385 (1949); H. C. Brown and R. S. Fletcher, *J. Am. Chem. Soc.*, **71**, 1845 (1949), for a general discussion.

(11) A. Streitwieser, Jr., *Chem. Revs.*, **56**, 571 (1956).

Unfortunately *exo* and *endo* isomerism is not possible in the bicyclo(2.2.2)octyl system and therefore a direct test of the above phenomenon cannot be made. From the data in Table I it can be argued that very little, if any, rate enhancement is occurring. At 25° the acetolysis of bicyclo-(2.2.2)octyl-2 *p*-bromobenzenesulfonate is 53 times faster than the cyclohexyl *p*-bromobenzenesulfonate and the cyclopentyl *p*-bromobenzenesulfonate is 37 times faster than the cyclohexyl derivative. These results can be rationalized on the basis of I-strain as applied to 5- and 6-membered rings.[12] On the other hand, lack of significant rate enhancement need not necessarily exclude carbon participation in the transition state.[13] It should be noted that product analysis shows that 35% of the products is rearranged bicyclo(3.2.1)octanol-2.

In order to ascertain whether or not carbon participation or non-classical ion formation is occurring to any appreciable extent, the solvolysis of the optically active bicyclo(2.2.2)octyl-2 *p*-bromobenzenesulfonate was undertaken to determine the stereochemical course of the reaction. The acetolysis of the optically active *p*-bromobenzenesulfonate ester yielded an optically active acetate mixture which was reduced to the corresponding optically active alcohols. The alcohol mixture consisted of 65% bicyclo(2.2.2)octanol-2 and 35% *trans*-bicyclo(3.2.1)octanol-2. Important to note is the complete absence of *cis*-bicyclo(3.2.1)-octanol-2. It has been previously demonstrated that the *cis*-bicyclo(3.2.1)octanol-2 is the thermodynamically more stable isomer.[8] The complete absence of the *cis* isomer provides evidence that rearrangement to an open carbonium ion is unlikely since under these circumstances one would expect to obtain a mixture consisting largely of the *cis* isomer. The observation that only the *trans*

is formed is consistent with the prediction based on the formation of a non-classical ion. Since the non-classical ion is dissymmetric, the product formed, besides being *trans*, should also be optically active. Oxidation of the alcohol mixture did indeed produce an optically active ketone. The activity could only reside in the bicyclo(3.2.1)octanone-2, since the bicyclo(2.2.2)octanone-2 possesses a plane of symmetry.

The non-classical ion intermediate requires that the bicyclo(2.2.2)octanol-2 portion of the solvolysis product should be active, and that furthermore the configuration should be retained. Separation of the alcohol mixture by vapor phase chromatography yielded a sample of bicyclo(2.2.2) octanol of 96% purity whose sign of rotation showed that retention of configuration had occurred and whose magnitude of rotation indicated the possibility of complete retention. Unfortunately, the size of the sample used and the small rotation observed permits us only to say that retention occurred to the extent of $82 \pm 15\%$. This datum cannot exclude the open carbonium ion entirely, but it certainly permits one to say that if the open carbonium plays a role, it is only to a minor extent and that the non-classical or bridged-ion intermediate plays the major role in the reaction. The rate of solvolysis was also followed by polarimetric means and it was observed that the polarimetric rate is very similar to the titrimetric rate. Whether internal return occurs or not cannot be measured by our limited data, but may well prove to be important in this reaction, as it has in others.[8]

Our data also do not permit us to draw any conclusions with regard to C_6-C_2 hydrogen shifts since the amount of retention of optical activity in the bicyclo(2.2.2)octanol-2 could accommodate the occurrence of a hydride shift leading to a small amount of racemization

Absolute Configurations:

(1R:2R:5R)-(−)-*trans*

(1R:5R)(−) (1R:2S:5R)-(−)-*cis* (2S)-(+)

A sample of *cis*-bicyclo(3.2.1)octanol-2 was converted to the acid phthalate and resolved *via* its brucine salt to yield after hydrolysis (−)-*cis*-bicyclo(3.2.1)octanol-2, $[\alpha]^{25}D -8.2°$. The alcohol was oxidized by chromic anhydride to the ketone, $[\alpha]^{24}D -55°$. It will be recalled that (−)-*trans*-bicyclo(3.2.1)octanol-2 was isolated from the solvolysis product of the *p*-bromobenzenesulfonate ester of (+)-bicyclo(2.2.2)octanol-2 and that oxidation of this rearranged alcohol gave the (−)-ketone, isolated as its semicarbazone derivative.

The optical rotatory dispersion of the (−)-bicyclo(3.2.1)octanone-2 (Fig. 1) shows that this ketone exhibits a negative cotton effect. Application of the octant rule[14] provides one with the absolute configuration of the (−)-ketone as 1R:5R. Since the (−)-*cis*-and (−)-*trans*-bicyclo(3.2.1)octanol-2 have been oxidized to the (−)-ketone their absolute configurations are 1R:2S:5R and 1R:2R:5R, respectively.

(12) H. C. Brown and G. Ham, *J. Am. Chem. Soc.*, **78**, 2735 (1956).

(13) M. J. S. Dewar, *Ann. Reports*, **48**, 113 (1951).

(14) W. Moffit, A. Moscowitz, R. B. Woodward, W. Klyne and C. Djerassi, unpublished work cited by C. Djerassi in "Optical Rotatory Dispersion," McGraw–Hill Book Co., Inc., New York, N. Y., 1960.

Based on the mechanism proposed for the rearrangement of the *p*-bromobenzenesulfonate ester of (+)-bicyclo(2.2.2)octanol-2 to (−)-*trans*-bicyclo(3.2.1)octanol-2, the absolute configuration of (+)-bicyclo(2.2.2)octanol-2 is assigned the 2S configuration.

Acknowledgment.—This work was supported in part by research grant CY-4065, National Institutes of Health, Public Health Service. We wish to thank Dr. M. O'Dwyer for obtaining the rotatory dispersion data and Prof. E. Grunwald for many helpful discussions.

Experimental[15]

Bicyclo(2,2,2)octene-2 was prepared by condensation of 1,3-cyclohexadiene and ethylene following the procedure described by Walborsky and Loncrini.[6]

Water-free Peracetic Acid.[16]—Phosphorus pentoxide (120 g.) was suspended in 500 ml. of anhydrous benzene and cooled in ice. Peracetic acid (30%, 150 ml.) was added carefully with stirring and cooling. The cold solution was filtered and stored in the ice-box until used.

2,3-Epoxybicyclo(2.2.2)octane.[6]—To 50 g. of bicyclo-(2.2.2)octene-2 and 5 g. of anhydrous sodium acetate in 125 ml. of anhydrous benzene was slowly added 500 ml. of anhydrous peracetic acid in benzene over a period of 2 hours. The temperature of the mixture was kept below 20° during the addition. The reaction mixture was allowed to remain at room temperature for 2 hours, freed from excess of peracetic acid by washing with dil. alkali, water and dried over anhydrous sodium sulfate. Evaporation of the solvent *in vacuo* gave 50 g. (87%) of product which was purified by sublimation; m.p. 190–192° (s.t.).

Bicyclo(2.2.2)octanol-2.[6]—2,3-Epoxybicyclo(2.2.2) octane (46 g.) was reduced by lithium aluminum hydride in the usual manner. The best yield was obtained when the decomposition was effected with ammonium chloride solution. Working up the reaction mixture gave the alcohol 45 g. (95%), m.p. 208–210° (s.t.). The *p*-nitrobenzoate, m.p. 96–98°, the *p*-bromobenzenesulfonate ester,[6] m.p. 80–81° and the acetate,[6] b.p. 105° at 20 mm., 61–62° (2 mm.), n^{25}D 1.4705, were prepared.

Bicyclo(2.2.2)octyl-2 Acid Phthalate.—Bicyclo(2.2.2)-octanol-2 (30 g., 0.238 mole) was mixed with an equimolar quantity of resublimed phthalic anhydride (35.2 g.) and the mixture dissolved in 90 ml. of anhydrous pyridine. After being heated in an oil-bath at 100° for 4.5 hours, the reaction mixture was poured into 500 ml. of cold water and extracted thoroughly with benzene. The combined benzene extract was washed several times with 10% sulfuric acid, water, and dried over anhydrous sodium sulfate. Evaporation of the solvent gave a solid (47.6 g., 70% yield) which was recrystallized from benzene and few drops of low boiling point petroleum ether; m.p. 155°.

Anal. Calcd. for $C_{16}H_{18}O_4$: C, 70.05; H, 6.61. Found: C, 70.06; H, 6.70.

Product Analysis in the Solvolysis of Bicyclo(2.2.2)-octyl-2-*p*-Bromobenzenesulfonate.—Pure bicyclo(2.2.2)-octyl-2 *p*-bromobenzenesulfonate (6 g., 0.0173 mole) was allowed to react in 550 ml. of dry glacial acetic acid containing sodium acetate (0.0313 *M*) for 600 minutes (*ca.* 12 half-lives) at 50°. The cooled solution was diluted with 1.5 l. of water and extracted three times with 200-ml. portions of pentane. The aqueous layer was diluted again with 1 l. of water and extracted similarly with pentane. The combined pentane extract was washed thoroughly with water, allowed to stand for 2 hours over anhydrous sodium carbonate and then dried over anhydrous sodium sulfate. The pentane solvent was stripped through a 12″ column and the residue was distilled without an attempt at fractionation, to give a colorless liquid (2.4 g., 82.7%), b.p. 60–61° (2 mm.), n^{25}D 1.4702.

Reduction of the Acetolysis Product.—To a slurry of 1.1 g. of lithium aluminum hydride in 25 ml. of anhydrous ether was added a solution of 2.0 g. (0.00119 mole) of the solvolysis acetate in 15 ml. of ether and allowed to stir at room

(15) Melting points and boiling points are uncorrected. Analyses were performed by E. Thommen, Basel, Switzerland.

(16) L. Horner and E. Jurgens, *Ber.*, **90**, 2184 (1957).

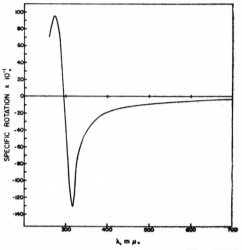

Fig. 1.—Rotatory dispersion curve of (−)-bicyclo[3.2.1]-octanone-2 (dioxane).

temperature for 30 hours. The reaction mixture was decomposed carefully with water and worked up in the usual manner to give 1.3 g. (85%) of the solvolysis alcohol, m.p. 195–206° (s.t.).

Analysis of the Alcohols by Vapor Phase Chromatography.—The retention times of pure *trans*-bicyclo(3.2.1)octanol-2 and pure bicyclo(2.2.2)-octanol-2, on a 3-ft. 30% glycerol-on-chromosorb column, were found to be 13.9 and 15.6 minutes, respectively. The optimum resolution was found to be at 93° with a flow rate of 200 ml./min. of helium gas as a carrier.

The alcohol from the solvolysis reaction was dissolved in absolute ethanol and passed through the column under the above conditions. Two peaks were obtained, beside the air and the solvent peaks, at 13.9 and 15.6 minutes, which overlapped partially. The areas under the two peaks were traced and their ratios were determined by weighing and by the use of a planimeter. The percentage of *trans*-bicyclo(3.2.1) octanol-2 from three different runs was 35 ± 3%.

Resolution of Bicyclo(2.2.2)octyl-2 Acid Phthalate.—Racemic bicyclo(2.2.2)octyl-2 acid phthalate (47 g.) was dissolved in a minimum of hot ethyl acetate and an equivalent amount of brucine was added. After standing overnight, feather-like crystals started to separate and after three days a total of 35 g. of the salt were filtered off. Another 23 g. separated out which was crystallized from ethyl acetate and combined with the first crop. The combined amount of the brucine salt was then recrystallized from ethyl acetate several times until a constant melting point, 135–145°, and a constant degree of rotation were obtained. The rotations observed for three consecutive crystallizations were, [α]^{25}D −25.90°, −26.14° and −26.70° (chloroform; *c*, 0.12, 0.15, 0.14), respectively. The amount of the brucine salt at this stage decreased to 47 g.

The brucine salt (47 g.) was dissolved in benzene and shaken three times with 50-ml. portions of 2 *N* hydrochloric acid. The benzene layer was washed with water and extracted with sodium bicarbonate solution. Acidification of the cold aqueous solution with cold dilute sulfuric acid liberated the acid phthalate which was filtered and dried. A total of 19 g. was recovered, m.p. 150–155°, [α]^{25}D −6.40° (chloroform, *c* 0.52).

The original ethyl acetate mother liquor which contained the other diasteroisomer was decomposed with hydrochloric acid and purified through the sodium salt as described above to give the enantiomorphic acid phthalate enantiomorph (15 g.).

Several fractional crystallizations of the individual enantiomorphs were carried out with each of the partially resolved acid phthalates until a constant melting point, 157–158°, and a constant degree of rotation was achieved.

In this manner, 15.5 g. of levorotatory bicyclo(2.2.2)octyl-2 acid phthalate $[\alpha]^{25}D$ −7.03° (chloroform, c 0.521), and 8 g. of the dextrorotatory enantiomorph $[\alpha]^{25}D$ + 6.86° (chloroform, c 0.643), were obtained.

Anal. Calcd. for $C_{16}H_{18}O_4$: C, 70.05; H, 6.61. Found: C, 70.31; H, 6.80.

Conversion of Bicyclo(2.2.2)octyl-2 Acid Phthalates Enantiomorphs to the Corresponding Alcohols.—In a typical experiment 8.3 g. of optically pure (−)-bicyclo-(2.2.2)octyl-2 acid phthalate, m.p. 157–158°, was dissolved in a solution of 10 g. of sodium hydroxide in 75 ml. of water and steam distilled. The liberated alcohol was collected together with *ca.* 200 ml. of water. The solid alcohol (2.5 g.) was filtered off and the aqueous solution after being saturated with sodium chloride, was extracted 4 times with 50-ml. portions of pentane. The combined pentane extract was washed with water and dried over anhydrous sodium sulfate. Evaporation of the solvent *in vacuo* gave 1.1 g. of additional alcohol, a total of 3.6 g. (94%), m.p. 210–211°. The alcohol was purified by sublimation and crystallization from pentane; m.p. 216–217° (s.t.), $[\alpha]^{25}D$ −7.45° (chloroform, c 0.750).

Similarly, 7 g. of optically pure bicyclo(2.2.2)octyl-2 acid phthalate (+) was converted to the corresponding alcohol, $[\alpha]^{25}D$ +6.80° (chloroform, c 0.615).

Anal. Calcd. for $C_8H_{14}O$: C, 76.12; H, 11.18. Found: C, 76.19; H, 11.01.

(+)-Bicyclo(2.2.2)octyl-2 *p*-Bromobenzenesulfonate.—To 1.5 g. of optically pure (−)-bicyclo(2.2.2)octanol-2 dissolved in 10 ml. of anhydrous pyridine was added gradually and with cooling and stirring 3.1 g. of recrystallized and dried *p*-bromobenzenesulfonyl chloride. After being left in the ice-box for 65 hours, the reaction mixture was poured on ice, and the separated crystalline solid (3.8 g., 93%) was filtered and dried. After three crystallizations from low-boiling petroleum ether, it gave m.p. 88–88.5°, $[\alpha]^{25}D$ + 1.2° (glacial acetic acid, c 1.40).

Anal. Calcd. for $C_{14}H_{17}O_3Br$: C, 48.70; H, 4.96. Found: C, 48.49; H, 5.05.

When the above reaction was repeated with 0.4 g. of the alcohol and the reaction mixture in pyridine was left only 20 hours, bicyclo(2.2.2)-octyl-2 *p*-bromobenzenesulfonate was obtained in 72.7% yield with an identical activity.

(+)-Bicyclo(2.2.2)octyl-2 Acetate.—Optically pure (+)-bicyclo(2.2.2)octanol-2 (1.5 g.) was dissolved in a mixture of 10 ml. of redistilled acetic anhydride and 15 ml. of glacial acetic acid and heated in an oil-bath at 75° for 7 hours. The reaction mixture was poured on ice and extracted 4 times with 50-ml. portions of ether. The combined ethereal extract was washed with water, and with a saturated solution of sodium bicarbonate and dried over anhydrous sodium sulfate. The solvent was stripped through a fractionating column and the residue was distilled *in vacuo* to give 1.8 g. (90%) of (+)-bicyclo(2.2.2)octyl-2 acetate, b.p. 58–59° (2 mm.), $[\alpha]^{25}D$ +4.03° (neat), $n^{25}D$ 1.4705.

Anal. Calcd. for $C_{10}H_{16}O_2$: C, 71.37; H, 9.59. Found: C, 71.23; H, 9.56.

Acetolysis of (−)-Bicyclo(2.2.2)octyl-2 *p*-Bromobenzenesulfonate in Glacial Acetic Acid.—Optically pure (−)-bicyclo(2.2.2)octyl-2 *p*-bromobenzenesulfonate (7 g.) was solvolyzed in 800 ml. of dry glacial acetic acid containing sodium acetate (0.032 *M*) in a bath at 50° for 15 hours. The reaction mixture was worked up in a similar manner to that of the racemic compound. The resulting acetate (2.9 g., 84%) had b.p. 60° at 2 mm., $n^{25}D$ 1.4702, $[\alpha]^{25}D$ +0.215° (neat).

Product Analysis.—The mixture of (+)-acetates obtained from the solvolysis of (−)-bicyclo(2.2.2)octyl-2 *p*-bromobenzenesulfonate was reduced to the corresponding alcohols by lithium aluminum hydride in the usual manner. The product of the reduction was sublimed *in vacuo* without fractionation; m.p. 185–201°, $[\alpha]^{25}D$ +3.41° (chloroform, c 10.0).

The alcohol mixture (0.75 g.) was separated by use of a preparative vapor phase chromatography column[17] employing the same conditions mentioned under analysis of the racemic product. Bicyclo(2.2.2)octanol-2 (6.2 mg., 96 ± 1% pure) and 2 mg. of *trans*-bicyclo(3.2.1)octanol-2 (98 ± 1% pure) were obtained. The activity of the samples

(17) The separation was performed by Dr. W. F. Ulrich, Beckman Instrument Co.

was measured at 25°, with a recording Rudolf optical rotatory dispersion apparatus and using pure dioxane as the solvent.

The 6.2-mg. sample of (+)-bicyclo(2.2.2)octanol-2 was dissolved in 1 ml. of dioxane and the dispersion curve was measured and compared with the curve obtained from an optically pure ($[\alpha]^{25}D$ −7° (CHCl₃)) authentic sample of bicyclo(2.2.2)octanol-2 of an identical concentration. Specific rotations were calculated every 10 mμ in the region 300–600 mμ. for both the authentic sample and the solvolysis alcohol. From these data the percentage retention of activity was determined at each point and then averaged to obtain the average percentage retention. The average mean deviation was determined. The result of this analysis showed that retention of activity had occurred to the extent of 82 ± 15%.

The *trans*-bicyclo(3.2.1)octanol-2 was shown to have negative rotation but, due to the small sample (2 mg.) and the large errors involved, the magnitude of rotation was not determined.

Oxidation of the Solvolysis Alcohols.—The mixture of (+)-alcohols obtained from the reduction of the solvolysis product, without purification, was oxidized by chromic anhydride in acetic acid in the usual manner. The mixture of ketones was steam distilled from the reaction mixture and the distillate was saturated with sodium chloride, extracted thoroughly with ether, the ethereal layer washed and dried over anhydrous sodium sulfate. Evaporation of the solvent *in vacuo* gave the ketones, m.p. 158–60°.

The crude ketone (0.20 g.), in 2 ml. of ethanol was heated for 2 minutes on the steam-bath with semicarbazide hydrochloride (0.30 g.) and sodium acetate (0.30 g.) dissolved in 1 ml. of water. On dilution with water, the semicarbazone precipitated (0.26 g., 90%), m.p. 186–187°. It was recrystallized twice from acetonitrile; m.p. 191–192°, $[\alpha]^{25}D$ −0.97° (chloroform, c 4.00).

Anal. Calcd. for $C_9H_{15}N_3O$: C, 59.64; H, 8.34; N, 23.19. Found: C, 59.38; H, 8.42; N, 23.37.

The same set of experiments were repeated starting with the acetate obtained from the solvolysis of (+)-bicyclo-(2.2.2)octyl-2 brosylate. The resulting semicarbazone gave $[\alpha]^{25}D$ +0.92° (chloroform, c 3.38).

cis-Bicyclo(3.2.1)octyl-2 Acid Phthalate.—*cis*-Bicyclo-(3.2.1)octanol-2 (10 g.) prepared as previously described[8] was converted to the acid phthalate following the procedure used for bicyclo(2.2.2)octyl-2 acid phthalate. Bicyclo-(3.2.1)octyl-2 acid phthalate (17 g.) was recrystallized from benzene–petroleum ether (30–60°); m.p. 114–117°.

Anal. Calcd. for $C_{16}H_{18}O_4$: C, 70.05; H, 6.61. Found: C, 70.31; H, 6.63.

Resolution of *cis*-bicyclo(3.2.1)octyl-2 Acid Phthalate.—The acid phthalate (15 g.) was dissolved in the minimum amount of acetone and an acetone solution of brucine alkaloid (21.5 g., 1 equ.) was added. The salt separated immediately was dissolved in a mixture of acetone and methanol and allowed to stand in the ice-box overnight to yield 23 g. of a crystalline solid, m.p. 120–124°, $[\alpha]^{24}D$ −22.7° (chloroform, c 1.4). After two recrystallizations from 2-butanone and one crystallization from ethyl acetate, 10 g. of the salt was decomposed in the usual manner to give the active acid phthalate (3.5 g.) which was further purified by extraction with a saturated solution of sodium bicarbonate followed by acidification. The acid phthalate had m.p. 107–110°, $[\alpha]^{24}D$ −11.6° (chloroform, c 1.55), and its infrared spectrum was identical with that of the racemic bicyclo(3.2.1)-octyl-2 acid phthalate.

(−)-*cis*-Bicyclo(3.2.1)octanol-2.—Bicyclo(3.2.1)octyl-2 acid phthalate (3 g.) was dissolved in 40 ml. of 10% sodium hydroxide and steam distilled. The distillate was saturated with sodium chloride and extracted thoroughly with ether, washed and dried. Evaporation of the solvent gave the alcohol (0.9 g.), m.p. 178–180° (s.t.), $[\alpha]^{24}D$ −8.2° (chloroform, c 1.4). Vapor phase chromatography showed that active bicyclo(3.2.1)octanol-2 consists of 86 ± 1% of the *cis* isomer. On a 3-ft. glycerol column (30% glycerol-on-chromosorb) at 93° with a helium flow-rate of 200 ml./ min., the *cis* isomer has a retention time of 18.2 minutes.

(−)-Bicyclo(3.2.1)octanone-2.—Active bicyclo(3.2.1)-octanol-2 was oxidized as previously described[8] to the corresponding ketone. The ketone was purified by sublimation and chromatography on an alumina column; m.p. 125–126° (s.t.), $[\alpha]^{24}D$ −55.5° (chloroform, c 4.0), λ_{max}

TABLE II

SOLVOLYSIS OF BICYCLO(2.2.2)OCTYL-2 p-BROMOBENZENE-
SULFONATE[a] AT 25 ± 0.05°

Time, sec.	$(a - x)$	$\frac{2.303}{\log a/a - x}$	k_1, sec.$^{-1} \times 10^6$
0	3.420	0.00	..
25,500	2.722	.2281	8.95
27,200	1.827	.6264	9.32
106,800	1.310	.9599	8.99
169,500	0.756	1.5096	8.91
284,400	0.253	2.6040	9.16

Av. 9.07 ± 0.25

[a] 0.02850 M.

287 (ε 18); RD in dioxane (c 2.73), 23–24°: $(\alpha)_{700}$ −36.5, $(\alpha)_{589}$ − 52, $(\alpha)_{317}$ −1306, $(\alpha)_{275}$ + 949, $(\alpha)_{260}$ +700.

The semicarbazone was prepared in the usual manner,[8] m.p. 167–69°, $(\alpha)_D$ −31.0° (chloroform, c 4.7).

Kinetics: Solvents.—The acetic acid was purified by refluxing with chromic anhydride, azeotropic distillation with benzene and collection of the purified acetic acid. The water content was determined by cryoscopy and sufficient acetic anhydride was added to make the solvent anhydrous and in addition to compensate for the water that is formed when sodium carbonate is allowed to react with acetic acid to make the standardized sodium acetate solution. The concentration of acetic anhydride was further determined by Kilpi's anthranilic acid method.

Titrations.—Analyses were performed with approximately 0.05 N standard perchloric acid and sodium acetate in glacial acetic acid. The standard perchloric acid was prepared from 60% aqueous acid which was compared with Bureau of Standards potassium acid phthalate. The sodium acetate reagent was obtained by dissolving reagent grade sodium carbonate in glacial acetic acid. Titrations were carried out with 5-ml. micro-burets. The best indicator was found to be brom phenol blue (1% solution in glacial acetic acid) and the end-point was approached from the acid side. The standard sodium acetate and perchloric acid were compared from time to time; the perchloric acid titer was found to be constant over a long period of time.

Rate Measurements.—The compound to be solvolyzed was weighed into a volumetric flask and made up to volume with the sodium acetate solutions (0.03–0.04 M). The amount of material used was calculated so that the solution would still contain sodium acetate at the end of the reaction. About 6-ml. portions of the solutions were sealed in ampoules and immersed in a suitable thermostat. At suitable time intervals an ampoule was removed and the reaction was interrupted by immersing it into ice. The ampoule was then brought to room temperature by placing in a beaker containing water, opened and a 5-ml. aliquot was removed, brought to acidity with perchloric acid and then titrated with standard sodium acetate to a bright faint yellow end-point.

First-order rate constants k, where $k = \frac{1}{t} \ln (a/a-x)$, a being the initial concentration in moles/liter of the material, t the elapsed time, and x the concentration of consumed base, were calculated. The results are summarized in the Tables II and III.

Polarimetric Measurements.—Polarimetric determinations carried out in this work were done with the aid of a

TABLE III

SOLVOLYSIS OF BICYCLO(2.2.2)OCTYL-2 p-BROMOBENZENE
SULFONATE[a] AT 50.97 ± 0.05°

Time, sec.	$(a - x)$	$\frac{2.303}{\log a/a - x}$	k_1, sec.$^{-1}$ 10^4
0	4.419	0.00	..
18,000	2.637	.5166	2.87
36,000	1.690	.9613	2.67
54,000	1.105	1.2864	2.57
72,000	0.714	1.8231	2.53
94,800	0.445	2.259	2.42

Av. 2.61 ± 0.26

[a] 0.02838 M.

Bellingham and Stanley model type polarimeter and a 2-dcm. polarimeter tube (unless specified). The measurements were carried out in a completely dark room using the sodium D line (λ 5893 Å.) (unless specified).

Rate of Solvolysis of (−)-Bicyclo(2.2.2)octyl-2 p-Bromobenzenesulfonate.—(−)-Bicyclo(2.2.2)octyl-2-p-bromobenzenesulfonate was weighed in a volumetric flask (high concentration suitable for polarimeter reading) and made up to mark with pure glacial acetic acid containing sodium acetate (calculated to react completely with the liberated p-bromobenzenesulfonic acid). The flask was thermostated in the bath at 25° and at suitable time intervals readings were taken in the following way. The solution was filtered off from the suspended particles by decantation into a specially designed filtration apparatus (which was thermostated during filtration) and a weak pressure of nitrogen was applied. The clear solution was transferred quickly and quantitatively to the polarimeter tube which was also thermostated by having water from the bath circulating around it. The average of ten readings from both sides of the tube was recorded which showed a maximum deviation of ±0.010° from each separate reading. The solution was returned back to the flask and thermostated. The green mercury light with suitable filter was used, and polarimetric rate constants were calculated using the equation

$$2.303 \log 10 \frac{\alpha_0 - \alpha\infty}{\alpha_t - \alpha\infty} = kt$$

Table IV summarizes the results obtained in a typical run.

TABLE IV

RATE OF SOLVOLYSIS OF (−)-BICYCLO(2.2.2)OCTYL-2 p-
BROMOBENZENESULFONATE[a] AT 25 ± 0.05°

Time, sec.	α	$\left(\frac{\alpha\infty - \alpha\infty}{\alpha t - \alpha\infty}\right)$	$\frac{2.303 \log}{\left(\frac{\alpha\infty - \alpha\infty}{\alpha t - \alpha\infty}\right)}$	k_1, sec.$^{-1} \times 10^6$
0	−0.155	1	0	...
13,020	− .128	1.122	0.1152	8.90
28,920	− .97	1.310	.2701	9.30
70,920	− .049	1.760	.5670	8.00
117,120	+ .021	3.550	1.267	10.80
160,120	+ .045	5.440	1.6941	10.60
.....	+ .090	...	....	...

Av. 9.4 ± 1.4

[a] Brosylate = 0.276 M; NaOAc = 0.302 M.

From: *J. Am. Chem. Soc.* **83**, 1397–1401 (1961)

[CONTRIBUTION FROM THE DEPARTMENT OF CHEMISTRY, THE UNIVERSITY OF WISCONSIN, MADISON 6, WIS.]

Ionic Reactions in Bicyclic Systems. II. Carbonium Ion Reactions in Bicyclo[2.2.2]-octane and Bicyclo[3.2.1]octane Derivatives

BY HARLAN L. GOERING AND MARTIN F. SLOAN[1]

RECEIVED SEPTEMBER 24, 1960

Deamination of 2-aminobicyclo[2.2.2]octane (III, X = NH₂) and hydrolysis of the corresponding [2.2.2]bicyclic *p*-toluenesulfonate (III, X = OTs) give mixtures of bicyclo[2.2.2]octan-2-ol (III, X = OH) and *exo*-(*axial*)-bicyclo[3.2.1]-octan-2-ol (IVa, X = OH). The isomeric *endo*-(*equatorial*)-bicyclo[3.2.1]octan-2-ol (IVb, X = OH) is not formed in these reactions. Acetolysis of *equatorial*-bicyclo[3.2.1]octan-2-yl *p*-toluenesulfonate (IVb, X = OTs) proceeds with complete retention of configuration (equatorial acetate is the only substitution product). Acid-catalyzed addition of acetic acid to bicyclo[2.2.2]octene gives a ternary mixture of bicyclo[2.2.2]octan-2-yl, and *axial*- and *equatorial*-bicyclo[3.2.1]octan-2-yl acetates (III, IVa and IVb; X = OAc).

Introduction

Bicyclo[2.2.2]octan-2-yl (III) and *exo*-(*axial*)-bicyclo[3.2.1]octan-2-yl (IVa) systems are related to the same carbonium ion system. The latter can be represented as (a) an equilibrium between the two classical structures I or (b) a bridged "non-classical" cation II. In addition to ionization reactions of 2-substituted bicyclo[2.2.2]- and [3.2.1]-octanes, this carbonium ion system can be produced by protonation of bicyclo[2.2.2]- and [3.2.1]octenes.

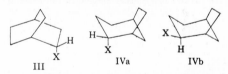

There are only a few reports in the literature concerning product studies of reactions involving this carbonium ion system. It has been observed[2] that 2-bromobicyclo[2.2.2]octane (III, X = Br) rearranges to 2-bromobicyclo[3.2.1]octane (IV, X = Br) when refluxed with silver bromide in carbon tetrachloride. This parallels the report[3] that hydration of bicyclo[2.2.2]octene (V) with aqueous sulfuric acid also results in rearrangement and gives bicyclo[3.2.1]octan-2-ol (IV, X = OH). The configurations of these products were not determined. These results have been quoted as evidence that

bicyclo[3.2.1]octane systems are more stable than the isomeric [2.2.2]bicyclic systems.[4-6]

On the other hand, hydrolysis of bicyclo[2.2.2]-octan-2-yl *p*-bromobenzenesulfonate, bromide and chloride (III; = O₂SC₆H₄Br, Br and Cl) is reported to give the unrearranged product, [bicyclo2.2.2]octan-2-ol (III, X = OH).[4] Nitrous acid deamination of 2-aminobicyclo[2.2.2]octane (III, X = NH₂) also is reported to give the unrearranged alcohol III (X = OH) as the major product.[7] However, in this case it was recognized that the product is not homogeneous.[7] As has been pointed out,[4,5] these results are not necessarily inconsistent with those mentioned in the preceding paragraph. The first two reactions are reversible[8] carbonium ion processes (*i.e.*, thermodynamic control) whereas the latter are irreversible[8] (*i.e.*, kinetic control). These results then suggest that the carbonium ion system gives

(1) Wisconsin Alumni Research Foundation Fellow 1956–1958; National Science Foundation Fellow 1958–1960.

(2) W. E. Doering and M. Farber, *J. Am. Chem. Soc.*, **71**, 1514 (1949).

(3) M. S. Newman and Y. T. Yu, *ibid.*, **74**, 507 (1952).

(4) H. M. Walborsky, *Experientia*, **9**, 209 (1953).

(5) A. Streitwieser, Jr., *Chem. Revs.*, **56**, 571 (1956).

(6) W. R. Vaughan and A. C. Schoenthaler, *J. Am. Chem. Soc.*, **80**, 1956 (1958).

(7) M. Farber, Ph.D. Thesis, Columbia University, 1949.

(8) Reversible carbonium ion processes are those in which the products are formed reversibly from the intermediates, *i.e.*, the intermediates are formed repeatedly. In irreversible processes the intermediates are converted to products irreversibly.

bicyclo[2.2.2]octan-2-yl derivatives faster than the isomeric bicyclo[3.2.1]octan-2-yl derivatives but that the latter are more stable.

This analysis can also accommodate the reports that acid-catalyzed addition of acetic acid to bicyclo[2.2.2]octene (V)[4] and bicyclo[3.2.1]oct-2-ene (VI)[9] give bicyclo[2.2.2]octan-2-yl acetate (III, X = OAc), if it is assumed that these are irreversible processes. However, it seems unlikely that these reactions (and the additions of hydrogen bromide and hydrogen chloride to V which also are claimed to give unrearranged adducts)[4] are irreversible carbonium ion processes.

On the basis of the reports that irreversible carbonium ion reactions of bicyclo[2.2.2]octan-2-yl systems do not result in rearrangement, it has been concluded that the carbonium ion does not have a "non-classical" or bridged structure such as II.[4,5] This, of course, would not unequivocally rule out the bridged structure, but as has been pointed out,[5] a bridged ion would be expected to give rise to some of the more stable bicyclo[3.2.1] isomer.

In other problems concerning the Wagner–Meerwein interconversion of bicyclo[2.2.2]- and [3.2.1]-octan-2-yl and octen-2-yl systems we investigated the rates and stereochemistry of solvolysis of the bicyclo[2.2.2]- and [3.2.1]-p-toluenesulfonates (III and IV, X = OTs)[10,11] and the stereochemistry of the deamination of 2-aminobicyclo[2.2.2]octane (III, X = NH₂).[12]

In the first of these studies it was discovered that under solvolyzing conditions the isomeric bicyclo[2.2.2]octan-2-yl and *axial*-bicyclo[3.2.1]octan-2-yl p-toluenesulfonates (III and IVa, X = OTs) are interconverted by internal return.[11] Thus it is clear that the same products would have to result from the isomeric p-toluenesulfonates—the product compositions might differ for the two p-toluenesulfonates because some product is formed before equilibration of the unsolvolyzed p-toluenesulfonates is complete.

In the second study[12] it was found that deamination of optically active 2-aminobicyclo[2.2.2]octane gives an active product (alcohol). This, however, when oxidized gave an optically active ketone. Since active bicyclo[2.2.2]octan-2-ol cannot give an active ketone, it was obvious that this irreversible carbonium ion process (deamination) resulted in rearrangement.

Because of these findings we have reinvestigated the (a) deamination of the amine (III, X = NH₂), (b) acid-catalyzed addition of acetic acid to bicyclo[2.2.2]octene (V) and (c) hydrolysis of the p-toluenesulfonate (III, X = OTs). We have also investigated the acetolysis products of *equatorial*-bicyclo[3.2.1]octan-2-yl p-toluenesulfonate (IVb, X = OTs). As mentioned above, the *axial*-p-toluenesulfonate (IVa, X = OTs) gives the same product as the [2.2.2]-p-toluenesulfonate (III, X = OTs) because of the rapid interconversion during solvolysis.

(9) K. Alder, H. Krieger and H. Weiss, *Ber.*, **88**, 144 (1955).

(10) H. L. Goering, R. W. Greiner and M. F. Sloan, *J. Am. Chem. Soc.*, **83**, 1391 (1961).

(11) H. L. Goering and M. F. Sloan, *ibid.*, **83**, in press (1961).

(12) M. F. Sloan, Ph.D. Thesis, University of Wisconsin, 1960.

V   VI

Results

Deamination of 2-Aminobicyclo[2.2.2]octane (III, X = NH₂)

.—The bicyclic amine (III, X = NH₂) was prepared by hydrogenation of 5-aminobicyclo[2.2.2]oct-2-ene.[10] Aqueous nitrous acid deamination of the amine gave bicyclooctanol in 67% yield. Deamination of the amine (III, X = NH₂) in acetic acid followed by saponification of the resulting acetate gave bicyclooctanol (65% yield) which had the same melting point and infrared spectrum as the product resulting from deamination with aqueous nitrous acid. Olefins were not detected; however, bicyclo[3.2.1]- and [2.2.2]octene are highly volatile[9,13] and may have been lost during isolation of the product.

The melting point of the deamination product was about ten degrees lower than that of pure bicyclo[2.2.2]octan-2-ol (III, X = OH). It was not depressed when mixed with pure III (X = OH) or changed by recrystallization or sublimation. The p-nitrobenzoate derivative, after recrystallization to constant melting point, melted about six degrees lower than pure bicyclo[2.2.2]octan-2-yl p-nitrobenzoate.

The infrared spectrum of the deamination product corresponded in detail to that of a binary mixture of bicyclo[2.2.2]octan-2-ol (III, X = OH) and *axial*-bicyclo[3.2.1]octan-2-ol (IVa, X = OH). The absence of bands characteristic of *equatorial*-bicyclo[3.2.1]octan-2-ol showed that this isomer was not present.

Gas chromatography also showed the deamination product to be a binary mixture of III and IVa (X = OH). However, the composition could not be determined by this method because the broad peaks were not completely resolved. The composition of the product was found to be 36% IVa (X = OH) and 64% III (X = OH) by infrared analysis. Control experiments showed that the deamination products (III and IVa, X = OAc and OH) are stable under the conditions of the deamination experiments.

Solvolysis of Bicyclo[2.2.2]octan-2-yl p-Toluenesulfonate (III, X = OTs) and *endo-(equatorial)*-Bicyclo[3.2.1]octan-2-yl p-Toluenesulfonate (IVb, X = OTs)

.—Bicyclo[2.2.2]octan-2-ol was prepared by saponification of the corresponding acetate which in turn was obtained by hydrogenation of the vinyl acetate–cyclohexadiene adduct.[10] The infrared spectrum of the alcohol and the p-toluenesulfonate derivative showed that they were not contaminated with isomeric bicyclo[3.2.1]octan-2-yl derivatives.

Pure bicyclo[2.2.2]octan-2-yl p-toluenesulfonate (III, X = OTs) was allowed to solvolyze in 80% aqueous acetone at 50° for a period corresponding to at least 99% reaction (see reference 11 for rate data). A slight excess of pyridine was added at the outset to keep the solution from becoming acidic.

(13) C. A. Grob, M. Ohta, E. Renk and A. Weiss, *Helv. Chim. Acta*, **41**, 1191 (1958).

The product, bicycloöctanol (olefins were not detected), was isolated in 82% yield and purified by sublimation in such a way as to avoid fractionation. Gas chromatography and the infrared spectrum showed that the product was a pure binary mixture of bicyclo[2.2.2]octan-2-ol (III, X = OH) and *axial*-bicyclo[3.2.1]octan-2-ol (IVa, X = OH). This mixture contained 45% (infrared analysis) of the [3.2.1]isomer. The equatorial [3.2.1]isomer (IVb, X = OH) was not present. Because bicyclo-[2.2.2]octan-2-yl *p*-toluenesulfonate and *axial*-bicyclo[3.2.1]octan-2-yl *p*-toluenesulfonate are rapidly equilibrated (by internal return) during solvolysis it is apparent that both would give the same products.

endo-(*equatorial*)-Bicyclo[3.2.1]octan-2-yl *p*-toluenesulfonate (IVb, X = OTs)[10,11] was allowed to solvolyze for ten half-lives at 60° in acetic acid containing a slight excess of sodium acetate. Saponification of the resulting acetate gave pure *equatorial*-bicyclo[3.2.1]octan-2-ol (IVb, X = OH) in 96% yield. The melting point and infrared spectrum were the same as those of alcohol from which the equatorial *p*-toluenesulfonate was prepared.

Addition of Acetic Acid to Bicyclo[2.2.2]octene (V).—Bicyclo[2.2.2]octene (V) was prepared by Wolff–Kishner reduction of bicyclo[2.2.2]oct-5-en-2-one[13] which in turn was obtained by oxidation of *endo*-bicyclo[2.2.2]oct-5-en-2-ol.[10] The addition of acetic acid to V was catalyzed by 0.09 M *p*-toluene-sulfonic acid. The crude product was saponified without purification and the unreacted olefin was removed by extraction with silver nitrate. The residual alcohol fraction, after purification by recrystallization, had an infrared spectrum that corresponded in complete detail to that of a ternary mixture of bicyclo[2.2.2]octan-2-ol (III, X = OH) and *axial*- and *equatorial*-bicyclo[3.2.1]octan-2-ol (IVa and IVb, X = OH). Gas chromatography (glycerol- and diglycerol-on-Celite) gave two peaks, IVa (X = OH) and a mixture of III and IVb (X = OH). From the relative intensities of the characteristic peaks in the infrared spectrum it appeared that there were about equal amounts of the three components.

When pure bicyclo[2.2.2]octan-2-yl acetate (III, X = OAc) was submitted to the conditions of the addition experiment, rearrangement occurred. The product, after saponification and purification, had an infrared spectrum that was indistinguishable from that of the ternary mixture of III, IVa and IVb (X = OH) described in the preceding paragraph. This experiment shows that under the present conditions the addition is a reversible carbonium ion process.

Discussion

The present work shows that both deamination of 2-aminobicyclo[2.2.2]octane (III, X = NH₂) and solvolysis of bicyclo[2.2.2]octan-2-yl *p*-toluene-sulfonate result in substantial rearrangement. These findings not only invalidate the earlier conclusions[4,5] concerning the nature of the cation but in fact indicate that a bridged ion (II), common to the bicyclo-[2.2.2]octan-2-yl and *axial*-bicyclo[3.2.1]octan-2-yl

systems, is involved.[14] In other words, the present results suggest that ionization involves participation by the bridging ethylene group.

Structure II for the ion nicely accounts for the stereochemical relationship between reactant and product. The usual relationship[15] is observed; *i.e.*, the atoms from which (C_1) and to which (C_2) migration occurs are inverted. It would indeed be difficult to explain the stereospecificity of the solvolysis in terms of the classical carbonium ion Ib. If this ion were the precursor for the bicyclo[3.2.1]-octyl product, formation of at least some of the more stable equatorial isomer would be expected. The bridged structure also accommodates the internal return phenomenon (interconversion of the isomeric *p*-toluenesulfonates III and IVa) associated with the solvolysis.[11] It should also be mentioned that the reactivities of the isomeric *p*-toluenesulfonates (III and IVb, X = OTs) are quite consistent with this picture.[11,16] That a bridged ion apparently is involved in this system is not surprising in view of the fact that analogous bridged ions are presumably involved in both the *exo*-2-norbornyl[14] and 7-norbornyl systems.[17]

A concerted process involving solvent attack at C_1 simultaneous with rearrangement and departure of the leaving group would also give the observed stereochemical result. In this connection it is significant that the kinetic experiments indicate nucleophilic participation by solvent is not involved.[11]

The completely stereospecific solvolysis of *endo*-(*equatorial*)-bicyclo[3.2.1]octan-2-yl *p*-toluenesulfonate (IVb, X = OTs) is most interesting. This not only shows that different carbonium ions are involved in irreversible carbonium ion reactions of the epimeric bicyclo[3.2.1]octan-2-yl derivatives but also suggests that in this case a bridged ion (VII) is also involved. According to this interpretation, with this isomer ionization involves participation by the bridging methylene group. It would be difficult to account for the stereospecificity (complete retention of configuration) on the basis of the classical carbonium ion Ib. On the other hand, attack by solvent at either of the two equivalent carbon atoms in VII would give the observed product, *i.e.*, the equatorial isomer. In another problem additional evidence that the symmetrical non-classical ion VII is involved in this system is being sought.

VII

Additional information concerning the nature of the intermediates in these systems results from the acid-catalyzed addition of acetic acid to bicyclo-

(14) For leading references concerning bridged or "non-classical" carbonium ions see ref. 5 and 17.

(15) P. D. Bartlett, Chap. 1 in H. Gilman's "Organic Chemistry," Vol. III, John Wiley and Sons, Inc., New York, N. Y., 1953.

(16) Because the significance of internal return cannot be assessed quantitatively the true rates of ionization of the isomeric *p*-toluene-sulfonates cannot be determined. However, the estimated rates are somewhat larger for each isomer than would be expected if the corresponding classical carbonium ion were the initially formed intermediate.

(17) S. Winstein, F. Gadient, E. T. Stafford and P. E. Klinedinst, *J. Am. Chem. Soc.*, **80**, 5895 (1958).

[2.2.2]octene, the only reversible carbonium ion process investigated. Under the conditions used in the present work (0.09 M HOTs, reflux six hours)[18] a ternary mixture of bicyclo[2.2.2]octan-2-yl (III, X = OAc) and *axial*-(IVa, X = OAc) and *equatorial*-bicyclo[3.2.1]octan-2-yl acetate (IV, X = OAc) is formed. The same ternary mixture is obtained when pure bicyclo[2.2.2]octan-2-yl acetate (III, X = OAc) is submitted to the conditions of the addition reaction.[19]

The results presented in this paper indicate that a "non-classical" or bridged ion (II) results from the ionization of bicyclo[2.2.2]octan-2-yl and *exo-*(*axial*)-bicyclo[3.2.1]octan-2-yl derivatives. Apparently an isomeric bridged ion (VII) results from the ionization of *endo-*(*equatorial*)-bicyclo[3.2.1] octan-2-yl derivatives. If this interpretation is correct, the energy barrier between II and VII is sufficiently high so that in irreversible processes there is no interconversion (the products from III and IVa are different from those of IVb). However, under reversible conditions, e.g., the acid-catalyzed addition of acetic acid and isomeric rearrangements (equilibration) of the acetates, the carbonium ions related to the isomeric bicyclo[3.2.1] octan-2-yl derivatives (II and VII) are interconverted.

Experimental

2-Aminobicyclo[2.2.2]octane (III, X = NH₂).—Hydrogenation[20] of 5-aminobicyclo[2.2.2]oct-5-ene[10] gave the hydrochloride of III (X = NH₂), m.p. > 320° (lit.[20] m.p. 345–350°), in 90% yield. The free amine (III, X = NH₂) melted at 143–144° (lit.[20] m.p. 140–141.5°).

Bicyclo[2.2.2]octan-2-ol (III, X = OH).—Hydrogenation of bicyclo[2.2.2]oct-5-en-2-yl acetate[10] over 10% palladium-on-carbon and then lithium aluminum hydride reduction[21] of the saturated acetate gave III (X = OH) in 25% yield (based on cyclohexadiene). After recrystallization from petroleum ether and sublimation (90°, aspirator vacuum) it melted at 220.9–222.2°(lit.[22,23] m.p. 216–217°); infrared bands: 9.15, 9.70, 10.20, 10.70, 11.00 and 11.80 μ (carbon disulfide). Bands characteristic of *equatorial*-bicyclo[3.2.1]-octan-2-ol (IVb, X = OH) (9.40, 9.60, 10.10 and 10.30 μ) and *axial*-bicyclo[3.2.1]octan-2-ol (IVa, X = OH) (10.40 μ) were absent.

The *p*-nitrobenzoate derivative, m.p. 107.6–108.0° (petroleum ether), was prepared by a previously described method.[24]

Anal. Calcd. for C₁₅H₁₇O₄N: C, 65.44; H, 6.22. Found: C, 65.58; H, 6.04.

Bicyclo[2.2.2]octan-2-yl acetate (III, X = OAc) was prepared from the alcohol (anhydrous pyridine method)[25] in 81% yield, n^{25}D 1.4725 (lit.[23] n^{20}D 1.4712).

Bicyclo[2.2.2]octan-2-yl *p*-Toluenesulfonate (III, X = OTs).—The *p*-toluenesulfonate derivative was prepared from pure alcohol by a previously described method.[10] After recrystallization from 60–68° petroleum ether to a constant melt-

ing point, 54.2–55.0°, the yield was 2.80 g. (70%); infrared bands: 9.10, 10.10, 10.30, 10.85, 11.05, 11.50, 12.10, 12.30, 13:10, 14.20, 14.65 and 15.05 μ (carbon disulfide). Bands characteristic of *equatorial*-bicyclo[3.2.1]octan-2-yl *p*-toluenesulfonate (IVb, X = OTs) (10.55, 11.30, 11.70 and 12.00 μ) and *axial*-bicyclo[3.2.1]octan-2-yl *p*-toluenesulfonate (IVa, X = OTs) (10.65, 11.25, 11.75, 13.55 and 13.90 μ) were absent.

Anal. Calcd. for C₁₅H₂₀O₃S: C, 64.25; H, 7.19; solvolysis equiv., 280.4. Found: C, 64.41, H, 7.00; solvolysis equiv., 283.4 ± 1.3 (av. of 11 detn.[11]).

endo-(equatorial)-**Bicyclo[3.2.1]octan-2-yl *p*-toluenesulfonate (IVb, X = OTs)** was prepared from pure *equatorial*-bicyclo[3.2.1]octan-2-ol.[10] After two recrystallizations from an ether–pentane mixture this material melted at 80.1–80.8°, and the yield was 85%. Kinetic experiments[11] showed that this material was homogeneous; infrared bands: 10.55, 10.70, 10.95, 11.30, 11.40, 11.70, 12.00, 12.25, 13.55 and 15.05 μ (carbon disulfide).

Anal. Calcd. for C₁₅H₂₀O₃S: C, 64.25; H, 7.19; solvolysis equiv., 280.4. Found: C, 63.96; H, 7.21; solvolysis equiv., 281.2.

Bicyclo[2.2.2]octene (V).—Bicyclo[2.2.2]oct-5-en-2-one was prepared by oxidation of *endo*-bicyclo[2.2.2]oct-5-en-2-ol[10] with chromic acid.[26] After sublimation it melted at 75.0–83.5° (lit.[13] m.p. 79°). Bicyclo[2.2.2]octene, m.p. 116.4–117.5° (lit.[13] m.p. 115–117°,[13] 111–112°[27]), was prepared by Wolff–Kishner reduction of the ketone.[13]

Deamination of 2-Aminobicyclo[2.2.2]octane (III, X = NH₂). A. In Water.—Deamination of the amine hydrochloride, m.p. > 320°, was carried out by the method described by Wildman and Saunders[20] for deamination of the hydrochloride of *endo*-5-aminobicyclo[2.2.2]oct-2-ene. After one recrystallization from petroleum ether the yield of bicyclooctanol, m.p. 210.2–211.2° (cf. bicyclo[2.2.2]octan-2-ol, m.p. 220.9–222.2°), was 67%.

Pure bicyclo[2.2.2]octan-2-ol (III, X = OH), m.p. 220.9–222.2°, was submitted to the deamination conditions (methylamine hydrochloride, sodium nitrite and hydrochloric acid). After sublimation the recovered material (82% yield) melted at 221.1–222.1°. Its infrared spectrum was identical with that of the starting material.

B. In Acetic Acid.—To a stirred solution of 1.20 g. (0.00743 mole) of the amine hydrochloride in 8.5 ml. of dry acetic acid at room temperature was added 0.815 g. (0.0118 mole) of sodium nitrite over a period of 30 min. The two-phase (sodium chloride precipitates) mixture was allowed to stand at room temperature for 24 hr. Then an additional 0.200 g. of sodium nitrite was added, and the reaction was heated on a steam-bath for 1 hr. After cooling, it was poured into 30 ml. of cold 20% aqueous sodium hydroxide and extracted with pentane for 24 hours. The pentane solution of the acetate was washed with 5% hydrochloric acid and water. After drying, the pentane was removed by distillation and replaced with 40 ml. of 1 M methanolic potassium hydroxide. The resulting solution was refluxed for 1 hr., cooled and diluted with water, and then extracted with pentane for 24 hr. Removal of the pentane left 674 mg. of crude alcohol. After sublimation (90°, aspirator vacuum) the yield of product, m.p. 199.8–202.6°, was 66%. When mixed with bicyclo[2.2.2]octan-2-ol (m.p. 220.9–222.2°) the mixture melted at 206.7–212.2°. When mixed with *axial*-bicyclo[3.2.1]octan-2-ol[10] (m.p. 199.9–200.2°) the mixture melted at 197.8–202.0°. It was not changed by further recrystallization or repeated sublimations. The infrared spectrum was identical with that of the product from aqueous deamination (Part A).

Gas chromatography of the deamination product (ethyl acetate solution) using a 6-ft. column of 20% diglycerol-on-Celite (115°, helium flow rate 16 ml./min.) produced two broad, partially overlapping peaks with retention times of 19.5 and 21.5 min. The former was shown to be bicyclo[2.2.2]octan-2-ol (III, X = OH) and the latter *axial*-bicyclo[3.2.1] octan-2-ol(IVa, X = OH).

The infrared spectrum of the deamination product (alcohol) was an exact composite of those of bicyclo[2.2.2]octan-2-ol and *axial*-bicyclo[3.2.1]octan-2-ol. Bands characteristic of *equatorial*-bicyclo[3.2.1]octan-2-ol (9.40, 10.10 and

(18) The conditions under which this reaction was claimed to give the unrearranged adduct were not described (ref. 4). These are essentially the conditions under which the addition of acetic acid to bicyclo[3.2.1]oct-2-ene is reported to give III (X = OAc) (ref. 9).

(19) Preliminary results (M. F. Sloan) indicate a similar mixture is obtained from bicyclo[3.2.1]oct-2-ene.

(20) W. C. Wildman and D. R. Saunders, *J. Am. Chem. Soc.*, **76**, 946 (1954).

(21) W. E. Doering and H. H. Zeiss, *ibid.*, **72**, 147 (1950).

(22) W. C. Wildman and D. R. Saunders, *J. Org. Chem.*, **19**, 381 (1953).

(23) G. Komppa, *Ber.*, **68**, 1267 (1935).

(24) H. L. Goering and J. P. Blanchard, *J. Am. Chem. Soc.*, **76**, 5405 (1954).

(25) R. L. Shriner, R. C. Fuson and D. Y. Curtin, "The Systematic Identification of Organic Compounds," Fourth Edition, John Wiley and Sons, Inc., New York, N. Y., 1956, p. 212.

(26) A. Bowers, T. G. Halsall, E. R. H. Jones and A. J. Lemin, *J. Chem. Soc.*, 2548 (1953).

(27) H. M. Walborsky and D. F. Loncrini, *J. Am. Chem. Soc.*, **76**, 5396 (1954).

10.30 μ^{10}) were absent. Infrared analysis showed that the product consisted of $64 \pm 2\%$ bicyclo[2.2.2]octan-2-ol and $36 \pm 2\%$ axial-bicyclo[3.2.1]octan-2-ol.

The p-nitrobenzoate of the deamination product melted at 101.5–102.5° after single recrystallizations from aqueous ethanol and petroleum ether. When this derivative was mixed with bicyclo[2.2.2]octan-2-yl p-nitrobenzoate (m.p. 107.6–108.0°) the mixture melted at 104.0–106.5°.

Bicyclo[2.2.2]octan-2-yl acetate (III, X = OAc) was submitted to the conditions of the deamination (methylamine hydrochloride, sodium nitrite, acetic acid). After saponification pure bicyclo[2.2.2]octan-2-ol, m.p. 220.6–221.8°, was isolated in 76% yield. The infrared spectrum was identical with that of an authentic sample.

Hydrolysis of Bicyclo[2.2.2]octan-2-yl p-Toluenesulfonate (III, X = OTs).—A solution of 3.00 g. (0.0107 mole) of III (X = OTs), m.p. 54.2–55.0°, in 55 ml. of 80% aqueous acetone containing 0.95 ml. (0.0117 mole) of pyridine was heated at 50° for 40 hr. This corresponds to over 99% reaction.[11] The solution was cooled and the acetone was allowed to evaporate under an air jet until crystallization of the product began. Water was added, and the mixture was extracted several times with ether. The ether extract was washed with 5% hydrochloric acid, then with water, and dried (magnesium sulfate). Removal of the ether left 1.113 g. (82%) of alcohol. After sublimation (90°, aspirator vacuum) the melting point was 204.4–205.6°.

Gas chromatography of the hydrolysis product (ethyl acetate solution) using a 6-ft. column of 20% diglycerol-on-Celite (115°, helium flow rate 16 ml./min.) produced two broad, partially overlapping peaks. The retention times of these corresponded to bicyclo[2.2.2]octan-2-ol (III, X = OH) and axial-bicyclo[3.2.1]octan-2-ol (IVa, X = OH).

The infrared spectrum was similar to that of the product resulting from deamination of 2-aminobicyclo[2.2.2]octane, i.e., a composite of the spectra of III and IVa (X = OH). Bands characteristic of equatorial-bicyclo[3.2.1]octan-2-ol (IVb, X = OH) were not present. Infrared analysis showed that the mixture consisted of $55 \pm 2\%$ III (X = OH) and $45 \pm 2\%$ IVa (X = OH).

Acetolysis of equatorial-Bicyclo[3.2.1]octan-2-yl p-Toluenesulfonate (IVb, X = OTs).—A solution of 500 mg. (0.00178 mole) of IVb (X = OTs), m.p. 80.1–80.8°, and 155 mg. (0.00189 mole) of sodium acetate in 9 ml. of anhydrous acetic acid was heated at 60° for 9 days (over 99% reaction).[11] After cooling, the solution was poured into water and the resulting mixture was extracted with pentane for 24 hr. The pentane was removed by slow distillation and replaced with 25 ml. of 1 M methanolic potassium hydroxide.

After the resulting solution had refluxed for 1 hr., it was diluted with water and extracted with pentane for 24 hr. Removal of the pentane followed by sublimation (90°, aspirator vacuum) gave 217 mg. (96%) of equatorial-bicyclo[3.2.1]octan-2-ol (IVb, X = OH), m.p. 176.0–178.7°. The infrared spectrum was identical with that of authentic IVb (X = OH).[10]

Addition of Acetic Acid to Bicyclo[2.2.2]octene (V).—A solution of 512 mg. (0.00473 mole) of V in 10 ml. of 0.092 M p-toluenesulfonic acid in acetic acid was refluxed for 6 hr. Then solid sodium acetate was added to the cooled solution and the resulting solution was diluted with water and extracted with pentane for 14 hr. The pentane was removed by slow distillation and replaced with 25 ml. of 1M methanolic potassium hydroxide. After the resulting solution had refluxed for 1 hr., it was diluted with water and extracted with pentane for 24 hr. The pentane extract was washed with two 5-ml. portions of 20% aqueous silver nitrate, then with water, and dried (magnesium sulfate). Removal of the solvent followed by sublimation (90°, aspirator vacuum) of the residual solid gave 360 mg. (59%) of alcoholic material, m.p. 191.5–193.8°. After one recrystallization from petroleum ether the melting point was 199.4–201.5°.

The infrared spectrum of the product was a composite of those of bicyclo[2.2.2]octan-2-ol (III, X = OH) and axial- and equatorial-bicyclo[3.2.1]octan-2-ol (IVa and IVb, X = OH). The relative intensities of the bands at 11.80 μ (III), 10.10 μ (IVb) and 10.40 μ (IVa) indicated that approximately equal amounts of the three components were present.

Bicyclo[2.2.2]octan-2-yl acetate (III, X = OAc) was submitted to the conditions of the addition reaction. The yield of product, after one sublimation, was 68%, m. p. 194.5–196.8°. The infrared spectrum was indistinguishable from that of the alcohol resulting from saponification of the adduct obtained from the addition of acetic acid to V.

Infrared Analysis.—The compositions of the binary mixtures of III and IVa (X = OH) were determined by a previously described method.[28] The transmittance of samples was arbitrarily set at 100% at 2.4 μ for the calculations. The spectra of 10% carbon disulfide solutions of the samples were determined with a Baird model B double beam infrared spectrophotometer equipped with a sodium chloride prism. The same set of cells was used for all of the determinations. The method was checked with three synthetic mixtures of III and IVa (X = OH). The average difference between the experimental and actual values of the compositions of these three samples was 1.7%.

(28) H. E. Zimmerman, J. Am. Chem. Soc., **78**, 1168 (1956).

51 | Stereospecific Participation

One of the properties of the norbornyl solvolysis well accounted for by the bridged norbornyl cation is its stereospecificity, the kinetically determined product being entirely *exo,* even when this product is unstable thermodynamically relative to its *endo* epimer. Occasional attempts are still made to replace the concept of a bridged ion intermediate with rapidly equilibrating species including the classical ion with localized charge. In the work by dePuy, Ogawa, and McDaniel a norbornyl tosylate is constructed which has potential participating groups on both the *endo* and *exo* sides. The *endo* isomer, Ib, reacts with retention of structure and configuration, while the *exo* isomer reacts with Wagner-Meerwein (not homoallylic) rearrangement. It is clear that no classical ion intervenes in these solvolyses, but that each participating group holds the resulting bridged ion in a potential well which prevents its isomerization into the isomeric bridged ion.

The nature of the rearrangement product from *exo*-7-isopropylidene-2-norbornenyl tosylate, which is not a nortricyclyl acetate, indicates that for some reason this compound yields a homoallylic ion of the type symmetrical with respect to the double bond, as in formula XXXI of Winstein and Kosower (Paper No. 40).

It should be noted that the participation of a *saturated* bridge, as in 7-isopropylidene-*exo*-2-norbornyl tosylate (VI), also gives an intermediate ion which does not show any occurrence of the classical norbornyl cation from either epimer.

From: *J. Am. Chem. Soc.* **83**, 1668–71 (1961)

[CONTRIBUTION FROM THE DEPARTMENT OF CHEMISTRY, IOWA STATE UNIVERSITY, AMES, IOWA]

The Solvolysis of *exo-* and *endo*-7-Isopropylidene-dehydronorbornyl Tosylates

BY C. H. DEPUY, I. A. OGAWA AND J. C. MCDANIEL

RECEIVED OCTOBER 17, 1960

The tosylates of *exo-* and *endo*-7-isopropylidene-dehydronorborneol have been solvolyzed in glacial acetic acid containing sodium acetate. Both isomers solvolyzed with anchimeric assistance of the appropriate homoallylic unsaturation, the *exo* isomer with the 5,6- and the *endo* isomer with the 7,8-double bond. *Despite the fact that in both reactions a carbonium ion is generated at position 2, the two homoallylic ions are completely independent,* the ion from the *endo*-tosylate giving exclusively *endo*-acetate, the ion from the *exo*-tosylate giving exclusively rearranged acetate. Similar results were obtained on solvolysis of the dihydro compounds *exo-* and *endo*-7-isopropylidene-norborneol. The limits which these results place on the structure of homoallylic cations are discussed.

It is now well established that resonance interaction may take place between an electron-deficient center and a double bond not directly attached to the same carbon. When the site of unsaturation and the carbonium ion are separated by a single, saturated carbon atom, the system is known as "homoallylic," and the interaction as "homoallylic resonance." The interaction was first noted for cholesteryl cations,[1] and has been extensively investigated there, in the dehydronorbornyl system,[2] and with cyclopropylcarbinol compounds.[1b] Reactions involving such homoallylic participation are often characterized by an abnormally rapid rate of solvolysis relative to the

$$\begin{array}{c} \diagup \\ C=C \\ \diagup \quad \diagdown \\ \quad CH_2 \end{array} \; \diagdown C(+) \quad \longleftrightarrow \quad (+) \diagup C - C - C \diagdown \\ \quad\quad\quad\quad\quad\quad\quad\quad\quad CH_2$$

corresponding dihydro compound,[3] by the isolation of products containing a cyclopropane ring, and by stereochemical criteria (*e.g.*, solvolyses

occurring with retention of configuration). Despite the extensive amount of work which has been published on homoallylic systems, a number of important problems dealing with the nature of the intermediate ions remain unsettled.[1] In particular, the type of bonding involved in these ions is unclear, as well as the possible participation of classical carbonium ions in some of their reactions. In this paper we report studies which place important restrictions on the type of bonding in some homoallylic ions, and which also demonstrate, in a convincing manner, that classical ions cannot be involved in their reactions.

We recently reported methods for the synthesis of *endo*-7-isopropylidene-dehydronorborneol (Ia) from 6,6-dimethylfulvene and α-acetoxyacrylonitrile.[4] The alcohol group in this interesting molecule is dihomoallylic, being separated from both the 7,8- and 5,6-double bonds by a single saturated carbon atom. Participation is then possible, at least in theory, with either of the two double bonds. On stereochemical grounds, interaction with the 5,6-double bond would not be expected to be detectable kinetically in this system but, if important, could be demonstrated by the nature of the products resulting from the reaction. At the

(1) For recent, comprehensive discussions see (a) S. Winstein and E. M. Kosower, *J. Am. Chem. Soc.*, **81**, 4399 (1959), and (b) R. H. Mazur, W. N. White, D. A. Semenow, C. C. Lee, M. S. Silver and J. D. Roberts, *ibid.*, **81**, 4390 (1959).

(2) S. Winstein, H. M. Walborsky and K. Schreiber, *ibid.*, **73**, 5795 (1950).

(3) If the participation makes itself felt in the rate-determining step.

(4) C. H. DePuy and P. R. Story, *J. Am. Chem. Soc.*, **82**, 627 (1960).

same time, participation with the 7,8-double bond, if it occurred, would provide another example of homoallylic interaction of a type hitherto unknown. Previous attempts to demonstrate participation in analogous systems have been unsuccessful. Thus Martin and Bartlett[5] failed to detect any anchimeric assistance during the solvolysis of II, and

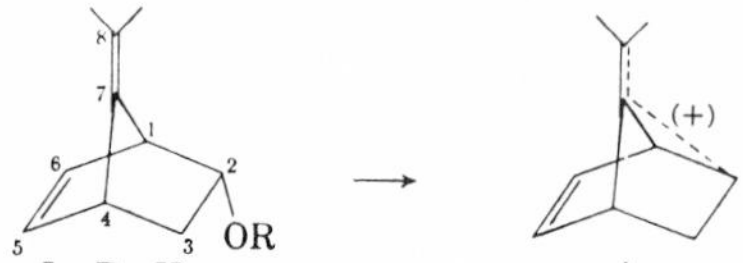

Ia, R = H
b, R = Ts
c, R = Ac-

A

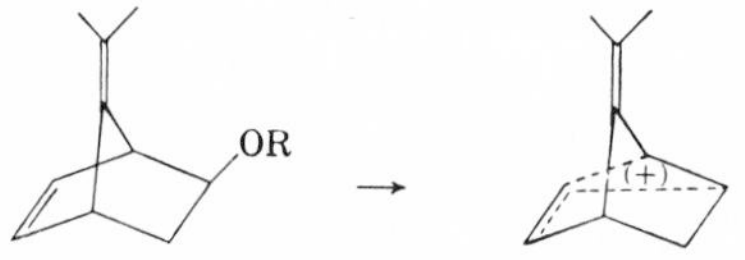

Va, R = H
b, R = Ts

B

van Tamelen and Judd[6] found no kinetic evidence for participation in III.

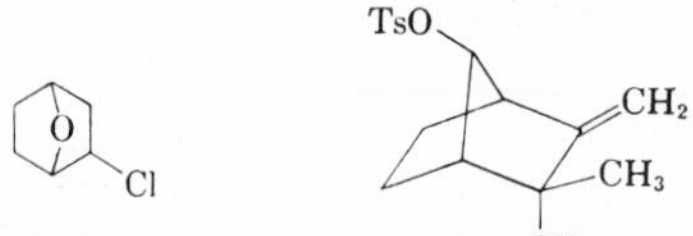

II   III

When Ib was allowed to solvolyze in glacial acetic acid containing sodium acetate and the rate of the reaction followed acidimetrically, it was immediately obvious that the ionization was strongly assisted by the presence of the 7,8-double bond. The rate constants for this solvolysis are reported in Table I, along with constants for several other bicyclic compounds for comparison. It can be seen from the data that the *endo*-tosylate Ib is about 2000 times more reactive than *endo*-dehydronorbornyl tosylate (VII) which displays no anchimeric assistance to solvolysis, and that it approaches *exo*-dehydronorbornyl tosylate (VIII) in reactivity. In the absence of participation the 7,8-double bond would be expected to be rate-depressing due to its inductive effect.

The demonstration of a rate enhancement in solvolysis is good evidence for participation in the transition state, but tells nothing about the fate of the homoallylic ion once formed. For instance, both *exo*- and *endo*-norbornyl tosylates give many of the same products on solvolysis, showing that participation may become important after the rate-determining step. Consequently, a study of the products of the acetolysis was indicated. The acetate formed in the reaction was carefully isolated, hydrolyzed to the corresponding alcohol and chromatographed. An 87% yield of pure, crystalline, unrearranged *endo*-7-isopropylidene-dehydronorborneol (Ia) was obtained. Even more

(5) J. C. Martin and P. D. Bartlett, *J. Am. Chem. Soc.*, **79**, 2533 (1957).

(6) E. E. van Tamelen and C. I. Judd, *ibid.*, **80**, 6305 (1958).

TABLE I

RATES OF ACETOLYSIS OF SOME BICYCLO[2,2,1]HEPTYL TOSYLATES

Compound	Temp., °C.	Rate	Ref.
Ib	50	$7.70 \pm 0.28 \times 10^{-4}$	
	30	$7.25 \pm 0.20 \times 10^{-6}$	
	(25)	$(3.70 \times 10^{-6})^a$	
IV	50	$3.24 \pm 0.11 \times 10^{-4}$	
	30	$3.90 \pm 0.09 \times 10^{-6}$	
	(25)	$(2.26 \times 10^{-6})^a$	
Vb	30	$6.27 \pm 0.10 \times 10^{-6}$	
VI	30	$1.76 \pm 0.05 \times 10^{-4}$	
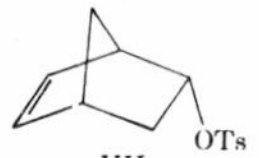 VII	25	2×10^{-9}	7
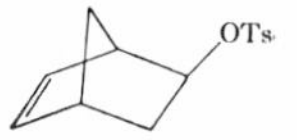 VIII	25	1.5×10^{-6}	7
 IX	25	$8.4 \times 10^{-8 b}$	8
 X	25	2.36×10^{-6}	9

a Calculated from the data at higher temperatures. *b* Calculated with the assumption that tosylates react at one-third the rate of brosylates.

strikingly, when the crude reaction mixture from the acetolysis was examined with the aid of gas chromatography, only a single, sharp peak characteristic of the *endo*-acetate was observed under conditions in which *exo*- and rearranged acetates (*vide infra*) were cleanly separable. Obviously the solvolysis had proceeded with a very high degree of specificity.

The most likely conclusion to be drawn from the stereospecificity of the solvolysis is that the two homoallylic ions A and B are independent of one another, and that no interconversion takes place under the conditions of the reaction. Two alternate explanations are possible, however. In the first of these, it could be imagined that for some reason participation with the 7,8-double bond is so much more favorable energetically than with the 5,6-double bond that, in an equilibrium between ions A and B, A predominates by a large factor. In the second possibility, A and B might be imagined to be resonance structures, the actual intermediate having, simultaneously, interaction between the cationic center and *both* double bonds, as in XII. This intermediate might, in theory, react with solvent to form *endo*-acetate Ic exclusively. Both of these possibilities would be ruled out if it could be shown that the ion B, formed by solvolysis of the *exo*-tosylate Vb, gave entirely different products.

(7) S. Winstein and M. Shatavsky, *ibid.*, **78**, 593 (1956).

(8) S. Winstein, B. K. Morse, E. Grunwald, H. W. Jones, J. Corse, D. Trifan and H. Marshall, *ibid.*, **74**, 1127 (1952).

(9) P. von R. Schleyer, private communication.

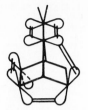

XII

The *endo*-alcohol Ia was readily available from the reduction of the corresponding ketone, but this reaction was highly stereospecific and gave only small, unisolable amounts of the *exo* isomer.[4] Equilibration of the crude hydride reduction product with aluminum isopropoxide in isopropyl alcohol gave an approximately 50–50 mixture of the two alcohols. These could not be separated by crystallization or column chromatography, but were readily separable by isolative gas chromatography using a 20% THEED[10]-on-Celite column one meter long. When prepared in this way the *exo*-alcohol was a crystalline solid which was converted to its tosylate and solvolyzed under the same conditions as for the *endo*-tosylate. As expected, the rate of the acetolysis of Vb was rapid at 30°, again indicating anchimeric assistance. The rate constant for the solvolysis is given in Table I. The reaction was carried out on a larger scale and the products were isolated. Gas chromatographic analysis of the crude acetate showed it to be a single compound, with a different retention time on g.p.c. from *either* the *exo*- or *endo*-acetate. Cleavage of the ester with LiAlH₄ afforded a white, crystalline alcohol, m.p. 102–103°, which was different from either *exo*- or *endo*-7-isopropylidenedehydronorborneol. It displayed infrared absorption bands at 6.36 and 13.8 μ, characteristic of a double bond in the norbornyl system[11] and, by analogy with the type of rearrangement taking place with *exo*-norbornyl tosylate, it was assigned structure XI.

These results make it very clear, then, that the two homoallylic cations A and B are neither identical nor interconvertible under the conditions of the reaction. Hence, *there are at least two distinct carbonium ions capable of existence at position 2, their formation depending upon the stereochemistry of the original tosylate.* The most striking of the two would seem to be A, since it appears likely that rearrangement to give the allylic carbonium ion analogous to XI would be favored thermodynamically. These results rule out classical character

to the carbonium ion, and demand an activation energy for the conversion of A to B.

It next seemed pertinent to investigate the analogous solvolyses in the 5,6-dihydro compounds, *exo*- and *endo*-7-isopropylidene-norbornyl tosylates, IV and VI. Here the analogous intermediates would be, from IV the homoallylic cation C, and from VI the non-classical cation D, resulting from

participation of the saturated β-carbon. The results in these cases were completely in accord with those reported above. Both tosylates solvolyzed rapidly compared to analogous tosylates which could not have anchimeric assistance to ionization. Again the *endo*-acetate was the exclusive product from acetolysis of the *endo*-tosylate (as evidenced by the appearance of only a single peak on g.p.c. analysis and the isolation, in 89% yield, of the corresponding alcohol after saponification and chromatography). The *exo*-tosylate gave none of the *endo*-acetate, but again formed a rearranged acetate. The alcohol produced upon saponification of this acetate was identical with that formed by partial hydrogenation of the rearranged alcohol XIa from the *exo*-dehydrotosylate above. Again no interconversion could be detected between the homoallylic and the nonclassical ions.

Two additional points of interest seem worthy of mention. The similarity between the rate constants for the solvolysis of the *exo*-7-isopropylidene-norbornyl (IV) and dehydronorbornyl (Ib) tosylates and those for *exo*-norbornyl (X) and dehydronorbornyl (VIII) tosylates indicates that the potential allylic character of the rearranging carbonium ion has little effect on the rate of the reaction. This may prove to be general, or may be due to unfavorable orientation of the π-electrons of the 7,8-double bond in this particular system. A second interesting comparison is between the rates of acetolysis of *endo*-7-isopropylidene-norbornyl tosylate (IV) and *endo*-7-isopropylidenedehydronorbornyl tosylate (Ib). Since electron donation from 5,6-unsaturation to the 7-position is known,[12] it might have been anticipated that the transition state for the solvolysis of the dehydronorbornyl system could be stabilized by an interaction such as that shown in XIII. Actually, however, the diene is less reactive than the mono-ene, and it

Vb

XIa, R = H
b, R = Ac

(10) Tetra-(hydroxyethyl)-ethylenediamine.
(11) L. Kaplan, H. Kwart and P. von R. Schleyer, *J. Am. Chem. Soc.*, **82**, 2341 (1960).
(12) S. Winstein, M. Shatavsky, C. Norton and R. B. Woodward, *ibid.*, **77**, 4183 (1955).

XIII

seems unlikely that this type of interaction is important.

Experimental

Melting points are uncorrected. Analyses were performed by Weiler and Strauss, Oxford, England. Gas chromatographic analyses were performed using a Perkin–Elmer model 154-C vapor Fractometer. The column used for the analysis of the alcohols was a 1 m. × 6 mm. Pyrex tube packed with 9% by weight THEED (tetra-(hydroxyethyl)-ethylenediamine) on 60-80 mesh Celite. The column used in preparative runs was a 1 m. × 15 mm. tube packed with 20% by weight THEED on Celite.

endo-7-Isopropylidene-bicyclo-(2,2,1)-5-hepten-2-ol (Ia), m.p. 74–75°, was prepared by the method of DePuy and Story.[4]

exo-7-Isopropylidene-bicyclo-(2,2,1)-5-hepten-2-ol was obtained by equilibration of Ia. The *endo*-alcohol (5 g., 0.03 mole), aluminum isopropoxide (6.8 g., 0.03 mole) and acetone (0.1 ml.) were dissolved in 100 ml. of dry isopropyl alcohol and the solution heated under reflux for 72 hours. Dilute acid was added, the products extracted with ether, the extracts washed and dried over anhydrous MgSO4. The solvent was carefully removed (the alcohols are very volatile) and the resulting oil analyzed by g.p.c. It contained about 43% *exo*-alcohol. The mixture was dissolved in pentane and as much *endo*-alcohol as possible allowed to crystallize, leaving a mixture containing about 60% *exo*-alcohol. A single pass through the preparative column was sufficient to separate about 200 mg. of the oil into two crystalline alcohols. Recrystallization from pentane gave the *exo*-alcohol in the form of long white needles, m.p. 56–57°.

Anal. Calcd. for $C_{10}H_{14}O$: C, 79.95; H, 9.39. Found: C, 79.65; H, 9.27.

endo-7-Isopropylidene-bicyclo-(2,2,1)-2-heptanol, m.p. 81–82°, was prepared by the method of DePuy and Story.[4]

exo-7-Isopropylidene-bicyclo-(2,2,1)-2-heptanol was prepared by equilibration of the corresponding *endo*-alcohol as described above. After isolation by g.p.c. and recrystallization from pentane it had a m.p. 62.5–63°.

Anal. Calcd. for $C_{10}H_{16}O$: C, 78.89; H, 10.59. Found: C, 78.64, 78.02; H, 9.07, 10.13.

Tosylates.—All tosylates were prepared from the alcohols by the method of Tipson.[13] The *endo*-tosylates have been described earlier.[4] The *exo*-tosylates decomposed on standing or heating and accurate melting points could not be obtained.

Kinetic Measurements.—The technique used was that of Winstein.[14] The bath temperatures were 49.99 ± 0.02° and 30.00 ± 0.03°. The acetolyses were run in sealed tubes each containing 5 ml. of solution, approximately 0.035 M in tosylate and 0.040 M in sodium acetate. The reactions gave good first-order plots over at least 50% of the reaction, but some curvature was observed at long reaction times. Several infinity points checked with calculated values to within a few per cent.

Product Analysis.—About 1.5 g. of each of the tosylates was allowed to solvolyze at 50° for 24 hours in 40 ml. of dry acetic acid which was 0.2 M in sodium acetate. The reaction mixture was poured into cold water and extracted with pentane. The extracts were washed with water, dried and the pentane removed. The product in each case showed only a single peak on g.p.c. analysis, under conditions which readily separated mixtures of the acetates of all four compounds. The acetates were hydrolyzed, the hydrolysis products extracted with pentane, dried and the solvent carefully removed. In each case the products crystallized immediately, and the alcohol was obtained in 85–90% yield after chromatography or recrystallization. The *endo*-tosylates gave these high yields of the corresponding *endo*-alcohols, identified by their infrared spectra and mixture melting points with authentic samples. The *exo*-tosylates gave two new alcohols.

Alcohol from Acetolysis of Vb.—This alcohol melted at 102.5–103.5°. It readily absorbed hydrogen over palladium-on-carbon and had infrared peaks at 6.36 and 13.7 μ, characteristic of the dehydronorbornyl system.

Anal. Calcd. for $C_{10}H_{14}O$: C, 79.95; H, 9.39. Found: C, 80.22; H, 9.38.

After the uptake of one molar equivalent of hydrogen the resultant dihydro alcohol was identical with that described below from the solvolysis of VI.

The alcohol from the acetolysis of VI melted at 86–87°.

Anal. Calcd. for $C_{10}H_{16}O$: C, 78.89; H, 10.59. Found: C, 78.64; H, 10.80.

(13) R. S. Tipson, *J. Org. Chem.*, **9**, 235 (1944).

(14) S. Winstein, C. Hansen and E. Grunwald, *J. Am. Chem. Soc.*, **70**, 812 (1948).

52 | Bicyclooctyl and Bicyclo-octenyl Cations

Paper No. 52, by Goering and Sloan, scrutinizes some of the ionic reactions in the bicyclo(2.2.2)octyl, bicyclo(2.2.2)octenyl, and bicyclo(3.2.1)octyl ring systems. The pair which undergo rapid interconversion do so with internal return, their tosylates isomerizing in acetic acid solution. The reaction rates are all faster than would be predicted for unassisted solvolysis, and by larger amounts when corrections are made for the fact that ionization, in a system with internal return, is faster than solvolysis. It is not clear how much bridged character the ion from I has, but some of its properties, including the stereospecificity with which it reacts, are abnormal for an ion with only allylic delocalization.

From: *J. Am. Chem. Soc.* **83,** 1992–99 (1961)

[CONTRIBUTION FROM THE DEPARTMENT OF CHEMISTRY OF THE UNIVERSITY OF WISCONSIN, MADISON 6, WIS.]

Ionic Reactions in Bicyclic Systems. III. Solvolysis of Bicyclooctanyl and Bicyclooctenyl p-Toluenesulfonates[1]

By Harlan L. Goering and Martin F. Sloan[2]

Received October 17, 1960

First-order rate constants for acetolysis and ethanolysis of (a) *endo*-bicyclo[2.2.2]oct-5-en-2-yl *p*-toluenesulfonate (I), (b) bicyclo[2.2.2]octan-2-yl *p*-toluenesulfonate (VII) and (c) *exo(axial)*-bicyclo[3.2.1]octan-2-yl *p*-toluenesulfonate (VIII) have been determined. Rate constants for the solvolysis of VII in 80% aqueous acetone and acetolysis of *endo(equatorial)*-bicyclo[3.2.1]octan-2-yl *p*-toluenesulfonate (XVI) have also been determined. Ionization of *endo*-bicyclo[2.2.2]oct-5-en-2-yl *p*-toluenesulfonate (I), which results in complete rearrangement to the bicyclo[3.2.1]oct-3-en-2-yl system, is anchimerically assisted. Solvolysis of bicyclo[2.2.2]octan-2-yl *p*-toluenesulfonate (VII) and *axial*-bicyclo[3.2.1]octan-2-yl *p*-toluenesulfonate (VIII) is accompanied by internal return which results in the interconversion (equilibration) of the two isomers during solvolysis. The reactivities of these isomers are consistent with the idea that ionization results in the formation of a common bridged ("non-classical") carbonium ion; *i.e.*, anchimeric acceleration is indicated.

Introduction

In the first paper in this series[3] it was shown that acetolysis of *endo*-bicyclo[2.2.2]oct-5-en-2-yl *p*-toluenesulfonate (I) gives *axial*-bicyclo[3.2.1]oct-3-en-2-yl acetate (IX). Deamination of *endo*-5-aminobicyclo[2.2.2]oct-2-ene also results in complete rearrangement to the bicyclo[3.2.1]oct-3-en-2-yl system.[3,4] On the other hand, solvolysis

(1) This work was supported in part by the Office of Ordnance Research.

(2) Wisconsin Alumni Research Foundation Fellow 1956–1958; National Science Foundation Fellow 1958–1960.

(3) H. L. Goering, R. W. Greiner and M. F. Sloan, *J. Am. Chem. Soc.*, **83**, 1391 (1961).

of the saturated analog, bicyclo[2.2.2]octan-2-yl p-toluenesulfonate (VII), or deamination of the corresponding amine results in only partial rearrangement to the bicyclo[3.2.1]octan-2-yl system.[5]

The Wagner–Meerwein conversion of the *endo*-bicyclo[2.2.2]oct-5-en-2-yl system to the bicyclo-[3.2.1]oct-3-en-2-yl system is not unexpected. By analogy with related systems, ionization of I would be expected to give the bicyclo[3.2.1]-allylic cation II. Evidence has been presented that *syn*-7-norbornenyl p-toluenesulfonate (III)[6,7]

I   II

and *trans*-5,6-dibromobicyclo[2.2.2]oct-2-ene (IV)[8] ionize in polar media to give the allylic carbonium ions. In each of these cases participation by the methylene group is manifested by a high reactivity. The conversion of *syn*-7-camphenyl p-toluene-

III

IV

sulfonate (V) to 1,1-dimethyl-2-hydroxymethyl-bicyclo[3.2.0]hept-2-ene (VI) by hydrolysis[9] indicates that here also ionization may involve direct formation of the allylic carbonium ion. However, in this case there is no apparent rate enhancement—the acetolysis rate of V at 140° is slightly smaller than that of its saturated analog.[9]

V   VI

In the present work the solvolytic reactivity of *endo*-bicyclo[2.2.2]oct-5-en-2-yl p-toluenesulfonate (I) in ethanol and acetic acid was determined to obtain information concerning the nature of carbonium ion reactions in this system. To assess the rate enhancement resulting from methylene participation the rates of acetolysis and ethanolysis of the saturated analog, bicyclo[2.2.2]octan-2-yl p-toluenesulfonate (VII),[5] were also determined.

(4) W. C. Wildman and D. R. Saunders, *J. Am. Chem. Soc.*, **76**, 946 (1954).

(5) H. L. Goering and M. F. Sloan, *ibid.*, **83**, 1397 (1961).

(6) S. Winstein and E. T. Stafford, *ibid.*, **79**, 505 (1957).

(7) S. Winstein and C. Ordronneau, *ibid.*, **82**, 2084 (1960).

(8) A. Gagneux and C. A. Grob, *Helv. Chim. Acta*, **42**, 1753 (1959).

(9) E. E. van Tamelen and C. I. Judd, *J. Am. Chem. Soc.*, **80**, 6305 (1958).

It was discovered that VII undergoes a reversible stereospecific isomeric rearrangement to *axial*-bicyclo[3.2.1]octan-2-yl p-toluenesulfonate (VIII) during solvolysis and for this reason solvolysis of the latter compound, and its epimer XVI, were also investigated.

Results

endo-Bicyclo[2.2.2]oct-5-en-2-ol, prepared and purified by a method described earlier,[10] gave a p-toluenesulfonate derivative which contained a reactive contaminant (probably the *exo* isomer).[4,11] Pure *endo*-bicyclo[2.2.2]oct-5-en-2-yl p-toluenesulfonate (I)[3] was obtained by recrystallization of this material from ethanol. When Compound I was derived from pure *endo*-bicyclo[2.2.2]oct-5-en-2-ol[3] the ethanol recrystallization was not necessary. Homogeneous samples of I, prepared by either of these ways, showed excellent first-order solvolytic behavior. The p-toluenesulfonate derivative I was shown to have the bicyclo[2.2.2]-oct-5-en-2-yl structure by conversion (hydrogenation) to bicyclo[2.2.2]octan-2-yl p-toluenesulfonate (VII).[5]

Specific first-order rate constants for acetolysis (30° and 42°) and ethanolysis (30° and 49°) are given in Table I. In each experiment the reaction was followed to at least 75% completion and nine or more values of the first-order constant were determined from appropriately spaced titrations. No trends in these values were observed and the rate constants were reproducible. A kinetic experiment is included in the Experimental section. With this compound, and all of the others investigated in the present work, the infinity titers corresponded to theory.

With one exception, the constants in Table I are average values (and deviations from the

TABLE I

SOLVOLYSIS OF *endo*-BICYCLO[2.2.2]OCT-5-EN-2-YL p-TOLU-ENESULFONATE (I)[a]

Temp., °C.	n[b]	$10^5 k$, sec.$^{-1}$
	Acetolysis	
30.07	2	2.97 ± 0.03
30.07	1[c]	3.10 ± .02
42.06	2	13.2 ± .05

$\Delta H^{\ddagger} = 23.1$ kcal./mole; $\Delta S^{\ddagger} = -3.0$ e.u. at 30°

	Ethanolysis	
30.07	3	0.323 ± 0.002
49.03	2	3.95 ± .05

$\Delta H^{\ddagger} = 25.0$ kcal./mole; $\Delta S^{\ddagger} = -1.2$ e.u. at 30°

[a] Initial concentration of I was 0.025 M in all experiments. [b] Number of independent kinetic experiments. [c] Contained 0.055 M sodium acetate.

average) of two or three independent kinetic experiments. The other is the average of nine determinations made during the single experiment. The activation parameters included in the table

(10) W. C. Wildman and D. R. Saunders, *J. Org. Chem.*, **19**, 381 (1953).

(11) This material, even after several recrystallizations from ether-pentane, gave apparent integrated first-order rate constants (ethanolysis and acetolysis) which decreased more than 60% during the first 50% reaction.

were computed in the usual manner.[12] The second entry in Table I shows that 0.055 M sodium acetate causes a slight positive salt effect. It was under these conditions that the product was shown to be *exo(axial)*-bicyclo[3.2.1]oct-3-en-2-yl acetate (IX).[8]

To determine the effect of the double bond in I on the reactivity, the rates of acetolysis and ethanolysis of the saturated analog, bicyclo[2.2.2]-octan-2-yl *p*-toluenesulfonate (VII), were investigated. The *p*-toluenesulfonate VII was prepared from pure bicyclo[2.2.2]octan-2-ol.[5] In this case the integrated first-order rate coefficient, k (eq. 1), for both acetolysis and ethanolysis decreased during the reaction. Both the initial rate constants (obtained by extrapolating plots of percentage reaction *vs.* integrated first-order rate coefficient to 0% reaction) and the rate and magnitude of the downward drift were reproducible. The integrated constants drifted down throughout the entire reaction. However, plots of log [ROTs]-*vs.* time became linear after about 30% reaction for acetolysis and about 40% reaction for ethanolysis. In other words, the instantaneous first-order rate constant, k_{inst} (eq. 2) drifted down during the early stages of the reaction and then became constant. In all cases, integrated constants calculated from data for the last 50% of reaction were steady.

$$k = (1/t) \ln ([ROTs]_0/[ROTs]_t) \qquad (1)$$
$$k_{inst} = -(d[ROTs]/dt)/[ROTs]_t \qquad (2)$$

. The pertinent kinetic experiments are summarized in Table II. Two values of the rate constants are given in the table. The first, $k_{i[2.2.2]}$, is the initial rate constant (obtained by extrapolating the integrated coefficients to 0% reaction) and the second, k_t, is the average of five or more values (and average deviation) of the integrated first-order constant for the final 50% of the reaction (*i.e.*, the zero-time titer was taken at about 50% reaction). The latter values correspond to the instantaneous first-order rate constant after it becomes steady—if integrated first-order constants are steady, k(eq. 1) = k_{inst} (eq. 2). The data in Table II show that the acetolysis behavior of VII is not affected by the presence of 0.05 M sodium acetate. One rate constant for the hydrolysis of VII in 80% acetone is included in Table II. In this case the rate constant also drifted downward (from 9.1×10^{-5} sec.$^{-1}$, 0% reaction, to 6.5×10^{-5} sec.$^{-1}$, 75% reaction). These are the conditions under which the product was shown to be a binary mixture of bicyclo[2.2.2]octan-2-ol and *axial*-bicyclo[3.2.1]octan-2-ol.[5]

The decrease in the rate constants for the solvolysis of bicyclo[2.2.2]octan-2-yl *p*-toluenesulfonate (VII) is due to rearrangement during solvolysis to the slightly less reactive *axial*-bicyclo-[3.2.1]octan-2-yl *p*-toluenesulfonate (VIII). That VIII is produced during solvolysis, rather than being present in the *p*-toluenesulfonate (VII) from the outset, was established as follows. The infrared spectrum of VII used in the kinetic experiments did not contain bands characteristic of the bicyclo[3.2.1] isomer VIII. Moreover,

(12) A. A. Frost and R. G. Pearson, "Kinetics and Mechanism," John Wiley and Sons, Inc., New York, N. Y., 1953.

TABLE II

SOLVOLYSIS OF BICYCLO[2.2.2]OCTAN-2-YL *p*-TOLUENESULFONATE (VII)[a]

Temp., °C.	n [b]	Added salt, 10^2 M	10^5 $k_{i[2.2.2]}$, [c] sec.$^{-1}$	10^5 k_t, [d] sec.$^{-1}$
Acetolysis				
30.07	2		0.68 ± 0.01	0.448 ± 0.001
49.03	2		$7.4 \pm .1$	$5.40 \pm .04$
49.03	2	2.99 NaOAc	$7.6 \pm .1$	$5.42 \pm .05$
49.03	2	5.50 NaOAc	$7.5 \pm .1$	$5.36 \pm .01$
49.03	1 [e]	5.50 NaOAc	$7.7 \pm .2$	$5.35 \pm .07$
Ethanolysis				
49.03	2		1.32 ± 0.01	0.978 ± 0.004
80% aqueous acetone [f]				
49.03	1		9.1 ± 0.2	

[a] Initial concentration of VII was 0.025 M. [b] Number of independent kinetic experiments. [c] Initial rate constant. [d] Rate constant after 50% reaction (*i.e.*, zero-point titer taken at about 50% reaction). [e] Sample of VII used in this experiment was prepared by recrystallizing analytically pure material (material used in other experiments) four times. [f] Composition based on volumes of pure components at 25° before mixing.

the acetolysis rate behavior and physical properties of an analytically pure sample of VII were unchanged by four additional recrystallizations (fifth entry in Table II).

The less reactive isomer formed during the solvolysis of bicyclo[2.2.2]octan-2-yl *p*-toluenesulfonate (VII) was identified as *axial*-bicyclo-[3.2.1]octan-2-yl *p*-toluenesulfonate (VIII) in the following way. Unreacted *p*-toluenesulfonate was isolated from an acetolysis reaction after 50% reaction. After recrystallization, the yield of recovered *p*-toluenesulfonate was 63%. The melting point (11° lower than that of pure VII) and infrared spectrum of this material were indistinguishable from those of a pure synthetic binary mixture of 30% VII and 70% VIII. Bands characteristic of *equatorial*-bicyclo[3.2.1]octan-2-yl *p*-toluenesulfonate (XVI) were absent.

The fact that the instantaneous first-order constants become steady after the initial downward drift indicates that a steady-state ratio of concentrations of VII and VIII is obtained; *i.e.*, the rearrangement is reversible and reaches equilibrium. This was confirmed by investigating the solvolytic behavior of *axial*-bicyclo[3.2.1]octan-2-yl *p*-toluenesulfonate (VIII).

Pure VIII was prepared from pure *axial*-bicyclo-[3.2.1]octan-2-ol.[5] In this case the integrated first-order coefficients drifted upward for both ethanolysis and acetolysis. As for the solvolysis of VII, plots of log[ROTs] *vs.* time become linear after about 30% acetolysis and 45% ethanolysis. Thus in this case the instantaneous rate constants show initial upward drifts and then become steady. Data for the acetolysis and ethanolysis of VIII are given in Table III.

That the upward drift in the rate was indeed due to isomerization to the more reactive bicyclo-[2.2.2] isomer VII was demonstrated by isolation of the unsolvolyzed *p*-toluenesulfonate from an ethanolysis experiment after 50% solvolysis. This material, isolated in 78% yield, had an infrared

TABLE III

SOLVOLYSIS OF axial-BICYCLO[3.2.1]OCTAN-2-YL p-TOLUENE-
SULFONATE (VIII) AT 49.03°[a]

Solvent	$10^5 k_{t[3.2.1]}$,[b] sec.$^{-1}$	$10^5 k_t$,[b] sec.$^{-1}$
HOAc	4.3	5.23 ± 0.07
HOAc	4.3	5.28 ± .03
EtOH	0.67	0.928 ± .020
EtOH	0.64	0.986 ± .034

[a] Initial concentration of VIII was 0.025 M.   [b] See footnotes c and d, Table II.

spectrum which corresponded in detail to a binary
mixture of 75 ± 5% VIII and 25 ± 5% VII.

The data presented in Tables II and III clearly
show that bicyclo[2.2.2]octan-2-yl p-toluenesulfonate (VII) and axial-bicyclo[3.2.1]octan-2-yl
p-toluenesulfonate (VIII) are interconverted during
solvolysis. The rate of interconversion (equilibration) is such that starting with either isomer a
steady-state ratio of the two isomers is reached
by about 30% solvolysis in acetic acid and 40%
solvolysis in ethanol. It should be noted that
values of k_t (these are the rate constants for the
steady-state ratio of VII and VIII) are essentially
the same for VII (Table II) and VIII (Table III).
The slight differences are probably due to the fact
that the zero-point titers were taken a little before
equilibration was complete. The following experiment was carried out to check this point more carefully. Solutions of pure VII and VIII in acetic
acid were prepared and heated simultaneously in
the 49.03° thermostat. The reactions were followed from 75% (zero time) to 95% completion.
The integrated rate constants for this portion of
the reaction (5.4 ± 0.2 × 10^{-5} sec.$^{-1}$ for VII and
5.2 ± 0.1 × 10^{-5} sec.$^{-1}$ for VIII) were steady and
the same (within experimental error) for the two
solutions.

The solvolytic behavior of the isomeric p-
toluenesulfonates VII and VIII is summarized
by the accompanying scheme. From the rate

SCHEME I

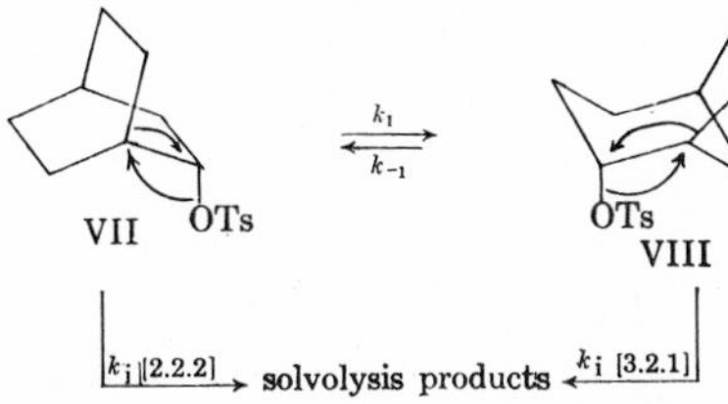

constants for solvolysis ($k_{i[2.2.2]}$ and $k_{i[3.2.1]}$;
Tables II and III) and the values of the first-order
constant after equilibration (k_t in Tables I and II)
the mole fraction of VII, F, in the equilibrated
unsolvolyzed p-toluenesulfonate can be determined
from eq. 3.[13] Because both the numerator and

$$(k_t - k_{i[3.2.1]})/k_{i[2.2.2]} - k_{i[3.2.1]}) = F \quad (3)$$

denominator are small differences between numbers
with rather large uncertainties, the value of F obtained in this way is not very accurate. This
treatment indicates that the mole fraction of VII

(13) W. G. Young, S. Winstein and H. L. Goering, J. Am. Chem.
Soc., 73, 1958 (1951).

(F) in the equilibrated unsolvolyzed p-toluenesulfonate is 0.32 ± 0.04 for acetolysis at 49° and 0.45
± 0.04 for ethanolysis at 49°. These values
correspond to equilibrium constants (K_{eq}) of
2.1 ± 0.4 for acetic acid and 1.2 ± 0.3 for ethanol
for the interconversion of VII and VIII. This
steady-state composition differs slightly from the
thermodynamic equilibrium composition because
the isomers are not consumed (solvolyzed) at
equal rates. The equilibrium mixture would contain slightly more of the more reactive isomer VII;
i.e., F would be higher and K_{eq} would be lower.
From the present data it is clear that the difference
in thermodynamic stability between VII and VIII
under these conditions is <0.5 kcal.

In principle, the composition of the unsolvolyzed
p-toluenesulfonate during the equilibration can be
determined by eq. 3 (in this case k_t would be replaced by the time-dependent instantaneous rate
constant, k_{inst} (eq. 2)).[13] This would enable
determination of the rate constant for equilibration,
$k_1 + k_{-1}$ (Scheme I). However, instantaneous
rate constants cannot be determined with an
uncertainty of less than about 25% of the total
range of the drift ($k_{i[2.2.2]} - k_t$). Thus only a
rough estimate of the rate of equilibration can be
made. Plots of k_{inst}[13] vs. time for the early stages
of the acetolysis of VII at 49° show that 3000
seconds is an upper limit for a half-life for equilibration (the period required for k_{inst} to drift
50% of the total change). This gives a lower limit
of 2 × 10^{-4} sec.$^{-1}$ for ($k_1 + k_{-1}$). From this value
and that of the equilibrium constant (k_1/k_{-1} =
2.1) it can be determined that under these condi-
tions lower limits for k_1 and k_{-1} are 1.4 × 10^{-4} sec.$^{-1}$
and 0.6 × 10^{-4} sec.$^{-1}$, respectively.

The rate of acetolysis of equatorial-bicyclo[3.2.1]-
octan-2-yl p-toluenesulfonate (XVI) at 49.03°
was also determined for comparison with the rates
of the other isomers. In this case excellent first-
order behavior was observed and $k = 3.05 ±
0.02 × 10^{-6}$ sec.$^{-1}$. It is under these conditions
that the acetolysis substitution product is equatorial-bicyclo[3.2.1]octan-2-yl acetate (i.e., the
geometric configuration is retained completely[5]).

Discussion

As mentioned in the Introductory section, acetolysis of endo-bicyclo[2.2.2]oct-5-en-2-yl (I) results
in complete rearrangement and gives axial-bicyclo-
[3.2.1]oct-3-en-2-yl acetate (IX).[3] This suggests
that ionization of I may involve methylene participation with direct formation of the relatively
stable allyl carbonium ion II or possibly a non-
classical ion X with substantial allylic character.
The bridged or non-classical structure X nicely

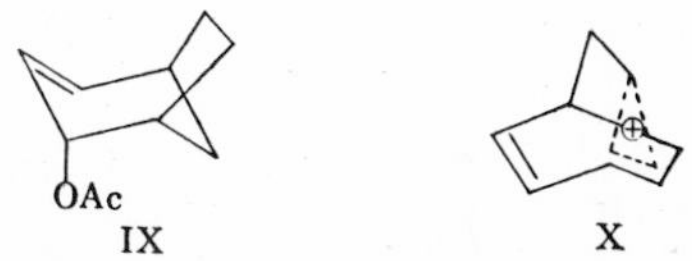

IX   X

accommodates the complete stereospecificity of the
reaction (only IX is formed[3]). However, it is
possible that II undergoes exclusive exo attack to

give IX.[14] It is significant in this connection that acetate ion results in only a small "normal"[15] positive salt effect and that $k_{HOAc}/k_{EtOH} = 9.2$ at 30°. This indicates nucleophilic participation by solvent is not important[16] or, in other words, acetolysis (and probably also ethanolysis) involves a carbonium ion intermediate. Thus concerted processes such as XI (which also would result in the stereospecific conversion of I to IX) seem unlikely.

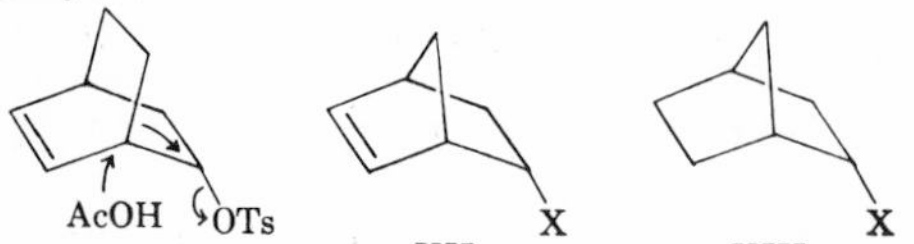

The most compelling evidence for participation by a neighboring group (in this case methylene) is a greater observed rate of ionization than would otherwise obtain. Relative rates of acetolysis of I, VII, VIII, XVI, endo-dehydronorbornyl p-toluenesulfonate (XII, X = OTs), endo-norbornyl p-toluenesulfonate (XIII, X = OTs) and cyclohexyl p-toluenesulfonate are given in Table IV. These data are helpful for estimating the unassisted ionization rate for endo-bicyclo[2.2.2]oct-5-en-2-yl p-toluenesulfonate (I).

TABLE IV

ACETOLYSIS REACTIVITIES OF BICYCLIC SYSTEMS

p-Toluene-sulfonate	Temp., °C.	$10^5 k$, sec.$^{-1}$	Relative reactivity[a]
I	30	2.97	105
VII	30	0.68[b]	24
	49	7.3[b]	
VIII	49	4.3[b]	14
XVI	49	0.305	1
Cyclohexyl[26]	25	4.7×10^{-3c}	0.34
	30	1.0×10^{-2}	
endo-Norbornyl (XIII)[19]	25	2.8×10^{-3d}	0.20
endo-Dehydronor-bornyl (XII)[18]	25	6.3×10^{-6d}	4.5×10^{-3}

[a] These values determined from rate constants in preceding column by comparing constants for pairs of compounds at the same temperature. [b] Initial rate constants. [c] Extrapolated from data for other temperatures taken from ref. 26. [d] One-third of the value reported for the corresponding p-bromobenzenesulfonate in the indicated reference.

As shown in Table IV, at 30° the rate of acetolysis of I is 4.4 times greater than that of its saturated analog, bicyclo[2.2.2]octan-2-yl p-toluenesulfonate (VII). However, the unassisted ionization rate would be expected to be lower for the unsaturated analog. The inductive effect of the double bond would lower the unassisted rate in I relative to VII, and non-bonded interactions between the tosyloxy group and the C_5- and C_6-hydrogen atoms (cis to the tosyloxy group) in VII would increase its rate (steric acceleration[17]) relative to that of I. It would appear that the relative unassisted rates for I and VII should be comparable to those for endo-dehydronorbornyl (XII)[18] and endo-norbornyl p-bromobenzenesulfonates (XIII, X = p-BrC$_6$H$_4$-SO$_3$).[19] Presumably in the latter two systems rates of ionization are not anchimerically assisted. As indicated in Table IV the rate of acetolysis of the saturated analog XIII at 25° is 44 times faster than that of XII. Thus, to a first approximation, in the absence of participation the rate of acetolysis of I would be expected to be about 1/44 as fast as that of VII or about 1/200 the observed rate.

There are several complications involved in this analysis. A minor one concerns the greater stability of bicyclo[2.2.2]octane and -octene systems relative to the corresponding bicyclo[2.2.1]heptane and -heptene systems.[20] This difference apparently results from the greater strain associated with rigid bicyclo[2.2.1] systems; or, to put it another way, bicyclo[2.2.2] systems are more flexible.[20] This flexibility (twisting) results in a reduction of eclipsed hydrogen–hydrogen interactions which may decrease the driving force for ionization in bicyclo[2.2.2] systems relative to bicyclo[2.2.1] systems (cf. rates of ionization of cyclopentyl and cyclohexyl derivatives[21]). Because of factors of this type the difference in the unassisted ionization rates for the saturated (VII and XIII) and unsaturated analogs (I and XII) may not be the same for [2.2.2]- and [2.2.1]bicyclic systems.

Of greater significance is the fact that for two reasons the rate of solvolysis of bicyclo[2.2.2]octan-2-yl p-toluenesulfonate (VII) does not correspond to the rate of unassisted ionization. In the first place, the rate of ionization of VII is apparently anchimerically accelerated. Secondly, because of ion pair return[15] (presumably internal return[22]) the rate of ionization of VII is greater than the rate of acetolysis.[23] As will be shown below, the rate of acetolysis of VII (which is about $^1/_5$ of the rate of ionization) is about 100 times greater than that estimated for unassisted ionization. Because of these complications the rate enhancement resulting from methylene participation in the acetolysis of I cannot be determined quantitatively. However, it is clear that the observed rate of acetolysis of I is at least 10^2 and perhaps over 10^3 times greater than if participation were not involved. Perhaps the endo-dehydronorbornyl system XII is the best model for estimating the unas-

(14) In principle, the two structures for the cation are distinguishable because II has a plane of symmetry whereas X is asymmetric. In another problem evidence is being sought as to whether or not the cation derived from active I (or the corresponding amine) is asymmetric.

(15) S. Winstein and A. H. Fainberg, J. Am Chem. Soc., 80, 459 (1958) and earlier papers in that series.

(16) S. Winstein, et al., ibid., 79, 4116 (1957); 75, 147 (1953); 73, 2700 (1951).

(17) H. C. Brown and H. L. Berneis, ibid., 75, 10 (1953).

(18) S. Winstein and M. Shatavsky, ibid., 78, 592 (1956).

(19) S. Winstein, B. K. Morse, E. Grunwald, H. W. Jones, J. Corse, D. Trifan and H. Marshall, ibid., 74, 1127 (1952).

(20) R. B. Turner, W. R. Meador and R. E. Winkler, ibid., 79, 4116 (1957).

(21) A. Streitwieser, Jr., Chem. Revs., 56, 571 (1956).

(22) S. Winstein, E. Clippinger, A. H. Fainberg, R. Heck and G. C. Robinson, J. Am. Chem. Soc., 78, 328 (1956).

(23) Apparently any ion pair return that might be involved in the acetolysis of I would not affect the rate of solvolysis (i.e., in this case the rate of solvolysis corresponds to the rate of ionization). This is because the expected product of ion pair return, axial-bicyclo[3.2.1]oct-3-en-2-yl p-toluenesulfonate, would solvolyze immediately. See A. H. Fainberg and S. Winstein, J. Am. Chem. Soc., 78, 2767 (1956), for a similar situation.

sisted rate for I. On this basis the rate enhancement amounts to a factor of 2.3×10^4 (Table IV).

Evidently, the interconversion of bicyclo[2.2.2]-octan-2-yl (VII) and *axial*-bicyclo[3.2.1]octan-2-yl *p*-toluenesulfonate (VIII), which accompanies solvolysis, involves internal return as illustrated by Scheme II. This is an expansion of Scheme I and includes the "intimate" ion pair intermediate (XIV)[22] common to the reversible isomerization and solvolysis. The bridged structure for the cation in XIV has been assigned[5] to accommodate the stereochemistry of the solvolysis; the bicyclo-[3.2.1]product has the *axial* configuration XV.[5] As will be shown below, the rates of ionization of VII and VIII are consistent with this assignment. Only the internal ion pair intermediate is included in this scheme. Presumably additional intermediates, including the dissociated bridged carbonium ion, are involved in the solvolysis-product forming reaction (k_8).[22] It is mechanistically significant that $k_{HOAc}/k_{EtOH} = 5.6$ for VII and 6.5 for VIII at 49° (this indicates a carbonium ion mechanism[16]) and that the addition of sodium acetate is essentially without effect (there are no indications of special salt effects[24] for solvolysis or isomerization).

SCHEME II

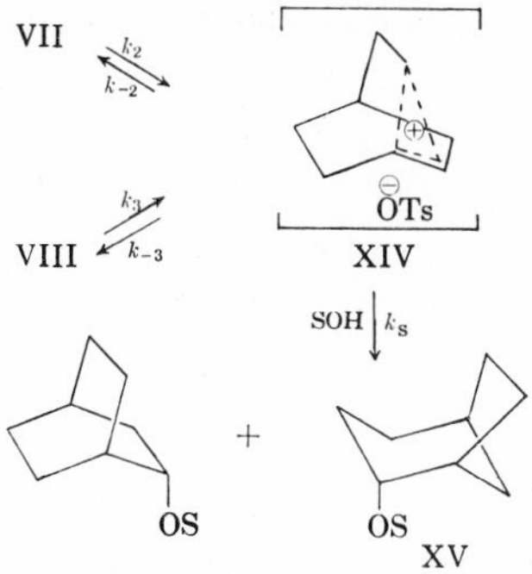

That the intramolecular interconversion of VII and VIII involves an ionic process as illustrated in Scheme II is indicated by the fact that it proceeds slower in ethanol than in acetic acid. Moreover, the data show qualitatively that the rate of equilibration relative to solvolysis is larger for acetolysis than ethanolysis; *i.e.*, k_{HOAc}/k_{EtOH} is larger for interconversion ($k_1 + k_{-1}$; Scheme I) than for solvolysis. This means that ($k_{-2} + k_{-3})/k_8$ is smaller for ethanolysis than acetolysis. It has been observed that for other systems the ratio of internal return to solvolysis is greater for acetolysis than ethanolysis.[15,25]

If a common bridged carbonium ion results from ionization of VII and VIII (*i.e.*, if methylene participation is involved with both isomers) the rates of ionization would be expected to be enhanced (anchimeric assistance). It is clear from the interconversion of VII and VIII (ion pair return) which accompanies solvolysis that the rate of ionization is greater than the rate of solvolysis; *i.e.*, the rate

of formation of XIV (ionization) is greater than that of production of solvolysis products.

The rates of ionization of VII and VIII (k_2 and k_3 in Scheme II) can be estimated as outlined below for VII. The rate of formation of that fraction of XIV which is converted to product is the rate of solvolysis, $k_{i[2.2.2]}$ (Scheme I and Table II). The rate of formation of the fraction of XIV involved in the isomerization can best be determined by considering the interconversion separately from solvolysis (*e.g.*, eq. 4). Two rate constants in eq. 4

$$\text{VII} \underset{k_{-2}}{\overset{k'_2}{\rightleftarrows}} \text{XIV} \underset{k_{-3}}{\overset{k'_3}{\rightleftarrows}} \text{VIII} \qquad (4)$$

(k'_2 and k'_3) differ from the corresponding constants (k_2 and k_3) in Scheme II in that the latter correspond to total rates of ionization and the former (eq. 4) correspond to rates of ionization of that fraction of substrate that is not converted to solvolysis product. Thus

$$k_2 = k'_2 + k_{i[2.2.2]} \qquad (5)$$

The value of $k_{i[2.2.2]}$ can be measured directly (Table II) and k'_2 can be estimated as follows. The rate constant for isomerization of VII to VIII, k_1 (Scheme I), is related to the constants in eq. 4 as

$$k_1 = k'_2/[1 + (k_{-2}/k_{-3})] \qquad (6)$$

As shown in the preceding section the lower limit for k_1 (Scheme I) is 1.4×10^{-4}. The value of k_{-2}/k_{-3} can be determined from the equilibrium constant for the interconversion ($K_{eq} = 2.1$) and eq. 7 by assuming that the value of the ratio k'_2/k'_3 corresponds to ratio of the initial rates of solvolysis of VII and VIII; *i.e.*, $k'_2/k'_3 = k_{i[2.2.2]}/k_{i[3.2.1]}$.

$$(k'_2/k'_3)/K_{eq} = k_{-2}/k_{-3} \qquad (7)$$

Thus for acetolysis at 49°

$$k_{-2}/k_{-3} = (7.4/4.3)/2.1 = 0.8$$

and with eq. 6 it can be shown that $k'_2 = 1.4(1 + 0.8) \times 10^{-4} = 2.5 \times 10^{-4}$. Thus the total rate of ionization of VII (k_2, Scheme II) computed from eq. 5 is $(2.5 + 0.7) \times 10^{-4}$ sec.$^{-1}$ or about 5 times larger than the rate constant for solvolysis ($k_{i[2.2.2]}$). A similar treatment for VIII gives a value of 1.7×10^{-4} sec.$^{-1}$ (acetolysis at 49°) for the total rate of ionization (k_3, Scheme II) which in this case is 4 times larger than the rate constant for solvolysis ($k_{i[3.2.1]}$).

It is difficult to estimate unassisted ionization rates for VII and VIII. Probably the best model for VII is the *endo*-norbornyl system XIII. In the absence of participation VII would be expected to be less reactive than XIII because of the aforementioned greater flexibility of the bicyclo[2.2.2] system. From Table IV it can be seen that VII solvolyzes over 10^2 times faster than XIII. This, however, underestimates the difference in ionization rates by a factor of 5 providing that the rate of solvolysis corresponds to the rate of ionization for XIII. Thus, there is little doubt but that methylene participation is involved in the ionization of VII.

It appears that ionization of *axial*-bicyclo[3.2.1]-octan-2-yl *p*-toluenesulfonate (VIII) is also anchimerically assisted. Its rate of solvolysis is 40 times greater than that of cyclohexyl *p*-toluenesul-

(24) S. Winstein and E. Clippinger, *J. Am. Chem. Soc.*, **78**, 2784 (1956).

(25) S. Winstein and K. C. Schreiber, *ibid.*, **74**, 2165 (1952); H. L. Goering, T. D. Nevitt and E. F. Silversmith, *ibid.*, **77**, 5026 (1955).

fonate[26] (Table IV). If the rate of solvolysis of cyclohexyl *p*-toluenesulfonate corresponds to its rate of ionization, the difference in rates of ionization is a factor of about 160. Thus the reactivities of VIII and VII appear to be consistent with the idea that each gives rise to a common bridged ion.[5]

Acetolysis of *equatorial*-bicyclo[3.2.1]octan-2-yl *p*-toluenesulfonate (XVI) gives acetate with retained configuration.[5] This suggests that ionization in this case also gives rise to a bridged ion (XVII).[5] It is possible that the rate of ionization is greater than that of acetolysis; internal return from the symmetrical "internal" ion pair intermediate would re-form the reactant and thus would not disturb the first-order solvolytic behavior. It is apparent that anchimeric acceleration, if present, is small. However, the present data are not inconsistent with the view that a bridged ion is involved in this case also.

TsO—

H XVI   XVII

Experimental

Materials.—The preparations and purification of *endo*-bicyclo[2.2.2]oct-5-en-2-yl (I),[3] bicyclo[2.2.2]octan-2-yl (VII)[5] and *equatorial*-bicyclo[3.2.1]octan-2-yl *p*-toluenesulfonate (XVI)[5] have been described earlier.

axial-Bicyclo[3.2.1]octan-2-yl *p*-toluenesulfonate (VIII) was prepared from the pure parent alcohol[3] by the method described for the preparation of VII.[5] After three recrystallizations from pentane the yield was 92%, m.p. 51.0–52.6°; Infrared bands: 9.50, 10.05, 10.65, 10.90, 11.25, 11.40, 11.75, 12.30, 12.40, 13.55, 13.90, 14.65 and 15.05 μ (carbon disulfide).

Anal. Calcd. for $C_{15}H_{20}O_3S$: C, 64.25; H, 7.19; solvolysis equiv., 280.4. Found: C, 64.38; H, 7.20; solvolysis equiv., 281.7 ± 1.2 (4 determinations).

Hydrogenation of *endo*-Bicyclo[2.2.2]oct-5-en-2-yl *p*-Toluenesulfonate (I).—A solution of I[3] in ether was hydrogenated at room temperature and atmospheric pressure over 5% palladium-on-barium sulfate. The theoretical amount of hydrogen was absorbed in 30 min., after which the reaction ceased. After removal of the catalyst (filtration) and solvent (distillation) the residual product was recrystallized from pentane. The melting point of this product was 54.6–55.2° (75% yield). Its infrared spectrum was indistinguishable from that of pure bicyclo-[2.2.2]octan-2-yl *p*-toluenesulfonate (VII), m.p. 54.2–55.0°.[5]

Kinetic Experiments.—The sealed ampule technique was used for the 49° and 42° experiments. The first point was taken as soon as possible after temperature equilibration and the reactions were quenched by cooling the ampules in ice. The ampules (which contained about 5.5 ml.) were then warmed to 25° after which the 5-ml. aliquots were measured and titrated. The reactions at lower temperatures were carried out in volumetric flasks. In these experiments the 5-ml. aliquots were measured at the temperature of the reaction and delivered into a flask cooled in ice-water and titrated immediately. Infinity titers for all experiments were obtained by heating aliquots in sealed ampules to 100° for a period corresponding to at least ten half-lives. In all cases observed infinity titers were within 2% of the calculated values.

A. Acetolysis.—Anhydrous acetic acid was prepared by refluxing reagent grade acetic acid with the calculated amount of acetic anhydride. The reactions were followed by titration of the aliquots with a standard 0.03 *M* solution of sodium acetate in acetic acid to the brom phenol blue end-point. In those experiments in which excess sodium

acetate was present, aliquots were delivered into an excess of standard perchloric acid in acetic acid and back-titrated with the standard sodium acetate solution.

B. Ethanolysis.—Reactions in anhydrous ethanol[27] and 80% aqueous acetone were followed by titrating aliquots to the brom thymol blue end-point with 0.03 *M* standard sodium methoxide in methanol. Typical acetolysis and ethanolysis experiments are summarized in Tables V and VI.

TABLE V

ACETOLYSIS OF *endo*-BICYCLO[2.2.2]OCT-5-EN-2-YL *p*-TOLUENESULFONATE (I) AT 30.07°

Time, 10^{-3} sec.	[ROTs] (10^2 *M*)	$10^5 k$, sec.$^{-1}$
0	2.19	
3.000	2.00	3.00
6.600	1.80	2.93
10.20	1.63	2.92
13.80	1.46	2.93
18.00	1.29	2.93
22.80	1.14	2.93
27.60	0.976	2.93
34.80	.786	2.95
42.00	.650	2.90
49.20	.512	2.95

Av. 2.94 ± 0.02

TABLE VI

ETHANOLYSIS OF BICYCLO[2.2.2]OCTAN-2-YL *p*-TOLUENESULFONATE (VII) AT 49.03°

Time, 10^{-3} sec.	[ROTs] (10^2 *M*)	$10^5 k$, sec.$^{-1}$
0	2.44	1.32[a]
11.52	2.12	1.24
17.28	1.97	1.24
23.04	1.85	1.21
28.80	1.73	1.19
35.22	1.62	1.17
40.80	1.52	1.16
47.82	1.41	1.14
54.90	1.32	1.13
62.10	1.23	1.11
86.22	0.964	1.08
99.90	.853	1.05
112.5	.748	1.05
125.1	.671	1.03
137.7	.590	1.03

Recalculation of data using 47.82×10^3 sec. as zero time

0	1.41	
7.080	1.32	1.01
14.28	1.23	0.978
38.40	0.964	.998
52.08	.853	.970
64.68	.748	.985
77.28	.671	.965
89.88	.590	.972

Av. 0.982 ± 0.012

[a] This value obtained by extrapolation to 0% reaction.

Isolation of Unsolvolyzed *p*-Toluenesulfonate. A. Acetolysis of Bicyclo[2.2.2]octan-2-yl *p*-Toluenesulfonte (VII).—A solution of 2.81 g. (0.01 mole) of VII, m.p. 54.2–55.0°, in 50 ml. of anhydrous acetic acid was heated at 49.03° for 190 min. (50% reaction). After cooling, the solution was poured into a flask containing 100 g. of crushed ice, and the resulting mixture was extracted with four 50-ml. portions of ether. The ether extracts were combined, washed with 10% sodium carbonate solution and dried over magnesium sulfate. The volume of ether was reduced to *ca.* 5 ml. under a stream of air and the resulting solution was diluted with 35 ml. of pentane. Crystallization was

(26) H. C. Brown and G. Ham, *J. Am. Chem. Soc.*, **78**, 2735 (1956).   (27) R. H. Manske, *ibid.*, **53**, 1104 (1931).

induced by cooling in Dry Ice, and the solvent was removed with a filter stick. Three recrystallizations of the residual material from ether–pentane yielded 886 mg. (63%) of material which melted at 42.5–43.7°. When mixed with VII, m.p. 54.2–55.0°, the mixture melted at 40.6–46.2°; when mixed with VIII, m.p. 51.0–52.6°, the mixture melted at 43.8–50.0°.

The infrared spectrum of the recovered tosylate was an exact composite of the spectra of VII[5] and VIII. The absence of bands at 10.55 and 12.00 μ showed that *equatorial*-bicyclo[3.2.1]octan-2-yl *p*-toluenesulfonate (XVI)[5] was not present. The *equatorial*-tosylate XVI is less reactive than VII or VIII and thus if present would survive the conditions of the isolation.

Quantitative infrared analyses were carried out by the method described in the previous paper[5] with the exception that synthetic mixtures were not analyzed. The bands used for analysis (0.4 *M* solutions in carbon disulfide) were 10.30 μ (VII) and 13.55 μ (VIII). The percentage transmittance at 2.8 μ was arbitrarily set at 100. The results indicated that the mixture contained 65 ± 5% VIII and 35 ± 5% VII.

B. Ethanolysis of *axial*-Bicyclo[3.2.1]octan-2-yl *p*-Toluenesulfonate (VIII).—A solution of 1.00 g. (0.0036 mole) of VIII, m.p. 51.0–52.6°, in 18 ml. of anhydrous ethanol was heated at 49.03° for 24 hr. (50% reaction). The solution was poured into 100 g. of crushed ice and the resulting mixture was extracted with five 30-ml. portions of ether. The ether extracts were combined, washed with dilute potassium hydroxide solution and water and dried over magnesium sulfate. After removal of the ether the solid residue was recrystallized four times from pentane. This gave 388 mg. (78%) of material which melted at 44.7–45.8°. The infrared spectrum differed from that described in A only in the relative intensities of the peaks. A quantitative infrared analysis indicated that the mixture contained 75 ± 5% VIII and 25 ± 5% VII.

A synthetic binary mixture consisting of 70% VIII and 30% VII melted at 42.8–43.8° after one recrystallization from pentane.

53 | Solvolytic Ring Closure to Nor-bornyl Acetate

Lawton (Paper No. 53) extended the method of LeNy and of Winstein (Papers 46, 48) into more familiar ground; he [a few weeks ahead of Bartlett and Bank, *J. Am. Chem. Soc.* **83**, 2591 (1961)] generated the norbornyl cation by the solvolysis of a 2-(Δ^3-cyclopentenyl)ethyl arenesulfonate and found that the double bond was responsible for an acceleration of two orders of magnitude in the rate of solvolysis, relative to the saturated analog. Ring closure in the products was 99.5% complete and the product was stereospecifically *exo,* as from norbornyl sulfonates.

From: *J. Am. Chem. Soc.* **83,** 2399 (1961)

1,5 PARTICIPATION IN THE SOLVOLYSIS OF β-(Δ³-CYCLOPENTENYL)-ETHYL p-NITROBENZENESULFONATE

Sir:

Although acetolysis of norbornyl brosylate (Ib) has been shown to proceed through the non-classical carbonium ion (II)[1,2] to *exo*-norbornyl acetate (Ia), a second possible product from ion II, β-(Δ³-cyclopentenyl)-ethyl acetate (IIIa), was not observed. For this reason, β-(Δ³-cyclopentenyl)-ethyl p-nitrobenzenesulfonate (IIIc) was prepared

I	II	III
a, R = acetyl	a, R = acetyl	
b, R = p-bromobenzene- sulfonyl	b, R = p-bromobenzene- sulfonyl	
	c, R = p-nitrobenzene- sulfonyl	

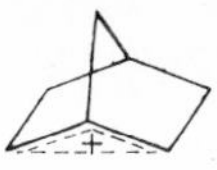

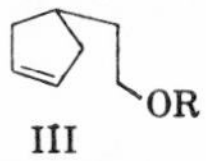

and solvolyzed in acetic acid at reflux temperature. The sole product of this acetolysis was *exo*-norbornyl acetate (Ia), b.p. 80°(11 mm.), n^{25}D 1.4563. Vapor phase chromatographic analysis[3] indicated less than 0.5% of acetate IIIa. The product was characterized further by hydrolysis to *exo*-norborneol,[4] m.p. 120–123°, and formation of the phenyl-urethan, m.p. 146–147°.

The required β-(Δ³-cyclopentenyl)-ethanol (III, R = H) was prepared as described by alkylation of ethyl cyanoacetate with Δ³-cyclopentenyl tosylate[5] and afforded a 60% yield of ethyl α-cyano-α-(Δ³-cyclopentenyl)acetate,[6] b.p. 143° (16 mm.), n^{25}D 1.4584, N-benzylamide, m.p. 115–116°, which upon hydrolysis with 50% aqueous ethanolic potassium hydroxide produced Δ³-cyclopentenyl-malonic acid, m.p. 149–150° dec., in 90% yield. Decarboxylation of the malonic acid in refluxing pyridine gave Δ³-cyclopentenylacetic acid, which without purification was reduced with lithium aluminum hydride to β-(Δ³-cyclopentenyl)-ethanol, b.p. 180–182°, n^{25}D 1.4691, phenylurethan, m.p. 62–64.5°, p-nitrobenzenesulfonate (IIIc), m.p. 65–67°. Hydrogenation of the unsaturated alcohol yielded ιβ-cyclopentylethanol,[7] b.p. 79–82°(10 mm.), n^{25}D 1.4559, p-nitrobenzenesulfonate, m.p. 74–75°.

Acetolysis of 0.04 *M* p-nitrobenzenesulfonate IIIc at 60° gave a first order titrimetric rate constant of 1.10 × 10⁻⁴ sec.⁻¹. This is about 95 times faster than the rate observed for acetolysis of β-cyclopentylethyl p-nitrobenzenesulfonate under the same conditions and indicates 1,5 participation of the double bond, presumably with formation of the non-classical structure II. Acetolysis of p-nitrobenzenesulfonate IIIc in 0.04 *M* sodium acetate in acetic acid also gave acetate Ia exclusively,

while acetolysis of p-bromobenzenesulfonate IIIb (an oil at room temperature) in acetic acid alone gave acetate Ia containing about 3% unsaturated acetate IIIa.[8]

Participation of the double bond with formation of the norbornyl structure gives additional information about the character of the non-classical carbonium ion. Aside from this inherent theoretical interest, the process provides a unique synthetic route to this, and possibly other, bicyclic systems.

The author wishes to thank the faculty and graduate students of the Department of Chemistry, University of Wisconsin, for their helpful discussions.

DEPARTMENT OF CHEMISTRY
UNIVERSITY OF WISCONSIN   RICHARD G. LAWTON
MADISON 6, WISCONSIN

RECEIVED APRIL 6, 1961

(1) S. Winstein and D. S. Trifan, *J. Am. Chem. Soc.*, **71,** 2953 (1949); **74,** 1147 (1952); **74,** 1154 (1952).

(2) J. D. Roberts and C. C. Lee, *ibid.*, **73,** 5009 (1951).

(3) Analysis was carried out with a 150 foot Golay "Ukon" column, 160°.

(4) Trace amounts of *endo* product were present as indicated by vapor phase chromatography.

(5) E. L. Allred, J. Sonnenberg and S. Winstein, *ibid.*, **81,** 5833 (1959); *J. Org. Chem.*, **25,** 26 (1960).

(6) Except where indicated, satisfactory analyses have been obtained for all new compounds.

(7) G. R. Yohe and R. Adams, *J. Am. Chem. Soc.*, **50,** 1505 (1928).

54, 55 | The Trishomocyclopropenyl and Related Cations

Papers 54 and 55, by Winstein and Sonnenberg, present a detailed experimental study of the *cis*- and *trans*-3-bicyclo(3.1.0) hexanols and the solvolysis of their tosylates. The following points of difference are observed and interpreted as indicating that the *cis* isomer solvolyzes by way of the nonclassical trishomocyclopropenyl cation II (see also Paper No. 41): (1) The *cis* undergoes ionization at an accelerated rate. Corrected for internal return, k_{cis}/k_{trans} is about 44. (2) The *cis* shows a special salt effect, the *trans* does not. Although it is not clear that the special salt effect need be confined to nonclassical ion pairs, there appears to be an empirical correlation to this effect. (3) The acetate products are stereospecifically *cis* from both isomers. (4) The *cis* gave only acetate product, the *trans* gave 33% olefin. (5) Solvolysis of the *cis* was attended by statistical distribution of deuterium among the 1-, 3-, and 5-positions when the deuterium was originally at C-3 alone or at C-1 and C-5 alone. (6) Solvolysis of the *trans*-tosylate under similar conditions yielded only about 7% redistribution of deuterium from the 3-position.

Paper No. 55 contains a general discussion of the theoretical possibility that a methylene group can be incorporated in place of a σ bond at any number of points in an aromatic system. The accessibility of such ions depends in large part upon a favorable geometry of the precursor molecule; in the present case it is greatly aided by the fact that the chair conformation of the cyclohexane ring is the same as that required for the trishomocyclopropenium ion to attain maximum electronic delocalization. The bishomocyclopropenium ion is not favorable enough to impart any acceleration to the solvolysis of Δ^3-cyclopentenyl tosylate (Table

III), although the reactivity of some *cyclobutenyl* compounds may be associated with homocyclopropenyl character in the cation.[1,2]

[1] E. F. Kiefer and J. D. Roberts, *J. Am. Chem. Soc.* **84**, 784 (1962).
[2] S. L. Manatt, M. Vogel, D. Knutson, and J. D. Roberts, *ibid.*, **86**, 2645 (1964).

From: *J. Am. Chem. Soc.* **83**, 3235–44 (1961)

[Contribution from the Department of Chemistry, University of California, Los Angeles 24, Calif.]

Homoconjugation and Homoaromaticity. III.[1] The 3-Bicyclo[3.1.0]hexyl System[2,3]

By S. Winstein and Joseph Sonnenberg
Received January 3, 1961

In order to study the nature of the theoretically interesting 3-bicyclo[3.1.0]hexyl cation, synthetic routes to 3-bicyclo[3.1.0]-hexanone and the epimeric bicyclohexanols have been devised. The cis- and trans-3-bicyclo[3.1.0]hexyl toluenesulfonates show contrasting behavior in acetolysis. Acetolysis is associated with a special salt effect and some anchimeric acceleration in the case of the cis epimer, but not the trans. Also, the cis-toluenesulfonate leads to cis-acetate with complete retention of configuration and no olefin, while the trans-toluenesulfonate gives rise to cis-acetate with complete inversion of configuration, together with considerable olefin. This behavior is suggestive of the intervention of a non-classical cation in acetolysis of the cis-toluenesulfonate, but not the trans.

Some years ago in another connection the question arose whether a 3-bicyclo[3.1.0.]hexyl cation I might have a symmetrical non-classical structure II. Examination of models suggested that the amount of reorganization and rehybridization required to make carbon atoms 1, 3 and 5 equivalent, as in the case of three alternate carbon atoms in chair cyclohexane, was not enormous. On the other hand, substantial quantum-mechanical delocalization energy could be anticipated on theoretical grounds[4,5] for a cation such as II. Therefore, structure II for the 3-bicyclohexyl cation appeared to us to be a definite possibility. It seemed to us also that the existence of a structure such as II would have far-reaching implications for organic chemistry.[1b] Therefore, we synthesized and studied the behavior of 3-bicyclo[3.1.0.]hexyl derivatives in acetolysis. Some of the results of this work are described and discussed in the present manuscript.

Synthesis of 3-Bicyclo[3.1.0.]hexanone.

Since neither 3-bicyclo[3.1.0.]hexanone (XI) nor the related alcohols XIII-C-OH and XIII-T-OH were known when we commenced this work, it was necessary to devise synthetic approaches to the 3-bicyclohexyl system. One of our two approaches involves formation of 3-bicyclo[3.1.0.]hexanone (XI) from cyclopropane-cis-1,2-diacetic acid (VII). The second method of synthesis involves methylene addition to Δ³-cyclopentenol (XII) to yield 3-bicyclo[3.1.0.]hexanol (XIII-OH).

While our work was in progress, a Communication by Hofmann, Orochena and Yoho[6a] appeared

which reported a synthesis of cyclopropane-cis-1,2-diacetic acid from 1,4-cyclohexadiene (III) by way of 7,7-dibromonorcar-3-ene (IV) and the 3,3-dibromocyclopropane-cis-1,2-diacetic acid (V-III). Our own synthesis of cyclopropane-cis-1,2-diacetic acid before the experimental details of their procedure were available[6b] was analogous to theirs, except that debromination of the dibromonorcarene IV was carried out before oxidation of the olefinic group to a dicarboxylic acid.

Treatment of 1,4-cyclohexadiene with dibromocarbene[7] gave rise to a satisfactory yield of dibromonorcarene[6b] IV, together with a small amount of tetrabromide[6b,8] V. Debromination of the dibromonorcarene IV proceeds in high yield with a large excess of sodium in moist methanol.[7,9,11]

(1) First two papers in this series: (a) I, S. Winstein, J. Sonnenberg and L. de Vries, *J. Am. Chem. Soc.*, **81**, 6523 (1959); (b) II, S. Winstein, *ibid.*, **81**, 6524 (1959).

(2) This research was supported by a grant from the Petroleum Research Fund administered by the American Chemical Society. Grateful acknowledgment is hereby made to the donors of this fund.

(3) The main results reported in the present manuscript were presented by S. Winstein at the Welch Foundation Conference on Molecular Structure and Organic Reactions, Houston, Tex., November 7–9, 1960.

(4) (a) E. Hückel, *Z. Physik*, **70**, 204 (1931); (b) J. D. Roberts, A. Streitwieser, Jr., and C. M. Regan, *J. Am. Chem. Soc.*, **74**, 4579 (1952).

(5) (a) M. Simonetta and S. Winstein, *ibid.*, **76**, 18 (1954); (b) C. F. Wilcox, Jr., S. Winstein and W. G. McMillan, *ibid.*, **82**, 5450 (1960).

(6) (a) K. Hofmann, S. F. Orochena and C. W. Yoho, *ibid.*, **79**, 3608 (1957); (b) K. Hofmann, S. F. Orochena, S. M. Sax and G. A. Jeffrey, *ibid.*, **81**, 992 (1959).

(7) W. E. Doering and A. K. Hoffmann, *ibid.*, **76**, 6162 (1954).

(8) A lachrymatory material, also reported by Hofmann, Orochena and Yoho,[6b] was observed in 2% yield in the present work. This proved to be benzyl bromide, formed probably from the adduct of dibromocarbene to 1,3-cyclohexadiene, a contaminant of the 1,4-cyclohexadiene employed.

(9) This dehalogenation also proceeds well with lithium and t-butyl alcohol in tetrahydrofuran[10] (unpublished work by P. Bruck).

(10) P. Bruck, D. Thompson and S. Winstein, *Chemistry & Industry*, 405 (1960).

(11) Norcar-3-ene has been prepared recently by H. E. Simmons directly from 1,4-cyclohexadiene with methylene iodide and the zinc-copper couple (H. E. Simmons, private communication).

Conversion of the norcarene VI to cyclopropane-*cis*-1,2-diacetic acid was carried out by ozonolysis in a 2:1 acetic acid–acetic anhydride mixture. The yield of acid (63%) was definitely better than in glacial acetic acid alone and far superior to that in ethyl acetate.[12]

The results of an attempted preparation of 3-bicyclo[3.1.0.]hexanone (XI) directly from the barium salt of cyclopropane-*cis*-1,2-diacetic acid were discouraging, so the Dieckmann condensation of the diethyl ester of the cyclopropane-*cis*-1,2-diacetic acid was resorted to. By this method the β-keto-ester X was obtained in over-all yields of 60–80% from the acid VII. By hydrolysis and decarboxylation the keto-ester X was converted to bicyclohexanone XI in 50% yield.

Methylene Addition to Δ³-Cyclopentenol.—After we developed a convenient preparation of Δ³-cyclo-pentenol[13] (XII), direct methylene addition appeared to provide an attractive possible alternative route to the 3-bicyclo[3.1.0.]hexyl system. Photolysis of diazomethane in the presence of Δ³-cyclo-pentenol (XII) or its acetate in ether solution yielded no bicyclic derivative. The diethyl ether solvent was apparently attacked in preference to the olefinic group.[14] Preliminary work on the addition of dibromocarbene to Δ³-cyclopentenyl derivatives showed that this method might be capable of development into a practical synthesis. However, our best results were obtained with the method of Simmons and Smith[16] for preparing cyclopropanes directly from olefins using methylene iodide and zinc–copper couple in ether.

A major problem in the olefin–methylene iodide synthesis of cyclopropanes is a good, reproducible zinc–copper couple. By modifying the procedure described by Hennion and Sheehan,[17] a fairly active zinc–copper couple was obtained which worked satisfactorily in the Simmons and Smith reaction. This method for preparing the couple is simple and easily reproducible. A similar procedure has recently been described.[18]

From the action of two parts methylene iodide and 4 parts zinc–copper couple on one part Δ³-cyclopentenol (XII), a gratifying 75% yield of 3-bicyclo[3.1.0.]hexanol was obtained. Vapor phase chromatographic analysis of the product showed less than 0.5% of one of the two epimeric bicyclo-hexanols, the addition being highly stereospecific. From the configurational assignments in a later section of this paper, it is the *cis*-3-bicyclo[3.1.0.]-hexanol (XIII-C-OH) which is produced by this method.

The above-described reaction of Δ³-cyclopentenol is, apparently, the first example of the addition of iodomethylzinc iodide to an unsaturated alcohol.

Not only does the hydroxyl group permit addition of methylene to the olefinic group, but it strongly facilitates this reaction. Thus, the reaction with Δ³-cyclopentenol is much more rapid and proceeds with much higher yield than with Δ³-cyclopentenyl acetate or cyclopentadiene. The latter two substances led to *ca.* 3% yields of bicyclic products under the identical conditions which gave rise to a high yield of bicyclohexanol from Δ³-cyclopentenol.

Oxidation of the 3-bicyclo[3.1.0.]hexanol (XIII-C-OH) from the Simmons–Smith reaction by means of chromium trioxide in pyridine gave rise to bicyclohexanone XI in good yield.

3-Bicyclo[3.1.0.]hexanone and its Reduction.—The 3-bicyclo[3.1.0.]hexanone differs from the previously reported 2-bicyclo[3.1.0.]hexanone[19] in physical properties and in melting point and ultraviolet spectral properties of the corresponding 2,4-dinitrophenylhydrazones. The infrared spectrum of the 3-bicyclohexanone XI is summarized in the experimental section together with the ultraviolet spectrum of ketone XI and those of Δ³-cyclopentenone, cyclopentanone and cyclohexanone for comparison.

The ultraviolet spectra of bicyclohexanone XI and its olefinic analog, Δ³-cyclopentenone, are of some interest in connection with the subject of "interactions[3,5,20] between non-conjugated chromophores." In the $n \rightarrow \pi^*$-region of the spectrum (*ca.* 2800 Å.), neither 3-bicyclo[3.1.0.]hexanone (XI) nor Δ³-cyclopentenone show the enhanced extinction coefficient characteristic of many β,γ-unsaturated ketones.[20a] Also, in the shorter wave length region of the spectrum down to *ca.* 1860 Å., neither compound shows evidence of any new $\pi \rightarrow \pi^*$ band such as those that appear in the spectra of certain β,γ-unsaturated ketones.[20b]

As regards the enhancement of the $n \rightarrow \pi^*$-extinction coefficient of certain β,γ-unsaturated ketones, Labhart and Wagniere[20b] have correlated this phenomenon with overlap of a non-bonding *p*-orbital on the oxygen atom with the bonding olefinic π-orbital. On this basis, no increase of $n \rightarrow \pi^*$-extinction coefficient would be anticipated for Δ³-cyclopentenone, since the pertinent overlap integral has a value of zero for symmetry reasons.[3] Since Δ³-cyclopentenone shows no increase in intensity of the $n \rightarrow \pi^*$-transition, none is expected for the bicyclohexanone XI.

Reduction of the 3-bicyclo[3.1.0.]hexanone by several methods gave rise to mixtures of the two epimeric *cis*- and *trans*-3-bicyclo[3.1.0.]hexanols (XIII-C-OH and XIII-T-OH). The reducing agents included lithium aluminum hydride in ether[21] at −78°, lithium tri-*t*-butoxyaluminohydride in tetrahydrofuran,[22] sodium borohydride in pyridine[23] and aluminum isopropylate in isopropyl

(12) A. L. Henne and P. Hill, *J. Am. Chem. Soc.*, **65**, 752 (1943).

(13) (a) S. Winstein, E. L. Allred and J. Sonnenberg, *ibid.*, **81**, 5833 (1959); (b) E. L. Allred, J. Sonnenberg and S. Winstein, *J. Org. Chem.*, **25**, 26 (1960); (c) J. Sonnenberg, unpublished work.

(14) This is in line with Meerwein's report[15] that diazomethane reacts in diethyl ether to give ethyl *n*-propyl and ethyl isopropyl ether as products.

(15) H. Meerwein, H. Rathjen and H. Werner, *Ber.*, **75**, 1610 (1942).

(16) (a) H. E. Simmons and R. D. Smith, *J. Am. Chem. Soc.*, **80**, 5323 (1958); (b) **81**, 4256 (1959).

(17) G. F. Hennion and J. J. Sheehan, *ibid.*, **71**, 1964 (1949).

(18) R. S. Shank and H. Schechter, *J. Org. Chem.*, **24**, 1825 (1959).

(19) N. A. Nelson and G. A. Mortimer, *ibid.*, **22**, 1146 (1947).

(20) (a) R. C. Cookson and N. S. Wariyar, *J. Chem. Soc.*, 2302 (1956); (b) H. Labhart and G. Wagniere, *Helv. Chim. Acta*, **42**, 2219 (1959)

(21) A. Streitwieser, Jr., and W. D. Schaeffer, *J. Am. Chem. Soc.*, **79**, 6233 (1957).

(22) H. C. Brown and R. F. McFarlin, *ibid.*, **78**, 252 (1956); **80**, 5372 (1958).

(23) W. G. Dauben, G. J. Fonken and D. S. Noyce, *ibid.*, **78**, 2579 (1956).

alcohol.[24] The proportions of the two epimeric alcohols in the product could be determined by vapor phase chromatography, and the results are summarized in Table I.

TABLE I

FORMATION AND EQUILIBRATION OF BICYCLOHEXANOLS FROM 3-BICYCLO[3.1.0.]HEXANONE

Method	Temp., °C.	10^3 moles ketone	% yield (recovery)	Isomer ratio in distilled alcohol cis:trans
		Reductions		
LiAlH₄–ether	−78	29.0	85	89:11
		25.0		87.5:12.5
LiAlH(OBu-t)₃–THF	25	2.1		88:12
NaBH₄–pyridine	75	2.3	44	64 ± 2:36 ± 2
Al(OPr-i)₃–i-PrOH	75	31.3		40:60
		1.0		44:56
		Equilibration		
Al(OPr-i)₃–i-PrOH	82	2.5ᵃ	89	72:28
		2.1ᵇ	62	76:24

ᵃ 90:10 cis:trans mixture of the 3-bicyclo[3.1.0.]hexanols. ᵇ 60:40 cis:trans mixture of the 3-bicyclo[3.1.0.]hexanols.

Equilibration of the two bicyclohexanols was carried out by the procedure of Eliel and Ro[24] using aluminum isopropylate with a trace of acetone in refluxing isopropyl alcohol. As summarized in Table I, a 74:26 equilibrium mixture of epimeric alcohols is approached from both directions.

From the 88:12 cis-rich alcohol mixtures obtained by hydride reduction of the bicyclohexanone, the pure cis-alcohol XIII-C-OH could be obtained by chromotography. The trans-alcohol XIII-T-OH could be obtained free from the cis epimer by chromatographic separation of the 60:40 trans-rich alcohol mixture from aluminum isopropylate reduction of the ketone.

Assignment of Configuration to the Bicyclohexanols.—The 3-bicyclo[3.1.0]hexyl derivatives can be expected to have a chair-like conformation resembling the chair conformation of cyclohexane and a puckered[25] conformation of the cyclopentane ring.[26] Due to the restriction of the fused 3-membered ring, the puckering of the cyclopentane ring occurs primarily at the 3-position and does not oscillate around the ring. For this reason the 5-membered ring may be expected to assume the Cs[27] or envelope[28] form, and the cis- and trans-3-bicyclo[3.1.0]hexanols will have largely equatorial and axial dispositions of the hydroxyl group, respectively. This is depicted in formulas XIII-C-OH and XIII-T-OH. With the available evidence it is possible to make a convincing assignment of configuration to the two bicyclohexanols obtained in reduction of 3-bicyclo[3.1.0]hexanone.

The results obtained in reduction of the bicyclohexanone and equilibration of the bicyclohexanols

(24) E. L. Eliel and R. S. Ro, J. Am. Chem. Soc., **79**, 5992 (1957).

(25) (a) J. G. Aston, S. C. Schumann, H. L. Fink and P. M. Doty, ibid., **63**, 2029 (1941); **65**, 341 (1943); (b) J. E. Kilpatrick, K. S. Pitzer and R. Spitzer, ibid., **69**, 2483 (1947).

(26) In carbonyl stretching frequency (1739 cm.⁻¹), the 3-bicyclo[3.1.0.]hexanone resembles cyclopentanone (1743 cm.⁻¹) much more closely than cyclohexanone (1709 cm.⁻¹). This resemblance exists also for the n → π*-absorption in the ultraviolet.

(27) K. S. Pitzer and W. Donath, J. Am. Chem. Soc., **81**, 3213 (1959).

(28) F. V. Brutcher, et al., ibid., **81**, 4915 (1959).

can be used to assign configurations to the epimeric 3-bicyclo[3.1.0]hexanols. Thus, reductions of relatively unhindered cyclohexanones with lithium aluminum hydride conventionally lead to a high proportion of the more stable equatorial alcohol,[23] while aluminum isopropylate tends to give more of the less stable axial alcohol. On this basis, the 3-bicyclo[3.1.0]hexanol favored at equilibrium and formed predominantly in the hydride reductions is the equatorial cis-alcohol XIII-C-OH. The bicyclohexanol which is formed predominantly by aluminum isopropylate reduction is therefore the axial trans-alcohol XIII-T-OH.

Observed relationships between other cis and trans pairs of cyclopentane derivatives as regards physical properties and relative stability also support the above configurational assignments to the 3-bicyclo[3.1.0]hexanols. In the cyclopentane series, the trans isomer tends to have the higher boiling point and refractive index.[29] With the 1,3-dimethylcyclopentanes, the cis isomer has been found to be the thermodynamically more stable one.[30] These are just the relationships which obtain with the cis-and trans-3-bicyclo[3.1.0]hexanols as regards boiling point, refractive index and relative stability.

Other chemical evidence strongly supports the above assignment of configuration to the 3-bicyclo[3.1.0]hexanols. One such piece of evidence is the facilitating stereospecific effect of the hydroxyl group of Δ³-cyclopentenol in the Simmons–Smith reaction. This must be due to some participation by the hydroxyl group in the mechanism of methylene addition by the iodomethylzinc iodide.[16] Without attempting to go into details, the hydroxyl participation must involve oxygen atom coördination to zinc. This would make the methylene addition to the olefinic group occur cis to the hydroxyl group, cis-3-bicyclo[3.1.0]hexanol (XIII-C-OH) being the expected product from an hydroxyl group-facilitated reaction.[31] Another important piece of chemical evidence supporting the stated configurational assignment to the bicyclohexanols is the relative behavior of the corresponding toluenesulfonates XIII-C-OTs and XIII-T-OTs in acetolysis, which is described below and in the subsequent paper. Anchimeric acceleration of ionization of the cis epimer XIII-C-OTs compared to the trans, with formation of a non-classical carbonium ion, is in line with the present configurational assignment, but could not be understood with a reversed one.

Rates and Salt Effects in Acetolysis.—In Table II are summarized the measured first-order rates of acetolysis of the cis- and trans-3-bicyclo[3.1.0]-hexyl toluenesulfonates (XIII-C-OTs and XIII-T-OTs), as well as the cyclopentyl ester which was examined for comparison. Rates were measured at 50° and 75° in anhydrous acetic acid both with and without added sodium acetate or lithium per-

(29) S. F. Birch and R. A. Dean, J. Chem. Soc., 2477 (1953).

(30) J. N. Haresnape, Chemistry & Industry, 1091 (1953).

(31) The stereospecific facilitating effect of the hydroxyl group in the reaction of Δ³-cyclopentenol with iodomethylzinc iodide is analogous to similar effects of the hydroxyl group in olefine addition reactions observed by Henbest [e.g., H. B. Henbest and R. A. Wilson, J. Chem. Soc., 1958 (1957)].

I-C   XIII-C-OTs

I-T   II

XIII-T-OTs   XIII-C-OAc

TABLE II

RATES OF ACETOLYSIS OF SOME TOLUENESULFONATES

[ROTs], $10^3 M$	Temp. °C.	Other solute	Concn., $10^2 M$	$10^5 k$, sec.$^{-1}$ Integ.	Graphical
*cis*-3-Bicyclohexyl					
18.0[a]	50.0	....	..	2.31 ± 0.02	2.34
18.2[b]	50.0	....	..	2.53 ± .05	2.56[e]
18.2[b]	75.0	....	..	40.9 ± .3	40.9[e]
12.6[c]	50.0	....	..	2.44 ± .02	2.43
9.0[d]	50.0	....	..	2.47 ± .05	2.43
9.0[c]	50.0	....	..	2.46 ± .04	2.51
12.6[b]	50.0	NaOAc	3.05	4.60 ± .08	4.75[f]
12.6[b]	75.0	NaOAc	3.05	69.0 ± .29	72.0[f]
9.9[d]	50.0	LiClO$_4$	0.40	5.40 ± .05	5.36
12.3[c]	50.0	LiClO$_4$	1.00	7.69 ± .06	7.64
9.4[d]	50.0	LiClO$_4$	2.00	10.5 ± .1	10.5
9.3[d]	50.0	LiClO$_4$	3.00	12.7 ± .2	12.7
12.9[c]	50.0	LiClO$_4$	4.00	14.9 ± .2	14.9
12.4[c]	50.0	LiClO$_4$	6.00	18.9 ± .3	19.0
12.5[c]	50.0	LiClO$_4$	8.00	22.1 ± .2	22.1
*trans*-3-Bicyclohexyl					
17.7[g]	75.0	....	..	....	3.80
5.3[g]	75.0	....	..	....	4.80
8.6[h]	50.0	....	..	0.266 ± 0.023	..
13.2[g]	75.0	NaOAc	3.05	....	5.10
8.3[h]	50.0	NaOAc	3.05	....	0.295
8.1[g]	75.0	LiClO$_4$	2.00	7.66 ± 0.07	7.64
8.0[g]	75.0	LiClO$_4$	4.00	9.92 ± .26	9.89
7.6[g]	75.0	LiClO$_4$	8.00	14.1 ± .2	14.0
Cyclopentyl					
22.3	50.0	....	..	3.60 ± .13	..
29.5	50.0	NaOAc	3.05	3.76 ± .05	..
28.2	75.0	NaOAc	3.05	54.1 ± .8	..

[a] Toluenesulfonate prepared from an 89:11 *cis:trans* mixture of the 3-bicyclo[3.1.0]hexanols; m.p. 46–48°. [b,c] Toluenesulfonates prepared from the chromatographed *cis*-3-bicyclo[3.1.0]-hexanol; m.p. 51.6–51.8° and 51.5–52.°0, respectively. [d] Toluenesulfonate prepared from *cis*-alcohol from the Simmons and Smith reaction; m.p. 50.6–51.6°. [e] At 50.0°; $\Delta H^{\pm} = 24.1$ kcal./mole; $\Delta S^{\pm} = -5.0$ e.u. [f] At 50.0°; $\Delta H^{\pm} = 23.7$ kcal./mole; $\Delta S^{\pm} = -5.2$ e.u. [g] Toluenesulfonate, m.p. 70.5–72.0°. [h] Toluenesulfonate, m.p. 70.8–71.3°.

chlorate. The latter salt was added especially to determine whether acetolysis of any of the substances was subject to a special salt effect.[32]

With cyclopentyl toluenesulfonate, added sodium acetate increased the first-order titrimetric rate constant, k_t, by amounts corresponding to the so-called "normal" salt effect.[32,33] In Table III is summarized the corresponding b-value derived from the fit of the salt effects to the linear relation[33] 1, where k_t^0 is the titrimetric rate constant at zero salt concentration.

$$k_t = k_t^0 [1 + b(\text{salt})] \quad (1)$$
$$k_t = k_{\text{ext}}^0 [1 + b(\text{LiClO}_4)] \quad (2)$$

With the *cis*-3-bicyclo[3.1.0]hexyl toluenesulfonate (XIII-C-OTs), added 0.03 M sodium acetate caused an unusually large rate enhancement, the apparent b-value being 30 compared to 1–2 for the cyclopentyl and Δ^3-cyclopentenyl analogs. Added lithium perchlorate definitely gave rise to a steep special salt effect at low concentrations, followed by the normal, more shallow, linear pattern of salt effects at the higher concentrations. Fitting the normal linear portion of the k_t *vs.* [LiClO$_4$] plot to eq. 2, where k_{ext}^0 is a rate constant which includes the special but none of the normal salt effect, one obtains a k_{ext}^0/k_t^0 ratio of 3.2. This measures the magnitude of the special salt effect.[32] The efficiency of lithium perchlorate in the special salt effect may be gauged from the value of 4 × $10^{-3} M$ for [LiClO$_4$]$_{1/2}$, the salt concentration which introduces half of the special salt effect.

By contrast with its *cis* epimer, the *trans*-3-bicyclo[3.1.0]hexyl toluenesulfonate (XIII-T-OTs) displayed little or no special salt effect in its acetolysis. With this epimer, there is some uncertainty in the k_t^0 value because of difficulties discussed more fully in the Experimental section. However, any special salt effect of lithium perchlorate is quite small. For example, a k_{ext}^0/k_t^0 value of 1.17 is obtained by applying eq. 2 to the k_t values at 0.02, 0.04 and 0.08 M lithium perchlorate concentrations and comparing the de-

rived k_{ext}^0 value with the k_t^0 values listed in Table III.

Solvolysis Products.—Vapor phase chromatographic analysis using *n*-decane as an internal standard showed that the product from solvolysis of the *cis*-3-bicyclo[3.1.0]hexyl toluenesulfonate (XIII-C-OTs) in acetic acid containing sodium acetate is quantitatively the bicyclohexyl acetate. The extent of olefin formation must have been less than 0.5%. On the other hand, the *trans*-3-bicyclo[3.1.0]hexyl toluenesulfonate (XIII-T-OTs) gave rise only to 67% of bicyclohexyl acetate. The remaining 33% must be attributed to olefin formation. Three new peaks were observed in vapor phase chromatography of the product, two of them with retention times similar to that of cyclohexene and the other with a somewhat longer retention time. However, the hydrocarbon fraction was not investigated further.

In order to determine the proportions of *cis* and *trans* isomers in the acetate products from solvolysis, they were reduced with lithium aluminum hydride and the product alcohols were ex-

(32) S. Winstein, *et al.*, (a) *J. Am. Chem. Soc.*, **76**, 2597 (1954); (b) *Chemistry & Industry*, 664 (1954); (c) *Experientia Suppl. II*, 137 (1955); (d) *J. Am. Chem. Soc.*, **80**, 169 (1958).
(33) S. Winstein and A. H. Fainberg, *ibid.*, **78**, 2763 (1956).

TABLE III

SUMMARY OF OBSERVED SALT EFFECTS IN ACETOLYSIS OF SEVERAL TOLUENESULFONATES

ROTs	Temp., °C.	Special salt effect	10⁵ k, sec.⁻¹		k_{ext}^0/k_t^0	b-Values LiClO₄	Av. fit % of k	b-Values NaOAc
			k_{ext}^0	k_t^0				
cis-3-Bicyclo[3.1.0]hexyl	50.0	Yes	7.87	2.48	3.17[a]	22.9	1.2	30[b]
trans-3-Bicyclo[3.1.0]hexyl	75.0	f	5.60	4.80	1.17	18.8	0.7	2.0[c]
Δ³-Cyclopentenyl[e]	50.0	No	0.436	0.438	0.99	30.4	1.0	1.8
Cyclopentyl[d]	50.0	No		3.60				1.5
Cyclohexyl[d]	50.0	No		0.179		37.2		

[a] (LiClO₄)₁/₂ is 4 × 10⁻³ M.   [b] Based on one point; includes contribution from the special salt effect.   [c] Value observed at 50.0° is 3.6.   [d] Data of Fainberg and Winstein.[34]   [e] Data of Joseph Sonnenberg.[13c]   [f] Small or none.

amined vapor phase chromatographically using a carbowax column. The product alcohols from both cis-and trans-toluenesulfonates were nearly pure cis, the one from cis-toluenesulfonate being at least 98.5% cis, and the one from trans-toluene-sulfonate being at least 99.5% cis. The results are summarized in Table IV. A control experiment on a 70:30 cis:trans mixture of 3-bicyclo-[3.1.0]hexyl acetates showed that the acetates quantitatively survived the reaction conditions and confirmed the reliability of the whole workup and analytical procedure (Table IV).

Discussion.—Examining the available evidence for any indication that a unique carbonium ion species may intervene in solvolysis of a 3-bicyclo-[3.1.0]hexyl toluenesulfonate, we come first to the question of anchimeric acceleration. As is brought out in Table V, the rate data do give some indication of slight anchimeric acceleration of solvolysis of the cis-3-bicyclo[3.1.0]hexyl toluene-sulfonate (XIII-C-OTs). However, the usual prob-lem exists regarding what is the best compound for comparison with the cis-toluenesulfonate in assess-ing anchimeric acceleration in the latter. Cyclo-pentyl and cyclohexyl toluenesulfonates, either of which might be suggested as models, differ between themselves by a factor of 20 in acetolysis rate at 50°.

TABLE IV

SUMMARY OF PRODUCTS OF ACETOLYSIS OF 3-BICYCLO-[3.1.0]HEXYL TOLUENESULFONATES WITH 0.10 M SODIUM ACETATE

Compound	Temp., °C.	[ROTs], 10² M	Time, hr.	Products, % Acetate	Olefin	Alcohol compn., % cis	trans
cis-ROTs	50.0	8.1	42.0	100	0[a]	98.5	1.5
trans-ROTs	75.0	8.5	38.5	66.5	33[b]	100	0[a]
	75.0	4.9	38.5	67.8		...	..
cis- and trans- ROAc[c]	75.0	7.3	38.5	101	0[a]	70	30

[a] < 0.5%.   [b] Difference between 100 and % yield of ace-tate.   [c] 70:30 cis:trans mixture.

Reference to Table V shows that the trans-3-bicyclo[3.1.0]hexyl toluenesulfonate ranks between the cyclohexyl and Δ³-cyclopentenyl analogs in reactivity, all three of these esters having closely similar acetolysis rate constants. On the other hand, the k_t for the cis-toluenesulfonate XIII-C-OTs is larger than that of the trans epimer by ca. one power of ten. Taking k_{ext}^0 for the cis-toluene-sulfonate XIII-C-OTs, since this is a better lower

(34) A. H. Fainberg and S. Winstein, J. Am. Chem. Soc., 78, 2780 (1956).

limit to the ionization rate constant, makes the cis:trans rate ratio ca. 30. This estimate of the degree of anchimeric acceleration of ionization of the cis-toluenesulfonate would be increased further if we allowed for the fact that the axial disposition of the toluenesulfonoxy group in the trans-ester XIII-T-OTs may be associated with slight steric acceleration (as in the case of the axial cis-4-t-butylcyclohexyl[35] ester).

TABLE V

REACTIVITIES OF SOME p-TOLUENESULFONATES IN ACETOLYSIS AT 50.0°

ROTs	10⁵ k, sec.⁻¹	Rel. k
Cyclopentyl	3.60	20.0
Δ³-Cyclopentenyl	0.438	2.4
trans-3-Bicyclo[3.1.0]hexyl	.266	1.5
Cyclohexyl[34]	.179	1.00
cis-3-Bicyclo[3.1.0]hexyl	2.48, 7.87[a]	13.8, 44[a]

[a] Based on k_{ext}^0.

Another indication that there is something unique about the solvolysis of the cis-toluenesulfonate XIII-C-OTs is the contrast between the cis and trans epimers XIII-C-OTs and XIII-T-OTs as regards stereochemistry and products of acetolysis. Thus, the trans epimer gives acetate XIII-C-OAc with complete inversion of configuration and a substantial fraction of elimination product. This is similar to the behavior of both the trans- and cis-4-t-butylcyclohexyl toluenesulfonates.[35] On the other hand, the cis-3-bicyclo[3.1.0]hexyl toluene-sulfonate (XIII-C-OTs) gives rise to cis-acetate XIII-C-OAc with complete retention of configura-tion and no accompanying olefin.

The most striking indication that a unique species intervenes in acetolysis of the cis-toluenesulfonate XIII-C-OTs is the special salt effect which is present in its acetolysis. A special salt effect does not occur in acetolysis of the cyclopentyl, Δ³-cyclopentenyl[13c] and cyclohexyl analogs and is either absent or quite small with the trans-toluene-sulfonate XIII-T-OTs. Here, as in other cases,[32] the special salt effect can be taken to be diagnostic for the occurrence of a carbonium ion pair with a relatively stable unique structure for the cation.

The anchimeric acceleration, stereochemistry, lack of olefin formation and special salt effect ob-served in its acetolysis all suggest that ionization of cis-3-bicyclo[3.1.0]hexyl toluenesulfonate (XIII-C-OTs) may indeed lead very predominantly to a non-classical ion II which leads stereospecifically to cis-acetate XIII-C-OAc. The anchimerically un-assisted ionization to the classical ion pair IC (rate

(35) S. Winstein and N. J. Holness, ibid., 77, 5562 (1955).

constant k_s) would, on this basis, be negligible. On the other hand, ionization of the *trans*-toluenesulfonate XIII-T-OTs, with the wrong configuration for anchimeric assistance, is entirely anchimerically unassisted (k_s). The classical intermeiate 1-T leads partly to olefin, while the non-classical ion II does not.

The indications of a unique intermediate in acetolysis of the *cis*-toluenesulfonate appeared to us to warrant isotopic labeling experiments which would provide a definite check for the occurrence of a cation with the symmetrical structure II. These are described and discussed in the following paper.

Experimental

7,7-Dibromonorcar-3-ene.—Dibromocarbene[7] was allowed to react with a 69:31 1,4-cyclohexadiene–benzene mixture prepared by the procedure of Wibaut and Haak.[36] An equimolar amount of bromoform (330 g., 1.7 moles) in dry *t*-butyl alcohol (90 ml.) was added in one portion to the 1,4-cyclohexadiene (140 g., 1.75 moles) in benzene. To this stirred solution a 50 molar % excess of 1 M potassium *t*-butylate in *t*-butyl alcohol was slowly added. The reaction product in 1 liter of pentane was washed with a total of 10 liters of water to remove most of the *t*-butyl alcohol. This precipitated tetrabromide V, which was washed with pentane and dried. This product (66 g.), m.p. 205–206° (reported[6b] m.p. 205–207°), was obtained in 18% yield based on the available bromoform.

The remaining yellow pentane solution was dried over anhydrous magnesium sulfate. The solvent was evaporated and the residue was distilled at 2.8 mm., a portion of the material boiling at 68° and the remainder at 91°. Absolute ethanol was added to the distillate and the product cooled to give a first crop of 95.5 g. of 7,7-dibromonorcar-3-ene, m.p. 37.8–38.8° (reported[6b] m.p. 36.8–37.0°). After a second and third crop were obtained, the remaining mother liquor was redistilled. The distillate partly solidified after standing in the refrigerator. After decanting off a small liquid portion which was used later, the solid was recrystallized from absolute alcohol. A total of 188 g. (44% yield based on the available diene and bromoform) of 7,7-dibromonorcar-3-ene was obtained. The recrystallizations were unpleasant because of the presence of a lachrymatory material.

The small liquid portion remaining was distilled through a Podbielniak column and, following a small forerun (b.p. 39.2–40.0° at 6.7 mm.), about a 5-g. fraction, b.p. 56–59° at 3.8 mm., was collected. This colorless fraction had strong lachrymatory character and appeared to be benzyl bromide on the basis of its infrared spectrum. It formed an *sec*-alkylisothiouronium picrate, m.p. 188–188.5° (reported[37] m.p. 188° for the benzyl bromide derivative).

Norcar-3-ene.—The 7,7-dibromonorcar-3-ene (48 g., 0.19 mole) was dissolved in ether (200 ml.) in a 5-liter 3-neck flask cooled in ice and equipped with a stirrer, Dry-Ice condenser, addition tube and dropping funnel. Metallic sodium (3 g. atom) was added in roughly 2-cc. pieces during the course of the reduction. At the same time wet methanol (10 ml. of water in 300 ml. of methanol) was added dropwise with rapid stirring; 2.25 hours was required for the addition of the sodium. After the reaction mixture was stirred for 2 hours, ether (50 ml.) was added, followed by additional sodium (1 g. atom) and wet methanol (200 ml.). The reaction mixture was stirred an additional 3 hours (sodium was still present) and then water (350 ml.) was added cautiously, followed by the addition of ether (50 ml.). The combined ether solution was separated and the aqueous layer extracted successively with pentane (100 ml.), ether (150 ml.) and pentane (150 ml.). The combined organic layer was washed with water (4 × 50 ml.), the last wash being neutral to litmus. The combined organic layer was dried over anhydrous magnesium sulfate and anhydrous calcium chloride, filtered, and distilled carefully to remove most of the pentane

and ether. The residue was fractionally distilled through a Podbielniak column and two colorless fractions were collected: (a) 1.05 g., b.p. 84–115°; and (b) 13.95 g. (77%), b.p. 115–115.5° at 751 mm., $n^{25.0}$D 1.4740. A small colored residue remained. In another similar run, 0.5 mole of 7,7-dibromonorcar-3-ene yielded an 88% yield of norcar-3-ene, b.p. 115–115.5°. Vapor phase chromatographic analysis (v.p.c.) of fraction b on didecyl phthalate indicated one symmetrical peak.

Anal. Calcd. for C_7H_{10}: C, 89.29; H, 10.71. Found: C, 88.88; H, 10.63.

The hydrocarbon is a colorless liquid with a slight odor. It adds bromine in carbon tetrachloride, and in 95% ethanol immediately decolorizes aqueous permanganate. The infrared spectrum contains absorption bands at 1648 (C=C) and 1018 cm.$^{-1}$ (cyclopropane ring), as well as other bands at 3052(sh), 2995, 2865, 2832, 1440, 731 and 654 cm.$^{-1}$. The ultraviolet spectrum in cyclohexane shows no maximum above 2150 Å., the extinction coefficient at 2160 Å. being only 59.

Cyclopropane-*cis*-1,2-diacetic Acid.—The norcar-3-ene (12 g., 0.128 mole) dissolved in glacial acetic acid (160 ml.) and acetic anhydride (80 ml.) was ozonized (3% approximate weight concentration of the ozone) between 0° and 20° until ozone was detected in the exit tube. Ozone was consumed immediately and the solution was clear during most of the reaction. Toward the end of the reaction, the reaction mixture became cloudy and precipitated some white semi-solid. The excess ozone in the system was flushed out with an oxygen stream before 30% hydrogen peroxide (35 ml.) and water (240 ml.) were added and the solution refluxed overnight.

The following day the water and acetic acid were removed by distillation at atmospheric pressure; the last traces were removed with the aid of a water aspirator. A slightly yellow solid remained which was recrystallized from ethyl acetate and washed with ether. An over-all yield of 63% of crude diacid was obtained in four experiments. Ozonolyses in acetic acid and/or ethyl acetate gave much poorer yields (30–45%). The initial sample of the diacid was obtained using glacial acetic acid as the solvent. A sublimation and recrystallization from ethyl acetate gave crystals, m.p. 131–132° (reported[6] 131–133°).

Anal. Calcd. for $C_7H_{10}O_4$: C, 53.16; H, 6.37. Found: C, 53.11; H, 6.32.

2-Carbethoxy-3-bicyclo[3.1.0]hexanone.—A mixture of cyclopropane-*cis*-1,2-diacetic acid (19.0 g., 0.12 mole), absolute ethanol (43.2 ml., 0.36 mole), dry toluene (22 ml.) and concentrated sulfuric acid (0.10 ml.) was placed in a 200-ml. distilling flask connected with a downward condenser and magnetic stirrer. When heated in a 110–115° oil-bath, an azeotropic mixture of alcohol, toluene and water began to distil at about 75°. Distillation was suspended when most of the toluene–alcohol azeotrope (76.7°) had distilled over. Distillation was continued after a fresh portion of alcohol and toluene was added and the procedure repeated. Toluene was finally added to remove all the ethanol by azeotropic distillation. The diester was not isolated but the residue used directly in the Dieckmann condensation.

After small pieces of sodium (4.5 g., 0.20 mole) were added at one time to the cooled residual toluene solution of the diester, the mixture was heated slowly to 110° while being stirred magnetically. (Approximately 3 ml. of absolute ethanol was added to reduce the induction period.) After a few minutes, a vigorous reaction commenced, and some ethanol distilled out. A cake of the sodium compound separated and the solution became orange. Dry toluene was added in order to keep the mixture fluid enough for efficient stirring. After the spontaneous reaction had abated, the mixture was refluxed for 30 minutes before being decomposed with ethanol. The cooled reaction mixture was then slowly poured into cold 10% acetic acid and the organic layer separated with the aid of pentane. The remaining aqueous portion was then extracted successively with two portions of pentane, toluene and ether. The united orange organic extract was then washed successively with water, 5% sodium bicarbonate, and water until neutral. Without drying the organic solution, the ether, pentane and toluene were removed by distillation. The residue was distilled under reduced pressure and this gave rise to 16.0 g. (79% over-all yield) of the keto-ester.

(36) J. P. Wibaut and F. A. Haak. *Rec. trav. chim.*, **67**, 85 (1948).

(37) N. D. Cheronis and J. B. Entrikin, "Semimicro Qualitative Organic Analysis," Interscience Publishers, Inc., New York, N. Y., 2nd Ed., 1957.

An analytical sample was prepared in a similar manner in 60% over-all yield, b.p. 85–86° (2.2 mm.), n^{27}D 1.4642.

Anal. Calcd. for $C_9H_{12}O_3$: C, 64.27; H, 7.19. Found: C, 64.21; H, 7.28.

The β-keto-ester is a colorless pleasant-smelling liquid which gives a purple color with ferric chloride. The infrared spectrum shows a small O–H absorption at 3460 cm.⁻¹. Other absorption bands occur at 1751, 1722, 1024 and 810 cm.⁻¹.

3-Bicyclo[3.1.0]hexanone.—Barium hydroxide crystals (28.2 g., 0.165 mole) were added to a mixture of water (282 ml.) and 2-carbethoxy-3-bicyclo[3.1.0]hexanone (16.0 g., 0.095 mole) in a 500-ml. round-bottom flask. The mixture was refluxed for 30 minutes (decomposition sets in suddenly) and then about 30 ml. was distilled and collected in pentane. The aqueous phase was returned to the flask and distillation continued. This process was repeated until ketone no longer distilled over (three times).

The combined pentane solution was first dried over calcium chloride for 15 minutes, then over anhydrous magnesium sulfate. The mixture was filtered, and then pentane was removed by distillation. The remaining residue was fractionally distilled through a Podbielniak column. Two fractions were collected and a small residue remained: (a) 0.44 g. (5%), b.p. 50–54° (24 mm.); (b) 3.92 g. (43%), b.p. 54–55° (25 mm.), $n^{2.50}$D 1.4590.

The analytical sample was prepared in a similar manner in 44% yield. On distillation through a Podbielniak column, the ketone boiled at 51–52° at 18 mm., $n^{25.0}$D 1.4590.

Anal. Calcd. for C_6H_8O: C, 74.97; H, 8.39. Found: C, 74.69; H, 8.43.

The bicyclohexanone is very volatile and has a pleasant odor resembling that of cyclopentanone. The analytical sample exhibited only one peak on v.p.c. using a Carbowax column. The infrared and ultraviolet spectra of the ketone are summarized in Table VI and VII.

TABLE VI

OBSERVED INFRARED ABSORPTION BANDS OF 3-BICYCLO-[3.1.0]HEXANONE

Cm.⁻¹	Cm.⁻¹	Cm.⁻¹	Cm.⁻¹	Cm.⁻¹	Cm.⁻¹
3462w	1763shs	1457m	1137s	962w	808m
3052m	1739vs	1407ms	1075w	918w	770shw
2915s	1700shm	1263s	1038m	903w	753m
2860ms	1643vw	1157s	1022shw	847vw	

The orange 2,4-dinitrophenylhydrazone of 3-bicyclo-[3.1.0]-hexanone was prepared in the usual manner and was recrystallized from aqueous alcohol; m.p. 149.2–149.8°; λ_{max}^{EtOH} 3595 Å., ε 23,100; $\lambda_{max}^{CHCl_3}$ 3625 Å., ε 23,600.

Anal. Calcd. for $C_{12}H_{12}O_4N_4$: C, 52.17; H, 4.38; N, 20.28. Found: C, 52.42; H, 4.15; N, 20.31.

cis- and trans-3-Bicyclo[3.1.0]hexanols.—A mixture of these alcohols was obtained from lithium aluminum hydride reduction of the bicyclohexanone. After the lithium aluminum hydride (1.1 g., 0.029 mole) was stirred magnetically with anhydrous ether (100 ml.) for 1 hour, the 3-bicyclo-[3.1.0]hexanone (2.8 g., 0.029 mole) in ether (75 ml.) was added dropwise over 30 minutes while being cooled in a Dry Ice–acetone-bath. The solution was stirred for 4 hours at −78°, then an additional hour at room temperature. While the solution was being cooled in ice, water (2.2 ml.) followed by 10% sodium hydroxide (1.75 ml.) was added. After the reaction mixture was stirred for 2 hours, the inorganic salts were filtered and the ethereal solution dried over magnesium sulfate. Distillation through a Podbielniak column gave 2.40 g. (85%) of 3-bicyclo[3.1.0]hexanol, b.p. 68–69.5° (17.5 mm.), $n^{25.0}$D 1.4774. Analysis by v.p.c. using a 2-meter column containing 25% Carbowax 1500 (polyethylene glycol) on 40–80 mesh firebrick operated at 140–150° showed the product to be an 89:11 cis–trans mixture.

Anal. Calcd. for $C_6H_{10}O$: C, 73.43; H, 10.27. Found: C, 73.61; H, 10.35.

The bicyclohexanone was reduced also on a small scale (200 mg.) with lithium tri-t-butoxyaluminohydride in tetrahydrofuran[22] and sodium borohydride in pyridine,[23] and the resulting alcohol mixtures were determined by v.p.c. (Table I).

TABLE VII

ULTRAVIOLET SPECTRA OF SEVERAL KETONES

Water		Isoöctane		Isoöctane	
λ_{max}, Å.		λ_{max}, Å.	ε	λ_{max}, Å.	ε
Cyclohexanone					
<1855ª	1980	<1860ª	840	2910sh	14.9
2764	21.0	2768sh	12.8	2950sh	14.6
		2847sh	14.6	3054sh	11.6
Cyclopentanone					
<1850ª	1260	1897	1100	2894	17.1
2799	22.0	2597	6.2	2935sh	15.5
		2684	9.5	2998	18.5
		2711sh	10.2	3057sh	13.0
		2768sh	13.3	3110	15.0
		2799	13.7	3234	6.7
		2864sh	16.2		
Δ³-Cyclopentenone					
<1860ª	4390	<1860ª	4300	2887sh	11.0
2593	48.5	2592	6.2	2941sh	10.0
		2676	8.1	2991	10.9
		2765	10.0	3104	8.4
		2803sh	9.7	3230	4.2
		2862	11.1		
3-Bicyclo[3.1.0]hexanone					
<1855ª	1460	<1860ª	1510	2860sh	13.7
2797	18.9	2600	5.7	2888	14.7
		2683	8.7	2993	15.1
		2766	11.8	3102	11.3
		2799	12.1	3217	4.6

ª Not a maximum.

A 20.4-g. (0.1 mole) quantity of distilled aluminum isopropoxide was added to 3-bicyclo[3.1.0]hexanone (3.0 g., 0.031 mole) in isopropyl alcohol (98 ml.) in a flask equipped with a downward condenser. The mixture was magnetically stirred and heated at 92° for 17 hours. After the reaction mixture was cooled, water (2 ml.), ether (40 ml.) and then 16 M sodium hydroxide (25 ml.) were added. The aqueous portion was extracted three times with pentane and ether and then the combined organic layer washed with brine. After the solution was dried over anhydrous magnesium sulfate, pentane and ether were distilled at atmospheric pressure, and the isopropyl alcohol was removed carefully at 96 mm. Using a Podbielniak column, a slightly yellow liquid (3.35 g.) with a distinct odor, distilling mostly at 78° (20 mm.), was obtained. A yellow residue remained. The v.p.c. analysis of the distillate indicated a 40:60 cis–trans mixture of the 3-bicyclo[3.1.0]hexanols, along with a 10% impurity of unknown identity.

For the equilibration of the cis- and trans-bicyclohexanols, isopropyl alcohol (40 ml.), acetone (0.7 ml.) and the 3-bicyclo[3.1.0]hexanol (0.24 g.) were added to a small quantity of freshly distilled aluminum isopropoxide in a 100-ml. round-bottom flask. After the reaction mixture was refluxed for 112 hours, 5 ml. was distilled and the cloudy mixture refluxed for another 24 hours. The mixture was worked up in the usual way, and the bicyclohexanols were isolated by distillation and analyzed by v.p.c. (Table I).

By careful chromatography on alumina, essentially pure cis-3-bicyclo[3.1.0]hexanol was obtained from the product of reduction of bicyclohexanone with lithium aluminum hydride. Distillation of the earlier fractions eluted with pentane yielded a material, b.p. 69° (19.5 mm.), n^{25}D 1.4771, with a cis-alcohol content greater than 98.5%.

From 900 mg. of cis-3-bicyclo[3.1.0]hexanol the toluenesulfonate, m.p. 52.0–52.4°, was prepared in the usual way in 66% yield.

Anal. Calcd. for $C_{13}H_{16}O_3S$: C, 61.88; H, 6.39; S, 12.71. Found: C, 61.77; H, 6.22; S, 12.49.

The toluenesulfonate formed directly from the lithium aluminum hydride reduction product from 3-bicyclo[3.1.0]-hexanone had m.p. 46–48°.

By systematic chromatography on alumina, 3-bicyclo-[3.1.0]hexanol, b.p. 75–76° (18 mm.), with the *trans* content greater than 97%, was obtained from the alcohol mixture which arises from aluminum isopropoxide reduction of bicyclohexanone. From 450 mg. of the *trans*-alcohol the toluenesulfonate, m.p. 71–72°, was prepared in 60% yield in the usual manner.

Anal. Calcd. for $C_{13}H_{19}O_4S$: C, 61.88; H, 6.39; S, 12.71. Found: C, 62.02; H, 6.22; S, 12.76.

Treatment of Δ^3-Cyclopentenol and its Acetate with Diazomethane.—An ethereal solution of diazomethane (0.02 mole) was added to Δ^3-cyclopentenol[13] (0.014 mole) in ether and irradiated by an internal ultraviolet source until the solution became colorless. This reaction was performed at three temperatures, room temperature, 0° and −78°. In all three experiments, a v.p.c. analysis of the ether residue on a Carbowax column showed only starting alcohol and several peaks right after the ether solvent peak. The starting alcohol was recovered in each case.

An ethereal solution of diazomethane (0.024 mole) and Δ^3-cyclopentenyl acetate[13,38] (0.014 mole) was allowed to stand several months at 0° until the yellow color disappeared. After distilling away most of the ether, the residue was analyzed by v.p.c. using a didecyl phthalate column. No bicyclic acetate was visible; only the starting acetate and a few new peaks, which appeared right after the ether solvent peak, were observed. The starting acetate was recovered as the corresponding alcohol.

Zinc–Copper Couple.—Couple A was one described by Howard[39] and recommended by Simmons and Smith.[16]

Couple B was prepared as follows. Mallinckrodt analytical reagent zinc dust (24.8 g., 0.38 mole) was washed successively with 3% hydrochloric acid (4 × 20 ml.), distilled water (3 × 25 ml.), 2% copper sulfate solution (2 × 40 ml.), and finally distilled water (3 × 50 ml.). The last water washings were decanted directly on a Büchner funnel. After most of the water was removed by suction (too much air drying by suction caused the couple to heat up), the zinc–copper couple was dried using a rotary vacuum dryer, and a uniform finely divided active couple was obtained. On a molar scale, less active couple was produced.

Methylene Addition to Δ^3-Cyclopentenyl Acetate and Cyclopentadiene.—Zinc–copper couple A (5.4 g.) was added in one portion to a solution of Δ^3-cyclopentenyl acetate[13,38] (6.3 g., 0.05 mole) and methylene iodide (13.4 g., 0.05 mole) in ether (50 ml.). The reaction mixture was stirred magnetically and refluxed for 48 hours with no noticeable effect. After the reaction mixture was filtered, the crude acetate was analyzed by v.p.c. on a Carbowax column. This analysis indicated the formation of 10–18% bicyclohexyl acetate, the yield varying with the couple and the reaction time. Since the *cis*- and *trans*-3-bicyclohexyl acetates are not separated on a Carbowax column, nor on didecyl phthalate or silicone columns, the acetate mixture was reduced to alcohol with lithium aluminum hydride in ether and worked up by the usual basic treatment. Analysis of the alcohol by v.p.c. on a Carbowax column showed it to be predominantly *cis*, but the presence of a little methylene iodide makes the analysis inaccurate because its retention time falls between those of the two 3-bicyclo[3.1.0]hexanols. On a didecyl phthalate column, methylene iodide is well separated from the bicyclohexanols, but these two alcohols are not separated from each other. The infrared spectrum of a 3-bicyclo[3.1.0]-hexanol fraction obtained by preparative v.p.c. of a combination of various reaction residues indicated that the bicyclohexanol contained no more than 10% of the *trans* epimer.

In an experiment similar to the one above, refluxing tetrahydrofuran being substituted in place of ether as the solvent, Δ^3-cyclopentenyl acetate gave only 1% bicyclic acetate as shown by v.p.c. analysis. The reaction of Δ^3-cyclopentenyl acetate and methylene iodide with a moderately active zinc–copper couple B gave a 2% yield of bicyclic acetate as shown by v.p.c. analysis after 48 hours of gentle refluxing in ether. The same zinc–copper couple worked smoothly with Δ^2-cyclopentenol, however.

An ethereal solution of methylene iodide (26.8 g., 0.1 mole) and freshly distilled cyclopentadiene (34 g., 0.52 mole) was added to a moderately active zinc–copper couple B (13.1 g., 0.2 mole), and the mixture was magnetically stirred

and refluxed for 48 hours. Work-up of the reaction mixture and v.p.c. examination of the fraction of intermediate boiling point indicated the presence of two new components with retention times appropriate for C_6-hydrocarbons. However, these were present in only very low yield, and the reaction mixture was not examined further.

cis-3-Bicyclo[3.1.0]hexanol from Δ^3-Cyclopentenol.—Anhydrous ether (60 ml.) was added to zinc–copper couple B prepared from 24.8 g. of zinc dust in a flask equipped with a magnetic stirrer, dropping funnel, reflux condenser and drying tube. To the above slurry, an intimate mixture of methylene iodide (53.4 g., 0.20 mole) and Δ^3-cyclopentenol[13] (8.4 g., 0.10 mole) was added rapidly. This was followed by anhydrous ether (40 ml.). After a short induction period (5 min.), an exothermic reaction occurred which lasted for several minutes.

After the mixture was refluxed for an hour, it was cooled and filtered through a Super-Cel pad on a Büchner funnel to remove the excess zinc which was thoroughly washed with ether. The filtrate was distilled carefully at atmospheric pressure (bath temperature to 80°) and a yellow solution remained to which pentane was added. On addition of water to the organic solution, a very slight exothermic reaction was noticed and a massive white precipitate formed. More water and pentane were added and the mixture was again suction filtered on a Super-Cel pad. Even after repeated pentane and ether washings, the smell of bicyclic alcohol persisted on the pad.

The pentane solution was separated and the aqueous portion continuously extracted with ether–pentane mixtures. The combined organic material developed a light purple color which was removed by washing with aqueous sodium thiosulfate. After the organic solution was dried over anhydrous magnesium sulfate, a crude distillation gave 7.6 g. of material, b.p. 63–69° (17 mm.). On v.p.c. analysis this crude product proved to be *cis*-3-bicyclo[3.1.0]hexanol contaminated with up to 2% of methylene iodide, 2% of the starting Δ^3-cyclopentenol, and the impurities contained in the latter, namely, 4% cyclopentanol and 2% of an unidentified component.[13] Fractionation of the crude product gave rise to a material, b.p. 68° (18 mm.), $n^{25}D$ 1.4781, whose infrared spectrum was identical to that of authentic *cis*-3-bicyclo[3.1.0]hexanol, $n^{25}D$ 1.4770.

The fractionated *cis*-3-bicyclo[3.1.0]hexanol (containing a trace of methylene iodide) gave rise to a *p*-toluenesulfonate, m.p. 46.2–49.5°. This crude product was dissolved in ether and washed with sodium thiosulfate and water. Recovery and recrystallization of the toluenesulfonate led to a 66% yield of colorless product, m.p. 50.5–51.4°, m.p. 50.5–51.5° on admixture with authentic *cis*-toluenesulfonate. On acetylation with acetic anhydride in pyridine, the fractionated alcohol gave rise to a quantitative yield of acetate. The analytical sample had b.p. 71° (15 mm.), $n^{25}D$ 1.4492.

Anal. Calcd. for $C_8H_{12}O_2$: C, 68.54; H, 8.63. Found: C, 68.49; H, 8.65.

Methylene iodide, which was not effectively removed from the *cis*-3-bicyclo[3.1.0]hexanol by fractional distillation, was eliminated by chromatography on alumina. Analysis of the chromatographed alcohol by v.p.c. on a Carbowax column showed the absence of *trans*-alcohol, and on didecyl phthalate the absence of methylene iodide.

In another experiment starting with Δ^3-cyclopentenol (7.8 g.) and a moderately active zinc–copper couple B, a work-up involving one filtration was used. After being refluxed for an hour, the reaction mixture was cooled to room temperature. When water was added, the reaction mixture became exothermic and ether refluxed for several minutes while precipitation occurred. The mixture was then suction filtered and washed several times with ether. The organic layer was separated and the aqueous layer extracted with ether. The combined ether solution was washed successively with brine, sodium thiosulfate solution, and finally with brine. The resulting colorless solution was dried over anhydrous magnesium sulfate and the ether removed. The resulting residue was chromatographed on alumina, ether being used to recover all the alcohol product. The slightly colored ether solution was washed with sodium thiosulfate solution, brine, dried and distilled. A crude distillation gave 7.5 g. (79%) of material, b.p. 65–66° (15 mm.). Redistillation through a Podbielniak column gave a fraction of *cis*-3-bicyclo[3.1.0]-hexanol, b.p. 76° (27 mm.), $n^{25}D$ 1.4775. As noticed with

(38) J. Sonnenberg, unpublished work.

(39) F. L. Howard, *J. Research Natl. Bur. Standards*, **24**, 677 (1940).

other samples of the *cis*-alcohol, the refractive index decreased on contact with air.

A 2.2-g. portion of the *cis*-3-bicyclo[3.1.0]hexanol was converted to acid phthalate by a procedure adapted from that of Levene and Mikeska.[40] Evaporation of the ether solution of the acid phthalate gave rise to 5.42 g. (98.5%) of material, m.p. 122–125°. This crude ester was recrystallized once from ether–pentane, which led to 3.6 g. (65%) of product, m.p. 125.5–126.5°. Recrystallization of a portion of this material led to a melting point of 126.0–127.0°.

Anal. Calcd. for $C_{14}H_{14}O_4$: C, 68.28; H, 5.73. Found: C, 68.49; H, 5.81.

Saponification of a 2.46 g. of acid phthalate, m.p. 125.5–126.5°, gave rise to 0.86 g. (88%) of *cis*-alcohol, b.p. 71.0–71.5° (22 mm.). From a redistillation a center cut, b.p. 66° (16 mm.), $n^{25}D$ 1.4770, was collected.

Anal. Calcd. for $C_6H_{10}O$: C, 73.43; H, 10.27. Found: C, 73.63; H, 10.53.

Oxidation of *cis*-3-Bicyclo[3.1.0]hexanol.—To a solution of chromic trioxide (4.5 g., 0.045 mole) in pyridine[41] (45 ml.), a solution of the alcohol (1.0 g., 0.01 mole) in pyridine (10 ml.) was added, and the resulting mixture was stirred magnetically at room temperature for 20 hours. During the first half-hour, the mixture turned from yellow to dark brown. Water (112 ml.) was added and the solution extracted with ether (3 × 100 ml.). The combined organic layer was washed successively with water, 1.8 M sulfuric acid, water, sodium bicarbonate, and water, and then dried over magnesium sulfate. The odor of pyridine was still present so the organic solution was washed with portions of hydrochloric acid. After washing away the acid as before and drying the resulting organic phase, the ether was removed by distillation and 0.50 g. (51%) of material, b.p. 49–50° (20 mm.), was isolated. The infrared spectrum of this material was identical with that of authentic 3-bicyclo-[3.1.0]hexanone.

Acetolysis Products.—A 102.8-mg. quantity of *cis*-3-bicyclo[3.1.0]hexyl toluenesulfonate, m.p. 50.6–51.4°, and 62.5- and 108.0-mg. samples of *trans*-toluenesulfonate, m.p. 70.8–71.3° and 69.5–70.3°, respectively, were each solvolyzed under the conditions summarized in Table IV. A control run with a 51.3-mg. sample of a 70:30 *cis–trans* mixture of 3-bicyclo[3.1.0]hexyl acetates, b.p. 68.5–70.5° (14 mm.), n^2D 1.4488, was also carried out (Table IV).

After the acetolysis solutions were cooled, the ampoules were opened and their contents transferred to a separatory funnel with the aid of pentane and water. Then a known weight of *n*-decane (53.0 mg. for the *cis*-toluenesulfonate) was added. A total of 45 ml. of distilled water was added to the acetolysis products and the decane, and this mixture extracted with pentane (4 × 50 ml.). The combined pentane solution was then washed successively with water (2 × 5 ml.), 5% sodium bicarbonate (1 × 5 ml.), and water (1 × 5 ml.). After the pentane solution was dried with magnesium sulfate, the pentane was carefully distilled through an efficient column with the bath temperature maintained below 60°. The inside of the column was washed with a small quantity of pentane, and the acetate residue analyzed directly by v.p.c. using a didecyl phthalate column. With the aid of a detector response factor determined on four synthetic mixtures of decane and *cis*-3-bicyclo[3.1.0]hexyl acetate, the yield of acetate is given by the relative v.p.c. areas of decane and acetate.

After the v.p.c. analyses of the acetates were performed, anhydrous ether was added to the remaining pentane solution and the pentane removed by azeotropic distillation. More anhydrous ether was added to the residue and the mixture cooled to 0°. As the mixture was being magnetically stirred and cooled, an ethereal 0.8 M lithium aluminum hydride solution (10 ml.) was added over several minutes. The reaction mixture was stirred for a half-hour at room temperature, and then the excess hydride decomposed by water (0.6 ml.) followed by 10% sodium hydroxide (0.5 ml.). Following an additional half-hour of stirring, the reaction mixture was allowed to stand overnight. The following day the mixture was carefully suction filtered and the salts washed thoroughly with ether. The ether solution was dried with anhydrous magnesium sulfate and the ether carefully distilled through an efficient column with the bath temperature maintained below 60°. After the inside of the column was washed with a small quantity of pentane, the alcohol residue was analyzed directly by v.p.c. on a Carbowax column.

The alcohol product from the *cis*-toluenesulfonate was very predominantly the *cis*-alcohol, no more than 1.5% of *trans*-alcohol being present. This was indicated by comparison with a synthetic mixture of 2% *trans*-alcohol in *cis*-alcohol from saponification of the acid phthalate. This synthetic mixture suggested that 0.5% of the *trans*-alcohol could be observed in the presence of the *cis*-alcohol. The v.p.c. analysis of the alcohol product from the *trans*-toluenesulfonate showed only *cis*-alcohol, no *trans*-alcohol being detected.

Control experiments showed that the extraction technique caused no change in the ratio of decane to acetate, and that conversion of acetate to alcohol introduced no error. The latter point was checked on pure *cis*-acetate and on the 70:30 *cis-trans* mixture.

Kinetic Measurements.—Cyclopentyl toluenesulfonate, m.p. 28–29° (reported[42,43] m.p. 28–29°; 27–28°), was prepared in the usual way.

Solvents and reagents for measurement of acetolysis rates in acetic acid, 0.01 M in acetic anhydride, by the sealed ampoule technique were prepared as usual.[33–35] In the acetolysis runs in the presence of sodium acetate, all three toluenesulfonates listed in Table II displayed infinity titers within *ca.* 1% of theoretical. With the *cis*-3-bicyclohexyl ester, the first-order rate constant drifted down slightly in a run due to the special salt effect of sodium acetate and the accumulation of the common ion salt, sodium toluenesulfonate.[32,44]

In the absence of sodium acetate the infinity titer was still close to theoretical in the case of cyclopentyl toluenesulfonate. However, it was only *ca.* 95% of theoretical in the case of the *cis*-3-bicyclohexyl ester. The reason for the low infinity titer was not further investigated, but steady first-order rate constants were obtained on the basis of the experimental infinity titers. With the *trans*-3-bicyclohexyl ester, an infinity titer could not be measured because of a darkening of the acetolysis solution. The first-order rate constant evaluated on the basis of the theoretical infinity titer drifted down in a run, making the values listed in Table II somewhat inaccurate. For the run at 75° with 0.0053 M ester, the $10^5 k$ value given by a plot of log $(a-x)$ *vs.* time is 5.72, 4.80 and 4.25 for the reaction ranges, 6–17%, 17–47% and 39–64%, respectively. The intermediate value of k is listed in Tables II and III. For the run at 75° with 0.0177 M ester, the $10^5 k$ value obtained graphically is 4.72 for the 1–38% reaction range and 3.80 for the 38–71% range. The lower figure is listed in Table II. It seems quite probable that the correct infinity titer to be employed under these conditions should be lower, as in the case of the *cis*-ester, but an experimental figure was not available.

In the presence of added lithium perchlorate, darkening of the acetolysis solutions prevented determination of an infinity titer with both *cis*- and *trans*-bicyclohexyl esters. Acetolysis was followed to *ca.* 60% and 30% solvolysis with the *cis*- and *trans*-esters, respectively, steady first-order rate constants being obtained on the basis of theoretical infinity titers.

Spectral Measurements.—The Δ^3-cyclopentenone was prepared by pyrolysis[45] of dicyclopentadienol-3. Fractionation of the ketone fraction through a Podbielniak column gave a sample of Δ^3-cyclopentenone, b.p. 39.0–40.5° (39 mm.), $n^{25}D$ 1.4521. On redistillation, material, b.p. 41–43° 41–43° (42–45 mm.), $n^{25}D$ 1.4518, was obtained (reported[45] b.p. 41° (40 mm.), $n^{20}D$ 1.4536).

The infrared spectral measurements were performed with the neat liquids in 0.018–0.031 mm. sodium chloride cells on a Perkin–Elmer model 21 double beam spectrophotometer with sodium chloride prisms.

The ultraviolet spectral measurements were carried out with a Cary model 14 spectrophotometer, the instrument being swept with nitrogen to exclude oxygen. To reach

(40) P. A. Levene and L. A. Mikeska, *J. Biol. Chem.*, **75**, 587 (1927).

(41) G. I. Poos, G. E. Arth, R. E. Beyler and L. H. Sarett, *J. Am. Chem. Soc.*, **75**, 422 (1953).

(42) (a) H. C. Brown and G. Ham, *ibid.*, **78**, 2735 (1956); (b) J. D. Roberts and V. C. Chambers, *ibid.*, **73**, 5034 (1951).

(43) S. Winstein, *et al.*, *ibid.*, **74**, 1127 (1952).

(44) S. Winstein, P. Klinedinst, Jr., and G. C. Robinson, *ibid.*, **83**, 885 (1961).

(45) K. Alder and F. H. Flock, *Ber.*, **89**, 1732 (1956).

From: *J. Am. Chem. Soc.* **83**, 3244–51 (1961)

1850 Å. it was necessary to use thin cells (0.1–cm. and 0.01–cm. path length), a maximum phototube voltage (setting 4 or 5), and a slit control of 25. In the far ultraviolet region a scanning speed of 0.5 Å./sec. with a chart speed of 2 in./

min. was used; in the near ultraviolet region a scanning speed of 2.5 Å./sec. with a chart speed of 2 in./min. was employed. Negligible scattering was found in the instrument down to 1850 Å.

[Contribution from the Department of Chemistry, University of California, Los Angeles 24, Calif.]

Homoconjugation and Homoaromaticity. IV. The Trishomocyclopropenyl Cation. A Homoaromatic Structure[1,2]

By S. Winstein and Joseph Sonnenberg

Received January 3, 1961

3-Deuterated-3-bicyclo[3.1.0]hexanols have been prepared and the corresponding toluenesulfonates acetolyzed in order to check for the occurrence of a uniquely symmetrical non-classical cation as an intermediate in solvolysis of the *cis*-toluenesulfonate. In acetolysis of the *trans*-toluenesulfonate very little redistribution of deuterium is visible in the solvolysis product. In acetolysis of the *cis*-toluenesulfonate, however, deuterium is distributed equally over carbon atoms 1, 3 and 5 in the product. Further, deuterium on the cyclopropane ring of the initial *cis*-toluenesulfonate is also symmetrically distributed during acetolysis. The results obtained are uniquely consistent with the intervention of the trishomocyclopropenyl cation as an intermediate in solvolysis of *cis*-3-bicyclo[3.1.0]hexyl toluenesulfonate. The theoretical relationship between trishomocyclopropenyl and cyclopropenyl cations is discussed, and some of the implications of the present results for organic chemistry are outlined. Regarding the trishomocyclopropenyl cation as the first example of a homoaromatic structure, the authors discuss a generalized concept of homoaromaticity.

The contrasting behavior of the *cis*- and *trans*-3-bicyclo[3.1.0]hexyl toluenesulfonates as regards anchimeric acceleration, special salt effects, stereochemistry and olefin formation in acetolysis[3] was an indication that the *cis*-epimer does indeed give rise to the symmetrical non-classical cation II. We had anticipated the possibility of such a structure for the 3-bicyclo[3.1.0]hexyl cation I on theoretical grounds. Suitable isotopic labeling of the 3-bicyclohexyl ring system was obviously the way to establish whether solvolysis does indeed involve an intermediate such as II with equivalent carbon atoms 1,3 and 5. In this paper we report and discuss the results of such a study which prove that the 3-bicyclo[3.1.0]hexyl cation does indeed have the non-classical structure II. Regarding this so-called trishomocyclopropenyl cation as the first-recognized homoaromatic structure, we go on to propose and discuss a generalized concept of homoaromaticity.[4]

$$\text{I} \qquad\qquad \text{II}$$

Deuterium Labeling and Kinetic Isotope Factor.—The simplest way to label the bicyclo[3.1.0]-hexyl ring system is by substitution of a deuterium atom for hydrogen on the carbinol carbon atom 3. For this reason, 3-bicyclohexanone was reduced with lithium aluminum deuteride as shown in the Reaction Scheme. The bicyclohexanone was derived from oxidation of a mixture of *cis*- and *trans*-

3-bicyclohexanols, designated A-OH and F-OH, respectively. A large portion of the deuterated *cis*-alcohol B-OH was separated from the contaminating *trans*-epimer by chromatography on alumina and then purified further by way of the crystalline acid phthalate.[3] Combustion analysis of the deuterated *cis*-alcohol B-OH showed it to have 9.85 atom % excess deuterium or 98.5% of theoretical for one deuterium atom per molecule.

Saponification of the non-crystalline portion of the acid phthalate of the deuterated alcohol gave rise to a 60:40 *cis–trans* mixture of deuterated alcohols. A small amount of deuterated *trans*-alcohol G-OH was isolated by preparative vapor phase chromatography, but this sample was still slightly impure.

Rates of acetolysis of the toluenesulfonates of the deuterated and ordinary *cis*-3-bicyclo[3.1.0]-hexanols B-OH and A-OH were determined simultaneously at 50.0°. From these rate runs, summarized more fully in the Experimental section, a small kinetic isotope effect is indicated, (k_H/k_D) being equal to 1.05.

Deuterium Scrambling and Spectra.—Acetolysis of the toluenesulfonate B-OTs of the deuterated *cis*-alcohol B-OH at 50° in acetic acid solvent 0.10 M in sodium acetate and reduction of the resulting acetate with lithium aluminum hydride in the usual way[3] gave rise to a *cis*-alcohol C-OH. The infrared spectra of the three *cis*-alcohols A-OH, B-OH and C-OH, summarized in the Experimental section, show qualitatively that solvolysis of B-OTs is accompanied by the type of deuterium scrambling expected from a symmetrical non-classical intermediate II.

The substitution of deuterium for hydrogen on the carbinol carbon atom 3 of the *cis*-3-bicyclo-[3.1.0]hexanol causes the appearance of a number of new infrared absorption bands, while others disappear or are shifted. The two most prominent new absorption bands in alcohol B-OH are the C-D stretching absorption at 2151 cm.$^{-1}$ and an absorption at 723 cm.$^{-1}$. These two bands can be

(1) This research was supported by a grant from the Petroleum Research Fund administered by the American Chemical Society. Grateful acknowledgment is hereby made to the donors of this fund.

(2) The main results presented in this manuscript were reported in outline form: (a) in a preliminary Communication, S. Winstein, J. Sonnenberg and L. de Vries, *J. Am. Chem. Soc.*, **81**, 6523 (1959); (b) by S. Winstein at the Welch Foundation Conference on Molecular Structure and Organic Reactions, Houston, Tex., November 7–9, 1960.

(3) S. Winstein and J. Sonnenberg, *ibid.*, **83**, 3235 (1961).

(4) S. Winstein, *ibid.*, **81**, 6524 (1959).

REACTION SCHEME

assigned to the deuterium on the carbinol carbon atom 3. The strong absorption band at 745 cm.$^{-1}$ in alcohol A-OH is absent in B-OH, and it can, therefore, be assigned to hydrogen on the carbinol carbon atom.

The infrared spectrum of the product alcohol C-OH shows all the bands of the deuterated B-OH as well as some additional ones. The 2151 and 723 cm.$^{-1}$ bands for carbinyl deuterium occur with decreased intensities in C-OH. The additional bands for C-OH not present for B-OH include the carbinyl hydrogen band at 746 cm.$^{-1}$ and two others, namely, at 2266 and 670 cm.$^{-1}$. As pointed out below, the latter two are quite clearly to be assigned to tertiary cyclopropyl deuterium.

Inspection of the infrared spectrum of cis-3-bicyclo[3.1.0]hexanol in the 3.2–3.6 μ region using lithium fluoride optics reveals three frequencies logically associated with cyclopropyl hydrogen atoms, 3070, 3028 and 3000 cm.$^{-1}$. For the trans-epimer the corresponding frequencies are at 3062, 3032 and 2995 cm.$^{-1}$. By analogy with the in-phase and out-of-phase vibrations at ca. 2926 and 2853 cm.$^{-1}$ for CH$_2$ groups and the band at ca. 2890 cm.$^{-1}$ for tertiary C–H observed in ordinary unstrained aliphatic compounds,[5] one can ascribe the 3070 and 3000 cm.$^{-1}$ frequencies for the cis-3-bicyclo[3.1.0]hexanol to the CH$_2$ group and the 3028 cm.$^{-1}$ band to the tertiary hydrogen atom of the cyclopropane ring. Analogously, the 3062 and 2995 cm.$^{-1}$ frequencies are due to methylene, and the 3032 cm.$^{-1}$ frequency arises from tertiary hydrogen in the trans-alcohol.[6]

(5) L. J. Bellamy, "The Infrared Spectra of Complex Molecules," John Wiley and Sons, Inc., New York, N. Y., 2nd Ed., 1958.

(6) S. E. Wiberly and S. C. Bunce, Anal. Chem., **24**, 623 (1952), have suggested the use of C–H stretching frequencies at 3.23 μ (3096 cm.$^{-1}$) and 3.23 μ (3013 cm.$^{-1}$) for identification of cyclopropane CH$_2$ groups. Their data indicated that a third band sometimes occurs in this region, but this additional band did not appear regularly and was not commented on. For a number of cyclopropane derivatives, A. R. H. Cole, J. Chem. Soc., 3807 (1954), has reported only a single cyclopropane hydrogen stretching frequency in the 3042–3058 cm.$^{-1}$ region. For the cyclopropane ring-containing alcohol, 2-bicyclo[5.1.0]octanol,

The assignment of the 3028 or 3032 cm.$^{-1}$ band for the cis- and trans-3-bicyclo[3.1.0]hexanols to the tertiary cyclopropyl hydrogen is supported by the fact that deuteration on the carbinol carbon atom 3 does not affect its intensity. On the other hand, the intensity is lowered in alcohol C-OH, which does have some tertiary cyclopropyl deuterium and thus less tertiary hydrogen. Also, 6,6-dibromobicyclo[3.1.0]hexane[7] (III) with no cyclopropyl methylene hydrogen atoms still shows a band at 3030 cm.$^{-1}$. Further support for the assignment is provided by the observations of Henbest, et al., on epoxides,[8] whose strained 3-membered ring has considerable analogy to the cyclopropane ring. These investigators have observed characteristic C–H stretching bands which are useful in identification of the epoxide group. In cyclohexene oxide, the methine C–H band occurs at ca. 3000 cm.$^{-1}$, while in the more strained cyclopentene oxide IV, which bears a close analogy to bicyclo[3.1.0]hexane, the methine C–H stretch occurs at 3037 cm.$^{-1}$, quite similar to the 3028 or 3032 cm.$^{-1}$ band observed with the bicyclohexanols. The new 2266 cm.$^{-1}$ band observed in the product alcohol C-OH, not present in the spectrum of the deuterated alcohol B-OH, is quite clearly to be ascribed to tertiary cyclopropyl deuterium, because the position of this new band is reasonably close to that which can be anticipated from the effect of isotopic substitution on the 3028 cm.$^{-1}$ C–H band.[9]

Conversion of Cyclopropyl to Carbinyl Deuterium.—It is quite obvious from the infrared spectra of A-OH, B-OH and C-OH and the band assignments discussed above that solvolysis of the

A. C. Cope and P. E. Peterson, J. Am. Chem. Soc., **81**, 1643 (1959), have reported bands at 3070 and 2990 cm.$^{-1}$, attributed to the cyclopropane CH$_2$ group.

(7) J. Sonnenberg, unpublished work.

(8) H. B. Henbest, G. D. Meakins, B. Nicholls and K. J. Taylor, J. Chem. Soc., 1459 (1957).

(9) A. Streitwieser, Jr., R. H. Jagow, R. C. Fahey and S. Suzuki, J. Am. Chem. Soc., **80**, 2326 (1958).

III   IV

3-deuterated B-OTs is attended by some loss of deuterium from the carbinol carbon atom 3 and some appearance of tertiary deuterium on the cyclopropane ring. In order to obtain independent evidence on the amount of deuterium on the cyclopropane ring and to demonstrate the return of deuterium from the cyclopropane ring to the carbinol carbon atom, the product alcohol C-OH was carried through another sequence of reactions.

Chromium trioxide oxidation of the scrambled alcohol product C-OH yielded the partially deuterated C-ketone. On reduction of this ketone with lithium aluminum hydride and separation of the cis-3-bicyclo[3.1.0]hexanol from the small amount of contaminating trans-epimer[3] by preparative vapor phase chromatography, partially deuterated cis-alcohol D-OH was obtained. The infrared spectrum of D-OH showed that it contained only cyclopropyl deuterium, the 2266 and 670 cm.[-1] bands being present and the carbinol C-D absorptions at 2151 and 723 cm.[-1] being absent. Combustion analysis of D-OH showed it to contain 64% of the original deuterium in B-OH.

Acetolysis of the toluenesulfonate D-OTs prepared from alcohol D-OH and the usual conversion of the product acetate to alcohol gave rise to cis-alcohol E-OH. In the infrared spectrum of this alcohol the cyclopropyl deuterium bands at 2266 and 670 cm.[-1] were weaker than in the spectrum of D-OH and the carbinol C-D bands at 2151 and 723 cm.[-1] were evident. Clearly, cyclopropyl deuterium was converted in part to carbinyl deuterium during solvolysis of D-OTs.

Quantitative Spectral Analysis of Deuterium Scrambling.—Absorbance measurements on the various cis-alcohols at some of the characteristic infrared frequencies as summarized in Table I give

at pertinent frequencies are listed in Table I. For example, one sees that the C/B ratio at the carbinyl deuterium frequency of 2151 cm.[-1] is 0.33, the value predicted on the basis of the nonclassical cation II. An average value of 0.32 ± 0.01 was obtained using two different instruments. The figure of 0.64 for the D/B ratio of deuterium content given by combustion analyses is also in line, (0.64/0.32) being equal within experimental error to the value 2.00 for the ratio of cyclopropyl to carbinyl deuterium predicted by equal distribution of the deuterium label among carbon atoms 1,3 and 5. Other ratios of infrared intensities listed in Table I further support the conclusion that solvolysis of cis-3-bicyclo[3.1.0]hexyl toluenesulfonate renders carbon atoms 1,3 and 5 effectively equivalent.

From Table I it is clear that in solvolysis of D-OTs, the fraction of deuterium which becomes carbinyl in type is close to one-third, the E/B ratio at 2151 cm.[-1] being close to the value of twoninths expected on the basis of the cation II. Similarly, the E/C and E/D ratios at cyclopropyl deuterium frequencies are very close to the predicted two-thirds. Thus, in solvolysis of D-OTs with deuterium solely on the cyclopropane ring, deuterium was again distributed equally among carbon atoms 1,3 and 5.

The occurrence of deuterium distribution during solvolysis of B-OTs is also substantiated by proton magnetic resonance spectra of alcohols A, B, C and D. The spectra of alcohols A and B indicate that the carbinyl proton resonates at the same frequency as the hydroxylic one. Comparison of the spectra of the four alcohols shows the line at +140 c.p.s. relative to water is due to tertiary cyclopropyl hydrogen. In Table II are summarized the area ratios of combined carbinyl and hydroxyl hydrogen to total hydrogen in the spectra of the four alcohols. Although this analysis is less accurate than the one based on infrared spectra, it is clear that the ratios are quite close to the ones calculated on the basis of the non-classical cation II.

TABLE I
INTENSITY RATIOS OF CHARACTERISTIC ABSORPTION BANDS IN THE cis-3-BICYCLO[3.1.0]HEXANOLS

Alcohol ratio	Carbinyl D 2151	Cyclopropyl D 2266 670	Carbinyl H 745	Predicted ratio[a]
C/B	0.33			0.33
C/A			0.63	0.67
D/A			.96	1.00
D/C		0.99 0.99		1.00
E/A			.81	0.78
E/B	.20			.22
E/C	.62	.65 .66		.67
E/D		.66 .67		.67
H/A			.06	.00[b]
H/B	.99			1.00[b]
H/C		.07		0.00[b]

Observed ratios at frequencies (cm.[-1])

[a] On the basis of the non-classical cation. [b] On the basis the classical cation.

TABLE II
ANALYSIS OF DEUTERIUM SCRAMBLING BY PROTON MAGNETIC RESONANCE SPECTRA

cis-ROH	Total no. H atoms	No. of carbinyl and hydroxyl H atoms	Area ratio; carbinyl + hydroxyl/total Calcd.	Found
A	10	2	0.200	0.183
B	9	1	.111	.115
C	9	1.67[a]	.186[a]	.183
D	9.33[a]	2	.214[a]	.230

[a] On the basis of non-classical cation II.

Solvolysis of trans-Toluenesulfonate.—The small amount of impure deuterated trans-alcohol G-OH was converted to crystalline toluenesulfonate G-OTs and acetolyzed similarly to the cis-epimer, except that the temperature was 75°. Conversion of the acetate product to alcohol in the usual way[3] gave rise to alcohol H-OH. The infrared spectrum of this material contained all the bands of alcohol B-OH and weak absorption bands attributed to C-OH. From Table I it is evident that no more than a few per cent. of redistribution of deuterium

a more quantitative view of the degree of deuterium scrambling in the various specimens. Some intensity ratios between various pairs of alcohols

occurs in solvolysis of the *trans*-toluenesulfonate G-OTs.

Classical *vs*. Non-classical Cations.—The previous paper[3] reported the contrasting behavior of the *cis*- and *trans*-3-bicyclo[3.1.0]hexyl toluenesulfonates in acetolysis. Thus, acetolysis is associated with a special salt effect and some anchimeric acceleration in the case of the *cis*-epimer, but not the *trans*. Also, the *cis*-toluenesulfonate leads to *cis*-acetate with complete retention of configuration and no olefin, while the *trans*-toluenesulfonate gives rise to *cis*-acetate with complete inversion of configuration, together with considerable olefin. It is instructive to compare the *cis*- and *trans*-bicyclohexyl toluenesulfonates with the *cis*- and *trans*-4-*t*-butylcyclohexyl[10] analogs for these both give inverted acetate and large amounts of olefin in acetolysis.

The behavior of the bicyclohexyl esters was suggestive of the intervention of the non-classical cation II in acetolysis of the *cis*-toluenesulfonate, but not the *trans*. It could be supposed that anchimerically assisted ionization of *cis*-toluenesulfonate gives rise to ion II which leads stereospecifically to *cis*-acetate. On the other hand, anchimerically unassisted ionization of *trans*-toluenesulfonate presumably leads to classical cation I-T which gives rise to *cis*-acetate, together with olefin. The observed deuterium scrambling during acetolysis of deuterated *cis*-3-bicyclo[3.1.0]hexyl toluenesulfonate B-OTs in exact accord with ion II-D provides compelling support for this interpretation.

As regards deuterium scrambling, the behavior of the *trans*-bicyclohexyl toluenesulfonate is in sharp contrast with that of the *cis*, just as in the case of the special salt effect, stereochemistry and elimination during acetolysis. This fact is very helpful in delineating the possible role of a classical ion in the deuterium scrambling during acetolysis of *cis*-toluenesulfonate. For example, one might attempt to explain this deuterium scrambling by way of three distinct classical cations in rapid equilibrium. However, the *trans*-toluenesulfonate solvolyzes by just such a classical cationic intermediate, and yet it displays very little deuterium scrambling in its acetolysis. Alternatively, one might consider a classical cation as a precursor of the non-classical one in accounting for the observed deuterium scrambling. On this basis, however, the *trans*-toluenesulfonate would also be expected to show extensive deuterium scrambling, but it does not. The behavior of the *trans*-toluenesulfonate indicates that a classical 3-bicyclo[3.1.0]hexyl cation neither equilibrates nor turns non-classical at a rate competitive with collapse to substitution and elimination products.

The deuterium scrambling, together with the special salt effect and stereochemistry in acetolysis, all are uniquely consistent with direct formation of the non-classical cation II by ionization of *cis*-3-bicyclo[3.1.0]hexyl toluenesulfonate. All the facts suggest that the (k_Δ/k_s) ratio, that is the ratio of anchimerically assisted and unassisted ionization rates, must be substantial and of the order of 30–50 or more. In the case of the *trans*-toluenesulfonate,

(10) S. Winstein and N. J. Holness, *J. Am. Chem. Soc.*, **77**, 5562 (1955).

only a small fraction (<10%) of the classical cation I-T first formed becomes non-classical, most of it collapsing to products without becoming bridged.

The kinetic isotope effect of the 3-deuterium atom on the rate of ionization of *cis*-3-bicyclo[3.1.0]-hexyl toluenesulfonate is of obvious interest, but the present work has not supplied a direct measure of it. The observed (k_H/k_D) ratio of 1.05 is smaller than the values reported for similar model systems, *e.g.*, 1.15 and 1.19 for cyclopentyl-1-*d*[9] and cyclohexyl-1-*d*[11] toluenesulfonates, respectively. However, the apparent (k_H/k_D) ratio of 1.05 applies to titrimetric rather than ionization rate constants. Since ion pair return accompanies acetolysis of *cis*-3-bicyclo[3.1.0]hexyl toluenesulfonate,[3] the titrimetric rate is only a fraction of the ionization rate and the residual toluenesulfonate rapidly becomes scrambled during a run. Until the extent of ion pair return and the kinetic isotope effect of deuterium on the cyclopropane ring are more directly assessed,[12] we should defer further discussion of the question of deuterium isotope effects.

Stereoelectronic Considerations.—The non-classical ion II, which may also be represented by IIa, may be expected to have a chair conformation, the atomic orbitals on atoms 1, 3 and 5 overlapping in such a manner that the electron cloud involved in the three-center bonding is concentrated on one side of the molecule. This orbital overlap is portrayed in IIb. While IIb is represented with tri-

(11) K. Mislow, S. Borčić and V. Prelog, *Helv. Chim. Acta*, **40**, 2477 (1957).

(12) This matter is being investigated in collaboration with Dr. S. Borčić of the Institute Rudjer Bošković, Zagreb, Yugoslavia.

gonal hybridization at atoms 1, 3 and 5 and overlapping *p*-orbitals, some rehybridization would be permissible. Also, we can anticipate that introduction of some angle strain to decrease the C–C–C angles at the CH$_2$ groups will be more than compensated for by increased delocalization energy.[13]

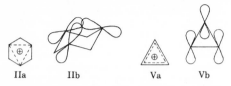

IIa   IIb   Va   Vb

The stereospecific attack by solvent or other nucleophiles on the non-classical cation II to regenerate a *cis* configuration in the product is quite similar to the stereospecific formation of β-cholesteryl or 3,5-cyclocholestan-6β-yl derivatives from the non-classical cholesteryl cation[13,14] VI, *exo*-5-norbornenyl derivatives from the 5-norbornenyl ion[2b,14d,15,16] VII or *anti*-7-norbornenyl derivatives from the *anti*-7-norbornenyl cation[17] VIII.

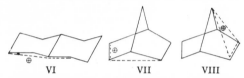

VI   VII   VIII

The Trishomocyclopropenyl Cation and the Generalized Concept of Homoaromaticity.

—The non-classical 3-bicyclo[3.1.0]hexyl cation II is related to the cyclopropenyl cation V by interposition of a CH$_2$ group between the CH groups on all three sides of the molecule. Because of this analogy, cation II may be referred to as "tris-homocyclopropenyl." This species may well be merely the first example in an interesting new chapter of organic chemistry, namely, homoaromatic chemistry. This general idea is explained below.

Simple molecular orbital theory applied to cyclic unsaturated systems predicts unique stability for those systems which have $(4n + 2)$ π-electrons.[18] These are the cases in which the bonding molecular orbitals are just fully filled. With the three-membered ring, two π-electrons are involved, unique stability being predicted for the cyclopropenyl cation V. This prediction has been confirmed recently with the preparation of relatively stable cyclopropenylium salts by Breslow.[19] With the 5-, 6- and 7-membered rings, the aromatic

(13) M. Simonetta and S. Winstein, *J. Am. Chem. Soc.*, **76**, 18 (1954).

(14) S. Winstein, *et al.*, *ibid.*, (a) **70**, 838 (1948); (b) **70**, 3528 (1948); (c) **78**, 4347, 4354 (1956); (d) **81**, 4399 (1959).

(15) S. Winstein, H. M. Walborsky and K. Schreiber, *ibid.*, **72**, 5795 (1950).

(16) S. Winstein, *Experientia Suppl. II*, 137 (1955).

(17) (a) S. Winstein, M. Shatavsky, C. Norton and R. B. Woodward, *J. Am. Chem. Soc.*, **77**, 4183 (1955); (b) S. Winstein and M. Shatavsky, *ibid.*, **78**, 592 (1956).

(18) (a) E. Hückel, *Z. Physik*, **70**, 204 (1931); (b) J. D. Roberts, A. Streitwieser, Jr., and C. M. Regan, *J. Am. Chem. Soc.*, **74**, 4579 (1952); (c) S. L. Menatt and J. D. Roberts, *J. Org. Chem.*, **24**, 1336 (1959).

(19) (a) R. Breslow and C. Yuan, *J. Am. Chem. Soc.*, **80**, 599 (1958); (b) R. Breslow and H. Höver, *ibid.*, **82**, 2644 (1960).

sextet of electrons is involved. This is contained in the cyclopentadienide ion IX, benzene X and tropylium ion XI, respectively, all three of these species being predicted by molecular orbital theory to have unique stability. Supporting evidence has long existed regarding cyclopentadienide ion and benzene, and the prediction has been strikingly confirmed more recently for tropylium ion by the preparation of very stable tropylium salts by Doering.[20]

Comparing the non-classical cation II with the cyclopropenyl analog V, we see that orbital overlap in II is not π, but intermediate between σ and π. Also, overlap and exchange integrals are 1, 3 rather than 1,2. Otherwise, the bicyclohexyl cation II is wave-mechanically analogous to the cyclopropenyl ion V. The two cations have the same pattern of molecular orbital energy levels,[18] with the resulting delocalization energy smaller for II than V, however. From this point of view the bicyclohexyl cation II is the trishomo counterpart of a species which fits the $(4n + 2)$ electron rule. Conceptually, this homo relationship may be generalized to include homo counterparts of the other aromatic examples of the $(4n + 2)$ rule. Thus, we can visualize pentahomocyclopentadienide ion XII, hexahomobenzene XIII and heptahomotropylium ion XIV. These are summarized and compared with their classical counterparts in Table III. Species XII could be visualized to arise from a material such as XV, structure XVI would

TABLE III
AROMATIC AND HOMOAROMATIC SPECIES FITTING THE $(4n + 2)$ RULE

n	$4n + 2$	Formula	Name
0	2	$C_3H_3^{\oplus}$	Cyclopropenyl
		$C_6H_9^{\oplus}$	Trishomocyclopropenyl
1	6	$C_5H_5^{\ominus}$	Cyclopentadienide
		$C_{10}H_{15}^{\ominus}$	Pentahomocyclopentadienide
1	6	C_6H_6	Benzene
		$C_{12}H_{18}$	Hexahomobenzene
1	6	$C_7H_7^{\oplus}$	Tropylium
		$C_{14}H_{21}^{\oplus}$	Heptahomotropylium

IX   X   XI

XII   XIII   XIV

↑–Y$^{\ominus}$ ↑–Y$^{\ominus}$

Y   Y

XV   XVI   XVII

(20) (a) W. v. E. Doering and L. H. Knox, *ibid.*, **76**, 3203 (1954); (b) see W. v. E. Doering and H. Krauch, *Angew. Chem.*, **68**, 661 (1956) for an excellent review of this and related matters.

represent one of the "Kekulé" structures for hexa-homobenzene, and the heptahomotropylium ion XIV could be formulated as the product of ioniza-tion of a material with structure XVII.

The question whether species XII–XIV will prove to be truly homoaromatic is one of balance between quantum-mechanical delocalization energy and the compression energy necessary to force classical structures (like the "Kekulé" structures of type XVI) into the same geometry. It is quite clear that quantum-mechanical delocalization ener-gies in homoaromatic cases XII–XIV will be less than in aromatic cases, perhaps *ca.* 40% as large,[2b,13,21] but the compression energies may not be large enough to preclude formation of hybrid homoaromatic structures. The balance seems no more discouraging for XII–XIV than for the trishomocyclopropenyl cation II, and we have experiments under way in an effort to prepare new homoaromatic compounds.

Homoconjugation and Homoaromaticity.—The concept of homoconjugation first arose in con-sidering the behavior of cholesteryl and *i*-choles-teryl derivatives in solvolytic reactions.[13,14] A non-classical intermediate VI was visualized which was termed "homoallyl." The latter designation is made clearer with formulas XVIIIa–c which portray a carbonium ion with a β-olefinic group and show explicitly the overlapping atomic *p*-orbitals on the two olefinic carbon atoms C_3 and C_4 and the cationic carbon atom C_1. The idea behind the homoallyl designation is that a methylene group (C_2) is a poor insulator of conjugation if the proper rotational positions about the C_1–C_2 and C_2–C_3 bonds are assumed. With proper rotational posi-tions, there is very appreciable 1,3-orbital overlap[13] of a type intermediate between σ and π. Semi-empirical molecular orbital calculations[13] sug-gest substantial stabilization from electron delocali-zation.

XVIIIa   XVIIIb

XVIIIc

From the above point of view, one may say that the homoallyl cation XVIII is homoconjugatively stabilized. In conjugation there is electron de-localization over adjacent carbon atoms. Homo-conjugation involves electron delocalization across intervening carbon atoms, a single intervening carbon atom in the case of cation XVIII. Such homoconjugation, involving electron delocalization across intervening carbon atoms, is present, also,

in the trishomocyclopropenyl cation II and the other visualized homoaromatic species XII–XIV. The striking behavior of the *cis*-3-bicyclo[3.1.0]-hexyl system has confirmed our anticipations on theoretical grounds that such homoconjugation could be important in systems possessing no π-elec-trons in the original classical structures.

If we consider the stepwise insertion of the methylene groups which convert species like the cyclopropenyl cation V and benzene X to their homoaromatic counterparts II and XIII, the designation bishomocyclopropenyl[22] is appropriate for cation VIII, and the pseudo-aromatic structure for tropilidene visualized by Doering[23] can be termed monohomobenzene. Only by explicit step-wise insertion of methylene groups may we ap-preciate the full ramifications of all the possible molecules which may represent discrete species. For illustration, monohomocyclopentadienide ion XX is a conceivable anion from proton removal from XIX. The homoaromatic species II and XII–XIV, with a methylene group inserted between all alternate CH groups, are unique in having complete equivalence of the classical contributing structures. While a systematic nomenclature system will ultimately be desirable, the designation "perhomo-aromatic" may be a useful one to distinguish cases like II and XII–XIV from analogs with fewer interposed methylene groups.[24]

XIX   XX

Experimental

cis-Alcohol B-OH.—3-Bicyclo[3.1.0]hexanone was ob-tained by oxidation of *cis*-3-bicyclo[3.1.0]hexanol[3] contain-ing a small proportion of *trans*-epimer with chromic trioxide in pyridine.[4] Reduction[3] of the ketone with lithium alu-minum deuteride in ether at −78° gave rise to a 5.0-g. quantity of crude deuterated alcohol. From chromatog-raphy on alumina[3] three main fractions were obtained: (a) 2.9 g. of the essentially pure *cis*-alcohol (maximum of 4% of the *trans*-alcohol); (b) an intermediate fraction which was mostly the *cis*-alcohol; and (c) the remaining residue which came off with the ether eluent.

Each alcohol fraction was converted separately to acid phthalate.[3a] Fraction a yielded 7.1 g. of crude acid ph-thalate, m.p. 118–121.5°. After two recrystallizations from ether–pentane, 4.9 g. (67%) of product, m.p. 122.5–125.5°, was obtained. A second crop of 1.3 g., m.p. 118–123°, was also obtained. The combined crude acid phthalates from fractions b and c amounted to 1.2 g. of material, m.p. 120–123.5°. The mother liquors from all the recrystallizations were combined and saved for later use in obtaining the deuterated *trans*-alcohol.

Saponification[3] of the 4.9 g. of acid phthalate, m.p. 122.5–125.5°, yielded 1.7 g. (87%) of the deuterated *cis*-alcohol, b.p. 67–68° (17.0 mm.). The center fraction of 1.4 g., b.p. 67.5° (17.0 mm.), $n^{25.0}D$ 1.4770 was used in all the analytical work. A v.p.c. analysis indicated the presence of only the *cis*-alcohol, no more than 0.5% of the *trans*-alcohol being present. Deuterium combustion analysis[25] indicated 9.85 atom % excess deuterium.

(21) (a) C. F. Wilcox, Jr., S. Winstein and W. G. McMillan, *J. Am. Chem. Soc.*, **82**, 5450 (1960); (b) S. Winstein and R. Piccolini, unpublished work.

(22) W. G. Woods, R. A. Carboni and J. D. Roberts, *J. Am. Chem. Soc.*, **78**, 5653 (1956).

(23) W. v. E. Doering, *et al.*, *ibid.*, **78**, 5448 (1956).

(24) This type of distinction is also desirable in the non-cyclic cases, such as those based on allyl. It is necessary to consider bishomoallyl as well as homoallyl.

(25) By Dr. J. Nemeth, Urbana, Ill.

Anal. Calcd. for C_6H_9DO: C, 72.68; H and D, 11.18. Found: C, 72.88; H and D, 11.09.

Saponification of the combined lower melting acid phthalates (2.5 g.) led to 0.90 g. of alcohol. A v.p.c. analysis indicated contamination by only 2% of the *trans*-isomer, so this material was used in the preparation of the deuterated *cis*-toluenesulfonate.

Conversion of deuterated *cis*-alcohol to toluenesulfonate[3] led to a 70% yield of product, m.p. 51.5–52.0°, in addition to a second crop, m.p. 51.0–51.5°, obtained from the last mother liquor.

Anal. Calcd. for $C_{13}H_{15}DO_3S$: C, 61.63; H and D, 6.76. Found: C, 61.79; H and D, 6.52.

Acetolysis of B-OTs.—The toluenesulfonate (m.p. 51.0–52.0°, 1.25 g., 5.0 mmoles) and 65 ml. of anhydrous acetic acid, 0.01 M in acetic anhydride and 0.1005 M in sodium acetate, was heated at 50.0° for 48 hours in a sealed flask. After the acetolysis products were subjected to the standard extraction and reduction procedure,[3] a v.p.c. analysis of the undistilled alcohol product indicated the presence of more than 99% of *cis*-alcohol. Distillation of the residue yielded 0.45 g. of *cis*-alcohol C–OH, b.p. 64–66° (18.5 mm.).

C-Ketone and *cis*-Alcohol D-OH.—Alcohol C–OH (*ca.* 0.45 g.) in pyridine (5 ml.) was oxidized[3] with chromic trioxide (2.3 g.) in pyridine (23 ml.) and worked up in the usual way. The product in ether was analyzed by v.p.c., and this showed the presence of the desired ketone, a relatively large amount of pyridine, and several minor impurities at times. No bicyclic alcohol was detected. The ketone in ether was reduced[3] with lithium aluminum hydride at −78° to yield 0.35 g. of alcohol product, b.p. 65–66° (16 mm.). A v.p.c. analysis indicated a 90:10 *cis–trans* mixture. Using preparative v.p.c., the *cis*-alcohol was purified and separated from the *trans*-alcohol. The deuterated *cis*-alcohol D-OH thus obtained was used in all the analytical work; $n^{25}D$ 1.4760. Deuterium combustion analysis[25] indicated 6.27 atom % excess deuterium. Conversion of alcohol D-OH (*ca.* 0.30 g.) to toluenesulfonate[3] gave rise to 0.35 g. of product, m.p. 50.5–51.5° after two recrystallizations.

Acetolysis of D-OTs.—Toluenesulfonate D-OTs (317 mg.) was dissolved in 16 ml. of anhydrous acetic acid, 0.01 M in acetic anhydride and 0.1005 M in sodium acetate, and was heated at 50.0° for 48 hours in a sealed ampoule. After the standard work-up and reduction procedure,[3] 0.10 g. of alcohol was obtained by distillation. A v.p.c. analysis of the distillate indicated that the *cis*-alcohol was contaminated with an unknown component (3%) with retention time slightly less than that of the *cis*-alcohol. Therefore, the *cis*-alcohol E-OH was reisolated using preparative v.p.c.

***trans*-3-Bicyclo[3.1.0]hexanol G-OH.**—The combined mother liquors from the preparation of the acid phthalate of deuterated *cis*-alcohol B-OH were saponified.[3] A v.p.c. analysis of the alcohol product indicated that it contained numerous components, most of them probably arising from the original chromic trioxide oxidation. However, the *trans*-alcohol constituted 40% of the bicyclic alcohol. Using preparative v.p.c., the *trans*-alcohol was isolated and partially purified. At the same time, more of the *cis*-alcohol was also collected.

The accumulated *trans*-alcohol (*ca.* 0.30 g.) was not pure, a small unknown component being present as evidenced by the asymmetrical peak on v.p.c. analysis. The infrared spectrum of the alcohol product exhibited C–D stretching absorption in the 4.5–5.0 μ region, which was weaker (about one third the absorbance) than that observed for the deuterated *cis*- alcohol B-OH. The infrared analysis of the deuterated *trans*-alcohol G-OH indicated the presence of 2% alcohol B-OH.

Conversion of alcohol G-OH (*ca.* 0.30 g.) to toluenesulfonate[3] gave 0.50 g. of crude product, m.p. 35–50°. One recrystallization from ether–pentane gave 0.35 g. of material, m.p. 58–66°. Utilizing fractional crystallization from ether–pentane, 0.22 g. of toluenesulfonate G-OTs, m.p. 68.5–70.0°, was obtained.

Acetolysis of Toluenesulfonate G-OTs.—The toluenesulfonate m.p. 68.5–70.0°, (0.22 g.) and 12 ml. of anhydrous acetic acid, 0.01 M in acetic anhydride and 0.1005 M in sodium acetate, was heated at 75.0° for 44.5 hours in a sealed ampoule. After the standard work-up and reduction[3] of the acetolysis product, alcohol H-OH was isolated using preparative v.p.c. The infrared spectrum of alcohol H-OH

indicated it was primarily the deuterated *cis*-alcohol B-OH contaminated with a small amount of the scrambled *cis*-alcohol C-OH.

Preparative V.p.c.—By the use of a $^3/_8$ inch copper tube column, 2.5 meters long, packed with 30% Carbowax 4000 suspended on 70% by weight of 40–60 mesh Johns–Mansville firebrick, and by attaching a collection system to the exit tube, it was possible to adapt the analytical[3] apparatus for separation of 0.2–0.5-ml. samples of the deuterated *cis*-

TABLE IV

OBSERVED INFRARED ABSORPTION BANDS OF THE ORDINARY AND DEUTERATED 3-BICYCLO[3.1.0]HEXANOLS (FREQUENCY OF ABSORPTION BANDS IN CM.$^{-1}$)

cis-Alcohols			trans-Alcohols	
A-OH	B-OH	C-OH	F-OH	G-OH
(3310–	(3310–	(3310––	(3280–	(3280–
3400vs)	3400vs)	3400vs)	3450vs)	3450vs)
3070w	3070w	3070w	3062m	3062m
3028s	3028s	3028s	3032ms	3032ms
3000m	3000m	3000m	2995m	2995m
				2950sh
(2920–	(2920–	(2920–	(2926–	(2926–
2937vs)	2937vs)	2937vs)	2941vs)	2941vs)
			2900sh	2900sh
2846m	2846m	2846m	2860s	2860s
2732vw		2732vw		
				2366vw^a
				2342vw^a
		2266m		
	2224w	2224vw		
				2193w
	2177mw	2177w		
	2151m	2151mw		2152m
	2137sh	2137sh		2135sh
	2124sh	2124sh		
	2086w	2086vw		2092w
	2038vw	2038vw		2030vw
1460sh	1454w	1454w	1460sh	
1434m	1435m	1435m	1445m	1453m
1360m	1359m		1363m	1372m
1342m		1351m	1346m	1353w
		1335m		1328w
1315m	1310w	1305m	1313m	
1290s	1288s	1288s	1293mw	1295s
	1260w	1272w		1274w
	1240vs	1242m		1245w
1230m		1225m		
			1210w	1208shw
				1190shw
1175m	1175ms	1175w	1170m	1177s
1165shw		1162sh	1155sh	
		1135m		
	1120sh^a			1125s
1102s	1108vs	1109s	1105s	1115shw^a
		1087s		
1068w				
	1062m	1060s		1060vs
1045vs	1044m	1041s	1048vs	
			1026m	1026m
1022sh	1019m	1020sh		1020sh
			1005w	1005w
		990s		
	978m	980sh		978shw
		964w	965w	965ms
956vs				
	941vs	944s	945shw	945w
935m	932sh	932sh		
		918m	919w	920w
		893w	899w	904w
	884vw^a		875shw	879w
856w	855w	854w	862w	860w
	821shw	821w	833w	
807s	810ms	811w	810s	812s
	794m	793w		
		776w		
			762s	763s
745s	746m			
	723s	723m		723vw^a
		670m		

^{a} Probably due to impurities.

and *trans*-bicyclohexanols with considerable success. The final alcohol fractions were of *ca*. 98% purity.

Spectral Measurements.—The quantitative infrared spectral measurements were made with two spectrophotometers, each operated as a double beam instrument. The following control settings were used with the Perkin–Elmer model 21 equipped with sodium chloride prisms: resolution, 960; gain, 5.5; response, 1; speed, 5; and suppression, O. The 2.5–16.0 μ range was scanned. The following control settings were used with the Beckman model IR-4 equipped with lithium fluoride prisms: gain, 2.0%; speed, 0.17 μ/min.; period, 2.0 sec.; and slit, 2 × standard. The 3.0–5.0 μ range was scanned. The liquid alcohols were determined neat in a 0.018-mm. sodium chloride cell compensated against a sodium chloride block.

The complete infrared spectra of the various *cis*- and *trans*-3-bicyclohexanols are given in Table IV for neat liquid films. The data for the 3.0–5.0 μ region are from the Beckman IR-4 instrument with lithium fluoride optics, and for the 5.0–16. μ region from the Perkin–Elmer model 21 instrument with sodium chloride optics. The frequency ranges in parentheses indicate uncertain positions of maxima because of broadness of absorption bands.

TABLE V

OBSERVED PEAK HEIGHTS OF CHARACTERISTIC ABSORPTION BANDS OF THE *cis*-3-BICYCLO[3.1.0]HEXANOLS

Alcohol	Carbinyl D 2151	Cyclopropyl D 2266	Cyclopropyl D 670	Carbinyl H 745
A-OH	0.0	0.0	0.0	0.710
B-OH	.246	.0	.0	.0
C-OH	.081	.098	.335	.445
D-OH	.0	.097	.331	.680
E-OH	.050	.064	.222	.574
H-OH[b]	.163		.016	.026
	(.245)		(.024)	(.039)

(In absorbance units)[a]

[a] Measured on Perkin–Elmer model 21 spectrophotometer equipped with sodium chloride optics; frequencies in cm.⁻¹. [b] The available material at hand was insufficient to fill the infrared cell. Therefore, the values need to be increased. A factor of 1.5 has been chosen so that the intensity at the 2151 cm.⁻¹ band represents about 100% deuterium. These increased values are given in the parentheses and are used in the calculations.

In Table V are summarized some of the quantitative measurements on the various alcohol specimens for the analysis of deuterium scrambling made in Table I.

Proton magnetic resonance spectra of the *cis*-3-bicyclo-[3.1.0]hexanols were measured by R. Gillespie using a Varian V-4300-B high resolution spectrometer equipped with a 12-inch magnet and super-stabilizer. The frequency was fixed at 40 Mc./sec., and a magnetic field of about 9400 gauss was used. Determinations were made on the pure neat liquids. Sample tubes of 5-mm. outside diameter were used, and a sealed capillary tube of about 1-mm. diameter filled with distilled water was placed inside the sample tube. Samples were spun during the measurements. The line of the water peak was used as reference to measure shifts. The shifts of the peaks were determined by the use of the 60 c.p.s. audio-frequency side band method. The sign of the shift is chosen to be positive when the resonance falls at a higher applied field than the reference. In Table VI are summarized the observations on undeuterated *cis*-3-bicyclo-[3.1.0]hexanol.

TABLE VI

	Relative area		
Cycles per second[a]	Obsd.	Theory	Hydrogen assignment
8	1.84	2	1,2
91	0.24		
112[b]	3.44	4	3,4
140	2.48	2	5
161	2.16	2	6,7

[a] Relative to water, uncorrected for a bulk diamagnetic effect at 40 Mc. [b] Sharp peak; little, if any, splitting.

Kinetic Measurements.—First-order rate constants for acetolysis of 0.01 *M* toluenesulfonates A-OTs and B-OTs at 50.0° were determined simultaneously by the procedure employed previously.[3] For the undeuterated A-OTs the observed $10^5 k$ was 2.46 ± 0.04, while for the deuterated B-OTs it was 2.35 ± 0.04. In the latter case, there was some indication of a slight upward trend in the rate constant during the run.

56 | Solvolytic Ring Closure to the Decalin System

Goering and Closson (Paper No. 56) report some substantial driving forces in the solvolysis of *cis*- and *trans*-5-cyclodecen-l-yl *p*-nitrobenzoates: The *cis* is faster than the saturated by a factor of 4.6, the *trans* by 1500. A really unique feature of this reaction is the internal return (with 2/3 retention of ^{18}O-isotope position in the carboxyl group) of the reactive *trans* isomer to the *p*-nitrobenzoate of *trans-cis*-l-decalol. In net effect this is a *cis* addition of carbon and benzoate to a double bond, whereas the net effect of solvolytic ring closures—including the two in this paper—is *trans* addition to a double bond. Such a *cis* internal return was looked for in vain in the solvolysis of a 2-(Δ^3-cyclopentenyl)-ethyl sulfonate to the norbornyl system.[1] These facts made the explanation of Goering and Closson, based on a proximity effect, attractive despite the shortage of analogies in the literature. If the *trans*-cyclodecenyl ring is staggered as fully as possible, there are the two interconvertible conformations II′ and II″, with the ester group equatorial and axial, respectively, which are proposed to yield normal double bond anchimerism in the former case and concerted or benzoate-initiated transannular migration in the latter.

---

[1] P. D. Bartlett, S. Bank, R. J. Crawford, and G. H. Schmid, *J. Am. Chem. Soc.* **87**, 1288 (1965).

From: *J. Am. Chem. Soc.* **83,** 3511–17 (1961)

[Contribution from the Department of Chemistry, The University of Wisconsin, Madison 6, Wis.]

Transannular Interactions. IV. Products and Rates of Solvolysis of *cis*- and *trans*-5-Cyclodecen-1-yl *p*-Nitrobenzoate in Aqueous Acetone[1]

By Harlan L. Goering and William D. Closson[2]

Received March 20, 1961

Transannular participation by the double bond is involved in the solvolysis of *cis*- (Ia) and *trans*-5-cyclodecen-1-yl *p*-nitrobenzoate (II) in aqueous acetone. In each case the first-order rate is enhanced (alkyl–oxygen cleavage is involved) and only bicyclic products are formed. At 120° the *trans*-*p*-nitrobenzoate II is about 300 times more reactive than the *cis* isomer Ia which in turn is more reactive than the saturated analog, cyclodecyl *p*-nitrobenzoate. The *cis* isomer Ia is converted to *cis-cis*-1-decalol (V). Solvolysis of the *trans*-*p*-nitrobenzoate II is accompanied by an isomeric rearrangement (*ca.* 18%) to an unreactive product. The solvolysis product is *trans-trans*-1-decalol (IV) and the rearrangement product is mainly *trans-cis*-1-decalyl *p*-nitrobenzoate (III). The rearrangement product III formed from carbonyl-O¹⁸-*trans*-*p*-nitrobenzoate II has two-thirds of the label in the carbonyl position.

An investigation of the solvolysis of *cis*-5-cyclodecen-1-yl *p*-toluenesulfonate (Ib) was reported in an earlier paper.[3] In that work it was found that at 30° the unsaturated *cis*-*p*-toluenesulfonate Ib ethanolizes ten times faster and acetolyzes seven times faster than the saturated analog cyclodecyl *p*-toluenesulfonate. From the solvolytic behavior and the formation of bicyclic solvolytic and rearrangement products, it was concluded that ionization probably involves "transannular"[4] participation by the double bond.

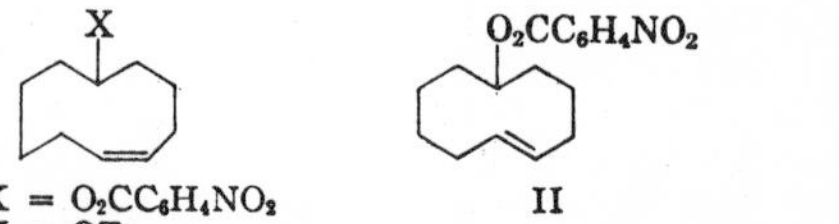

Ia, X = O$_2$CC$_6$H$_4$NO$_2$
b, X = OTs
c, X = OH

II

Transannular interactions involving carbon–carbon double bonds have been observed in other medium-sized ring systems. Pertinent examples

(1) This work was supported in part by the Research Committee of the Graduate School with funds given by the Wisconsin Alumni Research Foundation.

(2) Wisconsin Alumni Research Foundation Fellow 1956–1958; National Science Foundation Fellow 1958–1960.

(3) H. L. Goering, H. H. Espy and W. D. Closson, *J. Am. Chem. Soc.*, **81**, 329 (1959).

(4) Apparently the term "transannular" has not been defined explicitly. In the present discussion this adjective is restricted to those actions (reactions and interactions) between atoms or functional groups which are part of, or are directly attached to, the same ring and are separated by at least two ring members. The ring members to which interacting exocyclic functional groups are attached are not counted. This restriction excludes homoallylic and the usual type of neighboring group phenomena even when these are involved in cyclic systems.

include the acid-catalyzed (a) hydration of caryophyllene oxide,[5] (b) cyclizations of the maleic anhydride "adduct" of caryophyllene[6] and (c) conversion of pyrethrosin to cyclopyrethrosin.[7] The rates and products of solvolysis of *cis*-4-cycloöcten-1-yl *p*-bromobenzenesulfonate in acetic acid and trifluoroacetic acid[8] indicate that transannular participation by the double bond is involved in this case also. Similarly the acid-catalyzed conversion of 6-ketocyclodecyl *p*-toluenesulfonate to bicyclo-[5.3.0]decan-2-one apparently involves enolization followed by a unimolecular cyclization of the enol, *i.e.*, transannular participation by the enol double bond.[9]

In the present work the solvolytic reactivities of the *cis*- and *trans*-5-cyclodecen-1-yl systems were investigated. The *trans* system is far too reactive for preparation of the *p*-toluenesulfonate derivative and for this reason the *p*-nitrobenzoate derivative II was used. This paper describes an investigation of the products (stereochemistry) and rates of solvolysis (alkyl–oxygen cleavage) of *cis*-(Ia) and *trans*-5-cyclodecen-1-yl *p*-nitrobenzoate (II) in aqueous acetone. The stereochemistry of the cyclizations of these systems was of special interest in connection with recent suggestions that biogeneses of sesquiterpenes involve ionic cyclizations of unsaturated ten-membered ring intermediates.[10]

Results

Rate Measurements.—First-order rate constants for the solvolysis of *cis*-(Ia)[11] and *trans*-5-cyclodecen-1-yl *p*-nitrobenzoate (II)[11] are given in Table I. For comparison purposes, the reactivities of some other *p*-nitrobenzoates were measured and these data are also included in Table I. With two exceptions (cyclodecyl and *trans-cis*-1-decalyl *p*-nitrobenzoate, III) the constants given in the table are the average (and average deviation) of two independent kinetic experiments.

Solvolysis of *trans*-5-cyclodecen-1-yl *p*-nitrobenzoate (II) in 90% aqueous acetone at 100° and 120° resulted in the formation of about 0.82 equivalent of *p*-nitrobenzoic acid by a clean first-order process. The reactions were followed by titration of the *p*-nitrobenzoic acid and rate constants were determined from the rate of formation of acid. The "infinity" titers observed after ten half-periods at the reaction temperature were used to calculate the first-order constants. In each experiment the reaction was followed to about 80% completion. The rate was cleanly first-order and as can be seen from the small average deviations in Table I, the constants were reproducible. That alkyl–

(5) A. Aebi, D. H. R. Barton and A. S. Lindsey, *J. Chem. Soc.*, 3124 (1953).

(6) A. Nickon, *J. Am. Chem. Soc.*, **77**, 1190 (1955).

(7) D. H. R. Barton, O. C. Böckman and P. de Mayo, *J. Chem. Soc.*, 2263 (1960).

(8) A. C. Cope and P. E. Peterson, *J. Am. Chem. Soc.*, **81**, 1643 (1959); A. C. Cope, J. M. Grisar and P. E. Peterson, *ibid.*, **82**, 4299 (1960).

(9) H. L. Goering, A. C. Olson and H. H. Espy, *ibid.*, **78**, 5371 (1956).

(10) (a) J. B. Hendrickson, *Tetrahedron*, **7**, 82 (1959); (b) D. H. R. Barton and P. de Mayo, *Quart. Revs.*, **11**, 189 (1957); L. Ruzicka, *Experientia*, **9**, 357 (1953).

(11) H. L. Goering, W. D. Closson and A. C. Olson, *J. Am. Chem. Soc.*, **83**, 3507 (1961).

TABLE I

RATE CONSTANTS FOR SOLVOLYSIS OF *p*-NITROBENZOATE ESTERS (RX) IN AQUEOUS ACETONE[a]

p-Nitrobenzoate	Temp., °C.	[RX], 10^2 M	Solute, 10^2 M	$10^6 k$,[b] sec.$^{-1}$
90% aqueous acetone				
trans-5-Cyclo-	119.42	2.47		75.4 ± 0.2
decenyl (II)	99.71	2.3		12.5 ± .1
	99.68	2.3	2.6 HOPNB[c]	12.7 ± .4
	99.68	2.3	2.6 NaOPNB[c]	12.2 ± .2
cis-5-Cyclo-				
decenyl (Ia)	118.59	1.0	0.16 NaOPNB[c]	0.23 ± .01
Cyclodecyl	118.59	2.2	0.16 NaOPNB[c]	0.05[d]
trans-cis-1-Decalyl				
(III)	119.40	2.5		0.01[e]
α,α-Dimethylallyl	119.41	2.4		6.74 ± 0.02
80% aqueous acetone				
trans-5-Cyclo-				
decenyl (II)	99.71	2.2		38.7 ± 0.05

[a] Indicated solvent composition based on volumes of pure components at 25° before mixing. [b] Except for cyclodecyl and *trans-cis*-1-decalyl *p*-nitrobenzoates all constants are average values for two independent kinetic experiments. [c] HOPNB and NaOPNB are *p*-nitrobenzoic acid and sodium *p*-nitrobenzoate, respectively. [d] Upper limit estimated from 7.4% reaction after 432 hr. [e] Upper limit estimated from 2.4% reaction after 528 hr.

oxygen rather than acyl–oxygen cleavage is involved in this reaction is shown by both the products and the rate—there is no apparent reason why acyl–oxygen cleavage should be more rapid for II (or Ia) than for cyclodecyl *p*-nitrobenzoate.

As shown in Table I, the presence of 0.025 M sodium *p*-nitrobenzoate or *p*-nitrobenzoic acid had no detectable effect on the rate of solvolysis. Solvolysis of the *trans-p*-nitrobenzoate II in 80% acetone was about three times faster than in 90% acetone and resulted in the formation of about 0.85 equivalent of *p*-nitrobenzoic acid.

The difference between the observed and calculated "infinity" titers results from partial rearrangement of the reactant to an unreactive isomer, *i.e.*, solvolysis is accompanied by rearrangement as illustrated below. In this scheme k_s and k_r are first-order constants for solvolysis and rearrangement, respectively. The rate constants given in Table I are for the disappearance of II and thus correspond to $k_r + k_s$.

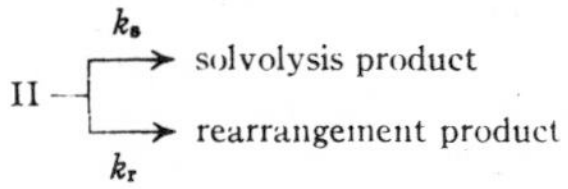

$$\text{II} \underset{k_r}{\overset{k_s}{\longrightarrow}} \begin{array}{l} \text{solvolysis product} \\ \text{rearrangement product} \end{array}$$

The rearrangement product is relatively unreactive and thus the rearrangement does not disturb the first-order rate of formation of *p*-nitrobenzoic acid. The ratio of rearrangement to solvolysis, k_r/k_s, can be determined readily from the observed and calculated "infinity" titers (*i.e.*, k_r/k_s is the difference between the calculated and observed titers divided by the observed titer). Values of k_r/k_s for various conditions are given in Table II. These were determined from the calculated titers and those observed at about ten half-periods. Each value is an average (and average deviation) of two independent experiments.

The data show that k_r/k_s is not affected by the presence of sodium *p*-nitrobenzoate or *p*-nitrobenzoic acid. The ratio decreases slightly with tem-

TABLE II

RATIO OF REARRANGEMENT (k_r) TO SOLVOLYSIS (k_s) FOR
0.02 M *trans*-5-CYCLODECEN-1-YL p-NITROBENZOATE IN
AQUEOUS ACETONE

Temp., °C.	Added solute, 10^2 M	$k_r/k_s{}^a$
	90% aqueous acetone	
118.6		0.226 ± 0.001
99.6		.203 ± .002
118.6	2.47 NaOPNB^b	.224 ± .001
99.6	2.47 NaOPNB^b	.191 ± .009
118.6	2.54 HOPNB^c	.235 ± .001
99.6	2.54 HOPNB^c	.205 ± .006
	80% aqueous acetone	
118.6		0.170 ± 0.001
99.7		0.164 ± 0.001

^{a} Average value and average deviation of two independent experiments. ^{b} Sodium p-nitrobenzoate. ^{c} p-Nitrobenzoic acid.

perature (rearrangement is more sensitive to temperature changes than solvolysis) and is lower for 80% acetone than for 90% acetone.

A discrepancy between the observed and calculated infinity titers would result from contamination of the reactant with an unreactive isomer as well as from formation of such an isomer during solvolysis. In the present case the unreactive isomer is formed during the solvolysis. This was demonstrated by showing that when II is contaminated with isotopically labeled (O^{18}) *trans-cis*-1-decalyl p-nitrobenzoate (III), which is the major component of the unreactive rearrangement product, the contaminant is completely removed by the method[11] (recrystallization) used to purify II for the kinetic experiments. Also, the fact that k_r/k_s is solvent and temperature dependent and reproducible shows that the unreactive isomer is formed during solvolysis.

Rate constants for the solvolysis of *cis*-5-cyclodecen-1-yl p-nitrobenzoate (Ia),[11] α,γ-dimethylallyl p-nitrobenzoate,[12] *trans-cis*-1-decalyl p-nitrobenzoate (III) and cyclodecyl p-nitrobenzoate in 90% aqueous acetone at 120° are included in Table I. In the case of α,γ-dimethylallyl p-nitrobenzoate the reaction was followed to over 80% completion; no trends were observed and the infinity titer was in good agreement with the calculated value.

The kinetic experiments with *cis*-5-cyclodecen-1-yl p-nitrobenzoate (Ia) were complicated by the low solubility and reactivity in 90% aqueous acetone. The measurements were made with 0.01 M solutions and the reactions were followed to 30–50% completion. The rate constants, computed using the calculated infinity titers, did not show any trends. Since pure *cis* p-nitrobenzoate Ia can be isolated in good yields after partial solvolysis, it appears that solvolysis is not accompanied by isomerization. The solvolyses of cyclodecyl and *trans-cis*-1-decalyl p-nitrobenzoates (III) were so slow that only approximate values for the first-order constants were obtained. These were calculated from the small amounts (a few per cent.) of acid produced after long periods of time. In the latter two cases the reaction probably involves acyl–oxygen rather than alkyl–oxygen cleavage.

(12) H. L. Goering and M. M. Pombo, *J. Am. Chem. Soc.*, **82**, 2515 (1960).

Thus k for these compounds is a conservative upper limit for the carbonium-ion process (alkyl–oxygen cleavage).

Solvolysis Products.—The products resulting from the simultaneous solvolysis and rearrangement of 0.03 M *trans*-5-cyclodecen-1-yl p-nitrobenzoate (II) in 90% acetone at 100° were isolated after twelve half-periods. Vapor phase chromatography (v.p.c.) indicated that a volatile product, which was not identified, is formed in 10–20% yield. The product was separated into an alcohol (60–69% yield) and a p-nitrobenzoate (15–18% yield) fraction by either column chromatography or sublimation. The alcohol fraction was identified as *trans-trans*-1-decalol (IV) by comparison of the infrared spectrum and p-nitrobenzoate derivative with those of an authentic sample. Vapor phase chromatography showed that this fraction contained 1–2% of a contaminant that had the same retention time as *trans-cis*-1-decalol.

Recrystallization of the p-nitrobenzoate fraction (the rearrangement product) gave pure *trans-cis*-1-decalyl p-nitrobenzoate (III) which was identified by comparison with an authentic sample. Saponification of the p-nitrobenzoate fraction gave a binary mixture of alcohols consisting of 85% *trans-cis*-1-decalol (v.p.c.) and 15% of a material which was not identified but had the same retention time as *trans-trans*-1-decalol (IV).

Control experiments showed that from 93–95% of the alcohol and 97–99% of the p-nitrobenzoate are isolated by the techniques used in the product studies. It was also found that ester interchange does not occur under the conditions of the solvolysis reaction.

The solvolysis product of *cis*-5-cyclodecen-1-yl p-nitrobenzoate (Ia) was also isolated. In this case a 0.03 M solution of Ia in 90% aqueous acetone was heated to 120° for 545 hours. This corresponds to about 36% reaction. The product (alcohol) and unchanged p-nitrobenzoate were isolated and separated in the manner described above; 65% of the original Ia was recovered. The solvolysis product obtained in 33% yield (based on the original amount of Ia) was identified as *cis-cis*-1-decalol (V) by comparison of v.p.c. retention time, the phenylurethan derivative and infrared spectrum with those of an authentic sample. Vapor phase chromatography indicated that this fraction was homogeneous.

When *cis*-5-cyclodecen-1-ol (Ic) was heated in 90% aqueous acetone under the conditions of the solvolysis reaction it was recovered unchanged. Thus Ic is not a solvolysis product and evidently *cis-cis*-1-decalol (V) is the initially formed product. It is apparent from the product that the solvolysis of Ia involves alkyl–oxygen cleavage.

Rearrangement of Carbonyl-O^{18} *trans*-5-Cyclodecen-1-yl p-Nitrobenzoate (II).—To obtain additional information about the rearrangement of II to *trans-cis*-decalyl p-nitrobenzoate (III) which occurs during solvolysis, the relative positions of the carboxyl oxygen atoms in the reactant II and product III were established. Carbonyl-O^{18}-II was solvolyzed in 90% acetone at 100° and the major rearrangement product, III, was isolated

after ten half-periods. The distribution of O^{18} in III (and also in II) was determined by saponification (acyl–oxygen cleavage), followed by re-conversion to the *p*-nitrobenzoate with unlabeled *p*-nitrobenzoyl chloride. The O^{18} content of the ester derived in this way corresponds to that of the ether–oxygen position of the original ester. The difference in O^{18} content before and after saponification and re-esterification corresponds to the O^{18} content of the carbonyl position of the original ester.

The results of the O^{18} experiments are summarized in Table III. Experiment 1 shows the O^{18} content of the reactant II. In the second experiment unreacted II was isolated after one half-life to determine if any scrambling occurs prior to reaction. Clearly there is little if any mixing of oxygen atoms in II during solvolysis. In experiment 3 the reaction was carried out in the presence of 0.05 M sodium *p*-nitrobenzoate. This experiment, in complete agreement with the kinetic results (*i.e.*, k_t/k_s is not affected by *p*-nitrobenzoate ion), shows that the rearrangement is intramolecular and that none of the label is lost under the conditions of the rearrangement. Experiments 4 and 5 are duplicate experiments and show the O^{18} distribution in III derived from carbonyl-O^{18} II (3.98 atom % excess O^{18}). These experiments show that the III has about one-third of the O^{18} in the alkyl–oxygen position.

TABLE III

OXYGEN-18 DATA FOR CONVERSION OF CARBONYL-O^{18} *trans*-5-CYCLODECEN-1-YL *p*-NITROBENZOATE (II) TO *trans*-*cis*-1-DECALYL *p*-NITROBENZOATE (III) IN 90% AQUEOUS ACETONE AT 99.6°

Expt.	Compound	Position	Atom % excess O^{18}
1	II[a]	Carbonyl-O	3.98 ± 0.04
2[b]	II	Alkyl-O	0.026 ± .012
3[c]	III	Total	3.99 ± .06
4	III	Alkyl-O	1.37 ± .01
5	III	Alkyl-O	1.33 ± .01

[a] Starting material. [b] The material was recovered from the solvolysis mixture after one half-life at 99.6°. [c] The experiment was carried out in the presence of 0.05 M sodium *p*-nitrobenzoate.

Discussion

The data in Table I show that in 90% aqueous acetone at 120° *trans*-5-cyclodecen-1-yl *p*-nitrobenzoate (II) solvolyzes over 300 times faster than the *cis* isomer Ia which in turn is about 5 times more reactive than the saturated analog, cyclodecyl *p*-nitrobenzoate. It is interesting to note that the *trans*-5-cyclodecen-1-yl system is even more reactive than the α,γ-dimethylallyl system by a factor of over ten. It was shown earlier that solvolysis of α,γ-dimethylallyl *p*-nitrobenzoate in aqueous acetone involves alkyl–oxygen cleavage.[12,13]

The high reactivities of Ia and II relative to cyclodecyl *p*-nitrobenzoate indicate that their rates of ionization (solvolysis) are accelerated by transannular participation by the double bond as illustrated for the two isomers by II′ and Ia′. In the absence of participation hydrolysis by acyl-oxygen cleavage would probably take over and the rates would be expected to be comparable with

(13) H. L. Goering and R. W. Greiner, *J. Am. Chem. Soc.*, **79**, 3464 (1957).

those of *p*-nitrobenzoates of saturated secondary alcohols. Presumably the unassisted ionization rates for Ia and II would be substantially lower than the rate of solvolysis of cyclodecyl *p*-nitrobenzoate. Thus the present data indicate that the ionization rates of Ia and II are accelerated by factors of over 5 and 10^3, respectively.

For several reasons these estimates are lower limits. In the first place, for reasons that will be presented in the Experimental section, the rate constant for cyclodecyl *p*-nitrobenzoate in Table I is a rough upper limit and in fact may be too high. Secondly, solvolysis of cyclodecyl *p*-nitrobenzoate may well involve acyl–oxygen cleavage in which case the solvolysis rate exceeds the ionization rate. Finally, the unassisted ionization rate for Ia and II would be expected to be slower than that for the cyclodecyl system. Introduction of a double bond in a ten-membered ring should relieve "medium ring" strain which presumably is responsible for the relatively high reactivity of the cyclodecyl system—cyclodecyl *p*-toluenesulfonate acetolyzes about 500 times faster than cyclohexyl *p*-toluenesulfonate.[14] The inductive effect of the double bond would also tend to lower the unassisted ionization rate somewhat.

In connection with the large driving force observed with the *trans*-*p*-nitrobenzoate II it is interesting to note that the ultraviolet spectrum of the corresponding ketone, *trans*-5-cyclodecenone,[11] contains a solvent-dependent band (λ_{max} 214.5 mμ, ε 2300, in 2,2,3,3-tetrafluoropropanol) which has been assigned to the photodesmotic transition[15]

The ultraviolet spectrum of *cis*-5-cyclodecenone[11] does not contain this band.[16] The possibility of a correlation between absorption resulting from such interactions and anchimeric acceleration observed with derivatives of the corresponding alcohols has been noted previously.[17] Thus both the spectra of the isomeric ketones and the relative anchimeric accelerations observed with the isomeric *p*-nitrobenzoates (Ia and II) indicate that stereoelectronic factors are more favorable for transannular interactions between the double bond and C_1 in the *trans*-5-cyclodecen-1-yl system than in the *cis* isomer.

Solvolysis of *cis*-(Ia) and *trans*-5-cyclodecen-1-yl *p*-nitrobenzoate (II) results in bond formation between C_1 and C_6 as illustrated by II′ and Ia′. It is interesting that these cyclizations are stereospecific. The *trans* isomer II gives the *trans*-decalyl system and the *cis* isomer Ia gives the *cis*-decalyl system.[18]

(14) R. Heck and V. Prelog, *Helv. Chim. Acta*, **38**, 1541 (1955).

(15) E. M. Kosower, W. D. Closson, H. L. Goering and J. C. Gross, *J. Am. Chem. Soc.*, **83**, 2013 (1961).

(16) W. D. Closson, unpublished results.

(17) For leading references see S. Winstein, L. de Vries and R. Orloski, *J. Am. Chem. Soc.*, **83**, 2020 (1961).

(18) It is interesting that this is the same stereochemistry as that involved in (a) the transannular cyclization of pyrethrosin to cyclopyrethrosin[7] (conversion of a *cis*-cyclodecene system to a *cis*-decalin derivative) and (b) the proposed biogenesis of eudesmol[10a] (transan-

In each case, solvolysis involves a *trans* addition of C_1 and solvent across the C_5,C_6-double bond. On the other hand, the isomeric rearrangement of II to III which accompanies solvolysis amounts to a *cis* addition of C_1 and the migrating *p*-nitrobenzoate group across the double bond. The isomeric rearrangement involved in the solvolysis of the *cis-p*-toluenesulfonate Ib is stereochemically analogous to the conversion of II to III; Ib isomerizes to *cis-trans*-1-decalyl *p*-toluenesulfonate during solvolysis (ethanolysis and acetolysis).[3]

H $\overset{|}{C}$OCOC₆H₄NO₂

II′

III, Ar = *p*-C₆H₄NO₂

IV

Ia′   V

Evidently the rearrangement of II to III involves "ion pair return," probably "internal return."[19] That the process is ionic is indicated by the fact the rate shows about the same sensitivity toward varying the ionizing power of the solvent as does the rate of solvolysis (k_s); cf. k_r/k_s for 80% and 90% acetone. It is clear that the rearrangement is intramolecular because k_r/k_s is not affected by the addition of *p*-nitrobenzoate ion and the O^{18} experiments show that rearrangement does not result in exchange with either *p*-nitrobenzoic acid or *p*-nitrobenzoate ion. The fact that rearrangement results in only partial equilibration of the oxygen atoms (the carbonyl oxygen atom retains its identity in part) suggests that the process involves internal return. Return from a "solvent separated"[19] ion pair is believed to result in complete equilibration of the oxygen atoms in the anion portion of the molecule.[20] On the other hand, cases are known in which internal return results in no or only partial equilibration of the oxygen atoms in a *p*-nitrobenzoate.[12,20,21]

The observation that carbonyl-O^{18} *trans*-5-cyclodecen-1-yl *p*-nitrobenzoate (II) remains discretely labeled throughout the solvolysis indicates that the reactant is not reformed by internal return, *i.e.*, it appears that the rate of solvolysis corresponds

to the rate of ionization. Internal return to give rearrangement product III results in some oxygen mixing and if only one intimate ion pair intermediate is involved in the ionization–dissociation process, internal return to reactant II should also result in mixing of the oxygen atoms. Internal return has been observed to result in equilibration of carboxyl oxygen atoms during the solvolysis of allylic *p*-nitrobenzoates[12,21,22a] and benzhydryl *p*-nitrobenzoate.[22b] However, more than one internal ion pair intermediate may be involved and thus the absence of oxygen equilibration during solvolysis does not rule out the possibility of internal return.

One feature of the stereochemistry of the transannular cyclizations of *cis*- and *trans*-5-cyclodecen-1-yl derivatives remains obscure. This concerns the stereochemical change at C_1. If the reactive conformations of the reactants are those illustrated by II′ and Ia′, displacement of the leaving group at C_1 by C_6 proceeds with inversion of configuration. This arrangement, which allows for nucleophilic attack by the double bond from the rear, seems to be the best one for accounting for the rather large driving force—anchimerically accelerated ionizations evidently invariably involve back-side internal displacements.[23]

However, there is another possibility. This is illustrated for the *trans* isomer by II″. If this conformation is the one involved in the cyclization, C_1 is substituted (by C_6) with retention of configuration. Although there are many precedents for intramolecular front-side displacements, *e.g.*, SNi reactions,[24] these usually occur when there is no alternative. Moreover, these probably often, if not generally, involve internal return from ion pair intermediates in which case front-side attack is not simultaneous with rupture of the original bond. It is not clear to what extent, if any, front-side nucleophilic attack can facilitate departure of a leaving group. Thus one is left with the dilemma that conformation II′ nicely accounts for the accelerated ionization, but makes it difficult to rationalize the migration of the ester group from C_1 to C_6 without complete equilibration of the carboxyl oxygen atoms. On the other hand, II″ can nicely account for the stereochemistry[25] and O^{18} results of the rearrangement—the analogous conformation was used to rationalize the isomerization of Ib to *cis-trans*-1-decalyl *p*-toluenesulfonate[3]—but it is not clear if such an arrangement can accommodate the rate enhancement. In another problem we are attempting to establish the relative configurations of C_1 in the reactant II and C_{10} in the solvolysis IV and rearrangement products III to settle this point.

The large driving force indicates that ionization of the *trans-p*-nitrobenzoate II results in the direct

nular cyclization involving a *trans* double bond to give a *trans*-decalin system).

(19) S. Winstein, E. Clippinger, A. H. Fainberg, R. Heck and G. C. Robinson, *J. Am. Chem. Soc.*, **78**, 328 (1956).

(20) S. Winstein and G. C. Robinson, *ibid.*, **80**, 169 (1958).

(21) M. M. Pombo and K. D. McMichael, unpublished work.

(22) (a) H. L. Goering and J. T. Doi, *J. Am. Chem. Soc.*, **82**, 5850 (1960); (b) J. F. Levy, unpublished results.

(23) For leading references see (a) A. Streitwieser, Jr., *Chem. Revs.*, **56**, 571 (1956), and (b) D. J. Cram, "Steric Effects in Organic Chemistry," M. S. Newman, ed., John Wiley and Sons, Inc., New York, N. Y., 1956, Chapt. 5.

(24) E. L. Eliel, *ibid.*, Chapt. 2.

(25) The *trans*-1-decalyl isomer resulting from an intramolecular isomeric rearrangement of either II′ or II″ would be expected to give the observed product III, *i.e.*, if the reaction is intramolecular the product resulting from *cis* addition would be expected in any event.

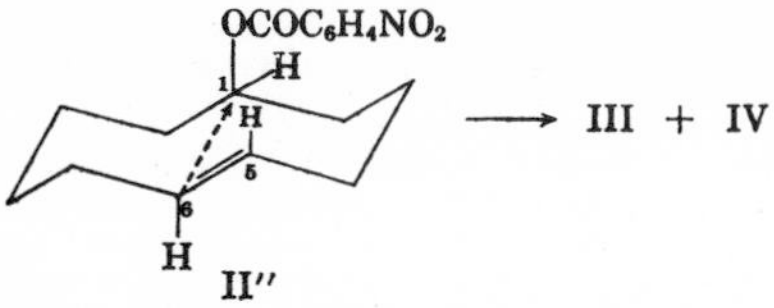

II''

formation of an ion pair in which the cation is the *trans*-1-decalyl carbonium ion VI or the non-classical ion VII. Similarly, the initially formed cation from the *cis*-*p*-nitrobenzoate is either the classical "rearranged" ion VIII or the bridged non-classical ion IX. The anchimeric accelerations and probably also the stereochemistry are explicable in terms of either the classical or non-classical ions.

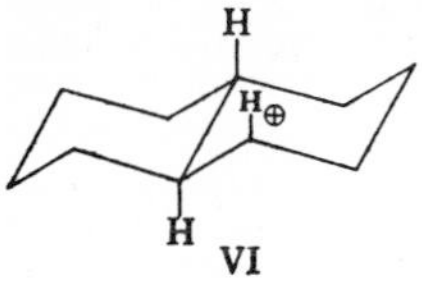

VI

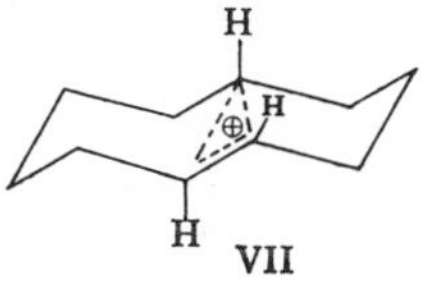

VII

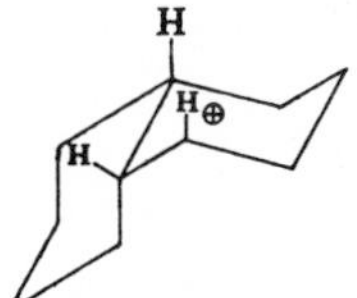

VIII

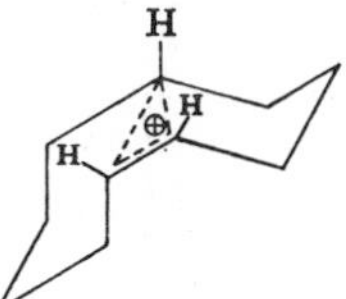

IX

It is of interest in this connection that nitrous acid deaminations of *trans-trans-* and *cis-cis-*1-decalylamine give the corresponding alcohols as the only substitution products,[26] *i.e.*, in both cases there is complete retention of configuration. Presumably these reactions involve the same carbonium ions involved in the solvolysis-product forming step in the present work. The results of the deamination reactions have been interpreted in terms of the classical carbonium ions VI and VIII.[27] The reason proposed[27] for the retention of configuration was that solvent attacks the carbonium ion along the path of easiest approach, the approach to form equatorial alcohol being less hindered than that to form axial alcohol.[27] If this interpretation is correct the classical carbonium ions can similarly accommodate the present results. On the other hand, the non-classical structures for the *cis*-(IX) and *trans*-1-decalyl carbonium ions (VII) account for the products derived from these ions in an obvious way. Indeed, intermediates of this type (*i.e.*, bridged ions) are generally used to rationalize stereospecific *trans* addition reactions (which are observed with both isomers in the present case) and replacement reactions which involve retention of configuration.[23] In other problems we are investigating the structures of bicyclic carbonium ions of this type.

Experimental

Materials.—The *cis*-(Ia) and *trans*-5-cyclodecen-1-yl *p*-nitrobenzoates (II) used in the present work are described in the preceding paper.[11] **Cyclodecyl *p*-nitrobenzoate,** m.p. 114.5–115.0° (ethanol) (lit.[28] m.p. 116°), was prepared[11] from cyclodecanol[9] in 93% yield. ***trans-cis*-1-Decalyl *p*-nitrobenzoate (III),** m.p. 116.0–116.5° (aqueous methanol) (lit.[26] m.p. 116°), was prepared[11] from *trans-cis*-1-decalol,[3] m.p. 48.0–48.5°, in 72% yield. **α,γ-Dimethylallyl-*p*-nitrobenzoate,** m.p. 53–54° (lit.[29] m.p. 54°), was prepared from the pure alcohol[12] in 32% yield. *p*-Nitrobenzoic acid, m.p. 240.3–240.9°, was purified by recrystallization from methanol. Sodium *p*-nitrobenzoate was prepared by shaking a solution of 0.119 mole of *p*-nitrobenzoic acid in 200 ml. of ether with 50 ml. of 2.0 *M* aqueous sodium hydroxide. The aqueous layer containing the salt was extracted with ether in a continuous extractor to remove any traces of excess acid and then evaporated until the salt crystallized. The salt was separated by filtration and dried to constant weight at 140° under reduced pressure. An aqueous solution of this salt had a *p*H of about 8.

Aqueous acetone was prepared by mixing pure acetone (fractionated from calcium chloride) and conductivity water. The pure components were equilibrated at 25° prior to mixing. Solvent compositions are based on the volumes of the pure components at 25°.

Kinetic Experiments.—Standard solutions of the substrates in aqueous acetone were prepared and distributed into ampules. Ester concentrations of 0.020 *M* to 0.025 *M* were used except in the case of *cis*-5-cyclodecen-1-yl *p*-nitrobenzoate (Ia) where the limited solubility necessitated lower concentrations. All concentrations and volumes were measured at 25°.

Aqueous acetone solutions develop an acid titer slowly when heated in the presence of oxygen at high temperatures.[30] For example, the titer of a 0.01 *M* solution of pure *p*-nitrobenzoic acid in 90% acetone increased about 35% in 200 hr. at 119° and then decreased slowly. The rate of production of acid by this process was too slow to affect the rate studies of the more reactive esters, *e.g.*, α,γ-dimethylallyl *p*-nitrobenzoate and II which at 119° have half-periods of 29 and 2.5 hr., respectively. However, it is obvious that it would seriously interfere with the less reactive esters. It was found that the acid-producing side reaction could be essentially eliminated by flushing the ampules several times with nitrogen before sealing them.[31] Titers of 0.01 *M* solutions of *p*-nitrobenzoic acid under nitrogen in ampules increased less than 1% when heated for 333 hr. at 119°. In all of the kinetic experiments, except those with the aforementioned reactive esters, ampules were flushed with nitrogen prior to sealing. Even so, it is clear that the acid-producing side reaction may be significant in experiments with cyclodecyl and *trans-cis*-1-decalyl *p*-nitrobenzoate (III), which at 119° react only to the extents of 7.4% in 432 hr. and 2.4% in 528 hr., respectively. Because of this complication the approximate constants in Table I for these two esters may be too high and thus should be considered to be rough upper limits.

The rate of acid formation was measured by potentiometric titration of aliquots with standard 0.025 *M* aqueous sodium hydroxide. A Beckman model G *p*H meter was used for the potential measurements. The first-order rate constants presented in Table I were calculated from the rate of acid formation in the usual manner.

Standard solutions of the *trans*-*p*-nitrobenzoate II under nitrogen in sealed ampules were heated for 10–12 half-lives to obtain the data presented in Table II.

Solvolysis Products. (A) ***trans*-5-Cyclodecen-1-yl *p*-Nitrobenzoate (II).**—A solution of 1.400 g. (4.61 mmoles) of II in 135 ml. of 90% aqueous acetone in a glass bomb was heated at 99.6° for 188 hr. (*ca.* 12 half-lives). The contents were diluted with 750 ml. of water and made basic to phenolphthalein with dilute sodium carbonate solution and the resulting solution was extracted with 40–60° petroleum ether in a continuous extractor for 71 hr. Gas chromatographic analysis of the petroleum ether solution with a 12-foot column of 20% saturated silver nitrate solution in polyethylene glycol (Carbowax 400) on Celite at 80° indicated the presence of olefin in amounts corresponding to 10–20% yield. The solution was concentrated and

(26) W. G. Dauben, R. C. Tweit and C. Mannerskantz, *J. Am. Chem. Soc.*, **76**, 4420 (1954).

(27) A. Streitwieser, Jr., *J. Org. Chem.*, **22**, 861 (1957).

(28) M. Kobelt, P. Barman, V. Prelog and L. Ruzicka, *Helv. Chim. Acta*, **32**, 256 (1949).

(29) M. M. Pombo, Ph.D. Thesis, University of Wisconsin, 1960.

(30) This has also been noted by M. Silver, private communication, 1960.

(31) This same method has been used recently by M. Silver, *J. Am. Chem. Soc.*, **83**, 404 (1961), to suppress the acid-forming reaction.

separated by chromatography on a column of 52 g. of Merck "acid-washed" alumina. Elution with petroleum ether yielded 0.019 g. of a colorless oil, probably olefin. Elution with 50% benzene in petroleum ether produced 0.226 g. (0.745 mmole, 16.1%) of a mixture of p-nitrobenzoates (fraction A) consisting chiefly of trans-cis-1-decalyl p-nitrobenzoate (III). Elution with ethyl ether yielded 0.480 g. (3.110 mmoles, 67.4%) of solid alcohol (fraction B) which consisted almost entirely of trans-trans-1-decalol (IV). The product could also be separated into fractions A and B by sublimation. For example, sublimation of the product from 1.392 g. of II (after removal of the petroleum ether) at 80° and 0.3 mm. gave 0.490 g. (69.2%) of solid alcohol (fraction B) and 0.241 g. (17.3%) of unsublimable p-nitrobenzoate (fraction A). Control experiments with synthetic mixtures indicated that 93–95% of the alcohol fraction, and 97–99% of the p-nitrobenzoate fraction could be recovered by this procedure.

Recrystallization of a 0.226-g. portion of the p-nitrobenzoate fraction (fraction A) from methanol gave 0.111 g. of trans-cis-1-decalyl p-nitrobenzoate (III), m.p. 116.0–116.8°. This was identified by comparison with a known sample. Another sample of fraction A (0.206 g.) was saponified by refluxing it in 20 ml. of 5% methanolic potassium hydroxide for 3.5 hr. The solution was diluted with 20 ml. of water and extracted with 40–60° petroleum ether in a continuous extractor for 27 hr. Gas chromatography of the liquid alcohol (after evaporation of the petroleum ether) with a 6-foot column of 1,2,3-tris-(2-cyanoethoxy)-propane on Celite at 155° indicated its composition to be 85% trans-cis-1-decalol and 15% material having the same retention time as trans-trans-1-decalol (IV).

Treatment of 0.270 g. (1.75 mmoles) of fraction B with 0.36 g. (1.94 mmoles) of p-nitrobenzoyl chloride yielded 0.41 g. (77%) of trans-trans-1-decalyl p-nitrobenzoate, m.p. 83.7–84.8° (petroleum ether) (lit.[26] m.p. 86°). This proved to be identical with an authentic sample. Gas chromatographic analysis of fraction B with a 6-foot column of 20% 1,2,3-tris-(2-cyanoethoxy)-propane on Celite at 155° showed it to consist of 98–99% trans-trans-1-decalol (IV) and 1–2% of material having the same retention time as trans-cis-1-decalol.

In a control experiment a synthetic solvolysis mixture composed of 0.102 g. of trans-cis-1-decalyl p-nitrobenzoate (III), 0.260 g. of trans-trans-1-decalol (IV) and 0.323 g. of p-nitrobenzoic acid in 40 ml. of 90% aqueous acetone was heated at 100° for 240 hr. The mixture of alcohol and p-nitrobenzoate was isolated as described above and separated into fractions A and B by vacuum sublimation. Analysis of the alcohol fraction (fraction B) by gas chromatography showed it to be pure trans-trans-1-decalol (IV). The p-nitrobenzoate fraction (fraction A) was saponified and the alcohol thus obtained was shown by gas chromatography to be pure trans-cis-1-decalol. Thus, ester interchange does not occur under the conditions of the solvolysis reaction.

(B) cis-5-Cyclodecen-1-yl p-Nitrobenzoate (Ia).—A solution of 0.891 g. (2.94 mmoles) of Ia and 0.096 g. of sodium p-nitrobenzoate in 100 ml. of 90% aqueous acetone was placed in a glass bomb and heated at 118.6° for 545 hr. The solvolysis product and unchanged Ia were then isolated from the solution in the same manner as described for the isolation of the solvolysis products of II. The petroleum ether solution of solvolysis product and unreacted III was concentrated and chromatographed on 50 g. of Merck "acid-washed" alumina. Elution with 50% benzene in petroleum ether yielded 0.585 g. (1.93 mmoles, 66%) of p-nitrobenzoate, m.p. 147–152°. Recrystallization from ethanol–ethyl acetate gave 0.470 g. (1.55 mmoles) of cis-5-cyclodecenyl p-nitrobenzoate (Ia), m.p. 153.5–155° (identical with authentic material). Elution with 50% ether in benzene yielded 0.152 g. (0.985 mmole, 34%) of alcohol, m.p. 60–80°. Gas chromatography of this material with a 6-foot column of 20% 1,2,3-tris-(2-cyanoethoxy)-propane on Celite at 160° showed only a single peak which had the same retention time as cis-cis-1-decalol (V). Treatment of this material with phenyl isocyanate yielded the phenylurethan of cis-cis-1-decalol, m.p. 116–117° (petroleum ether) (lit.[31] m.p. 118°). This derivative was identical with a known sample.

To test the stability of cis-5-cyclodecenol (Ic) under the conditions of the solvolysis reaction, a solution of 0.080 g. of Ic, 0.079 g. of p-nitrobenzoic acid and 0.061 g. of sodium p-nitrobenzoate in 50 ml. of 90% aqueous acetone was heated at 118.6° for 455 hr. The alcohol fraction was isolated in the usual manner and analyzed by v.p.c. The alcohol was homogeneous and had a retention time corresponding to that of Ic. Treatment of the residual oil with phenyl isocyanate yielded a phenylurethan, m.p. 110.5–111.5°, which was identical (mixture melting point and infrared spectra in CHCl₃) with an authentic sample,[6] m.p. 111.5–112.5°.

Oxygen-18 Experiments.—Carbonyl-O¹⁸ labeled trans-5-cyclodecenyl p-nitrobenzoate (II) and trans-cis-1-decalyl p-nitrobenzoate (III),were prepared from the corresponding alcohols and p-nitrobenzoyl chloride-carbonyl-O¹⁸ in the usual manner.[12,22] Solvolysis of labeled II and isolation of the labeled III so produced were carried out as described above for unlabeled II.

To check for washout of O¹⁸ during isolation, synthetic mixtures of carbonyl-O¹⁸ labeled III (0.982 atom % excess O¹⁸), trans-trans-1-decalol and p-nitrobenzoic acid were isolated and separated in the manner described above. The O¹⁸ content of the recovered III was found to be identical, within the limits of experimental error (0.990 and 1.004 atom % excess O¹⁸), with that of the original material.[12]

To determine the O¹⁸ content of the alkyl–oxygen position of labeled III obtained from the rearrangement of labeled II it was saponified and reconverted to p-nitrobenzoate with unlabeled acid chloride as follows. To 20 ml. of 5% methanolic potassium hydroxide was added 0.226 g. (0.745 mmole) of labeled rearrangement product (fraction A) and 4 ml. of water. After 4 hr. of refluxing, the solution was diluted with 70 ml. of water and extracted with 40–60° petroleum ether in a continuous extractor for 20 hr. The petroleum ether was evaporated and the residue was dissolved in 4 ml. of pyridine. The resulting solution was treated with 0.166 g. (0.895 mmole) of unlabeled p-nitrobenzoyl chloride at 0°. The solution was stirred 3 hr. at room temperature and 0.209 g. (0.690 mmole) of crude p-nitrobenzoate mixture was obtained. Several recrystallizations from methanol gave 0.0913 g. (0.301 mmole) of III, m.p. 116.0–116.8°. This material contains the same alkyl–oxygen atom as the rearrangement product.

In experiment 2, Table III, the alkyl–oxygen position of unsolvolyzed II was investigated after one half-life at 99.6°. The total p-nitrobenzoate fraction (consisting of unsolvolyzed II and rearrangement products) from a 90% aqueous acetone solution, originally containing 0.2916 g. of carbonyl-O¹⁸ labeled II in 75 ml. of solution, was isolated by removing the solvent under aspirator vacuum. The remaining slurry was dissolved in 50 ml. of ether which was washed with 25 ml. of 3 N sodium carbonate solution and water and then dried with magnesium sulfate. Evaporation of the ether followed by recrystallization of the residue from 5 ml. of 60–68° petroleum ether gave 0.120 g. of crude p-nitrobenzoate mixture. This was saponified with methanolic potassium hydroxide and reconverted to the p-nitrobenzoate derivative. Three recrystallizations from 60–68° petroleum ether gave 0.087 g. of II, m.p. 108.7–109.8°, which contained the same alkyl–oxygen as the II recovered from the reaction mixture. This sample contained <1% of the original excess O¹⁸.

An isotope dilution experiment, designed to test for the presence of III in the samples of II used in the kinetic experiments, was carried out. To 0.4394 g. of II was added 0.0881 g. of carbonyl-O¹⁸ labeled III which contained 0.982 atom % excess O¹⁸. The solids were mixed, dissolved in ether, and recovered by evaporating the ether under an air stream. The m.p. of the solid was 90–104°. Five recrystallizations (60–68° petroleum ether) gave 0.13 g. of material melting at 108.2–109.6°, which was identical in every way with the original sample of II. This material did not contain any detectable excess O¹⁸. This experiment shows that the method used to purify the trans p-nitrobenzoate II would have removed any III and thus demonstrates that the II used in the kinetic experiments did not contain III.

(32) W. Hückel, R. Danneel, A. Gross and H. Naab, Ann., **502**, 99 (1933).

(33) The O¹⁸ contents were determined by the method described in ref. 12.

57 | The Pi-Route to Bicyclooctyl Cations

Winstein and Carter (Paper No. 57) propose an apt name for the generation of a nonclassical ion by interaction of a double bond and an ionizing center ("the π route"), and they demonstrate the formation, by the π route, of the bridged ion which is intermediate in the solvolyses and interconversions of 2-bicyclo(2.2.2)-octyl and *exo*-(axial)2-bicyclo(3.2.1)octyl sulfonates (X and XII). As antici-pated from the work of LeNy, of Goering, and of Walborsky, the ion XI, which connects X and XII, is different from LeNy's ion VIII, which leads to IX (*endo*, equatorial).

From: *J. Am. Chem. Soc.* **83,** 4485–86 (1961)

THE π-ROUTE TO A BICYCLOÖCTYL NON-CLASSICAL CATION[1]

Sir:

Many cationic reaction intermediates possess the three-center bonding indicated by formula I. In some ways the most intriguing of these are those species in which the bridging group, G, is methylene. In such cases, species I involves a delocalized two-electron system. Pertinent examples are the norbornyl cation[2] V, species[3] II which is related to the 7-norbornyl and *trans*-2-bicyclo[3.2.0]-heptyl systems, and the octahydrodimethanonaphthyl cation[4] III. In principle, as well as in practice, such cations may be produced by anchimerically assisted ionization of substrates in which the neighboring group contributes either σ- or π-electrons. For the norbornyl cation V, the σ-route may be illustrated by acetolysis of *exo*-norbornyl bromobenzenesulfonate (IV-OBs), which is accelerated relative to the *endo*-epimer by a factor of *ca.* 10³ and which leads exclusively to racemic

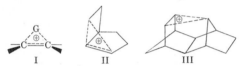

I   II   III

exo-norbornyl acetate[2] (*dl*-IV-OAc). Very recently, Lawton[5a] and Bartlett and Bank[5b] have provided examples of the π-route to the same cation. These investigators reported solvolyses of Δ³-cyclopentenylethyl arenesulfonates (VI) accelerated relative to the saturated analogs by factors ranging from 6 to more than 10², which gave rise essentially exclusively to *exo*-norbornyl solvolysis products.

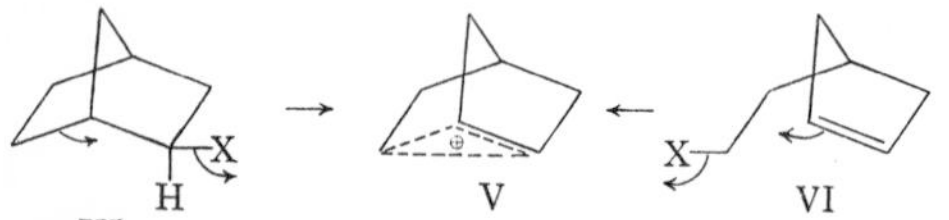

IV   V   VI

2-Bicyclo[2.2.2]- and [3.2.1]octyl systems (IX, X and XII), without the angle strain of their norbornyl analog, are even more instructive for carbonium ion theory. Thus, some time ago, Walborsky[6] had concluded that the bicyclo[2.2.2]octyl cation was classical. However, it is impossible to account for the behavior of the bicycloöctyl systems in solvolysis on the basis of classical cationic intermediates. Thus, Le Ny[7] and Goering and Sloan[8] have reported that acetolysis of Δ⁴-cycloheptenylmethyl bromobenzenesulfonate[7]

(VII) or *cis*-bicyclo[3.2.1]octyl toluenesulfonate[8] (IX-OTs) leads essentially exclusively to *cis*-2-bicyclo[3.2.1]octyl acetate (IX-OAc), none of the epimeric XV-OAc or the rearranged bicyclo-[2.2.2]octyl acetate XIII-OAc being observed. Evidently, acetolysis of the Δ⁴-cycloheptenyl-methyl and *cis*-bicyclo[3.2.1]octyl esters VII and IX-OTs provides π- and σ-routes, respectively, to the non-classical cation VIII, which then gives rise to the *cis*-bicyclo[3.2.1]octyl acetate IX-OAc. In solvolysis of the related bicyclo[2.2.2]octyl and *trans*-(*axial*)-bicyclo[3.2.1]octyl toluenesulfonates X and XII, Walborsky[9] and Goering[8] have shown recently that both substrates give rise to the same mixture of [2.2.2]- and *axial*-[3.2.1]-products XIII and XV, none of the epimeric *cis*-[3.2.1]-

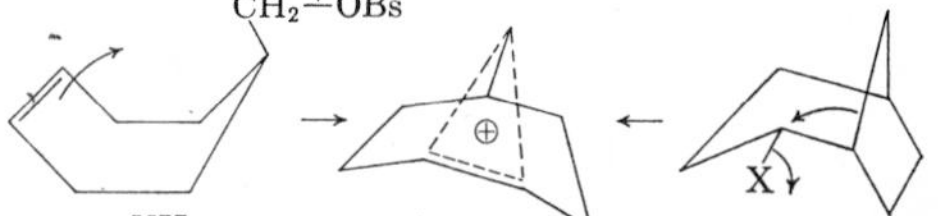

CH₂—OBs

VII   VIII   IX

product being observed. Also, the [2.2.2]acetate XIII-OAc from optically active [2.2.2]toluenesulfonate X is formed with complete retention of configuration. Anchimerically assisted ionization of X and XII apparently represents the σ-route to the non-classical cation XI which leads only to bicyclo[2.2.2]- and *axial*-bicyclo[3.2.1]octyl products.

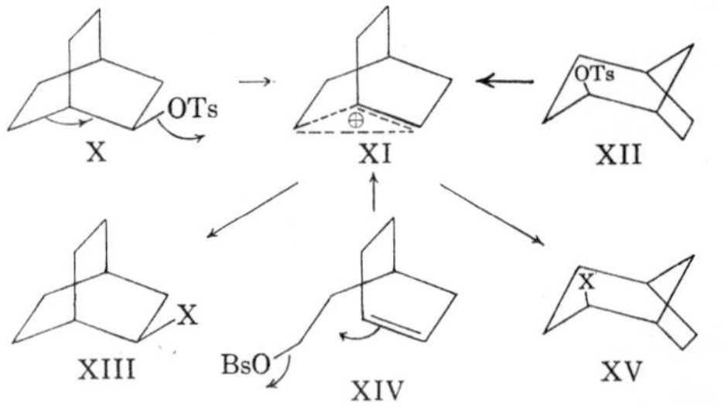

OTs   OTs

X   XI   XII

XIII   BsO   XIV   XV

For the π-route to cation XI, one can visualize starting with the Δ³-cyclohexenylethyl system XIV, instead of VII employed by Le Ny,[7] and we now have investigated the solvolysis of bromobenzenesulfonate[10] XIV, m.p. 25–26°. The corresponding alcohol, n^{25}D 1.4809, was obtained from hydroboration-oxidation of 4-vinycyclohexene using excess diene; m.p. of 3,5-dinitrobenzoate,[10] 63–64°. With 0.01 *M* XIV in a 0.02 *M* acetic acid solution of sodium acetate, good first order kinetics of acetolysis were observed, the rate constant at 75.1° being 7.4 × 10⁻⁶ sec.⁻¹. This value is four times the one obtained with the saturated analog[10] of XIV, m.p. 37–38°. From the acetolysis of XIV at 100° and treatment of the product with lithium aluminum hydride, there was obtained an alcohol mixture which vapor phase chromatographic anal-

(1) (a) Research supported by the National Science Foundation; (b) results reported by S. Winstein at Symposium on "Dynamic Stereochemistry" at XVIIIth International Congress of Pure and Applied Chemistry, Montreal, Canada, August 6–12, 1961.

(2) (a) S. Winstein and D. Trifan, *J. Am. Chem. Soc.*, **71**, 2953 (1949); **74**, 1147, 1154 (1952); (b) S. Winstein, *et al.*, *ibid.*, **74**, 1127 (1952).

(3) S. Winstein, F. Gadient, E. T. Stafford and P. E. Klinedinst, Jr., *ibid.*, **80**, 5895 (1958).

(4) S. Winstein and R. L. Hansen, *Tetrahedron Letters*, no. 25, 1 (1960).

(5) (a) R. G. Lawton, *J. Am. Chem. Soc.*, **83**, 2399 (1961); (b) P. D. Bartlett and S. Bank, *ibid.*, **83**, 2591 (1961).

(6) H. M. Walborsky, *Experientia*, **9**, 209 (1953).

(7) G. Le Ny, *Compt. rend.*, **251**, 1526 (1960).

(8) H. L. Goering and M. F. Sloan, *J. Am. Chem. Soc.*, **83**, 1397, 1992 (1961).

(9) H. M. Walborsky, M. E. Baum and A. A. Youssef, *J. Am. Chem. Soc.*, **83**, 988 (1961).

(10) Correct carbon and hydrogen analyses were obtained for all new compounds.

ysis showed was 20% cyclohexenylethanol and 80% of a 54:46 mixture of [2.2.2]-alcohol XIII-OH and *axial*-[3.2.1]-alcohol XV-OH, respectively. By preparative vapor phase chromatography, the three fractions were separated and identified further by m.p., m.p. of derivatives, and infrared spectrum:[8,9] (i) *axial*-alcohol XV-OH, m.p. 197–198°, m.p. of bromobenzenesulfonate, 62–63°, m.p. of *p*-nitrobenzoate, 94–95°, (ii) [2.2.2]-alcohol XIII-OH, m.p. 208–210°, m.p. of bromobenzenesulfonate, 79–80°, (iii) cyclohexenylethanol, m.p. of 3,5-dinitrobenzoate, 63–64°. Acetolysis of the mixed bromobenzenesulfonate, m.p. 44–55°, from the combined fractions (i) and (ii) led to a 53:47 mixture of alcohols XIII-OH and XV-OH.

In 0.02 M sodium formate in formic acid at 75.1°, the cyclohexenylethyl bromobenzenesulfonate XIV solvolyzes with a rate constant of 4.0×10^{-4} sec.$^{-1}$, faster than the saturated analog by roughly one power of ten. The isolated alcohol product from this formolysis is again the 54:46 mixture of [2.2.2]-alcohol XIII-OH and *axial*-alcohol XV-OH, the cyclohexenylethanol content now being almost negligible.

The present work shows that the unsaturated ester XIV tends to solvolyze predominantly by way of anchimerically assisted ionization to the non-classical cation XI. Thus, there is now unique and compelling evidence for this cation from the π-route of formation, as well as the σ, the distinction between the two carbonium ions VIII and XI being maintained whether the ions are produced by π- or σ-routes.

The pair of unsaturated systems, VII and XIV, which have been demonstrated to lead to isomeric non-classical ions and thus contrasting over-all structural and stereochemical results, represents only one example in a broader theme. The usual stereoelectronic considerations allow one to conceive other such pairs of unsaturated derivatives which would be related to isomeric bridged ions if these are formed in preference to classical ones. For example, a conceivable pair of systems includes Δ²-cyclopentenylethyl, related to ion II, and Δ⁴-cycloheptenyl, XVI, which is related to ion XVII and thus *cis*-2-bicyclo[3.2.0]heptyl derivatives XVIII.

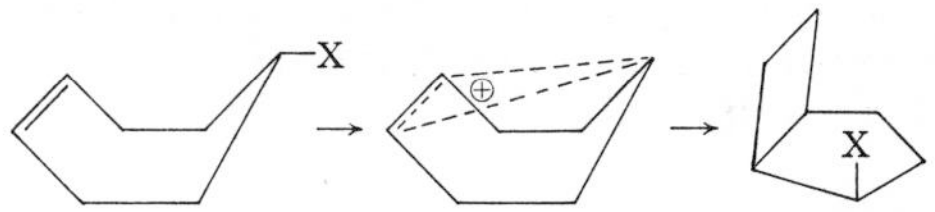

XVI → XVII → XVIII

DEPARTMENT OF CHEMISTRY
UNIVERSITY OF CALIFORNIA
LOS ANGELES 24, CALIFORNIA

S. WINSTEIN
PETER CARTER

RECEIVED SEPTEMBER 5, 1961

58 | Reactions of the Solvent Separated Ion Pair

In Paper No. 58, by Winstein, Klinedinst, and Clippinger, we include a representative of a large amount of systematic work clarifying the nature of the ion-pair intermediates in solvolysis. When a solvent-separated ion pair which would otherwise undergo ion-pair return is attacked by lithium perchlorate, the special salt effect is the result; when lithium bromide is used instead, the reaction is diverted from solvolysis to displacement. Neither reagent interferes with ion pair return from the intimate ion pair, and both show the same extrapolated ionization rate for zero ionic strength.

From: *J. Am. Chem. Soc.* **83**, 4986–89 (1961)

[CONTRIBUTION FROM THE DEPARTMENT OF CHEMISTRY, UNIVERSITY OF CALIFORNIA, LOS ANGELES 24, CALIF.]

Salt Effects and Ion Pairs in Solvolysis and Related Reactions. XXI.[1] Acetolysis, Bromide Exchange and the Special Salt Effect[2]

BY S. WINSTEIN, PAUL E. KLINEDINST, JR.,[3] AND E. CLIPPINGER[4]

RECEIVED JULY 19, 1961

The use of a salt like lithium bromide instead of lithium perchlorate permits one to gain further insight into the mechanism of the special salt effect. Diversion of reaction from solvolysis to formation of alkyl bromide by added bromide salts is very efficient in acetolysis of 1-anisyl-2-propyl *p*-toluenesulfonate and 3-anisyl-2-butyl *p*-bromobenzenesulfonate. At bromide salt concentrations in the normal salt effect range, formation of alkyl bromide shows good first-order behavior. The corresponding first-order rate constants for alkyl bromide formation, k_{RBr}, show a linear dependence on bromide salt concentration, extrapolation to zero salt concentration leading to an intercept, k_{ext}^0. For both the 1-anisyl-2-propyl and 3-anisyl-2-butyl systems, k_{ext}^0 values from bromide exchange are identical with k_{ext}^0 values from the special salt effect of lithium perchlorate. This agreement is evidence that bromide and perchlorate act as scavengers for the same solvolysis intermediates. Both trap the solvent-separated ion pair, but both permit internal return from the intimate ion pair

As brought out in previous papers of this series, it is necessary to distinguish between various carbonium ion intermediates in acetolysis. Solvolysis scheme I is designed for systems whose reac-

SOLVOLYSIS SCHEME I

$$\text{RX} \underset{k_{-1x}}{\overset{k_{1x}}{\rightleftarrows}} \text{R}\oplus\text{X}\ominus \underset{k_{-2x}}{\overset{k_{2x}}{\rightleftarrows}} \text{R}\oplus\|\text{X}\ominus \overset{k_{sx}^{III}}{\longrightarrow} \text{ROS}$$

$$k_{sx}^{III}(\text{M}\oplus\text{Y}\ominus)\downarrow$$

$$\text{RY} \underset{k_{-1y}}{\overset{k_{1y}}{\rightleftarrows}} \text{R}\oplus\text{Y}\ominus \underset{k_{-2y}}{\overset{k_{2y}}{\rightleftarrows}} \text{R}\oplus\|\text{Y}\ominus \overset{k_{sy}^{III}}{\longrightarrow} \text{ROS}$$

$$\text{I}_y \qquad\quad \text{II}_y \qquad\quad \text{III}_y$$

When $k_{1y} \gg k_{1x}$

$$\frac{1}{k_t} = \frac{1}{k_{ext\,x}}\left[1 + \frac{1}{a_x + b_{sx}(\text{MY})}\right]$$

$$k_{ext\,x} \equiv \left(\frac{k_1 k_2}{k_{-1}+k_2}\right)_x$$

$$a_x \equiv \left[\left(\frac{k_s^{III}}{k_{-2}}\right)\left(\frac{k_{-1}+k_2}{k_{-1}}\right)\right]_x$$

$$b_{sx} \equiv \left[\left(\frac{k_s^{III}}{k_{-2}}\right)\left(\frac{k_{-1}+k_2}{k_{-1}}\right)\right]_x$$

When $k_{1y} \ll k_{1x}$ and (MY) relatively constant

$$\frac{1}{k_{RY}} = \frac{1}{k_{ROS}} = \frac{1}{k_{ext\,x}}\left[1 + \frac{1}{a_x + b_{sx}(\text{MY})}\right]$$

If, also, (MY) is large

$$\frac{d\,(\text{ROS})}{d\,(\text{RY})} = a_y = \left[\left(\frac{k_s^{III}}{k_{-2}}\right)\left(\frac{k_{-1}+k_2}{k_{-1}}\right)\right]_y$$

tions proceed by way of intimate and solvent-separated ion pairs II and III, respectively, but not dissociated carbonium ions, and whose solvolysis product ROS arises from the solvent-

separated ion pair III.[2,5,6] It has been observed[2] that inclusion of salts such as lithium perchlorate in certain acetolyses gives rise to a steep special salt effect at low salt concentrations and a more shallow normal linear salt effect at higher concentrations. The steep special salt effect is evidently concerned with elimination of return from the solvent-separated ion pair[2,6] (external ion pair return), and it is due to diversion of solvent-separated ion pair $\text{R}\oplus\|\text{X}\ominus$ to a new species, $\text{R}\oplus\|\text{Y}\ominus$ by exchange with the added special salt MY.[2,6]

The use of a salt like lithium bromide permits one to gain further insight into the mechanism of the special salt effect and to extend the study of exchange reactions involving carbonium ion pair intermediates.[2,6] This is because ion pair return is very effective with the new ion pairs $\text{R}\oplus\|\text{Y}\ominus$ when Y is Br, covalent bromide RY being formed. Since the ionization rate constant k_{1y} of the latter is very much lower than that of the original arenesulfonate (k_{1x}), it accumulates during acetolysis in the presence of MY. In the present paper we report and discuss the results of a study of the acetolysis of 1-anisyl-2-propyl *p*-toluenesulfonate[7] and *threo*-3-anisyl-2-butyl *p*-bromobenzenesulfonate[5] in the presence of lithium or tetrabutylammonium bromide.

Bromide Exchange.—When lithium bromide or tetrabutylammonium bromide is added in acetolysis of 0.01 *M* 1-anisyl-2-propyl toluenesulfonate at 50.0°, these salts are very effective even at low concentrations in diverting reaction from solvolysis to formation of alkyl bromide as judged by Volhard titration. Because acetolysis products are unstable in the presence of hydrobromic acid, the exchanges were studied in the presence of sufficient lithium or tetrabutylammonium acetate to keep the solutions basic. At the higher bromide salt concentrations in the normal salt effect range, namely, the 0.03–0.09 *M* range, covalent bromide was formed to the extent of 85–89%. Under these conditions, the ratio of alkyl bromide to solvolysis product which are formed is relatively constant in

(1) Previous papers in this series: (a) XVIII, S. Winstein, M. Hojo and S. Smith, *Tetrahedron Letters*, No. **22**, 12 (1960); (b) XIX, S. Winstein, A. Ledwith and M. Hojo, *ibid.*, No. **10**, 341 (1961); (c) XX, A. Ledwith, M. Hojo and S. Winstein, *Proc. Chem. Soc.*, 241 (1961).

(2) Reported in summary: (a) S. Winstein, E. Clippinger, A. H. Fainberg and G. C. Robinson, *Chemistry & Industry*, 664 (1954); (b) S. Winstein, *Experientia Suppl. II*, 137 (1955); (c) VIth Reaction Mechanisms Conference, Swarthmore, Pa., Sept. 12, 1956; (d) S. Winstein, E. Allred and P. Klinedinst, Jr., Foreign Papers at VIIIth Mendeleev Congress of Pure and Applied Chemistry, Moscow, U.S.-S.R., March, 1959, p. 48.

(3) Research supported by the National Science Foundation.

(4) (a) National Science Foundation Predoctoral Fellow, 1952–1953; (b) U. S. Rubber Predoctoral Fellow 1953–(1954).

(5) S. Winstein and G. C. Robinson, *J. Am. Chem. Soc.*, **80**, 169 (1958).

(6) S. Winstein, P. E. Klinedinst, Jr., and G. C. Robinson, *ibid.*, **83**, 885 (1961).

(7) (a) S. Winstein, M. Brown, K. C. Schreiber and A. H. Schlesinger, *ibid.*, **74**, 1140 (1952); (b) A. H. Fainberg, G. C. Robinson and S. Winstein *ibid.*, **78**, 2777 (1956); (c) S. Winstein and A. H. Fainberg, *ibid.*, **80**, 459 (1958).

a run. So also is k_{RBr}, a first-order rate constant for RBr formation evaluated with the aid of eq. 1. In this equation $(RBr)_\infty$ and (RBr) are concentrations of developed alkyl bromide at infinity and time t, respectively. A typical such determination of k_{RBr} is illustrated in Table I. In all cases, the

TABLE I
KINETICS OF REACTION OF 0.0100 M 1-p-ANISYL-2-PROPYL p-TOLUENESULFONATE WITH 0.0278 M LITHIUM BROMIDE AND 0.00301 M LITHIUM ACETATE IN ACETIC ACID AT 50.0°

Time, 10^{-3} sec	Ml. AgNO$_3$ per aliquot	$10^5 k_{RBr}$, sec.$^{-1}$
0	2.378	..
2.10	2.316	4.42
4.50	2.255	4.30
7.50	2.188	4.23
10.56	2.126	4.23
14.16	2.057	4.35
18.60	1.987	4.41
23.40	1.934	4.31
42.96	1.798	4.14
∞	1.680	..

Mean 4.30 ± 0.07

bromide infinity titer was the same at 10 and 20 reaction half-lives, indicating that organic bromide was not solvolyzing to any measurable extent. The various determinations of k_{RBr} at the different

TABLE II
KINETICS OF BROMIDE EXCHANGE IN ACETOLYSIS OF 0.0100 M 1-p-ANISYL-2-PROPYL p-TOLUENESULFONATE AT 50.0°

Bromide salt	(MBr), $10^3 M$ Init.	Av.	(LiOAc) $10^3 M$	$10^5 k_{RBr}$, sec.$^{-1}$ Obsd.	Corr.
LiBr	2.78	2.37	3.01	4.30 ± 0.07	4.12
LiBr	4.64	4.21	2.01	$5.38 \pm .10$	5.06
LiBr	6.94	6.49	2.01	$6.74 \pm .14$	6.25
LiBr	9.02	8.58	2.00	$7.94 \pm .19$	7.29
Bu$_4$NBr	2.68	2.28	3.01	$3.64 \pm .06$	3.56
Bu$_4$NBr	4.46	4.04	5.04	$4.18 \pm .03$	4.04
Bu$_4$NBr	6.69	6.26	2.01	$4.90 \pm .06$	4.68
Bu$_4$NBr	8.76	8.31	2.00	$5.53 \pm .12$	5.24

concentrations of lithium and tetrabutylammonium bromide are summarized in Table II.

$$2.303 \log \left[\frac{(RBr)_\infty}{(RBr)_\infty - (RBr)} \right] = k_{RBr} t \qquad (1)$$

$$2.303 \log \left[\frac{(ROS)_\infty}{(ROS)_\infty - (ROS)} \right] = k_{ROS} t \qquad (2)$$

The behavior of *threo*-3-anisyl-2-butyl bromobenzenesulfonate toward added lithium bromide during acetolysis was quite analogous to that of the 1-anisyl-2-propyl analog. At concentrations of lithium bromide in the normal salt effect range, solvolyis was diverted to formation of covalent bromide to the extent of 93–96%. The determination of k_{RBr} at *ca.* 0.065 M lithium bromide at 25° is illustrated in Table III, while the results of two such runs are summarized in Table IV.

Corrections for Direct Reaction.—In the case of the 1-anisyl-2-propyl arenesulfonate, less reactive toward ionization than the 3-anisyl-2-butyl ester, it was necessary to estimate a correction for direct bimolecular reactions in which bromide ion is involved as a nucleophile in the rate-determining step. To assess the importance of such reactions, 1-phenyl-2-propyl toluenesulfonate is a good model

TABLE III
KINETICS OF REACTION OF 0.0100 M *threo*-3-ANISYL-2-BUTYL p-BROMOBENZENESULFONATE WITH 0.0634 M LITHIUM BROMIDE AND 0.00120 M LITHIUM ACETATE IN ACETIC ACID AT 25.00°

Time, 10^{-3} sec.	Ml. KSCN per aliquot	$10^6 k_{RBr}$, sec.$^{-1}$
0	0.755	..
1.14	0.885	107
2.28	1.000	106
3.42	1.100	105
4.56	1.190	105
6.42	1.320	106
8.76	1.455	108
12.78	1.590	103
∞	1.900	..

Av. 106 ± 1

TABLE IV
SUMMARY OF KINETICS OF CONVERSION OF 0.0100 M *threo*-3-ANISYL-2-BUTYL p-BROMOBENZENESULFONATE TO BROMIDE IN ACETIC ACID AT 25.00° [(LiOAc) = 1.20×10^{-3} M]

(LiBr), $10^3 M$		$10^6 k_{RBr}$, sec.$^{-1}$
Init.	Av.	
6.34	5.85	106 ± 1
3.16	2.71	76.0 ± 1.0

for the 1-anisyl-2-propyl ester, since the removal of the p-methoxyl group strongly retards ionization,[7] but is without appreciable effect on the more direct substitution and elimination reactions involving bromide ion as a nucleophile.[8] For this reason, the action of lithium and tetrabutylammonium bromides on 1-phenyl-2-propyl toluenesulfonate during acetolysis was investigated under the general conditions employed in the study of the 1-anisyl-2-propyl analog. As illustrated in Table V, k_{RBr} was relatively constant within a run with this substrate as well as the other two, and the results of the several runs with the 1-phenyl-2-propyl toluenesulfonate at 50° are summarized in Table VI.

TABLE V
KINETICS OF REACTION OF 0.0100 M 1-PHENYL-2-PROPYL p-TOLUENESULFONATE WITH 0.0278 M LITHIUM BROMIDE AND 0.0101 M LITHIUM ACETATE IN ACETIC ACID AT 50.0°

Time, 10^{-4} sec.	Ml. AgNO$_3$ per aliquot	$10^4 k_{RBr}$, sec.$^{-1}$
0	2.410	..
7.248	2.300	3.01
10.968	2.249	3.09
16.056	2.200	2.92
20.430	2.157	2.94
28.362	2.094	2.93
41.532	2.015	2.96
63.132	1.935	2.99
∞	1.850	..

Mean 2.98 ± 0.05

In the runs with 1-phenyl-2-propyl toluenesulfonate in the presence of substantial concentrations of bromide salt, alkyl bromide was formed to the extent of 65–77% at 0.03–0.08 M lithium bromide and 57–65% at 0.04–0.08 M tetrabutylammonium bromide. While the data are of some interest in

(8) (a) S. Winstein, D. Darwish and N. J. Holness, *J. Am. Chem. Soc.*, **78**, 2915 (1956); (b) I. D. R. Stevens, unpublished work.

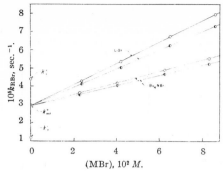

Fig. 1.—Effects of bromide salts in acetolysis of 1-*p*-anisyl-2-propyl toluenesulfonate at 50°: open circles, uncorrected k_{RBr} values; semi-closed circles, corrected k_{RBr} values.

connection with the subject of substitution and elimination by bromide ion as a nucleophile,[8] the present interest in them is because they afford an estimate of the rate of direct reactions of 1-anisyl-2-propyl toluenesulfonate with bromide salts.

TABLE VI

KINETICS OF BROMIDE EXCHANGE IN ACETOLYSIS OF 0.0100 M 1-PHENYL-2-PROPYL p-TOLUENESULFONATE AT 50.0°

Bromide salt	(MBr), 10^2 M Init.	Av.	(LiOAc) 10^2 M	Exchange, %	$10^6 k_{RBr}$, sec. $^{-1}$
LiBr	2.78	2.45	1.01	65	2.98 ± 0.05
LiBr	4.62	4.28	1.01	68	4.26 ± .06
LiBr	6.93	6.56	1.01	73	6.27 ± .10
LiBr	8.33	7.95	1.01	77	7.27 ± .21
Bu₄NBr	4.46	4.17	1.01	57	2.10 ± .06
Bu₄NBr	8.04	7.71	1.01	65	3.35 ± .08

The k_{RBr} values listed in Tables I–VI which are derived from kinetic runs in which the (RY/ROS) ratio is constant within a run are also equal to first-order solvolyses rate constants k_{ROS}, defined by eq. 2, where (ROS)$_\infty$ and (ROS) are concentrations of solvolysis product formed at infinity and time t, respectively. Also, k_{RBr} (or k_{ROS}) is equal to the first-order rate constant for disappearance of the arenesulfonate, RX. The k_{RBr} values for the 1-phenyl-2-propyl toluenesulfonate show a linear dependence on the average MBr concentration prevailing in the various runs so that they can be fit to eq. 3 with b_t equal to 148 for lithium bromide and 62 for tetrabutylammonium bromide. The k_t^0 value employed in eq. 3 is the acetolysis rate constant[7a] in the absence of salt,[9,10] 0.585 × 10^{-6} sec. $^{-1}$ at 50.0°. The b_t values to be expected if the only effect of the added bromide salts were normal salt effects on acetolysis can be estimated as 18 and 2.9 for lithium and tetrabutylammonium bromides, respectively. These are rough estimates based on observed regularities in the effects of various salts on various substrates.[10] The contribution to the first-order k_{RBr} values from direct

(9) The effect of the 0.0101 M lithium acetate in the runs may be judged[10] to be negligible [see S. Winstein and K. C. Schreiber, *J. Am. Chem. Soc.*, **74**, 2171 (1952)].

(10) (a) A. H. Fainberg and ·S. Winstein, *ibid.*, **78**, 2763 (1956); (b) S. Winstein, S. Smith and D. Darwish, *ibid.*, **81**, 5511 (1959); (c) S. Smith, unpublished work.

reaction with bromide ion may be taken equal to $[k_t^0(MBr)\Delta b_t]$, where k_t^0, (MBr) and Δb_t refer to eq. 3: (MBr) is the average bromide salt concen-

$$k_{RBr} = k_t^0 [1 + b_t(MBr)] \qquad (3)$$

tration in the run, and Δb_t is the difference between observed and expected b_t values for a given bromide salt.

By evaluating the $[k_t^0(MBr)\Delta b_t]$ contributions to the k_{RBr} values of 1-phenyl-2-propyl toluenesulfonate at the average (MBr) values in the runs with the 1-anisyl-2-propyl ester, the corrections were estimated for the contribution of direct reactions with bromide to the k_{RBr} values observed with the 1-anisyl-2-propyl arenesulfonate. As is clear from the measured and corrected k_{RBr} values in Table II, the corrections represent only a small fraction of the observed k_{RBr} values.

With the more reactive *threo*-3-anisyl-2-butyl system, any contribution to the observed k_{RBr} values is quite negligible, judging by the behavior of *threo*-3-phenyl-2-butyl toluenesulfonate. A control experiment with the latter substrate showed that its rate of direct reaction with lithium bromide is quite low compared to the k_{RBr} values obtained with the 3-anisyl-2-butyl system.

k_{ext}^0 **Values.**—Plots of the k_{RBr} values *vs.* the average bromide salt concentration in each run are shown in Fig. 1 for the 1-anisyl-2-propyl system. It is quite clear that both the corrected and uncorrected k_{RBr} values display the normal linear salt effect pattern in the 0.03–0.10 M salt concentration range. Also, extrapolation to zero salt concentration leads to an identical intercept, k_{ext}^0, when either corrected or uncorrected k_{RBr} values are employed. It is significant that the same k_{ext}^0 intercept value is obtained from both lithium and tetrabutylammonium bromide salts. This is shown graphically in Fig. 1 and numerically in Table VII.

TABLE VII

COMPARISON OF k_{ext}^0 VALUES FROM EFFECTS OF PERCHLORATE AND BROMIDE SALTS

System	Salt	$10^5 k_{ext}^0$, sec. $^{-1}$
1-An-2-PrOTs[a] 50.0°	Bu₄NBr	2.92
	LiBr	2.91
	LiClO₄	2.85
3-An-2-BuOBs[b] 25.0°	LiBr	5.01
	LiClO₃	5.05

[a] 1-Anisyl-2-propyl p-toluenesulfonate. [b] 3-Anisyl-2-butyl p-bromobenzenesulfonate.

It is quite clear from Fig. 1 that the k_{ext}^0 value for the 1-anisyl-2-propyl system is much above k_t^0, the titrimetric acetolysis rate constant in the absence of salt, and yet it is considerably below k_1^0, the ionization rate constant without added salt. The most interesting comparison is that between k_{ext}^0 obtained from k_{RBr} values and k_{ext}^0 obtained previously[7b] with lithium perchlorate as the special salt. As shown in Table VII, the two kinds of k_{ext}^0 values agree well within experimental error.

It is interesting to compare also for the 3-anisyl-2-butyl system the k_{ext}^0 values from lithium bromide and from lithium perchlorate as salts. The two k_{RBr} values for this system at 25° lead to a k_{ext}^0 intercept of 5.01×10^{-5} sec.$^{-1}$. Again, as is summarized in Table VII, this k_{ext}^0 from lithium bromide as the salt is within experimental error identical with the k_{ext}^0 given by lithium perchlorate.[5]

Bromide and Perchlorate as Scavengers.—The agreement between k_{ext}^0 values from bromide exchange and from lithium perchlorate-accelerated solvolysis is evidence that bromide and perchlorate act as scavengers for the same solvolysis intermediates. In the special salt effect of salts such as lithium perchlorate, elimination of ion pair return is only partial; the best working hypothesis has been that perchlorate acts as a scavenger for the solvent-separated ion pair, thus eliminating external ion pair return.[2,5-7] Evidently, bromide does this also.[2] On the other hand, both perchlorate and bromide permit internal return from the intimate ion pair. While both perchlorate and bromide trap the solvent-separated ion pair, the eventual products are different in the two cases. When perchlorate is the scavenger, solvolysis product is formed; when the scavenger is bromide, mainly alkyl bromide is produced.

The diversion of intermediate III by added salt MY is represented in solvolysis scheme I, the subscript x being used for RX and its related ion pairs, while y as subscript is employed for RY and its ion. pairs. A subscript x or y outside a bracket pertains to all the rate constants within the brackets. When MY is lithium perchlorate, no RY accumulates, and the accelerated solvolysis rate constant k_t is given by the expression shown in the solvolysis scheme.[6] This is written for the situation where MY exists very largely as ion pairs and these are the species which exchange with ion pairs III$_x$. At high MY concentration, all III$_x$ is diverted to III$_y$, no return from III$_x$ is permitted, and k_t is equal to $k_{ext\ x}$, the rate constant inclusive of internal return but without external ion pair return.

When MY is a bromide salt, diversion of III$_x$ to III$_y$ results in RY accumulation, since k_{1y} is small compared to k_{1x}. Where MY concentration is relatively constant, k_{RY} is given by an expression shown in the solvolysis scheme, which is, in fact, identical with the one for k_t in the case of a special salt such as lithium perchlorate. At high MBr concentrations, all III$_x$ is diverted to III$_y$, and k_{RBr} becomes equal to $k_{ext\ x}$, just as does k_t for lithium perchlorate-accelerated solvolysis.

When diversion of $R^\oplus || X^\ominus$ to $R^\oplus | Br^\ominus$ is quite complete, the solvolysis product ROS arises by the k_{sy}^{III} path in the solvolysis scheme. Also, as

shown in the scheme, the ratio of solvolysis and bromide exchange products, $[(ROS)/(RY)]$, is equal to the parameter a_y. The latter is related to the efficiencies of internal and external ion pair return associated with acetolysis of the alkyl bromide. Since $[(ROS)/(RY)]$ is observed to be quite small in the present work, ion pair returns associated with alkyl bromide are obviously very efficient. There is other evidence of the relatively greater importance of ion pair return for bromides compared to the corresponding arenesulfonates. For example, the polarimetric:titrimetric ratio of rate constants in acetolysis is much greater for *exo*-norbornyl bromide than for the bromobenzenesulfonate.[2,11]

Experimental

Arenesulfonates.—The 1-anisyl-2-propyl toluenesulfonate, m.p. 80.5–81.3°, acetolysis rate constant ($1.17 \pm 0.01) \times 10^{-5}$ sec.$^{-1}$ at 50.0°, and the *threo*-3-anisyl-2-butyl bromobenzenesulfonate, m.p. 97.5–98.5°, were specimens employed previously.[6] The 1-phenyl-2-propyl toluenesulfonate was available from previous work.[7a] Recrystallization gave rise to material, m.p. 91–92°.

Solvents and Salts.—Anhydrous acetic acid solvent was prepared in the usual way.[6] Lithium and tetrabutylammonium acetates were those previously described.[6] A stock solution of lithium bromide was prepared from Mallinckrodt N.F. grade material, water being destroyed with acetic anhydride. Lithium bromide solutions were standardized by Volhard titration.

Tetrabutylammonium bromide was prepared from Eastman Kodak Co. white label tetrabutylammonium iodide. The latter was treated with excess freshly prepared silver oxide in aqueous ethanol until the supernatant liquid tested free of iodide ion. The mixture was filtered and the filtrate was carefully neutralized with aqueous hydrobromic acid. Solvent was removed under reduced pressure and the crude product was twice recrystallized from ethyl acetate. The m.p. of the product, 102.7–103.5° (reported[12] 118°), was unchanged after several further recrystallizations. The equivalent weight of the material by Volhard titration was 324 (calcd. 322.4). There are apparently two crystalline forms of tetrabutylammonium bromide since a modification of m.p. 119° has been obtained by D. Darwish and I. D. R. Stevens[13] in these laboratories. The latter also obtained the 103° modification with correct carbon, hydrogen and bromine analyses.

Kinetic Measurements.—Consumption of bromide ion was followed by pipetting a 5-ml. aliquot of reaction solution into a separatory funnel containing 25 ml. of pentane and 10 ml. of water. The mixture was given forty vigorous shakes, the aqueous layer was drained off, another 10 ml. of water was added and the procedure repeated. The combined aqueous extracts were acidified with nitric acid and excess standard aqueous silver nitrate was added from a calibrated buret. The excess silver nitrate was back-titrated with standard potassium thiocyanate solution.

(11) E. Clippinger, unpublished work.

(12) M. B. Reynolds and C. A. Kraus, *J. Am. Chem. Soc.*, **70**, 1709 (1948).

(13) D. Darwish and I. D. R. Stevens, unpublished work.

59 | Ring Closure Involving Hydroxyphenyl Groups

Baird and Winstein explore the conditions under which an aromatic ring participates in the ionization at a site four carbon atoms away. An ordinary phenyl group is not as active as a double bond in this respect; but a p-hydroxyphenyl group ionized by a very strong base increases the rate of ionization and leads to 50–60% yields of spirodienones such as III. In acid media the dienone-phenol rearrangement converts these spirodienones into ar-β-tetralol, and reasons are given for thinking that the tetramethylenephenonium ion is intermediate in the direct formation of such tetrahydronaphthols and their ethers by ring closure. The potential well created in alkaline medium serves to trap the phenonium intermediate.

From: *J. Am. Chem. Soc.* **84,** 788–92 (1962)

[Contribution from the Department of Chemistry, University of California, Los Angeles 24, Calif.]

Neighboring Carbon and Hydrogen. XLVI.[1] Spiro-(4,5)-deca-1,4-diene-3-one from Ar₁⊖-5 Participation

By Richard Baird[2] and S. Winstein

Received October 27, 1961

When the aryl group is *p*-hydroxyphenyl, Ar₁-5 participation in the phenoxide anion of 4-aryl-1-butyl arenesulfonates, designated by the symbol Ar₁⊖-5, should lead to the corresponding spiro-dienones. Kinetic investigation of the behavior of 4-*p*-hydroxyphenyl-1-butyl *p*-bromobenzenesulfonate in basic solution shows that conditions are relatively unfavorable for Ar₁⊖-5 participation in methanol but are quite favorable in *t*-butyl alcohol as solvent. Correspondingly, spiro-(4,5)-deca-1,4-diene-3-one is isolated in low yield from reaction in methanol and in much better yield from *t*-butyl alcohol as a reaction medium. In the dienone–phenol rearrangement of the dienone to 5,6,7,8-tetrahydro-2-naphthol, the protonated dienone intermediate is analogous to the spiro-cationic intermediate in Ar₁-5-assisted solvolysis of 4-*p*-anisyl-1-butyl bromobenzenesulfonate. Therefore, the quantitative conversion of dienone to the tetrahydronaphthol in formic acid furnishes further insight into the behavior of spiro-cationic intermediates from Ar₁-5 participation.

With suitable 4-aryl-1-butyl arenesulfonates, Ar₁-5-assisted ionization[3] leads to spiro-cationic intermediates which give rise to tetralins as final products. When the aryl group is *p*-hydroxyphenyl, as in 4-*p*-hydroxyphenyl-1-butyl *p*-bromobenzenesulfonate (I-OBs), one can conceive of a process involving participation of the phenoxide ion group of the anion I-OBs. This would lead to the spiro-dienone III. Modifying the Ar₁-5

symbol[3] to indicate the anionic nature of the participating group,[4] such formation of dienone III from anion II-OBs can be designated Ar₁⊖-5. As indicated already in a preliminary Communication,[5] it is possible to find conditions which favor conversion of II-OBs to dienone III, and the results of this study of the formation and behavior of III are presented and discussed in the present manuscript.

Syntheses.—Most of the compounds in this study were prepared from 4-*p*-anisylbutanoic acid, which was obtained by the procedures of Fieser[6] and Martin.[7] Reduction of this acid with lithium

(1) Paper XL: S. Winstein and M. Battiste, *J. Am. Chem. Soc.*, **82,** 5244 (1960); paper XLI: S. Winstein and R. L. Hansen, *Tetrahedron Letters*, **No. 25,** 1 (1960); paper XLII: S. Winstein and R. L. Hansen, *J. Am. Chem. Soc.*, **82,** 8206 (1960); paper XLIII: D. Kivelson, S. Winstein, P. Bruck and R. L. Hansen, *ibid.*, **83,** 2938 (1961); paper XLIV: S. Winstein and P. Carter, *ibid.*, **83,** 4485 (1961); paper XLV: J. Sonnenberg and S. Winstein, *J. Org. Chem.*, **27,** in press.

(2) National Science Foundation Predoctoral Fellow, 1953–1955, 1956–1957. Present address: Dept. of Chem., Yale University, New Haven, Conn.

(3) (a) S. Winstein, R. Heck, S. Lapporte and R. Baird, *Experientia*, **12,** 138 (1956); (b) R. Heck and S. Winstein *J. Am. Chem. Soc.*, **79,** 3105 (1957).

(4) For similar symbolism in the case of neighboring functional groups, see F. L. Scott, R. E. Glick and S. Winstein, *Experientia*, **13,** 183 (1957).

(5) S. Winstein and R. Baird, *J. Am. Chem. Soc.*, **79,** 756 (1957).

(6) (a) L. F. Fieser and V. Desreux, *ibid.*, **60,** 2255 (1938); (b) L. F. Fieser and E. B. Hershberg, *ibid.*, **58,** 2314 (1936).

(7) E. L. Martin, *ibid.*, **58,** 1440 (1936).

TABLE I

SUMMARY OF SOLVOLYSIS RATE CONSTANTS FOR p-SUBSTITUTED 4-PHENYL-1-BUTYL p-BROMOBENZENESULFONATES

p-Substituent	Solvent	Temp., °C.	[ROBs], 10^2 M	Added base	Concn., 10^2 M	$10^5 k$, sec.$^{-1}$
HO	HCOOH	75.0	2.99	LiOCHO	3.35	$7.2^{a,b}$
HO	HCOOH	75.0	3.01	LiOCHO	6.96	$7.4^{a,c}$
H	MeOH	50.0	3.03	......	..	1.019 ± 0.004
CH$_3$O	MeOH	50.0	2.90	......	..	$1.076 \pm .005$
HO	MeOH	50.0	3.11	......	..	$1.104 \pm .006$
HO	MeOH	50.0	3.16	NaOCH$_3$	3.16	$8.3^{a,d}$
HO	MeOH	50.0	1.58	NaOCH$_3$	3.16	$8.9^{a,e}$
HO	MeOH	50.0	3.58	NaOCH$_3$	7.16	$15.4^{a,f}$
HO.	MeOH	50.0	3.00	NaOCH$_3$	18.47	$30.8^{a,g}$
HO	t-BuOH	50.0	2.04	KOBu-t	2.38	49.2 ± 0.8
HO	t-BuOH	50.0	0.504	KOBu-t	0.992	49.5 ± 1.9
HO	t-BuOH	50.0	0.447	KOBu-t	0.498	49.9 ± 1.4
HO	t-BuOH	25.0	2.05	KOBu-t	2.38	4.16 ± 0.03

^{a} Extrapolated initial rate constant. ^{b} Integrated rate constant drifts from 6.6 at 15% to 5.2 at 91% reaction. ^{c} Integrated rate constant drifts from 7.3 at 12% to 5.4 at 90% reaction. ^{d} Instantaneous value is 4.8 at 69% reaction. ^{e} Instantaneous value is 7.1 at 89% reaction. ^{f} Instantaneous value is 8.6 at 82% reaction. ^{g} Instantaneous value is 28.1 at 97% reaction.

aluminum hydride provided 4-p-anisyl-1-butanol, and this was converted to the p-bromobenzenesulfonate.[3b,8]

dimeric and polymeric products

+ olefin

Cleavage of the 4-p-anisylbutanoic acid with hydrobromic acid according to Fieser[9] provided 4-p-hydroxyphenylbutanoic acid. Reduction of the latter with lithium aluminum hydride under vigorous conditions provided 4-p-hydroxyphenyl-1-butanol (I-OH). Although 4-p-hydroxyphenyl-1-butyl p-bromobenzenesulfonate (I-OBs) could be obtained in fair yield directly from 4-p-hydroxyphenyl-1-butanol, the best route to this ester was from 4-p-hydroxyphenylbutanoic acid. Treatment of this material with an excess of dihydropyran and a trace of acid, followed by reduction with lithium aluminum hydride, led to 4-[p-(2-tetrahydropyranoxy)-phenyl]-1-butanol. This compound was converted to the p-bromobenzenesulfonate ester in the usual manner, and then the pyranyl group was removed by gentle acid hydrolysis.

Ar$_1$-5 Participation.—In searching for Ar$_1^{\ominus}$-5 participation, a combination of kinetic measurements and product examination was employed. In the kinetic exploration for Ar$_1^{\ominus}$-5 participation it was necessary to know the behavior of 4-p-hydroxyphenyl-1-butyl p·bromobenzenesulfo-

(8) S. Winstein and R. Heck, J. Am. Chem. Soc., **78**, 4801 (1956).
(9) L. F. Fieser, M. T. Leffler, et al., ibid., **70**, 3196 (1948).

nate (I-OBs) in neutral solvolysis. Pertinent solvolysis rate constants for this compound and two related ones are summarized in Table I.

In formic acid solvent, the first-order solvolysis rate constant of I-OBs drifted down in a run, but this is most logically ascribed to esterification of the phenolic group which converts I-OBs to a less reactive derivative. The drift is not due to partial reaction of I-OBs by way of the phenoxide ion II-OBs or to reaction involving formate ion attack, since the initial, instantaneous first-order formolysis rate constant was insensitive to the concentration of added lithium formate. Using the initial rate constant for I-OBs, the relative formolysis rates of the p-hydroxy, p-methoxy and unsubstituted 4-phenyl-1-butyl p-bromobenzenesulfonates at 75° are in the sequence 2.13:1.77:1.00 (Table II). Formolysis of the 4-phenyl-1-butyl ester proceeds ca. 19% by the Ar$_1$-5-assisted route,[3b] and the p-methoxy derivative ca. 54% by this route.[3b] With the p-hydroxy ester I-OBs, Ar$_1$-5 participation is apparently slightly more important in formolysis than it is in the p-methoxyl case.

TABLE II

RELATIVE RATES OF SOLVOLYSIS OF p-SUBSTITUTED 4-PHENYL-1-BUTYL p-BROMOBENZENESULFONATES

p-Sub-stituent	Relative rates	
	HCOOH, 75°	MeOH, 50°
H	1.00^a	1.00
CH$_3$O	1.77^a	1.06
HO	2.13	1.08

^{a} Based on data of Heck.[3b]

In methanol in the absence of added base, the 4-p-hydroxyphenyl-, 4-p-anisyl- and 4-phenyl-1-butyl p-bromobenzenesulfonates solvolyze with nearly identical rate constants (Tables I and II). In the relatively nucleophilic methanol solvent, Ar$_1$-5-assisted ionization[3b] is essentially negligible in all three cases.

Kinetic Search for Ar$_1^{\ominus}$-5 Participation.—As shown in Table I, the rate of methanolysis of the 4-p-hydroxyphenyl-1-butyl ester I-OBs is markedly increased by addition of sodium methoxide. However, the Ar$_1^{\ominus}$-5-assisted reaction of the phenoxide ion II-OBs is not the only process which is taking place, since it would be expected to exhibit first-order kinetics. Instead, first-order rate constants depended on the added sodium methoxide concentration and also drifted down in a run. At high sodium methoxide concentrations it is evident that a higher order (presumably second-order) process is dominating, but at the lower base concentrations the initial rates are too high to be explained in this way. An additional complication occurs at low base concentrations, due to the incomplete conversion of the phenol to the phenoxide ion. Measurements of the equilibrium constant for this process, using the closely related phenol, 2-p-hydroxyphenylethanol,[10] indicate, however, that the phenol is initially at least 90% in the form of the phenoxide ion even at the lowest base concentrations.

While the data for basic methanol suggest that $Ar_1^{\ominus}$-5 participation is developed by addition of sodium methoxide, they also show that at no concentration of added base could the $Ar_1^{\ominus}$-5-assisted process be made dominant by a large factor over both unassisted solvolysis and reaction involving methoxide ion attack.

The situation in t-butyl alcohol as solvent is more favorable for $Ar_1^{\ominus}$-5 participation. In this solvent, good first-order kinetics, dependent only on the concentration of the phenoxide ion, are observed with 4-p-hydroxyphenyl-1-butyl p-bromobenzenesulfonate. The rate is independent of the base concentration, as long as sufficient t-butoxide is used to convert the phenol to the phenoxide ion. In basic t-butyl alcohol the observed first-order rate constant (Table I) is $ca.$ fifty times as great as the solvolysis rate constant in neutral methanol at the same temperature. Since t-butyl alcohol is a poorer ionizing solvent than is methanol,[11] the unassisted as well as Ar_1-5-assisted solvolysis rates of 4-p-hydroxyphenyl-1-butyl p-bromobenzenesulfonate in t-butyl alcohol would be expected to be less than those in absolute methanol. Thus it is clear that $Ar_1^{\ominus}$-5-assisted reaction of I-OBs is very dominant in basic t-butyl alcohol.

Product Isolation.—Using the kinetic data as a guide to the conditions favorable for $Ar_1^{\ominus}$-5 participation, the non-phenolic products of basic solvolysis of bromobenzenesulfonate I-OBs in both methanol and t-butyl alcohol were examined. From both solvents there was obtained a neutral product which led to a white crystalline solid, m.p. 34–35°, on recrystallization from pentane at low temperatures. The yield of this material was 20% from methanol and as high as 50–60% from t-butyl alcohol.

The following chemical evidence showed the above compound to be spiro-(4,5)-deca-1,4-diene-3-one[5] (III). It showed the correct carbon–hydrogen analysis for $C_{10}H_{12}O$. Also, it reacted with 2,4-dinitrophenylhydrazine and with semicarbazide to give a red 2,4-dinitrophenylhydrazone, C_{16}-$H_{16}O_4N_4$, and a semicarbazone, $C_{11}H_{15}ON_3$, respectively. Quantitative hydrogenation of the compound over reduced platinum oxide required 2.04 ± 0.04 moles of hydrogen and led to a new ketone whose 2,4-dinitrophenylhydrazone showed the correct carbon–hydrogen analysis for the derivative of the tetrahydro ketone, $C_{16}H_{20}O_4N_4$. Finally, the compound underwent dienone–phenol rearrangement[12] to give an almost quantitative yield of authentic 5,6,7,8-tetrahydro-2-naphthol.

The structure of the neutral compound, m.p. 34–35°, was further verified by spectral evidence. Thus the infrared spectrum of the compound exhibited strong absorption maxima in chloroform solution at 1594, 1617, 1655 and 1707 cm.$^{-1}$, which is consistent with an $\alpha,\beta-\alpha',\beta'$-unsaturated carbonyl structure.[13] The ultraviolet absorption spectrum exhibited an absorption maximum in methanol at 242 mμ with ϵ equal to 16,000 (log ϵ 4.21). The ultraviolet spectrum of the 2,4-dinitrophenylhydrazone, $C_{16}H_{16}O_4N_4$, possessed absorption maxima at 390, 253 and 223 mμ in methanol with log ϵ 4.53, 4.21 and 2.92, respectively. Dreiding[14a] has reported a maximum at 242.5 mμ in ethanol with log ϵ equal to 4.2 for the closely related spiro-(5,5)-undeca-1,4-diene-3-one (IV). The corresponding 2,4-dinitrophenylhydrazone possessed λ_{max} equal to 391 mμ (EtOH) (log ϵ 4.53). The infrared maxima of Dreiding's dienone are reported as 1664, 1623 and 1600 cm.$^{-1}$, in close agreement with ours. Burnell and Taylor[15] had previously reported λ_{max} equal to 235 mμ for dienone IV, but failed to specify the solvent used.

The present work shows that $Ar_1^{\ominus}$-5-assisted ionization of suitable substrates, such as the 4-p-hydroxyphenyl-1-butyl arenesulfonate I-OBs, can provide a useful synthetic route to spiro-dienones. Since our first report[5] of the preparation of dienone III in this way, several other dienones, such as IV,[14a] V,[14b] VI[14c] and VII[14d] have been prepared similarly.

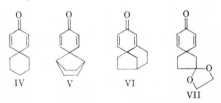

$$IV \qquad V \qquad VI \qquad VII$$

Ar_1-5 Intermediates.—There is evidence[3] that spiro-cationic intermediates such as IXa and IXb are involved in solvolyses of certain 4-p-anisyl-1-butyl derivatives (VIII). Some of the evidence is quite direct; for example, with VIIIb, reaction by way of the spiro-cation IXb leads to rearranged tetralin Xb. With VIIIa the evidence for the spiro-cation IXa is less direct. In interpreting the solvolysis of 4-anisyl-1-butyl p-bromobenzenesulfonate (VIIIa) previously,[3] the assumption was

(10) The equilibrium constant for this phenol will be reported in a subsequent paper.

(11) The **Y**-values for methanol and t-butyl alcohol are −1.090 and −3.26, respectively; A. H. Fainberg and S. Winstein, *J. Am. Chem. Soc.*, **78**, 2770 (1956).

(12) A. L. Wilds and C. Djerassi, *ibid.*, **68**, 1715 (1946).

(13) L. J. Bellamy, "The Infra-red Spectra of Complex Molecules," Methuen and Co., Ltd., London, 1958, p. 118.

(14) (a) A. S. Dreiding, *Helv. Chim. Acta.*, **40**, 1812 (1957); (b) R. Barner, A. S. Dreiding and H. Schmid, *Chemistry and Industry*, 1437 (1958); (c) S. Masamune, *J. Am. Chem. Soc.*, **83**, 1009 (1961); (d) S. Dorling and J. Harley-Mason, *Chemistry and Industry*, 1551 (1959).

(15) R. H. Burnell and W. I. Taylor, *J. Chem. Soc.*, 3486 (1954).

made that the spiro-cation IXa gave rise only to tetralin Xa and not to any open chain products.

VIIIa, R = H
b, R = CH₃

IXa, R = H
b, R = CH₃

Xa, R = H
b, R = CH₃

An intermediate XI analogous to IXa can be independently obtained from the dienone III which is derived *via* Ar₁⊖-5 participation. Thus, addition of a proton to the carbonyl oxygen atom of dienone III gives XI which is like IXa except for a hydrogen atom instead of a methyl group on oxygen. In this instance the spiran structure is pre-formed, and it is possible to determine whether tetralin is, in fact, formed from the spiro-cation and whether any ring opening occurs.

III   XI

When authentic spiro-(4,5)-deca-1,4-diene-3-one (III) was treated in buffered formic acid for one half-life of the parent bromobenzenesulfonate I-OBs, a yield in excess of 95% of authentic 5,6,7,8-tetrahydro-2-naphthol was isolated from the reaction mixture. Since the open chain products from the solvolysis of 4-*p*-anisyl-1-butyl derivatives have been shown not to cyclize under the reaction conditions,[16] the tetrahydronaphthol must have come from rearrangement of the dienone. It seems clear that spiro-cation XI leads essentially exclusively to the substituted tetralin and negligibly to open-chain products. This result serves to confirm the previous assumption[3] regarding the behavior of the related spiro-cation IXa.

Experimental

4-*p*-Anisylbutanoic acid was prepared from succinic anhydride, anisole and aluminum chloride *via* 3-*p*-anisoylpropanoic acid by the procedures of Fieser[6] and Martin.[7] The acid, b.p. 194–195.5° (9.9 mm.), m.p. 56–6.5°, was-obtained in 78.5% yield from anisole.

4-*p*-Anisyl-1-butanol[3a] was prepared in 93% yield by lithium aluminum hydride reduction of the above acid; b.p. 160–160.9° (8 mm.), n²⁵D 1.5248, m.p. 3.0–4.0°.

4-*p*-Anisyl-1-butyl *p*-Bromobenzenesulfonate.—Preparation of this substance was carried out by the low temperature method.[8] This provided the *p*-bromobenzenesulfonate in 62% yield, m.p. 41.5–43.5° (ether–pentane), reported[3b] m.p. 43–45°.

4-*p*-Hydroxyphenylbutanoic acid was prepared from 4-*p*-anisylbutanoic acid by the method of Fieser.[9] This procedure gave rise to the desired acid in 64% yield from anisole; m.p. 106–108°, reported[9] m.p. 107–108°.

4-*p*-Hydroxyphenyl-1-butanol.—Reduction of 4-*p*-hydroxyphenylbutanoic acid with 1.5 moles of lithium aluminum hydride for 24 hours was unsuccessful, due to the formation of an insoluble salt. When a large excess of the hydride was used (4:1 molar ratio) with a longer reflux period, the acid was reduced in 92% yield. Addition of 166

g. of the acid in 1500 ml. of anhydrous ether to a slurry of 115 g. of lithium aluminum hydride in 1000 ml. of dry ether and refluxing for one week yielded 141 g. of 4-*p*-hydroxyphenyl-1-butanol, b.p. 144–146° (0.5 mm.), m.p. 55.5–58.0°. A small portion purified for analysis by sublimation melted at 56.5–57.8°.

Anal. Calcd. for C₁₀H₁₄O₂: C, 72.27; H, 8.49. Found: C, 72.18; H, 8.75.

4-*p*-Hydroxyphenyl-1-butyl *p*-Bromobenzenesulfonate. From 4-*p*-Hydroxyphenyl-1-butanol.—A solution of 25 g. of 4-*p*-hydroxyphenyl-1-butanol in 300 ml. of Karl Fischer grade pyridine was cooled to −30° and to this was added 50 g. of Eastman Kodak white label *p*-bromobenzenesulfonyl chloride. After the chloride had dissolved, the solution was warmed up to 0° for 60 minutes, and the solution then poured into a large excess of ice-water. The oil was taken up in ether and the aqueous solution extracted once more with ether. The combined extracts were washed in the usual way and the bulk of the solvent was removed on the steam-bath, the remainder being taken off under reduced pressure.

When the resulting oil was dissolved in methylene chloride–hexane, it usually crystallized partially after 1–2 weeks in the ice-box.

When the oil was dissolved in 300–400 ml. of methanol, treated with charcoal at 0° for a few minutes and then filtered and diluted with ice-water until a second phase appeared, seeding with the above crystals usually induced extensive crystallization in *ca.* 24 hours at 0°. Filtration of the pasty solid obtained gave a material which when dissolved in methylene chloride and dried with magnesium sulfate crystallized readily on the addition of hexane to the point of oiling and seeding. A second recrystallization yielded long prisms, m.p. 59.5–61.5°, in 50% yield. This compound was completely soluble in 5% sodium hydroxide and was reprecipitated (as an oil) by carbon dioxide.

Anal. Calcd. for C₁₆H₁₇O₄SBr: C, 49.88; H, 4.45. Found: C, 49.74; H, 4.40.

From 4-*p*-Hydroxyphenylbutanoic Acid.—To a solution of 362 g. of Matheson, Coleman and Bell dihydropyran and 10 drops of concd. sulfuric acid in 350 ml. of anhydrous ether was added 155 g. of 4-*p*-hydroxyphenylbutanoic acid, and the solution was allowed to stand overnight at room temperature. This solution was then added over 1.5 hours to a slurry of 41 g. of lithium aluminum hydride in 1 liter of anhydrous ether, and the solution stirred under reflux for about 2.5 hours more. This solution was then treated with 82 ml. of water and 66 ml. of 10% sodium hydroxide according to the procedure of Leonard.[17] The resulting ether solution was concentrated to about 800 ml. and then washed several times with very dilute (*ca.* 1%) potassium hydroxide solution, and dried over a mixture of magnesium sulfate and potassium carbonate.

The oil resulting upon removal of the solvent was dissolved without further purification in 800 ml. of Karl Fischer grade pyridine, cooled to −20°, and treated with 286 g. of Eastman Kodak white label *p*-bromobenzenesulfonyl chloride by the low temperature method.[8] The product was isolated by pouring the mixture into ice-water and inducing it to crystallize. The solid was filtered with suction and washed thoroughly with water and dried in vacuum over potassium hydroxide. Recrystallization from ether–pentane afforded the pyranyl ether of 4-*p*-hydroxyphenyl-1-butyl *p*-bromobenzenesulfonate, m.p. 57–60°, in 77% yield.

The bulk of the above product (304 g.) was slurried in 2.5 liters of methanol and treated with a cooled mixture of 200 ml. of concentrated sulfuric acid and 400 ml. of water. This mixture was seeded with 4-*p*-hydroxyphenyl-1-butyl *p*-bromobenzenesulfonate and allowed to stand overnight in the ice-box. By this time most of the material had crystallized and water was added at intervals to bring out the rest, the final volume of solution being *ca.* 5 liters. The solid was washed with water and immediately dissolved in about 1500 ml. of methylene chloride. This solution was washed thoroughly with saturated sodium bicarbonate solution, dried and the product crystallized by the addition of hexane. The *p*-hydroxyphenylbutyl *p*-bromobenzenesulfonate, m.p. 59.3–61.7°, was obtained in 68% yield from 4-*p*-hydroxyphenylbutanoic acid.

(16) R. Heck and S. Winstein, *J. Am. Chem. Soc.*, **79**, 3108 (1957).

(17) N. J. Leonard, S. Swan, Jr., and J. Figueras, Jr., *J. Am. Chem. Soc.*, **74**, 4622 (1952).

5,6,7,8-Tetrahydro-2-naphthol was prepared from 2-naphthol by the method of Bamberger and Kitschalt.[18] The tetrahydronaphthol, m.p. 59.0–60.3°, $n^{25}D$ 1.5710 (supercooled), when mixed with 4-p-hydroxyphenyl-1-butanol, m.p. 56.5–57.8°, was liquid at room temperature.

Kinetic Measurements.—Anhydrous formic acid was prepared from J. T. Baker analyzed 98–100% formic acid. The water content, determined by density measurements, was between 0.10 and 0.14% by weight. Dioxane was purified according to Fieser.[19] Perchloric acid in dioxane was prepared by addition of the calculated amount of Merck 60% perchloric acid to purified dioxane, the solution being standardized against sodium acetate in acetic acid which in turn had been prepared by addition of a weighed amount of J. T. Baker analyzed, ACS reagent grade sodium carbonate to redistilled acetic acid. Lithium formate in anhydrous formic acid was prepared by addition of a weighed amount of anhydrous lithium formate, prepared by Arnold Fainberg, to purified formic acid, and was then standardized against the perchloric acid in dioxane. Brom cresol green was used as an indicator and the procedures used in the kinetic runs were those previously employed.[8]

Absolute methanol was prepared from J. T. Baker analyzed absolute methanol by treatment with magnesium turnings according to Lund and Bjerrum.[20] The water content, as determined by Karl Fischer titration, was 0.004% by weight. Standard solutions of sodium hydroxide and of p-toluenesulfonic acid in methanol were prepared by addition of the appropriate amounts of carbonate-free saturated sodium hydroxide solution and of Eastman Kodak white label p-toluenesulfonic acid monohydrate to absolute methanol. The sodium hydroxide solution was standardized against Mallinckrodt ACS potassium acid phthalate in a predominantly aqueous medium using phenolphthalein as the indicator, and the p-toluenesulfonic acid standardized against this base in the presence of excess ethanol using brom phenol blue as an indicator. When excess 4-p-hydroxyphenyl-1-butanol was added to the sodium hydroxide–p-toluenesulfonic acid titration, no detectable shift in end-point color or position was observed. Titrations in this system with phenoxides present therefore proceeded to the free phenol stage, so that phenoxide was indistinguishable from methoxide.

Sodium methoxide in absolute methanol for the kinetic measurements was made by dissolving the appropriate amounts of sodium metal, pre-washed with anhydrous methanol, in the requisite amount of the anhydrous methanol. These solutions were standardized by pipetting aliquots into an excess of standard p-toluenesulfonic acid in methanol and back titration of the excess acid with the standard sodium hydroxide in methanol using brom phenol blue as before. These were the same conditions as were used for the aliquots taken in the kinetic measurements, the p-toluenesulfonic acid solution being used as a quench for the reaction.

All of the above standard solutions were stable over a period of months and were checked at intervals.

t-Butyl alcohol was purified by distillation of Braun Co. t-butyl alcohol over sodium. Potassium t-butoxide in t-butyl alcohol was prepared in the same manner as was sodium methoxide in methanol. The titration techniques were identical to those used above, except that pipets had to be calibrated especially for t-butyl alcohol because of its high viscosity.

Kinetic runs were carried out in volumetric flasks at 25.00° or in sealed ampoules at 50.00° and 75.00°, except for the measurements in t-butyl alcohol at 50°. These rates were too fast to be quenched adequately at 25°, and the use of lower temperatures froze the t-butyl alcohol. For these measurements the rates were run in stoppered volumetric flasks at 50.0°, and aliquots quickly pipetted at room temperature in such a way that the pipet did not warm up. This procedure reduced the precision of the measurements somewhat, especially at the late points because of exposure to carbon dioxide in the air each time the flask was opened.

Product Isolation.—In 200 ml. of absolute methanol containing 0.03156 M sodium methoxide was dissolved an equal number of moles (2.4318 g.) of 4-p-hydroxyphenyl-1-butyl p-bromobenzenesulfonate. This mixture was main-

tained at 50.0° for 40 hours. It was then cooled and diluted with an equal volume of pentane. The solution was poured into 800 ml. of an ice–water mixture, the pentane layer separated and the aqueous solution extracted 20 more times with pentane. The combined pentane extracts were washed with water, with 1% sodium hydroxide solution and with saturated salt solution, then dried over magnesium sulfate. The pentane was distilled through a 12-inch Vigreux column and the product purified by sublimation in vacuum at 100°. This sublimate was recrystallized from pentane at −70° to give white needles, m.p. 33.8–35.0°, in ca. 20% yield.

Anal. Calcd. for $C_{10}H_{12}O$: C, 81.04; H, 8.16. Found: C, 80.81; H, 8.21.

The compound possessed an absorption maximum in the ultraviolet at 242 mμ (ϵ 16,000). It gave a red 2,4-dinitrophenylhydrazone, m.p. 140.5–143.5°, λ_{max} (MeOH) 390, 253 and 223 mμ (log ϵ 4.53, 4.21 and 2.92, respectively).

Anal. Calcd. for $C_{16}H_{16}O_4N_4$: C, 58.53; H, 4.91. Found: C, 58.63; H, 5.08.

In 995 ml. of 0.0253 N potassium t-butoxide in anhydrous t-butyl alcohol was dissolved 7.71 g. of 4-p-hydroxyphenyl-1-butyl p-bromobenzenesulfonate, and the solution was held for 5 hours at 50.0°. The solution was then diluted with 1 liter of pentane and poured into ca. 3 liters of a mixture of ice and water. The pentane was separated and the solution extracted 4 more times with pentane and then twice with 50% pentane–ether. The combined extracts were washed 3 times with water and then dried with magnesium sulfate. The bulk of the solvent was distilled through a Vigreux column until the boiling point rose to about that of t-butyl alcohol. The residue was dissolved in ether and washed 3 times more with water, re-dried and the solvent removed on the steam-bath, the last traces being taken off under reduced pressure. The product, b.p. 83.5–85.0° (1.3 mm.), obtained in 50% yield (a high boiling residue remaining in the pot), crystallized on standing; m.p. 35–36.2°. Recrystallized from pentane, the product, m.p. 35.5–36.5°, was identical in all respects with that obtained from methanol. In addition to the red 2,4-dinitrophenylhydrazone, it formed a semicarbazone, m.p. 224–225.5° dec.

Anal. Calcd. for $C_{11}H_{18}ON_3$: C, 64.36; H, 7.37. Found: C, 64.56; H, 7.19.

Dienone–Phenol Rearrangement of spiro-(4,5)-Deca-1,4-diene-3-one in Formic Acid.—In 113 ml. of anhydrous formic acid containing 0.03349 M lithium formate was dissolved 0.4981 g. of the dienone isolated from t-butyl alcohol, and the solution was then heated at 75° for 2.8 hours in a flask protected from moisture. The solution was then cooled and the formic acid was distilled at reduced pressure keeping the pot temperature at or below 40°.

When all of the acid had been removed, the residue was dissolved in dry ether and filtered through glass wool to remove most of the salts. The flask and salts were washed with dry ether and the combined ether solutions were treated with 1.1 g. of lithium aluminum hydride and allowed to stand overnight. The excess hydride was discharged with ethyl acetate, followed by water and then 40% hydrochloric acid, and the product isolated by extraction with ether. Distillation at reduced pressure yielded an oil which yielded a ca. 100% yield of 5,6,7,8-tetrahydro-2-naphthol, m.p. 56–60° (without recrystallization), when seeded with a minute seed of the naphthol. The melting point of a mixture of the product with authentic 5,6,7,8-tetrahydro-2-naphthol was undepressed (58–60.5°). Recrystallization of 0.46 g. of the product from hexane gave 0.40 g. of material with m.p. 60.5–61.0°.

Quantitative Hydrogenation of Spiro-(4,5)-deca-1,4-diene-3-one.—When 0.1008 g. of spiro-(4,5)-deca-1,4-diene-3-one, dissolved in 18 ml. of absolute t-butyl alcohol, was hydrogenated in the presence of reduced platinum oxide, 2.04 ± 0.04 moles of hydrogen was rapidly absorbed. The catalyst was removed by filtration and the solvent distilled through an 18-inch Podbielniak column. The residue was converted to a 2,4-dinitrophenylhydrazone, orange in color, m.p. 161.9–162.8°, 0.11 g. being obtained. In the ultraviolet the 2,4-dinitrophenylhydrazone possessed λ_{max} (MeOH) 363 and 229 mμ, with ϵ 22,500 and 17,000, respectively.

Anal. Calcd. for $C_{16}H_{20}O_4N_4$: C, 57.82; H, 6.07. Found: C, 57.93; H, 6.11.

(18) E. Bamberger and M. Kitschalt, *Ber.*, **23**, 885 (1890).

(19) L. F. Fieser, "Experiments in Organic Chemistry," 2nd Edition, D. C. Heath and Co., New York, N. Y., 1941, p. 368.

(20) H. Lund and J. Bjerrum, *Ber.*, **64**, 210 (1931).

60 | 1,3-Rearrange-ment in the *n*-Propyl Cation

Reutov and Shatkina showed that the isotopic rearrangement of the *n*-propyl group noted by Roberts and Halmann (Paper No. 21) was actually a 1,3- and not a 1,2-interchange as had formerly been supposed. *n*-Propylamine, labeled with radioactive carbon in the 1-position, underwent 8% conversion on nitrous acid deamination into *n*-propyl alcohol-3-^{14}C, with none of the radiocarbon being at the 2-position. Although the possibility is considered that hydrogen might have shifted from C-2 to C-1 and then from C-3 to C-2, the authors point out the improbability that an appreciable amount of isopropyl cation, once formed, would go on to rearrange into a primary cation. It is therefore most probable that there is a direct hydrogen migration from C-3 to C-1 in the *n*-propyl cation, competing with both the direct attack of solvent on the ion and the isomerization by α shift into isopropyl products. This result is of great interest, not only because it detects a kind of rearrangement which had always been extremely elusive, but because it appears to be relevant to the question of the protonated cyclopropane [A. A. Aboderin and R. L. Baird, *J. Am. Chem. Soc.* **86**, 252, 2300 (1964)].

From: *Tetrahedron* **18**, 237–43 (1962)

REARRANGEMENT OF ALKYL-CATIONS FORMED DURING REACTION BETWEEN NITROUS ACID AND ALKYLAMINE PERCHLORATES

O. A. REUTOV and T. N. SHATKINA

Department of Chemistry, University of Moscow and Academy of Medical Sciences of the U.S.S.R.

(*Received* 15 *September* 1961)

Abstract—In the reaction of nitrous acid with n-propylamine perchlorate labelled with ^{14}C at the nitrogen-bonded carbon, no rearrangement of the n-propyl cation chain, but isomerization of the type:

$$CH_3—CH_2—{}^{14}CH_2{}^+ \rightleftarrows {}^+CH_2—CH_2—{}^{14}CH_3$$

with simultaneous isomerization of n-propyl cation to isopropyl cation takes place.

A similar isomerization has been observed in the reaction of nitrous acid with the perchlorate of cyclohexylamine-1^{14}C. This results in the linking of the hydroxyl in a portion of the resultant cyclohexanol molecules to carbon atoms not participating in the C-N bond of the original cyclohexylamine.

ROBERTS and Halmann have described[1] the rearrangement of the propyl cation

$$CH_3—CH_2—{}^{14}CH_2{}^+ \rightleftarrows {}^+CH_2—{}^{14}CH_2—CH_3$$

during the reaction between ^{14}C-labelled n-propylamine and nitrous acid:

$$CH_3—CH_2—{}^{14}CH_2—NH_2·HClO_4 \xrightarrow{HNO_2} CH_3—{}^{14}CH_2—CH_2—OH$$

This interesting conversion, being the simplest case of a pinacoline rearrangement, attracted the attention of chemists and has taken its place in modern text books of organic chemistry. Its mechanism has been described in terms of the simplest non-classical cation:

$$\underset{CH_2 \text{------} CH_2}{\overset{CH_3}{\diagup \overset{\oplus}{\diagdown}}}$$

It has recently been shown that the propyl free radical in carbon tetrachloride solution does not undergo skeleton rearrangement. Instead isomerization occurs, the hydrogen atom migrating from the β-position.[2]

$$CH_3—CH_2—{}^{14}CH_2· \rightleftarrows ·CH_2—CH_2—{}^{14}CH_3$$

Bearing in mind the quite frequently observed analogy in behaviour of radicals and cations we have analysed the aforementioned work of Roberts and Halmann[1] and have found their conclusion as to the nature of the propyl cation rearrangement is not the only possible one.

On the basis of the activity of ethylamine formed in the reactions,

$$CH_3—CH_2—{}^{14}CH_2—NH_2·HClO_4 \xrightarrow{HNO_2} CH_3—CH_2—CH_2—OH \xrightarrow{KMnO_4}$$

$$CH_3—CH_2—COOH \xrightarrow{HN_3} CH_3—CH_2—NH_2 + CO_2$$
$$\text{active}$$

[1] J. Roberts and M. Halmann, *J. Amer. Chem. Soc.* **75**, 5759 (1953).
[2] O. A. Reutov and T. N. Shatkina, *Dokl. Akad. Nauk S.S.S.R.*, **133**, No. 2 (1960); *Tetrahedron* **18**, 305 (1961).

these authors[1] concluded that ^{14}C is in the two-position of the resultant n-propyl alcohol (CH_3—$^{14}CH_2$—CH_2—OH). Their assumption that radioactive carbon-14 should be bound to nitrogen in the ethylamine molecule was lacking in experimental evidence.

If ^{14}C actually belongs to the methyl group of the ethylamine molecule, then the propyl cation must have undergone isomerization as a result of hydride ion migration, rather than pinacoline rearrangement.*

Repeating the work of Roberts and Halmann under the specified conditions, we found that the propyl cation does not undergo chain rearrangement but isomerization, similar to that shown for the propyl radical†, namely

$$CH_3—CH_2—^{14}CH_2^+ \rightleftarrows {}^+CH_2—CH_2—^{14}CH_3$$

The reaction of n-propylamine perchlorate with nitrous acid affords n-propyl and isopropyl alcohols

$$CH_3—CH_2—^{14}CH_2—NH_2 \cdot HClO_4 \xrightarrow{HNO_2} CH_3—CH_2—CH_2OH + CH_3—CH(OH)—CH_3$$

Oxidation of the n-propyl alcohol with potassium permanganate gives propionic acid which is further oxidized by potassium bichromate to acetic acid and carbon dioxide

$$CH_3—CH_2—CH_2—OH \xrightarrow{KMnO_4} CH_3—CH_2—COOH \xrightarrow{K_2Cr_2O_7} CH_3—COOH + CO_2$$

The acetic acid activity passes over wholly to methylamine during Schmidt cleavage of the acid and to methane during fusion with alkali as the sodium salt.

$$CH_3—COOH \begin{cases} \xrightarrow{HN_3} {}^{14}CH_3—NH_2 + CO_2 + N_2 \\ \xrightarrow{NaOH} {}^{14}CH_4 + Na_2CO_3 \end{cases}$$

It is, therefore, clear that the molecules of n-propyl alcohol formed in the reaction of n-propylamine-1 ^{14}C with nitrous acid contain radioactive carbon-14 only in the 1 and 3 positions. Similarly, it has been shown that isopropyl alcohol contains ^{14}C in 1 and 3 (but not in 2) positions.

The isomerization of the n-propyl cation may be either a single migration of the hydride ion from the β-position:

$$CH_3—CH_2—^{14}CH_2^+ \rightleftarrows CH_2 \oplus {}^{14}CH_2 \rightleftarrows {}^+CH_2—CH_2—^{14}CH_3 \qquad (I)$$
$$\overset{|}{H}$$

or a two stage migration from the α-position:

(a) $$CH_3—CH_2—^{14}CH_2^+ \rightleftarrows CH_3—\overset{+}{C}H—^{14}CH_3$$

(b) $$CH_3—\overset{+}{C}H—^{14}CH_3 \rightleftarrows {}^+CH_2—CH_2—^{14}CH_3 \qquad (II)$$

Evidence in favour of the second mechanism is provided by the the formation of

---

* It should be noted that isomerization of n-propyl cation to isopropyl cation during the reaction between n-propylamine and nitrous acid has been reported.[3] Considerable amounts of isopropyl alcohol were revealed among the reaction products, the yield of n-propyl alcohol being 7% and that of isopropyl alcohol 32%).

† Roberts *et al.*[4] in very interesting experiments with other amines (2-aryl-1-ethylamine-1-^{11}C) have given irreproachable proof of the existence of skeleton rearrangements in reactions with nitrous acid.

[3] V. Mayer and Fr. Forster, *Chem. Ber.* **9**, 535 (1876); F. C. Whitmore and R. S. Thorpe, *J. Amer. Chem. Soc.* **63**, 1118 (1941).
[4] J. D. Roberts and C. M. Regan, *J. Amer. Chem. Soc.* **75**, 2069 (1953).

isopropyl alcohol in this reaction and from studies of hydrogen exchange in paraffins.[5] On the other hand, the literature[6] reveals only the formation of isopropyl alcohol (without n-propyl alcohol) from the action of nitrous acid on isopropylamine.*

Hence, whether the isomerization takes place in one or two stages has yet to be determined.

The tendency to isomerize with migration of the hydride ion is doubtlessly more or less a general property of alkyl cations. Roberts et al.,[7] for example, have observed such isomerization of ethyl cation in the reaction of ethylamine with nitrous acid. Quite likely such isomerization also takes place during Demyanov interconversion of alicycles.

Based on this assumption it may be concluded that in the formation of cyclohexanol in the reaction of nitrous acid with cyclohexylamine, the hydroxyl group is not necessarily bound only to the carbon which previously participated in the bond with the amine group. This has been proved experimentally. Cyclohexylamine labelled with ^{14}C at the N-linked carbon was synthesised according to the following scheme:

$$Br—(CH_2)_5—Br \xrightarrow[\text{(b) hydrolysis}]{\text{(a) } Na^{14}CN} HOO^{14}C—(CH_2)_5—^{14}COOH \xrightarrow[\text{heating}]{BaCO_3}$$

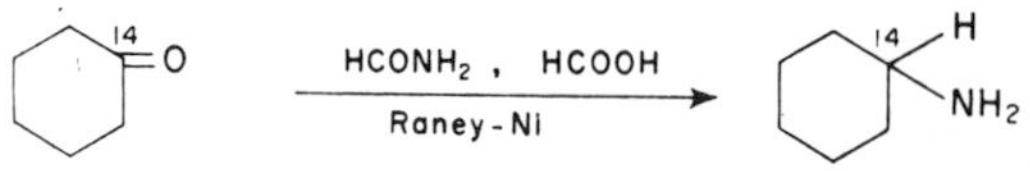

The following degradation proves that the cyclohexylamine was labelled only at the carbon atom bound to nitrogen. Cyclohexylamine was oxidized to cyclohexanone and the latter converted with hydrazoic acid to aminocaproic acid and then to pentamethylenediamine. The latter was found to be inactive.

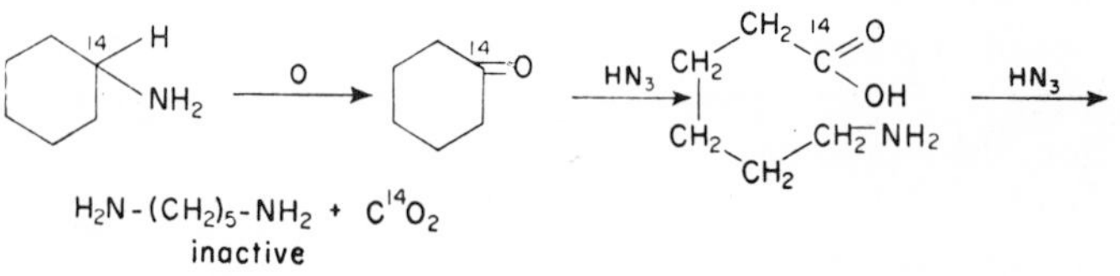

The reaction of ^{14}C amino-carbon labelled cyclohexylamine perchlorate with nitrous acid leads to a mixture of cyclohexanol and cyclopentylcarbinol

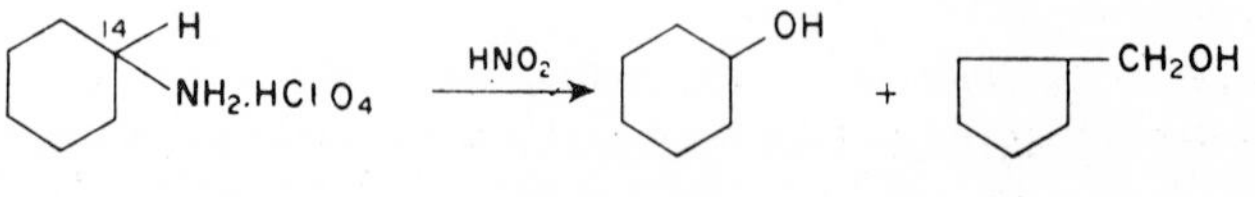

---

* The results of this investigation require verification. For the n-propyl alcohol to form the more stable isopropyl cation it must isomerize to the less stable n-propyl cation ($CH_3—\overset{+}{C}H—CH_3 \rightarrow {}^+CH_2—CH_2—CH_3$) so that if the isomerization does take place at all it should occur only to a small extent and only small amounts of n-propyl alcohol would be present in the reaction mixture.

[5] V. N. Setkina, D. N. Kursanov and E. V. Bochkova, Prob. Kinet. Katal. 9, 234 (1957).
[6] V. Mayer and Fr. Forster, Chem. Ber. 9, 535 (1876).
[7] J. Roberts and J. Hancey, J. Amer. Chem. Soc., 74, 5943 (1952).

In order to ascertain the position of the ^{14}C in the cyclohexanol, the latter was subjected to the following degradation:

$$HOOC - (CH_2)_5 - NH_2 \xrightarrow{\;HN_3\;} H_2N - (CH_2)_5 - NH_2 + C^{14}O_2$$
$$\text{active}$$

Pentamethylenediamine was found to active* (3·8 ± 0·3% of the original cyclohexanone activity).

This proves that the hydroxyl of some cyclohexanol molecules is not attached to the amino-binding carbon of the original cyclohexylamine molecule. Hence, the cyclohexyl cation intermediate undergoes isomerization as a result of hydride anion migration.

The rearrangement of the propyl free radical[2] and of alkyl cations considered in the present paper, resulted in an investigation concerning the rearrangement of alkyl anions by the carbonization of n-propylsodium. The action of metallic sodium on propyl-1-^{14}C chloride yields propylsodium-1-^{14}C which on carbonization gives only n-butyric-2-^{14}C acid:

$$CH_3-CH_2-{}^{14}CH_2-Cl \xrightarrow[\text{(toluene)}]{Na} CH_3-CH_2-{}^{14}CH_2^{(-)}Na^{(+)} \xrightarrow[\text{(toluene)}]{CO_2}$$

$$CH_3-CH_2-{}^{14}CH_2-COOH \xrightarrow{HN_3} CH_3-CH_2-{}^{14}CH_2-NH_2 \xrightarrow{O} CH_3-COOH + {}^{14}CO_2$$
$$\text{inactive}$$

Hence, the n-propyl anion $CH_3-CH_2-{}^{14}CH_2^{(-)}$ does not undergo rearrangement during carbonization.

EXPERIMENTAL

I. *Synthesis of propylamine*-1-^{14}C *perchlorate*

1. *Preparation of propionitrile*-1-^{14}C.[1] To a solution of 21·6 g (0·33 mole)K ^{14}CN (total activity 10 mc) in 35 ml water and 35 ml ethylene glycol 43 ml (0·33 mole) diethyl sulphate was added dropwise at 35°. After 18 hr at 20°, the 85–100° fraction was distilled off. Sulphuric acid (15 ml 18 N) was then added, and the supernatant layer separated and dried (fused CaCl₂). The fraction boiling at 94–97° was collected. Weight 5·4 g (30% of the theoretical), total activity 3 mc (Reported[9]: b.p. 97–97·2°).

---

* The low percentage of rearrangement of the cyclohexyl cation may perhaps be explained by its rapid reaction with the solvent to form cyclohexanol.
  A similar view has been advanced by Streitwieser and Coverdall[8] to explain the fact that not less than 94% *cis*-cyclohexanol-2-d is formed in the reaction of *cis*-cyclohexylamine 2-d perchlorate with nitrous acid.

[8] A. Streitwieser and C. E. Coverdall, *J. Amer. Chem. Soc.* **81**, 4275 (1959).
[9] R. Schiff, *Chem. Ber.* **19**, 567 (1886).

2. *Hydrogenation of propionitrile*-1-[14]C. Propionitrile-1-[14]C (4 g; 0·07 mole); total activity 1 mc[*] in 15 ml absolute ether was added with stirring to 6 g (0·16 mole) $LiAlH_4$ in 200 ml absolute ether at 0°. The mixture was stirred for 3 hr, followed by the dropwise addition of 3 ml water, 2 ml 20% NaOH and an additional 9 ml water. Propylamine was distilled from the reaction mixture into 7 ml perchloric acid and the solution evaporated to dryness *in vacuo* at 30–35°. Weight 5·15g (50% of theoretical), radioactivity presented in Table 1.

II. *Reaction of propylamine*-1-[14]C *and nitrous acid*[1]

To a solution of 5·13 g (0·05 mole) propylamine-1-^{14}C in 4·5 ml 35% perchloric acid at 25°, a solution of 4·8 g (0·07 mole) sodium nitrite in 7 ml water was added over a period of 1 hr and the mixture maintained for another hr at 25°, and then 10 ml propyl and 10 ml isopropyl alcohols were

TABLE 1. DISTRIBUTION OF RADIOACTIVITY IN PROPYL-[14]C
ALCOHOL OBTAINED IN THE REACTION OF
PROPYLAMINE-1-^{14}C WITH HNO_2

Compound	Radioactivity pulses/min mmole
1. Propylamine-1-[14]C	$295 . 10^3$
2. Propionic acid	$10·9 . 10^3$
3. Acetic acid	$0·879 . 10^3$
4. Methylamine	$0·877 . 10^3$
5. Sodium carbonate	0·0
% Rearrangement	$8·0 \pm 0·8$

$$\% \text{ Rearrangement} = \frac{\text{pulses/min mmole } CH_3COOH \cdot 100}{\text{pulses/min mmole } CH_3CH_2COOH}$$

added to the carriers and 28 ml of the mixture distilled off. The distillate was acidified with conc HCl, redistilled and then saturated with anhydrous K_2CO_3. After removal of the aqueous layer, the iso-propyl alcohol (10·4 g) at 81–83° and propyl alcohol (4·41 g) at 97–98·5° was collected. (Reported[10] b.p. of isopropyl alcohol 80·7–81·4° and propyl alcohol 97·2–97·25°).

III. *Determination of position of carbon* 14 *in propyl*-[14]C *alcohol*

1. *Oxidation of propyl*-[14]C *alcohol.* Propyl alcohol (4 g; 0·066 mole) prepared as in II was mixed with a solution of 4 g (0·038 mole) anhydrous sodium carbonate in 15 ml water and cooled in ice. A solution of 14 g (0·09 mole) potassium permanganate in 300 ml water (kept below 5°) was added and the mixture allowed to stand 12 hr at 20°. The filtrate from the MnO_2 was concentrated *in vacuo* at 35–40° to 30–40 ml and acidified with 66% H_2SO_4. Propionic-^{14}C acid was extracted with ether and the ethereal extract dried (fused Na_2SO_4). After removal of the solvent on a water bath, the acid (2·15 g; 43%), was distilled at 140–141°, n_D^{15} 1·3894 . (Reported b.p. 140·9°, n_D^{28} 1·3859). The radio-activity of propionic-^{14}C acid is given in Table 1.

2. *Oxidation of propionic*-[14]C *acid.*[12] Propionic-^{14}C acid (1 g; 0·013 mole), 12·8 g (0·043 mole) potassium dichromate and 120 ml 18 N H_2SO_4 were heated in a current of N_2 at 100° for 3 hr. Acetic acid was removed by steam distillation with ca. one l. water, the solution made alkaline with 0·1 N NaOH (simultaneous determination of acid) was concentrated *in vacuo* at 40–50° to ca. 10 ml. The residue was quantitatively transferred into a volumetric flask of such volume that the acetic acid concentration was ca. 10 mg/ml. The radioactivity of the acid is given in Table 1.

3. *Schmidt conversion of acetic acid to methylamine.*[1] To 88·5 mg (0·001 mole) sodium acetate-^{14}C in 0·5 ml absolute chloroform with stirring and cooling, 0·5 ml conc H_2SO_4 and then at 45–55° 2 ml 1·3 N hydrazoic acid in chloroform was added and the mixture maintained for 1 hr at 45–55°. The

[*] Propionitrile-1-[14]C (1·8 g) diluted with 2·2 g inactive propionitrile.

[10] W. Atkins and T. Wallace, *J. Chem. Soc.* **103**, 1471 (1913).
[11] A. Zander, *Liebigs Ann.* **224**, 62 (1887); P. Guye and E. Mallet *Ch. Zbl. I.* 1314 (1902).
[12] P. Nahinsky and S. Ruben, *J. Amer. Chem. Soc.* **63**, 2275 (1941).

solution was made alkaline with 10% aqueous NaOH during cooling with ice, the chloroform layer was removed and the methylamine steam distilled into 5 ml 5 N HCl. The solution of methylamine hydrochloride was evaporated to dryness and the salt purified by repeated addition of water and evaporation. After recrystallization from absolute alcohol, 67·7 mg (93%), m.p. 232–233° was obtained. (Reported[13] m.p. 232–233·5°). Results of activity measurements given in Table 1.

4. *Fusion of sodium acetate-*[14]*C with sodium hydroxide.* Sodium acetate-[14]C (85 mg; 0·001 mole) was fused with 80 mg (0·002 mole) NaOH until cessation of methane evolution; the residue was dissolved in 12 ml water and the activity of the resultant sodium carbonate measured. Results are given in Table 1.

IV. *Synthesis of cyclohexylamine*-1-[14]C

1. *Preparation of pimelic-1,7-*[14]*C acid.*[14] A mixture of 2·86 g (0·044 mole) K[14]CN (total activity 55 mc) 4·6 g (0·040 mole) distilled pentamethylene bromide, 3 ml water and 13 ml alcohol was boiled for 3 hr; the solvent evaporated *in vacuo*; 10 ml conc HCl added and the mixture boiled again for 2 hr. Pimelic-1,7-^{14}C acid was extracted with ether and the ethereal extract dried (Na$_2$SO$_4$). After removal of the solvent in a current of nitrogen, pimelic-1,7,-^{14}C acid (3·02 g) was dried in a vacuum desiccator. According to titrimetric data the acid is 94%, i.e. the yield is 81% of theoretical.

2. *Preparation of cyclohexanone-1-*[14]*C.*[14] A mixture of 3·0 g (0·019 mole) pimelic-1,7,-^{14}C acid and 0·1 g (0·005 mole) barium carbonate was gradually heated (1 hr) to and then maintained at 325° for 3 hr. During the heat treatment 1.7 g cyclohexanone-1-[14]C (79%) was distilled over, n_D^{20} 1·4498, m.p. 2,4-dinitrophenylhydrazone 161–163°. (Reported[15] n_D^{21} 1·4503, m.p. of 2,4-dinitrophenylhydrazone 162°.)

3. *Preparation of cyclohexylamine-1-*[14]*C.*[16] To 50 g (1 mole) of the formamide-formate mixture, 50 g (1 mole) 85% formic acid and 0·5 g Raney nickel, during 1·5 hr, 24 g (0·25 mole) cyclohexanone-1-[14]C* was added dropwise, the reaction mixture heated for 2·5 hr at ca. 115° and then evaporated to dryness after addition of 250 ml conc HCl. Excess 50% KOH was added to the residue and the mixture boiled 18–20 hr until complete elimination of ammonia. Cyclohexylamine-1-^{14}C was separated from the aqueous layer and distilled into 130 ml 18% perchloric acid. The solution was evaporated to dryness, the residue (16·08 g; 50%) washed with benzene and with ether and dried in a vacuum desiccator.

V. *Reaction of cyclohexylamine-1-*[14]C *with nitrous acid*[8]

To an ice cooled solution of 15·7 g (0·08 mole) cyclohexylamine-1-^{14}C in 50 ml water and 7 ml 60% perchloric acid, a solution of 6·5 g (0·09 mole) sodium nitrite in 30 ml water was added dropwise. After stirring for 6 hr at 0°, another 1 g (0·014 mole) sodium nitrite was added. The mixture was allowed to stand for 18 hr at 0–2° and then for 24 hr at 20°. The supernatant layer of cyclohexanol-^{14}C and cyclopentylcarbinol-^{14}C was removed and the lower layer, after saturation with sodium chloride, was extracted with ether. The combined ethereal extract and upper alcohol layer was washed with 10% H$_2$SO$_4$ and with water and dried (Na$_2$SO$_4$). After removal of the ether, 1 g of cyclohexanol carrier was added and the 159–161° fraction (2·88 g) collected. (Reported[17,18] b.p. cyclohexanol 160·5°; cyclopentylcarbinol 162·5–163·5°.)

VI. *Determination of carbon-14 position in cyclohexanol-*[14]C

1. *Oxidation of cyclohexanol-*[14]*C and cyclopentylcarbinol-*[14]*C.*[19] To 2·88 g of the alcohol mixture in 15 ml water and 1·8 ml conc H$_2$SO$_4$, 2·2 g (0·022 mole) CrO$_3$ in 50 ml water was added dropwise and the mixture left overnight at 20°. After distilling off ca. 20 ml, the distillate was saturated with anhydrous K$_2$CO$_3$ and the separated layer of cyclohexanone-^{14}C and cyclopentaldehyde-^{14}C extracted with ether. The ethereal solution was evaporated and the residue in 20 ml water was boiled for 1·5 hr

---

* 1·7 g Cyclohexanone-1-^{14}C were diluted to 24 g by reagent cyclohexanone.

[13] M. Sommelet, *C.R. Acad. Sci. Paris*, **178**, 219 (1924).
[14] R. J. Speer, M. Z. Humphries and A. Roberts, *J. Amer. Chem. Soc.* **74**, 2443 (1952).
[15] O. Wallach, *Liebigs Ann.* **353**, 331 (1907).
[16] A. N. Kost and I. I. Grandberg, *Zh. Obschii. Khim.* **25**, 1432 (1955).
[17] V. V. Markovnikov, *Liebigs Ann.* **302**, 21 (1898).
[18] N. D. Zelinski, *Chem. Ber.* **41**, 2629 (1908).
[19] N. Ya. Demyanova, *Sbornik Izbrannykh Trudov Akademika* pod (red. A. E. Favorskovo) p. 266 (1936).

with excess freshly precipitated silver oxide. Cyclohexanone-^{14}C was steam distilled from the reaction mixture and 1·8 g isolated after saturating the solution with anhydrous K_2CO_3. To the aqueous layer, 0·5 g of cyclohexanone carrier was added, the mixture shaken vigorously, and the cyclohexanone (0·45 g) again isolated. Sodium bisulphite (14 ml; 36% solution) was added to the combined cyclo-hexanone-^{14}C layers and the mixture left overnight. The bisulphite–cyclohexanone-^{14}C compound was washed with ether and the cyclohexanone-^{14}C liberated by addition of 20 ml boiling saturated K_2CO_3 solution. The cyclohexanone-^{14}C (1·16 g) was isolated by cooling and a further quantity (0·28 g) was obtained by addition of 0·5 g cyclohexanone carrier. For the activity measurements, cyclohexanone-^{14}C was converted to the 2,4-dinitrophenylhydrazone, m.p. 161–162° (from alcohol). The radioactivity is presented in Table 2.

TABLE 2

Activity of products pulses/min. mmole	Reaction	Deamination of cyclohexylamine-1-^{14}C I	Oxidation of cyclohexylamine-1-^{14}C II
Cyclohexanone (as 2,4-dinitrophenyl-hydrazone)		355 . 10³	405 . 10³
Pentamethylene-diamine (as picrate)		13·4 . 10³	0·0
% Rearrangement		3·8 ± 0·3	0·0

2. *Reaction of cyclohexanone-^{14}C with hydrazoic acid.*[20] A solution of 1·39 g (0·014 mole) cyclo-hexanone-^{14}C in 20 ml water was saturated at 0° with hydrogen chloride and then 1·5 g (0·023 mole) sodium azide added in portions. The mixture was stirred for 4 hr at 20°, the temp. was then gradually raised to and maintained at 90° for 4 hr and finally the solution was evaporated to dryness *in vacuo*. The hydrochloride of δ-amino-n-caproic acid was extracted with boiling absolute alcohol and after distillation of the solvent the hydrochloride (1·93 g) was dried in a vacuum desiccator.

3. *Reaction between δ-amino-n-caproic acid and hydrazoic acid.*[20] The hydrochloride of δ-amino-n-caproic-^{14}C acid (0·8 g; 0·006 mole) was heated *in vacuo* with 1·5 ml conc H_2SO_4 until complete elimination of HCl and 5 ml (0·01 mole) 2 N hydrazoic acid in benzene added to the residue. The liberated CO_2 was absorbed in sodium carbonate-free sodium hydroxide. The mixture was allowed to stand 24 hr at 20°, heated 3 hr at 50° and the benzene finally removed *in vacuo*. Water (30 ml) and ca. 11 g barium carbonate (until complete precipitation of SO_4^{-2} ions) was added to the residue, barium sulphate was filtered off, washed repeatedly with water and the filtrate after acidification evaporated to dryness.

In order to measure the radioactivity of pentamethylenediamine hydrochloride it was converted to the picrate, m.p. 226–228°. The latter was recrystallized twice from alcohol; m.p. 228–229°. (Reported[21] m.p. 225–230°). The results of the activity measurements are given in Table 2.

VII. *Experiments showing the original cyclohexylamine to be labelled only at the amino-linked carbon*

1. *Oxidation of cyclohexylamine-1-^{14}C to cyclohexanone.*[22] To a solution of 10·4 g (0·05 mole) cyclohexylamine-1-^{14}C perchlorate in 30 ml water, 200 ml 5% potassium permanganate was added; the mixture brought to pH 8 with 40% NaOH and a further 4 ml 0·5N of alkali added. The mixture was heated for 30 min at 90–100°. Cyclohexanone was steam distilled from the acidified solution; the distillate saturated with anhydrous K_2CO_3 and the cyclohexanone-1-^{14}C (1·5 g; 32%) isolated, n_D^{16} 1·4495, m.p. 2,4-dinitrophenylhydrazone 160–161°.

2. *Determination of position of carbon-14 in cyclohexanone-1-^{14}C.* This was carried out as in Experiments VI 2, 3. Results of activity measurements are given in Table 2 (column II).

[20] R. B. Loftfield, *J. Amer. Chem. Soc.* **73**, 4707 (1951).
[21] K. Yoshimira, *Biochem. Z.* **28**, 19 (1910).
[22] E. F. Phares, *Arch. Biochem. Biophys.* **33**, 176 (1951).

61 | Mechanisms in the Dicyclopenta-diene System

Cristol, Seifert, Johnson, and Jurale show that acid-catalyzed addition to the double bond of dicyclopentadiene and dihydrodicyclopentadiene (5,6-trimethylenenorbornane) yields different isomeric mixtures with respect to the ring geometry, depending upon the addend and solvent. The predominating *endo-exo* conversion of the trimethylene or allylene ring in these and solvolytic reactions is qualitatively interpretable in terms of the bridged ion VII (regarded as a resonance hybrid of VIII and IX). However, it is not obvious why methanol should exert a different selectivity in reaction between the active sites in VII from that shown by formic or acetic acid. Some possible ways of accounting for the facts by including protonated double bonds and classical ions also in the reaction scheme are discussed. The relative amounts of *exo-* and *endo*-methyl ethers from methanolysis of the tosylates III and VI are not the same as from acid-catalyzed addition of methanol to the corresponding olefins.

From: *J. Am. Chem. Soc.* **84**, 3918–25 (1962)

[Contribution from the Department of Chemistry, University of Colorado, Boulder, Colo.]

Bridged Polycyclic Compounds. XIX. Some Addition and Solvolysis Reactions in Norbornane Systems[1]

By Stanley J. Cristol, Wolfgang K. Seifert, Donald W. Johnson and J. Byrne Jurale

Received June 14, 1962

Acid-catalyzed additions of acetic acid, formic acid and water to *endo*-dihydrodicyclopentadiene (I) lead to products in which almost complete ring isomerizations (to III, or its analogs) has occurred. On the other hand, addition of methanol (or of water in methanol solvent) to I or to dicyclopentadiene (II), followed by hydrogenation, gives a mixture containing about 1 part of *endo* skeleton unrearranged product (VI, Y = OMe, OH) to 6 parts of *exo* skeleton product III. Solvolysis of the toluenesulfonates of III and VI in methanol both give a large preponderance of *exo* product (*ca.* 30:1 = III:VI). Addition of methanol or of acetic acid to norbornadiene (X) gives substantially more dehydronorbornyl methyl ether (XI, Y = OMe) or dehydronorbornyl acetate (XI, Y = OAc) in the mixture with nortricyclyl products XII (Y = OCH₃, OCO-CH₃) than solvolysis of the *p*-bromobenzenesulfonate of either XI or XII. Possible explanations of these results are discussed.

Ionic additions to *endo*-1,2-dihydrodicyclopentadiene (I) and to *endo*-dicyclopentadiene (II) have been reported to give products III (or the dehydro analogs) with *exo* configuration of addenda and also with rearranged, *i.e.*, *exo* ring skeletons.[2] *exo*-Dicyclopentadiene (IV) is reported,[2f] in contrast, to add HY reagents without rearrangement and thus to give products identical with those from II. In general, then, isomers with *endo* ring skele-

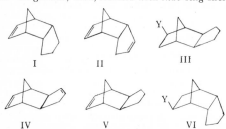

tons were not observed from addition to olefins with either *endo* or *exo* ring systems. In addition, it has been reported[3] that the *exo-exo* product III (Y = OAc) resulted from the acetolysis of the *p*-toluenesulfonate related to either *exo*-III or its epimer, or of the *p*-toluenesulfonate of *endo*-VI or its epimer. At the time most of the work listed in references 2 and 3 was done, techniques for analysis of very minor constituents were not available, so that products with *endo* ring systems might

(1) Previous paper in series: S. J. Cristol, J. R. Douglass, W. C. Firth, Jr., and R. E. Krall, *J. Org. Chem.*, **27**, 2711 (1962).

(2) See, *inter alia:* (a) H. A. Bruson and T. W. Riener, *J. Am. Chem. Soc.*, **67**, 723 (1945); (b) **67**, 1178 (1945); (c) **68**, 8 (1946); (d) P. D. Bartlett and A. Schneider, *ibid.*, **68**, 6 (1946); (e) F. Bergmann and H. Japhe, *ibid.*, **69**, 1826 (1947); (f) P. D. Bartlett and I. S. Goldstein, *ibid.*, **69**, 2553 (1947); (g) M. Gates and P. S. Malchick, *ibid.*, **76**, 1378 (1954); (h) K. Alder, F. H. Flock and H. Wirtz, *Chem. Ber.*, **91**, 609 (1958); (i) P. Wilder, Jr., C. F. Culbertson and G. T. Youngblood, *J. Am. Chem. Soc.*, **81**, 655 (1959); (j) S. J. Cristol, W. K. Seifert and S. B. Soloway, *ibid.*, **82**, 2351 (1960).

(3) (a) R. S. Barnes, Ph.D. thesis, Harvard University, 1951; (b) P. D. Bartlett, Abstracts of Papers, 12th National Organic Chemistry Symposium, June, 1951, p. 1.

understandably be missed. We decided, therefore, to reinvestigate selected portions of this problem, and our initial results in this and analogous systems are reported herein.

Addition of formic acid to *endo*-dihydrodicyclopentadiene (I) or to *endo*-dicyclopentadiene (II) and of acetic acid (catalyzed by 1.5% of sulfuric acid) to II led (after hydrogenation, where applicable) preponderantly, as suggested by earlier work,[2] to products with *exo* ring skeletons and *exo* substituents (III, Y = OCHO, OCOCH₃). The products were investigated by saponification or lithium aluminum hydride reduction to the alcohols; it was observed that the alcohol mixtures, which were largely III (Y = OH), were contaminated with small amounts of *endo* skeleton isomers VI (Y = OH). When we first began work on this problem, infrared analytical procedures were the best available to us, and our results indicated that the *endo* ring system was being converted to *exo* in substantially over 90% of the product. Work was not conducted with *exo*-olefin V, as it was felt that analytical methods were not precise enough to analyze mixtures using infrared techniques. Hydration of *endo*-olefin I with 22% sulfuric acid in water gave a product which was principally *exo* skeleton III (Y = OH), as reported earlier.[2a,d] This product was now analyzed by vapor-phase chromatography and contained about 2% *endo* skeleton; the reaction conversion was about 45%, and the remaining olefin was not isomerized. Again there appeared to be no reason to study the *exo*-olefin V, in view of the almost complete rearrangement observed with I.

The results described above appeared consistent with the idea that the products were derived largely, if not entirely, from a single *product-determining* intermediate, presumably a non-classical carbonium ion such as VII, for which the resonance structures VIII and IX can be written. This intermediate presumably could be the immediate precursor of both *endo* and *exo* products. Reaction

VII   VIII

IX

of VII with solvent at position **a** would lead to *endo* products VI, while reaction at **b** would lead to *exo* products III. The *exo* stereochemistry of the nucleophilic portion Y of the addendum seemed strong evidence for the cation VII.[2g,3,4]

A relief from the monotonous complete or nearly complete rearrangement of *endo* to *exo* ring skeleton occurred on addition of methanol to I and to II. Treatment of I with methanol containing 22% of (96% aqueous) sulfuric acid for four hours at reflux gave a mixture of methyl ethers III and VI (Y = OCH_3) in a ratio of 85.5 to 14.5. Of particular interest was the fact that the water present in the solution led to a small yield of alcohols III and VI (Y = OH) in approximately the same ratio, rather than the 50 : 1 ratio observed in aqueous sulfuric acid. The product mixture was analyzed and separated by gas chromatography.

Small amounts of the pure III and VI (Y = OCH_3) were isolated and their infrared spectra and relative retention volumes were compared with similar properties of ethers synthesized by methylation of the known alcohols III and VI (Y = OH). Addition of methanol to II gave a mixture of ethers that, after hydrogenation, again gave analysis for 14.5% *endo* skeleton VI (Y = OCH_2). Analytical data were reproducible to about ±0.5% for the ethers and ±1.0% for the alcohols. When the *exo*-olefin V was treated similarly, the product mixture contained the ethers III and VI in the ratio of 96.5 : 3.5 and alcohol by-products in the same ratio. Products were not significantly isomerized or interconverted under reaction conditions, nor was *endo*-olefin converted to *exo*-olefin under these conditions. Mixtures of olefins I and V led to mixtures of III and VI compatible with those anticipated from the results above.

These results appeared exciting to us, as they indicated that methanol had succeeded in trapping an intermediate in the addition reaction to I and to II before that intermediate had a chance to rearrange completely to the intermediate or intermediates which lead to III and VI (or their dehydro analogs) in the high ratio observed with water or with acetic acid. One may assume, for example, that an intermediate such as VII is the one that partitions itself to give the high ratio of III to VI, but that a second *product-determining* cationic intermediate precedes (or accompanies) its formation from I and that coördination of the nucleophile with the first-formed intermediate competes with rearrangement of one to the other.

It has been noted a number of times[5] that cationic intermediates produced by deamination of aliphatic primary amines give different ratios of products (where rearrangements or partitions between various products are involved) from similarly formulated cationic intermediates produced by solvolysis reactions. This usually has been rationalized on the basis of either the formation of "hot" carbonium ions[5a] by the exergonic loss of nitrogen from the alkanediazonium ions, or by the compression of the relative heights of activation energy barriers in the various reactions[5b] possible to the alkanediazonium ion. In addition, Winstein and his collaborators[6] have noted a number of cases where different methods of preparing presumably identical cations by addition to olefins or by solvolysis gave differing mixtures of products and therefore must involve at least two *product-determining* intermediates. They have discussed the possible nature of such intermediates in some detail.

As we were now confronted with data where addition to isomeric olefins led to differing mixtures of the same addition products, it seemed worthwhile to extend our studies in various ways. It seemed possible to assume that intermediates which could best be represented by the classical ions VIII and IX were formed early in the addition reaction by protonation of I and V, respectively, and that in methanol (a relatively poor ionizing solvent compared with water[7]) and with either methanol or water as nucleophilic reagent (relatively strong nucleophiles compared with acetic and formic acid[7,8]), these early intermediates had been trapped before rearranging completely to the intermediate or mixture of intermediates, that under other circumstances appeared to be the common precursor (or precursors) of the final products. It seemed necessary, then, to study other reactions that might also lead to these intermediates. We therefore undertook a study of the products of solvolysis of the *p*-toluenesulfonates III and VI (Y = $OSO_2C_6H_4CH_3$-*p*) in methanol to see if they would lead to different mixtures of methyl ethers. Bartlett and Barnes[3] had already looked at these systems in acetic acid, absolute ethanol and 80% ethanol and had noted that good (and different) first-order rate constants were observed with each isomer, indicating that the isomers do not rearrange to each other in these solvents. Product studies in acetic acid indicated that III (Y = $OCOCH_2$) was the product of acetolysis of both tosylates.[3] These data suggested that solvolysis to an intermediate ion pair[9] led entirely to products (presumably through other ion intermediates) with

(4) S. Winstein and D. Trifan, *J. Am. Chem. Soc.*, **71**, 2193 (1949); **74**, 1154 (1953).

(5) (a) D. J. Cram and J. E. McCarty, *ibid.*, **79**, 2866 (1957); (b) A. Streitwieser, Jr., *J. Org. Chem.*, **22**, 861 (1957); (c) M. S. Silver, *J. Am. Chem. Soc.*, **83**, 3482 (1961); (d) B. M. Benjamin, P. Wilder, Jr., and C. J. Collins, *ibid.*, **83**, 3654 (1961).

(6) (a) S. Winstein and M. Simonetta, *ibid.*, **76**, 18 (1954); (b) S. Winstein and N. J. Holness, *ibid.*, **77**, 5562 (1955); (c) S. Winstein, *Experientia Suppl. II*, 137 (1955); (d) S. Winstein and E. S. Kosower, *J. Am. Chem. Soc.*, **81**, 4399 (1959).

(7) E. Grunwald and S. Winstein, *ibid.*, **70**, 846 (1948); S. Winstein and A. H. Fainberg, *ibid.*, **79**, 5937 (1957).

(8) C. G. Swain, *ibid.*, **70**, 1119 (1948); C. G. Swain, R. B. Mosely and D. E. Bown, *ibid.*, **77**, 3727, 3731 (1955).

(9) S. Winstein, E. Clippinger, A. H. Fainberg, R. Heck and G. C. Robinson, *ibid.*, **78**, 328 (1958), and references cited therein.

no internal return to rearranged toluenesulfonates, so that there might be a possibility, if ions such as VIII and IX were formed, of capturing them before rearrangement. In fact, however, we found that solvolysis of the *endo*-tosylate VI in methanol (either with or without added sodium acetate) led to a mixture of methyl ethers III and VI containing 3.3 ± 0.3% of VI, while *exo*-tosylate III gave a mixture containing 2.9 ± 0.4% of *endo*-ether VI. These results are comparable with those reported for addition of methanol to *exo*-olefin V (which gives 3.5 ± 0.6% of ether VI), but markedly different from those obtained with *endo*-olefin I (14.5% of ether VI). It seems clear then that the solvolysis reaction, which has been shown to involve generally a series of ion pairs and/or relatively free ions,[9] either gives an ion immediately with a structure (possibly like VII) similar to that of the immediate precursor of the final products, or allows sufficient life-time in the cationic states to allow any possibly different original cations from III and VI tosylates to lose their original identities, either by transformation to a mesomeric ion such as VII or by equilibrium between the original ions.

Comparison of addition *vs.* solvolysis in another system may now also be made. Treatment of norbornadiene (X) with methanol containing 10% sulfuric acid for one week at room temperature gave a mixture of dehydronorbornyl methyl ether (XI, Y = OCH₃) and nortricyclyl methyl ether (XII, Y = OCH₃) in a ratio of 33:67, while treatment of X with acetic acid containing 1% sulfuric acid for 1.5 hr. at room temperature gave the corresponding acetates XI and XII (Y = OCOCH₃) in the ratio 25:75.[10] In both cases the reaction was run only part way and no 2:1 addition product was formed. On the other hand, solvolysis (at room

temperature) of the *p*-bromobenzenesulfonate XI (Y = OSO₂C₆H₄Br-*p*) in methanol (with or without pyridine present) gave a mixture of methyl ethers XI and XII containing 7.9 ± 0.3% of ether XI, while solvolysis of the brosylate XII gave a mixture containing 6.7 ± 0.3% of ether XI. Solvolysis of the brosylate XI in acetic acid (with or without sodium acetate) at room temperature gave an acetate mixture containing 8.0 ± 0.3% of acetate XI and 92.0 ± 0.3% of acetate XII, while that of

brosylate XII gave a mixture containing only 4.7 ± 0.4% of acetate XI.[11,12] Less than 1% of *endo* product was found in any case.

Experiments to show that the various products are substantially unisomerized under reaction conditions have been conducted.

Recently Dauben and Cargill[13] have shown that addition of acetic acid to quadricycloheptane (XIV) also leads to a mixture of acetates XI and XII, but in this case to about equal amounts of each isomer.

The data we have obtained seem to require several cationic intermediates in these additions and/or solvolysis reactions. Much recent evidence and discussion are pertinent to these data.[6,14] In particular, acid-catalyzed addition reactions of protonic species are believed to proceed through alternate routes as shown in eq. 1 to 4 or 1a to 4a. In the first extended discussions of acid-catalyzed hydration, Taft[14b] assumed that the initial π-complex formed by protonation of the olefin (eq. 1) is isomerized to an open carbonium ion (eq. 2) before reaction with water (eq. 3). Later results[6b,14e,15] suggest that under certain conditions the π-complex (or equivalent hydrogen bridged cation[6b]) reacts directly with solvent or with anion (eq. 4 and 4a) resulting in *trans* addition, while in other systems the non-stereospecific paths represented by eq. 1, 2 and 3 or 1a, 2 and 3a were followed. The relative values of k_2 compared with k_4 (or k_{4a}) in any given set of conditions then controls the stereochemical result.

$$>C{=}C< + H_2OS \rightleftharpoons \overset{H^+}{\underset{}{>C{=}C<}} + HOS \quad (1)$$

$$or >C{=}C< + HX \rightleftharpoons \overset{H^+}{\underset{}{>C{=}C<}} + X^\ominus \quad (1a)$$

$$\overset{H^+}{\underset{}{>C}}{=}C< \overset{k_2}{\rightleftharpoons} >\overset{H}{\underset{}{C}}{-}\overset{}{C}^\oplus< \quad (2)$$

$$>\overset{H}{\underset{}{C}}{-}C^\oplus + HOS \longrightarrow >\overset{H}{\underset{HOS}{C}}{-}\overset{}{C}{-} + >\overset{H}{\underset{}{C}}{-}\overset{H\overset{+}{O}S}{\underset{}{C}}{-} \quad (3)$$

$$or >\overset{H}{\underset{}{C}}{-}C^\oplus + X^- \longrightarrow {-}\overset{H}{\underset{X}{C}}{-}\overset{}{C}{-} + {-}\overset{H}{\underset{}{C}}{-}\overset{X}{\underset{}{C}}{-} \quad (3a)$$

(10) The fact that norbornadiene gives mixtures of dehydronorbornyl and nortricyclyl ethers and esters upon addition of alcohols and carboxylic acids has already been reported. *Cf.* H. Bluestone, S. B. Soloway, J. Hyman and R. E. Lidov, U. S. Patent 2,730,548 (January 10, 1956); U. S. Patent 2,738,356 (March 13, 1956); U. S. Patent 2,782,238 (February 19, 1957); and L. Schmerling, J. P. Levisi and R. W. Welch, *J. Am. Chem. Soc.*, **78**, 2819 (1956); H. Krieger, *Suomen Kemistilehti*, **33B**, 183 (1960). These experiments were run under conditions leading to some 2:1 addition products, and are therefore not necessarily comparable to ours.

(11) J. D. Roberts, C. C. Lee and W. H. Saunders, *J. Am. Chem. Soc.*, **77**, 3034 (1955), report that brosylate XI gives 11% of acetate XI and 89% of acetate XII on acetolysis at 45°.

(12) S. Winstein and H. J. Schmid (unpublished work) have also noted a different ratio of acetate products XI and XII from brosylates XI and XII; see footnote 23 in ref. 6d. In addition, solvolysis of brosylate XI is accompanied by rearrangement to brosylate XII (S. Winstein, private communication).

(13) W. G. Dauben and R. L. Cargill, *Tetrahedron*, **15**, 197 (1961).

(14) (a) M. J. S. Dewar, "Electronic Theory of Organic Chemistry," Oxford University Press, London, 1949, p. 144; (b) R. W. Taft, Jr., *J. Am. Chem. Soc.*, **74**, 5372 (1952); (c) E. L. Purlee and R. W. Taft, Jr., *ibid.*, **78**, 5807 (1956); (d) P. Riesz, R. W. Taft, Jr., and R. N. Boyd, *ibid.*, **79**, 3724 (1957); (e) C. H. Collins and G. S. Hammond, *J. Org. Chem.*, **25**, 911 (1960).

(15) G. S. Hammond and T. D. Nevitt, *J. Am. Chem. Soc.*, **76**, 4121 (1954).

$$>C=C< + HOS \xrightarrow{k_4} \overset{H}{\underset{\underset{\oplus}{HOS}}{-C-C-}} \qquad (4)$$

$$\text{or} >C=C< + X^- \xrightarrow{k_{4a}} \overset{H}{\underset{X}{-C-C-}} \qquad (4a)$$

It would appear possible to explain our data on additions to I and to V (or to their dehydro analogs) using similar models for intermediates. The carbon–carbon double bond in the *endo*-olefin I could be protonated from the *exo* side to give the π-complex XV or from the *endo* side to give the alternate π-complex XVI. Correspondingly, the *exo*-olefin V would give XVII and XVIII. The π-complexes with *exo* protons obviously can not lead directly to *exo*-Y products, as *trans* ring opening of such π-complexes would lead to ethers or alcohols related to XIX or XX with the Y groups having *endo* configurations. These were not found in the reaction mixture, although we would easily have been able to detect as little as 1% of these materials. These π-complexes, then, if formed, must either lose protons to return to unisomerized olefin[14] or isomerize to carbonium ions. It might be anticipated that XV would isomerize either to the carbon-bridged mesomeric cation VII or to the classical *endo* ion VIII, while XVII might correspondingly isomerize to VII or to IX. These, as discussed above, could be the immediate precursors of the products III and VI. Thus, if XV and XVII are the sole π-complexes formed, it is necessary to assume that the classical carbonium ions VIII and XI, or one of these with VII, are involved in the addition reaction.

XV   XVI

XVII   XVIII

XIX   XX   XXI

On the other hand, it may be assumed that the *endo*-protonated π-complexes XVI and XVIII are involved. The formation of these π-complexes should be less favored than that of XV and XVII, as *exo* addition is usually observed to norbornenes.[16] However, if the formation of π-complexes is reversible (eq. 1) and if the *trans* "ring-opening" reaction (eq. 4) of say, XVI, is significantly faster than that of XV,[17] then the compositions of the

(16) K. Alder, F. H. Flock and H. Wirtz, *Ber.*, **91**, 609 (1958).

product mixtures can be accommodated in the following way. Protonation of I gives XV and XVI; XV isomerizes to VII with the anchimeric assistance associated with the carbon–carbon bond migration. Compound XVI, on the other hand, is more susceptible to attack by nucleophiles than XV and is less ready to isomerize to VII or to VIII, as no anchimeric assistance is possible in this isomerization; XVI then may lead to products related to VI directly, maintaining the *endo* ring system, or may yield an *exo* solvated VIII ion, which can collapse to products VI or isomerize to VII (or to IX). Similar reaction schemes can be devised beginning with V. Under conditions where the sum of the lifetimes of the cationic states is high, for example, in water, where the stability of ions is inherently great, or in acetic acid or formic acid (where the nucleophilicity of the solvent is low) there will be time for rearrangement to intermediates which lead largely to *exo* ring systems. When the reaction is conducted under conditions where cationic species are captured relatively rapidly (for example, in methanol), rearrangements are relatively less complete and products with original ring skeletons may be obtained by direct reaction of π-complexes or by transformation of these to selectively solvated cations.

A comparison of results of solvolysis in methanol and in acetic acid of the *p*-bromobenzenesulfonates of *exo*-dehydronorborneol XI and nortricyclenol XII (Y = OBs) with addition of these solvents to norbornadiene (X) and quadricycloheptane (XIV)[13] also seems to require the intermediacy of several different cationic species. Solvolyses of XI and XII brosylates in methanol give mixtures of XI and XII that appear to differ slightly, although the differences lie just on the edge of experimental error estimates; in acetic acid, however, the differences are well outside experimental error. The differences are of such a nature as to indicate that each isomer isomerizes (in ring skeleton) slightly less than the average; these differences would, of course, be increased were the isomeric brosylates not isomerizing to each other.[12] Thus the cationic species seems to remember its origin. Addition of solvents to the diene X or the tetracyclic compound XIV[13] gives mixtures of products XI and XII (Y = OCH$_3$ or OCOCH$_3$) that differ substantially from those obtained in the solvolysis experiments.

Winstein and Kosower[6d] have discussed the rates and products of solvolyses of XI and XII derivatives and similar compounds in an extensive and elegant paper, and have suggested that the slight differences in product composition may be due to solvolysis in one case to a symmetrical homoallylic mesomeric ion XXII and in the other case to an unsymmetrical ion XXIII.[18] Here it must

(17) It has been observed that the ring opening of the epoxide XXI with lithium aluminum hydride is very difficult (D. W. Johnson and L. K. Gaston, private communication). This may be analogous to the reaction of XV.

(18) Winstein and Kosower[6d] suggest that norbornenyl *p*-bromobenzenesulfonate (XI) gives the unsymmetrical ion XXIII in the solvolysis, while the nortricyclyl bromobenzenesulfonate XII gives the symmetrical ion XXII. In view of the marked stereochemical requirement generally observed for anchimeric assistance to solvolysis (*anti*-coplanarity of neighboring and leaving group seem required[19]),

be assumed that capture by nucleophile competes with transformation of XXII to XXIII or *vice versa*. An alternative possibility is that both bromobenzenesulfonates give the same cationic species, which react at least in part with solvent in the "solvent-separated ion pair" stage,[9] in such a way that solvent reacts somewhat more readily in that position closest to the departing counter anion. A distinction between these unsymmetrically solvated species and classical non-mesomeric carbonium ions cannot be drawn from product data such as are available.

XXII   XXIII   XXIV

XXV   XXVI   XXVII

Again it can be assumed that the addition reactions to X involve different intermediates from solvolysis reactions. Several π-complexes (or hydrogen-bridged cations) may be postulated for the addition reaction represented by eq. 1. It is clear that, as *no* significant amount of *endo* product XXVII is observed in addition of either methanol or acetic acid, any XXIV which is formed either reverts to starting diene or is transformed to one of the carbonium ion species (XXII, XXIII or "classical" ions). Presumably XXII or XXIII would lead largely to nortricyclyl products as are found in solvolyses. On the other hand, an *endo*-π-complex, which might be represented as XXV, if one double bond is involved, or as XXVI, if it is assumed that the hydrogen orbital overlaps with the π-orbitals of both double bonds,[20] might be involved. It would be anticipated that either XXV or XXVI would lead by *trans* ring opening to the *exo* products XI or, of course, could rearrange to carbonium ions.

There is, of course, the possibility that addition to norbornadiene and to dihydrodicyclopentadiene involves some simple *cis* addition mechanism, similar perhaps to those postulated for the *cis* addition of chlorine to phenanthrene[22] in acetic acid or for the *cis* addition of acetyl nitrate to olefins.[23] Such *cis* addition mechanisms may be particularly attractive in these norbornene systems where *cis*

the opposite products might ordinarily be anticipated from XI and XII *p*-bromobenzenesulfonates.

(19) (a) D. H. R. Barton and R. C. Cookson, *Quart. Revs.*, **10**, 44 (1956); (b) S. J. Cristol and R. P. Arganbright, *J. Am. Chem. Soc.*, **79**, 3441 (1957).

(20) The possible interactions of the two double bonds in norbornadiene and norbornadiene derivatives have been discussed as has the structure of silver ion π-complexes.[21]

(21) (a) J. G. Traynham and J. R. Olechowski, *J. Am. Chem. Soc.*, **81**, 571 (1959); (b) C. F. Wilcox, Jr., S. Winstein and W. G. McMillan, *ibid.*, **82**, 5450 (1960); (c) C. F. Wilcox, Jr., and R. R. Craig, *ibid.*, **83**, 4258 (1961).

(22) P. B. D. de la Mare and N. V. Klassen, *Chemistry & Industry*, 498 (1960).

(23) F. G. Bordwell and E. W. Garbisch, Jr., *J. Am. Chem. Soc.*, **82**, 3588 (1960).

bimolecular eliminations have been found to be favored over *trans*.[24]

The mechanisms involved in transformation of XIV to an equimolar mixture[13] of acetates XI and XII are even more obscure. Very little information appears to be available on the mechanisms of additions to cyclopropanes. It seems remarkable, however, that this addition gives more olefinic product XI than does addition to the diene.

With the data described herein it is not possible to decide among the various possibilities for reaction paths; in particular, it is not possible to state whether or not the *endo* protonated complexes are involved as intermediates in the addition reactions. However, consideration of the product-composition data in both the *endo*-dihydrodicyclopentadiene case and the norbornadiene case is of interest. In each case, it would appear that about 20% of the "abnormal" product (with I, the *endo* ring skeleton product VI, and with X, the dehydronorbornyl product XI) may be accounted for by the "normal" path—that is, the path assumed by the solvolyses or by addition to V. The remaining 80% of the products VI or XI must come from another path. Studies with deuterium-labeled solvents would appear to promise interesting results, as it is clear that *endo*-protonated intermediates such as XVI, XVIII, XXV and XXVI would lead to *trans* addition of H and Y. This work is in progress.

Acknowledgments.—Acknowledgment is made to the donors of the Petroleum Research Fund, administered by the American Chemical Society, for partial support of this research. In addition, the authors are indebted to the Air Force Office of Scientific Research for partial support of this work, to the Shell Development Co. for samples of norbornadiene and to Professors Paul D. Bartlett, Herbert C. Brown, John D. Roberts and Saul Winstein for critical discussions.

Experimental

Addition of Water to *endo*-Dihydrodicyclopentadiene (I).— A mixture of 2.06 g. (15.3 mmoles) of *endo*-dihydrodicyclopentadiene I (containing about 2% of V and a trace of II or IV) and 17.7 g. of 22 wt. % aqueous sulfuric acid was heated at reflux with magnetic stirring for 4 hours. The cooled mixture was extracted 4 times with 15-ml. portions of ether. The combined ethereal solution was washed with sodium carbonate solution and water and the ether was removed by distillation. After azeotroping the water off with benzene, 1.74 g. of oil remained, which still contained a considerable amount of starting olefin I. The hydrated fraction by analysis showed 2% of VI (Y = OH) and 98% of III (Y = OH) (vapor phase chromatographic analysis).

In another experiment under identical conditions, using a less pure starting material, a mixture of III and VI (Y = OH) melting at 44–49° was obtained in 42% yield after distillation, b.p. 68.5° (0.6 mm.), which gave analysis for 3.2% of VI (Y = OH); m.p. of pure III (Y = OH) reported[2a,j] 53–54°.

Alcohol VI (Y = OH) was found to be stable under these reaction conditions. Olefin I did not isomerize when treated with 10% or 50% aqueous sulfuric acid for 0.5 hour (identification by melting point and infrared spectrum).

Methyl *exo*-5,6-Trimethylene-*exo*-2-norbornyl Ether (III, Y = OCH₃).—A solution of 1.52 g. (10 mmoles) of alcohol III[2j] (m.p. 52.8–53°) in 5 ml. of dry benzene was heated to reflux with 0.48 g. (20 mmoles) of sodium hydride for 1 hour. Methyl iodide (1.56 g., 11 mmoles) was added to the cooled mixture and heated for 1 hour at reflux temperature. The

(24) S. J. Cristol and E. F. Hoegger, *ibid.*, **79**, 3438 (1957).

TABLE I

PRODUCTS OF ADDITION OF METHANOL AND WATER TO OLEFINS I, II AND V IN METHANOL SOLVENT

Reaction	Reactants	Yield, %	Ratio^a of methoxyln. to hydran. prod.	Found Y = OCH₃		Found Y = OH		Calculated Y = OCH₃
				III	VI	III	VI	VI
1	II	89^e	12^{c,e}	85.2^e	14.8^e	83.2^e	16.8^e	...
2	I^f	81	33^b	85.5^f	14.5^f	87.9	12.1	...
3	V^g	90	11^{c,e}	96.5^e	3.5^e	97.3^e	2.7^e	...
4	29% I^h 71% V	88	..	94.0	6.0	...	...	6.7^{h,i}

^{a,b,c} This ratio depends on the amount of water present in the methanol reaction mixture and on the method of isolation of the alcohols III and VI (Y = OH) (fractionation by distillation^b or vapor phase chromatography^c). ^{b} The low hydration yield is due to hold-up in the distillation flask of this small scale run and therefore the 12.1% of VI (Y = OH) is not as good as the corresponding data of run 1. ^{d} Percentages are calculated as ethers III and VI (Y = OCH₃) being 100% and alcohols III and VI (Y = OH) being 100%. ^{e} After hydrogenation of the addition product. ^{f} The starting material (m.p. 0–2°)^{2j} contains about 2% of V and a trace of II or IV. The latter is the reason for the presence of about 1% or less of unsaturated ethers in the 14.5% of isolated VI (infrared). ^{g} The starting material contains about 7% of a mixture of II and IV. ^{h} The preparation of the starting material is described in ref. 2j (Table I, expt. 10); it is free of II and IV. ^{i} Calculation based on values of reactions 2 and 3; an additional error is introduced into this calculation by the analytically^{2j} determined composition of the reactants. Therefore, the calculated value is considered to be in excellent agreement with that observed.

solution was filtered; the inorganic solid was washed with benzene, dissolved in water and the aqueous solution extracted with ether. The combined ether and benzene solutions were washed with water, potassium hydrogen sulfate solution and water. The solution was dried over calcium sulfate and the solvents were removed under reduced pressure. Distillation gave 0.95 g. (57% yield) of product, n^{22}D 1.4867, b.p. 43–44° (0.2 mm.). The product gave analysis for 96.3% of III (Y = OCH₃). Pure III (Y = OCH₃) was isolated by preparative gas phase chromatography; infrared spectrum in carbon disulfide: 9.10 (strong) and 7.34 μ; there are weak absorptions at 7.95, 9.65 and 12.63 μ which are not present in the *endo* isomer VI (Y = OCH₃).

Anal. Calcd. for $C_{11}H_{18}O$: C, 79.46; H, 10.91. Found: C, 79.65; H, 11.03.

Methyl *endo*-5,6-Trimethylene-*exo*-2-norbornyl Ether (VI, Y = OCH₃).—One gram (6.6 mmoles) of alcohol VI,^{2j} (m.p. 81–82.5°) was treated with 0.48 g. (20 mmoles) of sodium hydride as described above. After reaction with 2.8 g. (19 mmoles) of methyl iodide, in an additional 2 ml. of benzene for 2 hours at reflux temperature, the mixture was worked up as described for III (Y = OCH₃); b.p. 40–43° (0.2 mm.). The yield was 230 mg. (21% of theor., 50% of the starting alcohol was recovered by distillation), n^{22}D 1.4924; vapor phase chromatography shows the absence of any III (Y = OCH₃). Infrared spectrum in carbon disulfide was 9.14 (strong) and 7.27 μ; there is a weak absorption at 12.20 μ, which is not present in III (Y = OCH₃).

Anal. Calcd. for $C_{11}H_{18}O$: C, 79.46; H, 10.91. Found: C, 79.58; H, 10.70.

Addition Reactions of Methanol to *endo*-1,2-Dihydrodicyclopentadiene (I), *exo*-1,2-Dihydrodicyclopentadiene (V), *endo*-Dicyclopentadiene (II) and a Mixture of I and V.—A mixture of 5 to 20 mmoles of olefin and an amount of 22 wt. % methanolic sulfuric acid (96%), which corresponds to a 50-fold molar ratio of methanol to olefin, was heated at mild reflux for 4 hours. Two volumes of water was added and the mixture was extracted four times with five 10-ml. portions of ether. The combined ethereal solution was washed with water, sodium carbonate solution and water. The excess of the ether was distilled off and the water was removed by azeotroping with benzene at normal pressure. The last trace of benzene was removed at 25° (10 mm.). The hydration products III and VI boil about 15° higher at 0.08 mm. than the ethers III and VI and therefore can be separated by distillation. However, in small scale runs the preferred method was to distil alcohols and ethers together and separate them by vapor-phase chromatography. No fractionation of VI from III (Y = OH or OCH₃) in excess of the experimental error of their analyses occurred during distillation, since the forerun and the afterrun contained the stereoisomers III and VI in the same ratio as the main fraction; the *endo* isomers VI (Y = OH and OCH₃) were found to have slightly higher boiling points than their corresponding *exo* isomers III (Y = OH and OCH₃); the data in Table I represent the average of duplicate analyses.

Reactions 2 and 3 were repeated several times with described results. In all reactions the identity of VI (Y = OCH₃) with authentic VI (Y = OCH₃) synthesized as described above was proven by isolation of VI (Y = OCH₃) from the addition products by preparative gas phase chromatography and comparison of infrared spectra. At the same time any amount of unsaturated ethers (these have slightly shorter retention times on Carbowax than VI (Y = OCH₃), but are not separated from VI) originating from small amounts of II and IV present in the starting olefins, were detected by their infrared absorption at 14.35 μ.^{2j}

In reaction 1 of olefin II these unsaturated ethers are the primary products. Their infrared spectra show bands of approximately equal intensity at 14.35 and 9.10 μ. Thus amounts of unsaturated ethers present in isolated VI (Y = OCH₃) of reactions 2, 3 and 4 can be estimated, since the absorption at 14.35 μ is absent in pure VI (Y = OCH₃).

Since the mixture of unsaturated ethers and alcohols (reaction 1) could not be separated into stereoisomers with a Carbowax column, it was hydrogenated quantitatively with platinum dioxide in ethyl acetate solvent at room temperature for 2.5 hours giving a mixture of III and VI (Y = OCH₃). The hydrogenated product was isolated by filtration, washing of the catalyst with ethyl acetate and removal of the solvent by distillation.

In reaction 3 the sum of VI (Y = OCH₃) and unsaturated ethers was 10.8% by analysis. The value of 3.5% (Table I) for VI (Y = OCH₃) obtained after hydrogenation as described above was confirmed by treating 32 mg. of the crude methanol adduct of V (reaction 3) with excess bromine in carbon tetrachloride for several hours at room temperature; the vapor phase chromatogram showed a ratio of III:VI (Y = OCH₃) = 96:4. In another addition of methanol to 99% pure^{2j} V an amount of 3.5% of VI (Y = OCH₃) was found.

In run 4 an olefinic by-product (5% yield) was isolated, which had absorption at 14.35 and 3.30μ and did not yield a phenyl azide adduct. The yield and composition of the hydration product in reaction 4 was not determined.

When the pure methyl ethers III and VI were treated under addition reaction conditions, only slight isomerization was observed. Analyses indicated that VI isomerized to a mixture containing 1.7% of III, while III gave a mixture containing 0.2% of VI. Neither ether gave any alcohol, while alcohol III gave a slight conversion to 2% of ether III.

Addition of Formic Acid to *endo*-1,2-Dihydrodicyclopentadiene (I).—A mixture of 1.37 g. (10.2 mmoles) of I and 1.41 g. (30.6 mmoles) of formic acid was heated at 93–103° for 45 minutes. The excess formic acid was distilled at reduced pressure and then 950 mg. (52%) of formate ester, b.p. 57–65° (0.15 mm.), n^{23}D 1.4910 (lit.^{2j} 1.4911), was obtained. The ester was reduced with lithium aluminum hydride to a mixture of alcohols III and VI (Y = OH). This mixture was analyzed by various procedures and gave results indicating a content of 4.4 to 7.2% of III. Good analytical procedures were not yet developed at the time of this preliminary experiment, so these results are not as precise as those for hydration or methanol addition.

Addition of Acetic Acid to *endo*-1,2-Dihydrodicyclopentadiene (I).—A solution of 2.68 g. (20.0 mmoles) of I, 0.1 ml. of 96% sulfuric acid and 12.1 g. of glacial acetic acid was heated at reflux for 1.2 hr. The solution was then cooled, diluted with two parts of water and extracted several times with ether. The combined ethereal extracts were washed with water, aqueous sodium carbonate, and water again and then dried over anhydrous calcium sulfate. Distillation gave 2.15 g. (55%) of ester,[2j] b.p. 64–70° (0.14 mm.), n^{25}D 1.4934. The ester was saponified with ethanolic potassium hydroxide and the resulting alcohol isolated. The alcohol product was analyzed by infrared estimation of the product urethanes (a procedure now known to be less satisfactory than vapor-phase chromatography) and contained $4 \pm 2\%$ of III and $96 \pm 2\%$ of VI.

Vapor phase chromatographic analyses were conducted on a Perkin–Elmer vapor fractometer, model 154-C, or a Beckman GC-2 gas chromatograph using helium as carrier gas. The isomeric alcohols and their methyl ethers were determined quantitatively on a 3-meter by 6-mm. copper column packed with approximately 25% Carbowax 20M on C-22 firebrick purchased from Wilkens Instrument and Research, Inc.

The ethers were analyzed at $124 \pm 1°$ and at a flow rate of 97–99 cc./min.

The analyses of the isomeric alcohols were generally conducted at 60 cc./min. and $150 \pm 2°$. The compositions of *exo*- and *endo*-dihydrodicyclopentadiene (I and V) mixtures were determined on a 4-meter Ucon polyglycol LB-550-X (two Perkin–Elmer "R" columns in series). The analyses were carried out at $125 \pm 2°$ with a helium flow of 50–55 cc./min.

A 3 microliter sample normally was used for the quantitative determinations. Larger samples were used when material was to be collected, but in these cases a poorer separation of the isomers was obtained.

The percentage compositions of a mixture were generally determined by planimeter measurement of the peak areas of the vapor-phase chromatogram. In some cases the areas were measured by the method of triangularization. When both methods were used on the same chromatogram, they gave values differing by less than 1%.

To determine that the relative thermal conductivities of the olefins and ethers are close enough to one to give accurate percentage composition data by peak area calculations, a synthetic mixture was prepared and analyzed. The prepared sample was 47.4% in olefin and 52.6% in the corresponding ethers. Calculation of the peak areas of the chromatogram indicated a composition of 48.0% olefins, 52.0% ethers, thus showing that the thermal conductivities are nearly the same and the peak areas are proportional to the weight percentage composition.

The ethers and alcohols showed the following order of retention volumes: VI (Y = OH) > III (Y = OH) > VI (Y = OCH₃) > III (Y = OCH₃). The isomeric unsaturated ethers had a slightly shorter retention time than VI (Y = OCH₃) and were not resolved well from each other or from VI.

Solvolysis of *endo*-5,6-Trimethylene-*exo*-2-norbornyl *p*-Toluenesulfonate (VI, Y = OTs).—The toluenesulfonate ester, m.p. 49.0–50.5° (lit.[3] 48–49°), was prepared from alcohol VI, m.p. 81.5–82.5°.[2j] A solution of 323 mg. (1.05 mmoles) and 90 mg. (1.1 mmoles) of anhydrous sodium acetate in 25 ml. of anhydrous methanol was heated at gentle reflux. After 11 hours the solution was allowed to cool, water was added, and the mixture was extracted with 4 portions of ethyl ether. After the solution was dried over magnesium sulfate, the ether was removed by distillation, benzene was added to the residue, then distilled to remove any remaining water. Calculation of the peak areas of the vapor-phase chromatogram indicated the presence of 3.3% (two analyses, 3.0% and 3.6%) of VI (Y = OCH₃) in III (Y = OCH₃).

The solvolysis was repeated on 30 mg. (0.13 mmole) of the tosylate in 3.0 ml. of absolute methanol. After the usual work-up vapor-phase chromatographic analysis showed 3.4% of VI ether.

Solvolysis of *exo*-5,6-Trimethylene-*exo*-2-norbornyl *p*-Toluenesulfonate (III, Y = OTs).—The *p*-toluenesulfonate ester was prepared from *exo*-trimethylene-*exo*-norborneol (III, Y = OH),[2j] and then was hydrogenated to remove any

unsaturation which had been present in the parent alcohol. Recrystallization from ligroin gave product melting at 65.3–67.5° (lit.[3] 60–61°). A solution of 701 mg. of this material in 70 ml. of absolute methanol was heated at reflux for 12.5 hr. and then cooled. Water was added, the solution was extracted with ether and the ethereal solution was dried over calcium sulfate. The solvent was removed by distillation and residual water was azeotroped off with benzene. Gas chromatographic analysis of the residue showed 2.7% of VI ether. After vacuum distillation, analysis of the product showed 3.2% of VI. A repeat experiment gave a product with 2.8% of VI, while one with sodium acetate present gave a product containing 3.0% VI and 97.0% of III (Y = OCH₃).

Acid-catalyzed Addition of Methanol to Norbornadiene (X).—Norbornadiene (5 g., 0.0545 mole) was added to absolute methanol (70 g., 2.18 moles) containing 8.11 g. of 96% sulfuric acid (10% sulfuric acid solution in methanol) which had been cooled to 0°. The reaction mixture was stirred for 0.5 hr. at 0° and then for 5 hours at room temperature. The reaction mixture was poured into water and extracted with pentane. The pentane solution was washed once with water, then with 10% sodium carbonate and then dried over anhydrous magnesium sulfate. Most of the pentane was removed, and the methyl ethers formed were analyzed by vapor-phase chromatography (modified Aerograph, master A-100, equipped with a 1 mv. Brown recorder) on a 2-meter × 6-mm. Carbowax 20M column. Analysis showed 65.5% of nortricyclyl methyl ether (XII) and 34.5% of *exo*-dehydronorbornyl methyl ether (XI). The addition had proceeded a few per cent. and no diadduct was formed.

In another experiment the addition was carried out at 5° for 5.5 hr. and allowed to stand at room temperature for 26 hr. Analysis showed that the reaction had proceeded approximately 64% to completion and a small amount of diadduct was formed. Analysis of the monoadduct showed 70% of XII and 30% of XI.

Analysis of a reaction mixture which had been allowed to stand at room temperature for 1 week gave 33% of XI and 67% of XII.

The nortricyclene ether XII was saturated to 2% potassium permanganate solution and had n^{25}D 1.4638. It had the characteristic nortricyclene peak at 12.35 μ.[25] The nuclear magnetic resonance spectrum (Varian A-60 spectrometer) showed no peaks below 6.7 τ, indicating no unsaturation. Compound XII was not extractable from pentane into aqueous silver nitrate, and did not isomerize to XI under addition conditions.

Anal. Calcd. for $C_8H_{12}O$: C, 77.43; H, 9.68. Found: C, 77.67; H, 9.51.

The unsaturated ether XI reacted rapidly with potassium permanganate and had n^{25}D 1.4611. The nuclear magnetic resonance spectrum showed two almost mirror image quartets centering at 3.9 and 4.2 τ, showing two different olefinic protons. This compound was extractable into 30% aqueous silver nitrate. It was stable under addition conditions and did not isomerize to XII.

Anal. Calcd. for $C_8H_{12}O$: C, 77.43; H, 9.68. Found: C, 77.40; H, 9.71.

Acid-catalyzed Addition of Acetic Acid to Norbornadiene (X).—Norbornadiene (16.7 g., 0.182 mole) was added to 43.5 ml. of glacial acetic acid containing 1 ml. of 40% sulfuric acid. The mixture was stirred for 1.5 hr. at room temperature. The reaction mixture was worked up in the same manner as the methanol-addition reactions and analyzed in an identical manner except for column temperature. The mixture showed 76% of nortricyclyl acetate (XII) and 24% of *exo*-dehydronorbornyl acetate (XI).

The nortricyclyl acetate XII did not react with potassium permanganate and was not extractable into aqueous silver nitrate. It had the infrared peak at 12.3 μ characteristic of nortricyclenes,[25] and had n^{25}D 1.4677. The n.m.r. spectrum had no peaks below 5.4 τ, indicating no unsaturation. Neither XII nor XI rearranged under addition conditions.

Anal. Calcd. for $C_9H_{12}O_2$: C, 71.02; H, 7.95. Found: C, 71.15; H, 7.93.

The unsaturated ester XI reacted with aqueous potassium permanganate and was extractable from pentane with 25%

(25) G. T. Youngblood, C. D. Trivette, Jr., and P. Wilder, Jr., *J. Org. Chem.*, **23**, 684 (1958).

aqueous silver nitrate. It had n^{25}D 1.4639. The n.m.r. spectrum showed two different olefinic proton multiplets centering at 3.85 and 4.11 τ.

Anal. Calcd. for $C_9H_{12}O_2$: C, 71.02; H, 7.95. Found: C, 70.89; H, 7.90.

Acetolysis of *exo*-Dehydronorbornyl *p*-Bromobenzenesulfonate.—*exo*-Dehydronorbornyl *p*-bromobenzenesulfonate, m.p. 79–81°[26] (prepared from alcohol, with analysis as 99% pure, 500 mg., 1.8 mmoles), was added to 50 ml. of glacial acetic acid and allowed to stand in the dark at room temperature for 24 hr. The solvolysis mixture then was poured into ice-water and extracted five times with 50-ml. portions of pentane. The combined pentane solution was then extracted once with water and once with 5% sodium carbonate, and dried over anhydrous magnesium sulfate. The pentane was removed by distilling through a fractionating column to minimize loss of product. The products then were analyzed by gas chromatography as 92.0% nortricyclyl acetate (XII) and 8.0% dehydronorbornyl acetate (XI). Results were essentially identical (92.2%

(26) S. Winstein, H. M. Walborsky and K. Schreiber, *J. Am. Chem. Soc.*, **72**, 5795 (1950).

XII and 7.8% XI) when potassium acetate was present in the solvolysis mixture.

Acetolysis of Nortricyclyl *p*-Bromobenzenesulfonate.—The procedure was as above except that the reaction time was 3 days.

The *p*-bromobenzenesulfonate, m.p. 80–82°,[26] was prepared from nortricyclyl alcohol of 99% purity by analysis (vapor-phase chromatography). The solvolysis products contained 95.4% of nortricyclyl acetate (XII) and 4.6% of dehydronorbornyl acetate (XI). With potassium acetate present, the product was 95.0% nortricyclyl acetate and 5.0% dehydronorbornyl acetate.

Methanolysis of Nortricyclyl *p*-Bromobenzenesulfonate.—The methanolysis reactions were run in the same fashion as the acetolyses except that the reaction time was 10 hr. at room temperature. Analysis showed 93.0% of nortricyclyl methyl ether (XII) and 7.0% of dehydronorbornyl methyl ether (XI). In the presence of pyridine, the product analysis was 93.5% XII and 6.5% XI.

Methanolysis of *exo*-Dehydronorbornyl *p*-Bromobenzenesulfonate.—The reaction time was 3.2 hr. at room temperature. The methyl ether product was 92.0% of XII and 8.0% of XI in the presence or absence of pyridine.

Errata

Page 425, right-hand column, line 2 from bottom,

4.4 to 7.2% of III *should read* 4.4 to 7.2% of VI

Page 426, left-hand column, line 17 from top,

4 ± 2% of III and 96 ± 2% of VI *should read* 4 ± 2% of VI and 96 ± 2% of III

62 | The Long-Lived Norbornadienyl Cation

Story and Saunders have provided the first NMR study of a nonclassical carbonium salt at equilibrium. 7-Norbornadienyl fluoborate in liquid sulfur dioxide gives well-separated signals for two, two, two, and one proton (Figure 1). This eliminates all the structures with C_{2v} or higher symmetry which might be written for the ion. Structure IVa and the classical ion would have four equivalent protons; IVc, the "methinated benzene" formula, demands six equivalent protons. Although IVb and XVI both require the observed number of kinds of hydrogen atoms, there remain some remarkable features of this spectrum which could scarcely have been anticipated. The signal of the 7-hydrogen, uniquely recognizable in both the spectrum of 7-norbornadienyl chloride and that of the fluoborate, moves from 5.8τ *upfield* to 6.5 in going from the unionized molecule to the carbonium ion. At the same time it acquires the appearance of a triplet, reasonable if bonding is appearing from C-7 to C-2 and C-3. The olefinic signal at 3.2τ moves down to 2.4 and becomes further split, while that at 3.4τ moves up to 3.7 and *loses* its fine structure, in going from molecule to ion. And while the 7-proton seems slightly *more* shielded as it begins to share a positive charge, the signal assigned to the bridgehead protons, which acquire no charge, moves downfield 1.6 ppm, the largest change in the spectrum attending the ionization process. Thus this opening of a new experimental possibility for studying carbonium ions has also raised some problems calling for further study.

In this and other papers on the NMR spectra of tautomeric and mesomeric systems, it is pointed out that the NMR method has an inherent limitation. Electronic spectra record transitions which happen faster than the atoms in a molecule can change their positions, and electronic spectra can therefore, upon occasion, give evidence of the composition of a tautomeric mixture or of the unique structure of a resonance hybrid. In contrast, there are many chemical reactions which take place faster than the transitions in the NMR spectrometer. Slowly interconverting mixtures of tautomers register as such in the NMR; beyond a certain speed of interconversion, mixtures of tautomers and resonance hybrids are indistinguishable. In the study of nonclassical ions it must be borne in mind that a molecular species is never *more* mesomeric than it appears to be from its NMR spectrum; but it may be *less* so.

Story and Saunders point out that in this uncertainty, from the NMR evidence, as to whether the 7-norbornadienyl cation is IVb, XVI, or a rapidly interconverting mixture of the bond structures of which XVI is a hybrid, one may naturally give some weight to the chemical evidence (including ionization accelerated by 10^{14}) which speaks for a transition state strongly stabilized by charge delocalization. If we adopt this view and accept the NMR analysis, we conclude that the positive charge in the ion resides principally on C-2 and C-3 as opposed to C-7. This leads to the remarkable preference for reaction with lithium aluminum hydride at C-2 or C-3 to produce the unstable hydrocarbon XV in high yield. The authors propose that only hydride can do this because, even if all anionic scavengers of the cation showed a kinetic preference for reacting at this position, the rapid reionization of the product would cause conversion into the thermodynamically more stable 7-substituted product.

In the π route to bridged ions, of which this may be regarded as a specialized example, it is normal for the reactivity of the ion to reside chiefly at the carbon atoms which were originally doubly bonded. In the 7-norbornadienyl cation this tendency is reinforced by the unfavorable bond angle at C-7, much less accepting of a positive charge than C-2 or C-3. Indeed, the only reason for reactivity appearing at C-7 at all must be the exceptional strain that develops when a product of reaction at C-2 is fully formed.

From: *J. Am. Chem. Soc.* **84**, 4876–82 (1962)

[A JOINT CONTRIBUTION FROM BELL TELEPHONE LABORATORIES, MURRAY HILL, N. J., AND THE DEPARTMENT OF CHEMISTRY, YALE UNIVERSITY, NEW HAVEN, CONN.]

Structure of the 7-Norbornadienyl Carbonium Ion[1]

BY PAUL R. STORY[2a] AND MARTIN SAUNDERS[2b]

RECEIVED JUNE 29, 1962

The first direct and detailed physical evidence for the structure of an aliphatic non-classical carbonium ion has been obtained from the nuclear magnetic resonance spectrum of 7-norbornadienyl fluoroborate. The spectrum in liquid sulfur dioxide and in nitromethane indicates an unsymmetrical structure. Rearrangement of the bicyclic skeleton is ruled out by conversion of the fluoroborate to the corresponding acetate and to the corresponding methyl ether.

Introduction

The solvolyses of certain related carbocyclic molecules including cyclopropyl carbinyl (I), norbornyl (II) and norbornenyl derivatives (III) have provided a fund of information concerning the nature of the carbonium ion intermediates and the subject of non-classical structures and charge delocalization in general.[3] Structures involving

non-classical delocalization of electrons have been proposed for the intermediate carbonium ions hypothesized in these and other systems in order to explain remarkably enhanced rates of solvolysis of certain derivatives. The information obtained

(1) A portion of this work has been reported in preliminary form; P. R. Story and M. Saunders, *J. Am. Chem. Soc.*, **82**, 6199 (1960).

(2) (a) Bell Telephone Laboratories, Murray Hill, N. J. (b) Department of Chemistry, Yale University, New Haven, Conn.

(3) For comprehensive discussions see: (a) S. Winstein and E. M. Kosower, *J. Am. Chem. Soc.*, **81**, 4399 (1959); (b) R. H. Mazur,

W. N. White, D. A. Semenow, C. C. Lee, M. S. Silver and J. D. Roberts, *ibid.*, **81**, 4390 (1959).

thus far consists chiefly of analysis of the products and rates of the solvolysis reactions. However, the precise structure or structures involved in each case are not obtainable from such indirect information. Ultraviolet spectra of a presumed non-classical species have been obtained in one system confirming the presence of the intermediate ion, but yielding no specific structural information.[4]

The problem has been one of obtaining some direct structural information concerning these non-classical carbonium ion intermediates. Nuclear magnetic resonance (n.m.r.) spectroscopy has been shown to be a very powerful structural tool and has been effectively used on the relatively stable heptamethylbenzeneonium[5] and triphenylmethyl carbonium ions.[6] It was, therefore, considered likely that similar useful information could be obtained regarding these bicyclic, aliphatic ions.

The 7-norbornadienyl system has been found to possess the necessary prerequisites to allow application of this technique to an aliphatic, non-classical system for the first time. This system was considered most advantageous because of the apparent stability of the C.7 carbonium ion as indicated by the remarkable rate enhancement observed in solvolysis of 7-norbornadienyl chloride[7] and because several useful derivatives were readily available.[8] The system was further made attractive by the very interesting non-classical structures possible for the 7-carbonium ion and because the principal structures already proposed (IV)[7] could easily be distinguished by n.m.r. spectroscopy.

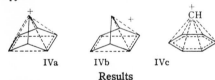

IVa   IVb   IVc

Results

7-Norbornadienyl Fluoborate.—Of the several possible ways in which the 7-norbornadienyl carbonium ion could be generated and presented for n.m.r. analysis, preparation of a salt from the corresponding chloride (7-chloronorbornadiene (VI)) was considered to be most promising. Acid generation of the ion from the alcohol or ether is considered risky because of the ease of protonation of the double bonds and subsequent rearrangement. Either of the two most commonly used reagents for salt preparation from halides, silver perchlorate or silver fluoborate at first appeared acceptable. The choice of liquid sulfur dioxide as the most satisfactory solvent, however, was found to dictate the use of silver fluoborate because of the limited solubility of silver perchlorate. Silver fluoborate was also preferred because of the explosive hazard of silver perchlorate and organic perchlorate salts.

(4) G. Leal and R. Pettit, *J. Am. Chem. Soc.*, **81**, 3160 (1959).

(5) W. v. E. Doering, M. Saunders, H. G. Boynten, H. W. Earhart, E. F. Wadley, W. R. Edwards and G. Laber, *Tetrahedron*, **4**, 178 (1958).

(6) R. Dehl, W. R. Vaughan and R. S. Berry, *J. Org. Chem.*, **24**, 1616 (1959); R. S. Berry, R. Dehl and W. R. Vaughan, *J. Chem. Phys.*, **34**, 1460 (1961).

(7) S. Winstein and C. Ordronneau, *J. Am. Chem. Soc.*, **82**, 2084 (1960).

(8) P. R. Story, *J. Org. Chem.*, **26**, 287 (1961).

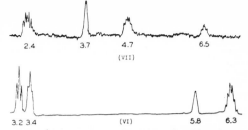

Fig. 1.—N.m.r. spectrum of 7-norbornadienyl fluoroborate and chloride in sulfur dioxide. Peak positions are given in p.p.m. relative to tetramethylsilane internal standard as 10 p.p.m.

Sulfur dioxide was chosen as the best solvent to prepare and display the carbonium ion salt because it is transparent, readily obtainable in a pure, dry state and remains liquid at temperatures down to −75°. Also, it has been used previously as a solvent for conductivity measurements of stable carbonium ion salts.[9]

Silver fluoborate has been found to react quantitatively with 7-norbornadienyl chloride (VI) to yield 7-norbornadienyl fluoborate (VII). The chloride VI was prepared directly from 7-t-butoxynorbornadiene (V)[8] by treatment with acetyl chloride as illustrated in eq. 1. The fluoborate VII was

$$\text{(1)}$$

also prepared in nitromethane, but less satisfactorily because of the higher freezing point of this solvent. The fluoborate VII did, however, appear to be slightly more stable at higher temperatures in nitromethane than in sulfur dioxide.

The N.m.r. Spectra.—The n.m.r. spectra of the fluoborate VII reaction solutions, after removal of silver chloride by centrifugation or filtration, were determined at temperatures ranging from −50° to about +50° with no apparent temperature effects, except that the solutions rapidly decomposed at temperatures over about 0°. The salient features of the spectra were not affected, however, until decomposition was nearly complete; the decomposition products merely added to the baseline noise. The n.m.r. spectrum of 7-norbornadienyl fluoborate (VII) in sulfur dioxide at −10° is recorded in Fig. 1. For comparison, the spectrum of the chloride precursor VI in sulfur dioxide is also shown.

The n.m.r. of the fluoborate VII in nitromethane was essentially identical to that in sulfur dioxide, except for a slight downfield shift in all the peak

(9) H. P. Leftin and N. N. Lichtin, *J. Am. Chem. Soc.*, **79**, 4275 (1957).

positions, the absorptions occurring at $\tau = 2.30$, 3.60, 4.64, 6.30. The peak at $\tau = 2.30$ had the same fine structure as in sulfur dioxide. The general shape of the other peaks was also unchanged. The n.m.r. spectrum of the chloride VI in nitromethane was also unchanged with absorptions at $\tau = 3.25$, 3.41, 5.8, 6.40. Quite fortuitously, nitromethane absorption at $\tau = 5.6$ did not interfere with the spectrum.

The addition of tetramethylsilane had no effect on the spectra of any of the samples. The ultraviolet spectra of the relatively concentrated solutions prepared for n.m.r. spectral analysis showed no absorption above 330 mμ, the cutoff wave length of liquid sulfur dioxide, as might be expected.[10]

Reactions of the Fluoborate VII.—Treatment of a sulfur dioxide solution of the fluoborate VII with acetic acid, after removal of a near quantitative yield of silver chloride (>96%), gave 7-norbornadienyl acetate (VIII)[8] exclusively in 50% yield (isolable).

The fluoborate VII was also converted exclusively to 7-methoxynorbornadiene (X) by treatment of the sulfur dioxide solution with 2-methoxy-2-methyl-1,3-dioxolane (IX). These reactions are shown in eq. 3. The reaction of the fluoborate VII with 2-deuterio-2-methyl-1,3-dioxolane (XII), which was worked-up by adding the methoxydioxolane IX, gave only high molecular weight materials distilling with difficulty over a wide temperature range. Furthermore, the fluoborate

$$(2)$$

VII did not react with deuteriotriphenylmethane over a four-hour period at low temperature in sulfur dioxide. This reaction was also worked up by the addition of IX to yield, in this case, 7-methoxynorbornadiene (X) containing no deuterium as determined by n.m.r.

Discussion

Structure of the Non-classical Ion.[11]—It is immediately obvious from its n.m.r. spectra that the

(10) If we are permitted to compare this ion to the cyclopropenyl carbonium ion, with which it is formally analogous, we see that the dipropylcyclopropenium ion has only end absorption in the ultraviolet; R. Breslow and H. Höver, J. Am. Chem. Soc., **82**, 2644 (1960).

(11) The information presented here will not, of course, differentiate between a non-classical ion or a mixture of rapidly equilibrating classical structures. However, since the only evidence published thus far (ref. 3a, 7) favors the non-classical structure, we shall argue in terms of this concept. This footnote was prompted by statements of one of the referees.

fluoborate VII is unsymmetrical, thereby eliminating structures IVa and IVc and implying IVb. We have assigned the peaks, which have areas in the ratio 1:2:2:2, to the 7-hydrogen, the bridgehead (1,4)-hydrogens and two *different* pairs of olefinic hydrogens. The peak at $\tau = 2.42$ is most reasonably interpreted as two overlapping triplets, strongly suggesting that the usual norbornadiene olefinic hydrogen triplet,[12] as seen in the chloride VI, is split by *coupling of the olefinic hydrogens with one additional hydrogen* with a coupling constant of about 5 c.p.s. The other peaks of the spectrum, at 3.74, 4.73 and 6.52, can be reasonably assigned to: remaining olefin (5,6), bridgehead (1,4) and bridge (7) hydrogens, respectively.

Since the spectrum of the fluoborate VII is unchanged in nitromethane, the possibility that the ion is a solvent adduct such as XIII is excluded.

XIII

The apparent coupling between the 7-hydrogen and the olefinic hydrogens (2,3) also argues against XIII as a possible structure.

It is interesting that the hydrogens on the three carbons presumed to carry the positive charge are all at higher field than might be expected. The 7 proton is upfield from its counterpart in the chloride, although below norbornadiene, and the two olefin hydrogens, while shifted downfield from their positions in the chloride, are not as low as some examples (tropylium, cyclopropenium) might lead one to predict. However, in these examples the protons considered lie in the plane of the carbocyclic ring and thus are shifted downfield by the diamagnetic anisotropy of the distributed charge as well as by the charge itself. In the norbornadienyl ion, however, the hydrogens considered are substantially out of the plane of the carbons. Thus, the geometry is closer to that of cyclopropane than cyclopropenium. The same diamagnetic anisotropy effect which causes cyclopropane to appear at abnormally high field may be involved in determining the positions of the hydrogens in norbornadienyl.

Chemical Evidence.—The structure IVb deduced from the n.m.r. spectra is consistent with all the chemical facts so far available. While this evidence will not distinguish between IVa, b or c or even show that the ion is non-classical, it does demonstrate that rearrangement has not occurred and implies interaction between C.7 and at least one pair of olefinic carbons.

The fluoborate VII was found to be converted exclusively to 7-norbornadienyl acetate (VIII)[8] in about 50% yield. The acetate VIII could not be obtained in a quantitative yield, but this was attributed to the rather inefficient isolation procedure and the necessary small scale of the reaction since no other products could be detected by G.P.C. or infrared analysis of the crude product.

(12) F. S. Mortimer, J. Mol. Spect., **3**, 528 (1959).

Meerwein[13] has shown that several carbonium ion salts, including triphenylmethyl fluoborate, will abstract alkoxy groups from 2-alkoxy-1,3-dioxolanes to yield 1,3-dioxolenium salts as shown in eq. 3. Triphenylmethyl fluoborate has also been shown to abstract hydrogen from 1,3-dioxolanes.

$$(3)$$

(Ph)₃CH

+ XI

(Ph)₃COCH₂CH₃

+ XI

In similar fashion, 7-norbornadienyl fluoborate (VII) was converted to 7-methoxynorbornadiene (X) in 57% yield by the addition of 2-methoxy-2-methyl-1,3-dioxolane (IX) to a sulfur dioxide solution of the fluoborate VII at low temperature (eq. 2). The reaction appeared to be rapid and complete since the solution was quite stable on immediate warming to room temperature. The crude methyl ether X was found to be at least 95% pure by G.P.C. analysis. Claisen distillation gave essentially no residue. The 2-methyl-1,3-dioxolenium fluoborate (XI) was obtained in 53% yield, m.p. 172–175°. Authentic dioxolenium fluoborate (XI) melts at 164–166° dec. Examination of the apparently impure salt revealed that it was not quite completely soluble in sulfur dioxide. The n.m.r. spectrum of the sulfur dioxide solution was identical with authentic dioxolenium fluoborate (XI) except that it contained a trace of impurity (5%). The sulfur dioxide-insoluble material was probably silver chloride or silver fluoborate carried along as the acetonitrile complex.[14]

In order to obtain a rough estimate of the acidity of the carbonium ion and to check for any non-observable carbon skeleton rearrangement or equilibria which could incorporate deuterium but not be evidenced by reaction products, the fluoborate VII was treated with 2-deuterio-2-methyl-1,3-dioxolane (XII); g.p.c. analysis of the product which was isolated by treating the reaction mixture with the methoxydioxolane (IX) showed no norbornadiene and only a very slight trace of a material with the same retention time as 7-methoxynorbornadiene (X). There were no volatile products. However, impure 2-methyl-1,3-dioxolenium fluoborate (XI) was isolated from the reaction in 48% yield. Examination of the n.m.r. spectrum of the sulfur dioxide solution revealed about 7% impurity. Otherwise the product was identical with authentic XI.

There appear to be two reasonable explanations for these unexpected results. The fluoborate may have reacted as anticipated to give 7-deuterionorbornadiene or the tricyclic olefin, 2-deuteriotricyclo[4.1.0.0³,⁷]heptene-4 (XV), which did not survive the reaction conditions. Alternatively, the dioxolane XII may have been attacked at one of

the oxygens with subsequent ring opening as shown in eq. 4.

$$(4)$$

or condensation to give high mol. wt. products

The fluoborate VII was found not to react with deuteriotriphenylmethane. There was no evidence of the characteristic yellow color of the trityl ion during the reaction. Furthermore, 7-methoxynorbornadiene (X), which was obtained as the only product (the reaction was not checked for trityl methyl ether) by working up the reaction as before with IX, contained no deuterium as demonstrated by its n.m.r. spectrum. This result should probably not be interpreted to mean that the 7-norbornadienyl carbonium ion (IVb) is less acidic than the trityl carbonium ion. It is, however, probably considerably more stable than its reactions and thermal instability would indicate. Because of the reactive double bonds it has more attractive decomposition paths open to it.

Convincing additional evidence for interaction of the *anti* double bond (C.2,3) and a developing carbonium ion at C.7 is provided by the lithium aluminum hydride reduction of 7-chloronorbornadiene (VI) which gave not only the expected norbornadiene (XIV) but also, quite remarkably, tricyclo[4.1.0.0³,⁷]heptene-4 (XV) as the major product.[15] The most probable reaction mechanism for the formation of XV is shown in eq. 5. The stereochemistry of the reduction at C.7 is unknown.

$$(5)$$

XIV, 12%   Y = H, D   XV, 88%

Ionization of the carbon–chlorine bond probably does not proceed to an appreciable extent before carbon–hydrogen bond formation begins. Moreover, the high degree of stereochemical control exerted by the non-classical ion thus indicates a high correspondence between carbon–chlorine bond breaking and electron transfer from the double

(13) H. Meerwein, K. Bodenbenner, P. Borner, F. Kunert and K. Wunderlich, *Ann.*, **632**, 38 (1960); H. Meerwein, V. Hederich, H. Morschel and K. Wunderlich, *ibid.*, **635**, 1 (1960).

(14) H. Meerwein, V. Hederich and K. Wunderlich, *Arch. Pharm.*, **291**, 541 (1958).

(15) P. R. Story, *J. Am. Chem. Soc.*, **83**, 3347 (1961).

bond to C.7.[16] Winstein's solvolysis of the chloride has led to the same conclusion.[7]

No previous reactions of 7-substituted norbornenes or norbornadienes have resulted in ring closure products such as XV because they were equilibrium processes and the strain involved in the tricyclic structure forced the equilibrium in favor of the bicyclic structure. Hydride reduction, on the other hand, is essentially irreversible and reaction at any carbon other than C.7 results in a ring-closed product.

While lithium aluminum hydride reduction of VI does not favor one non-classical cationic structure over another, it does provide the first direct chemical evidence of the type of transannular interaction proposed in the 7-norbornadienyl and *anti*-7-norbornenyl systems.

Extent of the Non-classical System.—All the available evidence is, therefore, consistent with IVb as the structure of the 7-nonbornadienyl non-classical carbonium ion, with one reservation. It is not clear to what degree, if any, the *syn* double bond (5,6) participates in charge delocalization. The n.m.r. spectral evidence is probably best described as inconclusive regarding this point. However, the slight upfield shift of the 5,6-hydrogens in the carbonium ion compared to their position in the chloride VI probably indicates any interaction to be slight at most. Participation in charge delocalization by the *syn* double bond, as shown in IVb, is based solely on the fact that 7-chloronorbornadiene (VI) was observed[7] to solvolyze *ca.* 800 × faster than *anti* - 7 - chloronorbornene (IIIb). This evidence must also be regarded as inconclusive, however, since it is in the realm of possibility that the rate difference is due largely to a ground state–transition state effect. Consequently, structure XVI must also be considered as a likely representation of the carbonium ion. For convenience, the carbonium ion will be

XVI

referred to henceforth as IVb with the tacit understanding that XVI is equally as likely a true representation.

Possible Interconversion of Non–classical Structures.—The evidence is thus strongly in favor of non-classical homoallylic stabilization of a cationic center at C.7. The n.m.r. evidence shows that this stabilization takes the form of the non-classical structure IVb in the fluoborate salt VII. Moreover, IVb is, *at least initially*, the expected structure. Because the double bond *syn* to the leaving group cannot participate *directly* at C.7 in the early stages of the formation of the non-classical ion, we see that structure IVb is exactly

the structure one would, *a priori*, predict in every ionization at C.7 which is promoted by non-classical ion formation.

The observation that the olefin peaks are unchanged up to 50° indicates that the interconversion of the isomeric forms of IVb through the transition state IVa occurs slower than at twice per second in the range studied. This barrier may be rationalized by assuming that considerable energy is necessary to move the bridge away from one double bond before any benefit from interaction with the other double bond is felt. A considerable distortion from the symmetrical geometry as in IVa is therefore implied.

In view of the remarkable evidence of DePuy, *et al.*,[17] it is not too surprising to find that interconversion if possible of the non-classical structures IV requires an activation energy. Reactions such as diazotization of the amine, 7-aminonorbornadiene, which will generate a positive charge at C.7 but are not primarily dependent on non-classical ion formation, may possibly yield one of the symmetrical structures (IVa,IVc) directly.

Acknowledgments.—We thank Mr. E. W. Anderson for determination of some of the n.m.r. spectra. P. R. S. is grateful for the many helpful suggestions and stimulating discussions provided by his colleagues in the Chemistry Department, Bell Telephone Laboratories.

Experimental

N.m.r. spectra were determined on 60 mc. Varian Associates n.m.r. spectrometers. Peak positions are reported in p.p.m. relative to tetramethylsilane internal standard as 10 p.p.m.

Silver fluoborate was in part prepared by the method of Olah and Quinn[18] and in part supplied by Chemical Procurement Laboratories. This material was dried over phosphorus pentoxide *in vacuo* before being stored, and warmed in a high vacuum just before use.

Sulfur dioxide was Matheson anhydrous grade and in several experiments was dried further by distillation from phosphorus pentoxide. The sulfur dioxide was, in every case, removed from the container in the vapor state.

Nitromethane.—Eastman spectrograde was further rigorously purified by Pocker's method.[19]

Deuteriotriphenylmethane was prepared by the addition of 99.6% deuterium oxide to triphenylmethylsodium.[20] Recrystallization from ethanol and from benzene gave colorless crystals, m.p. 92.5–93.5. The n.m.r. spectrum in carbon tetrachloride showed no detectable aliphatic hydrogen.

7-*t*-Butoxynorbornadiene (V) was prepared as previously reported.[8]

2-Methoxy-2-methyl-1,3-dioxolane (IX) was prepared according to Meerwein's procedure[12] for preparing the corresponding 2-ethoxy-2-methyl-1,3-dioxolane. These workers

(16) This is not too surprising, perhaps, considering the instability of the C.7 cation. For example, 7-norbornayl tosylate solvolyzes 10⁴ slower than cyclohexyl tosylate. [S. Winstein, M. Shatavsky, C. Norton and R. B. Woodward, *J. Am. Chem. Soc.*, **77**, 4183 (1955)]. The reduced bond angle at C.7 is presumably partly responsible, putting more s-character into the incipient empty p-orbital, thus making C.7 more electronegative. It may, in fact, be that the olefinic carbons have become positive relative to C.7 in the 7-norbornadienyl cation.

(17) It was shown that the carbonium ions XVII and XVIII, derived from *endo-* and *exo-*7-isopropylidenedehydronorbornyl tosylates, respectively, were not interconvertible under the solvolysis

XVII   XVIII

conditions; C. H. DePuy, I. A. Ogawa and J. C. McDaniels, *J. Am. Chem. Soc.*, **82**, 2398 (1960).

(18) G. A. Olah and H. W. Quinn, *J. Inorg. Nucl. Chem.*, **14**, 295 (1960).

(19) Y. Pocker, *J. Chem. Soc.*, 240 (1958).

(20) H. D. Zook and W. L. Rellahan, *J. Am. Chem. Soc.*, **79**, 881 (1957).

employed the general method of Alexander and Busch,[21]; b.p. 75° (105 mm.), infrared (neat): 3.35(m), 3.43(m), 7.20(s), 8.60(s), 9.43(s), 9.70(s), 10.46(m), 11.2(broad, s)μ; n.m.r. (ca. 1 molar in carbon tetrachloride): 6.09(m), 6.85 (s), 8.58(s).

2-Methyl-1,3-dioxolenium fluoborate (XI) was prepared according to Meerwein's method[18] from 2-methoxy-2-methyl-1,3-dioxolane (IX), m.p. 164–166° dec., n.m.r. (ca. 1 molar in sulfur dioxide): 4.64(s), 7.23(s).

7-Chloronorbornadiene (VI).—To a stirred solution of 61 g. (0.37 mole) of t-butyl ether (V) in 400 ml. of acetyl chloride (reagent grade), 0.5 ml. of water was added dropwise. Anhydrous hydrous hydrogen chloride was then bubbled in for about 5 minutes. Heating was begun and the mixture was refluxed for 1 hour. During this period, hydrogen chloride was bubbled in for two 5-minute periods. A nitrogen atmosphere was provided throughout the reaction time. The excess acetyl chloride was rapidly removed through a Claisen head at 70 mm. Immediate distillation through a spinning band column yielded 33 g. (70%) of 7-chloronorbornadiene (VI), b.p. 77° (55 mm.). This material was shown by infrared, n.m.r. and g.p.c. analysis to be identical to authentic chloride.[1,8] It should be noted that on a few occasions yields were as low as 57% with only 22% conversion, the unreacted ether V being recovered.

7-Norbornadienyl Fluoborate (VII).—A solution of 0.254 g. (0.002 mole) of chloride VI, which was purified immediately before use by preparative scale g.p.c. using a 5′ × ⁵/₈″, 15% Apiezon-M column, in 2 ml. of sulfur dioxide was slowly added over 15 minutes to a stirred solution-suspension of 0.500 g. (0.0026 mole) of silver fluoborate in 2 ml. of sulfur dioxide. The silver fluoborate was incompletely soluble in this volume of sulfur dioxide. Silver chloride began to precipitate immediately upon addition of chloride VI. After addition was complete, the solution was stirred for an additional 15 minutes. The volume of the solution was then reduced to 2–3 ml. by application of a vacuum. After centrifugation, the solution was pipetted into an n.m.r. tube which was then sealed. Sealed tubes were stored in Dry Ice until used. Addition of tetramethylsilane had no effect on the n.m.r. spectrum.

The entire operation, except centrifugation, was conducted in either a nitrogen-atmosphere dry-box as described above or on a vacuum line using standard techniques. Cooling, which allowed the reaction to be conducted at various temper tures ranging from −80° to −15°, was effected by passing nitrogen through a copper tube immersed in liquid nitrogen or a Dry Ice–solvent-bath, then through the jacketed reaction apparatus. Solutions prepared at lower temperatures, below −30°, were discovered to be uniformly better. Solutions prepared above this temperature frequently were discolored when a portion of the solution inadvertently became too warm. Successful preparation always gave colorless solutions. Further, the relatively concentrated n.m.r. solutions showed no ultraviolet absorption above 330 mμ at ca. −80°. Some preparations were carried out in liquid sulfur dioxide which had been distilled from phosphorus pentoxide, with no detectable improvement. Solutions of the fluoborate VII were stable for periods of at least one week, and possibly longer, at Dry Ice temperatures.

Nitromethane solutions of the fluoroborate VII were prepared at −20° to −15° in exactly the same fashion. These solutions were, however, invariably discolored presumably due to the necessary higher temperature.

Reaction of Fluoroborate VII with Acetic Acid.—A solution of the fluoroborate VII was prepared in the usual way from 0.3844 g. (0.0030 mole) of chloride VI and 0.650 g. (0.0033 mole) of silver fluoborate in a total of 10 ml. of sulfur dioxide at −50°. The reaction mixture was allowed to stir for 30 minutes, whereupon it was centrifuged and decanted. The white precipitate was washed twice with sulfur dioxide. The washings were combined and added to 3 ml. of glacial acetic acid. The white precipitate, which was presumed to be silver chloride (soluble in concentrated ammonium hydroxide) was washed with distilled hot water and dried overnight at 140° to yield a constant weight of 0.4198 g. (96.4%) of silver chloride.

After 20 ml. of methylene chloride was added to the acetic acid–sulfur dioxide solution, the sulfur dioxide was

evaporated away at room temperature inside the dry-box. The methylene chloride solution was washed with water and sodium bicarbonate solution and dried over anhydrous sodium sulfate. The solvent was then removed by slow Claisen distillation in an argon atmosphere. Isolation of the product by g.p.c. using a 40″ × ⁵/₈″ 10% Ucopolar on Fluoropak preparative scale column at 130° yielded 0.2290 g. (50%) of 7-norbornadienyl acetate (VIII) which was shown by infrared, n.m.r. and g.p.c. to be identical to authentic acetate VIII.[8] No other products could be detected by g.p.c. analysis of the crude product. Neither did infrared and n.m.r. analysis of the crude product reveal other products.

Reaction of Fluoborate VII with 2-Methoxy-2-methyl-1,3-dioxolane (IX).—The fluoborate VII was prepared on a vacuum line, using standard techniques, from 2.00 g. (0.158 mole) of chloride VI and 3.11 g. (0.160 mole) of silver fluoborate in approximately 100 ml. of sulfur dioxide at −70°. To this stirred solution, 2.5 g. (0.21 mole) of methoxydioxolane IX was added over 15 minutes. The silver chloride was not removed prior to addition of the dioxolane IX. This solution was then stirred for 5 minutes, whereupon removal of the sulfur dioxide was begun at reduced pressure. Concomitantly, 50 ml. of methylene chloride was added in small portions. The reaction flask was removed to the dry-box and the contents filtered free of a white precipitate which was washed with two small portions of methylene chloride. The combined washings were washed with water and sodium bicarbonate solution and dried over anhydrous sodium sulfate. The solvent was carefully removed and the product was distilled (Claisen-Vigreux) to yield 1.1 g. (57%) of 7-methoxynorbornadiene (X), b.p. 74–75° (56 mm.), infrared (neat): 3.21(w), 3.31(m), 3.42(m), 3.50(w), 6.42(w), 8.95(s), 13.6(s) μ; n.m.r. (ca. 1 molar in carbon tetrachloride). 3.55(3), 3.65(m), 6.60(m), 7.00(s).

Anal. Calcd. for $C_8H_{10}O$: C, 78.65; H, 8.25. Found: C, 78.63; H, 8.44.

Examination of the distillation pot revealed very little residue and the distilled product was shown by g.p.c. to be at least 92% pure.

The white precipitate was washed with about 30–50 ml. of acetonitrile. The remaining silver chloride was washed with water and dried to constant weight to give 2.16 g. (95.2%). Anhydrous ether was added to the acetonitrile solution to precipitate a white solid which was filtered off and dried in vacuo at room temperature for 2 days to give 1.47 g. (53%) of apparently impure 2-methyl-1,3-dioxolenium fluoborate (XI), m.p. 172–175°. The melting point of authentic XI is reported,[18] and has been observed in this Laboratory, as 164–166°. The fluoborate mI was dissolved in sulfur dioxide and found to be only about 90% soluble. The n.m.r. spectrum of this solution, except for a small amount of impurity (< 5%), was identical to that of the authentic fluoborate XI.

Reaction of the Fluoborate VII with Deuteriotriphenylmethane.—7-Norbornadienyl fluoborate (VII) was prepared in the usual way on the vacuum line from 2.00 g. (0.158 mole) of chloride VI and 3.11 g. (0.160 mole) of silver fluoborate in about 75 ml. of sulfur dioxide; 6.70 g. (0.273 mole) of deuteriotriphenylmethane was introduced into the mixture and stirred for 2 hours at −30° to −40° and 2.5 hours at −65°. The characteristic intense yellow color of the trityl carbonium ion was at no time apparent. A yellow color characteristic of the fluoborate VII reaction solutions which have been held at relatively high temperatures (−30°) was evident at the end of 2 hours. Consequently, the temperature was lowered to −65° for the remainder of the reaction time (2.5 hours); 2.50 g. (0.212 mole) of 2-methoxy-2-methyl-1,3-dioxolane (IX) was then introduced all at once with immediate dissipation of the yellow color. Solutions which were worked-up without addition of a quenching agent such as IX decomposed to give black intractable solids. This mixture was worked-up as described above and the crude product was examined by g.p.c. and found to contain no norbornadiene. Distillation through a small Claisen-Vigreux column yielded 0.95 g. (49%) of 7-methoxynorbornadiene (X), b.p. 70–71° (52 mm.). N.m.r. and infrared examination of this material revealed that it was identical to authentic ether X and contained no detectable deuterium as shown by careful integration. Triphenylmethane was also found to give no

(21) E. R. Alexander and H. M. Busch, J. Am. Chem. Soc., 74, 554 (1952).

visible reaction with the fluoborate VII prepared as above in nitromethane solution. This reaction was not examined further.

Preparation of 2-Deuterio-2-methyl-1,3-dioxolane (XII).— A modified procedure of Claus and Morganthau[22] for the reduction of *ortho* esters was used to reduce 2-methoxy-2-methyl-1,3-dioxolane (IX) with lithium aluminum deuteride. Benzene could not be used as Claus and Morganthau had done since it and the product XII boil at almost exactly the same point. Toluene was found to be unsatisfactory because it formed an azeotropic mixture ($\sim$ 1:1) with the product XII which could only be separated by g.p.c. Consequently, 2.36 g. (0.225 equiv. wt.) of lithium aluminum deuteride was added to 26 g. (0.22 mole) of IX in a small reaction flask equipped with stirrer and condenser and cooled in a Dry Ice–acetone-bath. If the mixture is not cooled it becomes violent after about 5 minutes. The cooled mixture is slowly warmed and finally refluxed for 3–4 hours. The product was distilled (Claisen) directly from this mixture to yield 6.0 g. (32%) of 2-deuterio-2-methyl-1,3-dioxolane (XII), b.p. 82–84°; g.p.c. analysis indicated a purity of 96%. The reported[23] boiling point of 2-methyl-1,3-dioxolane is 82°. Before use the deuteriodioxolane XII was purified by preparative scale g.p.c. The n.m.r. was consistent with the assumed structure and no C.2 hydrogen could be detected. Reduction of the methoxydioxolane IX with lithium aluminum hydride gave

(22) C. J. Claus and J. L. Morganthau, *J. Am. Chem. Soc.*, **73**, 5005 (1951).

(23) H. J. Dauben, B. Loken and H. J. Ringold, *ibid.*, **76**, 1359 (1954).

authentic 2-methyl-1,3-dioxolane as indicated by its infrared, n.m.r. and boiling point; infrared (carbon tetrachloride): 3.31(m), 3.44(m), 4.70(m), 8.88(s), 9.47(s), 11.6(s) μ; n.m.r. (carbon tetrachloride, 1 molar): 6.20 (10), 8.74 (s).

Reaction of Fluoborate VII with 2-Deuterio-2-methyl-1,3-dioxolane (XII).—The fluoroborate VII was prepared as usual on the vacuum line from 1.00 g. (0.008 mole) of silver fluoborate in about 40–50 ml. of sulfur dioxide at about $-75°$. To this stirred mixture, 1.20 g. (0.013 mole) of deuteriodioxolane (XII) was added all at once and stirring was continued for 4 hours. At the end of this period, 0.97 g. (0.008 mole) of methoxydioxolane (IX) was added and the reaction was worked-up as usual. Warming of the reaction mixture without addition of IX resulted in complete decomposition. Impure 2-methyl-1,3-dioxolenium fluoborate (XI) was obtained in 48% yield (0.67 g.), m.p. 174+° dec. As before, this salt was incompletely soluble in sulfur dioxide. The n.m.r. spectrum of the sulfur dioxide solution revealed about 7% impurity; otherwise, it was identical with authentic material.

Examination of the crude ether-soluble product by g.p.c. indicated the absence of norbornadiene or its possible isomers. Very little volatile material could be detected. However, two very small unresolved peaks appeared at approximately the retention time of 7-methoxynorbornadiene (X), but were insufficient to characterize. Excess dioxolanes IX and XII were, of course, removed in the water wash. The infrared of the crude product was inconclusive, except that the norbornadiene nucleus could not be detected. Claisen distillation gave a wide boiling point range, 100–150° (0.2 mm.), and no identifiable products.

63 | A Dissenting View

At the "Transition State" Symposium of the London Chemical Society in 1961, H. C. Brown spoke with a resounding voice of dissent. We recommend that the reader read this paper in full, then turn to the commentary on page 461.

From: *Chem. Soc. (London) Spec. Publ.* **16,** 140–62 (1962)

Strained Transition States

By Herbert C. Brown

(Purdue University, Lafayette, Indiana, U.S.A.)

INITIALLY, following the pioneering studies of Kehrmann in 1889[1] and of Meyer in 1894,[2] steric effects occupied a respectable position in organic chemistry. Indeed, in the 1920's, consideration of such effects constituted a major section of organic theory, as evidenced by the large amount of space devoted to them in books such as the advanced treatise by Cohen.[3]

The immense success of the electronic theory of organic reactions, as developed by Stieglitz, Robinson, and Ingold in the 1920's and 1930's, led naturally to the attempt to account for all chemical behaviour in terms of electronic effects.[4] Many phenomena which today are recognized as resulting from steric forces were attributed to the operation of pure electronic factors.[4, 5] As a consequence of the major emphasis on the electronic interpretation of chemical behaviour, attention to the role of steric effects in organic theory sank to a very low ebb.

For example, the excellent book published in 1940 by Hammett played a large part in introducing the quantitative methods of physical chemistry into organic chemistry.[6] Yet any consideration of steric effects is conspicuously absent from its pages. Perhaps the prevalent view of the times is best expressed in the words of a textbook published in 1941: "Steric hindrance . . . has become the last refuge of the puzzled organic chemist."[7]

It was evident that if steric effects were again to receive serious consideration as a major factor in chemical theory, it would be necessary to obtain quantitative, rather than qualitative, data on steric phenomena. A new tool was needed.

MOLECULAR ADDITION COMPOUNDS

Consideration of the ionization of simple acids and bases has played an important part in the development of modern theories of organic chemistry. Indeed, many of the currently accepted theoretical concepts receive their most direct and best confirmation from acid–base phenomena.[8–10] It is probable that the major contribution of this reaction to the development of organic theory is due not to any inherent importance of the ionization reaction, but rather to the lack of other simple reversible reactions of wide applicability.

It was pointed out by G. N. Lewis that the essential process in the ionization of classical acids and bases is the co-ordination of the proton with the free electron-pair of the base.[11] He suggested, therefore, that molecules such as boron trichloride and stannic chloride, which possess the ability to accept the electron pair of a base, should also be considered acids. Irrespective of whether this definition is accepted, it is apparent that the co-ordination of such Lewis acids with bases represents a simple reversible process of far greater versatility than the original reaction involving the transfer of a proton.

$$H^+ \quad\quad + \text{ :Base} = H\text{:Base}^+$$
$$\tfrac{1}{2}(BH_3)_2 + \text{ :Base} = H_3B\text{:Base}$$
$$BF_3 \quad\quad + \text{ :Base} = F_3B\text{:Base}$$
$$BMe_3 \quad\quad + \text{ :Base} = Me_3B\text{:Base}$$
$$AlMe_3 \quad\quad + \text{ :Base} = Me_3Al\text{:Base}$$
$$GaMe_3 \quad\quad + \text{ :Base} = Me_3Ga\text{:Base}$$

In studying molecular addition compounds, we can introduce wide variations in the structures of both components. Consequently, we are in a position to study in detail the effect of structure and of substituents upon the stability of the molecular addition compounds. In this way it is possible to evaluate the importance of the classical electronic effects, induction and resonance, as well as steric effects arising from the conflicting steric requirements of the two components.

There is an additional advantage in the study of these systems. Classical acid–base reactions must be studied in water or related solvents. Interpretation of the results is frequently rendered difficult because of the problem of separating solvent effects from the structural interactions under examination. On the other hand, molecular addition compounds can be examined in the vapour phase or in non-polar solvents, greatly simplifying the analysis of the data.

The proton is a charged particle of negligible steric requirements. As long as organic theory concerned itself primarily with the factors controlling the addition or removal of a proton from an organic moiety, it was natural that the theory should emphasize the role of the electrical factor in organic phenomena to the exclusion of the steric factor. Extension of the study of acid–base phenomena to Lewis acids with varying steric requirements has led to a clearer appreciation of the steric factor in organic theory.[12]

STERIC EFFECTS IN BIMOLECULAR DISPLACEMENTS

Considerable quantitative data have now been accumulated to show that the stability of a given molecular addition compound is a function of the conflicting steric requirements of the substituents on the acid and on the base, as well as their electronic contributions. Thus, in the addition compound (I) it is observed that the stability decreases with the increasing steric requirements of the substituents R and R′, while maintaining their electronic contributions sensibly constant.[13]

(I) —N·BR$_3$ —N····CR$_3$····I   (II)
      R′   R′

Similarly, in the reaction of substituted pyridine bases with alkyl iodides, it is observed that the rate of reaction is a function of the steric requirements of the substituents, R and R′.[14]

—N + CR$_3$ I ⟶ $\overset{+}{\text{N}}$—CR$_3$ I$^-$
  R′   R′

Indeed, a careful examination of the influence of the steric requirements of the substituents on the stability of the molecular addition compounds and on the rates of the related displacement reactions revealed a simple relationship between the strains in the molecular addition compounds (I) and those in the related transition states (II) for the displacement reaction.[13]

STERIC EFFECTS IN UNIMOLECULAR SOLVOLYSES

These studies of molecular addition compounds led to the conclusion that three alkyl groups attached to a tetrahedral nitrogen atom, such as in trimethylamine, or to a carbon atom, such as in t-butyl chloride, constitute a centre of strain.[15] Such strain would obviously be relieved in the ionization of a tertiary chloride to form the planar carbonium ion (III) and should therefore provide a powerful driving force for the ionization.

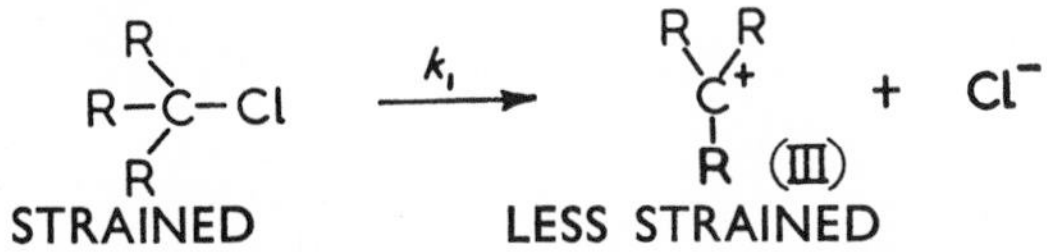

$$
\begin{array}{ccc}
\text{R} & & \text{R} \quad \text{R} \\
\text{R--C--Cl} & \xrightarrow{k_1} & \text{C}^+ \quad + \quad \text{Cl}^- \\
\text{R} & & \text{R} \ (\text{III}) \\
\text{STRAINED} & & \text{LESS STRAINED}
\end{array}
$$

Data have now accumulated to support the conclusion that large bulky groups in the tertiary halide markedly increase the rate of ionization.[16, 17]

It appears reasonable that a carbonium ion containing large bulky groups would exhibit a decreased tendency to react by substitution to give (IV) which would regenerate the original strained system, and an enhanced tendency to undergo elimination to give (V).[18]

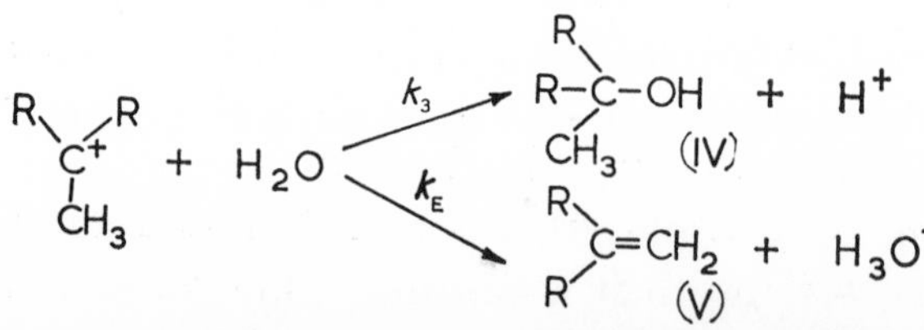

$$
\begin{array}{c}
\text{R} \quad \text{R} \\
\text{C}^+ \ + \ H_2O \ \substack{\xrightarrow{k_3} \\ \xrightarrow{k_E}} \\
\text{CH}_3
\end{array}
\quad
\begin{array}{c}
\text{R--C--OH} \ + \ H^+ \\
\text{CH}_3 \quad (\text{IV}) \\
\text{C=CH}_2 \ + \ H_3O^+ \\
(\text{V})
\end{array}
$$

Thus the solvolysis of t-butyl chloride in 80% aqueous ethanol yields 16% of isobutene (VI) whereas the related tertiary halide, 2,3,3-trimethyl-2-butyl chloride, yields 61% of the olefin (VII).[18]

The suggestion is now supported by a great deal of accumulated data.[19] However, alternative electronic interpretations have been suggested.[20]

STERIC EFFECTS IN BIMOLECULAR ELIMINATIONS

Convincing evidence is now available to support the conclusion that, in bimolecular elimination reactions, the preferred transition state will contain the four atoms concerned in the reaction in a planar *trans* arrangement (VIII).[21, 22]

In the case of a molecule which can eliminate in two possible directions, to yield two isomeric olefins, the two possible transition states can be represented as (IX) and (X).[23]

(VIII)   (IX)   (X)

In the absence of appreciable steric interactions, the transition state (X) should be somewhat more stable than (IX) because of the greater possibilities of hyperconjugation between the incipient double bond and the alkyl groups. The reaction will therefore proceed preferentially through this transition state to give a predominant yield of the more highly alkylated of the two possible olefins—a manifestation of elimination in accordance with the Saytzeff rule.[24]

This situation will be altered by the existence of steric effects. Such steric effects should arise from any one of three changes: (1) an increase in the steric requirements of the alkyl group R, (2) an increase in the steric requirements of the leaving group X, and (3) an increase in the steric requirements of the attacking base B.

It should be apparent from structure (X) that an increase in the steric requirements of the group R should result in increased steric interactions between the groups R and X. Such interactions will make the attainment of the transition state (X) more costly in energy. On the other hand, an increase in the steric requirements of R should have much less effect on the transition state (IX).

On the basis of these considerations an increase in the steric requirements of R would be expected to result in a decreased tendency for the reaction to proceed through the transition state (X) (Saytzeff elimination) and an increased tendency for the reaction to proceed through the less strained transition state (IX) (Hofmann elimination). Similarly, an increase in the steric requirements of X should likewise increase the steric interactions between R and X, and result in an enhanced tendency for the elimination to proceed *via* the less strained transition state (IX) (Hofmann elimination). Finally, an increase in the steric requirements of the base B (all other factors being maintained sensibly constant) should again result in a decreased stability of the transition state (X) relative to (IX).

In fact the data reveal a regular trend from Saytzeff to Hofmann elimination with the increasing steric requirements of the alkyl group R, with the increasing steric requirements of the leaving group X, and with the increasing steric requirements of the attacking base B.[23] The data consequently support this interpretation of the influence of steric strains on the transition states of bimolecular eliminations. However, alternative views have recently been discussed.[25]

THE QUESTION OF NON-CLASSICAL CARBONIUM IONS

In recent years considerable research has been devoted to solvolytic processes.[26] There has been major interest in the factors influencing the rates of ionization of organic halide and sulphonate esters.

$$RX \underset{k_{-1}}{\overset{k_1}{\rightleftharpoons}} R+ + X-$$

$$R+ + SH \rightarrow RS + H+$$

It was recognized early that derivatives with the benzylic structure undergo solvolysis at a rate considerably greater than that of the related aliphatic composition. Thus the solvolysis of αα-dimethylbenzyl chloride (XII) in 90% aqueous acetone at 25° proceeds at a rate some 600-fold greater than that of t-butyl chloride (XI).

The enhanced rate of solvolysis of αα-dimethylbenzyl chloride is attributed to resonance stabilization of the incipient carbonium ion in the transition state (XIII). (It is convenient to represent the incipient carbonium ion in the transition state as the actual carbonium ion. However, it is important to recognize that in the actual transition state the leaving group is still partially bonded to the carbonium carbon atom.)

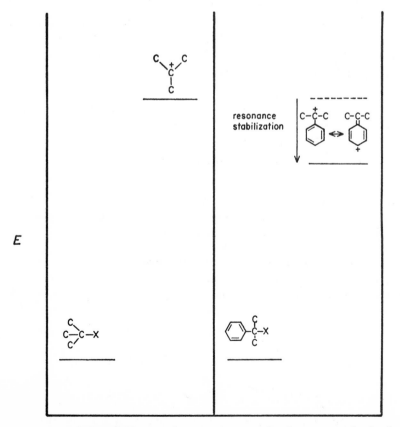

Consequently, the enhanced rate is primarily the result of the existence of a transition state which is lower in potential energy than the corresponding transition state in t-butyl chloride (Fig. 1).

FIG. 1. *Effect of classical resonance in facilitating solvolysis.*

Similarly, the enhanced rates of solvolysis of dimethyl-neopentyl-methyl chloride[16] or of tri-ti-butylmethyl *p*-nitrobenzoate[17] are attributed to strains in the initial state, strains which are partly relieved in the transition state. In other words the lower energy of activation in these solvolyses is due to an increase in the energy of the initial state relative to the transition state (Fig. 2).

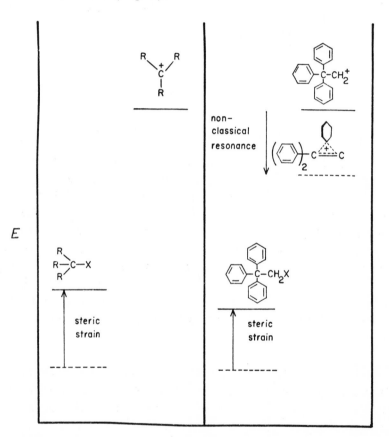

FIG. 2. *Effect of steric strain and postulated non-classical resonance in facilitating solvolysis.*

In recent years, numerous other cases of enhanced solvolysis rates have been observed.[26] In many instances these enhanced rates have been attributed to "non-classical resonance", and so-called "non-classical" structures have been assigned to the carbonium ions (XIV)–(XVII) formed in the solvolysis.

However, essentially every case where non-classical structures have been suggested involve strained initial states (Fig. 2). This raises the question of how much, if any, of the effect is due to non-classical resonance and how much to the strain in the molecular structure.

Suggestions for non-classical structures and resonance have multiplied fantastically in recent years, often without any reasonable scientific basis, and it is obviously impractical to examine all of them in detail. Accordingly, several years ago we decided to restrict our study to the four systems (XIV)—(XVII) in an effort to assess the relative importance of strain and non-classical resonance in the observed phenomena. Our study of the phenonium ion system has been concluded. This discussion will briefly review our work on this problem and will present our conclusions as to the importance of the phenonium ion in the reactions of phenethyl derivatives. Other systems will be considered in less detail.

Tools for the Study of Non-classical Carbonium Ions

Carbonium ions are reactive intermediates with very short lifetimes. As a result, it is possible to attribute many properties to such intermediates without the possibility for direct experimental test of their validity. Obviously it would be desirable to find a model system which would be sufficiently closely related to carbonium ions to provide a means of testing the many suggestions for unusual stabilities for carbonium ions of specific structures.

One reasonable model for carbonium ions (XVIII) would be the corresponding organoborines (XIX). However, these are difficult to work with, and, in the case of the more complex structures, they would be exceedingly difficult to synthesize. The corresponding ketones (XX) appear to offer major advantages in this regard.

Isotopes provide another major tool. The isotope may either be used as a tag, or as a substituent exerting a secondary isotope effect, to test some of the consequences of the non-classical formulations suggested to account for the observed enhanced rates.

Finally, we can make use of a powerful nucleophile to trap the newly-formed carbonium ion in order to establish whether the ionization proceeds to produce a single non-classical structure or a rapidly equilibrating set of classical carbonium ions.

It is remarkable that in spite of the huge volume of work in which such ions are suggested, there have been remarkably few critical studies to test the essentialness of the recommended interpretation.

The Non-classical Cyclodecyl Ion

One exception to the above statement is provided by the so-called non-classical cyclodecyl carbonium ion.

It was observed that cyclodecyl toluene-p-sulphonate undergoes solvolysis at an enhanced rate, 376 times that of cyclohexyl toluene-p-sulphonate.[32, 33] Moreover, the solvolysis is accompanied by transannular hydride shifts, so that the substituent appears at positions in the ring which did not contain the original toluene-p-sulphonyl group.[34] It therefore appeared reasonable to suggest that the solvolysis might proceed *via* the formation of a non-classical cyclodecyl ion (XXI).[32]

However, it was shown that the transannular deuterated derivative (XXIII) solvolyzes at the same rate as the undeuterated compound (XXII). This argues against transannular hydrogen participation in the ionization stage.[34]

$k_1 = 4.60 \times 10^{-5} \, \text{sec.}^{-1}$ $k_1 = 4.55 \times 10^{-5} \, \text{sec.}^{-1}$

(XXII)   In acetic acid at 25°   (XXIII)

Similarly, it was observed that the rate of reaction of sodium borohydride with cyclodecanone is very slow,[35] corresponding to the fast rate of solvolysis of the toluene-*p*-sulphonate. In other words, those factors which favour the transformation from the tetrahedral toluene-*p*-sulphonate to the trigonal carbonium ion resist the related conversion from the corresponding trigonal ketone into the tetrahedral carbinol. Indeed, a plot of log k_1 for the solvolysis of the toluene-*p*-sulphonates against log k_2 for the reaction of the cyclic ketones with sodium boro-hydride[35] yields a reasonably good linear relationship for compounds with from five to ten ring members (Fig. 3).

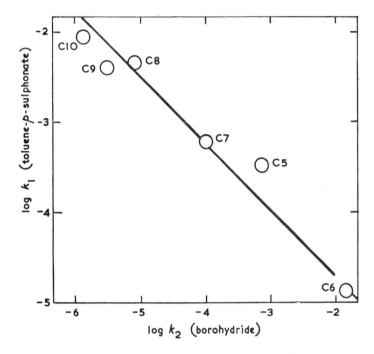

FIG. 3. *Free-energy relationship between the rate constants for the acetolysis of the cyclic toluene-*p*-sulphonates and the rate constants for the reaction of the cyclanones with sodium borohydride.*

THE NON-CLASSICAL PHENONIUM ION

The non-classical phenonium ion was originally introduced to account for the striking stereochemical results in the solvolysis of the *erythro-* and *threo*-3-phenyl-2-butyl toluene-*p*-sulphonates.[36] It has also been used to account for the relatively fast solvolysis exhibited by 2,2,2-triphenylethyl toluene-*p*-sulphonate (XXIV) and related derivatives.[28, 37]

However, a careful consideration of the problem indicates that the fast rate of solvolysis may arise from other factors. Thus the toluene-*p*-sulphonate is a highly substituted derivative. Relief of steric strain in the ionization stage may provide part or all of the observed driving force for

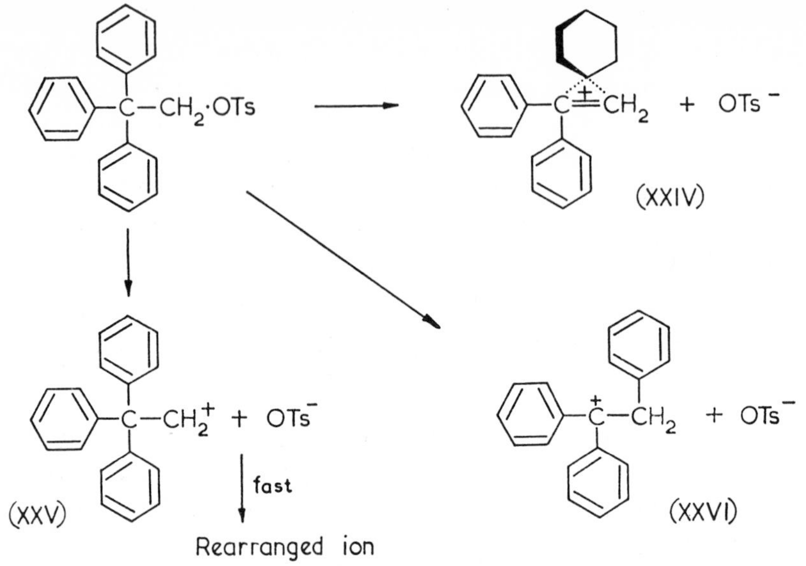

(XXIV)

(XXV)

fast

Rearranged ion

(XXVI)

the enhanced rate, with rearrangement of a phenyl group occurring as a fast second stage to give (XXV).

Finally, there is the possibility that the fast rate may arise from a direct rearrangement into the more stable tertiary carbonium ion (XXVI). In this event the phenonium structure would represent a transition state with a partially formed tertiary carbonium ion, and not a stabilized intermediate.

In order to arrive at an understanding of the importance of the phenonium ion in the solvolytic reactions of phenylethyl derivatives, it appears desirable to examine the behaviour of symmetrical structures. In such systems, rearrangement to a more stable carbonium ion will not be a factor in the experimental behaviour.

The solvolysis of 2,3-dimethyl-3-phenyl-2-butyl chloride[38] (XXVII) in 80% aqueous ethanol at 25° proceeds at a normal rate, not significantly faster than that of 2,3,3-trimethyl-2-butyl chloride (XXVIII) and slower than that of 2,3,3-trimethyl-2-pentyl chloride (XXIX).

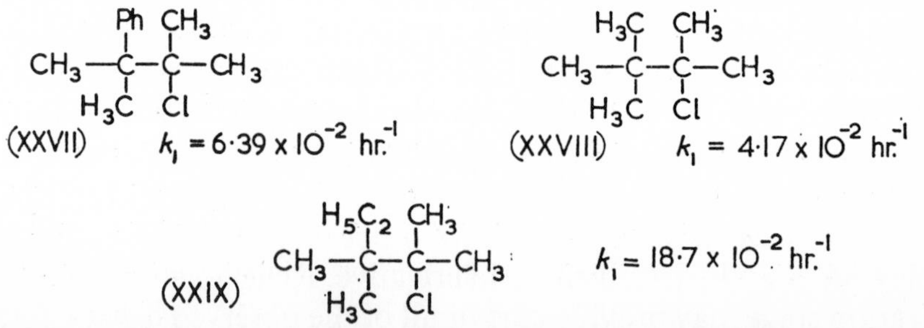

(XXVII) $k_1 = 6.39 \times 10^{-2}$ hr.$^{-1}$

(XXVIII) $k_1 = 4.17 \times 10^{2}$ hr.$^{-1}$

(XXIX) $k_1 = 18.7 \times 10^{-2}$ hr.$^{-1}$

It may be argued that in this system the tertiary carbonium ion is too stable to require assistance by the neighbouring phenyl group.

The related primary system, phenethyl toluene-*p*-sulphonate (XXX) exhibits no rate enhancement in the solvolysis in acetic acid over ethyl toluene-*p*-sulphonate (XXXI).[39] In this system it is argued that the lack of phenyl-participation arises from the openness of the rear side of the carbonium ion—it is so open to solvation by the solvent that the phenyl group cannot compete.

$$PhCH_2-CH_2 \quad k_1 = 2 \cdot 88 \times 10^{-7} sec.^{-1} \qquad CH_3-CH_2 \quad k_1 = 7 \cdot 72 \times 10^{-7} sec.^{-1}$$
$$\text{(XXX)} \quad OTs \qquad\qquad\qquad\qquad \text{(XXXI)} \quad OTs$$

Consequently, we are thereby restricted to an examination of secondary–secondary systems as possessing the proper balance between high activity of the carbonium ion and significant shielding of the rear side toward solvation.

The 1,2,2-triphenylethyl system has been exceedingly thoroughly studied by Collins and Bonner.[40] They used a triple labelling technique to establish the mechanism of the solvolysis and the rearrangement, and concluded that their results required that the ionization proceed through an open carbonium ion (XXXII). Moreover, the solvolysis of the optically active 1,2,2-triphenylethyl toluene-*p*-sulphonate proceeds with predominant retention of configuration, in spite of the conclusion[41] that only open classical carbonium ions are involved.

(XXXII)

It has been argued that these results must not be extrapolated to other secondary systems because the secondary benzylic carbonium ion may be too stable to make a demand upon the neighbouring pheynyl groups.[41]

Although no details have been presented, it has been reported by Winstein and Roberts[42] that in the acetolysis of *trans*-2-phenyl-cyclopentyl-*p*-bromobenzenesulphonate the possibility of phenyl participation does not influence the stereochemistry of the reaction. It was suggested that this might be the result of unfavourable angles for phenyl participation in the five-membered ring system, and more favourable conditions might exist in the corresponding cyclohexyl system.

However, this is not borne out by the experimental results. There is no evidence for any enhancement in the solvolysis (in acetic acid at 75°) of *trans*-2-phenylcyclohexyl toluene-*p*-sulphonate (XXXIII) as compared to the *cis*-isomer (XXXIV).[43] It has been argued that the energy required

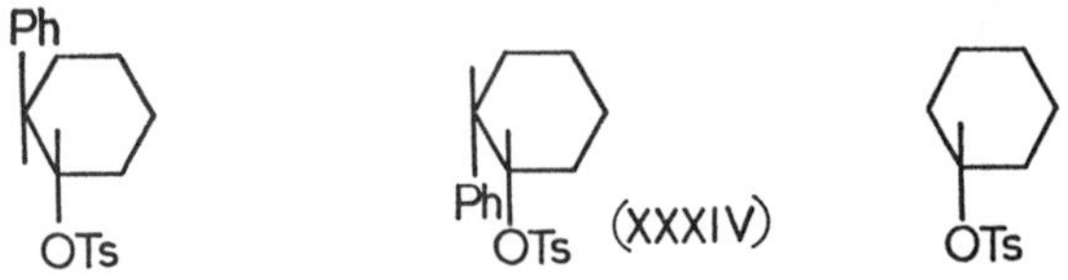

(XXXIII)   (XXXIV)

k_1: $7.95 \times 10^{-6} sec.^{-1}$ $7.7 \times 10^{-5} sec.^{-1}$ $4.14 \times 10^{-5} sec.^{-1}$

to place the phenyl group in an axial position suitable for participation would be prohibitive.[44]

By this time one has the feeling that he has something very nebulous by the tail.

Even in the case of 3-phenyl-2-butyl toluene-*p*-sulphonate (XXXV), the rate data[28] (in acetic acid at 49·6°) do not support phenyl participation in the ionization stage (XXXVI).

$$CH_3 \cdot CH \cdot CH \cdot CH_3$$
Ph, OTs (*threo*)
k_1: $2.38 \times 10^{-6} sec.^{-1}$ (XXXV)

$$CH_3 \cdot CH_2 \cdot CH \cdot CH_3$$
OTs
k_1: $4.3 \times 10^{-6} sec.^{-1}$ (XXXVI)

In acetic acid at 49·6°

The stereochemical results may support the formation of the phenonium intermediate immediately following the ionization stage. However, it should be recognized that the observed results do not *require* that the solvolysis proceed through such an intermediate. Attention is called to the 1,2,2-triphenylethyl system where the solvolysis proceeds with predominant retention even though the reaction involves open classical carbonium ions.

This discussion has emphasized the question of the importance of phenonium intermediates in the solvolysis of simple phenethyl derivatives. The results clearly indicate that the simple, unsubstituted phenyl group does not provide any significant driving force in the ionization of symmetrical derivaties.

Even in the case of 2,2,2-triphenylethyl toluene-*p*-sulphonate it can be argued that the phenonium ion does not make a major contribution to the solvolysis. The linear relationship observed between the logarithm of the rates of solvolysis of the toluene-*p*-sulphonates and the rates of the reaction of the corresponding ketones with sodium borohydride argues strongly for simple steric assistance as a major factor in the solvolysis rate (Fig. 4).

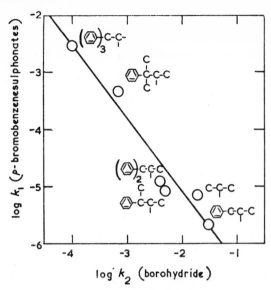

FIG. 4. *Logarithm of the rates of solvolysis of 2-substituted ethyl toluene-p-sulphonates and the rates of reaction of the corresponding ketones with sodium borohydride.*

THE NON-CLASSICAL TRICYCLOBUTONIUM ION

The fast rate of solvolysis of cyclopropylmethyl toluene-p-sulphonate and similar derivatives was originally attributed to the formation of the symmetrical tricyclobutonium ion (XXXVII), stabilized by non-classical resonance.[29]

In this way it was suggested that one could account both for the fast solvolysis rates and the rearrangements observed during solvolysis.

However, Hart and Sandri[45] showed that a number of secondary and tertiary derivatives containing cyclopropyl groups undergo solvolysis with similar rate enhancements but without rearrangements. Moreover, it was shown[46] that the deuterium derivative fails to exhibit any significant difference in rate over the hydrogen analogue.

$$
\begin{array}{cc}
\underset{H_2C}{\overset{H_2C}{\diagdown}}\!\!\!-CH \cdot CH_2 \cdot OTs & \underset{D_2C}{\overset{D_2C}{\diagdown}}\!\!\!-CH \cdot CH_2 \cdot OTs \\
1 \cdot 00 & 1 \cdot 00
\end{array}
$$

In acetic acid at 25°

Moreover, in our studies, it was observed that cyclopropyl groups have retarding effects on the reaction of ketones,[47] related to their rate-enhancing effects in the solvolysis of the toluene-*p*-sulphonates.

Roberts and his co-workers[48] have now replaced his original proposal of a single non-classical species by a rapidly equilibrating set of non-classical bicyclobutonium ions (XXXVIII).

It does not appear to be possible at the present time to distinguish these experimentally from the corresponding set of equilibrating classical ions.

BICYCLIC NON-CLASSICAL IONS

The last major stronghold of non-classical carbonium ions appears to be the bicyclic structures. The observation that *exo*-norbornyl toluene-*p*-sulphonate is 350 times as reactive as the *endo*-derivative and that the solvolysis of both compounds proceeds to give the *exo* products has been interpreted[30] as requiring the existence of a non-classical species (XXXIX), instead of a rapidly equilibrating pair of classical carbonium ions (XL).

The resonance stabilization is presumed to be important in the transition state for the *exo* toluene-*p*-sulphonate, but not for the *endo*. The predominant formation of the *exo* product is attributed to covalent bonding at the rear of the carbonium ion, so that the attack by solvent or other nucleophile must occur from the front-side.

Let us consider the validity of these arguments as a requirement for a non-classical species.

The fact that the *exo*-compound solvolyzes faster than the *endo* does not necessarily mean that the *exo* exhibits an enhanced rate. Rather, it may mean that the rate of the *exo* derivative is normal and that of the *endo* compound is unusually slow.

Can we conceive of any factor which might cause the *endo* derivative to be unusually slow?

Actually, an examination of the path which would be followed by the departing toluene-*p*-sulphonyl group reveals that it will be required to pass unusually close to the *endo* hydrogen atoms at the 5- and the 6-position. Consequently, we may be observing steric hindrance to ionization in the *endo* compound, rather than non-classical rate acceleration in the *exo*.

The stereochemistry of the substitution likewise does not require bonding at the rear side of the carbonium ion. It is well known that substitution from the *endo* direction of the norbornyl system is greatly hindered compared to approach from the *exo* direction. On this basis the lack of attack from the rear side of the carbonium ion is to be attributed not to the fact that the rear side is covalently bonded to saturated carbon, but to the fact that the rear side is sterically protected by the unusual steric requirements of bicyclic systems.

These arguments reveal that there is a reasonable alternative to non-classical structures in accounting for the behaviour of bicyclic carbonium ions. It appears desirable to test this alternative interpretation by experiment and we are presently engaged in this.

CONCLUSIONS

To sum up, our studies indicate that phenyl bridging is not an important factor in the ionization of phenyl substituted alkyl toluene-*p*-sulphonates except in very exceptional circumstances. Even in the case of 2,2,2-triphenylethyl toluene-*p*-sulphonate the major driving force toward ionization appears to be relief of steric strain.

In the case of cyclopropylmethyl halides and toluene-*p*-sulphonates, there appear to be no advantages in considering the ionization to proceed to a non-classical tricyclobutonium ion or to a set of three rapidly equilibrating ions. Instead, the results are most simply explained in terms of a rapidly equilibrating set of carbonium ions, classical in structure. We agree with Winstein and Kosower[49] that the enhanced rates observed in the solvolysis of these compounds is primarily due to their strained condition.

In the bicyclic system our experimental work has not yet reached a stage on which to base a definite conclusion. However, there exist a number of major difficulties in accounting for the observed data in terms of non-classical interactions. The possibility that steric hindrance to ionization and steric hindrance to substitution may be major factors in the observed behaviour of bicyclic derivatives appears to have been ignored.

The author does not wish at this time to urge the adoption of any particular interpretation. It appears desirable, however, to call attention to the existence of possible alternative explanations and to urge that interpretations in terms of non-classical intermediates be made with the same care and the same sound experimental basis as that which is customary in other areas of experimental organic chemistry.

The studies reported in this publication were made possible by grants from the National Science Foundation, and the Atomic Energy Commission.

References:
[1] Kehrmann, *J. prakt. Chem.*, 1889, **40**, 257.
[2] Meyer, *Ber.*, 1894, **27**, 510.
[3] Cohen, "Organic Chemistry," 5th ed., Edward Arnold and Co., London, 1928, Vol. I, Ch. 5.
[4] Remick, "Electronic Interpretation of Organic Chemistry," John Wiley and Sons, New York, 1944.
[5] Brown, *J. Chem. Soc.*, 1956, 1248.
[6] Hammett, "Physical Organic Chemistry," McGraw-Hill, New York, 1940.
[7] Ray, "Organic Chemistry," J. B. Lippincott Co., New York, 1941, p. 522.
[8] Watson, "Modern Theories of Organic Chemistry," 2nd ed., Oxford University Press, 1941.
[9] Wheland, "The Theory of Resonance," 2nd ed., John Wiley and Sons, New York, 1955.
[10] Brown, McDaniel, and Hafliger, "Dissociation Constants," Ch. 14 in "Determination of Organic Structures by Physical Methods," ed. Braude and Nachod, Academic Press, New York, 1955.
[11] Lewis, *J. Franklin Inst.*, 1938, **226**, 293.
[12] Brown, *J. Chem. Educ.*, 1959, **36**, 424.
[13] Brown, Gintis, and Domash, *J. Amer. Chem. Soc.*, 1956, **78**, 5387.
[14] Brown and Cahn, *J. Amer. Chem. Soc.*, 1955, **77**, 1715.
[15] Brown, *Science*, 1946, **103**, 385.
[16] Brown and Fletcher, *J. Amer. Chem. Soc.*, 1949, **71**, 1845.
[17] Bartlett and Swain, *J. Amer. Chem. Soc.*, 1955, **77**, 2801.
[18] Brown and Fletcher, *J. Amer. Chem. Soc.*, 1950, **72**, 1223.
[19] Brown and Moritani, *J. Amer. Chem. Soc.*, 1955, **77**, 3623.
[20] Hughes, Ingold, and Shiner, jun, *J. Chem. Soc.*, 1953, 3827.
[21] Hückel, Tappe, and Legutke, *Annalen* 1940, **543**, 191.
[22] Cristol, *J. Amer. Chem. Soc.*, 1947, **69**, 338.
[23] Brown and Moritani, *J. Amer. Chem. Soc.*, 1956, **78**, 2203.
[24] Dhar, Hughes, Ingold, Mandour, and Maw, *J. Chem. Soc.*, 1948, 2093.
[25] Banthorpe, Hughes, and Ingold, *J. Chem. Soc.*, 1960, 4054.
[26] Streitweiser, *Chem. Rev.*, 1956, **56**, 571.
[27] Brown, Brady, Grayson, and Bonner, *J. Amer. Chem. Soc.*, 1957, **79**, 1897.
[28] Winstein, Morse, Grunwald, Schreiber, and Corse, *J. Amer. Chem. Soc.*, 1952, **74**, 1113.
[29] Roberts and Mazur, *J. Amer. Chem. Soc.*, 1951, **73**, 2509.
[30] Winstein and Trifan, *J. Amer. Chem. Soc.*, 1952, **74**, 1149.
[31] Winstein, Walborsky, and Schreiber, *J. Amer. Chem. Soc.*, 1950, **72**, 5795.
[32] Heck and Prelog, *Helv. Chim. Acta*, 1955, **31**, 1541.

[33] Brown and Ham, *J. Amer. Chem. Soc.*, 1956, **78**, 2735.
[34] Prelog, *Record Chem. Progress*, 1957, **18**, 247.
[35] Brown and Ichikawa, *Tetrahedron*, 1957, **1**, 211.
[36] Cram, *J. Amer. Chem. Soc.*, 1949, **71**, 3863.
[37] Charlton, Dostrovsky, and Hughes, *Nature*, 1951, **167**, 986.
[38] Brown, Morgan, Chloupek, and Bernheimer, unpublished work.
[39] Winstein, Lindegren, Marshall, and Ingraham, *J. Amer. Chem. Soc.*, 1953, **75**, 147.
[40] Bonner and Collins, *J. Amer. Chem. Soc.*, 1956, **78**, 5587.
[41] Collins, Bonner, and Lester, *J. Amer. Chem. Soc.*, 1959, **81**, 466.
[42] Winstein and Roberts, *J. Amer. Chem. Soc.*, 1953, **75**, 2297.
[43] Funakabo, Moritani, Choe, and Murahishi, personal communication.
[44] Curtin and Schmukler, *J. Amer. Chem. Soc.*, 1955, **77**, 1105.
[45] Hart and Sandry, *J. Amer. Chem. Soc.*, 1959, **81**, 320.
[46] Borcic, Nikoletic, and Sunko, *Chem. and Ind.*, 1960, 527.
[47] Brown, Bernheimer, and Nishida, unpublished work.
[48] Mazur, White, Semenow, Lee, Silver, and Roberts, *J. Amer. Chem. Soc.*, 1959, **81**, 4390.
[49] Winstein and Kosower, *J. Amer. Chem. Soc.*, 1959, **81**, 4399.

Discussion on the Paper by

H. C. Brown

Professor R. E. Robertson (*National Research Council, Ottawa, Canada*). We have found an inverse secondary deuterium isotope effect from the hydrolysis of methyl halides and sulphonates and a similar inverse effect for γ-^{2}H-substitution in the corresponding n-propyl compounds. I wonder whether Professor Brown has used the method of deuterium substitution to test his hypothesis for those cases where he postulates interference between hydrogen and the leaving toluene-*p*-sulphonate group.

Professor Brown. It would be highly interesting to have data on the effect of *endo*-deuterium in the 6-position of *endo*-norbornyl toluene-*p*-sulphonate on its rate of solvolysis. Unfortunately, such data are not available. The hypothesis here presented would predict that this deuterium derivative should show a somewhat enhanced rate of hydrolysis over the parent compound.

Perhaps I might be permitted to mention here a remarkable result recently reported by Professor von Schleyer of Princeton University at the American Chemical Society in Washington. He synthesized 1,2-di-*p*-anisyl-2-norborneol and examined the carbonium ion produced in sulphuric acid by nuclear magnetic resonance. If the ion is non-classical, we should expect the two anisyl groups to be identical. On the other hand, if we are dealing with a rapidly equilibrating set of ions, the two anisyl groups should be distinct.

The nuclear magnetic resonance spectrum revealed the presence of two distinct anisyl groups.

Dr. J. W. Linnett (*Oxford University*). In connection with the two preceding papers, I would like to comment on non-classical structures for positive ions. First, the known bridge structure of diborane, with which $C_2H_6^{++}$ would be isoelectronic, seems to me to suggest that bridge structures for species like $C_2H_5^+$, $C_2R_4H^+$, etc., might have relatively low energies. After all, $C_2H_5^+$ contains the same number of electrons as B_2H_6, and a structure such as

$$H_2C \overset{\overset{H}{.}}{\smile} CH_2 \qquad \left(\text{or } H_2C \overset{.H.}{\smile} CH_2 \right)$$

is not therefore unreasonable. If such structures do have low energies, the mobility of hydrogen atoms in positive ions, which is observed in mass-spectrometric work, is understandable (cf. the paper by Dr. Maccoll). The second point is that it is not always necessary to suppose that these non-classical structures have an energy actually lower than the classical ones; they might be relatively easy transition states which decided the course a reaction would take.

Professor H. C. Brown (*Purdue University, Lafayette, Indiana, U.S.A.*). I hope that Dr. Linnett will concede that I am not unaware of the chemistry of diborane and related substances and of the bridge structures for these substances. Since bridge structures are well established in these substances, it was reasonable to consider the possibility of bridged structures for carbonium ions. However, all experiments which have been designed to test the importance of such structures in carbonium ions, under conditions where the physical organic chemists have postulated the formation of such intermediates have consistently yielded negative answers. I am not arguing against the possiblilty of bridged structures for solvated carbonium ions on theoretical grounds, but have attempted to point out that they appear to be ruled out on the basis of the available experimental evidence.

Permit me to clarify the term "solvated" carbonium ions used above. The physical organic chemist is primarily interested in carbonium ions formed as intermediates in solvolytic reactions and related processes. It should be pointed out that diborane and trimethylaluminum dimer possess their bridged structures only in the gas phase and in inert solvents. In diethyl ether trimethylaluminum loses its bridged structure and forms the simple monomeric etherate, $Me_3Al:OEt_2$. Similarly, in tetrahydrofuran diborane exists as the monomeric derivative. Most of the reactions of diborane appear to proceed *via* disruption of the bridged structure.

It is entirely possible that carbonium ions produced in the gas phase in the mass spectrometer possess bridged structures. However, the physical organic chemist is primarily interested in solvated carbonium ions. The evidence is overwhelming at present that such ions are best represented in their classical structures.

W. Gerrard (*Northern Polytechnic, London*). My purpose is to test opinion on the following statement, worded as two questions.

In the structure $>$C–X, when the bond C–X is being broken by solvolysis, does the carbonium structure $>$C$^{(+)}$ become flat concurrently as a consequence of the operation of one energy-change system, or is the flattening a subsequent occurrence energetically unconnected with the breaking of the C–X bond?

Secondly, what is the correlation between the answers to these questions and the resistance to solvolysis when the three groups of the structure $>$C are pinned back?

Professor Brown. As far as I know, there is no definite experimental evidence which bears on the point raised by Professor Gerrard in his first question. However, in terms of present thinking on the mechanism of such processes, it is more likely that the three groups attached to carbon approach coplanarity simultaneously with the lengthening of the C–X bond, achieving essential coplanarity at the moment the bond is ruptured.

With regard to the second question, Professor Doering has shown that the rate of solvolysis of 1-bromo bicyclo (2,2,2) octane is slow, but not remarkably so.

Presumably both the difficulty of solvating the rear of the carbonium ion and the strain introduced in approaching coplanarity of the carbonium centre are responsible for the reduced rate.

Dr. G. H. Whitham (*The University of Birmingham*). Your discussion has emphasized the possibility of accounting for the enhanced rates of solvolyses in bicyclic systems on other than "non-classical" grounds. Can you account for the observation that solvolyses in such systems occur with retention of configuration, without postulating a "non-classical" intermediate?

Professor Brown. It has been observed that the acetolysis of both *exo-* and *endo*-norbornyl toluene-*p*-sulphonates (I) and (II) yields *exo*-norbornyl acetate. This result has been attributed to the non-classical structure of the intermediate carbonium ion (III). It is postulated that the back-side of the carbonium ion is partially bonded to carbon-6 across the ring and that this bonding is responsible for the preferential substitution from the *exo*-side.

That this is not the only possible interpretation is indicated by our results on the hydroboration oxidation of norbornene (IV). *exo*-Norborneol is obtained in high purity with less than 1% of the *endo*-isomer indicated. Is this predominant formation of *exo*-norborneol (V) to be taken as evidence that there is non-classical bonding of the π-electrons of the double bond to the 5- and 6-carbon atoms across the ring?

Let us consider the possible role of steric effects in favouring substitution from the *exo* direction.

Solvolysis of the bridge head-substituted bicyclo[2,2,2]octane (VI) proceeds with retention of configuration.

Obviously there is no need to postulate non-classical bonding of the back-side of the carbonium carbon to the other bridgehead carbon in order to account for this substitution with retention of configuration.

Let us remove one of the ethylene bridges of this molecule. If we could retain the resulting boat structure (VII) of the cyclohexane derivative, we should not be surprised if substitution occurred predominantly from the less-hindered direction.

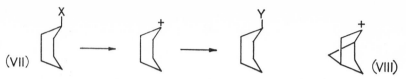

(VII)   (VIII)

We can retain cyclohexane in this form by introducing a methylene bridge and forming the 2-norbornyl cation (VIII). Here, also, substitution from the *exo* direction should be favoured sterically.

I, personally, find it much more reasonable that substitution should be directed along the less hindered approach to the carbonium carbon, rather than to postulate that the approach must be to the front-side because the back-side is bonded to a saturated carbon atom situated across the ring.

Permit me to point out another factor which may control the direction of substitution. These bicyclic carbonium ions are unusual in that they cannot be fully solvated from both directions. They undergo very rapid facile rearrangements. If such rearrangement is not the result of a non-classical structure, the carbonium ion must exist as a rapidly equilibrating set of ions. Professor von Schleyer's experiment, referred to previously, indicates that this is the case in the norbornyl system.

The very rapid movement of the ethylene bridge between the two adjacent positions of the cycopentyl ring system will prevent an accumulation of solvent in the *endo* direction and thereby favour substitution in the *exo* direction.

It is apparent that this proposal will predict the same stereochemistry as the more generally applied non-classical interpretation. Consequently, the stereochemical results do not appear to provide a really satisfactory basis for a decision between the alternative interpretations. For this reason my discussion emphasized rate phenomena. The question remains whether the observed rates exhibit enhancements which require major stabilization of the carbonium ions by non-classical resonance, or whether the rates are explicable in terms of less-stable equilibrating classical structures.

The discussion of the phenonium ion contains a piece of original and interesting evidence. This consists of a rather good correlation (Figure 4) between solvolysis rates of the substituted β-phenylethyl bromobenzenesulfonates and the borohydride reduction rates of the corresponding ketones and aldehydes. Winstein, Morse, Grunwald, Schreiber, and Corse (Paper No. 15) in 1952 pointed out that the effect of accumulation of groups at the β-carbon atom upon the driving force for phenyl participation could be due in part to relief of steric strain and in part to the contribution of the secondary or tertiary character at C-2 to the charge delocalization in the phenonium-like transition state. Brown's evidence makes it probable that the steric effect is the more important of the two.[1] This evidence, however, provides no test of the *mode of operation* of the steric effect in question. Brown appears to assume that both the borohydride reduction and the solvolysis are responding to changes in the direct steric pressure on the reaction center. These changes are more severe in the borohydride case (one O and one BH_4^- at C-1) than in the solvolysis (one H and one sulfonate), assuming that solvation requirements approximately cancel; yet the solvolysis is appreciably *more* sensitive to the range of structure changes examined than is the borohydride reduction. Indeed, if we should regard the cyclic ketones of Figure 3 as establishing a norm for the correlation between solvolysis and reduction rates, we should find that over a range of borohydride reduction rates normally associated with a range of 10^2 in solvolysis rates, the β-phenylethyl sulfonates are covering a range of about 10^4!

This exaggerated response of the β-phenylethyl solvolysis to steric effects presents no difficulty if the mechanism of it is that envisaged by Winstein and co-workers. The β substituents are pressing, not simply against C-1 and its attached atoms, but against each other. If at the transition state a β-phenyl group has moved a short distance toward the phenonium position, a larger amount of strain is relieved than in a simple rehybridization at C-1.

Because of its provocative style, Paper No. 63 has become one of the most quoted papers in the field, despite the modesty of its specific claims. Aspects of it have been discussed by several recent authors.[2] Also for our present purpose this paper seems to deserve careful attention.

Ten or so of the papers referred to in Paper No. 63 are in the present collection of reprints. Many others of this collection are pertinent to the subject of this paper. It seems, then, that the present reader should be in a strong position to

---

[1] We come to this opinion despite the fact that the linear free energy relationships between borohydride reduction and solvolysis prevail only in series of closely related compounds. Even the data of Figures 3 and 4 in this paper, if corrected by a suitable conversion factor between tosylates and brosylates and plotted on the same graph, would fall on lines of quite different slope.

[2] See, for example, D. J. Cram, *J. Am. Chem. Soc.* **86**, 3767 (1964); K. L. Servis and J. D. Roberts, *ibid.*, **86**, 3773 (1964); S. Winstein, *ibid.*, **87**, 381 (1965) and accompanying communications.

write his own commentary on this paper. We invite him to join us in a quiz inspired by Paper No. 63 and restricted in such a way that the answers are all to be found in this book.

1. In reference to the last paragraph on page 444, how many examples can you find of nonclassical ions being postulated in reactions of *unstrained* molecules?

2. In relation to tools for the study of nonclassical ions: Can you find cases in this book of the use of isotopes in critical studies of the ethyl, *n*-propyl, 2-butyl, pentamethylethyl, bicyclobutonium, norbornyl, norbornenyl, and trishomocyclo-propenyl cations?

3. What would a reader of Paper No. 15, by Winstein *et al.* in 1952, have predicted concerning rate acceleration in XXVII compared to XXVIII?

4. Expand the list of research tools mentioned by Brown to include all the general methods used by others in critical experiments on nonclassical ions in the papers of this collection.

5. What is the significance of the reservation ". . . the simple, unsubstituted phenyl group . . .," page 450, next to last paragraph?

6. Do you agree that all the facts explained by rapidly equilibrating bicyclo-butonium ions can be explained as well by rapidly equilibrating *classical* ions? If so, what makes them equilibrate so rapidly? If not, what facts require something beside classical ions?

7. At the top of page 453 it is suggested that steric hindrance by the *endo*-6-hydrogen atom against *departure* of an *endo* anion from C-2 may account for the 350-fold *exo/endo* rate ratio in solvolysis of 2-norbornyl derivatives. What are the *exo/endo* rate ratios in cases where no *endo*-6-H exists (norbornenyl and benzonorbornenyl)?

8. It is further proposed that the same type of steric hindrance to an approaching nucleophile may account for the kinetically determined *exo/endo* product ratio in norbornyl solvolysis (> 3000). (a) On this basis what would be the expected *exo/endo* product ratio in the *free radical* chlorination of norbornane or 7-oxanorbornane? What are the facts? (b) Why should it be so? (c) Is there any pertinent evidence on product ratios in the solvolysis of the *endo* and *exo* epimers of 2-bicyclo(3.2.1)octyl tosylate? (d) What is the *exo/endo* product situation in the solvolysis of *exo*- and *endo*-norbornenyl and benzonorbornenyl sulfonates?

9. Brown cites Collins' finding of predominant retention of configuration in displacements in the 1,2,2-triphenylethyl system, and suggests that Cram's retentions in the 3-phenyl-2-butyl, 3-phenyl-2-pentyl, and 2-phenyl-3-pentyl systems may be due to the same cause. (a) Are the degrees of stereospecificity in the two cases comparable? (b) On the basis of Collins' explanation of the retention, should Cram's retention be greater or less?

10. If you were going to add one interesting point to Figure 3, what would it be?

64, 68 | Deamination of Norbornyl-amines

Corey, Casanova, Vatakencherry, and Winter (Paper No. 64), and Berson and Remanick (Paper No. 68) have both explored one of the important subtleties of the norbornyl system, namely, the possibility that an extremely energetic reaction such as nitrous acid deamination may produce a classical norbornyl cation which will behave differently from the bridged ion. There would be no difficulty in obtaining final answers to some of the questions in these papers if one had several moles of fully resolved *exo-* and *endo*-norbornylamines and norbornyl *p*-bromobenzenesulfonates, labeled with deuterium at C-2, ^{13}C at C-5 and ^{14}C at C-6, and somewhat better VPC columns to separate substantial portions of all the products of deamination and solvolysis. The real-life problem is to obtain the answers with only certain of the desired tools. The different conclusions reached by the Corey and Berson teams reflect their attempts to push the data to the limit of their accuracy, to combine results obtained at different times and places and sometimes under different conditions, without any way of establishing what the ultimate limits of reliability of the data really were.

Both authors agree that the product of deamination of *exo-* and *endo*-2-norbornylamines contains clearly measurable amounts of *endo* in the largely *exo* product. By methods which are ingenious but too indirect for complete comfort, Corey concludes that the products of deamination of optically active *endo-* and *exo*-amines are identical within experimental error, and draws the further inference that the direct product of both deaminations is the classical norbornyl cation. Berson is convinced that optically active *endo-* and *exo*-amines give not only different amounts of *endo*-acetate (4.3% vs 2%) but also different amounts of optical activity in the *exo*-acetate (18% vs 11%); only the racemic portions of the products appear to be identical in that, according to the tracer work of Roberts, Lee, and Saunders (Paper No. 23), they have suffered identical amounts of 6,2- and 6,1-rearrangement. Both groups of investigators agree that the principal fate of the classical ion is conversion into the nonclassical ion, from which the racemic *exo*-acetate comes. Although completely identical products from both amines would have been persuasive evidence of a classical ionic intermediate, the kind of non-identity presented by Berson and Remanick's work opens more possibilities than can be narrowed down with the evidence at hand. Active *exo*-diazonium ion may yield classical ion by direct ionization, bridged ion by neighboring carbon participation, or active *endo*-acetate by displacement; active *endo*-diazonium ion may yield classical ion or active *exo*-acetate; classical ion may yield active *endo*-acetate, active *exo*-acetate, or bridged ion, which in turn produces only racemic *exo*-acetate. It would seem that if all departures from identical behavior of *endo* and *exo* were in the direction of more active *endo* product from *exo*-amine and more active *exo* product from *endo*-amine, then one might conclude that these deviations were due to direct displacement in the diazonium ion. However, it is the *endo*-diazonium ion which yields both more active *endo*-acetate and more active *exo*-acetate, so that these cannot both come entirely from S_N2 displacements on the diazonium ion. Within the precisions shown in Table I of Berson and Remanick, the *active endo-* and *exo*-acetates are formed in the same proportion from both epimeric amines; the results are therefore consistent with the formation of classical and nonclassical ions from both amines but in different proportions. The difference may be due either to some anchimerically assisted decomposition of *exo*-diazonium ion (which is not, of course, rate determining) or to direct formation of classical ion only, which becomes bridged more rapidly in the *exo* isomer because the anion is not in the way of the bridging.

Among the neat tricks in these papers is the Corey group's introduction of a carboxylate trapping group into the departing anion in *exo*-norbornyl benzenesulfonate. With it they showed that even in the intimate ion pair no classical ion can be trapped in acetolysis (contrary to deamination) to yield optically active product.[1] Berson and Remanick, finding too little active *endo*-norbornyl acetate for direct observation in a product, racemized the *exo*-acetate in its presence by acid which ionizes the *exo* far faster than the *endo,* then converted to norborneol and oxidized this to norcamphor, which has a specific rotation of 1,234° at 320 mμ.

---

[1] In a later experiment S. G. Smith and J. P. Petrovich, *Tetrahedron Letters* **1964**, 3363, found that even the strongly nucleophilic thiobenzoate group failed to intercept any unracemized carbonium ion in the acetolysis of (+)-*exo*-2-norbornyl *p*-trifluoromethylthionbenzoate and the accompanying O-to-S rearrangement.

From: *J. Am. Chem. Soc.* **85,** 169–73 (1963)

[CONTRIBUTION FROM THE CONVERSE LABORATORY OF HARVARD UNIVERSITY, CAMBRIDGE 38, MASS.]

On the Norbornyl Cation Problem

BY E. J. COREY, J. CASANOVA, JR.,[1a] P. A. VATAKENCHERRY[1b] AND ROLAND WINTER

RECEIVED AUGUST 2, 1962

Evidence is presented that deamination of *exo-* and *endo-*norbornylamines in acetic acid produces an unsymmetrical, essentially classical carbonium ion, but that the cation from solvolysis of *exo-*norbornyl arenesulfonates is essentially symmetrical.

The determination of structure and chemical properties of the various species which intervene in cationic rearrangements of carbon is central to the detailed understanding of such processes. The present formulations of these reactions, *e.g.* (1), usually include a

$$\underset{X_n}{\overset{C}{\underset{|}{C}}} \longrightarrow [\text{intermediate(s)}]^+ \xrightarrow{Y^-} \underset{X^{n-1}}{\overset{Y \; C}{\underset{|}{C}}} \quad (1)$$

consideration of whether rearrangement occurs *simultaneously* with ionization to give a bridged "non-classical" action, $C\!\cdot\!\!-\!\!\cdot C$ (anchimerically assisted ionization), or *after* ionization to a classical "carbonium ion." In either case there remains a question of whether the structure in which the migrating group forms a bridge across to the carbon atoms is a relatively stable intermediate which leads to product(s) directly by reaction with nucleophile or a transient on the way to a new (rearranged) classical carbonium ion. The intermediacy of such a bridged ion ought to assume increasing chemical significance as the ion becomes more stable than the alternative classical ions and as the energy barrier between these ions is diminished.

The behavior of a system in terms of these considerations might be expected to depend not only on the arrangement of carbon in the molecule but also on the nature of the process for cation generation and the interactions with neighboring solvent and solute molecules. Although it is already clear that the variable of the leaving group X is not trivial in the mechanistic scheme of things, the greater part of present knowledge on intermediates in carbonium ion rearrangements and on related matters, such as interaction of these intermediates with other ions and with solvent, is derived from the study of halide or sulfonate ester solvolysis. The use of other non-solvolytic reactions, *e.g.*, amine deamination, to distinguish between intermediate carbonium ion structures is rather less common for a number of reasons including in the case of amine deamination the inapplicability of kinetic analysis to the steps of interest and the irregularities which have been encountered in attempts to correlate product distribution with that from corresponding sulfonate ester or halide solvolysis in various systems.[2] It now appears

that in the case of deamination the enormous speed of decomposition of the diazonium ion is at least in part responsible for the apparent discrepancies.[3] This, in turn, suggests that the amine reaction, an obviously practical method of carbonium ion generation, may complement the solvolysis approach in the development of a more general understanding of interconverting classical and non-classical cations. Indeed, as will be apparent from what follows, it seems inappropriate to generalize on the basis of solvolysis results *alone*, however quantitative, since the problems of cationic rearrangements of carbon are intrinsically multidimensional as a result of the number and significance of the independent variables. A clear understanding of cation behavior may, in fact, require the study of a spectrum of processes for ion *generation* as well as the variation of carbon structure, stereochemistry and reaction medium.

The present paper deals with some experiments on amine deamination and solvolysis in the 2-norbornyl series which were performed to extend existing knowledge in this remarkably instructive system.[4] Winstein and Trifan have argued convincingly that the considerably greater solvolytic reactivity of *exo-*norbornyl arenesulfonate as compared to the *endo* isomer and the formation of racemic *exo-*acetate from acetolysis of optically active *exo-*sulfonate show that carbon–carbon σ-delocalization accompanies and assists ionization of the *exo* isomer. In addition, they consider that the symmetrical bridged ion is probably both the product of ionization and the direct precursor of *exo-*acetate, but they point out that an alternative formulation, a system of two equilibrated unsymmetrical non-classical ions, is not excluded. In the case of the solvolysis

of the *endo-*norbornyl arenesulfonate the mechanistic evidence is far less clear; it is not yet known, for example, whether *endo* → *exo* sulfonate rearrangement

(1) (a) U. S. Public Health (N. I. H.) postdoctoral fellow 1959–1961; (b) Research Associate under a grant (G-9999) from the National Science Foundation.

(2) *Cf.* H. Zollinger, "Diazo and Azo Chemistry," Interscience Publishers, Inc., New York, N. Y., 1961, pp. 93–101, 123–136.

(3) See, for example, the review by J. H. Ridd, *Quart. Revs.*, **15,** 418 (1961), which summarizes recent studies on "conformational control" of rearrangement in deamination reactions of acyclic systems and refs. 10 and 12 given below.

(4) See S. Winstein and D. Trifan, *J. Am. Chem. Soc.*, **74,** 1147, 1154 (1952).

precedes solvolysis. It has been proposed, however, that ionization in acetic acid leads to an unbridged norbornyl cation, possibly coördinated with solvent, which rearranges to the symmetrical cation and which to a much smaller extent associates with acetic acid to produce unrearranged *exo*-acetate. At 75° the unrearranged acetate amounts to 7–8% of the total reaction product as measured by the retention of optical activity. Apropos of the problem of formulating this reaction and the present work is the observation of Berson and Ben-Efraim[5] that the deamination of (+)-*endo*-norbornylamine in acetic acid affords *exo*-norbornyl acetate with *ca.* 23% retention of optical purity. This result was reconciled with the findings of Winstein and Trifan[4] by considering "that the excess unrearranged portion of the product acetate is derived by direct displacement of the solvent on the diazonium ion."[5] This hypothesis is inconsistent with the reasonable expectation that a concerted backside displacement reaction with solvent as nucleophile should be far less likely for amine deamination than for sulfonate solvolysis (*vide infra*). It seemed to us more likely that a *classical* carbonium ion is produced by loss of nitrogen from the *endo* diazonium cation and that this ion either reacts more rapidly with nucleophile (HOAc or AcO⁻) or rearranges less rapidly than the ion from solvolysis of the *endo*-sulfonate either because of a difference in reaction conditions[6] or a difference between the ions, *e.g.*, in geometry, energy content or environment.[7]

A crucial test of the Berson hypothesis would seem to be the deamination of optically active *exo*-norbornylamine. The *exo*-diazonium ion in this case is clearly not subject to concerted backside displacement for steric reasons and consequently, any retention of optical activity in the product must come from an optically active carbonium ion. We have found that the deamination of the optically active *exo*-amine in acetic acid under the conditions of Berson and Ben-Efraim and isolation of acetate *via* norboneol by their procedure gives acetate with about 15% retention of optical purity, and in addition that the product is a mixture of 96% *exo*-acetate and *ca.* 4% of the *endo*-acetate.[8]

Several Inferences Can Be Drawn from This Result. —First, it seems clear that an optically active carbonium ion must be formed despite the fact that carbon-carbon σ-participation to give a bridged ion is stereoelectronically favorable. Secondly, there must be an energy barrier between this ion and the symmetrically bridged cation. Thirdly, reaction of the unsymmetrical cation with solvent probably gives both *exo*- and *endo*-acetate with the former predominating heavily.[9] Whether the optically active cation formed in the deamination of the *exo*-amine originally possesses a shorter C_2–C_6 distance than the undistorted classical ion, with a commensurate increase in C_2–C_6 delocalization, cannot be decided at present. However, for the time being we prefer to consider that this intermediate

holds approximately to the geometry of the classical ion, essentially for the reasons given below and summarized in a general way in the recent excellent discussion of Martin and Bentrude.[10] In the highly exothermic,[11] direct loss of nitrogen from the norbornyl diazonium ion only a small activation energy is required (perhaps on the order of 5 kcal./mole) and only one mode of vibration is involved (C–N stretching). In the alternative C–C participation process simultaneous excitation of C–C bending modes and the C–N stretching mode is demanded, so that this route is disfavored on probability, *i.e.*, entropy, grounds to a degree which could well be critical in a system with low energy barriers.[12]

This view which leads to the conclusion that the retention of optical activity in deamination of *exo* norbornylamine is due to the formation of the classical norbornyl cation, also suggests the possibility that the classical cation may be a common intermediate for both rearranged and unrearranged products. If this were the case for the *exo*-amine it should also hold for the *endo* isomer and, in fact, the product analysis from *endo* and *exo* isomers should be about the same. In view of the reported 23% excess retention of optical activity in the deamination of optically active *endo*-norbornylamine, we have carried out an independent product analysis for the *endo* case using a different but essentially equivalent technique. This involved the deamination of *endo*-2-norbornylamine-2d_1 in acetic acid under the standard conditions. The acetates produced were converted to norborneol (LiAlH₄) which was subsequently oxidized to norcamphor (RuO₄–Freon). Deuterium analyses were performed by mass spectral measurements. Starting from amine containing 1.00 deuterium per molecule the norborneol and norcamphor which were obtained contained 1.00 and 0.42 atom deuterium per molecule, respectively.[13] The absence of 1,2-hydrogen shifting in the deamination was shown by

the fact that the deuterated norcamphor did not lose deuterium when treated with excess sodium methoxide–methanol under equilibrating conditions.[14] These results correspond (for the *exo* product[8]) to 16% excess retention of optical activity in the stereochemical experiment and as such are in close agreement with our results from *exo*-norbornylamine if both *exo*- and *endo*-amines are assumed to be converted essentially completely to a classical cation which serves as a common intermediate for both rearranged and unrearranged products.[15] This comparison of deuterium labeling

(5) J. A. Berson and D. A. Ben-Efraim, *J. Am. Chem. Soc.*, **81**, 4094 (1959).

(6) For example, the temperatures used for solvolysis and deamination experiments were 75° and *ca.* 20°, respectively.

(7) The decomposition of diazonium acetate ion pairs to produce (classical) carbonium-acetate ion pairs is a possibility which seems eminently suited to accommodate the experimental data.

(8) Since *exo*- and *endo*-acetates have the same sign and about the same magnitude of optical rotation, the figure given for % retention of optical purity refers to the *exo* isomer. It is quite possible that the retention of optical purity in the *endo* product is very much higher. This interesting point has not been checked chiefly because of obvious experimental difficulties of obtaining pure *endo*-acetate in sufficient quantity for rotation measurements.

(9) Predominance of *exo* attack on the classical cation is expected because of interference to *endo* attack by the *endo*-hydrogen at C₆. For a summary of related instances, see E. J Corey, P. A. Vatakencherry and R. Hartmann, *J. Am. Chem. Soc.*, **84**, 2611 (1962).

(10) J. C. Martin and W. G. Bentrude, *J. Org. Chem.*, **24**, 1902 (1959).

(11) A rough value $\Delta H = -3.6$ ev. (gas phase) can be estimated for the reaction $RN_2^+ \rightarrow R^+ + N_2$ from (1) the first ionization potential of N₂ (15.6 ev.) [F. H. Field and T. L. Franklin, "Electron Impact Phenomena," Academic Press, Inc., New York, N. Y., 1957, p. 62], (2) the ionization potential for a *sec*-alkyl radical (8 ev.) [J. J. Kaufman and W. S. Koski, *J. Am. Chem. Soc.*, **82**, 3262 (1960)], and (3) the homolytic dissociation energy for C–N₂⁺ (estimated at *ca.* 4 ev. from the known value of 4.5 ev. for *d* CH₃–CN). Assuming that the difference in solvation energies of R⁺ and RN₂⁺ is not large, it follows that diazonium ion decomposition is also highly exothermic in solution.

(12) See (a) D. J. Cram and J. E. McCarthy, *J. Am. Chem. Soc.*, **79**, 2866 (1957); (b) B. M. Benjamin, H. S. Schaeffer and D. J. Collins, *ibid.*, **79**, 6160 (1957); and (c) D. Y. Curtin and M. Wilhelm, *Helv. Chim. Acta*, **40**, 2129 (1957).

(13) The norborneol consisted of 95 ± 1% *exo* and 5 ± 1% *endo* isomer as determined by vapor phase chromatography.

(14) The possibility of 1,2-shifting of hydrogen does not appear to have been tested previously by direct experiment.

(15) A significant involvement of cation-acetate pairs seems likely on the basis of related deamination studies using acetic acid solvent; E. H. White

and optical activity experiments is valid providing it can be assumed that those reaction pathways which lead to rearrangement also lead to inversion. The assumption seemes completely justifiable since the two likely rearrangement processes fulfill this condition, *viz.*, rearrangement *via* the structures.

At this point mention should be made of the results of Roberts, *et al.*, which suggest that *ca.* 6% of 1,3-hydrogen rearrangement occurs in the deamination of an *exo-endo*-norbornylamine mixture (70:30) in water.[16] It is entirely possible that a small amount of such rearrangement might have occurred under the conditions of our experiment; we estimate that such a process could amount to *ca.* 5% of total reaction (at most) on the basis of n.m.r. spectrum of the partly deuterated norcamphor from *endo*-2-norbornyl-amine-$2d_1$ in which the bridgehead protons (7.43 and 7.62 τ) are downfield from the remaining protons in the molecule and almost completely separated (see Experimental section). The ratio of these peaks is 1.0:1.0 in norcamphor and 1.0:0.6 $\pm$ 0.05 in the deuterated norcamphor (total 0.42 deuterium per molecule). Obviously the occurrence of minor amounts of 1,3-hydrogen shifting can be interpreted in terms of a classical carbonium intermediate since the geometry of the norbornyl system itself favors such a rearrangement.

It also remains to consider the possibility that the norbornyl cation produced by deamination or the nearest molecules of solvent might be excessively energetic because of the exothermicity of diazonium decomposition. The possibility that part of the energy of reaction may initially be released as excess vibrational energy of the carbonium ion,[17] coupled with the complication that the times required for a vibration leading to rearrangement and collision with solvent are roughly comparable (*ca.* 10^{-13} sec.), makes it extremely difficult to anticipate the chemical consequences of highly exothermic decomposition in solution. Nonetheless, it seems most likely that the dominant effect of exothermic carbonium ion formation would be a higher than normal incidence of internal rearrangement and it is difficult to see how such a factor *per se* would be responsible for excess retention of optical activity in the norbornyl systems.[18]

The above-mentioned experiments on deamination were prompted partially by a related study which seemed to indicate a discrete existence for the classical or "unsymmetrical" norbornyl cation, the reaction of the isomeric norbornane-2-carboxylic acids with lead tetraacetate. In contrast to the anodic oxidation of

these optically active acids in methanol at high voltages which affords completely racemic *exo*-norbornyl methyl ether *via* a racemized or symmetric cation,[19] it has been found that the optically active *exo*- and *endo*-acids with lead tetraacetate in benzene yield norbornyl acetate (95% *exo* and small amounts of *endo*) with 43% *excess retention* of optical activity in *each* case.[20] In acetonitrile as solvent these optically active acids each give *exo*-norbornyl acetate with 34% retention of optical activity. Although the mechanism of oxidative decarboxylation with lead(IV) salts is not known in detail and although the identity of optical result for *exo*- and *endo*-norbornane-2-carboxylic acids in two different solvent systems might be coincidental, the mechanism shown below would seem best suited to accommodate all the facts including the obtention of characteristic carbonium ion rearrangements in other systems.[21-24] It is possible that the norbornyl radical precedes the cation, since the rates of oxidation of *exo*- and *endo*-acids are approximately the same. However, there is ample evidence[25] that the norbornyl radical is not prone to rearrangement at the reaction temperature of oxidation decarboxylation (*ca.* 80°) so that the carbonium ion is required as an intermediate; the assumption that the carbonium ion is a common intermediate for both rearranged and non-rearranged acetate is based on the correspondence of products from *exo*- and *endo*-acids and the rather small change in the fraction of rearrangement in going from benzene to the much more polar acetonitrile as solvent. It should also be noted that the yield and composition of product are not changed in the presence of oxygen at saturation.[19] The high net retention of optical activity as compared with solvolysis and amine deamination may be due to the dominant formation of classical carbonium-acetate ion pairs in non-polar media which favor rapid ion collapse.

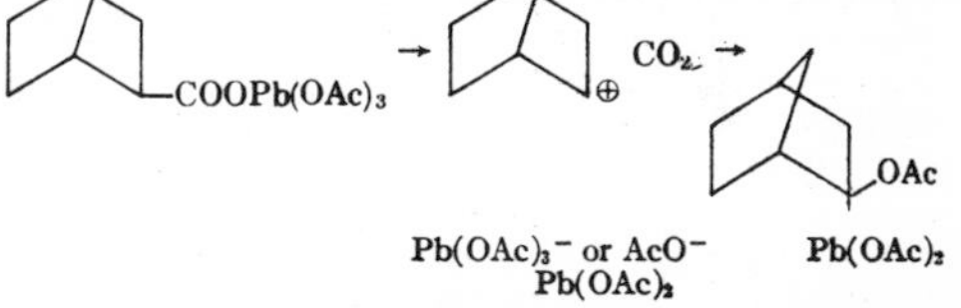

In view of the evidence that there is a significant energy barrier between the classical norbornyl cation and the symmetrical bridged ion and the formal possibility that the solvolysis of *exo*-norbornyl bromobenzenesulfonate might involve a pair of unsymmetrical bridged ions which are interconverted at a rapid rate relative to reaction with solvent acetic acid, we have carried out a test for an unsymmetrical intermediate in *exo*-sulfonate solvolysis. In this experiment the arenesulfonate was *m*-carboxybenzenesulfonate in which there is located a nucleophilic group (COO⁻ in basic medium) which can interact with the carbonium center *after*, but not *before*, ionization. The *m*-carboxybenzenesulfonate-carbonium ion pair can be expected to have an extremely fleeting existence (especially in media

and C. A. Aufdermarsh, *J. Am. Chem. Soc.*, **80**, 2597 (1958); **83**, 1179 (1961). The incidence of ion pairs provides a reasonable explanation (a) for the greater net retention of optical activity in *exo*- or *endo*-amine deamination as compared with *endo*-arenesulfonate solvolysis (*cf.* ref. 7), and (b) for the formation of slightly more *endo*-acetate from *endo*-amine than from *exo*-amine.

(16) J. D. Roberts, C. C. Lee and W. H. Saunders, Jr., *J. Am. Chem. Soc.*, **76**, 4501 (1954). These workers prefer to discuss such hydrogen rearrangement in terms of an *ad hoc* non-classical "nortricyclonium" ion.

(17) *Cf.* J. D. Polanyi, *J. Chem. Phys.*, **31**, 1338 (1959), and D. R. Herschbach, G. H. Kwei and J. A. Norris, *ibid.*, **34**, 1842 (1961).

(18) Preliminary experiments by Mr. Richard Atkinson in these laboratories using analytical gas chromatography indicate that no significant amount of *n*-propyl alcohol is formed in the deamination of pure isopropylamine, a possible indication of the unimportance of a vibrationally excited cation. The recent demonstration of "over-all" 1,3-hydride rearrangement in the deamination of *n*-propylamine may however be a consequence of exothermic diazonium ion decomposition (O. A. Reutov and T. N. Shutkina, *Tetrahedron*, **18**, 237 (1962)).

(19) E. J. Corey, N. L. Bauld, R. T. LaLonde, J. Casanova, Jr., and E. T. Kaiser, *J. Am. Chem. Soc.*, **82**, 2645 (1960).

(20) E. J. Corey and J. Casanova, Jr., *ibid.*, **85**, 165 (1963).

(21) G. Büchi and J. Marvel (personal communication) have ascertained that cyclobutanecarboxylic acid affords cyclobutyl, cyclopropylcarbinyl and allylcarbinyl acetates corresponding approximately to the mixtures encountered previously in the "bicyclobutonium" cation system; *cf.* R. H. Mazur, *et al.*, *J. Am. Chem. Soc.*, **81**, 4390 (1959).

(22) W. A. Mosher and C. L. Kehr, *ibid.*, **75**, 3172 (1953).

(23) L. L. McCoy and A. Zagalo, *J. Org. Chem.*, **25**, 824 (1960).

(24) Z. Valenta, *et al.*, *Tetrahedron Letters*, **20**, 25 (1960).

(25) J. A. Berson, C. J. Olsen and J. S. Walia, *J. Am. Chem. Soc.*, **82**, 5000 (1960).

of low polarity) since it can recombine with only slight molecular movement to give carboxylate ester; this expectation is reinforced by the results of the oxidative decarboxylation reactions with lead tetraacetate. Thus, if starting from optically active *exo*-norbornyl

ester an unsymmetrical norbornyl cartion-carboxy-sulfonate ion pair were formed, the product resulting from ionization might be the ester of optically active *exo*-norborneol. In practice the experiment was conducted by treating the *p*-nitrophenyl ester of the *m*-carboxybenzenesulfonate with two equivalents of alkali (which saponifies the *p*-nitrophenyl ester essentially instantaneously) and then conducting the ionization reaction in *t*-butyl alcohol or in tetrahydrofuran–water with slow addition of a third equivalent of alkali to maintain a slightly basic reaction solution. After the end of alkali addition no sulfonate ester remained and no *exo*-norborneol could be detected by vapor phase chromatography indicating the formation of carboxylate ester. The ester was saponified with alkali and the liberated *exo*-norborneol was then isolated and characterized. In both *t*-butyl alcohol and in aqueous tetrahydrofuran the *exo*-norborneol obtained was optically inactive within experimental error ($\pm 0.01°$ in $[\alpha]_D$) in runs starting with optically active *exo*-norborneol of $[\alpha]^{25}_D$ $-0.305°$ and $-1.87°$, respectively. Thus, it would seem that if the solvolysis of *exo*-norbornyl arenesulfonate does not produce the symmetrical ion, but a pair of interconverting unsymmetrical bridged ions, the interconversion rate is so rapid that for chemical purposes the ion may be taken as symmetrical.[26] In connection with this finding and the results reported above for amine deamination, there arises a question of whether the presence of certain neighboring anions (*e.g.*, sulfonate or halide) may facilitate carbonium-ion interconversion or rearrangement. Such an effect might be visualized for the norbornyl system as

Further research on this point is required.

Experimental[27,28]

(−)-*exo*-Norbornane-2-carboxylic Acid.—(−)-*endo*-Norbornane-2-carboxylic acid (15.42 g., 0.108 mole), prepared by the method of Berson and Ben-Efraim,[5] $[\alpha]^{25}_D$ $-14.43 \pm 0.25°$ (*c* 4.61, 95% ethanol, 1 dm.) calculated optical purity of 47.0 $\pm$ 0.9%, and phosphorus tribromide (100 g., 0.37 mole) were mixed and heated in an oil-bath at 160–170° with stirring for 6.5 hours. The red-orange reaction mixture was poured slowly onto *ca.* 500 g. of crushed ice while mixing. After 10 minutes this hydrolysate was extracted with four 50-ml. portions of ether, and the ether was washed with several portions of saturated salt solution. After drying over anhydrous sodium sulfate the ether was removed by distillation and the resulting colorless oil was distilled at 110–114° at 0.7 mm. The distillate crystallized in the receiver and amounted to 11.95 g. (77.5%). The infrared spectrum of this material in carbon disulfide was identical with (±)-*exo*-norbornane-2-carboxylic acid[5] and did not show contamination by the *endo* isomer. The optical rotation of this

substance, $[\alpha]^{25}_D$ $-12.63 \pm 0.20°$ (*c* 5.53, 95% ethanol, 1 dm.) leads to a calculated value of $45.3 \pm 0.7\%$ optical purity for the sample.[29]

(−)-*exo*-Norbornylamine Hydrochloride.—(−)-*exo*-Norbornane-2-carboxylic acid obtained in the previous experiment (11.92 g., 84.0 mmoles) in 50 ml. of chloroform was stirred at ice temperature and treated with 135 ml. of a dried solution contained 163 mmoles of hydrazoic acid in chloroform. To this solution was added 35 ml. (0.63 mole) of concentrated sulfuric acid over a 40-minute period. The cooling bath was removed and the vigorously stirred mixture was warmed carefully. Nitrogen evolution became vigorous above room temperature and subsided after several minutes. The mixture was refluxed for 2 hours then cooled and poured onto 200 g. of crushed ice. The chloroform layer was separated and the aqueous part was made strongly basic with cold concentrated sodium hydroxide (cooling, stirring) and extracted with two 75-ml. portions of ether. The combined ether extracts were dried over solid potassium carbonate and then treated with anhydrous hydrogen chloride. The filtered solid was washed with a small portion of ether and dried in vacuum. There was obtained 7.42 g. (64%) of white solid, m.p. 316–320° (dec.), $[\alpha]^{25}_D$ $-8.24 \pm 0.18°$ (*c* 5.04, CHCl₃, 1 dm.) whose infrared spectrum (CHCl₃) was entirely consistent with that of an amine hydrochloride.

The mother liquors from hydrochloride precipitation yielded an additional 1.83 g. upon being reprocessed; $[\alpha]^{25}_D$ $-7.64 \pm 0.49°$ (*c* 4.69, CHCl₃, 1 dm.).

Deamination of (−)-*exo*-Norbornylamine Hydrochloride.— A solution of (−)-*exo*-norbornylamine hydrochloride (6.43 g., 47 mmoles) in 50 ml. of glacial acetic acid was stirred and maintained at 17 ± 1° while solid sodium nitrite (6.43 g., 93.1 mmoles) was added in numerous small portions over 90 minutes. The mixture was stirred for an additional hour at this temperature, than overnight at room temperature. An additional 1.58 g. (22 mmoles) of sodium nitrite was added in small portions and stirring was continued for 1 hour more. The reaction mixture was poured onto 150 g. of crushed ice, and treated with 1 mole of sodium hydroxide in 150 ml. of water (stirring, cooling). The oil which separated was extracted into three × 75-ml. portions of ether, and the ether extracts, washed successively with saturated salt solution, 2 N hydrochloric acid, and saturated salt solution. The ether solution was dried over anhydrous magnesium sulfate and concentrated to *ca.* 50 ml. by slow distillation through a 4-foot Vigreux column. A small sample removed at this time was concentrated to remove the remainder of the ether and was analyzed by infrared and gas chromatography (4 ft. Carbowax 20 M, 50 ml. He/min.), and *exo*-norbornyl acetate was identified by comparison with an authentic sample as the major constituent (85.5%). The infrared spectrum differed from *exo*-norbornyl acetate by a strong 6.15 μ absorption, assigned to the nitrate.[6] The gas chromatogram showed three contaminants: (1) 1.5%, ret. time 1 min. 45 sec.; (2) 4%, ret. time 8 min. 15 sec.; (3) 9%, ret. time 11 min. 25 sec. The first and third of these impurities agreed well in retention time with those of norbornylene or nortricyclene and *exo*-norborneol, respectively.

The bulk of the reaction mixture above was shaken with 0.2 g. of platinum oxide catalyst at 60 p.s.i. in a Parr apparatus for 3 hours. Removal of the catalyst and concentration through a 4′ Vigreux column left a colorless oil which exhibited an infrared spectrum identical with *exo*-norbornyl acetate and a gas chromatogram which was consistent with the conversion of norbornylene to norbornane and *exo*-norbornyl nitrate to norbornyl acetate.

A mixture of hydrogenated product, 2.0 g. of acetic anhydride and 5.0 g. of acetic acid was refluxed gently for 3 hours, then distilled very slowly through a Holtzmann column. The fraction boiling at 131.5–132.0° (147 mm.)(1.97 g.) was collected. The infrared spectrum was identical with that of *exo*-norbornyl acetate and the gas chromatogram (4 ft. dinonyl phthalate, 140°) showed a single peak at a retention time of 19 min. 5 sec. The optical rotation of this sample was α^{25}_D $-0.892 \pm 0.011°$ (neat, 1 dm.), leading to a calculated[30] optical purity of 7.07 ± 0.29% and a net retention of optical purity in the reaction of 15%. Treatment with lithium aluminum hydride and analysis of the norbornols so produced by V.P.C. on a 20% Ucon 50 HB 280 x on Celite 545 column[31] at 160° showed a composition of 96 ± 1% *exo* and 4 ± 1% *endo*-norborneol.

N-Acetyl-*endo*-norbornylamine-2-*d*.—Norcamphor oxime (17.12 g.) was reduced with 6.0 g. of lithium aluminum deuteride (99.8% isotopically pure) in 370 ml. of ether at reflux for 48 hours. After decomposition of the reaction mixture with water and treatment of the ether phase and extracts with dry hydrogen chloride 10 g. of crude amine hydrochloride was obtained. The amine was then acetylated in concentrated aqueous solution containing excess alkali at 0° with acetic anhydride and the N-acetyl deriva-

(26) This type of experiment is clearly of interest for the *endo*-norbornyl arenesulfonate system as well as in other cases where a non-bridged cation may be formed prior to rearrangement. Further studies along these lines are in progress.

(27) Instruments used were: n.m.r. Varian A-60; infrared, Perkin–Elmer Infracord; V.P.C., F and M model 300.

(28) Microanalytical data from C. Daesslé, Montreal, Can.

(29) J. A. Berson and D. A. Ben-Efraim, *J. Am. Chem. Soc.*, **81**, 4083 (1959).

(30) J. A. Berson and S. Suzuki, *ibid.*, **81**, 4088 (1959).

(31) C. H. Depuy and P. R. Storey, *Tet. Letters*, **6**, 20 (1959).

tive was isolated by extraction and purified by chromatography on neutral alumina followed by sublimation to give 2.1 g. of pure N-acetyl-*endo*-norbornylamine-2-*d*, m.p. 127–128° (lit.[16] 124°), infrared absorption at 2.95, 6.05, 6.5 and 7.3μ,[32] deuterium content 1.00 atom per molecule (analysis performed by J. Nemeth, Urbana, Ill.).

endo-**Norbornylamine-2-*d* Hydrochloride.**—The above acetyl derivative (2.0 g.) was hydrolyzed at reflux for 40 hours with 30 ml. of 6 *N* hydrochloric acid. Evaporation under reduced pressure and crystallization of the residue from ether–cyclohexane gave 1.75 g. of the hydrochloride as colorless silky needles, m.p. 295° dec.

Deamination of *endo*-Norbornylamine-2-*d* in Acetic Acid.— The conditions of Berson and Ben-Efraim[5] were adhered to exactly using 1.70 g. of the amine hydrochloride, 8.95 ml. of glacial acetic acid, 0.945 g. of sodium acetate and 1.28 g. and 0.32-g. portions of sodium nitrite. Distillation of the crude product gave 947 mg. of acetate, b.p. 170° (bath) at 155 mm. This was converted to norborneol with lithium aluminum hydride-ether; isolation of the product by extraction with ether concentration and sublimation at 130° (155 mm.) gave 567 mg. of norborneol, m.p. 119–121°, which by V.P.C. analysis on a 4-meter tricyanoethoxypropane column (15% on firebrick) at 140° was shown to consist of 95 ± 1% *exo* and 5 ± 1% *endo*-norborneol. Deuterium analysis (performed by Mr. J. Nemeth) showed the presence of 1.00 atom deuterium per molecule.

Oxidation of Norborneol-*d*-to Norcamphor-*d* with Ruthenium-Tetroxide.—To a solution of 37 mg. of the above deuterated norborneol in 2 ml. of Freon 11 (trichlorofluoromethane) at 0° was added a slight excess (over one equivalent) of a bromine-free solution of ruthenium tetroxide[31]-Freon 11. After a few minutes a few drops of ether was added to destroy the excess oxidizing agent and the mixture was kept for 5 minutes, then filtered and concentrated and sublimed to give 23 mg. of norcamphor, m.p. 88–89°; infrared absorption (CCl₄) at 5.7, 6.9 and 7.1μ. Deuterium analysis of this and several check runs by mass spectrometer[34] showed the presence of 0.42 ± 0.003 deuterium atom per molecule.

Treatment of the deuteriated norcamphor (20 mg.) with 3 ml. of methanol and 2 ml. of *N* sodium hydroxide at reflux under nitrogen for 6 hours and resolation gave norcamphor (m.p. 88–89°) of essentially the original deuterium content (0.414 ± 0.003 deuterium per molecule), eliminating the possibility that 3-deuteriated 2-norbornyl acetate had been produced in significant amount in the deamination.

The n.m.r. spectrum of the deuteriated norcamphor differed from that of unlabeled norcamphor in that the relative intensities of the two peaks downfield at 7.43 and 7.62r) were 1.0 to 0.6 ± 0.05 in the former and 1.0 to 1.0 in the latter, the measurements being made in CCl₄ or CS₂ using a Varian A-60 spectrometer with electronic integration of signal. These two peaks can be assigned to the bridgehead positions since deuteration of the α-methylene group in norcamphor leaves their intensities unchanged and diminishes the upfield peaks.

p-**Nitrophenyl-(*m*-chlorosulfonyl) Benzoate.**—*p*-Nitrophenol (5.56 g., 40 mmoles) was added all at once to a solution of 9.56

g. (40 mmoles) of *m*-chlorosulfonylbenzoyl chloride[35] and pyridine (3.20 ml., 40 mmoles) in 110 ml. of dry benzene stirred vigorously at *ca*. 5°. After 10 minutes the mixture was stirred at 40–50° for 0.5 hour; filtered, and the solid washed with *ca*. 20 ml. of benzene. Combined filtrate and washing were evaporated to 50 ml. in vacuum, heated slightly to redissolve the solid, and cooled at about 5° for 0.5 hour. The white crystalline solid which separated was removed by filtration and dried in vacuum. A 64% yield (8.83 g.) was obtained, m.p. 128.5–132°. Two additional crystallizations from benzene (avoid excess heating) gave a sample for analysis, m.p. 135–136°.

Anal. Calcd. for C₁₃H₈O₆ NSCl: C, 45.69; H, 2.36; Cl, 10.38. Found: C, 45.76; H, 2.19; Cl, 10.33.

exo-**Norbornyl-[*m*-carbo-(*p*-nitrophenoxy)] Benzenesulfonate.** —A mixture of 0.4487 g. (4.0 mmoles) of *exo*-norborneol and 1.0251 g. (3.0 mmoles) of *p*-nitrophenyl-(*m*-chlorosulfonyl) benzoate at 5–10° was stirred and treated with 2.0 ml. (30 mmoles) of dry pyridine. The mixture was stirred at 15–20° for 2.5 hours, then filtered. The precipitate was washed with a small portion of benzene, and the combined filtrate and washing were evaporated at reduced pressure without heat. The residual oil was treated with about 5 ml. of toluene, filtered and the precipitate was washed with a small amount of toluene. The solution was then evaporated in vacuum. This process was repeated three times. The residual oil was triturated with pentane, dried at 1 mm. pressure and then used immediately in the solvolysis reaction; it is designated as XI below.

Solvolysis of Sulfonate XI in Tetrahydrofuran-Water.—A solution of 1.459 g. of oil XI (2.85 mmoles) in 59.64 ml. of 0.09885 *N* sodium hydroxide (5.70 mmoles) and 40 ml. of tetrahydrofuran was heated at 60°. A third mole (29.82 ml.) of sodium hydroxide was added over the next 7 minutes to maintain neutrality. After 1 hour the solution was cooled, made strongly basic with sodium hydroxide, and extracted with 2 × 30 ml. of pentane. The pentane was washed with 4 × 15 ml. of water, dried over sodium sulfate, and evaporated through a 4-foot Vigreux column. The residue crystallized on brief evacuation, and was essentially pure *exo*-norborneol (87 mg.) by V.P.C. on 2-ft. silicone gum rubber and TCEP.

Another reaction employing essentially identical conditions but starting with (−)-*exo*-norborneol ([α]²⁵D − 1.87 ± 0.14°) gave pure *exo*-norborneol ([α]²⁵D −0.007 ± 0.014°). This material showed a single peak when subjected to V.P.C. on a silicone rubber column.

Solvolysis of Sulfonate XI in *t*-Butanol.—A solution of 3.648 g. (8.75 mmoles) of oily XI in *ca*. 50 ml. of *t*-butyl alcohol (distilled from calcium hydride) was treated with 0.579 *N* benzyl-trimethylammonium hydroxide (29.38 ml.) in *t*-butyl alcohol. The volume was made up to 100 ml., and the solution was thermostated at 75°. One-fourth of an additional equivalent of base was added over 2 hours. After about 12 hours the *t*-butyl alcohol was removed by slow distillation through a 4-foot Vigreux column. A V.P.C. analysis of the distillate showed no norborneol but substantial norbornene. The residue was re-fluxed for 6 hours with 20 ml. of 6 *N* potassium hydroxide, and the hydrolysate was extracted with 3 × 30 ml. of pentane. Washing of the pentane with 3 × 4 ml. of water, concentration through a 4-foot Vigreux column and distillation of the residual oil (2.35 g.) through a Craig micro-still gave a fraction, b.p. 150–180°, which was purified further by V.P.C. *exo*-Norborneol obtained by collection from V.P.C. showed a rotation [α]²⁵D −0.08 ± 0.08°, starting with *exo*-norborneol of rotation [α]²⁵D − 0.305°.

(32) K. Alder, S. Stein, S. Schneider, M. Liebmann, E. Ralland and S. Schulze, *Ann.*, **525**, 183 (1936), have prepared *endo*-norbornylamine by catalytic reduction of norcamphor oxime.

(33) L. M. Berkowitz and P. N. Rylander, *J. Am. Chem. Soc.*, **80**, 6682 (1958).

(34) Consolidated Engineering Corporation, Type 21-103 C, see J. H. Benyon, "Mass Spectrometry and its Application to Organic Chemistry," Elsevier Press, New York, N. Y., 1960, p. 495.

(35) H. Limpricht and L. V. Uslar, *Ann.*, **102**, 250 (1857).

Errata

Page 466, above structural formula in right-hand column

1,2-hydrogen shifting in the deamination *should read* 3,2-hydrogen shifting . . .

Page 466, right-hand column, footnote 14,

1,2-shifting of hydrogen *should read* 3,2-shifting of hydrogen

65 | "Puckered" Cyclobutyl Tosylates

In previous studies of the solvolysis of cyclobutyl compounds (Papers 12, 30, 39, 42) these have appeared more reactive than would be projected from a consideration of their required valence angle and the behavior of the other cycloalkyl derivatives. The hypothesis of the bicyclobutonium ion (Paper No. 42) suggests that for some reason (presumably the achieving of better charge delocalization) ionization bends the cyclobutane ring into a tetrahedroid form with even narrower bond angles than before.

In Paper No. 65 Wiberg and Fenoglio report the solvolysis of a cyclobutyl tosylate which is forced, by the presence of an ethylene bridge, to be quite puckered. On any classical basis it might be expected to ionize less readily than undistorted cyclobutyl tosylate. Instead, the *equatorial* isomer, *endo*-5-bicyclo-(2.1.1)hexyl tosylate (I tosylate), undergoes acetolysis 10^3 times as fast as cyclobutyl tosylate, and three million times as fast as its axial (*exo*) isomer. Of the three modes of reaction characteristic of the bicyclobutonium ion, two are shown by I tosylate in acetic acid and the third in acetone containing chloride ion.

Details of the chemistry of this interesting ring system are given in other papers.[1,2]

---

[1] K. B. Wiberg, B. R. Lowry, and T. H. Colby, *J. Am. Chem. Soc.* **83**, 3998 (1961); K. B. Wiberg, B. R. Lowry, and B. J. Nist, *ibid.*, **84**, 1594 (1962); K. B. Wiberg and B. R. Lowry, *ibid.*, **85**, 3188 (1963).

[2] J. Meinwald and P. G. Gassman, *J. Am. Chem. Soc.* **82**, 2857, 5445 (1960); *ibid.*, **85**, 57 (1963); J. Meinwald, A. Lewis, and P. G. Gassman, *ibid.*, **82**, 2649 (1960); *ibid.*, **84**, 977 (1962); J. Meinwald, *Record Chem. Prog.* **22**, 39 (1961); J. Meinwald and A. Lewis, *J. Am. Chem. Soc.* **83**, 2769 (1961); W. D. Kumler, A. Lewis, and J. Meinwald, *ibid.*, **83**, 4591 (1961); J. Meinwald, P. G. Gassman, and J. J. Hurst, *ibid.*, **84**, 3722 (1962); J. Meinwald, C. Swithinbank, and A. Lewis, *ibid.*, **85**, 1880 (1963).

From: *Tetrahedron Letters* **1963,** No. 20, 1273–75

ON THE ACETOLYSIS OF <u>EXO</u> - AND <u>ENDO</u>-BICYCLO[2.1.1] -

HEXYL-5 TOSYLATES

By Kenneth B. Wiberg and Richard Fenoglio

Department of Chemistry, Yale University

New Haven, Conn.
(Received 12 June 1963)

Although good evidence has been found for anchimeric assistance

in the solvolytic reactions of unsaturated systems such as the 2-norbornen-

yl tosylates $(k_{exo}/k_{endo} = 8 \times 10^3)$[1] and the 7-isopropylidene 5-norbornen-

2-yl tosylates[2], the smaller rate factor observed with saturated systems

such as the 2-norbornyl tosylates $(k_{exo}/k_{endo} = 350)$[3] lends an element of

uncertainty in the interpretation of the results.[4]

We have observed that the bicyclo[2.1.1]hexyl-5 tosylates[5]

(1)   S. Winstein and M. Shatavsky, <u>J. Am. Chem. Soc.</u> 78, 592 (1956);
        S. Winstein, H. M. Walborsky and K. Schreiber, <u>J. Am. Chem. Soc.</u>
        72, 5795 (1950).

(2)   C. H. DePuy, L. A. Ogawa and J. C. McDaniels, <u>J. Am. Chem. Soc.</u>
        82, 2397 (1960).

(3)   S. Winstein and D. Trifan, <u>J. Am. Chem. Soc.</u> 74, 1147, 1154
        (1952).

(4)   H. C. Brown in <u>The Transition State</u>, Chemical Soc. Special Pub.
        No. 16, 140 (1962).

(5)   K. B. Wiberg, B. R. Lowry and T. H. Colby, <u>J. Am. Chem. Soc.</u>
        83, 3998 (1961).

give a remarkably large rate difference in acetolysis. The more reactive
endo-isomer (I) gave a rate constant of 2.79×10^{-3} sec^{-1} at 25°, whereas
the exo-isomer (II) gave a rate constant of 5.82×10^{-4} sec^{-1} at 164.2°.
The latter value corresponds to a rate constant at 25° of about 9×10^{-10}
sec^{-1} giving $k_{endo}/k_{exo} = 3 \times 10^{6}$. The acetolysis of I led to 80% ion-
pair return to 4-cyclohexenyl tosylate, 8% 4-cyclohexenyl acetate and
8% bicyclo[3.1.0]hexyl-2 acetate, plus some minor components. A
complete product study of the acetolysis of II has not as yet been made,
but a major product is 4-cyclohexenyl acetate.

I   II

The structure of I is similar to that of cyclobutyl tosylate, and
has the possibility of an anchimeric participation leading to a "bicyclobutonium" type ion.[6] The products of the reaction are those expected
from this type of participation: cyclobutyl tosylate gave cyclopropylcarbinyl acetate, cyclobutyl acetate, allylcarbinyl acetate and allylcarbinyl tosylate.[6] The product corresponding to cyclobutyl acetate was
not observed in the acetolysis of I, but it was obtained in the reaction in
acetone in the presence of halide ion.[5] The rate constant for the acetolysis

(6)   J. D. Roberts and V. C. Chambers, J. Am. Chem. Soc. 73, 5034
       (1951).

of cyclobutyl tosylate at 25° is about 3×10^{-6} sec $^{-1}$, [6,7] or about 10^3 lower than that for I. Thus, the extra bond angle deformation in I results in an accentuated rate of reactions.

The structure, II, is quite similar to that of 7-norbornyl tosylate (III), the acetolysis of which is characterized by the rate constant 6.4×10^{-15} at 25°.[8] The acetolysis of II is nearly 10^5 faster than that of III. The low rate of solvolysis of III is attributed to the bond angle deformation at the 7 position, which would be accentuated in the activated complex in which C_7 approaches a trigonal configuration.[8] This factor should be even more important in the reaction of II because of the smaller bridge involved. Thus, the higher rate of reaction of II suggests that here also, participation may be involved in the formation of the acetolysis activated complex.

The further details of the solvolytic reactions of I and II are presently under investigation. This work was supported by the U.S. Army Research Office, Durham, to whom we express our appreciation.

---

(7)   H. C. Brown and G. Ham, J. Am. Chem. Soc. 78, 2735 (1956).

(8)   S. Winstein, M. Shatavsky, C. Norton and R. B. Woodward, J. Am. Chem. Soc. 77, 4183 (1955).

66 The 1,2-Dianisyl-norbornyl Cation

Schleyer, Kleinfelter, and Richey (Paper No. 66) take advantage of the prolonged lifetime of 2-aryl- and 1,2-diarylnorbornyl cations in sulfuric and trifluoroacetic acids to determine whether the 1,2-diaryl ions are symmetrical with respect to the two aryl groups, or carry more of their charge at one or the other of the tertiary centers. Although the 1,2-dianisylnorbornyl cation, the one most thoroughly studied, was not stable in concentrated sulfuric acid, the instability consisted of the rapid sulfonation of one of the anisyl rings, which would not have occurred with such ease if the anisyl group had carried its proportional share of the positive charge, as in trianisylmethyl cation. The evidence from nuclear magnetic resonance is especially convincing that the two anisyl groups are not equivalently situated, even though a rapid equilibration of the two unsymmetrical structures is occurring at room temperature.

This result, analogous to that of Bonner and Collins (Paper No. 24) in the case of the ionization mechanism of 1,2,2-triphenylethyl acetate, may be due to the same cause generalized by Winstein *et al.* (Paper No. 15) for phenonium participation in competition with benzylic delocalization. It has not been determined in general whether norbornonium and benzylic delocalization are always entirely in competition, or whether they may to some extent reinforce each other. For this reason it may be a serious limitation on the present conclusions that there is an additional steric reason why the 1,2-diarylnorbornyl cations *should* be unsymmetrical in any case. Unlike the hypothetical 1,2-diphenylethylenephenonium ion, which could have existed with *trans* configuration, the symmetrical 1,2-dianisylnorbornonium ion would have to have its two anisyl groups *cis,* in which relation they can be only very imperfectly coplanar. For whatever reason, it is clear that one of the anisyl groups is involved in charge delocalization, while the other is not, and is probably tilted in a position to avoid interference with the other anisyl group.

From: *J. Am. Chem. Soc.* **85,** 479–81 (1963)

NON-CLASSICAL CARBONIUM IONS: THE STRUCTURE OF STABLE ARYL SUBSTITUTED NORBORNYL CATIONS[1]

Sir:

By their distinctive differences in behavior, two classes of carbonium ions may be recognized. "Clas-

(1) Preliminary accounts of this work were presented at National Meetings of the American Chemical Society: 141st, Washington, D. C., March, 1962, Abstracts, p. 28-O, and 142nd, Atlantic City, N. J., Sept., 1962, Abstracts, p. 56-Q.

TABLE I

ULTRAVIOLET SPECTRAL MAXIMA OF ARYL SUBSTITUTED
NORBORNYL CATIONS[a]

Diaryl ion precursor	Initial λ_{max}, mμ	Monoaryl analog	λ_{max}, mμ
Ia	340	Ig	337
Ib	349	Ih	350
Ic	349	Ih	350
Id	353	Ih	350
Ie	381	Ii	381
If	381	Ii	381

[a] In concentrated H_2SO_4. The monoaryl ions were chemically stable under these conditions,[6b] but the diaryl ions reacted and the ultraviolet maxima shifted with time.

TABLE II

N.M.R. SPECTRUM OF ION FROM If IN CF_3COOH SOLUTION

Position, τ	Multiplicity	Area	Assignment
2.28	Doublet ($^1/_2$ AB)	4	Aryl H, meta to OCH_3
2.83	Doublet ($^1/_2$ AB)	4	Aryl H, ortho to OCH_3
5.89	Sharp singlet	6	OCH_3 groups
6.75	Broad singlet	1	Bridgehead H
7.00	Broad singlet	4	CH_2's α to C+
7.4	Broad singlet	2	Remaining two
8.0	Broad singlet	2	CH_2's

TABLE III

APPROXIMATE HALF-TIMES FOR AROMATIC MONOSUBSTITUTION

Starting compound	Bromination[a]	Sulfonation (concd. H_2SO_4)	Sulfonation (84.3% H_2SO_4)
If	<1 minute	<1 minute	60 minutes
2-p-Anisylnorbornene	None detected[b]	>3000 hours	>3000 hours
Tri-p-anisylcarbinol	3 hours	2 hours	>3000 hours
p-t-Butylanisole	<1 minute	...	...
p-Methylanisole	...	<1 minute	30 minutes
p-Anisylmethylamine	<1 minute	<1 minute	30 hours

[a] A saturated solution of bromine in a 4.5 M solution of H_2SO_4 in CF_3COOH was added to an equal volume of a solution of aromatic compounds (about 0.25 M) in the same solvent.   [b] A side reaction of bromination on the bicyclic ring but not the aromatic ring with a half time of about 40 minutes limited the observation time.

sical" carbonium ions are formed from suitable precursors at normal rates predictable by electronic and structural considerations; such "simple" carbonium ions exhibit little sterospecificity in either their formation or in their reaction.[2] "Non-classical" carbonium ions, provided their precursors have the proper geometry, are generally formed with enhanced rates and their reactions are highly stereospecific. Despite many investigations, the structures of non-classical carbonium ions remain in doubt[3]; alternative possibilities include single mesomeric "bridged" structures or rapidly equilibrating simple ion mixtures.[3] We report here the preparation and structure proof of a stable, "non-classical" carbonium ion.

The unusual properties of carbonium ions in the bicyclo[2.2.1]heptane series have been widely interpreted to support a bridged structure.[2,4] Although a number of stable substituted monoarylnorbornyl cations have been studied,[5,6] the structure of such carbonium ions—bridged or simple—remains unproved because of the difficulty of obtaining unambiguous

(2) A. Streitwieser, Jr., "Solvolytic Displacement Reactions," McGraw-Hill Book Co., Inc., New York, N. Y., 1962; Chem. Revs., 56, 571 (1956).

(3) See H. C. Brown in "The Transition State," Special Publication No. 16, Chem. Soc., London, 1962; P. S. Skell and R. J. Maxwell, J. Am. Chem. Soc., 84, 3963 (1962).

(4) J. A. Berson in P. de Mayo, Ed., "Molecular Rearrangements," Interscience Publishers, Inc., New York, N. Y., in press.

(5) P. D. Bartlett, E. R. Webster, C. E. Dills and H. G. Richey, Jr., Ann., 623, 217 (1959); P. D. Bartlett, C. E. Dils and H. G. Richey, Jr., J. Am. Chem. Soc., 82, 5414 (1960).

(6) (a) N. C. Deno, P. T. Groves, J. J. Jaruzelski and M. M. Lugasch, ibid., 82, 4719 (1960); (b) N. C. Deno, P. von R. Schleyer and D. C. Kleinfelter, Tetrahedron Letters, No. 12, 414 (1961); (c) N. C. Deno, unpublished observations, privately communicated; (d) H. G. Richey, Jr., unpublished observations.

structural information. We believe that the symmetry properties of diarylnorbornyl carbonium ions (derived from 1,2-diarylnorbornanols, I[7]) make definitive determination of their structure possible.

For structures I, II and III

a, R = R' = C_6H_5
b, R = C_6H_5, R' = p-$CH_3C_6H_4$
c, R = p-$CH_3C_6H_4$, R' = C_6H_5
d, R = R' = p-$CH_3C_6H_5$
e, R = p-$CH_3C_6H_4$, R' = p-$CH_3OC_6H_4$
f, R = R' = p-$CH_3OC_6H_4$
g, R = H, R' = C_6H_5
h, R = H, R' = p-$CH_3C_6H_4$
i, R = H, R' = p-$CH_3OC_6H_4$

Ultraviolet Spectral Behavior.—Because of extended conjugation, diarylnorbornyl cations with bridged structure II should have ultraviolet spectra substantially different from those of analogous monoarylnorbornyl cations (II, R = H, R' = Ar). If the ions are rapidly equilibrating but asymmetric (III), corresponding monoaryl and diaryl cations should have the same ultraviolet chromophoric groups. The results (Table I) are in accord with the second but not the first prediction and favor asymmetric ion structures (III) for diaryl substituted norbornyl carbonium ions.

Thermodynamic Stability Measurements.—Barring steric influences, the nature and extent of which are hard to predict in this series, the dianisyl cation (from If) would be expected to be more stable thermodynamically than the monoanisyl cation (from Ii) if the structures of the ions are symmetrical (II), less stable (because of inductive effects of the non-conjugated aryl group) if the structures are asymmetrical (III). For the determination of thermodynamic stabilities of carbonium ions, the percentage of sulfuric acid in water at which the ion is half formed is a convenient measure; the more dilute the acid the more stable the ion.[6a] The evidence—ion from If half formed in 51% sulfuric acid, ion from Ii half formed in 41% sulfuric acid—favors asymmetrical ion structures (III).

Nuclear Magnetic Resonance Studies.—The n.m.r. spectrum of the dianisylnorbornyl ion (from If) indicated equivalence of both aryl rings (anisyl quartet and methoxyl singlet) and symmetry in the remainder of the molecule (Table II). Either symmetrical

(7) D. C. Kleinfelter and P. von R. Schleyer, J. Org. Chem., 26, 3740 (1961).

structure IIf or rapidly equilibrating asymmetrical structures IIIf are compatible with this result. The effect of cooling gave dramatic evidence in favor of rapidly equilibrating asymmetrical ion structures IIIf. The aryl proton peaks lost detail and collapsed into a single broad peak indicating impending non-equivalence of the aryl rings at the lowest temperature it was possible to achieve ($-70°$ in CH_2Cl_2). The corresponding aryl peaks of a model ion (from p-anisylcamphenilol)[5] under the same conditions did not alter significantly.

Chemical Behavior.—Under conditions of complete ionization, symmetrical ion IIf should not undergo rapid aromatic substitution because of the delocalization of positive charge into both aryl rings. Ions IIIf would have at any instant only one aryl ring conjugated with the charge; hence, substitution in the non-conjugated ring should be rapid. This latter prediction agrees with the results of semiquantitative experiments, comparing the rates of aromatic substitution of ions from If with the behavior of model compounds, by observing the changes in n.m.r. spectra (Table III).

We conclude on the basis of all four experimental criteria that diarylnorbornyl carbonium ions possess rapidly equilibrating asymmetric ion structures III. This result does not rule out the possibility of bridged structures for non-aryl substituted norbornyl or other non-classical carbonium ions, but it stresses the desirability of reopening the question of the structure of such intermediates.[3]

Acknowledgments.—This work was supported, in part, by a grant from the National Science Foundation (to P. R. S.). We wish to thank Professor Norman C. Deno for his interest, for providing stimulating ideas and discussion, and for experimental assistance.

(8) Alfred P. Sloan Research Fellow.

FRICK LABORATORY
PRINCETON UNIVERSITY   PAUL VON R. SCHLEYER[8]
PRINCETON, NEW JERSEY
DEPARTMENT OF CHEMISTRY
UNIVERSITY OF HAWAII   DONALD C. KLEINFELTER
HONOLULU, HAWAII
DEPARTMENT OF CHEMISTRY
PENNSYLVANIA STATE UNIVERSITY   HERMAN G. RICHEY, JR.
UNIVERSITY PARK, PA.

RECEIVED OCTOBER 24, 1962

67

The Conjugate Base of the Ethylene *p*-Hydroxyphenonium Ion

Baird and Winstein (Paper No. 67) pursue phenonium participation to its ultimate limit. The phenoxide ion corresponding to 2-*p*-hydroxyphenylethyl bromide undergoes first-order methanolysis about a million times faster than 2-*p*-anisylethyl bromide. A spectroscopically well-characterized intermediate is the direct product, its concentration rising and rapidly falling again. The rate constants of its formation and consumption are determined, and conditions are worked out for its isolation. The crystalline solid is characterized and shown to be the spirodienone IV (page 480), its methylene groups being entirely equivalent in the NMR. Direct measurements of its rate of reaction in methanol show a stability maximum at about pH 12. It is attacked by methoxide ion rapidly above pH 14, while below pH 8 it is protonated to the *p*-hydroxyphenonium ion, which is rapidly attacked by solvent. This is a way of generating and observing the ethylene-*p*-hydroxyphenonium ion from a neutral species which is isolated and observed by direct structural methods.

From: *J. Am. Chem. Soc.* **85**, 567–78 (1963)

[Contribution from the Department of Chemistry, University of California, Los Angeles 24, Calif.]

Neighboring Carbon and Hydrogen. LI.[1] Dienones from Ar₁⊖-3 Participation. Isolation and Behavior of Spiro(2,5)octa-1,4-diene-3-one

By Richard Baird[2] and S. Winstein

Received October 15, 1962

When the aryl group is *p*-hydroxyphenyl, Ar₁-3 participation in the phenoxide anion of 2-aryl-1-ethyl halides, designated by the symbol Ar₁⊖-3, leads to spiro(2,5)octa-1,4-diene-3-one. Kinetic investigation of the behavior of 2-*p*-hydroxyphenylethyl bromide in basic methanolic solution shows that conditions are very favorable for Ar₁⊖-3 participation; the intermediate spiro-dienone gives rise to monomeric methyl ether and higher molecular weight products in proportions dependent on the concentrations of methoxide and phenoxide ions. By spectroscopic methods it is possible to observe and study the kinetics of formation and decay of the intermediate spiro-dienone. Under specially designed conditions, it has been possible to isolate the unusually reactive spiro-dienone as a pure, crystalline solid and to study its behavior directly in solvolysis, hydrogenation, lithium aluminum hydride reduction and hydrogen bromide addition. The ultraviolet and n.m.r. spectra of the dienone are of some interest. Also, the acid-catalyzed rate of methanolysis of the spiro-dienone permits one to estimate the stationary state concentration of the ethylene phenonium ion intermediate in solvolysis of 2-*p*-anisylethyl toluenesulfonate. This is because the conjugate acid of the dienone may be taken as a model for the bridged-ion intermediate in anchimerically assisted ionization of a 2-*p*-anisylethyl derivative.

With suitable substrate structure and reaction conditions, it is possible to arrange for the formation of dienones through Ar₁⊖-participation of a neighboring phenoxide-ion group.[1a,3] In the case of Ar₁⊖-assisted formation of dienones, it has been indicated already in preliminary communications[3,4] that 2-*p*-hydroxyphenylethyl bromide (I-Br) gives rise under alkaline conditions to the intermediate dienone IV which can be detected spectroscopically[3] and even isolated in pure form.[4] The results of this study of the formation and behavior of this interesting substance are presented and discussed in the present manuscript.

(1) (a) Paper XLVI: R. Baird and S. Winstein, *J. Am. Chem. Soc.*, **84**, 788 (1962); (b) Paper XLVII: E. Friedrich and S. Winstein, *Tetrahedron Letters*, No. 11, 475 (1962); (c) Paper XLVIII: E. Hedaya and S. Winstein, *ibid.*, No. 13, 563 (1962); (c) Paper XLIX: S. Winstein, E. Vogelfanger, K. C. Pande and H. F. Ebel, *J. Am. Chem. Soc.*, in press; (e) Paper L: S. Winstein, E. Vogelfanger and K. C. Pande, *Chem. Ind.* (London), 2061 (1962).

(2) National Science Foundation Predoctoral Fellow, 1953–1955, 1956–1957. Present address: Dept. of Chem., Yale University, New Haven, Conn.

(3) S. Winstein and R. Baird, *J. Am. Chem. Soc.*, **79**, 756 (1957).

(4) R. Baird and S. Winstein, *ibid.*, **79**, 4238 (1957).

TABLE I

REACTION OF 2-*p*-HYDROXYPHENYLETHYL BROMIDE IN METHANOLIC AND ETHANOLIC SODIUM ALKOXIDE AT 25.00°

Run	Solvent	(RBr) 10^3 M	(NaOR) 10^3 M	Excess (NaOR):(RBr)	Initial 10^4k, sec.$^{-1}$	% rn. at exp. ∞^b	Range of integ. 10^3k (20–80% rn.), sec.$^{-1}$
1	EtOH^a	2.684	5.555	1:1	1.2	81.5	1.05–0.15
2	EtOH	3.502	17.54	4:1	1.4	85.3	1.27– .64
3	EtOH	3.494	17.63	4:1	1.2	84.9	1.57– .68
4	EtOH	3.019	33.10	10:1	1.4	88.7	1.23– .83
5	EtOH	3.284	72.34	20:1	1.32	95	1.18–1.03
6	EtOH	3.448	3.448	0:1	..	70	1.17 ± 0.04^c
7	EtOH	3.448	3.448	0:1	..	70	1.16 ± 0.04^c
8	MeOH^a	3.004	13.03	3:1	0.86	91	0.893–0.739
9	MeOH^a	3.000	13.03	3:1	0.87	89	0.796–0.665

^{a} Followed by base consumption; the other rates were followed by bromide ion production. ^{b} The experimental infinity was taken at 20 or more half-lives, based on the initial rate constant; the infinity values did not drift appreciably after this time. ^{c} Calculated on the assumption that the rate of disappearance of RBr is twice the rate of production of bromide ion.

Kinetic Search for $Ar_1^{\ominus}$-3 Participation.—Just as in the case of the $Ar_1^{\ominus}$-5 investigation,[1a,3] the search for $Ar_1^{\ominus}$-3 participation involved a combination of kinetic measurements and product examination. In the kinetic search for $Ar_1^{\ominus}$-3 participation, a study was made of the solvolytic behavior of the phenoxide ion II-Br from 2-*p*-hydroxyphenylethyl bromide (I-Br) in methanolic and ethanolic sodium alkoxide solution.

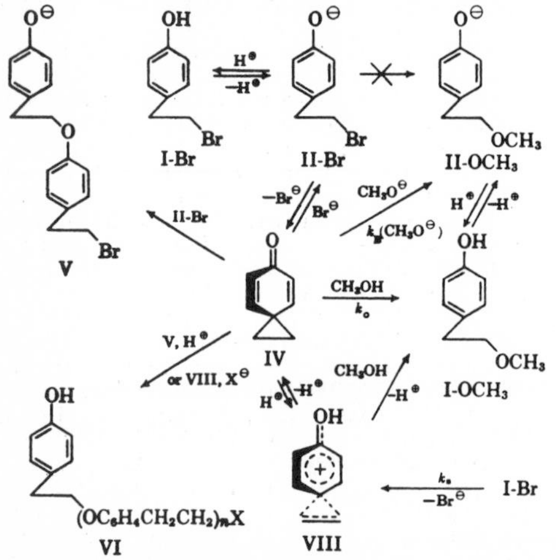

Fig. 1.—Reactions of 2-*p*-hydroxyphenylethyl bromide in anhydrous methanol at 25.0°.

As is clear from the summary in Table I, the initial value of the instantaneous[5] first-order rate constant obtained in these runs was independent of excess alkoxide ion employed. This is shown by runs 1–5 in Table I where the ratio of excess alkoxide:II-Br varies from 1:1 to 20:1. However, first-order kinetics were not well obeyed throughout the runs, first-order rate constants drifting downward in all of them.

In contrast with the *p*-hydroxyphenylethyl bromide, the corresponding methyl ether III-Br reacted much more slowly in absolute methanol containing sodium methoxide. Good second-order kinetics were observed in this case, k_2 being $(1.49 \pm 0.03) \times 10^{-5}$ l. mole^{-1} sec.$^{-1}$ at 25°. This corresponds to a pseudo first-order rate constant of 1.9×10^{-6} sec.$^{-1}$ at 0.13 M sodium methoxide, much smaller than the value of 8.6×10^{-4} sec.$^{-1}$ observed with the hydroxyphenylethyl

bromide I-Br. The situation is similar in ethanol as solvent, since the second-order rates of reaction of III-Br with ethoxide ion reported by DePuy[6] correspond to pseudo first-order rate constants which are lower than the one observed with I-Br by a factor of *ca.* 20 at the highest base concentration and *ca.* 400 at the lowest practical alkoxide concentration.

In both methanol and ethanol as solvents it is evident that the reaction of the phenoxide ion II-Br is substantially accelerated over the reaction of the ether III-Br with alkoxide ion. The contrast becomes much greater if the comparison is made between the first-order rate of II-Br and the neutral solvolysis of III-Br. The bromide III-Br is exceedingly slow in ethanol at 25°, but a crude estimate of its neutral solvolysis rate can be obtained from that of 2-*p*-anisylethyl *p*-toluenesulfonate (III-OTs) at 75°. Extrapolation[7] leads to an estimated difference of *ca.* 10^6 between the rate of II-Br and either the anchimerically unassisted or anchimerically assisted rate of ethanolysis of III-Br at 25°.

The anchimeric acceleration and essentially first-order kinetics observed in the alkaline solvolysis of I-Br can be interpreted in terms of the rate-determining formation of the spiro-dienone intermediate IV as in Fig. 1. The fate of this intermediate can be inferred from the following evidence. First of all, the products from the reaction in methanol consisted primarily of 2-*p*-hydroxyphenylethyl methyl ether (I-OCH₃), plus an ill-defined higher molecular weight product which appeared to consist of a mixture of products of general structure VI. The proportion of I-OCH₃ isolated varied with the excess of alkoxide used in the reaction, ranging from 57% when a 3:1 excess was employed to 82% when the ratio was 30:1. It seems certain that these products were formed *via* dienone IV rather than directly from I-Br or II-Br since the methyl ether of I-Br gives a quantitative yield of *p*-methoxystyrene under very similar conditions.[6]

In agreement with the product analysis, the experimental infinity values in the kinetic runs varied with the excess of alkoxide ion employed in the reaction. As shown in Table I, the reaction stopped at 81.5% of completion when a 1:1 ratio of excess ethoxide to II-Br was used. This value rose to 95% when the ratio of ethoxide to II-Br was increased to 20:1.

(6) C. H. DePuy and D. H. Froemsdorf, *J. Am. Chem. Soc.*, **79**, 3710 (1957).

(7) The anchimerically assisted and unassisted ethanolysis rate constants[8] for III-OTs are 6.6×10^{-6} sec.$^{-1}$ and 7.6×10^{-6} sec.$^{-1}$, respectively, at 75°. Applying a factor of 15 for the difference between a primary bromide and *p*-toluenesulfonate[9] and a factor of 15 for each 25° change in temperature gives an estimated rate constant of *ca.* 2×10^{-9} sec.$^{-1}$ for either anchimerically assisted or unassisted ethanolysis of III-Br at 25°.

(8) E. Jenny and S. Winstein, *Helv. Chim. Acta*, **41**, 807 (1958).

(9) A. Streitwieser, Jr., *Chem. Rev.*, **56**, 654 (1956).

(5) The initial, instantaneous first-order rate constant was obtained by extrapolation of a plot of concentration *vs.* time to zero time, graphical determination of the slope (dx/dt) and division by the concentration at zero time. Zero time could be established accurately as described in the Experimental section.

Since the purity of I-Br was established by analysis and melting point, it seems reasonable to attribute this incomplete reaction to the formation of dimeric V, by reaction between IV and ion II-Br. The bromine in V should be comparable in reactivity to that in the methyl ether III-Br, so that it would be expected to be essentially inert under the reaction conditions. Accordingly, this process results in consumption of II-Br without production of bromide ion, which would lead to deviation from first-order kinetics. It also explains the dependence of the product ratio and experimental infinity value on the excess of alkoxide ion used, as the latter is competing with ion II-Br for intermediate IV.

In order to test the above scheme, the rate of reaction of II-Br was measured in ethanol containing no excess ethoxide.[10] Under these conditions it was expected that two moles of II-Br would be consumed for every mole of bromide ion produced and that the reaction would stop at 50% (as measured by bromide ion produced), all of II-Br being converted to dimeric V at this point. In spite of the possibility of additional reactions of IV and incomplete conversion[10] of phenol I-Br to phenoxide II-Br, the above expectation is essentially correct as shown by runs 6 and 7 in Table I. The reaction stops at 70% reaction and reasonably good, non-drifting first-order rate constants[12] were obtained. As shown in Table I, the values of these rate constants were comparable in magnitude to the initial, instantaneous rate constants in runs 1–5.

Although the above scheme affords a good qualitative explanation of the reactions of II-Br and IV, the multiplicity of reactions possible at titrimetric concentrations makes a quantitative interpretation difficult. Thus, it was not possible to fit the over-all kinetic behavior of II-Br with any precision on the basis of titrimetric measurements, nor was it possible to establish a simple relationship between the excess of alkoxide ion used and the experimental infinity value obtained.

It was possible, however, to eliminate many of the side reactions observed at titrimetric concentration (0.03 M) and to clarify many of the above points by studying the reactions in more dilute solutions (10^{-4} to 10^{-5} M) making use of the characteristic spectroscopic properties of I-Br, II-Br, IV and II-OCH₃.

Spectroscopic Study of Ar₁⊖-3 Participation.—Both the reactant phenol I-Br and the product phenol I-OCH₃ exhibited similar ultraviolet spectra in methanol solvent. Maxima occurred at 285 mμ (ϵ 1500), 278 mμ (ϵ 1900) and near 225 mμ for both compounds. The first two maxima, the so-called B-bands,[13] were reasonably insensitive to substitution at the 2-position in the aliphatic portion of the molecule, but the latter maximum proved to be somewhat more sensitive, occurring at 229.5 mμ with I-Br and 224 mμ for I-OCH₃.

Addition of sufficient base to convert the phenols to their salts caused a characteristic[14] bathochromic shift. Thus the maximum at 224 mμ for 2-p-hydroxyphenyl-

ethanol (I-OH), which is essentially identical spectroscopically with I-OCH₃, was shifted to 241 mμ (ϵ 11,300) and the two maxima at 277.5 and 285 mμ became a single maximum at 295 mμ (ϵ 2700). The effect of added base on I-Br was more complex due to concurrent reaction, but qualitatively similar behavior was observed.

When a $ca.$ 10^{-4} M solution of I-Br in methanol was treated with a two- or threefold excess of sodium methoxide at 25°, only a small fraction of the phenol was converted to its sodium salt because of the unfavorable equilibrium involved at these concentrations.[11] Over the course of about thirty minutes, however, the phenolic maximum at 229.5 mμ slowly disappeared and a new maximum appeared at 274 mμ much more intense than the original phenolic maximum at 277.5 mμ. After about thirty minutes, this new maximum began to decrease and a phenolic maximum began to reappear near 229 mμ. After a total of sixty minutes this entire process was complete and the spectrum was similar to that of the initial solution, except that the phenolic maximum was now at 224 mμ, corresponding to the maximum of I-OCH₃ rather than I-Br.

The maximum at 274 mμ could not be attributed to any of the known phenols or their salts, and it was extremely unlikely that it was due to dimeric or analogous products since the spectra of such compounds resemble those of the monomers. A sample of p-hydroxystyrene, prepared by decarboxylation of p-hydroxycinnamic acid, exhibited a maximum at 260.5 mμ (ϵ 15,000) in methanol, which was shifted to 285 mμ (ϵ 18,000) by base. Both the styrene and its salt were stable under conditions where the 274 mμ peak rapidly disappeared, so that a fortuitous mixture of the styrene and its salt could not have given this maximum. The latter possibility was completely eliminated by the observance of the 274 mμ peak at more than one base concentration.

By a process of elimination it was possible to associate the maximum at 274 mμ with the intermediate dienone IV. This wave length was not inconsistent with this structure, since the related spiro(4,5)deca-2,5-dien-3-one[1a] (VII) possessed a maximum at 242 mμ, and the added conjugation provided by a cyclopropane ring was expected to cause a bathochromic shift.[15] However, this shift of 32 mμ was much larger than had been previously observed for cyclopropane conjugation,[15] so that it could not be used as compelling evidence for the structure of IV.

Spectroscopic Kinetic Studies.—For further kinetic studies, it was necessary to estimate the equilibrium constant for the equilibrium in eq. 1, since, for simplicity of kinetic treatment, it was desirable to have the substrate I-Br either completely ionized or almost completely un-ionized. Using the method of Stenström,[16] the value of K_m defined by eq. 2 was determined in absolute methanol, for 2-p-hydroxyphenylethanol (I-OH), assuming the value for I-Br would be almost identical. The measurements were not cor-

(10) This situation could not in fact be achieved because of incomplete conversion of phenol to phenoxide ion.[11] Nevertheless, as a first approximation the major part of the substrate was present as II-Br. For further comment, see subsequent paragraphs.

(11) J. W. Baker and A. J. Neale, $J.$ $Chem.$ $Soc.$, 3225 (1954).

(12) If two moles of substrate II-Br are consumed for every mole of bromide ion produced, $-d(II-Br)/dt = 2k(II-Br)$, where k is the rate constant for production of bromide ion. Integration gives $\ln (II-Br)_0 - \ln (II-Br) = 2k(t - t_0)$. Setting $(II-Br)_0 = a$, and $(Br^-) = x$, gives $(II-Br) = (a - 2x)$, and $\ln a - \ln (a - 2x) = 2k(t - t_0)$. Elimination of t_0 gives: $\ln (a - 2x_1) - \ln (a - 2x_2) = 2k(t_2 - t_1)$, which is the expression used to calculate k for runs 6 and 7.

(13) A. E. Gillam and E. S. Stern, "An Introduction to Electronic Absorption Spectroscopy in Organic Chemistry," Edward Arnold Ltd., London, 1955, p. 125.

(14) N. D. Coggeshall and A. S. Glessner, Jr., $J.$ $Am.$ $Chem.$ $Soc.$, **71**, 3150 (1949).

rected for ionic strength effects, since only an estimate of the magnitude of K_m was necessary. The values determined are given in the Experimental section, the average value of K_m being taken as $(3.25 \pm 0.25) \times 10^{-3}$ M. This meant that concentrations of sodium methoxide of 0.05–0.1 M were necessary to ensure

$$\text{ArO}^\ominus + \text{CH}_3\text{OH} \rightleftharpoons \text{ArOH} + \text{CH}_2\text{O}^\ominus \qquad (1)$$

$$K_m = (\text{ArOH})(\text{MeO}^\ominus)/(\text{ArO}^\ominus) \qquad (2)$$

(15) R. H. Eastman, $ibid.$, **76**, 4115 (1954).

(16) W. Stenström and N. Goldsmith, $J.$ $Phys.$ $Chem.$, **30**, 1683 (1926).

predominant conversion of I-Br to II-Br. Also, nothing could be gained by going in the other direction, since at 10^{-4} M sodium methoxide the equilibrium is still in the intermediate range and this is difficult to handle kinetically.[17] Both base and substrate are consumed at this concentration, and ca. 10% of the substrate is still present in the phenolic form I-Br. Lower concentrations were difficult to obtain because of reaction of the base with atmospheric carbon dioxide.

When preliminary kinetic measurements were made at base concentrations of 0.05 and 0.1 M, it was found that the intermediate IV was destroyed at a rate comparable to that at which it was formed. Since the base concentration was high compared to that of the substrate, any process leading to destruction of the intermediate could be treated as pseudo first order. This made both formation and destruction of IV first order so that the system resembles a radioactive parent–daughter series as in eq. 3. In this formulation k_2 is a complex rate constant, but it does not vary in any one run since base concentration is essentially constant.

$$\text{II-Br} \xrightarrow{k_1} \text{IV} \xrightarrow{k_2} \text{product (II-OCH}_3) \qquad (3)$$

$$[B] = \frac{[A]_0 k_1}{k_2 - k_1}(e^{-k_1 t} - e^{-k_2 t}) \qquad (4)$$

$$(k_2 - k_1)t_m = \ln(k_2/k_1) \qquad (5)$$

Because the reactant II-Br and product II-OCH$_3$ had similar ultraviolet spectra, the reaction was followed at the maximum of the intermediate (274 mμ). However, in order to evaluate the rate constants for the reaction by the usual kinetic method,[18] it was necessary to relate the concentration of IV to either that of II-Br or II-OCH$_3$. Since the molar extinction coefficient of IV was not available at the time these experiments were carried out, it was necessary to devise a method which did not require this information. The following method not only provided an estimate of the rate constants, but also proved convenient for the calculation of better values after more information about IV became available.

Provided that the rate constant for the second step in a series first-order sequence is enough smaller than that for the first step, the reaction will reach a point where only the second step is important and the value of this rate constant can be obtained from the slope of a plot of log (optical density) vs. time. This condition could not be obtained with the bromide II-Br, but with the corresponding iodide II-I the rate of the second step could just be measured at 0.01 M sodium methoxide concentration.

Once a method for evaluating k_2 was derived, the value of k_1 could be determined as follows: The integrated rate expression for a series first-order reaction is given in eq.[18] 4 where [B] represents the concentration of IV and [A]$_0$ the initial concentration of II-Br. As was stated above, this equation could not be evaluated without a way of relating [B] and [A]$_0$. However, on differentiation of expression 4 with respect to t, eq. 5 is obtained,[18] giving the value of t at which the concentration of IV is a maximum (t_m). By the use of a special rapid mixing flask[19] it was possible to determine t_m quite accurately, and eq. 5 could be solved by successive approximations. This value of t_m could be obtained without complication at 274 mμ since only the intermediate absorbed strongly at this wave length,

both substrate II-Br and product II-OCH$_3$ having minima here. The sensitivity of the value of k_1 to small errors in t_m was low, so that small errors in the latter were unimportant.

The value of k_1 obtained from this method is shown in run 2 in Table II. This value is known to be low because at the base concentration employed, the highest one at which k_2 could be evaluated, the substrate II-Br is less than 90% in the ionized form. Nevertheless, the value is of the same order of magnitude as the values for k_1 obtained titrimetrically (Table I). When another method, described later in this article, was derived for determining k_2 at base concentrations higher than 0.05 M, it was possible to determine k_1 under conditions where most of the substrate was in the phenoxide ion form (runs 3 and 4 in Table II). The values of k_1 in runs 3 and 4 are self consistent, but are larger than the titrimetric values of k_1 by a factor of ca. 2.3. As will be shown later, these values are believed to be correct, the titrimetric rate constants being low due to return by bromide ion.

TABLE II

SPECTROSCOPIC BEHAVIOR OF 2-p-HYDROXYPHENYLETHYL HALIDES (RX) AT 274 mμ IN ABSOLUTE METHANOL AT 25°

X	(RX), 10^3 M	(NaOMe), 10^2 M	$10^4 k_1$, sec.$^{-1}$	$10^4 k_2$, sec.$^{-1}$
I	5.08	0.994	5.1	9.2
Br	6.03	0.994	1.1	9.2[a]
Br	6.14	4.88	1.9	30.4[b]
Br	6.03	12.9	2.2	80.6[b]

[a] Assumed to be the same as in run above. [b] Calculated from decay rates of the intermediate.

The reaction of I-Br became much simpler in t-butyl alcohol as solvent. In this solvent, phenols are converted to their salts at much lower base concentrations than were required in methyl and ethyl alcohols, so that attack on IV by base could be made less serious. Both the bromide I-Br and the iodide I-I rapidly gave rise to an intense maximum at 271 mμ on addition of potassium t-butoxide, the reaction half-lives being less than 30 seconds at 30°. No species other than that absorbing at 271 mμ remained in the region 220 to 350 mμ after the treatment (except for iodide ion end absorption with I-I), and both the bromide I-Br and the iodide I-I gave the same optical density at 271 mμ when equivalent concentrations were used. The molar extinction coefficient (ϵ 22,200) calculated on the basis of complete conversion of I-Br or I-I was taken to be that of IV in t-butyl alcohol.

The chloride I-Cl reacted enough less rapidly than I-Br and I-I that it could be used for kinetic studies. However, competing reactions of II-Cl, etc., with IV were more significant with this derivative and the maximum absorption at 271 mμ was never as great as that obtained with I-Br and I-I. From the summary in Table III, it is evident that competing processes still cause a drift in the observed first-order rate constants, but this is much less serious than in methanol.

TABLE III

SPECTROSCOPIC BEHAVIOR OF 2-p-HYDROXYPHENYLETHYL CHLORIDE AT 271 mμ IN ABSOLUTE t-BUTYL ALCOHOL AT 30°

Run	(RX), 10^3 M	KOBu-t, 10^4 M	$10^4 k$ inst., sec.$^{-1}$	$10^4 k$ integ.,[a] sec.$^{-1}$	$\frac{\text{O.D.}_{max}[b]}{\text{O.D.}_\infty}$
1	3.21	3.60	3.00	3.03–2.49	0.90
2	3.21	1.01	3.01	3.05–2.58	.94
3	6.42	5.04	2.10	2.21–1.49	.88
4	3.21	35.3	1.41	1.38–0.93	.57

[a] This is the range of the integrated first-order rate constant from ca. 20–80% reaction. [b] O.D.$_\infty$ is the optical density of the intermediate obtained from the same concentration of the bromide or iodide.

(17) A. A. Frost and R. G. Pearson, "Kinetics and Mechanism," second edition, John Wiley and Sons, Inc., New York, N. Y., 1961, p. 195.

(18) Reference 17, p. 166.

(19) L. O. Winstrom and J. C. Warner, J. Am. Chem. Soc., 61, 1205 (1939).

Isolation of the Intermediate Dienone.—In view of the apparent stability of IV in *t*-butyl alcohol, attempts were made to concentrate solutions prepared from I-Br and potassium *t*-butoxide in this solvent. All such attempts, carried out at as low temperatures as possible by evaporation under reduced pressure, led to loss of the maximum at 271 mμ and the eventual isolation of a high-melting insoluble product which appeared to be polymeric.

When the preparation of IV was attempted in anhydrous ether, sodium hydride being used to convert I-Br to its salt, no reaction was observed. The sodium salt regenerated starting material on acidification and reacted normally on addition to a large excess of *t*-butyl alcohol. The use of a two-phase system was also attempted. Shaking solutions of I-Br in ether or pentane with aqueous sodium hydroxide yielded only high melting, ill-defined products.

A variation of the last method led to the successful isolation of the intermediate IV. When a strong aqueous potassium hydroxide solution was adsorbed on alumina,[20] and 2-*p*-hydroxyphenylethyl bromide dissolved in ether was passed through a chromatographic column of this alumina, effluent solutions were obtained which possessed a new maximum at 261 mμ in addition to the phenolic absorption at *ca.* 230 mμ.

By careful adjustment of column height and volume, flow rate and substrate concentration, solutions could be obtained which possessed only the maximum at 261 mμ. Estimation using the molar extinction coefficient obtained in *t*-butyl alcohol (ε 22,200) indicated an average concentration of IV in the vicinity of 10^{-3} *M* in a series of experiments run under essentially identical conditions. Dilution of samples of this solution with 99 volumes of *t*-butyl alcohol or methanol produced solutions exhibiting the previously observed ultraviolet absorption maxima for the intermediate at 271 and 274 mμ, respectively. In methanol containing 0.01 *M* sodium methoxide, the rate constant for disappearance of the absorption maximum, k_2, was within 1% of that previously observed (run 2 in Table II).

When carefully neutralized glassware was employed, the above ether solutions could be evaporated to give a white crystalline solid, which was soluble in ether, alcohols and in halogenated solvents. This substance could be recrystallized from ether–pentane at low temperatures in carefully neutralized apparatus, to give a low melting solid which possessed the correct carbon-hydrogen analysis for C_8H_8O. The spectral and chemical properties of the isolated compound were consistent with the dienone structure IV.

The infrared spectrum of the compound possessed strong absorption maxima for a highly conjugated carbonyl at 1650 cm.$^{-1}$ in carbon disulfide and 1640 cm.$^{-1}$ in chloroform, and in general was quite similar to that of spiro(4,5)deca-1,4-diene-3-one.[1a] The ultraviolet absorption maxima were also indicative of a highly conjugated carbonyl system, both in the position at which they occurred and in their intensity.[21,22] In addition, the positions of these maxima were unusually sensitive to the nature of the solvent,[23] λ$_{max}$ being shifted from 261 mμ in ether to 271 mμ in *t*-butyl alcohol, 274 mμ in methanol and *ca.* 282 mμ in water.

The nuclear magnetic resonance spectrum of dienone IV in CDCl$_3$ consisted of two sharp singlets of equal intensity at 8.31 and 3.56[24] p.p.m. on the τ-scale of

Tiers.[25] The positions of these peaks correspond closely with those observed for the cyclopropyl and vinyl hydrogens of dienone IVa at τ = 8.42 and 3.66 p.p.m., respectively.[24,26]

The lack of splitting of the vinyl hydrogens of IV is surprising but real, the resolution obtained being more than sufficient to show the characteristic triplet and quartet of diethyl ether under these conditions.

(6)

Some Reactions of the Intermediate.—In addition to the above-mentioned reaction with methoxide ion, the intermediate in dilute solution reacted with a variety of reagents to produce phenolic products. Thus, catalytic hydrogenation with reduced platinum oxide in ether required *ca.* one mole of hydrogen and the product, *p*-ethylphenol, was isolated in over 50% yield. The ultraviolet spectrum of the product indicated that it was actually formed in near quantitative yield, the difference being attributed to losses in the isolation of small quantities from very dilute solution. The same product was obtained in over 50% yield by dilute lithium aluminum hydride reduction. Addition of an ether solution of the intermediate to a large excess of hydrogen bromide in ether resulted in the formation of 2-*p*-hydroxyphenylethyl bromide, isolated in 50% yield with an 80% yield being observed spectroscopically. In dilute "neutral" or acidified methanol the ultraviolet maximum of the intermediate disappeared and the resulting spectrum was identical with that of 2-*p*-hydroxyphenylethyl methyl ether (I-OCH$_3$). Addition of more concentrated solutions of the intermediate to neutral or acidified solutions of sodium bromide in methanol caused the disappearance of up to one equivalent of bromide ion, the resulting solution exhibiting the solvolytic behavior of 2-*p*-hydroxyphenylethyl bromide in methanol. This behavior is reminiscent of the opening of ethylene oxide by chloride ion.[27]

When the precautions mentioned above concerning neutrality of the glassware were not taken, the solid isolated on evaporation of the ether solution was insoluble in all of the common organic solvents and melted above 160°. The intermediate itself, on standing, or more rapidly on heating to above its melting point, was converted to this material. The infrared spectrum of this solid was quite different from that of the intermediate, resembling that of *p*-anisylethyl bromide in most respects. A substance quite similar to the above solid was also obtained on treatment of fairly concentrated solutions of the intermediate in ether with stannic chloride etherate. The spectrum of the solid in the infrared was nearly identical with that of the solid previously obtained by treatment of 2-*p*-hydroxyphenylethyl bromide with potassium *t*-butoxide in moderately concentrated solution in *t*-butyl alcohol. All of these were presumed to be linear

(20) J. Castells and G. A. Fletcher, *J. Chem. Soc.*, 3245 (1956).

(21) E. A. Braude and E. R. H. Jones, *ibid.*, 498 (1945).

(22) L. Dorfman, *Chem. Rev.*, **53**, 47 (1953).

(23) For normal shifts see: R. B. Woodward, *J. Am. Chem. Soc.*, **63**, 1123 (1941).

(24) The nuclear magnetic resonance spectrum was determined with a Varian 60-megacycle high resolution spectrometer. Tetramethylsilane was used as an internal standard and the τ-values were obtained by imposing 200-cycle side-bands with a variable frequency audio-oscillator. The values obtained were not extrapolated to infinite dilution.

(25) G. V. D. Tiers, *J. Phys. Chem.*, **62**, 1151 (1958).

(26) R. Baird, unpublished work.

(27) A. A. Frost and R. G. Pearson, "Kinetics and Mechanism," 2nd edition, John Wiley and Sons, Inc., New York, N. Y., 1961, p. 292.

polymers of the type $HOC_6H_4(CH_2CH_2OC_6H_4)_nCH_2$-$CH_2X$ (VI).

Solvolytic Reactions of the Intermediate.—Solvolytic reactions of the intermediate were studied kinetically in absolute methanol as a function of pH by measurement of the rates of disappearance of the ultraviolet absorption maximum at 274 mμ. These rates were measured on solutions prepared by addition of 1 ml. of an appropriately concentrated ether solution of the intermediate to 99 ml. of the requisite methanol solution.

The reaction was accelerated by both acid and base, acid being much more effective than base. The reactions in the presence of base could be measured directly, using sodium methoxide solutions of known concentration. Because the concentration of the intermediate was so low, pseudo-first-order rate constants were obtained at each concentration. At low concentrations ($<3 \times 10^{-4}\ M$) the reaction was essentially independent of base concentration, the first-order rate constant reaching a minimum value of 3.1×10^{-4} sec.$^{-1}$. This was taken to be the rate constant, k_0, of the "uncatalyzed" rate.

In contrast to the behavior observed in basic solution, the decay rates of the intermediate in acid solution were so rapid that concentrations of acid lower than $10^{-7}\ M$ were required in order to obtain rates slow enough to be measurable. Dilution of solutions of perchloric acid in methanol failed to provide reproducible concentrations below $10^{-5}\ M$, so that it was necessary to use buffer solutions in order to attain the requisite acid concentrations.

Buffer solutions were prepared from mixtures of carboxylic acids and their sodium salts in methanol, the pH values being estimated from the pK values of Kilpatrick.[28] The use of buffers introduced two problems, that of general acid catalysis[29] and that of the so-called second-order salt effect.[30]

Correction for the small effect of general acid catalysis on the rate was made by extrapolation of a plot of the rate constant *vs.* acid concentration at constant ratio of buffer salt to buffer acid.[29] In these experiments the ionic strength was maintained constant by the addition of sodium perchlorate as indicated in Table IV. At the ionic strength used, 0.01 M, the rate constant for acetic acid was 1.2×10^{-2} l. mole^{-1} sec.$^{-1}$.

TABLE IV
ACID CATALYZED METHANOLYSIS OF THE INTERMEDIATE[a] WITH ACETIC ACID–SODIUM ACETATE BUFFERS AT 25°

Run	(NaOAc), $10^4\ M$	$\dfrac{\text{(NaOAc)}}{\text{(HOAc)}}$	Ionic strength,[b] $10^4\ M$	$10^4 k_2$, sec.$^{-1}$
1	97.1	1.0	97.1	9.93 ± 0.11
2	38.9	1.0	97.1	9.27 ± .12
3	9.72	1.0	97.1	8.97 ± .08
4	9.72	1.0	9.72	6.69 ± .17
5	97.1	0.5	97.1	16.7 ± .12
6	48.6	.5	97.1	15.15 ± .06
7	48.6	.5	97.1	15.35 ± .2
8	9.71	.5	97.1	14.73 ± .1
9	9.71	.5	9.71	10.04 ± .1

[a] Concentration of IV $3.8 \times 10^{-5}\ M$; all rates were followed spectroscopically at 274 mμ. [b] Sodium perchlorate was used to maintain ionic strength.

Correction for the second-order salt effect, primarily an effect of ionic strength upon the apparent ionization constant of the buffer acid, was accomplished as

(28) L. J. Minnick and M. Kilpatrick, *J. Phys. Chem.*, **43**, 259 (1939).
(29) L. P. Hammett, "Physical Organic Chemistry," McGraw-Hill Book Co., Inc., New York, N. Y., 1940, p. 215.
(30) J. Hine, "Physical Organic Chemistry," McGraw-Hill Book Co., Inc., New York, N. Y., 1956. p. 84.

follows. The hydrogen-ion concentration of a buffer system is given by eq. 7 and 8, where K_c is the concentration-dependent equilibrium constant of the buffer acid BH at a given ionic strength and K is the thermodynamic equilibrium constant.[31] Assuming that the normal salt effect on k_0 is negligible (as can be verified from measurements in basic solution), one can correct for the significant second-order salt effect on K_c by extrapolating the pseudo-first-order rate constant for the acid-catalyzed portion of the rate, $k_A(H^{\oplus})$, to zero ionic strength. This procedure has the advantage that it also corrects (approximately) for the normal salt effect on k_A. In acid solution, the rate constant $k_A(H^{\oplus})$ is related to the pseudo-first-order rate constant for solvolysis of the intermediate, k_2, as in eq. 9, so that k_A is given by eq. 10. Consequently, the intercept of a plot of $\log(k_2 - k_0)$ *vs.* $\sqrt{\mu}$ at $\mu = 0$ is given by eq. 11 and k_A at zero ionic strength can be obtained. The values of k_2 determined for acetic acid–sodium acetate buffers (runs 3 and 4 in Table V) were corrected in this way. The magnitude of the ionic strength effect can be seen by comparing runs 3 and 4 and runs 8 and 9 in Table IV.

$$[H]^{\oplus} = K_c([BH]/[B^{\ominus}]) \tag{7}$$

$$\log K_c = \log K + C\sqrt{\mu} \tag{8}$$

$$k_2 = k_A(H^{\oplus}) + k_0 \tag{9}$$

$$\log(k_2 - k_0) = \log k_A + \log[K([BH]/[B^{\ominus}])] + C\sqrt{\mu} \tag{10}$$

$$\log(k_2 - k_0)_{\mu=0} = \log k_A + \log[K([BH]/[B^{\ominus}])] \tag{11}$$

With glycolic and chloroacetic acids as catalysts, concurrent esterification of the acids by methanol rendered the data less precise than those with acetic acid, so that no corrections for ionic strength or general acid catalysis were attempted. The data listed in Table V were obtained from measurements at low ionic strength (0.011 M) and 1:1 buffer ratios, the pH values being taken as the pK values of the acids.

TABLE V
FIRST-ORDER RATE CONSTANTS FOR SOLVOLYSIS OF THE INTERMEDIATE[a] IN ABSOLUTE METHANOL AT 25.0°

Run	Added solutes	Concn., $10^3\ M$	pH[b]	$10^4 k_2$, sec.$^{-1}$ Obsd.	Calcd[d]
1	ClCH₂COOH ClCH₂COONa	1.05 1.05	7.9 ± 0.1	*ca.* 200	244
2	HOCH₂COOH HOCH₂COONa	1.0 1.0	8.85 ± 0.05	30	27.1
3	CH₃COOH CH₃COONa	..[c] ..[c]	9.46	8.47	8.37
4	CH₃COOH CH₃COONa	..[c] ..[c]	9.76	5.71	5.75
5	NaOCH₃	0.097	12.64	3.17 ± 0.07	3.16
6	NaOCH₃	0.307	13.13	3.29 ± .04	3.28
7	NaOCH₃	0.95	14.64	9.19 ± .05	8.87
8	NaOCH₃	51.4	15.35	31.8 ± .4	32.6

[a] Concentration of intermediate $3.8 \times 10^{-5}\ M$ in 99% methanol–1% ether; rates were followed spectroscopically at 274 mμ. [b] In this work pH refers to $-\log[CH_3OH_2^{\oplus}]$. For the buffered solutions, the pH was determined from the pK values of the buffer acids as described in the text. For the basic solutions the pH was taken as the difference between the log of the base concentration and the log of the autoprotolysis constant of methanol. [c] See Table IV. [d] Calculated using eq. 13.

The solvolysis rates of the intermediate dienone IV under all of the conditions are summarized in Table V and also presented in Fig. 2 in the form of a catalytic catenary. From Fig. 2 it is apparent that the rate reaches a rather broad minimum at intermediate pH values (11–13), where the rate is effectively due to the "uncatalyzed" reaction with solvent. Over the whole pH range, the over-all first-order decay constant, k_2, may be expressed as in eq. 12, where k_H and k_B are rate constants for the methoxonium and methoxide ion-

(31) S. Glasstone, "Textbook of Physical Chemistry," second edition, D. van Nostrand Co., Inc., New York, N. Y., 1946, p. 970.

catalyzed reactions, respectively. They are listed in Table VI. Using the autoprotolysis constant[32] of

$$k_2 = k_0 + k_A (H^\oplus) + k_B (MeO^\ominus) \qquad (12)$$

$$k_2 = \left[3.10 \times 10^{-4} + 1.52 \times 10^6 [H^\oplus] + \frac{1.32 \times 10^{-15}}{[H^+]} \right] sec.^{-1} \qquad (13)$$

methanol at 25°, 2.27 × 10⁻¹⁷, eq. 12 may be written in the form of 13. The ability of this equation to reproduce the values of k_2 in Table V is illustrated by the last column in that table.

TABLE VI

RATE CONSTANTS FOR CATALYZED AND "UNCATALYZED" SOLVOLYSIS OF INTERMEDIATE IV IN ABSOLUTE METHANOL AT 25°

Catalysis	Symbol	Value
"Uncatalyzed"	k_0	3.10×10^{-4} sec.$^{-1}$
Acid	k_A	$(1.52 \pm 0.03) \times 10^{-6}$ l.-mole^{-1}-sec.$^{-1}$
Base	k_B	$(5.84 \pm 0.24) \times 10^{-2}$ l.-mole^{-1}-sec.$^{-1}$

Over-all Reaction Scheme.—The over-all solvolytic scheme for the 2-p-hydroxyphenylethyl system in anhydrous methanol can be summarized as in Fig. 1. From the available evidence, it appears that all of the reactions of 2-p-hydroxyphenylethyl bromide I-Br in basic solution proceed by way of dienone IV. As indicated, this intermediate can react with a variety of nucleophilic species, the actual ratios of products depending on the relative concentrations of the various nucleophiles. This explains the published observations that 2-p-hydroxyphenylethyl halides react normally with amines[33] and sodium acetate,[34] but abnormally with hydroxide ion.[34] With the first two reagents, the primary fate of IV is reaction with amines or acetate ion. With the more strongly basic hydroxide ion, the concentration of phenoxide ions is much greater and a bigger spectrum of possible reactions of IV is available. Formation of IV also explains the fact that no styrene is formed when I-Br is treated with ethoxide ion, while the corresponding methyl ether III-Br gives quantitative conversion to olefin.[6]

Reaction of IV with bromide ion affords an explanation of the difficulties observed in fitting the kinetics of the titrimetric runs with I-Br. Return by bromide ion becomes more serious as reaction proceeds since more bromide ion is becoming available, and the kinetic situation becomes more complicated. It also explains the discrepancy between titrimetric and spectrophotometric rate constants, return being serious in 0.01 M solution but negligible in the 10⁻⁵ M spectrophotometric solutions. For this reason the rate constants obtained in runs 3 and 4 in Table III are believed to represent more accurately the true value of k_1 in the reaction of II-Br in methanol. The failure of the experiments in t-butyl alcohol directed toward isolation of IV can be attributed in part to the fact that concentration of such solutions increased the bromide ion concentration, with return-by bromide ion eventually leading to polymerization.

Relationship to Other Systems.—It is interesting to inquire whether Ar₁⊖-3-assisted solvolysis would contribute seriously to the methanolysis of 2-p-hydroxyphenylethyl bromide (I-Br) under initially neutral conditions. From the estimated value[35] of 7.2 × 10⁻¹⁵ for K_A of I-Br, the concentration of phenoxide ion II-Br would be ca. 8 × 10⁻⁹ M in a 0.01 M solution

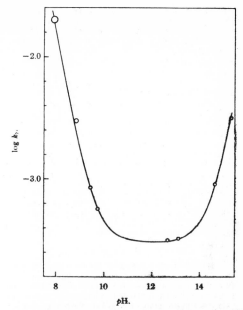

Fig. 2.—Catalytic catenary for solvolysis of dienone IV in absolute methanol at 25.0°. The circles represent experimental points; the solid line is calculated using eq. 13.

of I-Br. This would give rise to a rate of formation of dienone IV of ca. 2 × 10⁻¹¹ mole per liter per second at 25° and thus contribute a value of ca. 2 × 10⁻⁹ sec.⁻¹ to the instantaneous first-order rate constant for 0.01 M I-Br. This is as large as the rate constant for either Ar₁-3-assisted or unassisted ethanolysis of 2-p-anisylethyl bromide (III-Br) estimated earlier in this manuscript, so it is certainly competitive with the rate of Ar₁-3-assisted or unassisted methanolysis of 2-p-hydroxyphenylethyl bromide (I-Br). As reaction proceeds, however, acid is generated, and Ar₁⊖-3-assisted solvolysis will soon become negligible.

The rate of acid-catalyzed methanolysis of dienone IV to the methyl ether I-OCH₃ can lead to an estimate of the first-order rate constant for the dienone conjugate acid VIII, provided some measure of the basicity of IV is available. A very rough pK value for VIII can be based on Stewart's correlation[36] between the basicity of ketones and their infrared carbonyl stretching frequencies.[37] The frequency 1650 cm.⁻¹ (in CS₂) for IV leads to a value of +2 for the pK of VIII in water, suggesting that IV is considerably more basic than simple ketones, the pK values of which range from −4 to −8.[36] This is consistent with the high basicity reported[38] for the structurally similar 4-methylene-1,2,3,5,6-hexamethylcyclohexadiene-2,5.

On the basis of results obtained for bases of similar charge-type,[39,40] the value of pK for VIII would be expected to increase by ca. 1.5 pK units on going from water to methanol as solvent, suggesting a value of 3.5

(32) H. Goldschmidt and F. Aas, Z. physik. Chem., **112**, 423 (1924).

(33) (a) E. Späth and P. Sobel, Monatsh., **41**, 87 (1920); (b) C. S. Cheng, C. Ferber, R. T. Bashford, Jr., and G. F. Grillot, J. Am. Chem. Soc., **73**, 4081 (1951).

(34) J. V. Braun, Ber., **45**, 1282 (1912).

(35) This is based on K_m for the equilibrium in eq. 2 and the autoprotolysis constant for methanol.[32]

(36) R. Stewart and K. Yates, J. Am. Chem. Soc., **80**, 6355 (1958).

(37) It must be emphasized that Stewart's correlation was developed only for substituted acetophenones over a limited range of pK values (−4.5 to −8), so that such an extrapolation cannot be given much weight.

(38) W. von E. Doering, M. Saunders, H. G. Boyton, H. W. Earhart, E. F. Wadley, W. R. Edwards and G. Laber, Tetrahedron, **4**, 179 (1958).

(39) H. Goldschmidt and E. Mathiesen, Z. physik. Chem., **119A**, 439 (1926).

(40) A. L. Bacarella, E. Grunwald, H. P. Marshall and E. Lee Purlee, J. Org. Chem., **20**, 747 (1955).

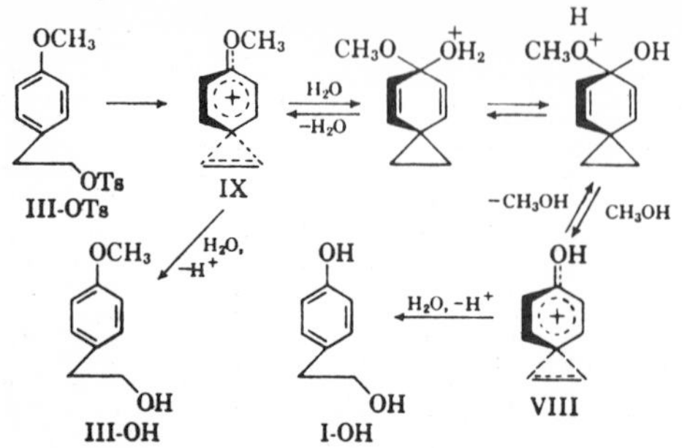

Fig. 3.—Possible interconversion of bridged ions.

for pK of VIII in the latter solvent. The use of the corresponding K-value (3×10^{-4}), together with the k_A value for acid-catalyzed methanolysis of IV, leads to a value of ca. 5×10^3 sec.$^{-1}$ for k_3, the first-order methanolysis rate constant for VIII (eq. 14). This corresponds to a half-life of ca. 10^{-3} second for VIII.

$$IV + H^+ \xrightleftharpoons{K} VIII \xrightarrow{k_3} I\text{-}OCH_3 \qquad (14)$$

If we use VIII as a model for the p-methoxyethylene phenonium ion IX, we can obtain a rough estimate of the stationary state concentration of the latter intermediate in the Ar$_1$-3-assisted solvolysis of 2-p-anisylethyl toluenesulfonate (III-OTs) shown in Fig. 3. For the latter substrate in ethanol, the estimated Ar$_1$-3-assisted ethanolysis[5,41] rate constant is ca. 3×10^{-8} sec.$^{-1}$ at 25°. This is the rate constant for formation of IX from III-OTs; using a rate constant for ethanolysis of intermediate IX the same as that of methanolysis of VIII leads to a stationary state concentration of IX equal to 4×10^{-11} times that of III-OTs. For 0.025 M III-OTs the estimated stationary state concentration of IX becomes 10^{-12} M.

The relatively long life of VIII, and by analogy with the intermediate IX, as well as other considerations, suggested the possibility that intermediate IX might be converted to VIII in an aqueous solvent by a route involving nucleophile solvent attack on the aromatic ring as depicted in Fig. 3. Such an interconversion would give rise to some p-hydroxyphenylethyl alcohol (I-OH) from hydrolysis of the p-anisylethyl ester III-OTs. However, when III-OTs was solvolyzed in buffered aqueous dioxane (NaHCO$_3$), the proportion of I-OH formed was shown to be less than 0.3%. Thus, reaction at the "cyclopropane ring" of IX predominates by a large factor over reaction at the methoxyl-bearing carbon atom of the "benzene ring."

Spectroscopic Considerations.—Formation of spiro-octa-1,4-diene-3-one (IV) represents the first reported synthesis of such a system by a reaction involving neighboring group participation, although Barton and Hendrickson[42] have observed the conversion of fucsin (X) into homofucsin (XI) on treatment with diazomethane, and Mustafa[43] reported a similar conversion of methylene-anthrone to XII. In both of these compounds, however, the presence of other functional groups mask the properties of the system found in IV. This is particularly true for the spectroscopic properties, so that only in the case of IV is it possible to make a direct comparison of the effects of various ring sizes and a methylene group on the ultraviolet spectrum of cyclohexadienones. In Table VII are given the ultraviolet

(41) (a) S. Winstein, C. R. Lindegren, H. Marshall and L. L. Ingraham, *J. Am. Chem. Soc.*, **75**, 147 (1953); (b) A. H. Fainberg and S. Winstein, *ibid.*, **78**, 2767 (1956).

(42) D. H. R. Barton and J. B. Hendrickson, *J. Chem. Soc.*, 1028 (1956).

(43) A. Mustafa and M. K. Hilmy, *ibid.*, 1434 (1952).

TABLE VII

ULTRAVIOLET MAXIMA (K-BANDS) OF CYCLOHEXADIENONES IN METHANOL SOLUTION

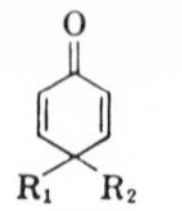

R_1, R_2	$\lambda_{max}^{(CH_3OH)}$, mμ	log ϵ	$\Delta\lambda$, mμ
CH$_3$-, CH$_3$-	227[b]	4.1[c]	
-(CH$_2$)$_5$-	242.5[d]	4.17	15
-(CH$_2$)$_4$-	242	4.20	~0
-(CH$_2$)$_3$-	274	4.34	32
CH$_2$=	280[e]	4.40[f]	6

[a] Except for the last two cases no correction is needed between methanol and ethanol; those two were both run in methanol. [b] Calculated by application of Woodward's rules (à la Dorfman[33]). The same value was obtained by subtracting 10 mμ for an α-substituent from the value for the known 2-methyl derivative[44] which has λ_{max} 237 mμ. This correction works very well in the cases cited by Dorfman.[33] [c] The epsilon is that of the 2-methyl derivative.[44] [d] The value given is that of Dreiding.[45] Burnell and Taylor[46] report λ_{max} 235 mμ for the same compound, but they do not specify the solvent. [e] Corrected for α-substituents by subtracting 10 mμ from the value for the dimethyl derivative reported by Filar and Winstein[47] for which λ_{max} 290 mμ. [f] This is the value observed in isoöctane; the compound is too reactive in methanol.

absorption maxima and intensities of several 4,4-disubstituted cyclohexadienones of this type. Unless otherwise noted, these data are for the compounds substituted only in the 4-position, appropriate corrections being made in two cases where α-methyl substituents are also present.

The position of the cyclopropane ring in IV is such that it must be at right angles to the plane of the 6-ring. In this position it appears to be almost as effective as a double bond in extending the conjugation

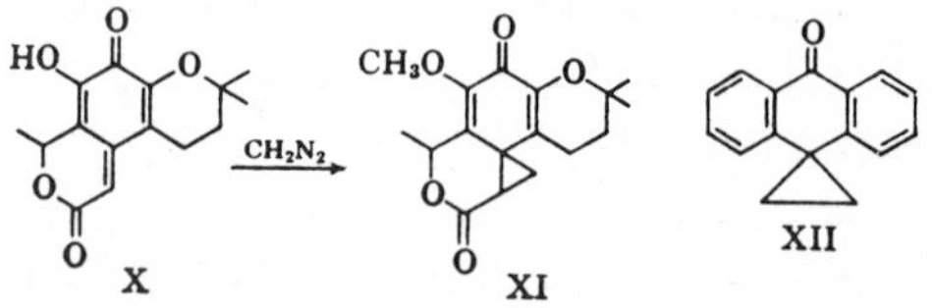

of the dienone system. Thus, the bathochromic shift, measured from the dimethyl compound, is +47 mμ for cyclopropane and ca. +53 for methylene. Other factors are no doubt involved, as witnessed by the shift (+15 mμ) introduced by 5- and 6-rings, but these should not greatly affect the above comparison.

Experimental

2-p-Hydroxyphenylethanol.—A solution of 23.5 g. of p-hydroxyphenylacetic acid in 250 ml. of anhydrous ether was added to a slurry of 11.7 g. of lithium aluminum hydride in 400 ml. of ether. The mixture was heated under reflux for 48 hours to complete reduction of the slightly soluble salt. The product was isolated by the addition of the minimum amount of dilute aqueous hydrochloric acid and extraction with ether; yield 9.2 g. (43%) of material, m.p. 89–91.5° (reported[34] m.p. 93°).

2-p-Anisylethanol was prepared by the method of La Forge.[48] This alcohol, b.p. 144–145° (11 mm.), $n^{25}D$ 1.5345, was obtained in 73% yield (reported[48] b.p. 130–132° (6.5 mm.).

2-p-Anisylethyl Bromide.—The p-toluenesulfonate ester of 2-p-anisylethanol was prepared from the alcohol by the low temperature method of Heck.[49] This ester (29 g.) was treated overnight at room temperature with 17.4 g. of Mallinckrodt NF lithium bromide in 200 ml. of Braun ACS acetone. The bulk of the solvent was then removed on the steam-bath, the solution diluted with 600 ml. of water and the product extracted with ether. Distillation at reduced pressure provided the bromide, b.p. 94.0–95.7° (2 mm.), $n^{25}D$ 1.5570, in 53% yield (reported b.p. 130–131° (11 mm.)[50]; b.p. 63° (0.15 mm.), $n^{25}D$ 1.5595).[51]

(44) M. Yanigita and S. Inayama, *J. Org. Chem.*, **19**, 1724 (1954).

(45) A. S. Dreiding, *Helv. Chim. Acta*, **40**, 1812 (1957).

(46) R. H. Burnell and W. I. Taylor, *J. Chem. Soc.*, 3486 (1954).

(47) L. J. Filar and S. Winstein, *Tetrahedron Letters*, No. **25**, 9 (1960).

(48) F. B. La Forge and W. F. Barthel, *J. Org. Chem.*, **9**, 250 (1944).

(49) R. Heck and S. Winstein, *J. Am. Chem. Soc.*, **79**, 3105 (1957).

(50) J. B. Shoesmith and R. J. Conner, *J. Chem. Soc.*, 2230 (1927).

Anal. Calcd. for C$_8$H$_{11}$OBr: C, 50.25; H, 5.16. Found: C, 50.19; H, 5.20.

2-p-Hydroxyphenylethyl bromide was prepared from 2-*p*-anisylethanol by the method of Späth and Sobel.[³¹ᵇ] After three recrystallizations from hexane, the bromide, m.p. 89.6–90.8°, was obtained in 46% yield (reported[³¹ᵇ] m.p. 89–91°).

Anal. Calcd. for C$_8$H$_9$OBr: C, 47.79; H, 4.51; Br, 39.74. Found: C, 47.89; H, 4.45; Br, 40.02.

This compound was further analyzed by treatment of two 0.0500-g. samples with 10-ml. portions of 1.2 M NaOH overnight, acidification with 6 N nitric acid and titration of the bromide ion by the Volhard procedure. Both samples gave 99.6% of the theoretical bromide ion.

2-p-Hydroxyphenylethyl iodide was synthesized from 2-*p*-anisylethanol by the procedure of Cheng.[³³ᵇ] The iodide, m.p. 112–113.5°, was obtained in 68% yield (reported[³³ᵇ] m.p. 113°).

2-p-Hydroxyphenylethyl Chloride.—A solution of 40 g. of 2 *p*-hydroxyphenylethyl iodide in 800 ml. of Braun ACS acetone was treated with 70 g. of anhydrous lithium chloride under reflux for 29 hours. The product was isolated as described for 2-*p*-anisylethyl bromide; yield 94% of the chloride, b.p. 97–99° (1.2 mm.), m.p. 55.3–57.0° (from hexane) (reported[³⁴] as a viscous liquid).

2-p-Hydroxyphenylethyl Methyl Ether.—To a mixture of 3 g. of reagent grade silver nitrate and 300 ml. of anhydrous methanol containing just enough brom phenol blue to give a detectable color was added a solution of 3 g. of 2-*p*-hydroxyphenylethyl bromide in 100 ml. of anhydrous methanol. Silver bromide began to precipitate at once, and 0.18 M sodium methoxide in methanol was added at such a rate as to keep the solution just slightly acidic (as measured by the color of the brom phenol blue). The solution was heated on the steam-bath to complete the reaction and the silver bromide removed by filtration through Celite. This solution was heated with solid sodium chloride to remove the unreacted silver nitrate and refiltered through Celite. Evaporation of the solvent and extraction of the salts with water led to the crude ether, which was converted to a 3,5-dinitrobenzoate with 3,5-dinitrobenzoyl chloride in pyridine. The 3,5-dinitrobenzoate, m.p. 102.2–103.1° from hexane, was obtained in a yield of 1.2 g.

Anal. Calcd. for C$_{16}$H$_{14}$O$_7$N$_2$: C, 55.49; H, 4.08. Found: C, 55.25; H, 3.98.

Saponification of this ester with potassium hydroxide in methanol, followed by recrystallization from methylene chloride–pentane and then ether–pentane, provided 2-*p*-hydroxyphenylethyl methyl ether as prisms, m.p. 41.7–42.5°.

Anal. Calcd. for C$_9$H$_{12}$O$_2$: C, 71.03; H, 7.95. Found: C, 70.81; H, 8.24.

p-Hydroxycinnamic acid was prepared according to the procedure in reference 52 for 2,4-dihydroxycinnamic acid. The acid, m.p. 215–216° dec., was obtained in 70% yield from *p*-hydroxybenzaldehyde [reported[⁵³] m.p. 206° dec.].

p-Hydroxystyrene was prepared in poor yield by the method used by Reichstein for 3-methoxy-4-hydroxystyrene.[⁵⁴] A mixture of 5 g. of *p*-hydroxycinnamic acid, 10 g. of redistilled quinoline and 1 g. of copper-bronze, heated at 220° for 5 minutes, led on extraction, sublimation at 0.9 mm. and recrystallization from pentane to *ca.* 20 mg. of styrene, m.p. 61–64.5° (reported[⁵⁵] m.p. 73.5°).

Kinetic Procedures. Solvents.—Anhydrous methanol and *t*-butyl alcohol were prepared as described previously.[¹ᵇ] Anhydrous ethanol was prepared in the same manner as anhydrous methanol and tested for water with Karl Fischer reagent. Methanol purified over magnesium always tested very slightly basic to neutralized brom phenol blue, and by dilution of known concentrations of standard perchloric acid was estimated to contain 10^{-5} to 10^{-6} M basic or buffering species. In the experiments in which especially neutral methanol was desired, the solvent was further purified by the method of Evers and Knox,[⁵⁶] by distillation over potassium acid phthalate–phthalic anhydride, followed by distillation over sodium, or by distillation over sulfanilic acid.[⁵¹] The second and third methods above gave methanol that was slightly less basic than that prepared by the method of Evers and Knox.

Standard alkoxide solutions were prepared as described previously.[¹ᵇ] The sodium ethoxide solutions were prepared and standardized immediately before use.

Mixing.—The rates measured in basic solution were rapid enough that mixing of reactants constituted a serious problem. In the earlier runs an alkoxide solution was quickly pipetted into

a phenol solution in a volumetric flask, the mixture diluted to the mark and aliquots taken. Both solutions were pre-equilibrated at 0.8° lower than the temperature of the bath to compensate for the heat of neutralization. Aliquots could then be pipetted as little as 90 seconds after the start of mixing.

For the reactions in methanol the two-chamber rapid mixing flask of Winstrom and Warner[¹⁹] was used for both the titrimetric and spectroscopic runs. This provided more thorough mixing and more rapid equilibration with the thermostat.

Methods of Following Rates.—Rates at concentrations of 0.01 M or greater were followed by titration. In methanol the procedures were identical with those described previously,[¹ᵇ] acid-base titrations being used. In all but one of the measurements in ethanol the extraction procedure of Fainberg[⁴⁷] was used, and the bromide ion produced was titrated by the Volhard procedure. For a quench, aliquots were pipetted into a mixture of pentane and dilute, halide-free, nitric acid in a small separatory funnel, and the mixture shaken vigorously, *ca.* forty times to ensure rapid neutralization of the base.

Rates at concentrations lower than 10^{-4} M were followed spectrophotometrically. These measurements were made in a Beckman DU spectrophotometer, thermostated by double thermospacers connected to a constant temperature circulating bath. The temperature of the cell compartment did not differ by more than 0.1° from that of the bath. Optical density measurements were made at a wave length which had been shown by qualitative measurements with a Cary (model 11PMS) recording spectrophotometer to represent the region of maximum absorption for the species being studied. Both cells in the Beckman DU were filled with the solvent used in the rate, excluding only the substrate, and the sample cell calibrated against the reference cell at the desired wave length. The kinetic solution was prepared and mixed as described previously and the kinetic sample cell washed several times with this solution and replaced in the thermostated compartment. The remainder of the solution was replaced in the thermostat and used to check the infinity value at the end of the rate. The sample cell, once filled, was left in the spectrophotometer during the entire run, and the optical density was measured as a function of time.

Buffer Solutions.—Buffer solutions in absolute methanol were prepared by treatment of a *ca.* 0.2 M solution of the appropriate acid with sufficient standard sodium methoxide in absolute methanol to give the desired buffer ratio, and then diluted to the appropriate concentration. The 0.2 M acid solutions were standardized by titration with sodium hydroxide in a predominantly aqueous medium, phenolphthalein being used as the indicator. The more concentrated buffer solutions were also titrated in this way, and agreed in all cases to within a few per cent of the expected titer. The ionic strengths of the buffer solutions were increased in some cases by the addition of the appropriate amount of anhydrous sodium perchlorate in methanol to the buffer mixture before dilution.

Freshly prepared buffer solutions were used in all runs with acetic acid buffers since esterification of the acid by methanol was a serious problem on prolonged standing. A 0.1927 M solution of acetic acid in methanol titrated 0.1780 M after *ca.* 36 hours at room temperature. With the stronger acids, glycolic and chloroacetic acids, this problem was more serious and only approximate *p*H values are given for these solutions.

Equilibrium Constants.—The equilibrium constant, K_m, for *p*-hydroxyphenylethanol was determined spectroscopically in absolute methanol at approximately 25°. The molar extinction coefficients of the phenolic and phenoxide forms of the phenol were determined from the spectra in 0.09 M methanolic sulfuric acid and 0.16 M methanolic sodium methoxide, respectively. The wave length of 241 mμ was used for this work because it afforded the largest difference in molar extinction coefficients between the phenolic and phenoxide forms. The optical density of solutions of the diluted phenol (1.08 × 10^{-4} M) containing varying amounts of base was determined at this wave length, and the concentrations of the phenol and phenoxide ion were calculated by the usual method.[¹⁶]

The value of K_m is not strictly constant, but decreases with increasing base concentration so that the extent of ionization increases slightly more rapidly with increasing base concentration than expected. This most likely is due to a salt effect.[³⁵]

The equilibrium constant for the analogous reaction in *t*-butyl alcohol was also investigated spectrophotometrically. Qualitative measurements with a series of solutions indicated that at concentrations above 10^{-4} M, the phenol was completely converted to its salt, but at lower concentrations conversion dropped off sharply, presumably due to the action of atmospheric carbon dioxide on the lower base concentrations. Consequently, no exact value was determined for the equilibrium constant in this solvent.

Product Runs in Absolute Methanol. With 0.13 M Sodium Methoxide.—To a solution of 6.03 g. (0.030 mole) of 2-*p*-

(51) W. H. Saunders, Jr., and R. A. Williams, *J. Am. Chem. Soc.*, **79**, 3712 (1957).

(52) R. Adams, Editor-in-Chief, "Organic Reactions," Vol. I, John Wiley and Sons, Inc., New York, N. Y., 1942, p. 250.

(53) T. Zincke and F. Leisse, *Ann.*, **322**, 224 (1902).

(54) T. Reichstein, *Helv. Chim. Acta*, **15**, 1450 (1932).

(55) H. Schmid and P. Karrer, *ibid.*, **28**, 722 (1945).

(56) E. C. Evers and A. G. Knox, *J. Am. Chem. Soc.*, **73**, 1739 (1951).

(57) A. H. Fainberg and S. Winstein, *ibid.*, **78**, 2770 (1956).

hydroxyphenylethyl bromide in 500 ml. of anhydrous methanol in a one-liter volumetric flask was added 500 ml. of 0.258 M sodium methoxide in absolute methanol. Both solutions were pre-equilibrated at 25.0° before mixing. The flask was then placed in a 25.0° bath for 3 hours, and subsequently cooled in an ice-bath and neutralized to brom phenol blue with p-toluenesulfonic acid in methanol. The methanol was then distilled at reduced pressure so as to keep the pot temperature below 25° until $ca.$ 100 ml. of solution remained. This solution was poured into water and the mixture extracted six times with ether. The extracts were washed with a small amount of water, with saturated salt solution and then dried over magnesium sulfate. The solution was filtered and the bulk of the ether removed on the steam-bath through a 12-inch Vigreux column. The residue was distilled at reduced pressure to give three fractions: 1, b.p. 126.5–128° (3.3 mm.), m.p. 39.5–42.5°, weighing 2.35 g.; 2, b.p. 128–135° (3.3 mm.), weighing 0.17 g.; 3, b.p. 215–220° (0.8 mm.), weighing 0.89 g.

Fraction 1, which amounted to 57% of the theoretical, was recrystallized from ether–pentane to give 1.3 g. of material, m.p. 42–44°, which did not depress when mixed with authentic 2-p-hydroxyphenylethyl methyl ether.

With 1 M Sodium Methoxide.—This run was carried out exactly as the one above except that the solution was neutralized with sulfuric acid in methanol and was filtered to remove most of the salts. The salt-paste obtained on filtration was dissolved in water and washed six times with ether. The combined extracts were added to the bulk of the methanol and the reaction worked up as for the lower base concentration above.

TABLE VIII

EQUILIBRIUM CONSTANT MEASUREMENT FOR 2-p-HYDROXY-
PHENYLETHANOL[a] IN ABSOLUTE METHANOL AT 25°

Optical density 241 mμ	(HOAr) (ArO$^-$)	Total (NaOMe) $\times 10^4$ M	$10^3 K_m$ M
0.013	100	..[b]	..
.031	100	..[c]	..
.230	4.005	9.007	3.53
.357	2.157	15.25	3.22
.543	1.049	29.90	3.08
.733	0.5083	59.79	3.01
1.099	0.01	1600	..

[a] Concentration, 1.018×10^{-4} M. [b] Contains 0.090 N sulfuric acid. [c] Contains no added base or acid.

On distillation, a main fraction, b.p. 127–128° (3.4 mm.), m.p. 38–42° (without recrystallization), weighing 3.74 g., was obtained in 82.4% yield. The melting point of a mixture of this compound with authentic 2-p-hydroxyphenylethyl methyl ether was undepressed. On treatment with 3,5-dinitrobenzoyl chloride in pyridine, a 3,5-dinitrobenzoate ester, m.p. 101.8–103.9°, weighing 6.92 g., was obtained in 66.5% over-all yield (from 2-p-hydroxyphenylethyl bromide).

Experiments Directed toward Isolation of Dienone Intermediate. 2-p-Hydroxyphenylethyl Bromide with Sodium Hydride in Ether.—A solution of 1.0 g. of 2-p-hydroxyphenyl bromide in 50 ml. of Mallinckrodt anhydrous ether was stirred with an excess of sodium hydride with protection from moisture until the evolution of hydrogen had ceased. The solution was then filtered through sintered glass under nitrogen pressure into a dry 125-ml. flask, and was allowed to stand tightly stoppered in this flask for 24 hours at room temperature. At the end of this time a portion of this solution was diluted 100-fold and the ultraviolet spectrum run in a 1-mm. cell. Intense maxima were observed at 257–258 mμ, and at 301 mμ, similar to those exhibited by the sodium salts of other phenols in absolute alcoholic solvents. No strong absorption in excess of the above was observed at 261 mμ. Dilution of the ether solution further, $e.g.$, to run the spectrum in a 1-cm. cell, gave the spectrum of the parent 2-p-hydroxyphenylethyl bromide.

Addition of a small sample of the above solution to dilute aqueous sulfuric acid, extraction with ether and drying over magnesium sulfate led to an oil which crystallized immediately when seeded with the parent compound, 2-p-hydroxyphenylethyl bromide, to give a solid, m.p. 83–87°, without recrystallization.

A portion of the above ether solution, when poured into a large excess of t-butyl alcohol, gave at once a strong maximum at 271 mμ for the dienone, and a weaker maximum at 230 mμ. The maximum at 271 mμ had increased about 5% on rerunning the spectrum after about 5 minutes, indicating that the formation of this maximum was actually occurring in t-butyl alcohol and not in the ether.

Reaction with Potassium t-Butoxide in t-Butyl Alcohol.—A solution of 0.025 mole of 2-p-hydroxyphenylethyl bromide in 50 ml. of absolute t-butyl alcohol and a second solution of 0.026

mole of potassium t-butoxide in an equal volume of t-butyl alcohol were added simultaneously through two separate addition funnels to a well-stirred 100-ml. portion of anhydrous t-butyl alcohol in a 500-ml. three-necked flask. This addition was carried out over the course of an hour at room temperature. At the end of this time, two 5-ml. aliquots of this solution were taken and one was filtered through Celite to remove the colloidal solid, the other being diluted with two volumes of pentane and washed four times with water, and dried over potassium carbonate. The ultraviolet spectra of both solutions thus treated were determined over the range 250–300 mμ, but neither solution exhibited maxima other than those attributable to phenolic species.

The bulk of the solution was diluted with two volumes of pentane and the solid precipitate filtered with suction. This residue was washed thoroughly with water and then recrystallized from benzene to give a white solid, m.p. 137–145°. The infrared spectrum was quite similar to that of 2-anisylethyl bromide, especially with respect to aromatic substitution patterns and the strong aromatic–aliphatic ether band at 1235 cm.$^{-1}$.

Anal. Calcd. for HOC$_6$H$_6$(OC$_4$H$_9$)$_4$Br: C, 72.8; H, 6.19. Found: C, 72.88; H, 6.11.

In another experiment, a mixture of 0.0045 mole of 2-p-hydroxyphenylethyl bromide and 100 ml. of 0.045 M potassium t-butoxide in t-butyl alcohol was shaken for 3 minutes and then diluted with 600 ml. of pentane and washed with 300-ml. portions of ice-water. The pentane solution was then dried over potassium carbonate and the solvent removed under reduced pressure. A small amount of solid remained which exhibited only characteristic phenolic spectral maxima in t-butyl alcohol in the ultraviolet.

To a solution of 0.0036 mole of 2-p-hydroxyphenylethyl iodide in 100 ml. of t-butyl alcohol was added, in small portions, 100 ml. of a solution of 0.036 M potassium t-butoxide in t-butyl alcohol over a period of 60 seconds. After 2 minutes, solid sodium bicarbonate was added and the mixture shaken vigorously for 60 seconds more and then diluted with 3 volumes of pentane and poured into water. The pentane phase was separated and washed twice with water, dried over potassium carbonate, and the ultraviolet absorption spectrum determined. Again, no maxima other than those attributable to phenolic species were observed.

Isolation of Dienone.—A basic alumina was prepared by shaking 1 kg. of alumina (Harshaw, activated powder, catalyst grade, 90% Al$_2$O$_3$, #A1–0101–P) with a solution of 100 g. of reagent grade potassium hydroxide in 75 ml. of water until a homogeneous mixture was obtained.[30] Passage of solutions of 2-p-hydroxyphenylethyl bromide in anhydrous ether through columns made of this alumina resulted in effluent solutions possessing absorption maxima at 261 and $ca.$ 230 mμ in the ultraviolet. The absolute and relative intensities of the two maxima varied with the ratio of alumina to the bromide, the flow rate, the amount of ether passed through the column, and the length of time the effluent solution was kept. On standing for varying periods of time, solutions possessing both maxima exhibited an increase in the maximum at 230 mμ at the expense of that at 261 mμ.

A variety of conditions and times were investigated and the following set of conditions was found to lead consistently to ether solutions containing only the maximum at 261 mμ: A solution of 3.25 g. of 2-p-hydroxyphenylethyl bromide (free from non-phenolic species such as 2-anisylethyl bromide) in 150 ml. of Mallinckrodt anhydrous reagent grade ether was forced with gentle air pressure onto a column made from a slurry of 325 g. of the basic alumina in a 66-mm. (inside diameter) chromatography column. The column was then eluted with anhydrous ether at a flow rate of 40–50 ml. per minute. The first 100 ml. of the ether passing through the column was discarded, and the next 700 ml. was collected in a 1-liter erlenmeyer flask.

All glassware used from this point on (including the flask above) was thoroughly cleaned in hot detergent solution and the surface neutralized by successive rinses with water, dilute acetic acid, distilled water, dilute ammonium hydroxide, and distilled water, and then dried in an oven.

The above 700 ml. of solution was shaken with a mixture of sodium bicarbonate and anhydrous potassium carbonate, and then filtered. Aliquots (2.00 ml.) of this solution were diluted to 25 ml. with ether and the ultraviolet spectrum determined in the range 220–300 mμ. From the homogeneity of this spectrum (absence of maxima at 230 mμ) the purity of the product could be verified. Solutions with a visible maximum at 230 mμ were not used. From the optical density of the above solution at 261 mμ, assuming the same molar extinction coefficient as in t-butyl alcohol (22,200), the concentration of the intermediate could be estimated to be $ca.$ 10^{-3} M and from the known volume of the original ether solution the yield of the intermediate could be estimated to be about 2%, or $ca.$ 84 mg.

The above solution could be concentrated at reduced pressure to $ca.$ 4×10^{-3} M where it was stable for about a week. Evaporation of the solution to dryness at reduced pressure and room temperature led to a white solid. This compound could be recrystallized from ether–pentane at low temperatures to give white needles, m.p. 40–43° (one run), m.p. 43–46° (different preparation).

This solid, immediately after preparation, was soluble in alcoholic solvents, ether, chloroform, carbon disulfide and acetone, but difficultly soluble in pentane. After standing for some time, or after drying under vacuum, or heating to above its melting point, the substance was no longer soluble in the above, or any common solvents, and possessed a melting point in the range 160–200°. One sample, after drying under vacuum, was analyzed and possessed the correct carbon–hydrogen analysis for spiro-(2,5)octa-1,4-diene-3-one, although it had changed to the high-melting solid before the analysis was performed.

Anal. Calcd. for C_8H_8O: C, 79.97; H, 6.71. Found: C, 79.66; H, 6.81.

Isolation of the solid was required only for carbon–hydrogen analyses and for infrared spectra. Other experiments and reactions were performed in ether solution or in solvents containing 1% ether obtained by dilution of one volume of the partially concentrated ether solution of the intermediate with 99 volumes of the appropriate solvent. Thus, for the kinetic studies of the decay rate of the intermediate, a solution of *ca.* 4×10^{-3} *M* intermediate in anhydrous ether, which could be stored for about a week, was diluted 1 to 99 with the appropriate kinetic solvent, to give a solution for which for all practical purposes was not affected by the presence of 1% ether. The spectrum of the stock solutions was checked periodically and when phenolic absorption was detected a new stock solution was prepared.

Reactions of the Dienone. Reaction with Lithium Aluminum Hydride.—A freshly prepared solution of the intermediate in 700 ml. of anhydrous ether, prepared as described previously, was added to a slurry of 5 g. of lithium aluminum hydride in 800 ml. of dry ether over a 70-min. period, and the mixture was stirred for 15 additional minutes. The excess hydride was discharged with 50 ml. of water and then 500 ml. of 20% hydrochloric acid was added and the ether phase separated. The aqueous phase was separated and extracted twice more with ether. The combined ether extracts were washed with water, saturated sodium bicarbonate solution, saturated sodium chloride solution and then dried over magnesium sulfate. The volume of this solution, after filtration, was measured, and the ultraviolet spectrum of this solution, appropriately diluted, was measured with a Cary recording spectrophotometer. At this time, a sample of the original ether solution of the intermediate was diluted 2 to 25 ml. and its ultraviolet spectrum determined. From the optical density of this control, which indicated that only the intermediate was present in the original ether solution, the concentration of the intermediate was obtained (assuming ϵ 22,200). On this basis, 5.56×10^{-4} mole of the intermediate had been added to the lithium aluminum hydride, and from the spectrum of the product solution the spectroscopic yield of *p*-ethylphenol was 4.35×10^{-4} mole, or 78.5% of the theoretical. The spectrum was identical with that of *p*-ethylphenol.

The ether was distilled through a bubble-plate column, and the residue treated with 0.7 g. of 3,5-dinitrobenzoyl chloride in pyridine, yielding a 3,5-dinitrobenzoate, m.p. 130–131.5°. The melting point of a mixture of this compound with authentic *p*-ethylphenol 3,5-dinitrobenzoate showed no depression. The derivative was obtained in the amount of 0.088 g., representing a 55% over-all yield (64% of the amount observed spectroscopically).

With Hydrogen Bromide in Ether.—A freshly prepared solution of the intermediate in 650–700 ml. of ether was rapidly added to 1 liter of a 0.06 *M* solution of anhydrous hydrogen bromide in ether. The excess acid was removed by extraction with saturated sodium bicarbonate solution and the solvent evaporated on the steam-bath. This procedure provided a solid, m.p. 84.5–88.5° without recrystallization, weighing 0.069 g. Recrystallization from hexane yielded 0.064 g., m.p. 88.5–90.5°. The melting point of a mixture of this substance with 2-*p*-hydroxyphenylethyl bromide was undepressed.

The ultraviolet spectra of the original solution of the intermediate befor: treatment with hydrogen bromide, of the hydrogen bromide in ether solution, and of the solution resulting on their admixture, were determined. The first solution exhibited only a maximum at 261 m*μ* for the intermediate, with no phenolic maxima. The hydrogen bromide solution exhibited a gradual increase in absorption toward the lower wave length range, but no maxima whatsoever. The product solution exhibited a phenolic maximum, which when corrected for the small underlying contribution from the hydrogen bromide was identical with that of 2-*p*-hydroxyphenylethyl bromide in ether. Using the previously derived value of 22,200 for the ϵ of the intermediate at 261 m*μ*, and the known ϵ for the bromide at 229.5 m*μ* of 11,800, the yield of the 2-*p*-hydroxyphenylethyl bromide observed spectroscopically could be estimated to be 79–82%, and that actually isolated was 47–50% over-all yield from the intermediate.

Catalytic Hydrogenation.—A freshly prepared solution of 5.9 $\times 10^{-4}$ mole of the intermediate in 750 ml. of ether was concentrated to *ca.* 23–25 ml., with precautions being taken to neutralize the surface of the glassware and to avoid overheating of the

product. This solution was added to a slurry of reduced platinum oxide (obtained from 14 mg. of PtO_2) in ether, and the volume of hydrogen consumed was measured. Because of the high partial pressure of ether and the method of introduction of the sample, the uptake of hydrogen could only be roughly estimated as 1 ± 0.2 mole of hydrogen per mole of intermediate.

The resultant solution was filtered to remove the catalyst and the ultraviolet spectrum determined. The spectrum was identical with that of *p*-ethylphenol and corresponded to *ca.* 5.6 $\times 10^{-4}$ mole (*ca.* 95% yield). The ultraviolet spectrum of the concentrated solution of the intermediate, a portion of which had been kept aside and run at the same time as that of the product, indicated that the intermediate at this concentration was stable for the time required for hydrogenation in the absence of hydrogen and the catalyst.

Evaporation of the ether from the above product and treatment of the residue with 3,5-dinitrobenzoyl chloride in pyridine gave a 3,5-dinitrobenzoate, m.p. 129.5–131.5° (from hexane), weighing 0.106 g. (52% over-all yield). The melting point of a mixture of this compound with the 3,5-dinitrobenzoate of *p*-ethylphenol was undepressed.

Reactions with *p*-Toluenesulfonic Acid and Sodium Bromide.— A solution of the intermediate in ether, prepared by the usual chromatographic procedure, was concentrated to 50 ml. and the concentration determined from the ultraviolet absorption maximum. The remainder of the solution (49 ml.) was added to 0.083 g. of sodium bromide in methanol and the total volume brought up to 100 ml. with anhydrous methanol, making the solution 0.081 *M* in sodium bromide and 0.00359 *M* in the intermediate, the solvent being *ca.* 50% methanolic ether.

From the above solution, 5.021-ml. aliquots were quickly pipetted into 5.021-ml. portions of 0.02713 *M p*-toluenesulfonic acid in methanol. These solutions were titrated to neutrality as in the kinetic runs with standard sodium methoxide in methanol, using brom phenol blue as the indicator. These solutions required 4.015 ml. of 0.002929 *M* sodium methoxide per aliquot as compared to the blank measurements which required 4.630 ml. per aliquot. The difference of 0.615 ml. between the solution of the intermediate and the blank amounted to *ca.* 100% of the intermediate present in an aliquot. Pipetting larger amounts of the intermediate into the above amount of acid or adding the same amount of intermediate solution to larger amounts of acid led to consumption of 91–94% of the acid theoretically possible.

The only reaction in the above procedure which consumes acid is one in which bromide ion or *p*-toluenesulfonate ion is incorporated into the products; the incorporation of methoxide ion on methanol does not consume acid. The fact that bromide ion was incorporated was demonstrated by the fact that solutions of the intermediate plus sodium bromide tested basic to neutralized brom phenol blue. After such solutions had stood for 7 hours, only 0.205 ml. of 0.03863 *M p*-toluenesulfonic acid in methanol was consumed by an aliquot. After 12 hours this dropped to 0.160 ml., corresponding to 26% of the intermediate originally present. Titration for bromide ion by the procedure of Fainberg[47] accounted for the other 74% of the original intermediate.

A new solution of the intermediate was prepared and concentrated to 21 ml. The concentration was determined as before, and 20 ml. of this was diluted to 100 ml. with anhydrous methanol, giving a solution 0.00360 *M* in the intermediate and containing no sodium bromide. Aliquots of this solution were pipetted into equal volumes of 0.0271 *M p*-toluenesulfonic acid in methanol and also into equal volumes of the acid containing 0.0069 *M* sodium bromide.

Of the above solutions, those containing sodium bromide decreased in titer by about 0.00387 millimole, corresponding to the trapping of 21.5% of the possible acid by the intermediate. Those with no added bromide ion showed no measurable decrease.

Addition of the sodium bromide solution (0.0416 *M*) to the solution of the intermediate in *ca.* 20% methanolic ether caused the mixture to become strongly basic (toward brom phenol blue), the color intensifying as more sodium bromide was added. Neither the sodium bromide solution nor that of the intermediate tested basic before admixture.

Search for Methoxyl Cleavage of 2-*p*-Anisylethyl *p*-Toluenesulfonate.—A solution of 2-*p*-anisylethyl *p*-toluenesulfonate (0.001 *M*) in 40° aqueous dioxane, buffered with 0.005 *M* sodium bicarbonate, was prepared. Its ultraviolet absorption was then determined in the region 240–250 m*μ*; 100 ml. of this solution was then treated with one ml. of 4 *M* sodium hydroxide and its ultraviolet spectrum again determined in the 240–250 m*μ* region. Both solutions were run against the appropriate reference solutions minus the substrate. The differences between these two solutions were then determined (corrected for the 1% dilution caused by the sodium hydroxide). These values are tabulated in column 2 in Table IX.

The original solution of 2-*p*-anisylethyl *p*-toluenesulfonate was then solvolyzed for 20 hours at 75°. This represented more

TABLE IX

OPTICAL DENSITY DIFFERENCES BETWEEN NEUTRAL AND BASIC
SOLUTIONS OF 2-*p*-ANISYLETHYL *p*-TOLUENESULFONATE

Wave length, mμ	O.D. differences before solvolysis	O.D. differences after solvolysis	Net change in differences
242	0.000	0.008	0.008
243	− .002	.004	.006
244	.012	.003	.008
245	.009	.004	− .005
246	.017	.007	− .010

than 20 half-lives for this compound as estimated from known
rates in other solvents using the Winstein–Grunwald equation.[58]

The neutral and basic solutions obtained after solvolysis were
examined spectroscopically and the optical density differences
are tabulated in column 3 of Table IX.

Subtraction of the difference in column 2 from those in column
3 gives column 4. The net differences in column 4 represent the
spectral contributions of any phenolic species present after solvolysis which were not present before, *i.e.*, any cleavage product.
These net differences are very small (within experimental error
of zero), and since 2-*p*-hydroxyphenylethanol has a maximum
at 241 mμ (ε 10,150) in basic solution, it can be estimated from
these differences that less than 0.2% of the 2-*p*-anisylethyl *p*-
toluenesulfonate undergoes cleavage during solvolysis.

(58) S. Winstein, E. Grunwald and H. W. Jones, *J. Am. Chem. Soc.*, **73**,
2700 (1951).

68

See commentary on page 463.

From: *J. Am. Chem. Soc.* **86,** 1749–55 (1964)

[Contribution from the Department of Chemistry, University of Southern California, Los Angeles 7, Calif.]

The Nitrous Acid Deamination of the Norbornylamines.   Carbon and Nitrogen Rearrangements of Norbornyl Cations[1]

By Jerome A. Berson[2] and Allen Remanick

Received August 16, 1963

The deaminations of optically active *endo*- and *exo*-norbornylamines in glacial acetic acid lead to different amounts of retention of optical purity in the *exo*-acetate product, in contrast to the report of Corey that the per cent retention was independent of the stereochemistry of the starting material.   The sources of the discrepancies are examined.   The results do not require the postulate of a common carbonium ion precursor of the products from the two amines.   A survey is made of the racemizing processes that occur in norbornyl cations.   The competition between hydride shift and conversion to solvolysis product as a function of solvent is discussed.

Since the earlier investigation[3] of the nitrous acid deamination of *endo*-norbornylamine in this laboratory, it has become possible to analyze the products with far greater precision than was then accessible to us. Heretofore,[3] detection of *endo*-norbornyl product in the presence of a large amount of *exo*- could not be pushed below about 7% of the former. With capillary gas chromatography, however, it is possible to detect as little as 0.5% or even less of *endo*-norborneol in the *exo* isomer. A re-examination of the product from the deamination of *endo*-norbornylamine[3] by this technique has now revealed the presence of 4–5% of the *endo*-alcohol. Accordingly, we undertook a reinvestigation of this deamination as well as that of *exo*-norbornylamine.

Results

Quantitative Basis for Determination of the Stereochemical Outcome of the Deaminations.—To determine the extent of racemization in a deamination of an optically active amine, it sometimes is convenient or necessary to rely upon indirect correlations of the optical purities of reactant and product. In the case of *endo*-norbornylamine (I*n*) we have heretofore assumed that its synthesis[3] from the corresponding acid II*n*[4] *via* the Schmidt reaction does not involve racemization. This assumption, combined with the correlations of *endo*-acid II*n* with *exo*-acid II*x*[4] and of the latter with *exo*-alcohol IV*x* and acetate[5] III*x*, provided the basis for a study[3] of the stereochemistry of the deamination

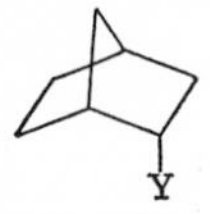

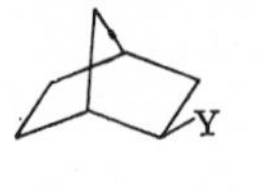

In, Y = NH₂
IIn, Y = CO₂H
IIIn, Y = OAc
IVn, Y = OH

Ix, Y = NH₂
IIx, Y = CO₂H
IIIx, Y = OAc
IVx, Y = OH

of I*n*. Although Schmidt reactions generally are found to occur with complete retention of configuration,[6] there could be cause for apprehension in the *exo*-norbornyl series. The conditions of the reaction, which involve the use of concentrated sulfuric acid,

are disturbingly reminiscent of those in which clear examples of heterolyses have occurred[7–9] to give carbonium ion intermediates. The known behavior of the 2-norbornyl cation[10] would then ensure partial or complete racemization. Accordingly, it seemed prudent to establish an independent correlation of the optical purities of *exo*-norbornylamine (I*x*) and *exo*-norbornyl acetate (III*x*), our projected reactant and product in the deamination study. This was effected as shown in Chart I.   The Schmidt reaction with (+)-

Chart I

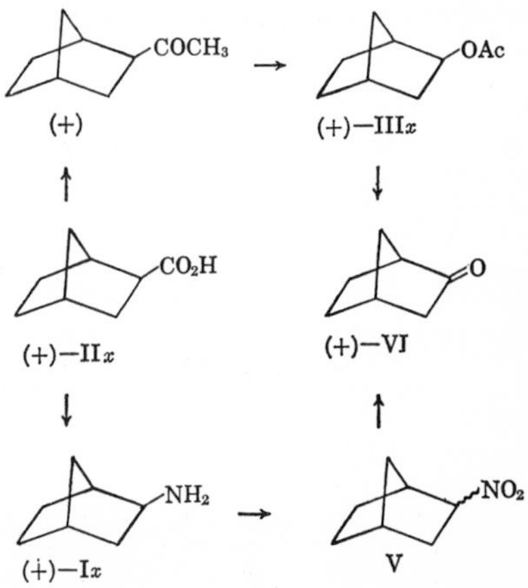

(+)   →   (+)–III*x*

(+)–II*x*   →   (+)–VI

(+)–I*x*   →   V

exo-norbornanecarboxylic acid (II*x*), 23.0% optically pure,[4] led to (+)-*exo*-norbornylamine (I*x*), oxidation of which with anhydrous peracetic acid[11] gave 2-nitronorbornane (V). In a Nef reaction, the crude optically active nitro compound V was converted by aqueous alkali to (+)-2-norbornanone (VI). The maximum rotation of VI was known by its correlation[12] with *exo*-norbornyl acetate (III*x*), and those of the reference compounds II*x* and III*x* were derived by isotopic dilution analysis.[4,5] The optical purity of the (+)-norbornanone (VI) derived from 23.0% optically pure

(1) This work was supported in part by a grant from the Petroleum Research Fund administered by the American Chemical Society.   Grateful acknowledgment is hereby made to the donors of this fund.

(2) To whom inquiries should be directed at the Department of Chemistry, University of Wisconsin, Madison, Wis.

(3) J. A. Berson and D. A. Ben-Efraim, *J. Am. Chem. Soc.*, **81**, 4094 (1959).

(4) J. A. Berson and D. A. Ben-Efraim, *ibid.*, **81**, 4083 (1959).

(5) J. A. Berson and S. Suzuki, *ibid.*, **81**, 4088 (1959).

(6) *Cf. inter alia*, A. Campbell and J. Kenyon, *J. Chem. Soc.*, 26 (1946).

(7) R. K. Hill and O. T. Chortyk, *J. Am. Chem. Soc.*, **84**, 1064 (1962).

(8) (a) C. Schuerch and E. H. Huntress, *ibid.*, **71**, 2223 (1949);   (b) P. A. S. Smith in "Molecular Rearrangements," P. de Mayo, Ed., Interscience Publishers, Inc., New York, N. Y., 1963, Part 1, p. 544–545;   (c) R. F. Brown, N. M. van Gulick, and G. H. Schmid, *J. Am. Chem. Soc.*, **77**, 1094 (1955), and references therein cited.

(9) (a) O. Wallach, *Ann.*, **379**, 182 (1911);   **369**, 63 (1909);   (b) L. Bouveault and Levallois, *Compt. rend.*, **146**, 180 (1908).

(10) (a) S. Winstein and D. Trifan, *J. Am. Chem. Soc.*, **74**, 1147 (1952); (b) *ibid.*, **74**, 1154 (1952).

(11) *Cf.* W. D. Emmons, *ibid.*, **79**, 5528 (1957).

(12) K. Mislow and J. G. Berger, *ibid.*, **84**, 1956 (1962).

acid (+)-IIx via amine Ix and nitro compound V was 22.4%, as calculated from the above-described correlations. In other words, the net retention in the Schmidt reaction could not have been less than about 97%. We therefore felt confident in the optical purity of the exo-amine Ix. With the Schmidt reaction in the exo series now having been shown to be stereochemically safe, we assumed that the conversion of endo-acid IIn to endo-amine In also was free from racemization.

Since (+)-endo-norborneol (IVn) having 65% of the highest reported[10a] rotation was oxidized[13] to (+)-norbornanone (VI) with 59% of the maximum rotation calculated on the basis of Chart I, it appears that the optical resolution of IVn acid phthalate[10b] was about 91% complete.

Nitrous Acid Deaminations.—In glacial acetic acid, both endo-In and exo-Ix norbornylamines reacted with nitrous acid (generated in situ by addition of sodium nitrite) to give norbornyl acetates as the predominant products. Small quantities of norborneols, norbornyl nitrates, and hydrocarbons also were formed. These minor side products were separated from the norbornyl acetate fraction either by preparative vapor chromatography or by elution chromatography under conditions that were shown in control experiments not to fractionate the acetates epimerically or optically.

The acetate product from both the endo- and exo-amines consisted mainly of exo-norbornyl acetate, but small amounts of endo-acetate also were observed. The data of Table I show that a somewhat greater proportion of endo-acetate seemed to be formed from endo-amine than from exo-amine.

In the optically active series, the acetate products obtained from either amine were optically active, but the observed rotations were those of the mixtures of exo- and endo-acetates, these substances or the corresponding alcohols being essentially inseparable on a preparative scale by the distillation or gas chromatographic techniques at our disposal. In order to interpret the observed rotations in terms of optical purities, it was necessary to know not only the epimeric composition of the acetate mixture but also the specific rotation of one of the components. We determined the latter quantity by taking advantage of the observation[10] that exo-norbornyl acetate can be selectively racemized by p-toluenesulfonic acid under conditions that do not affect the optical purity of endo-norbornyl acetate. The optical rotation due to endo-acetate remaining after such treatment of the reaction product from endo-amine was too small to measure. However, lithium aluminum hydride cleavage of the selectively racemized acetate mixture and then oxidation of the resulting alcohols gave 2-norbornanone (VI). The optical rotatory dispersion curve of this substance had been reported by Mislow and Berger[12] and had shown that observable rotations in the ultraviolet region could be expected even from samples of low optical purity. Conversion to the ketone thus served as a convenient way of amplifying the optical activity. The rotation of the norbornanone sample derived from the deamination of endo-amine and treatment of the acetate product by the above procedure was kindly determined for us by Professor Kurt Mislow at two

wave lengths in the ultraviolet. From these data and the original product composition and rotation, it was possible to calculate the retentions of optical purity in both acetates as exo, 18 ± 0.6%; endo, 85 ± 12%. The experimental error in the latter figure is large enough so that the result cannot confidently be distinguished from complete retention in the formation of endo-acetate. In the deamination of endo-amine, therefore, a total of 21% (0.953 × 18 + 0.047 × 85) of the replacement of amino by acetoxy occurs by non-racemizing processes.

The above device used to obtain the optical purity of the endo-acetate product from endo-amine In was not conveniently applicable to the product from exo-amine Ix. Only about half as much (ca. 2%) endo-acetate IIIn was formed from Ix as from In, and it was therefore difficult to determine the composition of the product mixture accurately. This uncertainty introduced such a large error into the determination of optical purity of the IIIn product that the value would not have been reliable to better than a factor of two. Consequently, the optical purity of the exo-acetate formed from exo-amine was calculated from the two extreme assumptions regarding the optical purity of the IIIn present, i.e., no racemization, or racemization equivalent to that of IIIx. On this basis, exo-amine Ix gave exo-acetate IIIx with 11 ± 2% retention of optical purity.

The major differences in behavior of the two epimeric amines are: (i) The endo-amine gives about twice as much endo-acetate as does the exo-amine. (ii) The retention of optical purity in the exo-acetate is substantially greater in the product from endo-amine than in that from exo-amine. Further, little, if any, racemization is observed in the endo-acetate product from endo-amine. The results are summarized in Table I.

TABLE I

PRODUCTS FROM THE DEAMINATIONS OF THE NORBORNYLAMINES IN ACETIC ACID[a]

	From exo		From endo	
Product	Yield, %	Optical purity, %	Yield, %	Optical purity, %
Total acetate	87[b]	...	80[b]	...
Total alcohol	10[b]	...	16[b]	...
Total nitrate	2 ± 0.5[b]	...	4[b]	...
endo-Acetate	2 ± 0.5[c]	100[f]	4.7 ± 0.5[c]	85 ± 12
exo-Acetate	98[c]	11 ± 2	95.3[c]	18 ± 0.6[e]
endo-Alcohol	~1[d]	...	5.3 ± 0.5[d]	...
exo-Alcohol	~99[d]	...	94.7[d]	...

[a] Unless otherwise indicated, the experimental uncertainty in the figures is estimated to be 0.5-1 unit. [b] % of total recovered product. [c] % of acetate product fraction. [d] % of alcohol product fraction. [e] Calculated as described in text. [f] Assumed.

While this work[14] was in progress, there appeared a paper by Corey and co-workers[15] on the deamination of the norbornylamines. Neither our experimental results nor our theoretical conclusions are in agreement with those of Corey.

It was previously suggested[3] that at least part of the survival of optical activity in the deamination product from endo-amine In is attributable to direct displacement by solvent or lyate ion. Corey, et al., objected on

(13) J. A. Berson, J. S. Walia, A. Remanick, S. Suzuki, P. Reynolds-Warnhoff, and D. Willner, *J. Am. Chem. Soc.*, **83**, 3986 (1961).

(14) The major experimental results are cited by J. A. Berson in "Molecular Rearrangements," P. de Mayo, Ed., Interscience Publishers, Inc., New York, N. Y., 1963, Part 1, pp. 181–182 and 208–209.

(15) E. J. Corey, J. Casanova, Jr., P. A. Vatakencherry, and R. Winter, *J. Am. Chem. Soc.*, **85**, 169 (1963).

the grounds that "this hypothesis is inconsistent with the reasonable expectation that a concerted backside displacement reaction with solvent as nucleophile should be far less likely for amine deamination than for sulfonate solvolysis." By "less likely," the authors[15] presumably meant "competes less efficiently with carbonium ion-formation." It seems to us, however, that the opposite view, namely that the compressed energy scale[16] in deaminations brings the rates of several competing processes closer together, is equally reasonable *a priori*. The authors[15] then stated that in the deamination of *exo*-norbornylamine, "the *exo*-diazonium ion . . . is clearly not subject to concerted backside displacement for steric reasons and consequently, any retention of optical activity in the product must come from an optically active carbonium ion." In our opinion, this objection is insufficient to rule out the displacement mechanism, especially since concerted backside nucleophilic displacement reactions giving configurational inversions *are known for both endo and exo-norbornyl p-bromobenzenesulfonates.*[17]

Finally, Corey, *et al.*,[15] reported that the retentions of skeletal integrity in the deaminations of both *endo*- and *exo*-amines were essentially identical (15–16%) and suggested[15,18] that a classical optically active norbornyl cation was the common intermediate in the formation of the active products in each case. But the reported[15] identity is not in accord with our finding (Table I) that *exo*-acetate from *endo*-amine retains much more optical purity than that from *exo*-amine. In seeking the cause of the discrepancy between our results and those of Corey, *et al.*, we are led to point out that, in our hands, it is difficult to reproduce the results of these nitrous acid deaminations with high accuracy. Our result of 11 ± 2% for the retention of optical purity in the *exo*-acetate from *exo*-amine is the average of three separate runs, the relative reproducibility being only about one part in ten.[19a] It is also significant that the ^{14}C-scrambling pattern in the deamination of *endo*-norbornylamine is reproduced with poorer precision than is that in the solvolysis of the *p*-bromobenzenesulfonate,[19b] as has been pointed out.[3] Since Corey, *et al.*,[15] reported only one run for each amine, we do not know if they experienced the same difficulty. In any case, if the discrepancies between our results and Corey's are due to this cause, it would seem that those[15] whose mechanistic proposal requires identical stereochemical results of the *endo*- and *exo*-amine deaminations should bear the burden of proof.

It seems at least as probable, however, that the sources of the discrepancies lie in factors other than the irreproducibility of the deaminations. The three most likely such factors are: (1) Our results apply only to acetate products, which we separated from the accompanying small amounts of nitrates, alcohols, and hydrocarbons. Corey, *et al.*,[15] reduced the crude reaction mixtures catalytically, thus converting nitrate esters to norborneols, and then acetylated. Their rotations

thus reflect optical purities of acetates of three different origins in the deamination, *i.e.*, that formed as acetate, that formed as nitrate, and that formed as alcohol.

(2) The optical purity reported by Corey, *et al.*,[15] for the product from *exo*-amine was calculated on the assumption that the observed rotation is that of *exo*-acetate. These authors recognized that the optical purity of the *endo*-acetate product (their sample contained 4%) might be much higher, but seemed to feel that this would not affect the results appreciably. To be confident of this position, one would have to know the rotation of optically pure *endo*-acetate. This datum was not available to Corey, *et al.*, who stated that *exo*- and *endo*-acetates have "about the same magnitude of optical rotation." The uncertainty of this relationship has been alluded to previously,[3,5,13] and the matter is settled for the first time in the present paper (see Experimental). For reasons given in the Experimental, we are unable to convert Corey's observed rotation into a proper % retention figure. The reported value[15] is, however, unreliable even on the basis of the stated[15] assumption. The observed rotation[15] of −0.892° would then receive a contribution of up to −0.222° due merely to the presence of 4% of unracemized *endo*-acetate. In other words, as much as a quarter of the total rotation used[15] as a basis for the calculation of retention in the *exo* product could be attributable to *endo* product.

(3) In the case of the *endo*-amine, Corey, *et al.*,[15] used the scrambling of a deuterium label originally at C-2 as a measure of loss of skeletal integrity. Thus, *endo*-norbornylamine-2-*d* with 1.00 atom of deuterium per molecule gave norbornyl acetate, which upon ester cleavage and oxidation gave 2-norbornanone with 0.42 atom of deuterium per molecule (42% rearrangement of the label). This result was interpreted[15] as corresponding to 16% retention of optical activity and 84% racemization in a hypothetical stereochemical experiment and thus appeared to be in close agreement with the value of 15% retention found[15] for the *exo*-amine deamination. The conclusion was based on the assumption that the % racemization is measured by twice the % rearrangement, which is true only if deuterium scrambling measures *a single kind* of the two most likely racemization processes (Wagner Meerwein rearrangement and 6,2-hydride shift). To the extent that deuterium scrambling results from *both* of these, it is an exaggerated measure of the true amount of racemization, for, taken in combination, these

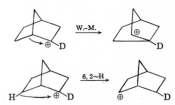

processes will produce skeletal rearrangement that is greater than half the racemization.[19b] That the apparent value[15] of 16% of product formed by nonracemizing processes in the *endo*-amine case (as measured by deuterium scrambling) is not incompatible with our observation of 21% (as measured by actual racemization) is shown by the following calculation.

(16) *Cf.* (a) A. Streitwieser, Jr., *J. Org. Chem.*, **22**, 861 (1957); (b) A. Streitwieser, Jr., and W. D. Schaeffer, *J. Am. Chem. Soc.*, **79**, 2893 (1957); (c) R. Huisgen and C. Rüchardt, *Ann.*, **601**, 1 (1956).

(17) S. J. Cristol and G. D. Brindell, *J. Am. Chem. Soc.*, **76**, 5699 (1954).

(18) *Cf.* also E. J. Corey and J. Casanova, Jr., *ibid.*, **85**, 165 (1963).

(19) (a) The variations in results do not seem to be attributable to optical fractionations occurring during the preparation of the *exo*-amine from *exo*-carboxylic acid, the Schmidt reaction being reproducible with high precision (see Experimental); (b) J. D. Roberts, C. C. Lee, and W. H. Saunders, Jr., *J. Am. Chem. Soc.*, **76**, 4501 (1954).

Corey, et al.,[15] examined the proton magnetic resonance spectrum of their norbornanone product in a search for 6,2-hydride shift but stated that they would not have detected 5% or less of such a process. Accordingly, we may take 5% as an upper limit of the total amount of 6,2-hydride shift. In terms of a threefold symmetric intermediate for hydride shift,[19b] this corresponds to 15% contribution of this path. For the purposes of this calculation, it is immaterial whether this is formulated as a discrete intermediate, e.g., VII; or the equivalent in terms of isotopic labeling, a 1:1:1 mixture of twofold symmetric nonclassical ions (VIII, IX, and X); or another operationally equivalent set of six classical ions. The total product acetate would then be made up of 21% of nonracemized,

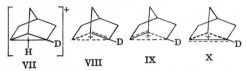

VII   VIII   IX   X

nonrearranged material, 15% of racemized material with 66.7% rearrangement, and 64% of racemized material with 50% rearrangement. The total % rearrangement would then be $0 + 10 + 32 = 42\%$, or just the observed[15] amount. This calculation shows that tracer scrambling, unless it is accompanied by a very accurate determination of the amount of 6,2-shift, is a deceptive measure of racemization in this system. In the experiment reported,[15] the inability to detect what superficially looked like a small amount of hydride shift could have led to a gross error in the estimate from tracer scrambling of % racemization.

Moreover, the assumption[15] of 0% hydride shift, which is necessary if the tracer scrambling result in the endo-amine deamination is to be equated directly with racemization, is incompatible with the proposed[15] mechanism. Since the cation derived from exo-amine deamination is suggested[15] to be the same as that from endo-amine deamination, it follows that if the latter does not suffer hydride shift, then the former also does not. But using Corey's figure of 15% retention for the exo-amine case and the known[19b] over-all 48% rearrangement in a ^{14}C-tracer scrambling experiment carried out under the same conditions, we calculate that the extent of rearrangement in the racemic portion of the product from exo-amine would be 48/0.85 = 56.5%. There is no way to achieve this much rearrangement without hydride shift. The calculated figure represents about 13% net 6,2-hydride shift ($3 \times 13 = 39\%$ contribution of the threefold symmetric path) in the racemic portion, and this same amount of hydride shift would have to occur in the case of endo-amine if the Corey mechanism held. A fit to the observed 42% over-all rearrangement figure for endo-amine would then require that the racemic portion of the product be 58% rearranged ($3 \times 0.13 \times 66.7 + 0.61 \times 50$) and that it make up 72% of the total product. The remaining 28% would then represent retention of skeletal integrity and hence of optical purity. This figure is almost twice as large as the 16% retention value deduced[15] from the assumption of 0% hydride shift in the endo-amine reaction. The latter assumption[15] leads, therefore, to an internal inconsistency, since either the value 16% retention, or the

mechanism proposed[15] to fit the value (or both) must be incorrect.[20a]

Although the proposal of complete mechanisms for the deaminations of the norbornylamines on the basis of the present evidence seems unwarranted,[20b] it is clear that the experimental results do not require the assumption[15] that all of the products derive from a carbonium ion.

Racemizing Processes in the Norbornyl Cation.— It is now possible to make a survey of the racemizing processes that occur in norbornyl cations. This involves comparisons of the extent of isotope-position rearrangement in the racemic portion of the product. For these calculations, the over-all ^{14}C-scrambling data of Roberts, Lee, and Saunders[19b] must be dissected in such a way as to omit from consideration that part of the product which involves neither isotopic scrambling nor loss of optical purity. This can be done by means of eq. 1, where R is the % rearrangement in the racemic portion of the product, N is the observed[19b] gross % rearrangement of isotope position, and P is the fraction of skeletal integrity retained. The quantity P is given by eq. 2, where F_x and F_n are the fractions of exo and endo products, and P_x and P_n are the respective optical purities.

$$R = N/(1 - P) \tag{1}$$

$$P = F_x P_x + F_n P_n \tag{2}$$

The experimental quantities required for eq. 1 and 2 are available from the data reported here and elsewhere,[4,5,10,19b,21] and are summarized in Table II, where calculated values for R are also given. It is assumed that racemization results from carbon and hydrogen shifts within cationic intermediates,[10,19b] not from the intervention of optically inactive neutral species such as norbornene or nortricyclene.[22] It is also assumed that the % rearrangement is insensitive to temperature, in agreement with the limited experimental test of the point.[19b]

At first glance, one gets the impression of a striking regularity of behavior of the cations in solvent acetic acid. The R-values for the acetolyses of endo- and exo-p-bromobenzenesulfonates appear to be identical within experimental error. Similarly, the R-values for deamination also are independent of the stereochemistry of the starting material, although the "deaminative" R seems to be different from the "acetolytic" R. Although these correspondences offer some superficially attractive bases for interpretation, the temptingly obvious conclusion that identical R's correspond to identical cation structures does not explain the apparently discordant R-values in aqueous solvent (Table II). From these data it seems that although the acetolytic racemizing processes are inde-

(20) (a) The apparent irreconcilability would be removed if there were a gross error in the ^{14}C-tracer experiment of Roberts, et al.,[19b] and the % rearrangement for the exo-amine product were 42.5% instead of 48%. This would allow 15% retention of skeletal integrity and 0% hydride shift. The discrepany seems much too large to be ascribed to experimental error. Furthermore, Roberts reports[19b] direct evidence for 6,2-hydride shift in the aqueous fluoroboric acid deamination of a mixed endo–exo amine sample. It seems entirely probable that 6,2-shift also would occur in acetic acid. (b) For a discussion of the intricacies of deamination mechanisms and related processes, see E. H. White and C. A. Aufdermarsh, J. Am. Chem. Soc., **83** 1179 (1961).

(21) S. Winstein and E. Clippinger, unpublished; E. Clippinger, Dissertation, University of California at Los Angeles, 1955.

(22) The evidence on this point is incomplete. For a review, see ref. 23.

TABLE II

ISOTOPE POSITION REARRANGEMENTS IN RACEMIZING PROCESSES OF NORBORNYL DERIVATIVES

Reactant	Solvent	Gross % rearr., N	F_x	F_n	P_x	P_n	R,[a] %
exo-ROBs	HOAc	60.6	1.00	0.00	0.00	..	60.6
exo-ROBs	75% acetone	54.5	1.00	.00	.00	..	54.5
endo-ROBs	HOAc	56.0	1.00	.00	.07	..	60.4
endo-ROBs	75% acetone	44.5	1.00	.00	.13	..	51.2
exo-RNH₂, HONO	HOAc	48.0[b]	0.98	.02	.11	1.00	54.0 ± 2
endo-RNH₂, HONO	HOAc	43.2[b]	0.95	.05	.18	0.85	54.6 ± 4

[a] Calculated from eq. 1; estimated uncertainty in R is about 0.5–1 unit unless otherwise indicated. [b] Value reported[19b] for the total product alcohol after lithium aluminum hydride reduction. This presumably is derived from acetate, alcohol, and nitrate (see Table I). We assume that the gross N is the same as the N for acetate. The resulting R is relatively insensitive to whether or not this assumption is strictly correct.

pendent of the geometry of the starting material, the hydrolytic ones are not.

To rationalize the results, the effects of ion-pair return must be taken into account. That solvolyses of norbornyl derivatives pass through ion-pair intermediates is clear from extensive previous studies by Winstein and his co-workers.[10,21,23a] The behavior of endo and exo derivatives differ, however. The intimate ion-pair from the exo compound returns to the covalent condition and is re-formed several times before actual solvolysis. This process results in rearrangement (or in the unsubstituted norbornyl case, racemization) of the starting substrate. The polarimetric vs. titrimetric rate ratio (k_α/k_t) shows that for every event leading to solvolysis product, exo-norbornyl p-bromobenzenesulfonate (exo-ROBs) is exposed to racemizing ion-pair formation about six times in acetic acid and about twice in 75% acetone. In the case of endo-ROBs, $k_\alpha = k_t$, so that if there is ion-pair return, it is without stereochemical consequences. If 6,2-hydride shift can occur in the ion-pair, the recycling in the exo derivative provides an opportunity for extra shuffling of the isotopic label that is denied to the endo. Although direct evidence on the question of hydride shift in ion-pairs derived from the parent norbornyl cation has not been available, these processes are facile in substituted norbornyl systems.[21,24,25] It therefore seems likely that the simple norbornyl system also experiences them, and that this is the most likely cause of the discrepancy between the exo and endo R-values in aqueous acetone. In principle, it is possible to dissect the over-all isotopic scrambling results in such a way as to reveal the extent of scrambling that occurs in each pass of exo-ROBs through the ion-pair condition, but it is doubtful that the accuracy[26] of the available data justify the calculation. Qualitatively, however, it is necessary to assume that the total contribution of 6,2-shift within the ion-pair to the over-all isotopic scrambling result is greater in aqueous acetone than in acetic acid if the results of Table II are to be explained in this way.

A quantitatively more significant comparison is that between the R-values for endo-ROBs in the two solvents. Here ion-pair return is not a factor, and the R-values measure scrambling processes that presumably occur at the solvated cation stage. The greater R-

value in acetic acid is in accord with the suggestion[10,19b,23b] that 6,2-shift follows Wagner–Meerwein rearrangement in the norbornyl cation and that the more highly nucleophilic aqueous solvent captures the cations more rapidly.

The R-values of Table II also bear on the question of the mechanism of solvolysis of endo-norbornyl p-bromobenzenesulfonate. It has been stated,[15] for example, that the possibility has not been excluded that the reaction may proceed by way of preliminary rearrangement of endo-sulfonate to the exo isomer. This would require identical R-values from endo and exo starting materials and thus appears to be in conflict with the 75% acetone results (Table II), where the discrepancy seems to be greater than experimental error.

The above analysis now permits a more meaningful examination of the R-values (Table II) for the deaminations in acetic acid of the norbornylamines. In these cases, R is essentially independent of the geometry of the starting amine. In the amine deaminations, there is no evidence that return to RN₂⁺ can occur once carbon–nitrogen heterolysis is achieved. Although such a process is not inconceivable,[27] until it has been demonstrated in this system, there seems to be no advantage in invoking it. The correspondence in R-values for the two amine systems is then most simply taken to mean that both systems get only one chance to racemize and shuffle isotopic label, and that the intermediates for the racemic portions of the products are the same in both cases. (Note that this is not the conclusion reached by Corey,[15] who proposed that the intermediates for the total products were the same.) This intermediate presumably is merely the solvated norbornyl cation. It may be significant that the extent of 6,2-hydride shift in this species in acetic acid solvent seems to be somewhat greater in the cation from exo- or endo-ROBs than in that from exo- or endo-RNH₂. The experimental error in the "deaminative" R, however, is large enough (see Table II) to suggest that, for the present, the apparent gap between it and the "acetolytic" R be interpreted with diffidence.

Experimental[28]

Optical Rotation of endo-Norbornyl Acetate in Solvent Acetic Acid.—To a sample of 0.2401 g. of endo-norborneol,[13] $[\alpha]_D$

(23) (a) For a review, see J. A. Berson in "Molecular Rearrangements," P. de Mayo, Ed., Interscience Publishers, Inc., New York, N. Y., 1963, Part 1, p. 168; (b) for discussion, see ibid., p. 145 ff.

(24) S. Winstein and A. Colter, unpublished; A. Colter, Dissertation, University of California at Los Angeles, 1956.

(25) W. G. Woods, R. A. Carboni, and J. D. Roberts, J. Am. Chem. Soc., 78, 5653 (1956).

(26) We are indebted to Professor J. D. Roberts for a discussion of this point.

(27) (a) For an example of internal return of a neutral species to a cation, see H. L. Goering and R. R. Josephson, J. Am. Chem. Soc., 83, 2588 (1961); (b) for an example of a reversible step in a diazonium salt decomposition, see J. M. Insole and E. S. Lewis, ibid., 85, 122 (1963); E. S. Lewis and J. E. Cooper, ibid., 84, 3847 (1962).

(28) Rotations at the sodium D line were measured at 25° in jacketed polarimeter tubes cooled with thermostated circulating water. The instrument was a Rudolph Model 80 high precision polarimeter reading directly to 0.001°. Capillary vapor chromatography was carried out with the Barber–Colman Model 20 instrument using argon carrier and a radium ionization detector with the operating variables specified. Packed column

+1.226° (CHCl₃), in a 2.00-ml. volumetric tube was added 0.3483 g. of acetic anhydride and 1.0 ml. of acetic acid. After 5 days at room temperature, the mixture was diluted to the mark with acetic acid and the rotation determined. On the assumption of complete reaction,[10] the sample showed $[\alpha]_D$ +10.5° (c 16.5 in acetic acid, l 1). Since the sample of *endo*-norborneol used had 65% of the rotation reported[10b] for the most highly resolved sample ($[\alpha]_D$ 1.89°, obtained from resolution of the acid phthalate) and gave 2-norbornanone with 59% of the rotation of optically pure (see below) material, the resolution of the acid phthalate[10b] was about 91% complete. The maximum rotation of *endo*-norborneol is thus $[\alpha]_D$ 2.08° (CHCl₃) and that of *endo*-norbornyl acetate $[\alpha]_D$ 17.8° (HOAc). Winstein and Trifan[10b] report $[\alpha]_D$ 14.00° (HOAc) for a sample of *endo*-norbornyl acetate of unspecified optical purity. However, since their most highly resolved sample was about 91% optically pure, the value 14.00° leads to a value of at least 15.4° for optically pure material. We have no information on the optical rotation of neat *endo*-norbornyl acetate or of *endo*-norbornyl acetate in solvent *exo*-norbornyl acetate. Since the rotation reported by Corey[15] is that of the undiluted liquid sample, we have no way of calculating % retention from his data.

Optically Active *exo*-Norbornylamine (Ix) by the Schmidt Reaction.—A solution of hydrazoic acid in chloroform, prepared from 10.5 g. of sodium azide, 10.5 ml. of water, 14.8 g. of concentrated sulfuric acid, and 100 ml. of chloroform, was dried over calcium sulfate and added to a solution of 10.5 g. of (+)-*exo*-norbornanecarboxylic acid,[4] $[\alpha]_D$ +6.40° (95% ethanol), 23% optically pure, in 50 ml. of chloroform. The mixture was cooled to 0°, stirred, and treated dropwise with 31 ml. of concentrated sulfuric acid. The ice bath was removed and the mixture allowed to come to room temperature, whereupon gas evolution began, followed by spontaneous boiling. After 15 min., the mixture was heated at reflux for 90 min., cooled to room temperature, and poured onto ice, the layers were separated, and the aqueous phase was washed with fresh chloroform. The aqueous layer was then made basic with dilute sodium hydroxide solution, the amine extracted with ether, and the ether layer dried over potassium hydroxide pellets. The ether layer was decanted and evaporated to dryness, and the residue was distilled *in vacuo* directly into tared 2.00-ml. volumetric tubes. The vacuum was broken by letting in dry nitrogen, and one of the tubes was removed, stoppered immediately, weighed, and made up to the mark with 5.58 N hydrochloric acid. The sample, 0.4384 g., showed α +1.077°, whence $[\alpha]_D$ +4.95° (in 5.58 N HCl). The procedure avoided handling of the exceedingly sensitive free amine, which rapidly forms a carbonate and therefore can be weighed in a conventional manner only with difficulty.

In a second run with the same batch of acid, there was obtained amine of $[\alpha]_D$ +4.72° (in 5.58 N HCl).

In a third run with acid of $[\alpha]_D$ +19.3°, 47.4 g. of acid gave 23.0 g. of amine, b.p. 77° (50 mm.). This material was assumed to have the same optical purity as the starting acid (69.5%). Another sample of amine was prepared from (−)-*exo*-acid of $[\alpha]_D$ −13.0°, 48% optically pure.

Correlation of *exo*-Norbornylamine (Ix) with 2-Norbornanone (VI).—To a magnetically stirred, ice-cooled solution of 3.3 ml. of 90% hydrogen peroxide in 15 ml. of ethylene chloride was added dropwise during 90 min. 14.7 g. of acetic anhydride. After completion of the addition, stirring was continued for 30 min. at 0° and 30 min. at room temperature. An additional 9 ml. of ethylene chloride was added, the mixture was heated to reflux, and 3.0 g. of *exo*-norbornylamine, $[\alpha]_D$ +4.72°, 23% optically pure, in 3 ml. of ethylene chloride was cautiously added dropwise during 30 min. There was a vigorous reaction, and a pale blue color remained at the end of the addition. After having been heated at reflux for another 15 min., the reaction mixture became yellow. Heating was continued for another 45 min., the mixture was cooled to 0°, washed with dilute ammonia and with water, dried over calcium sulfate, evaporated, and distilled. The product, a pale blue liquid, was collected as two arbitrary fractions, both with b.p. 72° (5 mm.). Fraction 1 weighed 0.87 g.; fraction 2 weighed 0.77 g.

Fraction 1 above was heated with 50 ml. of 10% sodium hydroxide on the steam bath for 1 hr. The mixture was cooled, poured into 3 N hydrochloric acid, and stirred for 3 hr. Extraction with ether gave a pale blue solution which, after having

been washed with water and dried over magnesium sulfate, was evaporated carefully under a Vigreux column. Two sublimations of the residue at aspirator pressure gave a crystalline solid which still retained a trace of blue color. Most of this was removed by treatment of a pentane solution of the material with charcoal, filtering, evaporating, and resubliming the residue. In this way there was obtained 0.107 g. of 2-norbornanone, vapor chromatographically homogeneous on a 40-m. tri-(β-cyanoethoxy)-propane (TCEP) capillary column at 107° and 10 p.s.i. The retention time and infrared spectrum were identical with those of authentic 2-norbornanone. The material had $[\alpha]_D$ +6.51° (c 5.3 in CHCl₃). The maximum rotation of 2-norbornanone calculated on the assumption that the Schmidt reaction involves complete retention is 28.3°. From the correlation[12] with *exo*-norbornyl acetate, it is 29.2°.

Acetolysis of Racemic *endo*-2-Norbornyl *p*-Bromobenzenesulfonate.—A sample of the racemic *p*-bromobenzenesulfonate[10a] was carefully recrystallized thrice from ether–pentane to constant m.p. 62°. This sample was free of hydroxyl impurity as judged by the infrared spectrum measured under conditions where 1% of norborneol could have been detected. A boiling solution of 0.227 g. of potassium acetate in 14.9 ml. of glacial acetic acid was treated in one portion with a solution of 0.625 g. of the sulfonate ester in 3.7 ml. of acetic acid. The mixture was boiled for 17.25 hr., diluted with water, and extracted with hexane. The hexane solution, after having been washed with bicarbonate and water, was dried over magnesium sulfate, and the hexane evaporated with a Vigreux column. The residue was distilled bulb-to-bulb, and the distillate was examined vapor chromatographically on the TCEP capillary column at 122° and 7 p.s.i. It was better than 99.9% homogeneous. The acetate was reduced with lithium aluminum hydride in ether, and the resulting alcohol was isolated by addition of sodium sulfate solution, washing the ether layer with water, drying with magnesium sulfate, and evaporating. Sublimation of the crystalline residue and examination on a 30-m. Ucon HB-550 capillary column at 70° and 80 p.s.i. showed it to be at least 99.5% *exo*-norborneol. No *endo*-norborneol could be detected. Under these conditions, the *exo*-alcohol emerged at 30.75 min. and the *endo* at 35 min. retention times. Contamination of *exo* by as little as 0.5% of *endo* would have been detected without difficulty, as was established by controls.

Amine Deaminations. A. *endo*-Norbornylamine (In).—The crude product obtained previously[3] from deamination of In in acetic acid contained[3] 5.8% of nitrate ester as indicated by elemental analysis for nitrogen. This material was re-examined on the TCEP capillary at 123° and 7 p.s.i. and showed peaks for acetate (80%), alcohol (16%), and a third peak emerging last (4%) which we assume was nitrate. The acetate was isolated by preparative vapor chromatography on a 6-m. × 4-cm. TCEP column (20% on Chromosorb P) at 115–120° and a flow rate of 700 ml./min. The order of retention times was different on this column, the alcohol emerging after the acetate and nitrate. Sample sizes were 0.4–0.5 ml. The alcohol was collected as a crystalline solid, which was shown to consist of 5.3% *endo*- and 94.7% *exo*-norborneols by capillary v.p.c. on the Ucon column. The acetate was collected as a colorless liquid, homogeneous on the TCEP capillary column, α_{obsd} −1.059° (neat, 1 dm.). After repassage through the preparative column, the acetate was distilled bulb-to-bulb. It had α_{obsd} −1.082° (neat, 1 dm.), $[\alpha]_D$ −1.24° (c 25 HOAc). Reduction of a sample with lithium aluminum hydride–ether gave a norborneol mixture which capillary v.p.c. on the Ucon column showed to be 95.3% *exo* and 4.7% *endo*. The experimental error in the absolute magnitude of these figures is about ±0.5%.

Optical Purity of *endo*-Acetate Product.—Another portion of the same reaction product was chromatographed on alumina under the conditions described in B. The acetate fraction, 3.05 g., homogeneous by v.p.c. (TCEP capillary), and 7.7 g. of *p*-toluenesulfonic acid monohydrate were made up to 53.5-ml. volume with glacial acetic acid, producing a solution 0.37 M in norbornyl acetate and 0.76 M in sulfonic acid. The solution was heated at 75–80° for 3.5 hr., poured onto ice, extracted with pentane, dried over magnesium sulfate, evaporated under a Vigreux column, and the residue distilled bulb-to-bulb to give 2.45 g. of a partially racemized acetate mixture. This material was converted to alcohols with lithium aluminum hydride in the manner described above, and the crystalline product sublimed to give 1.35 g. of material.

---

vapor chromatography was carried out with the Perkin–Elmer Model 154 instrument.

The mixture of alcohols, 2.03 g. of *p*-benzoquinone, 8.1 g. of aluminum *t*-butoxide, and 95 ml. of dry benzene were heated at reflux for 21 hr., cooled, allowed to stand overnight, and filtered from insoluble material, the filter cake was washed with ether, and the combined filtrate and washings were washed successively with ice-cold 10% sulfuric acid, 10% potassium hydroxide, and water. After having been dried over magnesium sulfate, the solution was evaporated under a Vigreux column and the residue sublimed to give 0.50 g. of 2-norbornanone. This material was completely free of norborneols (<0.1%) under conditions (2 m. × 0.5 cm., 20% Ucon LB-550-X on Chromosorb P, at 127° and 10 p.s.i. helium) where the ketone and alcohols were well separated (retention times of 12.9 and 18.9 min., respectively). This material was examined in duplicate solutions in the laboratory of Professor Kurt Mislow with an automatic recording Rudolph spectropolarimeter. The following data were recorded at 23°:

Solution 1, 1.435% in isooctane, showed observed rotations of +0.024° at 320 mμ and of +0.016° at 325 mμ in a 0.1-dm. tube. The specific rotations are thus $[\alpha]_{320}$ +17.6° and $[\alpha]_{325}$ +12.2°. From the respective values for the maximum rotations at these wave lengths[12] (1234 and 983°), the optical purity is calculated to be 1.3%.

Solution 2, 1.695% in isooctane, showed $[\alpha]_{320}$ +18.6° and $[\alpha]_{325}$ +13.0°, whence the optical purity is calculated to be 1.4%.

Control.—As a control experiment on the accuracy of the method at these low rotations and on the possibility of fractionation during oxidation and isolation, the following experiment was performed. A mixture of 0.522 g. of *endo*-norbornyl acid phthalate, $[\alpha]_D$ +2.554° (51.0% optically pure[13]) and 8.588 g. of racemic *exo*-norbornyl acid phthalate was converted to alcohols by steam distillation from 30% sodium hydroxide solution. The crude alcohols were oxidized to ketone by the Oppenauer procedure described above, and the resulting product (which was homogeneous by v.p.c.) was examined in the spectropolarimeter. It showed $[\alpha]_{320}$ +34.3°, $[\alpha]_{325}$ +30.0°, 2.9% optically pure. The optical purity anticipated from the gravimetric composition of the acid phthalate mixture was 2.92%.

B. *exo*-Norbornylamine (I*x*).—The conditions were those used[3] in the deamination of *endo*-amine. To a solution of 11.5 g. of (+)-*exo*-norbornylamine, 69.5% optically pure (see above), in 77 ml. of glacial acetic acid was added 11.5 g. of sodium nitrite

over a 2-hr. period. After standing overnight, the mixture was treated with 3 g. more of sodium nitrite and stirred an additional 2 hr. Then 30 ml. of water was added, and the mixture was stirred for an hour, cooled, and poured into 320 ml. of cold 20% sodium hydroxide solution while the temperature was kept below 25°. The mixture was extracted with pentane, the extract was washed with water, cold 10% hydrochloric acid, and water, dried over magnesium sulfate, evaporated with a Vigreux column, and the residue was distilled to give three fractions: (1) 0.92 g., b.p. 31–80° (23 mm.); (2) 0.88 g., b.p. 80–84° (23 mm.); (3) 5.36 g., b.p. 84–87° (23 mm.). Fraction 3 was chromatographed on Merck acid-washed alumina. The acetate fraction was cleanly eluted with 20% ether in pentane; the alcohol fraction was eluted with pure ether. The acetate fraction was distilled bulb-to-bulb. It was free of alcohol or nitrate contaminant and contained less than 1% of adhering solvent. Early chromatographic fractions of acetate had $[\alpha]_D$ +1.56° (*c* 20 in HOAc) and later ones had essentially the same rotation, $[\alpha]_D$ +1.61° (*c* 20 in HOAc). Lithium aluminum hydride reduction and analysis of the resulting alcohol mixture with the Ucon capillary column showed the acetate fraction to consist of 97.9% *exo* and 2.1% *endo* material. The alcohol fraction contained approximately 99% *exo* and 1% *endo* material. In a separate run, the composition of the reaction mixture before chromatography was determined by v.p.c. with the TCEP capillary column. This is the source of the figures for % acetate, % alcohol, and % nitrate given in Table I. Three runs under the same conditions followed by examination of the chromatographed acetate fraction gave the following results. Run 1: Amine from (−)-acid of 48% optical purity gave acetate of $[\alpha]_D$ −0.795° (*c* 21 in HOAc). The acetate had the composition 97% *exo*, 3% *endo*. Run 2: Amine from (+)-acid of 69.5% optical purity gave acetate of $[\alpha]_D$ +1.58° (HOAc) containing 98% *exo*, 2% *endo*. Run 3: Amine of the same origin as in run 2 gave acetate of $[\alpha]_D$ +1.46° (HOAc) containing 98% *exo*, 2% *endo*. Control experiments showed that chromatography by the above procedure caused neither fractionation of *endo*- and *exo*-acetates nor racemization of *exo*-acetate.

Acknowledgment.—We are much indebted to Professor Kurt Mislow of New York University for the measurement of the rotations in the ultraviolet.

69 | Bond Angle and Solvolysis Rate

One of the difficulties in assessing anchimeric assistance to reaction rates is in knowing what rate would be expected in the absence of participation of neighboring groups, when rates obviously respond to a variety of structural features. One important factor in ring compounds is known to be the change in strain attending the rehybridization from sp^3 to sp^2 on ionization, which is quite sensitive to constraints on the bond angle imposed by the ring system. Borohydride reduction (Papers 31, 63) in unhindered compounds responds in the opposite way to solvolysis because the direction of rehybridization is opposite, and this has provided evidence of an abnormal driving force in the ionization of cyclobutyl compared to other simple ring compounds.

In Paper No. 69 Foote develops another criterion, more nearly independent of steric effects than the borohydride reduction. All solvolysis rates of secondary tosylates lie either on or above a straight line if the logarithm of the solvolysis rate constant under standard conditions is plotted against the frequency of the C=O stretch in the infrared for the related ketone. The compounds which lie above the line are an interesting group, for they contain all the compounds suspected of yielding nonclassical ions. The equation of the straight line provides a means of predicting the *unassisted* solvolysis rates of secondary tosylates over eleven powers of ten, as far as the effect of angle is concerned.

From: *J. Am. Chem. Soc.* **86,** 1853–54 (1964)

Correlation of Solvolysis Rates and Estimation of Rate Enhancements

Sir:

The acetolysis rates of many arenesulfonates (RR'CHOSO$_2$Ar) are quantitatively correlated with the infrared carbonyl stretching frequencies of the corresponding ketones (RCOR'). Table I lists rates and frequencies of twenty compounds for which reliable data are available.[1]

TABLE I

Arenesulfonate	No.	log k_{rel}	$\nu_{C=O}$ for ketone, cm.$^{-1}$
Cyclohexyl	1	(0.00)^a	1716
Cycloheptyl	2	1.78^b	1705^c
Cyclooctyl	3	2.76^b	1703
Cyclononyl	4	2.70^b	1703^d
Cyclodecyl	5	2.98^b	1704
Cycloundecyl	6	2.05^b	1709^e
Cyclododecyl	7	0.50^b	1713^b
Cyclotridecyl	8	0.66^b	1713^d
Cyclotetradecyl	9	0.08^b	1714^d
Cyclopentadecyl	10	0.42^b	1715^d
Isopropyl	11	0.15^f	1718
2-Butyl	12	0.53^f	1721
Methylisopropylcarbinyl	13	0.93^f	1718
Methyl-*t*-butylcarbinyl	14	0.62^f	1710
7-Norbornyl	15	−7.00^{g,h}	1773
endo-8-Bicyclo[3.2.1]octyl	16	−4.11^i	1752
2-Adamantyl	17	−1.18^c	1727^c
α-Nopinyl	18	−0.73^j	1717
β-Nopinyl	19	0.04^j	1717
1,4-α-5,8-β-Dimethanoperhydro-9-anthracyl	20	2.67^k	1696

^{a} S. Winstein, B. K. Morse, E. Grunwald, H. W. Jones, J. Corse, D. Trifan, and H. Marshall, *J. Am. Chem. Soc.*, **74,** 1127 (1952). ^{b} H. C. Brown and G. Ham, *ibid.*, **78,** 2735 (1956). ^{c} See ref. 2. ^{d} T. Bürer and H. H. Günthard, *Helv. Chim. Acta*, **39,** 356 (1956). ^{e} N. J. Leonard and F. H. Owens, *J. Am. Chem. Soc.*, **80,** 6039 (1958). ^{f} S. Winstein and H. Marshall, *ibid.*, **74,** 1120 (1952). ^{g} S. Winstein, M. Shatavsky, C. Norton, and R. B. Woodward, *ibid.*, **77,** 4183 (1955). ^{h} C. J. Norton, Ph.D. Thesis, Harvard, 1955. ^{i} See ref. 3. ^{j} S. Winstein and N. J. Holness, *J. Am. Chem. Soc.*, **77,** 3054 (1955). ^{k} S. Winstein and L. deVries, unpublished work, quoted in R. Piccolini, Ph.D. Thesis, U.C.L.A., 1960.

Representation in the table has been limited to saturated, secondary arenesulfonates without hetero-

(1) Infrared spectra for which no literature reference is cited were measured in dilute solution (CCl$_4$) on a calibrated Perkin–Elmer 421 grating spectrograph by Mr. Donald Steele. Expanded scale, reduced slit width, and nitrogen sweep were used; frequencies are believed accurate to ±1 cm.$^{-1}$. Other infrared data were chosen from sources which reported similar measurement conditions. Many absorptions were doublets or multiplets; in these cases, weighted average peak positions are given. All acetolysis rates of toluenesulfonates or bromobenzenesulfonates are relative to cyclohexyl toluenesulfonate or bromobenzenesulfonate, respectively, at 25°.

substituents; in addition, the following types were specifically excluded: (1) compounds in which ground-state eclipsing interactions are relieved in the solvolytic transition state (for example, cyclopentyl and *endo*-2-norbornyl derivatives), and (2) compounds which have been shown to undergo anchimerically accelerated solvolysis (for example, *exo*-2-norbornyl and cyclobutyl derivatives).

Figure 1 is a plot of the data from Table I. The least-squares straight line through the points obeys the equation log k (relative to cyclohexyl, 25°) = −0.132·($\nu_{C=O}$ − 1720); the correlation coefficient is −0.97.'

A qualitative relationship between ketone frequency and solvolysis rate was observed by Schleyer and Nicholas[2] and would, indeed, be expected, since both carbonyl frequency and solvolysis rate are sensitive to bond angle and hybridization.[2-4] It is surprising, however, that the correlation should be so excellent for so many dissimilar compounds; the acetolysis rates cover a range of ten powers of ten, yet no rate varies from the line by much more than about one power of ten.

The correlation provides an extremely useful semiempirical relationship for the prediction of solvolysis rates. It also allows the magnitude of the combined effects of anchimeric acceleration and other interactions to be estimated by providing a "model" rate from which the effects of angle strain have been factored out.

As an example of the predictive usefulness of the correlation, Table II lists experimental and calculated data for several compounds which were not included in the calculation of the least-squares line, either because they were of slightly different type from those in Table I, or because the infrared data were considered somewhat less reliable. The calculated acetolysis rates agree extremely well with the experimental, even though several of the compounds are primary or unsaturated. It should be noted that although both polar substituents and conjugation affect rate and carbonyl frequency in the same way as angle strain (increased rates corresponding to decreased carbonyl frequencies), it is not clear that the relative effect would necessarily be of the same magnitude as for angle strain. Further testing of this point would be desirable.

Table III lists data for a number of compounds which were excluded from Table I because their acetolysis

(2) P. von R. Schleyer and R. D. Nicholas, *J. Am. Chem. Soc.*, **83,** 182 (1961).

(3) C. S. Foote and R. B. Woodward, *Tetrahedron*, in press.

(4) (a) J. O. Halford, *J. Chem. Phys.*, **24,** 830 (1956); (b) R. Zbinden and H. K. Hall, Jr., *J. Am. Chem. Soc.*, **82,** 1215 (1960); (c) H. C. Brown, *J. Chem. Soc.*, 1248 (1956).

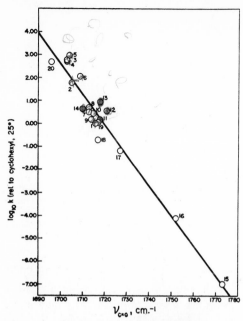

Fig. 1.—Acetolysis rates of arenesulfonates and carbonyl frequencies of corresponding ketones.

rates were considered to be accelerated either by ground-state eclipsing interactions or by anchimeric acceleration. All these compounds have rates which are *faster* than the rates calculated by the correlation; the difference is the sum of rate enhancements from anchimeric acceleration and steric effects (other than those of internal angle strain).

TABLE II

Arenesulfonate	$\nu C{-}O$ for ketone (or aldehyde), cm.$^{-1}$	Obsd.	Calcd.
		—log k_{rel}—	
Methyl	1728^{a,b}	-1.14^c	-1.1
Ethyl	1730^b	-1.45^c	-1.3
Benzyl	1709^b	1.73^f	1.5
trans-2-*t*-Butylcyclohexyl	1700^{e,f}	2.20^f	2.6
cis-2-*t*-Butylcyclohexyl	1700^{e,f}	2.61^f	2.6

^{a} Corrected from gas phase by subtracting 16 cm.$^{-1}$, which gives good agreement with solution values for acetaldehyde and propionaldehyde. ^{b} J. Depireux, *Bull. Soc. Chim. Belges*, **66**, 218 (1957). ^{c} See Table I, ref. *f.* ^{d} S. Winstein, E. Grunwald, and H. W. Jones, *J. Am. Chem. Soc.*, **73**, 2700 (1951). ^{e} Solvent not specified. ^{f} H. Goering, R. L. Reeves, and H. H. Espy, *J. Am. Chem. Soc.*, **78**, 4926, 4931 (1956).

This novel correlation is a further demonstration of the importance of angle strain and hybridization effects in organic reactions.[2,3,4c,5] It should be possible to extend the correlation to other types of reactions involving tetrahedral ground states and trigonal transition states (or *vice versa*).[6]

Acknowledgments.—The least-squares program and advice on its use were kindly supplied by Dr. Paul Haake. Computation was carried out on an IBM 7090

(5) C. S. Foote, *Tetrahedron Letters*, **No. 9**, 579 (1963).
(6) Schleyer has recently extended this correlation by adding terms for torsional strain, nonbonded interactions, and inductive effects: P. von R. Schleyer, Abstracts, 146th National Meeting of the American Chemical Society, Denver, Colo., Jan., 1964, p. 7C; P. von R. Schleyer, *J. Am. Chem. Soc.*, **86**, 1854 (1964).

TABLE III

Arenesulfonate	$\nu C{-}O$ for ketone, cm.$^{-1}$	Obsd.	Calcd.	log (acel.)
		—log k_{rel}—		
Cyclopropyl	1815^{a,b}	-5.32^c	-12.5	7.2
Cyclobutyl	1791^d	0.99^c	-9.4	10.4
Cyclopentyl	1748	1.51^c	-3.7	5.2
exo-2-Norbornyl	1751^d	2.71^c	-4.1	6.8
endo-2-Norbornyl	1751^d	0.18^c	-4.1	4.3
2-Bicyclo[2.2.2]octyl	1731^d	1.85^f	-1.5	3.4
2-Bicyclo[3.2.1]octyl (axial)	1717^d	1.62^f	0.4	1.2
2-Bicyclo[3.2.1]octyl (equatorial)	1717^d	0.47^f	0.4	0.1
endo-2-Bicyclo[2.2.2]oct-5-enyl	1735^g	2.49^f	-2.0	4.5
exo-2-Bicyclo[2.2.2]oct-5-enyl	1735^g	4.10^h	-2.0	6.1
exo-2-Norbornenyl	1745^g	2.42^i	-3.3	5.7
endo-2-Norbornenyl	1745^g	-1.48^i	-3.3	1.8
Nortricyclyl	1762^d	1.82^i	-5.6	7.4
anti-7-Norbornenyl	1780^j	4.11^{j,k}	-7.9	12.0
anti-8-Dicyclopentadienyl	1780^l	4.33^m	-7.9	12.2
syn-7-Norbornenyl	1780^j	-3.28^n	-7.9	4.6
anti-7-Benznorbornenyl	1792°	-1.22^o.	-9.5	8.3
exo-2-Benznorbornenyl	1756°	1.63^o	-4.8	6.4
endo-2-Benznorbornenyl	1756°	-2.22^o	-4.8	2.6
7-Dibenznorbornadienyl	1792^{p,q}	$-0.79^{q,t}$	-9.5	8.7
exo-8-Bicyclo[3.2.1]octyl	1752	-0.21^r	-4.2	4.0
9-Bicyclo[3.3.1]nonyl	1726	0.48^r	-0.8	1.3
5,5-Dimethyl-2-bicyclo[2.1.1]hexyl	1764^s	1.18^{s,t}	-5.8	7.0

^{a} In vapor. ^{b} W. B. De More, H. D. Pritchard, and N. Davidson, *J. Am. Chem. Soc.*, **81**, 5878 (1959). ^{c} J. D. Roberts and V. C. Chambers, *ibid.*, **73**, 5034 (1951). ^{d} See ref. 4b. ^{e} See Table I, ref. *a.* ^{f} H. L. Goering and M. F. Sloan, *J. Am. Chem. Soc.*, **83**, 1992 (1961). ^{g} Private communication from Dr. A. Gagnieux. ^{h} N. A. LeBel and J. E. Huber, *J. Am. Chem. Soc.*, **85**, 3193 (1963). ^{i} S. Winstein and M. Shatavsky, *ibid.*, **78**, 592 (1956); S. Winstein, H. M. Walborsky, and K. Schreiber, *ibid.*, **72**, 5795 (1950). ^{j} See Table I, ref. *h.* ^{k} See Table I, ref. *g.* ^{l} R. C. Cookson, J. Hudec, and R. O. Williams, *Tetrahedron Letters*, **No. 22**, 29 (1960). ^{m} R. B. Woodward and T. J. Katz, *Tetrahedron*, **5**, 70 (1959). ^{n} S. Winstein and E. T. Stafford, *J. Am. Chem. Soc.*, **79**, 505 (1957). ^{o} P. D. Bartlett and W. P. Giddings, *ibid.*, **82**, 1240 (1960); W. P. Giddings, Ph.D. Thesis, Harvard, 1959. ^{p} Solvent not specified. ^{q} J. Meinwald and E. G. Miller, *Tetrahedron Letters*, **No. 7**, 253 (1961). ^{r} See ref. 3. ^{s} J. Meinwald and P. G. Gassman, *J. Am. Chem. Soc.*, **85**, 57 (1963). ^{t} At 75°.

at the Computing Facility of the Department of Engineering, U.C.L.A. The author is particularly indebted to Prof. R. B. Woodward for encouragement and stimulation, and to Prof. P. D. Bartlett for interest in this work, which was originally presented in part in C. S. Foote, Ph.D. Thesis, Harvard, 1961. Part of this work was supported by Petroleum Research Fund Grant No. 1428 A 1, 4.

(7) Contribution No. 1613.

DEPARTMENT OF CHEMISTRY[7]   CHRISTOPHER S. FOOTE
UNIVERSITY OF CALIFORNIA
LOS ANGELES 24, CALIFORNIA

RECEIVED DECEMBER 27, 1963

70, 71 | Predicting Solvolysis Rates

In Papers 70 and 71 Schleyer supplements Foote's scheme with a specific formula for estimating effects of torsional (eclipsing) strain undergoing a change during ionization, and a discussion of nonbonded interactions such as determine conformational preferences in cyclohexanes and crossring interactions in norbornanes. He proposes that after any inductive effects have been allowed for, any large excess of observed over calculated solvolysis rate must be due to anchimeric assistance. In Paper No. 71 Schleyer tabulates 13 cases where the rates are as calculated within two powers of ten, and 18 cases showing rate enhancements running up to 13 powers of ten. Among these enhancements, listed by the logarithm of k_{obs}/k_{calc}, we find cholesteryl (3.7), *exo*-2-norbornyl (3.3), cyclobutyl (5.2), and *anti*-7-norbornenyl (12.9).

From: *J. Am. Chem. Soc.* **86,** 1854–56 (1964)

Estimation of Nonassisted Solvolysis Rates[1]

Sir:

Despite anticipated difficulties, many solvolysis rates
can be calculated with high accuracy very easily, using

(1) Presented at the Gordon Research Conference on Hydrocarbon
Chemistry, Colby Jr. College, New London, N. H., June, 1963, and at the

503

146th National Meeting, American Chemical Society, Denver, Colo., Jan., 1964, Abstracts, p. 7C.

TABLE I

CALCULATION OF SOLVOLYSIS RATES BY EQ. 1

No.	Compound	Ketone,[a] ν_{CO} cm.$^{-1}$	ϕ, deg.	GS − TS, non-bonded, kcal.	Log rel. rate Calcd.	Log rel. rate Obsd.[a]
1	7-Norbornyl	1773	60, 60	0.4	−7.0	−7.00
2	*endo*-8-Bicyclo[3.2.1]-octyl	1750	60, 60	0.6[b]	−4.2	−4.11
3	*endo*-2-Benznorbornenyl	1756	0, 40	0.4	−2.4[d]	−2.22
4	*endo*-2-Norbornenyl	1745	0, 40	0.4	−1.0[d]	−1.48
5	2-Adamantyl	1727	60, 60	0.6[b]	−1.1	−1.18
6	Cyclohexyl	1716	60, 60	0.0	−0.1	0.00
7	Cyclotetradecyl	1714	60, 60 ?	0.0	+0.1	+0.08
8	Isopropyl	1718	60, 60	0.0	−0.4	+0.15
9	*endo*-2-Norbornyl	1751	0, 40	1.3[c]	−0.2	+0.18
10	Cyclopentadecyl	1715	60, 60	0.0	0.0	+0.42
11	*cis*-4-*t*-Butylcyclohexyl	1716	60, 60	0.6[b]	+0.4	+0.42
12	Cyclododecyl	1713	60, 60	0.0	+0.3	+0.50
13	2-Butyl	1721	60, 60	0.6	−0.3	+0.53
14	3,3-Dimethyl-2-butyl	1710	60, 60	1.2	+1.5	+0.62
15	Cyclotridecyl	1713	60, 60	0.0	+0.3	+0.66
16	3-Methyl-2-butyl	1718	60, 60	1.4	+0.6	+0.93
17	Cyclopentyl	1740[e]	0, 20 ?	0.0	+1.5	+1.51
18	Cycloheptyl	1705	45, 45[f]	0.0[f]	+2.0	+1.78
19	*trans*-2-*t*-Butylcyclohexyl	1700	60, 60	0.6	+2.2	+2.20
20	*cis*-2-*t*-Butylcyclohexyl	1700	60, 60	1.2	+2.6	+2.61
21	1,4-α-5,8-β-Dimethanoperhydro-9-anthracyl	1696	60, 60	0.6	+2.8	+2.67

[a] Data from Foote.[5] [b] Axial cyclohexyl strain energy (E. L. Eliel, "Stereochemistry of Carbon Compounds," McGraw-Hill Book Co., Inc., New York, N. Y., 1962, p. 236). [c] See C. F. Wilcox, Jr., M. Sexton, and M. F. Wilcox, *J. Org. Chem.*, **28**, 1079 (1963). [d] Includes inductive factor $^1/_8$.[9] [e] This value would appear to be better than that usually quoted (*ca.* 1750 cm.$^{-1}$),[3,6] see C. L. Angell, *et al.*, *Spectrochim. Acta*, 926 (1959). [f] J. B. Hendrickson, *J. Am. Chem. Soc.*, **84**, 3355 (1962).

semiempirical but quite reasonable steric and conformational considerations. None of the underlying concepts is new[2] and the principles employed are well established in organic theory.

Bond Angle Strain.—Bond angle strain influences the rate of processes involving a change of carbon hybridization.[2,3] The ionization of a tosylate in the system C–C(OTs)–C is inhibited by a C–C–C angle constricted to a value less than 109.5°, while a C–C–C angle greater than 109.5° facilitates ionization.[2,3] The carbonyl stretching frequency of ketones is also sensitive to the internal C–CO–C bond angle.[3,4] Foote[5] has demonstrated dramatically the linear relationship which exists between these two factors.

For quantitative evaluation of the effect of bond angle strain on secondary tosylate acetolysis rates, compounds 1, 2, 5, 11, and 21 in Table I were selected. All are in the skew conformation around the reaction site (dihedral angles 60°), and all of the tosyl groups are in the axial conformation or are in equivalent steric environments. The first term of eq. 1 was deduced from the data of Table I. k_{rel} is the solvolysis rate relative to cyclohexyl tosylate in acetic acid at 25°, ν_{CO} is the carbonyl frequency (cm.$^{-1}$) of the ketone related to the secondary tosylate under consideration, and the strain is measured in kcal. Measured carbonyl frequencies of ketones[3,5] vary over 130 cm.$^{-1}$; bond angle

$$\log k_{rel} = (1715 - \nu_{CO})/8 + 1.32 \sum_i (1 + \cos 3\phi_i) + (GS - TS \text{ strain})/1.36 + \text{inductive term} \quad (1)$$

strain effects on solvolysis rates therefore should range over 10[16].

Torsional Strain.—Torsional strain can be evaluated with equal ease.[2] From a conformational viewpoint, carbonium ions, because of their sixfold rotational barrier,[6] should be essentially equally strained whatever their rotational arrangement.[7] Torsional strain effects on solvolysis rates can therefore be assessed from ground state considerations alone: compounds with eclipsed groupings around the reaction site will solvolyze more rapidly than compounds in skewed conformations.[2]

Angle ϕ is defined as the average smaller torsional angle around each of the C–C bonds adjacent to the tosyl group. Values of ϕ can vary between 0, and 60° and may be measured from models or otherwise estimated. Torsional strain variation with ϕ is evaluated from the usual equation,[7] $E_{torsional} = E_r/2 (1 + \cos 3\phi)$, where E_r is the barrier to single bond rotation. E_r does not vary greatly with ordinary changes in substitution[7]; the value of E_r adopted here, 3.6 kcal./mole, that of ethyl chloride and ethyl bromide,[7] was felt to be closest to the value expected for methyl rotation in an ethyl arenesulfonate. Activation free energies expressed in kcal. can be converted to powers of ten in rate at 25° by dividing by 1.36 ($\Delta F^* = -RT \ln k$). The second term of eq. 1 evaluates torsional strain; the maximum rate effect possible ($\phi = 0°, 0°$) is 10[5.3].

Nonbonded Interaction Strain.—In contrast to the above terms, nonbonded strain does not appear to give rise to very pronounced rate effects, amounting to only 10[1] or at most 10[2] for the relatively uncrowded secondary tosylates under consideration here. In principle, both steric acceleration and steric deceleration are possible depending on whether the solvolysis transition state is less or more crowded than the ground state.[2] Steric deceleration, in fact, is but rarely encountered,[8] evidently because leaving groups are generally able to find a propitious avenue for departure. Nonbonded strain effects can be evaluated (eq. 1, third term) by estimating ground state interactions of the tosyl group from conformational analogies or from experimental values and then deciding to what extent this nonbonded strain is decreased (or increased) in going to the transition state (*cf.* Fig. 1).

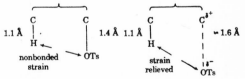

Fig. 1.—Analysis of nonbonded interactions and effect on rate.

(2) See H. C. Brown, *J. Chem. Soc.*, 1248 (1956), and references therein cited.

(3) P. von R. Schleyer and R. D. Nicholas, *J. Am. Chem. Soc.*, **83**, 182 (1961).

(4) J. O. Halford, *J. Chem. Phys.*, **24**, 830 (1956).

(5) C. S. Foote, *J. Am. Chem. Soc.*, **86**, 1853 (1964); Ph.D. Thesis, Harvard University, 1961.

(6) Compare CH$_3$BF$_2$ and CH$_3$NO$_2$.[7]

(7) D. J. Millen, "Progress in Stereochemistry," Vol. 3, P. B. D. De la Mare and W. Klyne, Ed., Butterworths, London, 1962, Chapter 4, D. J. Millen, *Chem. Ind.* (London), 1472 (1963).

(8) M. M. Donaldson, Ph.D. Thesis, Princeton University, 1958; *Dissertation Abstr.*, **22**, 738 (1961).

During ionization the tosyl C O bond is pictured to lengthen somewhat (Fig. 1) but not to "break" in attaining the transition state. Figure 1—one of many steric possibilities—depicts the situation found in axial cyclohexyl and *endo*-2-norbornyl derivatives, where strain relief accompanies ionization and steric acceleration results.

Bond angle, torsional, and nonbonded strain effects are sufficient in most cases to account quantitatively for observed solvolysis rates within 10^1 (Table I). Corrections for inductive effects ordinarily are not necessary for the compounds considered, except for those with a double bond or aryl ring β to the reaction site. The inductive term, $1/8$ in rate,[9] is applied in such cases. In this treatment, other effects expected to influence reaction rates (hyperconjugation, steric hindrance to solvation, etc.) do not appear to be important. Anchimeric assistance is considered in a separate communication.[10] Table I lists a representative display of compounds of diverse type ranging about 10^{10} in rate correlated satisfactorily by this treatment. The average deviation is $10^{\pm 0.25}$. Extension of these ideas to other systems and to other reactions is being pursued.

Acknowledgment.—Partial support of this work by a grant from the Petroleum Research Foundation is acknowledged with thanks.

(9) A. Streitwieser, *Chem. Rev.*, **56**, 571 (1956).
(10) P. von R. Schleyer, *J. Am. Chem. Soc.*, **86**, 1856 (1964).
(11) Alfred P. Sloan Research Fellow.

FRICK CHEMICAL LABORATORY   PAUL VON RAGUÉ SCHLEYER[11]
PRINCETON UNIVERSITY
PRINCETON, NEW JERSEY

RECEIVED FEBRUARY 12, 1964

The Nonclassical Carbonium Ion Problem: Reaction Rates[1]

Sir:

Three properties have become associated with "nonclassical" carbonium ions: (1) enhanced rates of formation, provided the precursor geometry is suitable (high *"exo–endo"* rate ratios of epimeric precursors); (2) high stereospecificity of kinetically controlled product formation; and (3) heightened propensity toward rearrangement. Carbonium ions with one or more of these unusual properties have often been assigned bridged structures implying increased stabilization by simultaneous and substantial charge delocalization over more than one carbon atom.[2] Recently, this concept has been questioned forcefully.[3] Rapidly equilibrating simple ions have been advanced as an alternative structural proposal.[3,4]

(1) Presented at the Gordon Conference on Hydrocarbon Chemistry, Colby Jr. College, New London, N. H., June, 1963, and at the 146th National Meeting, American Chemical Society, Denver, Colo., Jan., 1964, Abstracts, p. 7C.
(2) For reviews see (a) A. Streitwieser, Jr., "Solvolytic Displacement Reactions," McGraw-Hill Book Co., Inc. New York, N. Y., 1962; (b) J. A. Berson in P. de Mayo, Ed., "Molecular Rearrangements," Vol. 1, Interscience Publishers, Inc., New York, N. Y., 1963, Chapter 3; (c) C. W Rees and B. Capon, *Ann. Rept. Chem. Soc.* (London), **59**, 207 (1962); M. D. Johnson, *ibid.*, **58**, 167 (1961), and preceding articles in the same series.
(3) H. C. Brown in "The Transition State," Special Publication No. 16, The Chemical Society, London, 1962, pp. 140–158, 174–178; H. C. Brown and F. J. Choupek, *J. Am. Chem. Soc.*, **85**, 2322 (1963); H. C. Brown and H. M. Bell, *ibid.*, **85**, 2324 (1963) (*cf.*, however, S. Winstein, A. H. Lewin, and K. C. Pande, *ibid.*, **85**, 2324 (1963)); H. C. Brown, F. J. Choupek, and M. H. Rei, *ibid.*, **86**, 1246, 1247, 1248 (1964).

Of the three unusual properties associated with "nonclassical" ions, only one, enhanced reaction rate, can serve to distinguish between these structural alternatives. Both bridged and rapidly equilibrating ions would rearrange readily and both might give products with high stereospecificity.[3] Enhanced rates can be associated with simple carbonium ions only in two well-defined instances: (1) if the carbonium ion precursor suffers from steric or conformational strains, and these strains are relieved on ionization; or (2) if direct rearrangement to a more stable ion, e.g., from a potential primary to a tertiary ion, occurs during the ionization process. In the latter situation both the less stable simple ion and the bridged ion intermediates are by-passed, and there is also no possibility of rapidly equilibrating ions.

For a symmetrical nonclassical ion, in the absence of steric and conformational effects, enhanced rate of formation can only be associated with a bridged structure for the intermediate. The related and equivalent simple ions and their transition states must be less stable than those of bridged structure, by definition.

Acetolysis rates of a variety of secondary aliphatic tosylates can be calculated with unexpected accuracy by assessing bond angle, torsional, and nonbonded strain contributions; inductive terms are included only for unsaturated compounds.[5a] Tosylates such as *endo*-2-norbornyl, *endo*-2-norbornenyl, and *endo*-2-benznorbornenyl are successfully treated[5a]; there is no reason to suspect that the same approach should fail for their *exo* counterparts. Table I lists data for compounds for most of which anchimeric assistance has previously been postulated in the literature. The calculated rates[5a] are generally less, and are often greatly less, than those actually observed. These differences, estimates of the magnitude of anchimeric assistance, are listed in the last column of Table I.

The author believes this evidence is compelling for the existence of bridged carbonium ions. For compounds which either are symmetrical or cannot rearrange to a more stable ion, e.g., **3, 10, 15, 17**, the marked rate enhancements observed cannot reasonably and consistently[5] be explained on other than an electronic (delocalized) basis. In addition, compounds such as **6** and **12,** related by a common ionic pathway, must give a bridged ion, since *both* solvolyze with considerable anchimeric assistance. It would appear likely that most of the compounds with appreciable rate enhancement (Table Ia) give bridged ions on solvolysis.

The second group (Table Ib), with but slight anchimeric assistance ($< 10^2$), is borderline. Low rate enhancements in stereochemically favorable situations indicate that bridged ions, if present, must be of energy

(4) See, e.g., (a) C. J. Collins and B. M. Benjamin, *ibid.*, **85**, 2519 (1963); C. J. Collins, M. M. Staum, and B. M. Benjamin, *J. Org. Chem.*, **27**, 3525 (1962); W. A. Bonner and T. A. Putkey, *ibid.*, **27**, 2348 (1962), and earlier papers therein cited; (b) J. A. Berson and D. Willner, *J. Am. Chem. Soc.*, **84**, 675 (1962); **86**, 609 (1964); J. A. Berson and P. Reynolds-Warnhoff, *ibid.*, **84**, 683 (1962); **86**, 595 (1964); H. M. Walborsky, J. Webb, and C. G. Pitt, *J. Org. Chem.*, **28**, 3214 (1963); (c) P. S. Skell and R. J. Maxwell, *ibid.*, **84**, 3963 (1962); (d) E. J. Corey and J. Casanova, Jr., *ibid.*, **85**, 165 (1963); E. J. Corey, J. Casanova, Jr., P. A. Vatakencherry, and R. Winter, *ibid.*, **85**, 169 (1963); (e) P. von R. Schleyer, D. C. Kleinfelter, and H. G. Richey, Jr., *ibid.*, **85**, 479 (1963); (f) E. J. Corey and R. L. Dawson, *ibid.*, **85**, 1782 (1963); E. J. Corey and H. Uda, *ibid.*, **85**, 1788 (1963); (g) T. Norin, *Tetrahedron Letters*, **No. 1–2**, 37 (1964).
(5) P. von R. Schleyer, *J. Am. Chem. Soc.*, **86**, 1854 (1964); *cf.* (b) C. S. Foote, *ibid.*, **86**, 1853 (1964), and Ph.D. Thesis, Harvard University 1961.

TABLE I
ESTIMATION OF THE MAGNITUDE OF ANCHIMERIC ASSISTANCE BY THE METHOD OF REFERENCE 5a

No.	Tosylate	Ketone[a] ν_{CO}, cm.$^{-1}$	φ deg.	GS − TS, kcal. nonbonded	log rel. rate Calcd.	log rel. rate Obsd.[a]	log anch. assistance
	(a) Anchimeric assistance > 10^2						
1	anti-8-Dicyclopentadienyl	1780	60,60	0.3	−8.8[b]	4.33	13.1
2	anti-7-Norbornenyl	1780	60,60	0.3	−8.8[b]	4.11	12.9
3	7-Dibenznorbornadienyl	1792	60,60	0.1	−11.3[b]	−0.79	10.5
4	anti-7-Benznorbornenyl	1792	60,60	0.3	−10.3[b]	−1.22	9.1
5	7-Quadricyclyl	1746[c]	60,60	0.0	−4.9	3.31[d]	8.2
6	3-Nortricyclyl	1762	60,60	0.3	−6.2[b]	1.82	8.0
7	anti-8-Bicyclo[3.2.1]oct-2-enyl	1758[e]	60,60	0.2	−6.1[b]	−0.13[e]	6.0
8	7-syn-Norbornenyl	1780	60,60	0.1	−8.9[b]	−3.28	5.6
9	Cyclobutyl	1791	0,0	0.0	−4.2	0.99	5.2
10	exo-2-Benznorbornenyl	1756	0,45	0.3	−2.8[b]	1.63	4.4
11	exo-8-Bicyclo[3.2.1]octyl	1752	60,60	0.3	−4.4	−0.21	4.2
12	exo-2-Norbornenyl	1745	0,45	0.3	−1.4[b]	2.42	3.8
13	Cholesteryl	1721	60,60	0.0	−1.7[b]	2.01	3.7
14	exo-2-Bicyclo[2.2.2]oct-5-enyl	1735	0,60	0.4	0.5[b]	4.10	3.6
15	exo-2-Norbornyl	1751	0,40	0.3	−0.6	2.71	3.3
16	endo-2-Bicyclo[2.2.2]oct-5-enyl	1735	0,60	0.1	−0.7[b]	2.49	3.2
17	2-Bicyclo[2.1.1]hexyl	1764[f]	0,60	0.2	−3.3	−0.37[g]	2.9
18	Epicholesteryl	1721	60,60	0.4	−1.4[b]	1.40	2.8
	(b) Anchimeric assistance < 10^2						
19	Cyclopropyl	1815	0,0	0.0	−7.2	−5.32	1.9
20	9-Bicyclo[3.3.1]nonyl	1726	60,60	0.6	−1.0	0.48	1.5
21	exo-Trimethylenenorborn-exo-2-yl	1751	0,40	0.3	−0.6	0.84[h]	1.4
22	cis-3-Bicyclo[3.1.0]hexyl	1739[i]	0,40[j]	0.0	−0.2[b]	1.14[i]	1.3
23	axial-2-Bicyclo[3.2.1]octyl	1717	50,60	0.6	0.4	1.62	1.2
24	2-Bicyclo[2.2.2]octyl	1731	0,60	0.4	0.9	1.85	0.9
25	equat.-2-Bicyclo[3.2.1]octyl	1717	50,60	0.2	0.1	0.47	0.4
26	trans-3-Bicyclo[3.1.0]hexyl	1739[i]	0,40[j]	0.6[i]	0.2[b]	0.17	0.0
27	syn-8-Bicyclo[3.2.1]oct-2-enyl	1758[e]	60,60	1.1	−5.5	−5.54[e]	0.0
28	Cyclooctyl	1703	40,40?[k]	0.0?	2.8	2.76	0.0
29	Cyclononyl	1703	40,40?[k]	0.0?	2.8	2.70	−0.1
30	Cyclodecyl	1704	40,40?[k]	0.0?	2.7	2.98	+0.3
31	Cycloundecyl	1709	40,40?[k]	0.0?	2.1	2.05	0.0

[a] Data, unless otherwise indicated, taken from Foote.[8b]   [b] Corrections for inductive effects: −0.9 in log k for each double bond or phenyl ring and −0.5 in log k for each cyclopropane ring β to the reaction site.[8a]   [c] P. R. Story and S. R. Fahrenholtz, J. Am. Chem. Soc., 86, 1270 (1964).   [d] H. G. Richey, Jr., and N. C. Buckley, ibid., 85, 3057 (1963); P. R. Story and S. R. Fahrenholtz, ibid., 86, 527 (1964).   [e] N. W. LeBel and L. A. Spurlock, Tetrahedron, 20, 215 (1964).   [f] Value for 5,5-dimethylbicyclo[2.1.1]hexan-2-one (J. Meinwald and P. G. Gassman, J. Am. Chem. Soc., 85, 57 (1963)).   [g] At 75° (J. Meinwald, Abstracts, 18th National Organic Chemistry Symposium, American Chemical Society, Columbus, Ohio, June, 1963, p. 39).   [h] See ref. 2b.   [i] S. Winstein and J. Sonnenberg, J. Am. Chem. Soc., 83, 3235 (1961).   [j] Our experience [M. M. Donaldson, Ph.D. Thesis, Princeton University, 1958; Dissertation Abstr., 22, 738 (1961)] with locked cyclopentane rings suggests this estimate.   [k] J. Sicher in P. B. D. De la Mare and W. Klyne, Ed., "Progress in Stereochemistry," Vol. 3, Butterworths, London, 1962, Chapter 6; V. Prelog and J. G. Traynham in P. de Mayo, "Molecular Rearrangements," Vol. 1, Interscience Publishers, Inc., 1963, Chapter 9.

more nearly comparable with classical ions.[6] Compounds 25–31 have no significant anchimeric assistance and the data do not require the formulation of bridged intermediates. Further implications of this treatment will be discussed in the full report.

Acknowledgment.—Partial support of this work by a grant from the Petroleum Research Foundation is acknowledged with thanks.

(6) See Table I*i*, and ref. 4b, f, and g with regard to compounds 22, 23, and 24.

(7) Alfred P. Sloan Research Fellow.

FRICK CHEMICAL LABORATORY   PAUL VON RAGUÉ SCHLEYER[7]
PRINCETON UNIVERSITY
PRINCETON, NEW JERSEY

RECEIVED FEBRUARY 19, 1964

72 | Substituted Benzonorbornenyl Cations

Tanida, Tsuji, and Ishitobi (Paper No. 72) follow out the implications of the anchimeric assistance to ionization in the 7-benzonorbornenyl sulfonates by investigating the effects of substituents in the benzene ring on the rates of acetolysis. A range of rate constants of 386,000 is found between the nitro and the methoxy derivatives, corresponding to a ρ of -6.1 in a simple Hammett plot. The linearity of the Hammett plot is made perfect by two alternative devices: the use of $(\sigma + \sigma^+)$ as abscissa, or the use of $(\sigma_p^+ + \sigma_m^+)$ (Figures 3A and 3B, respectively). The latter method seems well founded since one of the participating positions is para to the substituent group, the other is meta to it. The use of the sum of meta and para substituent constants is in accord with the other evidence (such as that of Saunders and Story, Paper No. 62) that the norbornenyl double bond tends to participate symmetrically in ionization at C-7.

Up to a point the discussion in this paper is clear and elegant. The kinetic studies, as analyzed in Figures 1–3, favor a transition state in which both C-5(C-1′) and C-6(C-2′) are involved in participation, so that the transition state, written in valence bond notation, must include both structures shown in E (page 514), as well as the inevitable bond structures, common to all "σ-complex" transition states and intermediates, with charge at positions 3′, 5′, 4′, and 6′. We find the allusion to F as a possible "classical" structure for the carbonium ion confusing. In discussing the related case of 7-norbornenyl compounds, one might debate the isolated occurrence of the analogous structure K without violating well-accepted quantum mechanical principles. However, when

K

the charged atom is incorporated into a cyclohexadienyl (phenonium) ring derived from an aromatic structure, it is no more possible to divorce F from H, I, and

J than it would be to postulate the occurrence of one bond structure of any allylic cation without the other. We must assume, then, that the authors of Paper No. 72, in referring to F, have in mind the resonance hybrid of F, H, I, and J. Careful inspection of these structures will reveal that this resonance hybrid is a phenonium ion. Thus, unless we accord to the phenonium ion the dignity of being classical,[1] there is no permissible classical intermediate which can be discussed for the present reaction.

[1] There would, indeed, be every reason for considering this structure to be as "classical" as the reaction of aromatic substitution itself, but that is not the course that this curious nomenclature has taken in the hands of its promulgators (cf. Brown, "The Non-Classical Phenonium Ion," Paper No. 63, p. 447).

From: *J. Am. Chem. Soc.* **86**, 4904–12 (1964)

[CONTRIBUTION FROM THE SHIONOGI RESEARCH LABORATORY, SHIONOGI & CO., LTD., FUKUSHIMA-KU, OSAKA, JAPAN]

Substituent Effects and Homobenzylic Conjugation in *anti*-7-Benzonorbornenyl *p*-Bromobenzenesulfonate Solvolyses[1–4]

BY HIROSHI TANIDA, TERUJI TSUJI, AND HIROYUKI ISHITOBI

RECEIVED MARCH 20, 1964

A series of 4′-substituted *anti*-7-benzonorbornenyl *p*-bromobenzenesulfonates was prepared and the acetolysis of these sulfonates proceeds with retention of configuration. The relative rates of CH_3O, CH_3, H, Cl, Br, and NO_2 derivatives at 77.60° were 53.7, 5.7, 1, 0.045, 0.030, and 1.39×10^{-4}, respectively. The data indicate major participation by the aromatic ring, facilitating acetolysis. The rate data are not correlated by the Hammett relationship, $\log (k/k_0) = \rho\sigma$, or by the modified Hammett relationship, $\log (k/k_0) = \rho\sigma^{+}$. They are correlated with good precision by $(\sigma^{+} + \sigma)$ or by $(\sigma_p^{+} + \sigma_m^{+})$, yielding straight lines with $\rho = -2.40$ or -2.55. The implications of this correlation in terms of the precise nature of the participation in the transition state for the acetolysis are discussed.

The solvolytic behavior of norbornyl systems have provided many well-known examples for the demonstration of anchimeric assistance to ionization. Acetolytic reactivities (at 25°, relative to cyclohexyl *p*-bromobenzenesulfonate) of 5- and 7-norbornenyl and of 7- and 2-norbornyl *p*-bromobenzenesulfonates are summarized as[5]

The most remarkable rate enhancement was observed on the 7-*anti*-norbornenyl system.[6] The mere introduction of a double bond into the saturated 7-norbornyl system accelerated the acetolysis rate by a factor of 10^{11}. This large rate enhancement indicates participation by the double bond, facilitating ionization of the sulfonate group.

The solvolyses of 2- and 7-benzonorbornenyl derivatives were found by Bartlett and Giddings[7] to parallel qualitatively the results in the analogous norbornenyl system. In the case of *anti*-7-benzonorbornenyl *p*-bromobenzenesulfonate, the acetolysis rate was faster than that of 7-norbornyl *p*-bromobenzenesulfonate by a factor of 5×10^5, in contrast to the much larger factor of 10^{11} provided by the double bond of the *anti*-7-nor-

bornenyl derivative. The acetolysis rates of benzonorbornenyl *p*-bromobenzenesulfonates relative to cyclohexyl and the corresponding norbornyl *p*-bromobenzenesulfonate (shown in parentheses) at 25° are summarized[5,7a]

In spite of the smaller factor exerted by the aromatic ring in the *anti*-7-benzonorbornenyl derivatives, it is evident that participation must be quite important in accounting for the enhanced rates observed in these derivatives.

At the present time there is considerable discussion as to the precise nature of the participation in the solvolysis of derivatives of this kind, and of the precise structure of the carbonium ions produced in the ionization stage.[6b,8] It appeared to us that some light might be thrown on this interesting question by examining the effect of substituents in *anti*-7-benzonorbornenyl derivatives on the rate of acetolysis. Accordingly, we undertook the synthesis of a number of 4′-substituted *anti*-7-benzonorbornenyl *p*-bromobenzenesulfonates and a study of their rates of acetolysis.[9]

Results

Preparations.—Most of the 4′-substituted benzonorbornadienes (I, II, III, IV, and V), which were required in the present study as the starting materials, were prepared in high yields by our modification[10] of Wittig's procedure.[11] The introduction of a benzoyloxy group into the *anti*-7-position of the above dienes was achieved

(1) Paper V of a series on Bicyclic Systems; Paper IV: H. Tanida and T. Tsuji, *J. Org. Chem.*, **29**, 849 (1964).

(2) Some of the results of this paper appeared in preliminary form: H. Tanida, *J. Am. Chem. Soc.*, **85**, 1703 (1963).

(3) Presented, in part, at the 14th Organic Reaction Mechanism Symposium of the Chemical Society of Japan in Fukuoka, Oct., 1963.

(4) The ring system of benzonorbornadiene and its numbering are shown as

(5) For a recent review, see J. A. Berson, "Molecular Rearrangements," Vol. 1, P. de Mayo, Ed., Interscience Publishers, Inc., New York, N. Y., 1963, Chapter 3.

(6) (a) S. Winstein, M. Shatavsky, C. J. Norton, and R. B. Woodward, *J. Am. Chem. Soc.*, **77**, 4183 (1955); (b) S. Winstein, A. H. Lewin, and K. C. Pande, *ibid.*, **85**, 2324 (1963), and references therein.

(7) (a) P. D. Bartlett and W. P. Giddings, *ibid.*, **82**, 1240 (1960); (b) W. P. Giddings and J. Dirlam, *ibid.*, **85**, 3900 (1963).

(8) H. C. Brown and H. M. Bell, *ibid.*, **85**, 2324 (1963), and references therein.

(9) It should be pointed out that the effect of methoxy substituents in the 3′- and 6′-positions of *anti*-7-benzonorbornenyl system was previously examined by G. A. Wiley, and that in the mid-course of this work we learned Professor Streitwieser's prediction based on molecular orbital theory for a part of our results. Refer to A. Streitwieser, Jr., "Molecular Orbital Theory for Organic Chemists," John Wiley and Sons, Inc., New York, N. Y., 1961, p. 389.

(10) H. Tanida, R. Muneyuki, and T. Tsuji, *Bull. Chem. Soc. Japan*, **37**, 40 (1964).

(11) G. Wittig and E. Knauss, *Chem. Ber.*, **91**, 895 (1958).

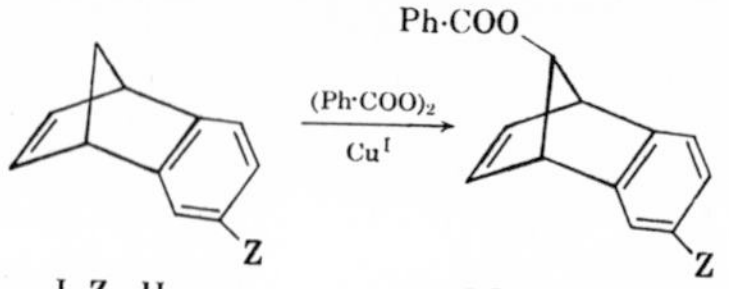

Ph·COO

(Ph·COO)$_2$
Cu^I

I, Z = H
II, Z = CH$_3$O
III, Z = CH$_3$
IV, Z = Cl
V, Z = Br

VI, Z = H
VII, Z = CH$_3$O
VIII, Z = CH$_3$
IX, Z = Cl
X, Z = Br, p-ClPhCOO
instead of PhCOO

VI
VII
VIII

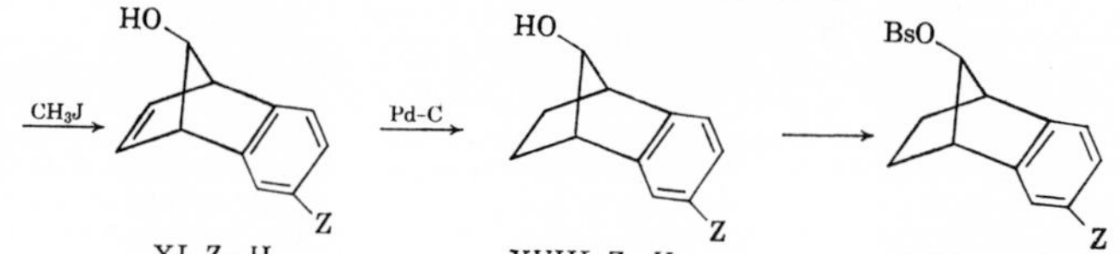

CH$_3$J

HO

Pd-C

HO

BsO

XI, Z = H
XII, Z = CH$_3$O
XIII, Z = CH$_3$

XVIII, Z = H
XIX, Z = CH$_3$O
XX, Z = CH$_3$

XXIV, Z = H
XXV, Z = CH$_3$O
XXVI, Z = CH$_3$

IX
X

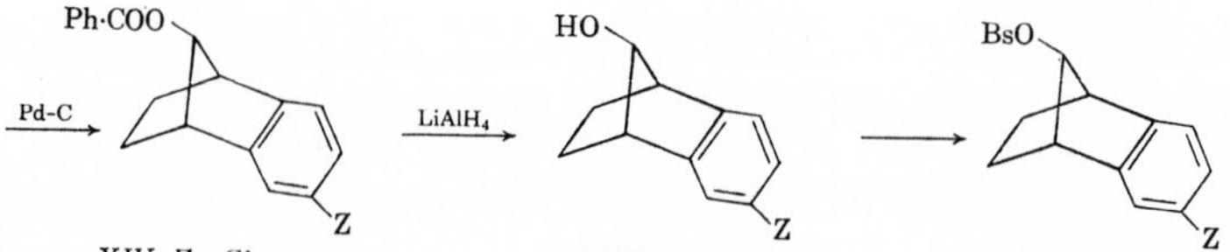

Pd-C

Ph·COO

LiAlH$_4$

HO

BsO

XIV, R = Cl
XV, R = Br
p-ClPhCOO
instead of PhCOO

XXI, R = Cl
XXII, R = Br

XXVII, Z = Cl
XXVIII, Z = Br

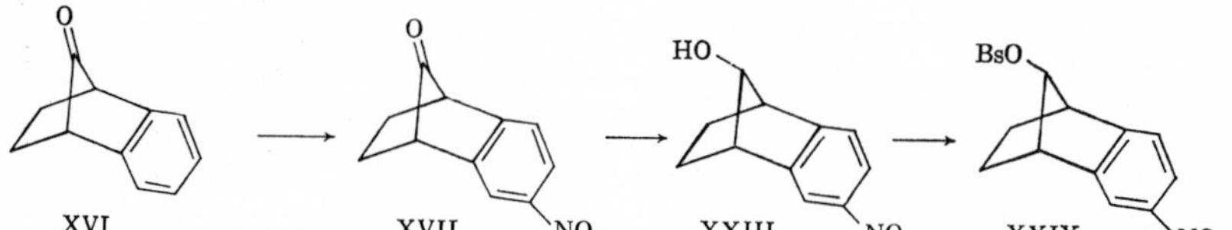

O

O

HO

BsO

XVI

XVII   NO$_2$

XXIII   NO$_2$

XXIX   NO$_2$

AcO

Z

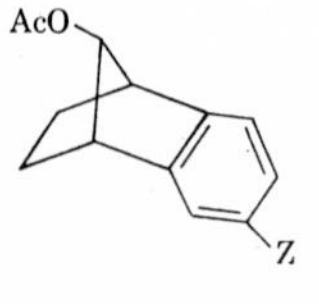

XXX, Z = H
XXXI, Z = CH$_3$O
XXXII, Z = CH$_3$

XXXIII, Z = Cl
XXXIV, Z = Br
XXXV   Z = NO$_2$

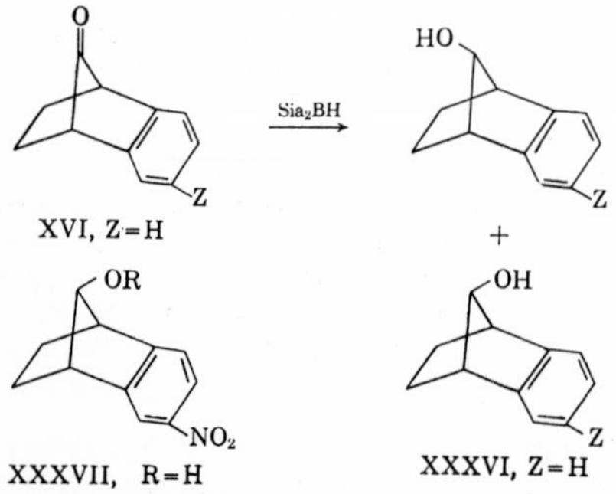

O

Sia$_2$BH

HO

+

OR

OH

XVI, Z = H

XXXVII, R = H
XXXVIII, R = CH$_3$CO

NO$_2$

XXXVI, Z = H

Z

by our method[12,13] yielding *anti*-7-benzoyloxybenzonorbornadiene (VI) and its 4'-methoxyl, 4'-methyl, and 4'-chloro derivatives (VII, VIII, and IX, re-

(12) H. Tanida and T. Tsuji, *Chem. Ind.* (London), 211 (1963).
(13) H. Tanida and T. Tsuji, *J. Org. Chem.*, **29**, 849 (1964).

spectively), and *anti*-7-*p*-chlorobenzoyloxy-4'-bromobenzonorbornadiene (X). Reactions of VI, VII, and VIII with methylmagnesium iodide gave *anti*-7-benzonorbornadienol (XI), *anti*-4'-methoxybenzonorbornadien-7-ol (XII), and *anti*-4'-methylbenzonorbornadien-7-ol (XIII), respectively, which on catalytic reduction over palladium–charcoal afforded the corresponding monoenols XVIII, XIX, and XX. Catalytic reduction of IX and X gave *anti*-7-benzoyloxy-4'-chlorobenzonorbornene (XIV) and *anti*-7-*p*-chlorobenzoyloxy-4'-bromobenzonorbornene (XV), respectively, which were transformed by lithium aluminum hydride into *anti*-4'-chlorobenzonorbornen-7-ol (XXI) and its 4'-bromo analog XXII. Our benzoyloxylation employed here gave only *anti* products, with no evidence of the epimers, in an agreement with the prediction based on the reaction mechanism.[13] Gas chromatographic analyses using authentic *syn* isomers confirmed these observations. Their orientations were established by comparison of the infrared spectra of

TABLE I

ACETOLYSIS RATES OF *anti*-7-BENZONORBORNENOL BROSYLATES

4'-Substituent	Temp., °C.	$k\psi$, sec.$^{-1}$	Calculated at 77.60°			
			ΔH^*, kcal.	ΔS^*, cal./deg.	$k\psi$,[c] sec.$^{-1}$	Rel. rate[c]
CH₃O	77.65 ± 0.03	8.27 × 10^{-4}				
	77.65 ± .03	8.00 × 10^{-4}				
	64.41 ± .03	1.56 × 10^{-4}	28.9	9.3	8.08 × 10^{-4}	53.7
	64.40 ± .02	1.52 × 10^{-4}				
	59.85 ± .02	8.44 × 10^{-5}				
CH₃	90.18 ± .03	3.38 × 10^{-4}				
	77.60 ± .03	8.60 × 10^{-5}	27.4	0.5	8.44 × 10^{-5}	5.7
	72.81 ± .03	4.77 × 10^{-5}				
H	97.75 ± .03	1.34 × 10^{-4}				
	95.75 ± .05	1.058 × 10^{-4b}	27.7	−2.1	1.49 × 10^{-5}	1
	77.65 ± .03	1.50 × 10^{-5}				
	74.79 ± .05	1.022 × 10^{-5b}				
Cl	120.55 ± .07	1.134 × 10^{-4}				
	103.55 ± .04	2.11 × 10^{-5}	32.2	4.7	6.63 × 10^{-7}	0.045
	93.85 ± .03	4.72 × 10^{-6}				
	77.65 ± .03	6.95 × 10^{-7}				
Br	104.28 ± .04	1.25 × 10^{-5}	. .	. . .		0.030[d]
NO₂	168.50 ± .20	4.62 × 10^{-5}	33.2	−3.9	2.07 × 10^{-9}	1.39 × 10^{-4}
	152.75 ± .15	1.107 × 10^{-5}				
7-Norbornyl brosylate[a]			35.7	−3.5	1.86 × 10^{-10}	1.25 × 10^{-5}

[a] S. Winstein, M. Shatavsky, C. Norton, and R. B. Woodward, *J. Am. Chem. Soc.*, **77**, 4183 (1955), and ROBs/ROTs rate ratio assumed to be 2.90. [b] Cited from ref. 7a. [c] Calculated from the least-square slopes of the Arrhenius plots. [d] Calculated on the assumption of that the slope of the Arrhenius plots is equal to that of the Cl compound.

XVIII, XIX, XX, XXI, and XXII with XI, XII, and XIII; the latter showed clearly an internal interaction between the hydroxyl group and the π-electrons of the double bond,[14] the ν_{OH} absorptions of XVIII, XIX, XX, XXI, and XXII appearing at 2.75–2.76 μ,[15] whereas those of XI, XII, and XIII were at 2.81 μ.[16]

The preparation of *anti*-4'-nitrozonorbornen-7-ol (XXIII) began with the nitration of benzonorbornen-7-one (XVI), which was available from XVIII by the Oppenauer oxidation.[7a] The nitration gave exclusively 4'-nitrobenzonorbornen-7-one (XVII),[17] which was led by sodium borohydride to the predominant formation of *anti*-4'-nitrozonorbornen-7-ol (XXIII).[18] The n.m.r. spectrum of XVII and the formation of 2-nitronaphthalene in high yield by dehydrogenation of XVII over palladium–charcoal unequivocally established that the position of the nitro group was originally 4'. The *anti* configuration of XXIII was confirmed by comparison of the infrared band of hydroxyl and the n.m.r. signal of C-7 hydrogen with those of an authentic sample of *syn*-4'-nitrobenzonorbornen-7-ol (XXXVII) described below.

The preparation of authentic *syn*-alcohols will be needed for the investigation of stereochemistry of the solvolysis products. Disiamylborane reduction[19] of

XVI yielded approximately equal amounts of *anti*- and *syn*-7-benzonorborneol (XVIII and XXXVI). The pure *syn*-alcohol was isolated by careful elution chromatography and its structure was confirmed by infrared and n.m.r. spectra (see Experimental). Gas chromatography of XXXVI recorded a distinguishable peak at shorter retention time than XVIII in line with expectation for the shielding effect of the benzo grouping on the hydroxyl group.[20] This observation was also obtained in the case of all but one of our 4'-substituted compounds which were prepared from the respective ketones.

The one exception was the 4'-nitro compound. The hard volatility of XXIII and XXXVII made it difficult for us to perform quantitative gas chromatographic analysis. Therefore, authentic samples of XXXVII and of XXXVII-acetate were prepared by nitration of XXXVI and XXXVI-acetate, and the positions of their nitro groups were determined by the n.m.r. spectra.

All of the *p*-bromobenzenesulfonates of the abovementioned *anti*-alcohols were prepared by standard procedures. The properties of the new compounds described here are summarized in Tables II, III, and IV (Experimental).

Solvolysis Rates.—The rates of acetolyses were carried out in the usual manner.[21] The solvolysis rates are summarized in Table I, together with the derived activation parameters. For comparison, the rate constants at 77.60° were calculated, using least square slopes derived from Arrhenius plots. The plots were good straight lines (Experimental).

The methoxy substituent in the 4'-position increases the rate by a factor of 53.7. A methyl group is effec-

(14) *Cf*. P. von R. Schleyer, D. S. Trifan, and R. Bacskai, *J. Am. Chem. Soc.*, **80**, 6691 (1958); M. Oki and H. Iwamura, *Bull. Chem. Soc. Japan*, **32**, 306 (1959).

(15) The measurements were carried out using a Perkin–Elmer Model 12C, LiF prism, 20-mm. cell, in carbon tetrachloride solution.

(16) Further support was obtained by behavior of the hydrogen at the 7-position in the n.m.r. spectra, attributed to diamagnetic anisotropy effects of the double bond: K. Tori, T. Muneyuki, T. Tsuji, Y. Hata, and H. Tanida, to be published (presented at the 16th Annual Meeting of the Chemical Society of Japan in Tokyo, April, 1963). Hydrogenation of the double bond causes an upfield shift of the *anti*-7-hydrogen of about 0.15–0.25 p.p.m. Also, *cf*. R. R. Fraser, *Can. J. Chem.*, **40**, 78 (1962).

(17) For the remarkable orientation effect of benzonorbornenes observed on aromatic substitution reactions, see H. Tanida and R. Muneyuki, *Tetrahedron Letters*, **No. 38**, 2787 (1964).

(18) It was previously noted by Bartlett and Giddings (ref. 7a) that the reduction of benzonorbornen-7-one by lithium aluminum hydride yields only the *anti* isomer. This marked stereospecificity of this reduction to yield the *anti* isomer favorably is unexpected and is being investigated in this laboratory.

(19) H. C. Brown and D. B. Bigley, *J. Am. Chem. Soc.*, **83**, 486 (1961); H. C. Brown and D. B. Bigley, *ibid.*, **83**, 3166 (1961).

(20) It was also noted that the *syn*-acetate exhibits shorter retention time than the *anti*-acetate, but this difference is much less than that of the alcohol.

(21) *E.g.*, S. Winstein, C. Hanson, and E. Grunwald, *J. Am. Chem. Soc.*, **70**, 812 (1948); S. Winstein, E. Grunwald, and L. L. Ingraham, *ibid.*, **70**, 821 (1948).

tive, causing an increase in rate of 5.7 over the parent compound. The chloro and bromo substituents result in a rate that is slower than the parent compound by factors of 0.045 and 0.030, respectively. Finally, the nitro substituent results in a rate that is very slow, 1.39 × 10⁻⁴ that of the parent compound.

Solvolysis Products.—In order to determine the products of the acetolysis, we carried out the solvolysis of each of the p-bromobenzenesulfonates in glacial acetic acid containing an equivalent quantity of sodium acetate.[21] In each case we isolated quantitatively an acetate whose infrared spectrum and other properties agreed with those of the authentic anti-acetate. These acetates were reduced to alcohols with lithium aluminum hydride. Careful gas chromatographic analyses carried out on the acetates and on the derived alcohols indicated only one product at the same retention times as those of the anti compounds. A quantitative experiment with authentic anti and syn epimeric alcohols XVIII and XXXVI demonstrated the absence of syn compound in the solvolysis product of XXIV in amounts greater than 0.3%.[22] The same demonstration was established on the solvolysis products of all our 4′-substituted compounds, except for the nitro compound. Since we could not find an effective gas chromatographic technique for the separation of the epimers of alcohols XXIII and XXXVII and acetates XXXV and XXXVIII, the analysis of the acetolysis product of XXIX was carried out by infrared spectrum. The infrared spectrum of the acetolysis product was consistent with that of XXXV, but quite different from that of XXXVIII. Quantitative estimation by the characteristic absorptions of XXXVIII at 1150 and 1645 cm.⁻¹ proved the absence of XXXVIII in the acetolysis product in amounts greater than 5%.

Discussion

Rates of Acetolysis.[23]—The effect of substituents on the rates of acetolysis of the anti-7-benzonorbornenyl p-bromobenzenesulfonate is very large, far larger than can be accounted for in terms of a simple inductive effect. There can be little doubt that the acetolysis reaction involves participation by the aromatic ring, and that the substituents markedly affect the contribution of the aromatic ring to facilitate the ionization of the sulfonate substituent.

Certainly, the huge range of reactivity of 386,000 from 4′-methoxy to 4′-nitro appears not to be compatible with any simple electrostatic influence of the substituent. It is of the same order of magnitude as the range of reactivity observed by Brown and Okamoto[24] in the solvolysis of the substituted t-cumyl chlorides where direct resonance interaction of the substituent with the carbonium carbon occurs.

In the case of the 4′-nitro substituent, the rate is very slow and it might be questioned whether participation is important here. However, the 4′-nitro derivative

undergoes solvolysis 11 times faster than 7-norbornyl p-bromobenzenesulfonate itself, in spite of the rate-retarding inductive influence of the nitrobenzo grouping. This points strongly to participation even in the case of the nitro derivative.[25]

These results clearly indicate that the transition state must involve participation of some kind by the aromatic ring.

Solvolysis Products.—The synthetic methods used to produce the 7-hydroxy derivatives yielded the anti-7-alcohols. By comparison of infrared and n.m.r. spectra with those of authentic syn isomers, the stereochemistry of the anti-7-alcohols were unequivocally established.

Solvolysis of the brosylates of these alcohols yielded acetates which were reduced to alcohols. Quantitative experiments by gas chromatography using authentic syn-alcohols demonstrated that the acetolysis of all but one of these brosylates proceeded with over-all retention of configuration. As the only exception, there may remain some questions for the case of the 4′-nitrobrosylate, because of the nonavailability of a precise analytical method. However, in this case also, we can say the acetolysis proceeds with retention of configuration within a limitation of about 95%. Consequently, these results strongly argue for participation by the aromatic ring.[26]

Correlation of Rate Data.—It is of considerable interest to know the precise nature of the participation of the aromatic ring in facilitating the ionization of the 7-sulfonate ester substituent. It is possible to conceive that this participation involves only interaction of the π-electron cloud, as indicated by the structure

$$BsO^{\delta^-}$$

A

Alternatively, the transition state may resemble the σ-complex which is usually proposed for typical aromatic substitution reactions.

$$BsO^{\delta^-} \qquad\longleftrightarrow\qquad BsO^{\delta^-}$$
$$\delta^+ \qquad\qquad\qquad \delta^+$$
$$OCH_3 \qquad\qquad\qquad OCH_3$$

B

Although the precise nature of the intermediate formed following ionization would be of interest, it is

(22) Bartlett and Giddings[7a] reported that the solvolysis of XXIV yielded pure anti-7-acetate. By the availability of the syn-alcohol, we confirmed their result.

(23) It has been shown that internal return may be an important factor to be considered in acetolyses. Refer to (a) S. Winstein, J. S. Gall, M. Hojo, and S. Smith, J. Am. Chem. Soc., 82, 1011 (1960); (b) S. Winstein and G. C. Robinson, ibid., 80, 169 (1958). However, the absence of data bearing on the point in the present system makes it necessary to base the present discussion on solvolytic rates.

(24) H. C. Brown and Y. Okamoto, ibid., 79, 1913 (1957), and references therein.

(25) This conclusion is supported by our observation that the 4′,5′-dinitro-anti-7-benzonorbornenyl p-bromobenzenesulfonate undergoes acetolysis at a rate much slower even than that of the 4′-nitro derivative.

(26) We noticed the formation of a small amount of the syn-alcohol XXXVI in the solvolysis of XXIV, when a more nucleophilic solvent, such as aqueous Cellosolve, rather than acetic acid was used. This observation also argues for participation in acetolysis. The relation between the stereochemistry of solvolysis product and the kind of solvent is being studied in this laboratory.

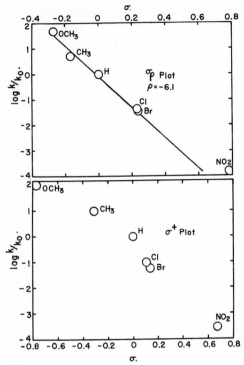

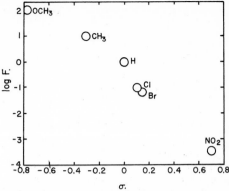

Fig. 2.—The $\rho-\sigma^+$ treatment of the partial rate factors.

Fig. 1.—A (upper): the $\rho-\sigma$ treatment of the relative acetolysis rates. B (lower): the $\rho-\sigma^+$ treatment of the relative acetolysis rates.

evident that the rate data can give information only with regard to the transition state, and not with respect to the intermediate formed subsequently.

It appeared that it might be possible to obtain information as to **the** precise nature of the interaction in the transition state by establishing whether the rate data are correlated by the Hammett σ-constant[27] or the Brown–Okamoto σ^+-constants.[28]

A plot of the relative rates of acetolysis (Table I) *vs.* the σ-constants yields a reasonable good correlation (Fig. 1A). However, the 4′-nitro derivative is distinctly above the line defined by the other points. That is to say, the nitro derivative appears to be considerably more reactive than would be predicted from the other data. We were originally concerned over the question whether the observed slow rate of the nitro compound established participation in this derivative. A point below the line might have been considered as evidence that participation is incomplete in this derivative. However, there appears to be no simple explanation for a point which is above the line. Moreover, the calculated value for the reaction constant, ρ, is −6.1, a value far larger than that observed for any reaction which is correlated satisfactorily by σ.

A simple plot of the rate data *vs.* σ_p^+ likewise provides an unsatisfactory correlation (Fig. 1B).[29] The

methoxy, methyl, and hydrogen points are correlated reasonably well, but the halo and nitro points are far below the line defined by the first-named points.

We considered the possibility that solvolysis might be proceeding through two concurrent reactions, involving participation at the points *meta* and *para* to the substituent.

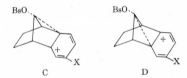

Accordingly, we calculated partial rate factors by use of the relationships

$$\text{obsd. relative rate} = F_{p-x} + F_{m-x}$$

$$\frac{\log F_{p-x}}{\log F_{m-x}} = \frac{\sigma_p^+ - x}{\sigma_m^+ - x}$$

However, this did not improve the correlation significantly (Fig. 2).

It is evident from the plots that the use of σ places the nitro derivative above the line, whereas the use of σ^+ places it below the line. Consequently, we considered the possibility that the use of the sum of σ^+ and σ might provide a satisfactory correlation. Accordingly, we plotted the rates relative to one-half the rate of the parent compound *vs.* $(\sigma^+ + \sigma_p)$, in which σ^+ was employed according to the manner described in ref. 26 (Fig. 3A). A reasonably good correlation was realized.

There are theoretical reasons why such a correlation might be anticipated. The mechanism of aromatic substitution is believed to involve the formation of a π-complex, followed by its transformation into a σ-complex.[30]

the methoxy, methyl, and halo groups, but predominantly *meta* to the nitro group. Consequently, σ_p^+ was used for the first four substituents and σ_m^+ for the nitro group. Since there are two equivalent positions in the parent compound, we used one-half the observed rate for the hydrogen compound.

(30) For example, see L. M. Stock and H. C. Brown, "Advances in Physical Organic Chemistry," Vol. 1, Academic Press, Inc., New York, N. Y., 1963, Chapter 2.

(27) (a) L. P. Hammett, "Physical Organic Chemistry," McGraw–Hill Book Co., Inc., New York, N. Y., 1940, Chapter VII; (b) D. H. McDaniel and H. C. Brown, *J. Org. Chem.*, **23**, 420 (1958).

(28) H. C. Brown and Y. Okamoto, *J. Am. Chem. Soc.*, **80**, 4979 (1958).

(29) It was considered that bonding would occur predominantly *para* to the

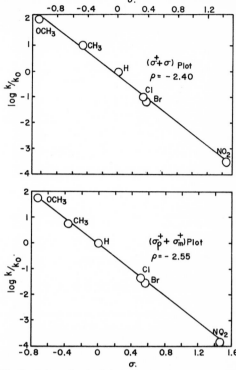

$$Z^+ + \bigcirc \rightleftarrows \bigcirc \cdot Z^+$$

The reaction rate should then depend on the stabilities of both the π- and σ-complexes.

$$\text{rate} = K_\pi k_\sigma [\text{ArH}][Z^+]$$

It is customary to ignore the contribution of the π-complex in favor of the much larger factor introduced by the σ-complex.[31]

According to this interpretation, the transition state for the acetolysis would be somewhere between the π-complex participation, indicated in A, and the σ-complex participation, indicated in B.

The data can also be correlated by $(\sigma_p^+ + \sigma_m^+)$ (Fig. 3B). In this case it can be argued that the participation involves contributions from both the *meta* and *para* positions simultaneously, so that both σ_p^+ and σ_m^+ contribute to the stability of the transition state.

E

Unfortunately, there does not appear to be any simple means for selecting between these alternative correlations and interpretation at the present time.

Rate data for 4′,5′-disubstituted derivatives may make it possible to select between these alternative possibilities, and we are currently investigating this question.

The Nature of the Carbonium Ion Intermediate.—The question remains as to the nature of the intermediate produced following the departure of the leaving group. Does it have the classical structure F, or the nonclassical structure G?

F   G

Unfortunately, the present data do not appear to provide any basis for selecting between these two alternative possibilities. Moreover, both intermediates would predict solvolysis with over-all retention, so that the observed stereochemistry of substitution does not permit a choice to be made. The results with the symmetrically substituted derivative now under study may indicate better whether the reaction proceeds

Fig. 3.—A (upper): the $(\sigma^+ + \sigma)$ plots of the relative acetolysis rates. B (lower): the $(\sigma^+ + \sigma^+)$ plots of the relative acetolysis rates.

through the formation of a symmetrical or an unsymmetrical transition state and thereby provide some evidence as to whether a classical or a nonclassical intermediate is formed in the ionization stage.

Experimental[34]

Properties and analyses of the new compounds prepared in the present study are summarized in Tables II, III, and IV.

Materials.—All of 4′-substituted benzonorbornadienes, which were used as starting compounds for the syntheses of the desired compounds, were obtained in good yields by our modification[10] of Wittig's procedure[11] for the addition of benzyne to cyclopentadiene. 4′-Methoxybenzonorbornadiene, b.p. 99–100° (4 mm.), n^{23}D 1.5642; 4′-methylbenzonorbornadiene, b.p. 110–112° (22 mm.), n^{24}D 1.5541; 4′-chlorobenzonorbornadiene, b.p. 112–112.5° (10 mm.), n^{21}D 1.5763; 4′-bromobenzonorbornadiene, b.p. 127–129° (10 mm.), n^{29}D 1.5191, were used.

An Example of Benzoyloxylation of the 7-Position of Benzonorbornadienes. *anti*-**7-Benzoyloxy-4′-methoxybenzonorbornadiene (VII).**—To a stirred mixture of 76.8 g. (0.446 mole) of 4′-methoxybenzonorbornadiene (II) and 357 mg. of freshly prepared cuprous bromide in 250 ml. of chlorobenzene there was added under a nitrogen atmosphere a solution of 30 g. (0.124 mole) of benzoyl peroxide in 140 ml. of chlorobenzene over a period of 3 hr. at about 80°. After the addition was completed, the reaction temperature was raised to 100° and stirred for 10 hr. Qualitative analysis by potassium iodide–starch paper indicated that no benzoyl peroxide remained after this period. During the course of the reaction, the color of the solution changed

(31) There have been some examples recently where the evidence indicates that this simplification is not satisfactory. Thus Benkeser[32] and Eaborn[33] have noted reactions in which the rates of substitution are better correlated by σ than by σ^+ constants.

(32) R. A. Benkeser, T. V. Liston, and G. M. Stanton, *Tetrahedron Letters*, No. **15**, 1 (1960).

(33) (a) C. Eaborn and J. A. Waters, *J. Chem. Soc.*, 542 (1961); (b) R. W. Bott, C. Eaborn, and J. A. Waters, *ibid.*, 681 (1963); (c) C. Eaborn and K. C. Pande, *ibid.*, 1566 (1960).

(34) Melting points were taken by capillary and are corrected. Boiling points are uncorrected. Unless stated otherwise, infrared spectra were determined with a Nippon Bunko IR-S spectrometer in carbon tetrachloride and carbon disulfide; n.m.r. spectra were determined at 60 Mc. with a Varian A-60 spectrometer using tetramethylsilane as internal standard in deuteriochloroform.

TABLE II

4'-SUBSTITUTED *anti*-7-BENZONORBORNENOL DERIVATIVES

4'-Subst.	7-Subst.[a]	M.p. or b.p. (mm.), °C.	Recrystn. solvent[e] or n_D (t, °C.)	Formula	Carbon, % Calcd.	Carbon, % Found	Hydrogen, % Calcd.	Hydrogen, % Found
CH₃O	HO	79	E	$C_{12}H_{14}O_2$	75.76	76.02	7.42	7.41
	AcO	115 (b.t.) (0.02)[b]	1.5382 (22)	$C_{14}H_{16}O_3$	72.39	72.22	6.94	6.95
	BsO	93.5–94.5	H	$C_{18}H_{17}BrO_4S$	52.81	52.97	4.19	4.30
CH₃	HO	95–96		$C_{12}H_{14}O$	82.72	82.44	8.10	8.14
	AcO	67.5–68.5	E	$C_{14}H_{16}O_2$	77.75	77.82	7.46	7.62
	BsO	97–98	E	$C_{18}H_{17}BrO_3S$	54.97	55.18	4.36	4.38
H	HO	105–106[c]						
	AcO	78–79 (0.3)	1.5333 (25)	$C_{13}H_{14}O_2$	77.20	76.91	6.98	6.72
	BzO	112–112.5	H	$C_{18}H_{16}O_2$	81.79	82.07	6.10	6.22
	BsO	135.4–136.4[d]	E					
Cl	HO	115	H	$C_{11}H_{11}ClO^f$	67.87	68.00	5.70	5.70
	AcO	110–112 (b.t.)[b] (0.05)	1.5459 (23)	$C_{13}H_{13}ClO_2$	65.97	66.16	5.54	5.58
	BzO	127–127.3	H	$C_{18}H_{15}ClO_2{}^g$	72.36	72.59	5.06	5.20
	BsO	91–92	E	$C_{17}H_{14}BrClO_3S$	49.35	49.51	3.41	3.43
Br	HO	125–126	HE	$C_{11}H_{11}BrO$	55.25	55.32	4.64	4.71
	BsO	83.5–84.5	HE	$C_{17}H_{14}Br_2O_3S$	44.56	44.86	3.08	3.18
NO₂	HO	114.5–115	C	$C_{11}H_{11}NO_3{}^h$	64.38	64.37	5.40	5.60
	AcO	94	HE	$C_{13}H_{13}NO_4{}^i$	63.15	63.45	5.30	5.50
	BsO	134.5	HE	$C_{17}H_{14}BrNO_5S^j$	48.13	48.28	3.33	3.33

[a] Substituent: AcO = acetoxy, BsO = *p*-bromobenzenesulfonyloxy, Bz = benzoyloxy. [b] Bath temperature. [c] Lit.[7a] m.p. 104.1–105.7°. [d] Lit.[7a] m.p. 132.5–135°. [e] Solvent: E = ether, H = *n*-hexane, C = carbon tetrachloride, HE = a mixed solvent of *n*-hexane and ether. [f] Calcd.: O, 8.22. Found: O, 8.43. [g] Calcd.: O, 10.71. Found: O, 10.69. [h] Calcd.: N, 6.83. Found: N, 6.75. [i] Calcd.: N, 5.67. Found: N, 5.47. [j] Calcd.: Br, 18.83. Found: Br, 18.97.

TABLE III

4'-SUBSTITUTED *anti*-7-BENZONORBORNADIENOL DERIVATIVES

4'-Subst.	7-Subst.[a]	M.p. or b.p. (mm.), °C.	Recrystn. solvent[b] or n_D (t, °C.)	Formula	Carbon, % Calcd.	Carbon, % Found	Hydrogen, % Calcd.	Hydrogen, % Found
CH₃O	HO	69.5–70.5	HE	$C_{12}H_{12}O_2$	76.57	76.55	6.43	6.39
	BzO[a]	91–91.5	H	$C_{19}H_{16}O_3$	78.06	77.95	5.52	5.57
CH₃	HO	109–110 (3)	1.5712 (27.5)					
	BzO[a]	90.5	H	$C_{19}H_{16}O_2$	82.58	82.56	5.84	5.92
Cl	BzO[a]	124.5–125	HE	$C_{18}H_{13}ClO_2{}^c$	72.85	72.83	4.42	4.51
Br	*p*-ClBzO	137.3–137.8	HB	$C_{18}H_{12}BrClO_2$	57.55	57.29	3.22	3.29

[a] Substituent: Bz = benzoyloxy, *p*-ClBzO = *p*-chlorobenzoyloxy. [b] Solvent: H = *n*-hexane, HE = a mixed solvent of *n*-hexane and ether, HB = a mixed solvent of *n*-hexane and benzene. [c] Calcd.: Cl, 11.95. Found: Cl, 11.75.

TABLE IV

4'-SUBSTITUTED *syn*-7-BENZONORBORNEOL DERIVATIVES

4'-Subst.	7-Subst.[a]	M.p. or b.p. (mm.), °C.	Recrystn. solvent[d] or n_D (t, °C.)	Formula	Carbon, % Calcd.	Carbon, % Found	Hydrogen, % Calcd.	Hydrogen, % Found
CH₃O	HO	64.5–66	c	$C_{12}H_{14}O_2$	75.76	75.72	7.42	7.42
H	HO	117–118		$C_{11}H_{12}O$	82.46	82.59	7.55	7.44
	AcO	125 (b.t.)[b] (3)	1.5377 (26)	$C_{13}H_{14}O_2$	77.20	77.42	6.98	7.01
Cl	HO	123–124	HE	$C_{11}H_{11}ClO$	67.87	67.70	5.70	5.90
Br	HO	123–124	HE	$C_{11}H_{11}BrO$	55.25	55.41	4.64	4.50
NO₂	HO	127–128.5	HE	$C_{11}H_{11}NO_3$	64.38	64.39	5.40	5.49
	AcO	95.5–96.5	HE	$C_{13}H_{13}NO_4$	63.15	63.25	5.30	5.36

[a] Substituent: AcO = acetoxy. [b] Bath temperature. [c] Purified by sublimation. [d] Solvent: H = *n*-hexane, HE = a mixed solvent of *n*-hexane and ether.

gradually from blue to brown. After cooling to room temperature, the reaction mixture was extracted with 10% aqueous sodium carbonate to remove benzoic acid, washed with water, and dried over anhydrous sodium sulfate. After removal of the solvent, 51 g. of crude II was recovered by vacuum distillation, leaving a viscous residue. High vacuum distillation of this residue gave 17 g. of crude VII, b.p. 167–171° (0.045 mm.), and left 24.4 g. of viscous high molecular product. Crude VII was purified by recrystallization from hexane to yield 11 g. (30.4%) of pure VII as colorless needles.

The benzoyloxy esters VI, VIII, IX, and X were prepared in a similar manner.

anti-4'-**Methoxybenzonorbornadien-7-ol** (**XII**).—To a solution of methylmagnesium iodide in ether, which was prepared from 23.4 g. of methyl iodide and 3.91 g. of magnesium turnings in 140 ml. of anhydrous ether, there was added dropwise a solution of 9.38 g. of VII in 270 ml. of anhydrous ether under nitrogen atmosphere. After heating for 2 hr. under reflux, the mixture

was poured into a concentrated aqueous solution of ammonium chloride. The separated ether layer was washed with 10% aqueous sodium thiosulfate and water, and dried over anhydrous sodium sulfate. A by-product, phenyldimethylcarbinol, was removed by vacuum distillation at about 110–120° (5 mm.). The residue (6.2 g.) was recrystallized from a mixed solvent of *n*-hexane and ether to give 5.44 g. (90%) of colorless prisms of XII.

anti-7-**Benzonorbornadienol** (**XI**) and *anti*-4'-**methylbenzonorbornadien-7-ol** (**XIII**) were similarly prepared from VI and VIII, respectively.

anti-4'-**Methoxybenzonorbornen-7-ol** (**XIX**).—Catalytic reduction of XII with palladium-on-charcoal yielded colorless prisms of XIX almost quantitatively.

Similarly, XVIII and XX were prepared from XI and XIII, respectively.

anti-7-**Benzoyloxy-4'-chlorobenzonorbornene** (**XIV**) and *anti*-7-*p*-**chlorobenzoyloxy-4'-bromobenzonorbornene** (**XV**) were obtained in quantitative yield by catalytic reduction of IX and X, respectively, with palladium-on-charcoal in ethanol. Both are colorless crystals.

anti-4'-**Chlorobenzonorbornen-7-ol** (**XXI**).—To a suspension of 1.14 g. of lithium aluminum hydride in 120 ml. of anhydrous ether was added over 1.5 hr. a solution of 7.94 g. of the benzoyl ester XIV in 340 ml. of ether at such a rate as to maintain gentle reflux. After an additional 2.5 hr. of reflux, the mixture was treated cautiously with wet ether and then with water. It was poured into chilled water, and 10% hydrochloric acid was added until the inorganic precipitate was dissolved. The layers were separated and the aqueous layer was extracted twice with 100-ml. portions of ether. The combined ether layers were dried, evaporated, and a by-product, benzyl alcohol, was removed under vacuum. Recrystallization of the residue from *n*-hexane yielded 3.63 g. (75%) of XXI.

anti-4'-**Bromobenzonorbornen-7-ol** (**XXII**) was similarly obtained.

4'-**Nitrobenzonorbornen-7-one** (**XVII**).—To a solution of 1.0 g. of benzonorbornen-7-one (XVI) in 3 g. of 80% sulfuric acid 671 mg. of powdered potassium nitrate was slowly added at 40°. After stirring for 2 hr., the reaction mixture was poured onto ice and extracted with ether. The ether solution was washed with water and aqueous sodium bicarbonate, dried, and evaporated. The residue was recrystallized from ether to give 825 mg. of XVII (64.3%) as colorless prisms, m.p. 126–126.5°; n.m.r. (in CDCl₃): two aromatic H at 1.8–1.9 τ,[35b] one aromatic H at 2.5–2.7,[35b] two bridgehead H at 6.5 τ.

Anal. Calcd. for C₁₁H₉O₃N: C, 65.02; H, 4.46; N, 6.89. Found: C, 65.08; H, 4.75; N, 7.06.

Dehydrogenation of XVII.—The mixture of 100 mg. of the ketone XVII with 50 mg. of 20% palladium-on-charcoal was heated at 330–350° for 2 hr. An evolution of gas was noticed. The reaction mixture was extracted with ether, washed with water, dried over sodium sulfate, and evaporated. Treatment of the residue with Merck alumina in pentane followed by recrystallization from alcohol gave 24 mg. of 2-nitronaphthalene, m.p. 78.5–79°, which was identified with an authentic sample.

anti-4'-**Nitrobenzonorbornen-7-ol** (**XXIII**).—To a solution of 1.81 g. of XVII in 100 ml. of anhydrous methanol was slowly added a powder of 0.84 g. of sodium borohydride. After stirring for 3 hr. at room temperature and then for 1 hr. under reflux, the mixture was treated with water to decompose the excess of sodium borohydride, the methanol was removed, and water was added to yield an oil, which was extracted with ether. The ether extract was washed with water and aqueous sodium bicarbonate, dried over sodium sulfate, and evaporated. Recrystallization of the residue gave 1.30 g. (70%) of XXIII as colorless needles; infrared: ν_{OH} 2.76 μ (LiF prism, 20-mm. cell, in CCl₄ solution); n.m.r. (in CDCl₃): two aromatic H at 1.8–2.0,[35a] one aromatic H at 2.6–2.8 τ,[35b] C₇-H at 6.15 (multiplet), two bridgehead H at 6.75 τ (quartet).

The acetate of XXIII (**XXXV**) showed the following n.m.r. (in CDCl₃): two aromatic H at 1.8–2.0,[35a] one aromatic H at 2.6–2.8,[35b] C₇-H at 5.4 (multiplet), two bridgehead H at 6.53 τ (quartet).

anti-4'-**Methoxybenzonorbornen-7-ol** *p*-**Bromobenzenesulfonate** (**XXV**).—To 3.31 g. of 4'-methoxybenzonorbornen-7-ol in 8.5 ml. of anhydrous pyridine was added 4.44 g. of *p*-bromobenzenesulfonyl chloride. The solution was left in a refrigerator for over a week. Upon addition of the mixture to ice and water, an oil was isolated and extracted with ether. The ether solution was washed twice with 5% aqueous acetic acid and aqueous sodium bicarbonate, and dried over anhydrous sodium sulfate. After evaporation of ether, the residue was kept in a refrigerator for completion of crystallization. The crystals which formed were recrystallized from ether to give colorless needles. The yield was 5.57 g. All other *p*-bromobenzenesulfonates were obtained in a similar way.

anti-**Benzonorbornen-7-ol Acetate** (**XXX**).—To 0.20 g. of *anti*-7-benzonorbornenol in 0.6 ml. of anhydrous pyridine was added 0.13 g. of acetic anhydride and the mixture allowed to stand for a few days in a refrigerator with a calcium tube. The mixture was poured onto ice and extracted with ether. The ether solution was washed with 1% hydrochloric acid and aqueous sodium bicarbonate, and dried over anhydrous sodium sulfate. Evaporation of the ether gave crude acetate in quantitative yield and distillation at 78–79° (0.3 mm.) gave the pure product.

The other acetates were prepared in the same way.

syn-7-**Benzonorbornenol** (**XXXVI**).—2-Methylbut-2-ene (18.2 g.) was dissolved in a solution of 3.54 g. of sodium borohydride in 70 ml. of diglyme and the mixture, cooled to 0°, was treated with 17.6 g. of boron trifluoride etherate to form disiamylborane. To the reagent at 0° was added 7.9 g. of benzonorbornen-7-one (XVI) in 20 ml. of diglyme and the reaction mixture maintained at 0° for 3 hr. with stirring, then left overnight at room temperature. Oxidation at room temperature with 100 ml. of 3 N sodium hydroxide followed by 80 ml. of 30% hydrogen peroxide produced 7.9 g. (98%) of the mixture of *anti*- and *syn*-7-benzonorbornenol (XVIII and XXXVI). Analysis by gas chromatography (polyethylene glycol succinate column at 180°) showed 46% *anti*-, 54% *syn*-alcohol. The *syn*-alcohol XXXVI was isolated by elution chromatography on Florisil with a mixed solvent of petroleum ether and ether; infrared, ν_{OH} 2.79 μ (LiF prism, 20-mm. cell, in CCl₄ solution).

The n.m.r. of XXXVI (in CDCl₃): C₇-H at 5.96 (triplet), two bridgehead H at 6.81 τ (quartet). For reference, the n.m.r. of XVIII (in CDCl₃): C₇-H at 6.15 τ (multiplet), two bridgehead H at 6.84 τ (quartet).

syn-**Benzonorbornen-7-ol acetate** was prepared in a manner similar to that used for XXX; n.m.r. (in CDCl₃): C₇-H at 5.16 τ (triplet), two bridgehead H at 6.62 τ (quartet). For reference, the n.m.r. of XXX (in CDCl₃): C₇-H at 5.46 (multiplet), two bridgehead H at 6.66 τ (quartet).

syn-4'-**Methoxybenzonorbornen-7-ol**, *syn*-4'-**chlorobenzonorbornen-7-ol**, and *syn*-4'-**bromobenzonorbornen-7-ol** were prepared by the Oppenauer oxidation of the corresponding *anti*-alcohols followed by disiamylborane reduction. The isolation of these *syn*-alcohols was achieved in a manner similar to that used for XXXVI. The Oppenauer oxidation was carried out according to the method which Bartlett and Giddings[7a] used for the preparation of XVI.

syn-4'-**Nitrobenzonorbornen-7-ol** (**XXXVII**).—To a solution of 30 mg. of XXXVI in 1 ml. of nitromethane, a solution of 20 mg. of concentrated nitric acid (d 1.38) in 67 mg. of 98% sulfuric acid was slowly added at 0°. After stirring for 2 hr., the reaction mixture was worked up in a manner similar to that used for XVII. The yield was 13 mg.; n.m.r. (in CDCl₃): two aromatic H at 1.8–2.0,[35a] one aromatic H at 2.5–2.7,[35b] C₇-H at 5.73 (triplet), two bridgehead H at 6.69 τ (quartet).

syn-4'-**Nitrobenzonorbornen-7-ol Acetate** (**XXXVIII**).—To a solution of 25 mg. of *syn*-benzonorbornen-7-ol acetate in 1 ml. of acetic anhydride was added 17 mg. of fuming nitric acid (d 1.50) at 0°. After standing at 0° for 5 hr., then at room temperature for a day, the reaction mixture was worked up in a manner similar to that used for XVII; n.m.r. (in CDCl₃): two aromatic H at 1.8–2.0,[35a] one aromatic H at 2.6–2.8,[35b] C₇-H at 5.1 (triplet), two bridgehead H at 6.5 τ (quartet).

Structure of Acetolysis Products.—The acetolysis solution was allowed to remain in a constant temperature bath for more than 10 half-lives of each of the *p*-bromobenzenesulfonates, concentrated by distilling the acetic acid under slightly reduced pressure, diluted with ether, and treated with water and solid sodium bicarbonate to remove acetic acid. After drying over anhydrous sodium sulfate, the ether solution was evaporated on a steam bath and the residue was pumped for some time in a vacuum desiccator. The infrared spectrum of the residue was identical with that of each of the authentic *anti*-7-benzonorbornenyl acetates and the yield was quantitative. The residue was added dropwise to excess lithium aluminum hydride in ether, causing gentle boiling with each drop, and refluxed for a few hours. Water was added cautiously until no further reaction occurred; then 5% aqueous hydrochloric acid was added until all precipitate had dissolved. The ether layer was separated, washed with sodium carbonate solution, and dried over sodium sulfate. The residue obtained after evaporation of the ether had an infrared spectrum identical with that of each of the authentic anti-7-benzonorbornenols. Quantitative gas chromatographic analyses of these derived alcohols with authentic *syn*-alcohols under the following conditions demonstrated the absence in amounts greater than 0.3% of *syn* compounds in the solvolysis products. Exceptionally, the solvolysis product of the 4'-nitro compound was investigated by comparison of the infrared spectrum using the charts of authentic *anti*- and *syn*-alcohols.

Gas Chromatographic Analyses of the Solvolysis Products.—A standard column of 3 m. × 6 mm. stainless steel tubing was employed with helium as carrier gas in a Shimazu gas chromatograph Model GC-1B: the column was packed with 5% by weight

---

(35) (a) An AB part (multiplet) of an ABK system; (b) a K part (second-order doublet) of an ABK system.

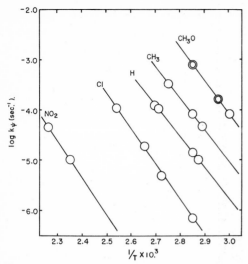

Fig. 4.—Arrhenius plots of the acetolysis rates of *p*-bromobenzene-sulfonates: O, one run; ⊚, two runs.

of diethylene glycol succinate suspended on acid-washed, 30–60 mesh Chromosorb W. Analyses were carried out under the following conditions: for XVIII and XXXVI, at 180° with a flow rate of 100 ml./min., the retention time of 5.6 min. to XXXVI and of 8.5 min. to XVIII; for XIX and its *syn* epimer, at 100° with 100 ml./min.; for XXI and its *syn* epimer, at 200° with 100 ml./min.; for XXII and its *syn* epimer, at 200° with 100 ml./min.; for XXX and its *syn* epimer, at 170° with 100 ml./min.

Kinetic Measurements.—The chosen acetolysis conditions and procedures were similar to those of Bartlett and Giddings,[7a] which in turn had been chosen to be similar to those of Winstein, *et al.*[21]

Reagent grade acetic acid was heated under reflux with about 4% potassium permanganate for 5 hr., distilled, dried over phosphorus pentoxide, and then redistilled. The distilled acid was further purified by collecting the fraction boiling at 117–118° after refluxing with 3% of acetic anhydride, and stored for use with addition of 1% acetic anhydride. Sodium acetate standard solution was made by dissolving anhydrous sodium carbonate in acetic acid and by refluxing for 5 hr. with sufficient acetic anhydride to remove the water of neutralization, and its concentration was adjusted to 0.104 M at room temperature. Perchloric acid standard solution was prepared by adding reagent grade 70% perchloric acid to the solution of the above acetic acid and sufficient acetic anhydride to remove the water; the concentration was approximately 0.02 M.

Samples of sulfonate ester were weighed into 30-ml. volumetric flasks so that solutions approximately 0.10 M in ester would be obtained, then filled to 30 ml. with the sodium acetate–acetic acid solution. Rate constants were determined by the infinity titer method; zero time meant that the complete solution and thermal equilibrium had been reached. Aliquots, usually eight 3-ml. portions of a reaction solution at reaction temperature, were pipetted directly from the volumetric flask into the constant temperature bath at recorded times and drained into 20 ml. of purified dioxane.[36]

(36) Refer to L. F. Fieser, "Experiments in Organic Chemistry," 3rd Ed., D. C. Heath and Co., Boston, Mass., 1955, p. 285.

In necessary cases, aliquots were pipetted from the flask at a constant temperature into ampoules. The sealed ampoules were placed in the constant temperature bath at once and individual ampoules were removed at recorded times and plunged into ice-cold water. "Infinity" ampoules were removed after at least ten half-lives and usually two were taken for each run. The contents of each ampoule were diluted with 20 ml. of dioxane. Two drops of a saturated solution of brom phenol blue in acetic acid was added, and the residual sodium acetate was titrated with the perchloric acid solution. Disappearance of the yellow indicator color was taken as the end-point. Plots of log ($A_\infty - A_t$) *vs.* time where A_∞ and A_t are titers at "infinity" and at any time were uniformly linear. The slopes multiplied by −2.303 gave the pseudo-first-order rate coefficients. Data from a representative run are presented in Table V.

TABLE V

ACETOLYSIS OF XXV. A TYPICAL RUN AT 64.41 ± 0.03°

Time, min.	Ml. of HClO₄ required	$A_t - A_\infty$	log ($A_t - A_\infty$)
10	13.16	12.50	1.0969
25	12.16	11.50	1.061
50	9.84	9.18	0.9628
70	8.42	7.76	.8899
105	6.19	5.53	.7427
130	4.99	4.33	.6365
160	3.89	3.23	.5092
210	2.63	1.97	.2945
∞	0.66		
∞	0.66		

The plot of log ($A_t - A_\infty$) *vs.* time was linear with slope -4.055×10^{-3} min.⁻¹; multiplied by −2.303/60, this gave the rate coefficient, 1.56×10^{-4} sec.⁻¹.

Calculation of the enthalpy and entropy of activation was performed by the usual method.[37] Plots of log k_ψ *vs.* $1/T$ formed straight lines for all compounds, as shown in Fig. 4, and their slopes were calculated by the method of least squares.

An Example of Calculation of Partial Rate Factor.—For CH₃O compound

$$k_{p-\mathrm{OCH_3}} + k_{m-\mathrm{OCH_3}} = \text{obsd. rate constant}$$

$$\frac{k_{p-\mathrm{OCH_3}}}{k_\mathrm{H}/2} + \frac{k_{m-\mathrm{OCH_3}}}{k_\mathrm{H}/2} = \text{rel.} \times 2 = 107.4$$

$$F_{p-\mathrm{OCH_3}} + F_{m-\mathrm{OCH_3}} = 107.4 \qquad (1)$$

$$\frac{\log F_{p-\mathrm{OCH_3}}}{\log F_{m-\mathrm{OCH_3}}} = \frac{\sigma^+_{p-\mathrm{OCH_3}}}{\sigma^+_{m-\mathrm{OCH_3}}} = \frac{-0.778}{+0.047} = -16.5 \qquad (2)$$

from eq. 1 and 2, we obtained

$$F_{p-\mathrm{OCH_3}} = 106.4, \quad F_{m-\mathrm{OCH_3}} = 0.76$$

Acknowledgment.—We are indebted to Professor E. Ochiai and Dr. K. Takeda for their encouragement, to Professors H. Hart and J. F. Bunnett for helpful discussions, and to Mr. Tadashi Irie for the technical assistance. Grateful acknowledgment is also made to Professor H. C. Brown, who was on a visit to Japan, for valuable suggestions and discussions.

(37) Refer to J. F. Bunnett, "Technique of Organic Chemistry. Vol. VIII: Investigation of Rates and Mechanisms of Reactions. Part I," 2nd Ed., S. L. Friess, E. S. Lewis, and A. Weissberger, Ed., Interscience Publishers, Inc., New York, N. Y., 1961, p. 200.

Erratum

Page 510, structures XIV, XV, XXI, XXII

Change R *to* Z

73 | 1-Phenyl-1,2-norbornanediol

Collins, Cheema, Werth, and Benjamin (Paper No. 73) report the study of a pinacol rearrangement in the norbornane series by a combination of tritium labeling, ^{14}C labeling, and correlation of configuration. Their evidence points specifically to the reaction sequence shown on page 519, in which VI and VII are shown by direct chemical correlation to be related to phenylnorbornenes of opposite configurations. This inversion occurs only because the 6,1-hydride shift which converts E into F is fast compared to the 3,2-shift of the *endo*-hydrogen in E. This same 3-hydrogen in F is now *exo*, and migrates normally to complete the pinacol rearrangement. Strongly preferred migration of *exo*- over *endo*-hydrogen is an expected consequence of the bridging in ions E and F, but would not be anticipated in the total absence of such bridging.

The criterion of *solvolysis rate* fails to give much indication of bridging in the transition states for ionization of tertiary norbornyl esters.[1] The present evidence is thus in line with previous indications that it requires less neighboring group participation to control the stereochemistry of the product in solvolysis than to boost the rate (see, for example, Paper No. 15). The explanation of this may be the obvious one that even low-energy bonding implies the presence of the bonding atom within bonding distance, and hence may exclude front-side competition effectively. An ion of this type cannot safely be called "essentially classical,"[1] at least while high *exo/endo* preference remains in ionization rate, product control, and 3,2-migration.

Dr. Collins has pointed out in correspondence that if 6,1-hydride shift competes with Nametkin rearrangement it will explain the observed migration of some *endo* methyl in the racemization of camphene [W. R. Vaughan, C. T. Goetschel, M. H. Goodrow, and C. L. Warren, *J. Am. Chem. Soc.* **85**, 2282 (1963)].

[1] H. C. Brown and H. M. Bell, *J. Am. Chem. Soc.* **86**, 5003 (1964); H. C. Brown and M. H. Rei, *ibid.*, **86**, 5004–08 (1964).

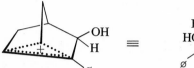

(−) VI   E

F   F

(+) VII

From: *J. Am. Chem. Soc.* **86,** 4913–17 (1964)

[Contribution from the Chemistry Division of Oak Ridge National Laboratory, Oak Ridge, Tennessee]

Molecular Rearrangements. XXI. The Pinacol Rearrangement of 2-Phenylnorbornane-2,3-*cis-exo*-diol[1a]

By Clair J. Collins, Zafarullah K. Cheema,[1b] Richard G. Werth,[1b] and Ben M. Benjamin

Received June 8, 1964

The rearrangement of 2-phenylnorbornane-2,3-*cis-exo*-diol (VI) in concentrated sulfuric acid at 0° takes place with intramolecular migration of hydrogen from C-3 to C-2. Rearrangement of the norbornane carbon skeleton also occurs, with an accompanying 6,1-shift of hydrogen. The configuration of the product, 3-*endo*-phenyl-2-norbornanone (VII), is inverted with respect to the configuration of reactant (VI). The results, attained with tritium, carbon-14, and stereochemical studies, can best be accommodated by assuming nonclassical carbonium ion intermediates.

Introduction

In connection with their work on the performate oxidation of 2-phenylnorbornene (IV), Kleinfelter and Schleyer[2] noted that one of the compounds available through their route—namely, 2-phenylnorbornane-2,3-*cis-exo*-diol (VI)—upon being heated with a dilute aqueous dioxane–sulfuric acid mixture yielded 3-*endo*-phenyl-2-norbornanone (VII). The stereochemical relationship of reactant VI and product VII was

not specified. The fact that phenyl is *endo* in both VI and VII precludes a simple loss of tertiary hydroxyl followed by a 1,2-shift of hydrogen during the rearrangement. Three conceivable, but unattractive, mechanisms remain as possibilities. The first, secondary hydroxyl loss followed by migration of the phenyl, seems unlikely, since tertiary hydroxyl removal should be preferred, and, further, there is apparently no documented case[2,3] of migration of an *endo* substituent in the rearrangement of a norbornyl compound. The second mechanism is formation of the tertiary carbonium ion A, followed by loss of the proton at C-3 and preferential reprotonation from the *exo*-direction.[2] This mechanism is identical with the theory of "vinyl dehydration" proposed many years ago by Tiffeneau[4] and effectively negated, whenever tested, by the demonstration that deuterium undergoes intramolecular 1,2-shift during pinacol rearrangement.[5,6] The third mechanism, rearrangement of the norbornyl carbon skeleton either through classical or nonclassical ions with an accompanying hydride shift,[7] also presents an

a priori appearance of unlikelihood. Unlikely because: (a) we would expect the tertiary, benzyl-type carbonium ion A to be much more stable[8,9] than the bridged ion E, and (b) we would not expect A, once formed, to

rearrange to the secondary carbonium ion B (see the discussion later in this paper).

Kleinfelter and Schleyer[2] clearly state the foregoing three mechanistic possibilities without choosing between "vinyl dehydration" and skeletal rearrangement. The prejudice of one of us[10] against "vinyl dehydration" as a serious contender, and the knowledge that in spite of its apparent unlikelihood, one of the remaining mechanisms must operate, caused us to investigate the pinacol rearrangement of VI. Our approach to the problem was to combine studies of the consequences of tritium and carbon-14 labeling during the transformation VI → VII with an examination of its stereochemistry. We used concentrated sulfuric acid at 0° to bring about the rearrangements, rather than the conditions employed by Kleinfelter and Schleyer, because of the known[5] tendency of warm, dilute acids to favor exchange of hydrogen α to carbonyl groups.

The first series of experiments was concerned with the synthesis and rearrangement of 2-phenylnorbornane-2,3-*cis-exo*-diol-3-³H₁ (VIa). The reaction sequence is shown in Chart I and was carried out twice. In the first experiments the molar radioactivities, in millicuries, for selected compounds in the series were: IIIa, 1.177; IVa, 0.6192; Va, 0.6266; VIa, 0.6263; and VIIa, 0.3058. Thus approximately half of the tritium was retained during the rearrangement of VIa → VIIa and subsequent work-up, signifying that at least half of the reaction proceeded with intramolecular migration of tritium. In order to determine whether the partial loss of radioactivity was a con-

(1) (a) This paper is based upon work performed at Oak Ridge National Laboratory, which is operated by Union Carbide Corp. for the Atomic Energy Commission. Previous paper: C. J. Collins, M. M. Staum, and B. M. Benjamin, *J. Org. Chem.*, **27**, 3525 (1962). (b) Research Participant of the Oak Ridge Institute of Nuclear Studies.

(2) D. C. Kleinfelter and P. von R. Schleyer, *J. Am. Chem. Soc.*, **83**, 2329 (1961).

(3) J. Berson in "Molecular Rearrangements," P. de Mayo, Ed., Interscience Publishers, Inc., New York, N. Y., 1963, Chapter 3, p. 159.

(4) M. Tiffeneau, *Bull. soc. chim.*, **33**, 759 (1923).

(5) C. J. Collins and co-workers, *J. Am. Chem. Soc.*, **81**, 460 (1959).

(6) W. B. Smith and co-workers, *ibid.*, **81**, 997 (1959).

(7) J. D. Roberts, C. C. Lee, and W. H. Saunders, Jr., *ibid.*, **76**, 4501 (1954).

(8) C. J. Collins and B. M. Benjamin, *ibid.*, **85**, 2519 (1963), and previous papers.

(9) P. von R. Schleyer, D. C. Kleinfelter, and H. G. Richey, Jr., *ibid.*, **85**, 479 (1963).

(10) C. J. Collins, *Quart. Rev.* (London), **14**, 363 (1960).

sequence of duality of mechanism or of exchange of hydrogen for the tritium in VIIa during work-up, we

It remained only to establish the stereochemistry of the transformation VI → VII. The stereochemical

CHART I

CHART II

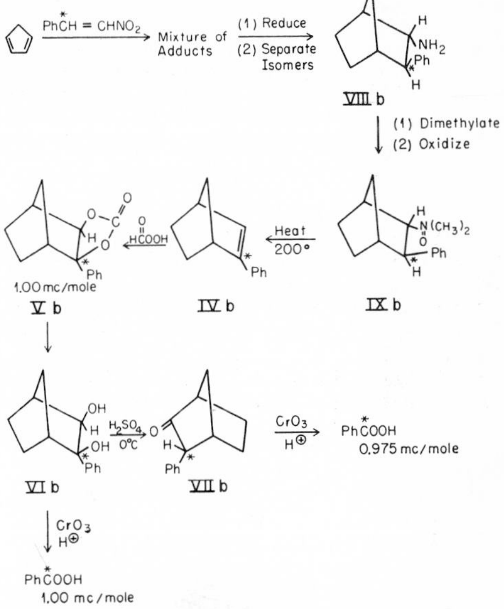

study is outlined in Chart III. Optically pure ketone (+)-VII was formed upon rearrangement of the optically pure glycol (−)-VI. Since the enantiomers (+)-IV and (−)-IV in the sequence shown in Chart III both yield the same (+)-ketone (VII), it is clear that (−)-VI afforded (+)-VII whose configuration had been inverted during the rearrangement.

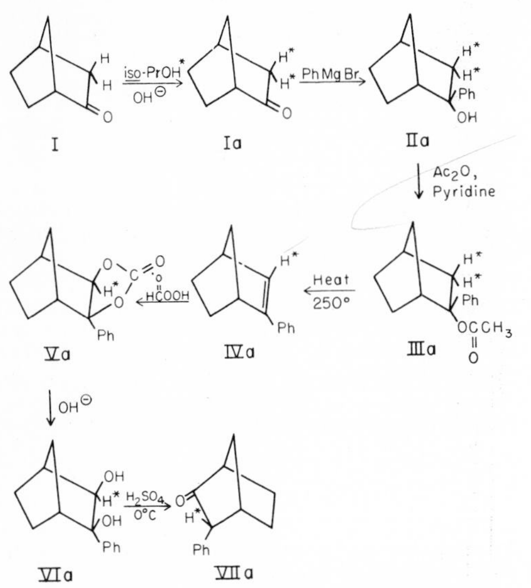

repeated the experiment, but isolated the product quickly and, in addition, kept wash solutions as nearly neutral as possible. Tritium determinations, in millicuries per mole, for key compounds in the second experiments were: Va, 0.4901; VIa, 0.4869; and VIIa, 0.4148; corresponding to 15% loss of the tritium during rearrangement of VIa. Finally, a crude kinetic experiment was performed which indicated that in very weakly basic solution exchange of tritium for the hydrogen of VII is complete within a few hours. It has been established, therefore, that the hydrogen at position 3 of the glycol VI migrates intramolecularly to the extent of more than 85%, and it is possible that the intramolecularity is complete. From these results we can see that "vinyl dehydration" is not an important mechanism in the rearrangement of VI. Since the two remaining mechanisms require inversion of configuration during rearrangement, VIIa is drawn to show that the inversion has taken place.

Our next series of experiments was constructed to differentiate rearrangement of the norbornyl carbon skeleton from secondary hydroxyl removal followed by a C-2 → C-3 migration of the *endo*-phenyl. The sequence is shown in Chart II, in which the asterisk now refers to the carbon-14 label. The results are unequivocal, demonstrate that the labeled carbon remains attached to phenyl during rearrangement, and show conclusively that secondary hydroxyl removal followed by a Nametkin-type phenyl migration to the secondary (C-3) position cannot have occurred to any significant extent.

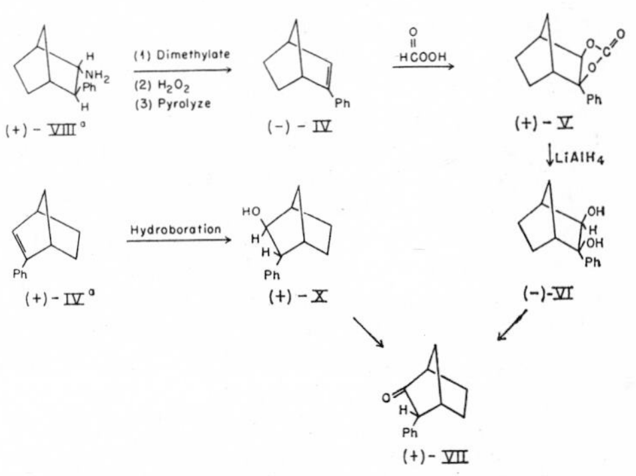

CHART III

Thus pinacol rearrangement of 2-phenylnorbornane-2,3-*cis-exo*-diol (VI) proceeds with intramolecular migration of hydrogen from C-3 to C-2, the configuration of the ketone VII produced is inverted with respect to the configuration of VI, and the phenyl remains attached to the same carbon atom throughout the rearrangement. One mechanism which can be written for these results includes the formation of the classical carbonium ion A, followed by rearrangement through ions B and C (with accompanying 6,1-shift of hydrogen) to the classical ion D, which then yields the ketone VII. This mechanism, however, does not tell us why the *exo*-hydrogen of ion D undergoes such easy migration to the 2-position, whereas the *endo*-hydrogen in ion A does not. Further, rearrangement of the stable tertiary benzyl-type ion A to the secondary ion B seems unlikely. A much more satisfactory interpreta-

suggests that the open ion A could lose a proton from C-6 with concurrent bonding at C_6–C_2 to produce a tricyclane which, upon reprotonation, would produce the open ion D. Professor Brown's suggestion has the twofold advantage that it not only removes the necessity for the unlikely rearrangement A → B, but it can be tested by carrying out the pinacol rearrangement of VI in deuterium- or tritium-containing sulfuric acid. The ketone VII so produced should then contain deuterium or tritium in the 6-*exo*-position. The intermediacy of a tricyclane, however, must still involve carbonium ion intermediates and thus leaves unexplained the very important reason for the disinclination for migration of the *endo*-hydrogen of VI, a phenomenon which has already been noticed for *endo*-alkyl groups.[2,3] The steric interpretation[11] for the low *endo*:*exo* ratio of solvolysis rates for norbornyl derivatives is of no help here, nor were we able to conceive any other steric reason for our results.[11a]

Following the experiment suggested by Prof. Brown, our next effort will be the synthesis and rearrangement, in cold, concentrated sulfuric acid, of 2-phenylnorbornane-2,3-*cis-endo*-diol (XI). We would like to know whether ketone VII can be produced during the reaction and, if so, whether the *exo*-hydrogen at C-3

tion (despite our earlier reluctance to consider them) employs the nonclassical, bridged intermediates E and F, in which E rearranges to F accompanied by a hydride shift, possibly through an ion similar to the tricyclonium ion postulated by Roberts.[7] Migration of the 3-*endo*-hydrogen in E is not possible because of bridging from the 6-position to the *same* side of C-2

to which the hydrogen, if it migrated, would shift. In ion F, however, bridging is on the opposite side from the *exo*-hydrogen at C-3, which can now migrate without difficulty.

It seems to us remarkable that the tertiary, benzyl-type carbonium ion E, generated in cold, concentrated sulfuric acid should prefer the nonclassical structure. Perhaps the favorable geometry of the 1-, 2-, and 6-carbons and the added driving force attributed to the incipient formation of ketone VII are enough to overcome the usual[8,9] tendency of such carbonium ions to remain open and unbridged. Professor H. C. Brown

migrates intramolecularly and unaccompanied by rearrangement of the norbornane skeleton. Prof. J. D. Roberts has recently suggested (in a letter) the possibility for *endo* migration of the no. 3 hydrogen during rearrangement of the glycol XII, for it is con-

ceivable that the two methoxyl groups at positions 2

(11) H. C. Brown, F. J. Chloupek, and M.-H. Rei, *J. Am. Chem. Soc.*, **86**, 1246, 1247, 1248 (1964).

(11a) Note Added in Proof.—We have now carried out the rearrangement VI → VII in tritiated sulfuric acid. The uptake of tritium per mole of VII was only 0.067% of the molar radioactivity of the sulfuric acid. Oxidation of ketone VII so obtained afforded benzoic acid whose molar radioactivity was 0.033% that of the original sulfuric acid. This evidence, we believe, rules out the intervention of a tricyclane intermediate in the rearrangement VI → VII.

and 4 (in the phenyl) could stabilize the tertiary, classical, open carbonium ion at the expense of the bridged ion similar to E. When time permits, we hope to study the rearrangement of XII.

Experimental

Procedures developed by Kleinfelter and Schleyer[2,12] for the synthesis and rearrangement of 2-phenylnorbornanone-2,3-*exo-cis*-diol were used with the following exceptions: (a) 2-Phenylnorbornene was prepared by pyrolysis of 2-*exo*-phenyl-2-*endo*-norbornyl acetate which gave a product containing only 1–2% of phenylnortricyclene; (b) quantitative conversion of 2-*endo*-phenyl-2,3-*cis-exo*-norbornylene carbonate to the *cis-exo*-diol was accomplished by lithium aluminum hydride reduction of the carbonate; and (c) 3-*endo*-phenyl-2-borbornanone (VII) was obtained by the pinacol rearrangement of the diol VI at 0° in 96% sulfuric acid. Pertinent aspects of the reaction procedures in the tritium, carbon-14, and optically active series are described in detail.

2-Norbornanone-3-³H₁ (Ia).—To 20 ml. of tritiated isopropyl alcohol was added 0.25 g. of sodium, and when this had all dissolved, 15 g. of norcamphor was added. The mixture was heated for 1.5 hr. and then the isopropyl alcohol was evaporated under vacuum. The residue was taken up in ether and washed with water. The ether layer was dried with magnesium sulfate. After evaporation of the ether, there remained 15 g. of the tritiated ketone Ia.

2-*endo*-Phenyl-2,3-*cis-exo*-norbornylene-3-*endo*-³H₁ Carbonate (Va).—The product (Ia) from above was combined with an additional 7.8 g. of ketone and then converted to 2-*exo*-phenyl-2-*endo*-norbornanol-3-³H₁ (IIa).[12] The carbinol IIa was treated with acetic anhydride in pyridine to give the acetate (IIIa), 1.177 mc./mole, which was next heated under reflux in a metal bath at 270° for 5 min. The mixture was dissolved in ether and washed with sodium bicarbonate solution. After distillation, the product, 2-phenylnorbornene-3-³H₁ (IVa), 0.6192 mc./mole, was shown (g.p.c.) to contain only about 1% of phenylnortricyclene. The olefin, 5 g., was converted to 2.3 g. of tritiated carbonate (Va, 0.6266 mc./mole) by the method of Kleinfelter and Schleyer[2] and was then hydrolyzed[2] to the glycol VIa, 2.1 g., 0.6263 mc./mole.

3-*endo*-Phenyl-2-norbornanone-3-³H₁ (VIIa).—The diol VIa, 2.0 g., was added to 100 ml. of 98% sulfuric acid at −8°. The mixture was stirred for 0.5 hr. and then poured onto ice. The ketone was recovered by ether extraction. The ether solution was washed thoroughly with 50 ml. of Na₂CO₃ solution which showed appreciable amount of tritium activity. The ketone was distilled; b.p. 108° at 0.5 mm.; radioactivity assay, 0.3058 mc./mole.

In a second experiment, the carbonate Va, 0.4901 mc./mole, was converted to glycol VIa, 0.4869 mc./mole, which was then subjected to the conditions of pinacol rearrangement. The ketonic product VIIa was washed quickly with sodium bicarbonate solution and distilled; the distillate contained 0.4148 mc./ mole of tritium. A small amount of radioactivity appeared in the sodium bicarbonate washings. The ketone was shown by n.m.r. analysis to contain no detectable amount of 2-phenylnorbornanone (no doublet at 2.94 p.p.m.). The products from both of the foregoing experiments were combined, and dissolved in ether; the ether solution was washed with two 100-ml. portions of 1 N sodium hydroxide. The recovered ketone was nonradioactive. Thus all the tritium was in the labile 3-*exo*-position. After the above treatment with basic solution, the material still contained no observable amount (n.m.r.) of the 3-*exo*-phenyl epimer. Hydrogen exchange is thus much more rapid than epimerization to the 3-*exo*-phenyl-2-norbornanone.

2-Phenylnorbornene-2-C¹⁴ (IVb).—β-Nitrostyrene-α-C¹⁴ was synthesized from benzaldehyde-*carbonyl*-C¹⁴ and nitromethane.[13] Cyclopentadiene and the labeled β-nitrostyrene were converted through the Diels–Alder reaction, followed by reduction of the Diels–Alder product to 3-*exo*-phenyl-2-*endo*-norbornylamine-3-C¹⁴ (VIIIb) according to the method described in the literature for the nonradioactive compound.[14–16]

(12) D. C. Kleinfelter and P. von R. Schleyer, *J. Org. Chem.*, **26**, 3740 (1961).

(13) "Organic Syntheses," Coll. Vol. I, John Wiley and Sons, Inc., New York, N. Y., 1932, p. 413.

(14) W. E. Parham, W. T. Hunter, and R. Hanson, *J. Am. Chem. Soc.*, **73**, 5068 (1951).

The primary amine was then treated with formic acid and formaldehyde to give N,N-dimethyl-3-*exo*-phenyl-2-*endo*-norbornylamine.[16] About a 20% yield of a mixture of epimeric 3-phenylnorbornanones was isolated from the reaction mixture. The tertiary amine, 18.3 g., was mixed with 60 ml. of methanol and 32 g. of 30% hydrogen peroxide, and the mixture was stirred for 5 days. Excess hydrogen peroxide was destroyed by the addition of a few mg. of Adams catalyst. Solvents were evaporated under vacuum at 40–50° and the sirupy amine oxide was transferred to a distilling flask. It was heated slowly under vacuum (0.5 mm.) to 250° during which treatment a distillate appeared over a range of 70–130°; the liquid was dissolved in ether, then washed with dilute hydrochloric acid, and finally redistilled to yield 5.3 g. of product, b.p. 80–83° (0.5 mm.). It was shown to be pure 2-phenylnorbornene-2 by comparison of its n.m.r. spectrum with that of an authentic sample.

3-*endo*-Phenyl-2-norbornanone-3-C¹⁴ (VIIb).—The carbon-14-labeled olefin IVb was treated with performic acid. The carbonate Va obtained from this reaction was crystallized from ethanol to give 5.1 g. of crystals, m.p. 101°; radioactivity assay, 0.3955 mc./mole. It was reduced with lithium aluminum hydride to give 4.2 g. of oily diol VIb whose infrared spectrum was identical with that of the nonradioactive material. A 300-mg. portion of the diol VIb was oxidized with chromic acid in acetic acid to give 160 mg. of benzoic acid; radioactivity assay, 0.3967 mc./mole. The remainder of the diol was treated with sulfuric acid at 0° as described above to give ketone VIIb. A sample of ketone VIIb, 480 mg., was oxidized with chromic acid to give 193 mg. of benzoic acid, whose radioactivity assay was 0.3868 mc./mole.

(−)-2-Phenylnorbornene ((−)-IV).—3-*exo*-Phenyl-2-*endo*-norbornylamine (VIII) was mixed with an equimolar amount of tartaric acid and the resulting salt was fractionally crystallized from absolute ethanol. A fraction, [α]²⁵D 42.5° (c 1, H₂O), m.p. 192–194°, was obtained whose specific rotation was unchanged after two further crystallizations.

Anal. Calcd. for C₁₇H₂₃NO₆: C, 60.52; H, 6.87. Found: C, 59.00; H, 7.20.

The free (+)-amine VIII was obtained by treating an aqueous solution of the tartaric acid salt with sodium hydroxide and extracting the solution with ether. The amine, [α] 32.6°, which remained after the ether was evaporated was not suited for analysis because it rapidly absorbed carbon dioxide. The hydrochloride was prepared and crystallized from alcohol, m.p. 235–236°, [α]²⁵D 47.6° (c 1, ethanol).

Anal. Calcd. for C₁₃H₁₈NCl: C, 69.78; H, 8.11. Found: C, 70.06; H, 8.16.

The amine VIII was also resolved through fractional crystallization from acetone of its *d*-10-camphorsulfonic acid salt, m.p. 210–211°, [α] 46.2° (c 1, ethanol).

Anal. Calcd. for C₂₃H₃₃NO₄S: C, 65.84; H, 7.93. Found: C, 65.82; H, 7.78.

The resolved (+)-amine, 24.9 g., was treated for 4 hr. at reflux temperature with 34 g. of 90% formic acid and 27 g. of 37% formaldehyde. From the reaction mixture was isolated 10.8 g. of ketonic material and 16.9 g. of tertiary amine Im. Without further purification the optically active amine was oxidized over a period of 4 days (room temperature) with a solution of 25 ml. of 30% hydrogen peroxide in 30 ml. of methanol. After the excess peroxide had been destroyed, all solvent was evaporated and, without further purification, the amine oxide was pyrolyzed at 250° and 0.8 mm. The distilled material was washed with dilute hydrochloric acid and was then redistilled; yield 3 g., [α]²⁵D −180.3° (c 1, ethanol). The n.m.r. spectrum was the same as that of the authentic material.

(+)-3-*endo*-Phenyl-2-norbornanone ((+)-VII).—Optically active olefin (−)-IV, 2.6 g., was converted to the carbonate (+)-V which was crystallized from ethanol; m.p. 123°, [α]²⁵D 63.2°, (c 1, ethanol).

The carbonate (+)-V was reduced with lithium aluminum hydride to produce the solid diol (−)-VI, which was crystallized from hexane; m.p. 80°, [α] −24.7° (c 1, ethanol). The infrared spectrum was indistinguishable from that of racemic VI.

(−)-2-Phenylnorbornane-2,3-*cis-exo*-diol (−)-VI), 1.4 g., was treated with 25 ml. of sulfuric acid at 0° for 10 min. The product was isolated, after pouring the mixture onto ice, and

(15) G. I. Poos, S. Kleis, R. R. Wittekind, and J. D. Rosenau, *J. Org. Chem.*, **26**, 4898 (1961).

(16) T. Weinstock, N. Schwartz, and M. F. Kormendy, *ibid.*, **26**, 5247 (1961).

then distilled. A quantitative yield, 1.3 g., of solid ketone (+)-VII was obtained, m.p. 55–55.5°, [α] 141° (c 1, ethanol). The melting point and specific rotation were the same after two crystallizations from hexane. The n.m.r. spectrum was identical with that of the racemic sample.

Anal. Calcd. for $C_{13}H_{14}O$: C, 83.83; H, 7.58. Found: C, 82.7 ; H, 7.41.[17]

In one model experiment a batch of racemic ketone VII, prepared by our method, crystallized after being stored in the refrigerator. Subsequently all samples of the ketone crystallized if they did not contain detectable amounts of the *exo*-phenyl epimer. The ketone has previously been reported[2] as a liquid. It was crystallized from ice-cold hexane; m.p. 33–35°.

(+)-3-*endo*-**Phenyl-2-*exo*-norbornanol** ((+)-**X**).—Partially resolved (−)-3-*exo*-phenyl-2-*endo*-norbornylamine ((−)-VIII) was recovered from the mother liquors after resolution of (+)-VIII. It was converted to the (+)-2-phenylnorbornylene-2, [α] 103.7° (57.5% optically pure). This olefinic material, 5.9 g., was dissolved in 43 ml. of diglyme, and 1.1 g. of sodium borohydride was added. To the mixture was then slowly added 4.5 g. of boron trifluoride dietherate in 10 ml. of diglyme. The mixture was stirred for 3.5 hr. after which 7.5 ml. of 3 *N* sodium hydroxide was added, followed by 7.5 ml. of 30% hydrogen peroxide. Stirring was continued for 0.5 hr. and the contents of the flask were washed with ether and water into a separatory funnel. The water layer was removed and the ether layer was washed three times with water. The ether was evaporated and the residue was distilled. Most of the material, 4 g., was collected at 125–126° at 0.15 mm. It partially crystallized; [α] 52.8° (c 1, ethanol).

Anal. Calcd. for $C_{13}H_{16}O$: C, 82.93; H, 8.57. Found: C, 82.06; H, 8.37.

Oxidation of (+)-X to (+)-VII.—To 17 ml. of pyridine cooled in an ice bath was carefully added 2 g. of chromium trioxide. After the yellow complex had been formed, there was added 2 g. of carbinol (+)-X dissolved in 5 ml. of pyridine. The mixture

was stirred at room temperature for 2 hr., after which time it was mixed with 200 ml. of water. The aqueous solution was extracted with three portions of ether, and the ether extracts were washed with water and dilute hydrochloric acid. After evaporation of the ether, the product was distilled to give 1 g. of ketone (+)-VII; b.p. 103–106° at 0.1 mm., [α] 74.8° (c 1, ethanol, 53% optical purity). The infrared spectrum indicated the presence of a small amount of unreacted carbinol.

Summary of Evidence for Assignment of *endo*-Phenyl Configuration in Ketone VII.—At the suggestion of a referee we summarize our evidence which establishes the *endo* configuration of the phenyl group in ketone VII: (1) Borohydration of olefin IV gave 3-*endo*-phenyl-2-*exo*-norborneol (X) whose configuration is assumed from the established[18] stereochemical course for borohydration of norbornene, α-pinene, camphene, and other similar bicyclic olefins. Oxidation of X with chromium trioxide in pyridine afforded a ketone (VII) whose n.m.r. spectrum was identical with that of the ketone VII obtained upon rearrangement of VI in sulfuric acid.

Further evidence for the correctness of the assigned *endo*-phenyl configuration of VII can be obtained by comparing its n.m.r. spectrum with that of 3-*exo*-phenylnorbornanone-2 obtained by the Nef reaction[2] or by isomerization of VII in alkaline solution. The signal for the tertiary proton at C-3 of ketone VII appears as a doublet, $J = 4.5$ c.p.s. at 3.27 p.p.m. downfield from the signal for tetramethylsilane. The signal for the same proton of the "Nef" ketone appears as a doublet, $J = 3.1$ c.p.s. at 2.93 p.p.m. It has been shown[19] that the *exo* protons in bicycloheptyl compounds are less shielded than *endo* protons and appear at lower fields. This then establishes VII as having a 3-*exo* proton. The doublet separation of 3.1 c.p.s. for the "Nef" ketone probably arises from coupling of the 3-*endo* proton with the 7-*anti* proton[20] rather than with the 4-bridgehead proton (which should be nearly zero).[21] Details of the n.m.r. spectra of several phenyl-substituted norbornane compounds will be the subject of a later paper.

---

(17) Carbon and hydrogen analyses were performed by Huffman Microanalytical Laboratories, Wheatridge, Colo. The analysis of the ketone is somewhat low about 1%, because this compound reacts with oxygen from the air and is converted to a mixture of *cis*-3-benzoylcyclopentanecarboxylic acid and other oxygen-containing compounds.

(18) H. C. Brown, "Hydroboration," W. A. Benjamin, Inc., New York, N. Y., 1962, pp. 126–131.

(19) J. I. Musher, *Mol. Phys.*, **6**, 93 (1963).

(20) J. Meinwald and Y. C. Meinwald, *J. Am. Chem. Soc.*, **85**, 2514 (1963).

(21) P. Laszlo and P. von R. Schleyer, *ibid.*, **86**, 1171 (1964).

74, 75 | The Long-Lived Norbornyl Cation

Schleyer, Watts, Fort, Comisarow, and Olah (Paper No. 74) demonstrate the enormous possibilities of Olah's new medium for studying carbonium ions at equilibrium. In liquid sulfur dioxide containing excess antimony pentafluoride 2-, 1-, and 7-norbornyl chlorides are all converted into 2-norbornyl hexafluoro-antimonate, which can be hydrolyzed to 2-norborneol. At intermediate stages in the conversion of the 1- and 7-compounds, controlled by operating over a range of temperature, hydrolysis products indicate the presence of the difficultly accessible 1- and 7-norbornyl cations, respectively, neither of which appears to be converted into the other. This treatment is evidently a potent method for converting any carbonium ion into its most stable isomer, and will therefore, among other things, give new information about relative stabilities of some species not otherwise easily interconverted.

The NMR spectrum of the 2-norbornyl cation is examined at temperatures down to $-120°$, at which point it shows three structureless peaks of relative areas 4, 1, and 6. From $-5°$ to $+37°$ the spectrum is a single line, and at $-120°$ there is no sign of the broadening that would precede a further resolution.

The three-peak spectrum corresponds to a higher degree of equivalence among different protons than is predicted by the norbornonium ion, and a higher degree of equivalence than is allowed by the tracer product studies of Roberts, Lee, and Saunders (Paper No. 23). The transition occurring between $-60°$ and $-5°$ is readily identified as due to the speeding up of the 3,2-hydride shift to the point where it is faster than the spin transitions in the NMR spectrometer. Combined with the 6,2-hydrogen shift and 1,2-carbon shift or its nonclassical equivalent, this isomerization makes all positions in the 2-norbornyl cation equivalent. The

3,2-shift, which can be frozen out, is found by Saunders, Schleyer, and Olah (Paper No. 75) to have an activation energy of 10.8 kcal and a pre-exponential factor of $10^{12.3}$ sec^{-1}. For the reactions which cannot be frozen out, it is only possible to say that they must have rate constants at least as fast as 300,000 sec^{-1} at $-120°$, otherwise some broadening of the NMR spectral lines would be observed. We know (Paper No. 23) that the 6,2-shift is not as fast as reaction of the carbonium ion with solvent. As expected, only the 1,2-shift behaves toward NMR and chemical criteria alike as if it is in fact a mesomerism and not a rapid reaction at all.

If we assume that the 6,2-hydride shift has the same A factor as the 3,2-shift we can estimate a corresponding value of 4.8 kcal for its activation energy, and a value of its rate constant at 25° of 6×10^8 sec^{-1} in SO$_2$-SbF$_5$ solvent.

The work of Roberts, Lee, and Saunders (Paper No. 23) indicated that in acetic acid, where only 30% of the product involved either 6,1- or 6,2-hydride shift, the reaction of norbornonium ion with the solvent must have a rate constant 3.3 times that of the hydride shift. We have the supplementary information[1] that racemization in the acetolysis of *exo*-2-norbornyl *p*-bromobenzenesulfonate is at least 99.95% complete, hence the process leading to it within the cation proceeds with a rate constant at least $2,000 \times 3.3 = 6,600$ times that of the 6,2-hydride shift. It is possible, of course, that the powerful ionizing solvent of Papers 74 and 75 reduces the difference in rate between different rearrangements within the ion. However, if we chose to regard the racemization as an equilibration of classical ions, the best estimate[2] that we could make of its rate constant in SO$_2$-SbF$_5$ would be by the use of this factor, leading to

$$k_{\text{rac}}^{25°} = 6,600 \times 6 \times 10^8 = 4 \times 10^{12} \text{ sec}^{-1}$$

This happens to be about the rate of passage of a transition state over the barrier in rate theory; any reaction occurring so fast has zero activation energy and the migrating carbon would be at just as low an energy when midway in its migration as at the beginning or end. Thus an attempt to avoid the bridged ion leads to the tentative conclusion that *all* states between the classical limits, including the symmetrical state, are of equal energy, and that C-6 flops about randomly in an untidy box. No such picture of decaying molecular structure results if we attribute the racemization to the direct formation of the bridged ion with planar symmetry, and no absurdly high rate constants are required.

[1] S. Winstein, E. Clippinger, R. Howe, and E. Vogelfanger, *J. Am. Chem. Soc.* **87**, 376 (1965).

[2] S. Winstein, *ibid.*, **87**, 381 (1965).

From: *J. Am. Chem. Soc.* **86,** 5679–80 (1964)

Stable Carbonium Ions. X.[1] Direct Nuclear Magnetic Resonance Observation of the 2-Norbornyl Cation

Sir:

An unusually intensive research effort has been devoted to the study of bicyclo[2.2.1]heptyl cations, their rearrangements, rates of formation, and structure.[2-11] We wish to report the direct observation of the 2-norbornyl cation as the SbF_6^- salt in SbF_5 or SbF_5–liquid SO_2 solution,[12] the analysis of the n.m.r. spectra of such solutions,[13] and the discovery of new rearrangements in the norbornane series.

The n.m.r. spectra of 2-*exo*-norbornyl chloride and fluoride (I) are expectedly complex, but when either halide is dissolved in SbF_5 or in SbF_5–liquid SO_2 the same one-peak spectrum is observed at temperatures between −5 and +37° (Fig. 1). This broadened peak

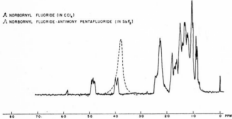

A NORBORNYL FLUORIDE (IN CCl₄)
A NORBORNYL FLUORIDE-ANTIMONY PENTAFLUORIDE (IN SbF₅)

Fig. 1.—N.m.r. spectra of 2-*exo*-norbornyl fluoride (I, X = F) and the 2-norbornyl cation at + 37°.

appears near −3.75 p.p.m. in neat SbF_5 and near −3.1 p.p.m. in SbF_5–SO_2, relative to external tetramethylsilane. If the solution in SbF_5–SO_2 is cooled to −60°, separation of the n.m.r. spectrum into three bands of areas 4 (−5.35 p.p.m.), 1 (−3.15 p.p.m.), and 6 (−2.20 p.p.m.) occurs (Fig. 2). If the solution at −60° is warmed to room temperature the single line pattern (at −3.1 p.p.m.) is restored, and this warming–cooling cycle can be repeated many times, indicating the chemical stability of the ion in solution. The identity of this ion as the 2-norbornyl cation follows not only from the analysis of these n.m.r. spectra, discussed in the accompanying communication,[13] but

(1) Part IX: G. A. Olah, *J. Am. Chem. Soc.*, in press.

(2) S. Winstein and D. S. Trifan, *ibid.*, **74**, 1147, 1154 (1952); S. Winstein, *et al.*, *ibid.*, **74**, 1127 (1952); J. D. Roberts, C. C. Lee, and W. H. Saunders, Jr., *ibid.*, **76**, 4501 (1954).

(3) For work through early 1962, see J. A. Berson in "Molecular Rearrangements," Vol. 1, P. de Mayo, Ed., Interscience Publishers, Inc., New York, N. Y., 1963, Chapter 3, pp. 111–231.

(4) E. J. Corey and J. Casanova, Jr., *J. Am. Chem. Soc.*, **85**, 165 (1963); E. J. Corey, J. Casanova, Jr., P. A. Vatakencherry, and R. Winter, *ibid.*, **85**, 169 (1963).

(5) P. von R. Schleyer, D. C. Kleinfelter, and H. G. Richey, Jr., *ibid.*, **85**, 479 (1963).

(6) H. C. Brown in "The Transition State," Special Publication No. 16, The Chemical Society, London, 1962, pp. 154, 155, 175–178; H. C. Brown and F. J. Chloupek, *J. Am. Chem. Soc.*, **85**, 2322 (1963); H. C. Brown, F. J. Chloupek, and M.-H. Rei, *ibid.*, **86**, 1246, 1247, 1248 (1964).

(7) J. A. Berson and A. Remanick, *ibid.*, **86**, 1749 (1964).

(8) P. von R. Schleyer, *ibid.*, **86**, 1854, 1856 (1964).

(9) R. Hoffmann, *J. Chem. Phys.*, **40**, 2480 (1964); *J. Am. Chem. Soc.*, **86**, 1259 (1964).

(10) C. A. Bunton, K. Khaleeluddin, and D. Whittaker, *Tetrahedron Letters*, 1825 (1963); P. Beltrame, C. A. Bunton, A. Dunlop, and D. Whittaker, *J. Chem. Soc.*, 658 (1964).

(11) W. Hückel and M. Heinzel, *Tetrahedron Letters*, 2141 (1964).

(12) For experimental details, see G. A. Olah, E. B. Baker, J. C. Evans, W. S. Tolgyesi, J. S. McIntyre, and I. J. Bastien, *J. Am. Chem. Soc.*, **86**, 1360 (1964).

(13) M. Saunders, P. von R. Schleyer, and G. A. Olah, *ibid.*, **86**, 5680 (1964).

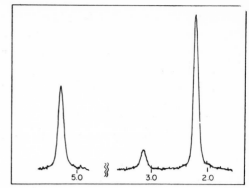

Fig. 2.—N.m.r. spectrum of the 2-norbornyl cation at −60°.

also from the hydrolysis[12] of the ion, which produced only 2-*exo*-norbornanol (III) in good yield and in high purity.

The same 2-norbornyl cation can be generated in other ways and from other precursors. If 2-*exo*-norbornyl chloride (I, X = Cl) is dissolved in a solution of $AgSbF_6$ in liquid SO_2 containing a small amount of SbF_5, the same ionic species is formed. Treatment of norbornene (II) with $HSbF_6$ (HF + SbF_5) in SbF_5 gives the same result. More surprising is the behavior of 1-chloronorbornane (IV) and 7-chloronorbornane (V), since both compounds are legendary in their inertness toward normal ionization conditions.[3,8,14] When either IV or V was dissolved in a solution of SbF_5–SO_2 at low temperatures, the n.m.r. spectra indicated little carbonium ion formation. When these solutions were warmed to −10° and then cooled to −60°, the characteristic 2-norbornyl signals (Fig. 2) were observed. The rearrangements of IV and V to the 2-norbornyl cation were confirmed by hydrolysis; both solutions gave principally 2-*exo*-norbornanol (III) (see Tables I and II). These rearrangements are without precedent in the literature.[3,14]

TABLE I

ANALYSIS OF HYDROLYSIS PRODUCTS FROM 7-CHLORONORBORNANE (V) IN SbF_5–SO_2

Hydrolysis after warming to (°C.)	7-Norbornanol (VII), %	2-*exo*-Norbornanol (III), %
−50	70	30
−35	53	47
−20	5	95

TABLE II

ANALYSIS OF HYDROLYSIS PRODUCTS FROM 1-CHLORONORBORNANE (IV) IN SbF_5–SO_2

Hydrolysis after warming to (°C.)	1-Chloro-norbornane (IV), %	1-Norbornanol (V), %	2-*exo*-Norbornanol (III), %	Other, %
−50	34	65	0.5	0.5
−35	1	11	87	1[a]
−20	0	5	94	1[a]

[a] Two minor products.

The fact that even simple aliphatic carbonium ions are stable in SbF_5 solution suggests that such conditions should afford a maximum opportunity for rearrange-

(14) See P. von R. Schleyer and R. D. Nicholas, *ibid.*, **83**, 2700 (1961); R. C. Fort, Jr., and P. von R. Schleyer, *Chem. Rev.*, **64**, 277 (1964), and references therein cited.

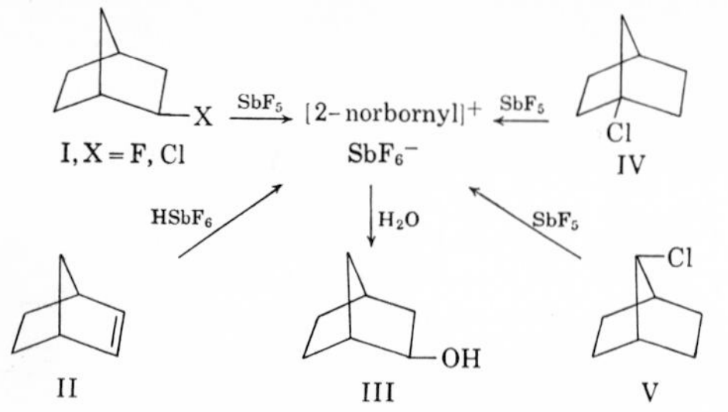

ment.[12,15] In a given series the carbonium ions of greatest over-all stability tend to form.[12,15] It is quite clear from the literature that the 2-norbornyl cation is considerably more stable than either the 1-norbornyl cation, the 7-norbornyl cation, or other bicycloheptyl cations of different carbon skeleton. One such structure is ion VI, which has been observed to be interconvertible with the 7-cation.[16] In an attempt to gain

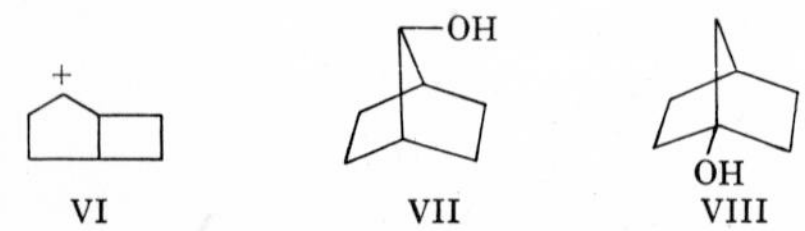

some insight into the course of rearrangement of IV and V to the 2-norbornyl cation, we have carried out hydrolyses of solutions of these chlorides. The chlorides were dissolved in SbF_5–SO_2 at $-70°$, warmed to temperatures given in Tables I and II, cooled back to $-70°$, and hydrolysed at this low temperature. Tables I and II summarize the data. From 7-chloronorbornane (V) only 7-norbornanol (VII) and 2-exo-

norbornanol (III) were obtained (Table I). 1-Chloronorbornane (IV) was somewhat more inert.[17] At the lowest temperatures (Table II) some starting material was recovered. The major reaction products were 1-norbornanol (VIII) and III, although traces of unidentified substances were also detected by capillary gas chromatography.

We have no positive evidence for the mechanisms of the rearrangements of the 1- and 7-norbornyl compounds IV and V to the 2-norbornyl cation. The hydrolysis experiments suggest that the 1-norbornyl and 7-norbornyl cations are not interconvertible. The simplest conceptual mechanism for the transformation of IV to the 2-cation is a simple 1,2-hydride shift, while V might rearrange to the 2-cation either by a direct 1,3 hydride shift or by the fragmentation sequence shown below.

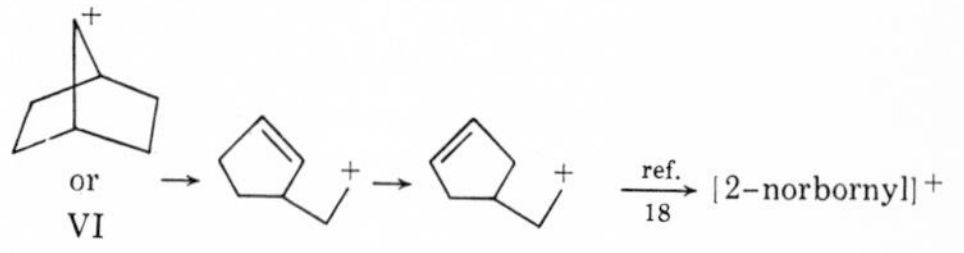

Acknowledgments.—We would like to thank the Alfred P. Sloan Foundation and the National Science Foundation for partial support of this research at Princeton University.

(15) Paul von R. Schleyer, R. C. Fort, Jr., W. E. Watts, M. B. Comisarow, and G. A. Olah, *J. Am. Chem. Soc.*, **86**, 4195 (1964).

(16) S. Winstein, F. Gadient, E. T. Stafford, and P. E. Klinedinst, Jr., *ibid.*, **80**, 5895 (1958).

(17) The acetolysis of 1-norbornyl tosylate is one-sixteenth the rate of 7-norbornyl tosylate: C. J. Norton, Ph.D. Thesis, Harvard University, 1955.

(18) R. G. Lawton, *J. Am. Chem. Soc.*, **83**, 2399 (1961); P. D. Bartlett and S. Bank, *ibid.*, **83**, 2591 (1961).

(19) Alfred P. Sloan Research Fellow, 1962–1966; J. S. Guggenheim Fellow, 1964–1965; Fulbright Research Fellow, 1964–1965.

(20) National Science Foundation Predoctoral Fellow, 1963–1964.

DEPARTMENT OF CHEMISTRY   PAUL VON R. SCHLEYER[19]
PRINCETON UNIVERSITY   WILLIAM E. WATTS
PRINCETON, NEW JERSEY 08540   RAYMOND C. FORT, JR.[20]
DOW CHEMICAL COMPANY   MELVIN B. COMISAROW
EASTERN RESEARCH LABORATORY   GEORGE A. OLAH
FRAMINGHAM, MASSACHUSETTS 01702

RECEIVED SEPTEMBER 23, 1964

From: *J. Am. Chem. Soc.* **86,** 5680–81 (1964)

Stable Carbonium Ions. XI.[1] The Rate of Hydride Shifts in the 2-Norbornyl Cation

Sir:

The n.m.r. spectrum of the 2-norbornyl cation, as its SbF_6^- salt, undergoes significant changes with alteration in temperature. At $-120°$, 2-*exo*-norbornyl fluoride in mixed SbF_5–SO_2–SO_2F_2 solvent consists of three peaks at -321 (area 4), 189 (area 1), and -132 c.p.s. (area 6) from external tetramethylsilane (at 60 Mc.). No important change appears up to $-60°$, but at higher temperature the peaks broaden and coalesce near $-23°$ to a single peak, which sharpens to 20 c.p.s. half-width at $3°$ (Fig. 1).[1] An analysis of these spectra allows us to determine the rates and activation parameters of hydride shifts occurring in the norbornyl cation.

Three rearrangements have been established for the 2-norbornyl cation.[2] These are the Wagner–Meerwein rearrangement (1), the 6,2- (or 6,1-) hydride shift (2), and the 3,2-hydride shift (3) (Chart I).

CHART I[a]

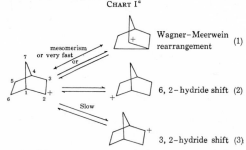

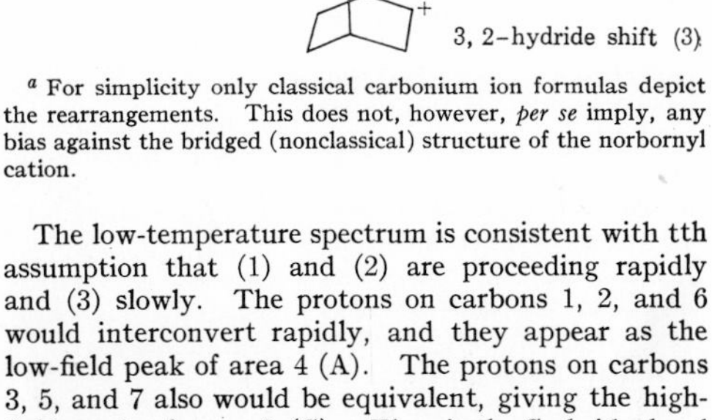

Wagner–Meerwein rearrangement (1)

6, 2 – hydride shift (2)

3, 2 – hydride shift (3)

[a] For simplicity only classical carbonium ion formulas depict the rearrangements. This does not, however, *per se* imply, any bias against the bridged (nonclassical) structure of the norbornyl cation.

The low-temperature spectrum is consistent with tth assumption that (1) and (2) are proceeding rapidly and (3) slowly. The protons on carbons 1, 2, and 6 would interconvert rapidly, and they appear as the low-field peak of area 4 (A). The protons on carbons 3, 5, and 7 also would be equivalent, giving the high-field peak of area 6 (C). The single C_4 bridgehead proton gives the signal at intermediate field (B).

(1) Part X: P. von R. Schleyer, W. E. Watts, R. C. Fort, Jr., M. B. Comisarow, and G. A. Olah, *J. Am. Chem. Soc.* **86,** 5679 (1964).
(2) See ref. 2–11 of part X.[1]

At higher temperatures all rearrangements occur rapidly to render the hydrogens equivalent on the n.m.r. time scale. A single peak results.

Since the 3,2-hydride shift (3) is assumed responsible for interconversion resulting in a single line, it is this process which is most amenable to quantitative rate analysis. A single 3,2-shift transforms three of the A protons to C and one to B protons. The same 3,2-shift converts the B proton and three of the C protons to A protons. The line shape of the n.m.r. spectrum can be

$$\text{B (1)} \underset{\text{one proton}}{\overset{}{\rightleftharpoons}} \text{A (4)} \underset{\text{three protons}}{\overset{}{\rightleftharpoons}} \text{C (6)}$$

calculated readily when spin–spin coupling is not important.[3−6] Since the lines have less than 5 c.p.s. half-width at low temperature, this approximation should hold.[7] A general computer program coded in Fortran language has been written which allows the calculation using the number of sites, the relative transition probabilities, and the observed chemical shifts as input data.

Curves calculated for a series of rate constants agree well with spectra taken at different temperatures (Fig. 1). From these correspondences, the rates in Table I were obtained. The activation enthalpy for the 3,2-

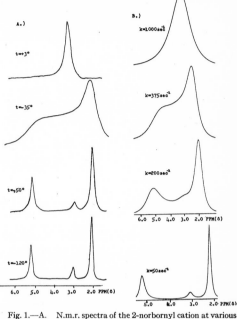

Fig. 1.—A. N.m.r. spectra of the 2-norbornyl cation at various temperatures. B. Calculated spectra for the 2-norbornyl cation for various rates of 3,2-hydride shifts.

TABLE I

CALCULATED RATES OF 3,2-HYDRIDE SHIFTS IN THE 2-NORBORNYL CATION

T, °C.	Half-width, c.p.s.	k, sec.$^{-1}$
+12.9	7.2	10,000
+ 7.0	12	6,000
+ 3.8	13.3	5,500
− 2.0	27	2,900
− 6.5	29	2,600
−11.2	51	1,550
−16.2	66	1,200
−19.3	98	850
−25.5	a	525
−29.0	a	375
−30.2	a	325
−33.5	a	225
−35.9	a	175
−38.2	a	150
−44.5	a	75
−46.0	a	72

a Rate determined from ratio of peaks when several peaks are present or from shape of collapsed spectrum.

hydride shift from the usual Arrhenius plot is $E_a − 10.8 \pm 0.6$ kcal./mole. The pre-exponential factor is $A = 10^{12.3}$ sec.$^{-1}$.

It is interesting to consider the information concerning the rates of processes 1 and 2. If these were slowed significantly at low temperatures, the low-field peak should have responded first by broadening. No such broadening was observed even at −120°. Assuming arbitrarily that the Wagner–Meerwein rearrangement (1) and the 6,2-hydride shift (2) occur at the same rate, the line shapes and half-widths of the low-field peak were calculated. A rate constant of 300,000 sec.$^{-1}$ or less should have produced an easily observable broadening of the low-field peak. We conclude that the rate of processes 1 and 2 must

be greater than this figure *even at −120°*. If the pre-exponential factor were 10^{13} for these processes, this would correspond to an activation energy less than 5.5 kcal./mole. Of course, with lower pre-exponential terms the limiting activation energy would be correspondingly higher.

At −120° the 3,2-hydride shift (3) is slower than the 6,2-hydride shift (2) and the Wagner–Meerwein rearrangement (1) by a minimum of $10^{8.8}$. In mixed SbF$_5$–SO$_2$ClF–SO$_2$ solvent we observed the spectrum of the 2-norbornyl cation at temperatures as low as −143°. Although there was a general line broadening of all peaks (probably due to the viscosity of the system), the extra line broadening of the low-field peak was still less than 5 c.p.s., corresponding to a minimum of the rate ratios in excess of 10^9. The large difference in the rates of these processes requires explanation in any consistent view of the nature of the norbornyl cation and the associated energy surface.[1,2]

Acknowledgments.—We would like to thank the National Science Foundation for partial support of this research at Yale University and at Princeton University.

(8) Alfred P. Sloan Research Fellow, 1962–1966; J. S. Guggenheim Fellow, 1964–1965; Fulbright Research Fellow, 1964–1965.

(3) R. Kubo, *Nuovo Chim., Suppl.*, **6**, 1063 (1957).
(4) P. W. Anderson, *J. Phys. Soc. Japan*, **9**, 316 (1954).
(5) R. A. Sack, *Mol. Phys.*, **1**, 163 (1958).
(6) M. Saunders, *Tetrahedron Letters*, **No. 25**, 1699 (1963).
(7) S. Alexander, *J. Chem. Phys.*, **37**, 967 (1962).

DEPARTMENT OF CHEMISTRY   MARTIN SAUNDERS
YALE UNIVERSITY
NEW HAVEN, CONNECTICUT
DEPARTMENT OF CHEMISTRY   PAUL VON R. SCHLEYER[8]
PRINCETON UNIVERSITY
PRINCETON, NEW JERSEY 08540
THE DOW CHEMICAL COMPANY   GEORGE A. OLAH
EASTERN RESEARCH LABORATORY
FRAMINGHAM, MASSACHUSETTS 01702

RECEIVED SEPTEMBER 23, 1964

Supplementary References

There are two critical articles on phenonium ions which, at the time of our publication deadline, had not yet appeared in print. H. C. Brown, K. J. Morgan, and F. J. Chloupek have submitted a review to the Journal of the American Chemical Society which tends to reverse the recent trend toward fragmentary communications. Its purpose is "to reopen the question and to consider the possibility that the reactions of these systems may involve a pair of rapidly equilibrating cations or ion pairs, rather than the stable phenonium ion now postulated by current theory."

C. J. Collins, B. M. Benjamin, and M. H. Lietzke, in the number of Liebigs Annalen in honor of W. Hückel's seventieth birthday, examine sets of special kinetic assumptions which would accommodate certain of Cram's stereochemical results on the basis of equilibrating classical ions.

The reader will also find much of interest in the following papers, which are among those published prior to mid-August, 1965. These papers are not covered by the index.

1. Solvolytic Ring Closures (the π route):
   Stereochemistry of single and multiple solvolytic ring closures:

   W. S. Johnson, D. M. Bailey, R. Owyang, R. A. Bell, B. Jaques, and J. K. Crandall, J. Am. Chem. Soc., 86, 1959 (1964).

   W. S. Johnson, S. L. Gray, J. K. Crandall, and D. M. Bailey, ibid., 86, 1966 (1964).

   W. S. Johnson, W. H. Lunn, and K. Fitzi, ibid., 86, 1972 (1964).

   W. S. Johnson and J. K. Crandall, ibid., 86, 2085 (1964).

   W. S. Johnson and R. Owyang, ibid., 86, 5593 (1964).

   The participation of a 3,4-double bond in formolysis:

   K. L. Servis and J. D. Roberts, J. Am. Chem. Soc., 86, 3773 (1964).

Hydride shifts attending the π route to the norbornyl cation:
  K. Humski, S. Borčić, and D. E. Sunko, <u>Croat</u>. <u>Chem</u>. <u>Acta</u>,
    37, 3 (1965).
Effect of methyl substitution:
  P. D. Bartlett and G. D. Sargent, <u>J</u>. <u>Am</u>. <u>Chem</u>. <u>Soc</u>., 87,
    1297 (1965).
Effect of chain elongation:
  P. D. Bartlett, W. S. Trahanovsky, D. A. Bolon, and G. H.
    Schmid, <u>J</u>. <u>Am</u>. <u>Chem</u>. <u>Soc</u>., 87, 1314 (1965).
Comparison of π and σ routes:
  P. D. Bartlett, W. D. Closson, and T. J. Cogdell, <u>J</u>. <u>Am</u>.
    <u>Chem</u>. <u>Soc</u>., 87, 1308 (1965).

2. <u>Solvolysis</u> <u>of</u> β-<u>Phenylethyl</u> <u>Systems</u>:
Experimental particulars and further discussion related to
Paper 63:
  H. C. Brown, R. Bernheimer, and K. J. Morgan, <u>J</u>. <u>Am</u>. <u>Chem</u>.
    <u>Soc</u>., 87, 1280 (1965).

3. <u>Phenonium</u> <u>Ions</u>, <u>Long-lived</u>, <u>NMR</u> <u>Spectra</u>:
Classical:
  G. A. Olah and C. U. Pittman, Jr., <u>J</u>. <u>Am</u>. <u>Chem</u>. <u>Soc</u>., 87,
    3507 (1965).
Bridged:
  G. A. Olah and C. U. Pittman, Jr., <u>ibid</u>., 87, 3509 (1965).
  L. Eberson and S. Winstein, <u>ibid</u>., 87, 3506 (1965).
Neighboring anthryl group in solvolysis:
  L. Eberson, J. P. Petrovich, R. Baird, D. Dyckes, and S.
    Winstein, <u>J</u>. <u>Am</u>. <u>Chem</u>. <u>Soc</u>., 87, 3504 (1965).

4. <u>Ions</u> <u>of</u> <u>the</u> <u>Norbornyl</u> <u>Type</u>:
Hindered ionization in 6,6-dimethylnorbornyl tosylate:
  P. v. R. Schleyer, M. M. Donaldson, and W. E. Watts, <u>J</u>. <u>Am</u>.
    <u>Chem</u>. <u>Soc</u>., 87, 375 (1965).
Solvolysis of tertiary norbornyl compounds:
  H. C. Brown and H. M. Bell, <u>J</u>. <u>Am</u>. <u>Chem</u>. <u>Soc</u>., 86, 5003,
    5007 (1964).
  H. C. Brown and M. -H. Rei, <u>ibid</u>., 86, 5004, 5008 (1964).
Four communications on norbornyl and apobornyl systems:
  S. Winstein, E. Clippinger, R. Howe, and E. Vogelfanger, <u>J</u>.
    <u>Am</u>. <u>Chem</u>. <u>Soc</u>., 87, 376 (1965).
  A. Colter, E. C. Friedrich, N. J. Holness, and S. Winstein,
    <u>ibid</u>., 87, 378 (1965).
  R. Howe, E. C. Friedrich, and S. Winstein, <u>ibid</u>., 87, 379
    (1965).
  S. Winstein, <u>ibid</u>., 87, 381 (1965).
Volume of activation in solvolysis of the 2-norbornyl bromo-
benzenesulfonates:

W. J. le Noble and B. L. Yates, _J_. _Am_. _Chem_. _Soc_., 87, 3515 (1965).

Stereoselectivity of chemical capture of the norbornyl cation:
H. L. Goering and C. B. Schewene, J. Am. Chem. Soc., 87, 3516 (1965).

5. <u>Long-lived</u> <u>Cyclopropylcarbinyl</u> <u>Cations</u>, <u>NMR</u> <u>Spectra</u>, <u>and</u>
   <u>Geometry</u> (compare discussion on p. 302):
   C. U. Pittman, Jr., and G. Olah, _J_. _Am_. _Chem_. _Soc_., 87, 2998 (1965).

Author Index

Aas, F., 485
Abd Elhafez, F. A., 127, 142, 143, 255
Abderhalden, E., 17
Aboderin, A. A., 67, 411
Abragam, D., 84
Adams, K. H., 267
Adams, Roger, 59, 180, 283, 369, 487
Adams, Rowland, 22-25, 26, 31, 78, 99, 124, 173, 288
Aebi, A., 391
Alder, K., 28, 31, 87, 88, 96, 130, 131, 350, 380, 420, 423, 469
Alekseev, S. V., 11
Alexander, E. R., 161, 268, 434
Alexander, S., 530
Allen, C. F., 62
Allison, J. B., 17
Allred, E. L., 299, 369, 373, 401
Amagat, P., 81
Amundsen, L. H., 122
Anderson, P. W., 530
Anderson, R. P., 319
Andrews, L. J., 57, 316
Angell, C. L., 504
Applequist, D. E., 214
Arcus, C. L., 23, 46, 79

Arganbright, R. P., 424
Armstrong, R., 30-34, 56, 61, 75, 88, 96, 130, 147, 148, 173, 213, 280, 294
Arndt, F., 269
Arth, G. E., 312, 319, 380
Arvin, J. A., 59
Ascherl, A., 10
Aschner, T. C., 131, 147, 321
Aston, J. G., 374
Atkins, W., 416
Aufdermarsh, C. A., 466, 495

Bacarella, A. L., 485
Bacskai, R., 328, 511
Baddeley, G., 32
Baer, H., 216
Baird, R., 67, 288, 406-410, 406, 411, 479-490, 479, 483
Baker, E. B., 527
Baker, J. W., 79, 131, 481
Ballinger, P., 259
Bamberger, E., 410
Bank, S., 389, 398, 528
Banthorpe, D. V., 454
Barman, P., 180, 195, 395

Barner, R., 408
Barnes, R. S., 420
Bartell, L. S., 334
Barthel, W. F., 486
Bartlett, P. D., 2, 4, 8,
  10, 14, 37, 46, 58, 69,
  79, 81, 83, 116, 126,
  135, 179, 186, 213-221,
  213, 216, 234, 247, 268,
  269, 316-322, 334, 351,
  355, 389, 398, 420, 476,
  501, 509, 528
Barton, D. H. R., 166,
  255, 391, 424, 486
Bashford, Jr., R. T., 485
Bassham, J. A., 68, 132
Bastien, I. J., 527
Bateman, L. C., 20, 24,
  51, 303
Battiste, M., 406
Bauer, E., 271
Bauld, N. L., 467
Baum, M. E., 326, 343-
  348, 344, 398
Baumgartner, F. N., 56
Beckmann, S., 31, 88, 96,
  130
Beeck, O., 121
Bell, H. M., 505, 509,
  518
Bellamy, L. J., 382, 408
Beltrame, P., 527
Bender, P., 220
Ben-Efraim, D. A., 466,
  468, 492
Benjamin, B. M., 259, 280,
  421, 466, 505, 520-525,
  520
Benkeser, R. A., 514
Bennett, W., 30-34, 56,
  75, 88, 96, 114-117, 118,
  119, 130, 132, 147, 148,
  155, 157, 173, 213, 278,
  280, 294
Bensley, B., 229
Benson, A. A., 68, 132
Bentrude, W. G., 466

Benyon, J. H., 469
Berger, J. G., 492
Bergmann, E., 5, 9
Bergmann, F., 18, 25, 83,
  284, 420
Bergstrom, C. G., 70-76,
  246, 276, 293, 303
Berkowitz, J., 218
Berkowitz, L. M., 469
Berlande, A., 162
Bernal, J. D., 231
Berneis, H. L., 364
Bernheimer, 455
Bernstein, H. I., 38
Bernstein, R. B., 265
Berry, R. S., 431
Berson, J. A., 341, 466,
  467, 468, 476, 492-498,
  492, 493, 496, 505, 509,
  520, 527
Bertram, J., 319
Beyerstedt, F., 237
Beyler, R. E., 312, 319,
  380
Beynon, J. H., 23, 26
Bigley, D. B., 511
Billen, G. N., 282
Birch, S. F., 138, 374
Bjerrum, J., 410
Blanchard, J. P., 352
Blanke, E., 60
Bloch, W., 195
Blom, J. H., 138
Bluestone, H., 422
Blumberg, P., 17
Bly, R. S., 326
Boarland, V., 210
Bochkova, E. V., 414
Bockenoogen, H. A., 195
Böckman, O. C., 391
Bodenbenner, K., 433
Böeseken, J., 8
Bolhofer, W. A., 61
Bondi, A., 255
Bone, W. A., 56
Bonner, W. A., 141-145,
  141, 144, 155, 254-263,

254, 455, 505
Bonner, W. H., 454
Boord, C. E., 60
Borčić, S., 210, 384, 455
Bordwell, F. G., 424
Borkowski, M., 179, 186,
277, 303
Borner, P., 433
Boschan, R. H., 46, 78,
237-244
Bothner-By, A. A., 210
Bott, R. W., 514
Bouveault, L., 492
Bowers, A., 352
Bowman, P. I., 58, 79
Bown, D. E., 421
Boyd, R. N., 422
Boyton, H. G., 431, 485
Brady, J. D., 454
Brattain, R. R., 73
Braude, E. A., 126, 233,
321, 483
Braun, J. V., 485
Breslow, R., 385, 432
Brewster, J. H., 182, 251
Brindell, G. D., 494
Brockway, L. O., 8
Brown, F., 37, 38, 49-51
Brown, H. C., 30, 37, 61,
81, 157, 179-183, 179,
182, 186-195, 186, 188,
193, 210, 249, 269, 277,
303, 304, 321, 344, 345,
364, 366, 373, 380, 438-
455, 454, 455, 471, 473,
476, 500, 504, 505, 508,
509, 511, 512, 513, 518,
522, 524, 527
Brown, M., 99, 124, 223,
288, 401
Brown, R., 271
Brown, R. F., 268, 492
Brown, T. L., 246, 249
Brown, W. G., 59, 71, 79,
83, 91, 282
Bruck, P., 331-332, 332,
333, 335, 372, 406

Bruehlman, R. J., 218
Brugger, W., 195
Brunel, L., 167
Brüngger, H., 21
Bruson, H. A., 319, 420
Brutcher, Jr., F. V.,
238, 374
Bruylants, P., 53, 127
Büchi, G., 467
Buckles, R. E., 6, 24,
78, 180, 237
Buckley, G. D., 131
Buckley, N. C., 506
Bunce, S. C., 382
Bunnett, J. F., 517
Bunton, C. A., 267, 269,
527
Burbach, J. C., 232
Bürer, T., 500
Burgess, K., 270
Burnell, R. H., 408, 486
Burness, D. M., 69
Burr, Jr., J. G., 135
Burt, C. P., 56
Burton, H., 36
Busch, H. M., 435
Butenandt, A., 19
Buu Hoi, N. -P., 39

Cahn, A., 454
Calas, R., 214
Callais, J., 84
Campbell, A., 492
Capon, B., 505
Carboni, R. A., 151, 153,
174, 280, 296, 316, 328,
339, 386, 496
Cargill, R. L., 422
Carlsmith, L. A., 283
Carr, E. P., 56
Carter, P., 398-399, 406
Casanova, Jr., J., 465-
469, 467, 493, 494, 505,
527
Caserio, Jr., F. F., 305
Caserio, M. C., 184,

302–313
Cason, J., 54, 62, 84
Castells, J., 483
Catchpole, A. G., 36, 233
Cauquil, G., 214
Chadwick, J., 32
Chakravorty, P. N., 23, 290
Chambers, V. C., 54, 115, 179, 186, 246, 276, 277, 321, 380, 472, 501
Charlton, J. C., 38, 51, 455
Chavanne, G., 8
Cheema, Z. K., 520–525
Cheng, C. S., 485
Cheronis, N. D., 283, 377
Chloupek, F. J., 505, 522, 527
Choe, 455
Chortyk, O. T., 492
Christiansen, W. G., 60
Christie, J. B., 256, 259, 263
Church, M. G., 20, 24
Ciereszko, L. S., 135
Ciotti, Jr., C. J., 251
Clapp, H. G., 81
Claus, C. J., 436
Clippinger, E., 86, 173, 174, 213, 222, 223, 224, 227, 240, 268, 288, 292, 364, 365, 394, 401–404, 401, 404, 421, 495, 526
Closson, W. D., 390–396, 390, 391, 393
Coggeshall, N. D., 481
Cohen, J. B., 454
Colby, T. H., 470, 471
Cole, A. R. H., 382
Coleman, G. H., 59
Coles, H. W., 321
Collins, C. H., 422
Collins, C. J., 141–145, 141, 144, 155, 161–170, 161, 254–263, 254, 259, 265, 280, 421, 455, 466,

505, 520–525, 520
Colter, A., 228, 496
Comisarow, M. B., 66, 527–528, 528, 529
Conant, J. B., 56, 70
Cone, L. H., 38
Conner, R. J., 486
Constan, N. D., 62
Cook, J. W., 167
Cookson, R. C., 166, 255, 373, 424, 501
Cooper, J. E., 496
Cooper, K. A., 37, 51, 303
Cope, A. C., 210, 382, 391
Coraor, G. R., 155
Corey, E. J., 214, 465–469, 466, 467, 493, 494, 505, 527
Corse, J., 46, 78–85, 87, 95, 107, 130, 181, 213, 237–244, 276, 317, 318, 344, 356, 364, 454, 500
Coryell, C. D., 83
Cottle, D. L., 11
Coulson, C. A., 56, 125, 294
Coverdall, C. E., 415
Cowdrey, W. A., 1, 9, 10, 13, 14, 20
Cox, E. F., 277, 281
Cox, Jr., J. C., 134
Cox, R. H., 195
Craig, D., 39
Craig, R. A., 60
Craig, R. R., 424
Cram, D. J., 6, 31, 38, 46, 51, 81, 99, 104–112, 114, 118, 127, 142, 143, 155, 158, 161, 224, 255, 265, 280, 394, 421, 455, 461, 466
Crawford, R. J., 389
Criegee, R., 234, 241
Cristol, S. J., 333, 420–427, 420, 424, 454, 494

Cross, P. C., 8
Crowfoot, D., 17, 19
Culbertson, C. F., 420
Curry, M. J., 241
Curtin, D. Y., 83, 143,
  166, 352, 455, 466
Curtis, Jr., O. E., 246

Dalle, P., 62
Danilov, S., 81
Danneel, R., 396
Darwish, D., 402, 403,
  404
Dauben, H. J., 436
Dauben, W. G., 255, 373,
  395, 422
Daudel, P., 39
Daudel, R., 39
Daughensbaugh, P. J., 17
Davidson, N., 501
Davies, R. H., 289
Davies, T. D., 37, 51
Davis, T. L., 62
Dawson, R. L., 505
Dean, R. A., 374
Deans, S. A. V., 74
Degnan, W. M., 220
Dehl, R., 431
de la Mare, P. B. D.,
  259, 424
de Mayo, P., 391
Demjanow, J., 56
Demjanow, N., 56
Demjanow, N. J., 53, 57,
  282
DeMore, W. B., 501
Demyanova, N. Ya., 417
Denisenko, Ya. I., 163
Denney, D. B., 233, 234
Denney, D. G., 233
Deno, N. C., 267, 268,
  476
Depireux, J., 501
DePuy, C. H., 355–358,
  355, 434, 468, 471, 480

Derfer, J. M., 60

Derx, H. G., 241
de Salas, E., 27, 28, 46,
  51, 57, 68, 79, 99, 131,
  255, 343
Desreux, V., 406
de Vries, L., 126, 299,
  332, 333, 338, 372, 381,
  393, 500
Dewael, A., 53, 127
Dewar, M. J. S., 28, 32,
  46, 79, 82, 114, 118,
  127, 134, 345, 422
DeWolfe, R. H., 22, 305
Dhar, M. L., 454
Diels, O., 17, 138
DiGiorgio, P. A., 60
Dillon, R. T., 8, 83,
  270
Dills, C. E., 476
Dirlam, J., 146, 314, 509
Dittmer, D. C., 268
Djerassi, C., 345, 408
Dodds, M. L., 321
Dodson, R. M., 70, 125,
  295
Doering, W. von E., 58,
  131, 134, 147, 210, 213,
  233, 268, 321, 349, 352,
  372, 385, 386, 431, 485
Doi, J. T., 394
Dojarenko, M., 282
Domash, L., 454
Donaldson, M. M., 334,
  504, 506
Donath, W., 374
Dorfman, L., 483
Dorling, S., 408
Dostrovsky, I., 18, 37,
  38, 51, 79, 81, 455
Doty, P. M., 374
Dreiding, A. S., 408, 486
Dryden, H. L., 326
Duncan, J. F., 265, 267
Dunitz, J. D., 126
Dunlop, A., 527
du Vigneaud, V., 120

Eaborn, C., 514
Earhart, H. W., 431, 485
Eastman, R. H., 481
Easty, D. M., 131
Ebel, F., 8
Ebel, H. F., 479
Edwards, T., 268
Edwards, W. R., 431, 485
Eichelberger, L., 5, 8
Eichelberger, W. C., 242
Eley, D. D., 231
Eliel, E., 374, 394, 504
Emmons, W. D., 492
Engelmann, H. M., 131
England, B. D., 37
Entrikin, J. B., 283, 377
Espy, H. H., 390, 391, 501
Evans, D. D., 127, 183
Evans, J. C., 527
Evans, M. G., 231
Evans, O. J., 37, 51
Evers, E. C., 487
Eyring, H., 28, 46, 79,
  119

Fahey, R. C., 382
Fahrenholtz, S. R., 506
Fainberg, A. H., 174,
  213, 222, 223, 224, 225,
  227, 228, 240, 248, 268,
  288, 291, 297, 303, 364,
  375, 376, 394, 401, 403,
  408, 421, 486, 487
Farber, M., 349
Favorskaya, T. A., 53,
  127
Fehnel, E. A., 218
Felkin, H., 326
Fenoglio, R., 471-473
Fenton, S. W., 210
Ferber, C., 485
Ferguson, L. N., 218
Fernholz, E., 19, 23
Fickes, G. N., 340
Field, F. H., 466
Fieser, L. F., 31, 85,
  251, 321, 406, 407, 410,
  517
Fieser, M., 31
Figueras, Jr., J., 409
Filar, L. J., 486
Fink, H. L., 374
Firth, Jr., W. C., 420
Fischer, E., 284
Fleming, G. H., 18, 81
Fletcher, G. A., 483
Fletcher, R. S., 30, 37,
  61, 81, 179, 186, 344,
  454
Flock, F. H., 380, 420,
  423
Flowers, D., 220
Fonken, G. J., 373
Foote, C. S., 500-501,
  500, 501, 504, 505
Ford, E. G., 23
Forster, Fr., 413, 414
Fort, Jr., R. C., 66,
  527-528, 527, 528, 529
Fortunatow, K., 57
Fowler, R. H., 231
Frahm, H., 220
Frank, V. S., 61
Franklin, T. L., 466
Fraser, R. R., 511
Fredga, A., 256
French, K. H. V., 58
Frenkiel, L., 195
Freudenberg, K., 4, 256
Freund, M., 57, 59, 118
Fridman, S. A., 53, 127
Friedrich, E. C., 86,
  479
Friess, 46
Froemsdorf, D. H., 480
Frost, A. A., 362, 482,
  483
Fugitt, C. H., 119, 132,
  148, 157, 278
Funakubo, E., 455
Fuoss, R. M., 231
Fuson, R. C., 56, 69, 71,
  168, 221, 283, 320, 352

Fuszgänger, R., 59

Gadient, F., 288, 333, 337, 351, 398, 528
Gagneux, A., 326, 361, 501
Galand, E., 57
Gall, J. S., 512
Garbisch, Jr., E. W., 424
Gassman, P. G., 501, 506
Gaston, L. K., 423
Gates, M., 420
Gebhart, Jr., H. J., 267
Gelfer, D., 81
Gephart, F. T., 23
Gerrard, W., 58
Giddings, W. P., 146, 314, 316-322, 318, 501, 509
Gillam, A. E., 481
Gintis, D., 454
Glasstone, S., 484
Glessner, A. S., 481
Glick, R. E., 237, 406
Glucksmann, C., 269
Godelot, M., 214
Goering, H. L., 55, 107, 220, 222, 226, 227, 228, 234, 293, 303, 316, 349-353, 350, 352, 360-367, 360, 361, 363, 365, 390-396, 390, 391, 392, 393, 394, 398, 496, 501
Goldberg, M. W., 18, 21
Goldschmidt, H., 485
Goldsmith, N., 482
Goldstein, B., 234
Goldstein, I. S., 420
Goodman, L., 46
Goodyear, S., 218
Gordon, A. S., 246
Gortler, L. B., 2
Gould, C. W., 158
Grace, J. A., 329
Graham, G. E., 137
Graham, W. H., 184, 302-

313
Grandberg, I. I., 417
Grayson, M., 454
Green, C., 56
Greene, J. L., 266
Greenlee, K. W., 60
Greiner, R. W., 227, 350, 360, 393
Grillot, G. F., 485
Grisar, J. M., 391
Grob, C. A., 226, 326, 350, 361
Gross, A., 396
Gross, J. C., 393
Groth, B. S., 131
Groves, L. H., 168
Groves, P. T., 476
Gruber, H., 167
Grunwald, E., 2, 23, 24, 28, 78-85, 78, 79, 84, 87, 91, 93, 95, 107, 115, 119, 130, 172, 180, 181, 182, 213, 217, 225, 227, 230, 231, 237, 255, 276, 291, 303, 316, 317, 318, 321, 344, 356, 358, 364, 421, 454, 485, 490, 500, 501, 511
Gudeman, E., 59
Günthard, H. H., 500
Gustavson, G., 54, 56
Gutowsky, H. S., 214
Gutt, J., 62
Guye, P., 416

Haak, F. A., 377
Hadwick, T., 267
Hafliger, O., 454
Hager, G. F., 131
Halford, J. O., 500, 504
Hall, Jr., H. K., 500
Haller, A., 271
Haller, H. L., 282
Halmann, M., 121-122, 155, 412
Halsall, T. G., 352

Ham, G., 179-183, 186, 210, 344, 345, 366, 380, 455, 473, 500

Hamilton, C., 220

Hammett, L. P., 14, 53, 61, 91, 114, 182, 188, 192, 454, 484, 513

Hammond, G. S., 292, 422

Hancey, J., 414

Hansen, R. L., 333-334, 333, 335-339, 337, 398, 406

Hansley, V. L., 74

Hanson, C., 24, 180, 181, 237, 321, 358, 511

Hanson, R., 148, 523

Haresnape, J. N., 374

Harley-Mason, J., 408

Harman, R. A., 119

Harrell, Jr., L. L., 320

Harris, E. E., 143

Harris, H., 30

Hart, H., 245, 246-252, 246, 279, 294, 455

Hartmann, R., 466

Hata, Y., 511

Hauser, C. R., 38, 79, 84

Hays, J. T., 131

Heck, R., 179, 186, 210, 224, 227, 237, 240, 288, 334, 364, 393, 394, 406, 407, 409, 421, 454, 486

Hedaya, E., 479

Hederich, V., 433

Hedestrand, G., 220

Heffler, M., 256

Heilbron, I., 23, 26, 252

Heinzel, M., 527

Heller, A., 230

Henbest, H. B., 374, 382

Hendrickson, J. B., 391, 486, 504

Henne, A. L., 373

Hennion, G. F., 373

Henry, P., 283

Hermans, P. H., 83

Herschbach, D. R., 467

Hershberg, E. B., 406

Herz, W., 195

Hess, H. V., 78, 237

Hess, K., 220

Hewitt, C. L., 167

Hickinbottom, W. J., 269

Hill, A. J., 220

Hill, P., 373

Hill, R. K., 492

Hilmy, M. K., 486

Hine, J. S., 68, 114, 118, 121, 131, 132, 148, 155, 278, 484

Hinshelwood, C., 37

Hodges, J., 23

Hoegger, E. F., 424

Hoffmann, A. K., 372

Hoffmann, R., 527

Hofmann, K., 299, 372

Hojo, M., 401, 512

Holness, N. J., 126, 298, 376, 384, 402, 421, 500

Holroyd, Jr., E. W., 114-117, 118, 119, 132, 148, 155, 157, 278

Holzman, G., 158

Horner, L., 346

Horning, E. C., 282

Horning, M. G., 282

Höver, H., 385, 432

Howard, F. L., 379

Howe, R., 86, 526

Huber, J. E., 501

Hückel, E., 339, 372, 385

Hückel, W., 98, 99, 396, 454, 527

Hudec, J., 501

Hudson, Jr., B. E., 84

Hughes, E. D., 1, 9, 10, 13, 14, 18, 20, 24, 36-40, 36, 37, 38, 46, 49-51, 51, 70, 79, 81, 83, 116, 233, 303, 316, 454, 455

Huisgen, R., 256, 494

Hulburt, H. M., 119

Humphries, M. Z., 417

Humphries, N. L., 167
Hunter, W. T., 148, 523
Huntress, E. H., 83, 492
Huyser, H. W., 195
Hyatt, A. A., 269
Hyman, J., 422

Ichikawa, K., 186-195,
  188, 249, 455
Inayama, S., 486
Ingold, C. K., 1, 4, 9,
  10, 13, 14, 18, 20, 24,
  36, 37, 38, 46, 49-51,
  51, 79, 83, 116, 157,
  248, 255, 256, 303, 316,
  454
Ingraham, L. L., 23, 46,
  65, 78, 93, 155, 173,
  180, 181, 217, 237, 255,
  267, 268, 321, 455, 486,
  511
Insole, J. M., 496
Ireland, R. E., 293
Ishitobi, H., 509
Iwamura, H., 511

Jagow, R. H., 382
James, A. T., 270
Japhe, H., 420
Jaruzelski, J. J., 268,
  476
Jeffrey, G. A., 372
Jeffrey, G. H., 59
Jenny, E., 480
Johannesen, R. B., 179,
  186
Johanson, S. B. H., 131
Johnson, D. W., 420-427,
  423
Johnson, E. A., 138
Johnson, E. R., 195
Johnson, F. O., 151, 153,
  174
Johnson, H. E., 210
Johnson, M. D., 505

Johnston, F., 58
Jones, E. R. H., 321, 352,
  483
Jones, H. W., 79, 87, 91,
  115, 119, 130, 181, 213,
  225, 276, 303, 317, 344,
  356, 364, 490, 500, 501
Jones, W. E., 271
Josephson, R. R., 496
Judd, C. I., 356, 361
Judefind, W. L., 136
Jurale, J. B., 420-427
Jurgens, E., 346
Just, G., 296
Juvala, A., 59

Kaiser, E. T., 467
Kamm, O., 17, 18, 21
Kaplan, L., 173, 357
Karabinos, J. V., 161
Karickhoff, M., 265
Karrer, P., 487
Kaspar, R., 234
Katz, T. J., 318, 501
Kaufman, J. J., 466
Kaye, I. A., 254
Kehr, C. L., 467
Kehrmann, Fr., 454
Keller, J., 82
Kellom, D. B., 143
Kenyon, J., 13, 492
Kepner, R. E., 36, 39, 79
Khaleeluddin, K., 527
Kharasch, M. S., 81
Kice, J. L., 234
Kiefer, E. F., 371
Kilmer, G. W., 120
Kilpatrick, J. E., 126,
  181, 189, 374
Kilpatrick, M., 484
Kimball, G. E., 4-5, 10,
  12, 254
Kirschbaum, G., 167
Kishner, N., 282
Kitschalt, M., 410
Kivelson, D., 406

Klassen, N. V., 424
Klein, F. S., 230
Kleinfelter, D. C., 475–
  477, 476, 505, 520, 523,
  527
Kleis, S., 523
Klinedinst, Jr., P. E.,
  228, 288, 333, 351, 380,
  398, 401–404, 401, 528
Kloetzel, M. C., 131
Klotz, I. M., 56, 70
Klyne, W., 166, 345
Knauss, E., 316, 319, 509
Knight, J. D., 158, 265
Knilling, W. v., 10
Knox, A. G., 487
Knox, L. H., 213, 385
Knutson, D., 371
Kobelt, M., 180, 182, 188,
  195, 395
Koelsch, C. F., 168
Kohler, E. P., 56, 70,
  195
Kohnstam, C., 229
Koll, W., 138
Komppa, G., 31, 88, 96,
  99, 130, 352
Konigsberger, C., 163
Kopineck, H. J., 125
Kormendy, M. F., 523
Kornblum, N., 137
Kornblum, R. B., 157
Korte, R., 289
Koski, W. S., 466
Kosower, E. M., 127, 176,
  232, 246, 285, 288–297,
  288, 306, 355, 393, 421,
  423, 455
Kost, A. N., 417
Kostanecki, St. v., 84
Kotel'nikoma, V. M., 163
Krall, R. E., 420
Krauch, H., 385
Kraus, C. A., 404
Krieger, H., 350, 422
Krueger, J., 62
Kubo, R., 530

Kühn, M., 59
Kuhn, R., 5, 8
Kunert, F., 433
Küng, W., 194, 210
Kursanov, D. N., 414
Kwart, H., 173, 321, 357
Kwei, G. H., 467

Laber, G., 431, 485
Labhart, H., 373
Ladenburg, K., 23, 290
La Forge, F. B., 486
LaLonde, R. T., 467
LaMer, V. K., 242
Lampe, V., 84
Landesman, H. K., 326
Langer, S. H., 246, 276
Langlois, D. P., 57, 118
Lapporte, S., 406
Laszlo, P., 524
Law, P. A., 245
Lawrence, C. A., 167
Lawson, E. J., 18
Lawton, R. G., 152, 369,
  398, 528
Leak, J. C., 162
Leal, G., 329, 339, 431
LeBel, N. A., 501, 506
Ledwith, A., 401
Lee, C. C., 68, 116, 118,
  120, 122, 130–139, 130,
  147–150, 147, 155, 213,
  276–284, 276, 294, 295,
  303, 343, 355, 369, 422,
  430, 455, 467, 494, 520,
  527
Leers, L., 265
Leffek, K. T., 334
Lefferts, E. B., 116, 269,
  334
Leffler, M. T., 283, 407
Leftin, H. P., 431
Legutke, G., 454
Leisse, F., 487
Lemin, A. J., 352
Le Ny, G., 152, 324–326,

326, 398

Lenze, F., 57, 118

Leonard, N. J., 59, 409, 500

Lepingle, M., 74

Lester, C. T., 254-263, 455

Levallois, F., 492

Levene, P. A., 13, 282, 380

Levine, J., 72

Levisi, J. P., 422

Levy, J., 84, 167

Levy, J. F., 394

Lewin, A. H., 505, 509

Lewis, C. E., 117, 271

Lewis, C. J., 60, 283

Lewis, E. S., 126, 496

Lewis, G. N., 454

Ley, J. B., 267

Lichtin, N. N., 431

Lidov, R. E., 422

Liebmann, M., 469

Likhosherstov, M. V., 11

Limpricht, H., 469

Lindegren, C. R., 46, 65, 155, 173, 267, 455, 486

Lindsey, A. S., 391

Linnemann, E., 118

Linstead, R. P., 59

Lipscomb, W. N., 273

Liss, T. A., 210

Liston, T. V., 514

Llewellyn, D. R., 267, 269

Llewellyn, J. A., 334

Locquin, R., 265, 269

Loebisch, W., 17

Loftfield, R. B., 180, 283, 418

Lohmann, K. H., 217

Loken, B., 436

Loncrini, D. F., 320, 321, 343, 352

London, F., 5

Long, F. A., 2, 268, 269

Longuet-Higgins, H. C.,

135

Lott, W. A., 60

Lowry, B. R., 470, 471

Lucas, H. J., 7-12, 7, 8, 9, 10, 12-15, 12, 14, 20, 28, 46, 63, 79, 83, 98, 117, 255, 270

Lugasch, M. M., 476

Lund, H., 410

Lutz, G. A., 8

Lynn, K. R., 265, 267

MacNulty, B. J., 37

Mailhe, A., 167

Malchick, P. S., 420

Mallet, E., 416

Malmberg, E. W., 177

Manatt, S. L., 371

Mandour, A. M. M., 454

Mannerskantz, C., 395

Manske, R. H., 168, 366

Marcy, W., 241

Marker, R. E., 17, 18, 19, 21

Markovnikov, V. V., 417

Marshall, H., 65, 81, 87, 130, 155, 173, 181, 213, 267, 276, 317, 344, 356, 364, 455, 486, 500

Marshall, H. P., 485

Martin, A. J., 270

Martin, E. L., 406

Martin, F., 60

Martin, J. C., 213-221, 356, 466

Martin, M., 39, 51

Martin, R. J. L., 37

Marvel, C. S., 283

Masamune, S., 408

Masterman, S., 1, 9, 13, 14, 20, 116

Matchett, J. R., 72

Mathiesen, E., 485

Matsen, F. A., 70

Mauguin, Ch., 11

Mauthner, J., 17

Maw, G. A., 454
Maxwell, R. J., 476, 505
Mayer, R. P., 265-271, 265, 266
Mayer, V., 413, 414
Mayor, R. H., 161
Mazur, R. H., 31, 53-64, 70, 116, 118, 127, 130, 155, 246, 276-284, 276, 293, 294, 302, 303, 355, 430, 454, 455, 467
McCarty, J. E., 255, 280, 421, 466
McCloskey, C. M., 59
McCoy, L. L., 467
McDaniel, D. H., 454, 513
McDaniel, J. C., 355-358, 434, 471
McElvain, S. M., 237, 241
McFarlin, R. F., 373
McIntyre, J. S., 527
McKennis, Jr., H., 26
McKenzie, A., 5, 255
McKenzie, Jr., S., 53, 60, 70
McMahon, R. E., 68, 114-117, 114, 118, 119, 121, 131, 132, 148, 155, 278
McMichael, K. D., 394
McMillan, W. G., 372, 386, 424
McNesby, J. R., 246
McNiven, N. L., 13
Meador, W. R., 343, 364
Meakins, G. D., 382
Meecham, S., 289
Meer, N., 5
Meerwein, H., 79, 98, 265, 266, 373, 433
Meinwald, J., 317, 470, 501, 506, 524
Meinwald, Y. C., 524
Meisenheimer, J., 233
Meislich, E. K., 143
Melander, L., 265
Meluch, W. C., 256
Menatt, S. L., 385

Meunier, V. C., 269
Meyer, J., 4
Meyer, L. H., 214
Meyer, V., 454
Michael, A., 8
Michiels, L., 74
Mickey, S., 84
Mikeska, L. A., 380
Millen, D. J., 504
Miller, E. G., 501
Miller, R. J., 10
Minnick, L. J., 484
Mislow, K., 256, 384, 492
Mitchell, N. W., 38
Moffitt, W. E., 56, 294, 345
Montfort, F., 98
Moreland, Jr., W. T., 182
Morgan, 455
Morganthau, J. L., 436
Moritani, I., 454, 455
Morrison, G. O., 131
Morschel, H., 433
Morse, B. K., 78-85, 87, 90, 95, 98, 107, 130, 181, 213, 255, 276, 317, 318, 344, 356, 364, 454, 500
Mortimer, F. S., 432
Mortimer, G. A., 373
Moscowitz, A., 345
Mosely, R. B., 421
Mosher, W. A., 134, 467
Moycho, S., 99
Mudrak, A., 161
Mulliken, R. S., 79, 83, 125, 232
Mumm, O., 62
Muneyuki, R., 509, 511
Murahishi, S., 455
Musher, J. I., 524
Music, J. F., 70
Mustafa, A., 486

Naab, H., 396
Nahinsky, P., 416

Naragon, E. A., 60, 117, 283
Nathan, W. S., 79
Neale, A. J., 481
Nelson, K., 234
Nelson, L. S., 122
Nelson, N. A., 373
Nevell, T. P., 27, 28, 46, 51, 57, 68, 79, 99, 131, 255, 343
Neville, O. K., 122, 133, 148, 157, 170, 278
Newman, M. S., 349
Nicholas, R. D., 500, 504, 527
Nicholls, B., 382
Nickon, A., 391
Niemann, C., 158
Nightingale, D., 180
Nikoletic, M., 455
Nishida, 455
Nist, B. J., 470
Noll, C. I., 269
Noller, C. R., 180
Nommensen, E. W., 59
Norin, T., 505
Norris, J. A., 467
Norton, C. J., 153, 172, 175, 213, 288, 317, 318, 321, 328, 332, 333, 335, 357, 385, 434, 473, 500, 509, 511, 528
Noyce, D. S., 373
Nybergh, B., 265
Nyman, G. A., 99
Nystrom, R. F., 59, 71, 83, 91, 162, 282

Ochs, R., 84
Ogawa, I. A., 355-358, 434, 471
Ogg, Jr., R. A., 4
Ohta, M., 350
Okamoto, Y., 512, 513
Oki, M., 511
Olah, G. A., 66, 434, 527-

528, 527, 528, 529-530, 529
Oldham, W. J., 138
Olechowski, J. R., 424
Olsen, C. J., 467
Olsen, S., 282
Olson, A. C., 234, 391
Olson, A. R., 2, 5, 9, 10
Ordronneau, C., 328-329, 337, 361, 431
Orekhoff, A., 267
Orloff, H. D., 166
Orloski, R., 393
Orochena, S. F., 372
Osthoff, R. C., 220
Otvos, J. W., 121
Owen, L. N., 51, 135
Owens, F. H., 500

Pande, K. C., 479, 505, 509, 514
Parham, W. E., 148, 523
Pariselle, H., 72, 74
Patterson, A. M., 172
Paul, M. A., 268, 269
Pauling, L., 76, 126
Pearson, R. G., 246, 276, 362, 482, 483
Peeling, M. G., 37, 51
Perizzolo, C., 267, 268
Perkin, W. H., 56, 59
Peters, R. A., 69
Peterson, P. E., 382, 391
Petrovich, J. P., 464
Pettit, R., 329, 339, 431
Pfeiffer, P., 14, 83
Phares, E. F., 418
Phillips, H., 13, 46
Piccolini, R., 328, 386, 500
Pitt, C. G., 340, 505
Pittman, V. P., 13
Pitzer, K. S., 181, 189, 255, 374
Planer, Prof., 17
Pöckel, I., 46, 58, 79,

Pocker, Y., 267, 434
Polanyi, J. D., 467
Polanyi, M., 5, 9, 75
Pollak, P. I., 83, 143
Pombo, M. M., 392, 394, 395
Poos, G. I., 312, 319, 380, 523
Popkin, A. H., 18, 81
Potter, H. T., 195
Powell, L. S., 11
Prelog, V., 179, 180, 182, 186, 188, 194, 195, 197-210, 210, 335, 384, 393, 395, 454, 455, 506
Pressman, D., 46, 83
Price, C. C., 46, 69, 161
Price, Jr., F. P., 188
Pritchard, H. D., 501
Pritchard, J. G., 269
Puntambeker, S. V., 269
Purlee, E. L., 422, 485
Putkey, T. A., 505

Quinn, H. W., 434

Raaen, V. F., 259, 265
Rainey, W. T., 254
Ralland, E., 469
Ramart-Lucas, Mme., 81
Rasmussen, R. S., 73
Rathjen, H., 373
Rawlinson, S. B., 32
Ray, F. E., 454
Read, J., 14
Rees, C. W., 505
Reeve, W., 265
Reeves, R. L., 501
Regan, C. M., 121, 127, 135, 142, 149, 155, 255, 339, 372, 385, 413
Rei, M. -H., 505, 518, 522, 527
Reichstein, T., 487
Reid, E. E., 139

Rellahan, W. L., 434
Remanick, A., 492-498, 493, 527
Remick, A. E., 454
Renk, E., 350
Reutov, O. A., 412-418, 412, 467
Reynolds, M. B., 404
Reynolds-Warnhoff, P., 341, 493, 505
Rhoads, S. J., 210
Richard, A., 269
Richardson, A. C., 255
Richey, Jr., H. G., 475-477, 476, 505, 506, 520, 527
Richter, H., 62
Rickert, H. F., 28, 87, 96, 131
Ridd, J. H., 465
Riegel, B., 70, 125
Riegel, B. M., 295
Rieke, C. A., 79
Riener, T. W., 319, 420
Riesz, P., 422
Ringold, H. J., 436
Ro, R. S., 374
Roberts, A., 167, 417
Roberts, I., 4-5, 10, 12, 14, 254
Roberts, J. D., 30-34, 30, 31, 53-64, 56, 57, 61, 68, 70, 74, 75, 79, 87, 88, 96, 114-117, 114, 115, 116, 118-120, 118, 119, 120, 121-122, 121, 122, 127, 130-139, 130, 131, 132, 135, 142, 147-150, 147, 148, 149, 151, 153, 155-159, 155, 157, 173, 174, 179, 180, 182, 184, 186, 195, 213, 214, 246, 255, 276-284, 276, 277, 278, 280, 281, 283, 293, 294, 295, 296, 302-313, 302, 303, 316, 321, 328, 339, 343, 355, 369,

371, 372, 380, 385, 386,
412, 413, 414, 422, 430,
454, 455, 461, 467, 472,
494, 496, 501, 520, 527
Roberts, R. M., 46, 237-
244, 237
Robertson, R. E., 334
Robinson, C. S., 38
Robinson, G. C., 174,
213, 222, 223- 235, 223,
224, 240, 248, 268, 288,
364, 380, 394, 401, 421,
512
Robinson, R., 4
Rogers, H., 214
Rogers, M. T., 56, 70,
173
Roland, H., 195
Rosenau, J. D., 523
Rosenwald, R. H., 8
Rothen, A., 13
Rothstein, E., 14
Royals, E. E., 320
Ruben, S., 416
Rüchardt, C., 256, 494
Ruzicka, L., 18, 21, 99,
135, 180, 195, 210, 391,
395
Rydon, H. N., 59
Rylander, P. N., 469

Sabatier, P., 167
Sack, R. A., 530
Sadek, H., 231
Saika, A., 214
Salmi, E. J., 289
Salmon, G., 163
Sandri, J. M., 246-252,
246, 279, 294, 455
Sarett, L. H., 312, 319,
380
Sauer, C. W., 57, 180,
195
Saunders, D. R., 352, 361
Saunders, M., 430-436, 430,
431, 485, 527, 529-530,

530
Saunders, Jr., W. H.,
130-139, 147-150, 147,
155, 213, 276, 295, 343,
422, 467, 487, 494, 520,
527
Sax, S. M., 372
Scaife, C. W., 131
Scanlan, J. T., 282
Scattergood, A., 241
Schaaf, E., 167
Schäfer, G., 233
Schaeffer, H. J., 161-
170, 161, 259, 280, 466
Schaeffer, W. D., 373,
494
Schechter, H., 373
Schenker, K., 194, 210
Schiff, R., 415
Schinz, H., 195
Schlatter, M. J., 59, 62
Schlenk, W., 84
Schlesinger, A. H., 26,
78, 99, 124, 176, 223,
288, 401
Schleyer, P. von R., 66,
293, 319, 328, 334, 356,
357, 475-477, 476, 500,
501, 504-505, 505-506,
504, 505, 511, 520, 523,
524, 527-528, 527, 528,
529-530, 529
Schmerling, L., 31, 96,
422
Schmid, G. H., 389, 492
Schmid, H., 408, 487
Schmid, H. J., 127, 153,
175, 293, 422
Schmidt, E., 10
Schmidt, W., 233
Schmukler, S., 166, 455
Schneider, A., 420
Schneider, P., 14
Schneider, S., 469
Schoenewaldt, E. F., 213
Schoenthaler, A. C., 349
Schöllkopf, U., 319

Schomaker, V., 126
Schreiber, K. C., 46, 78-
  85, 78, 81, 90, 92, 95,
  97, 99, 107, 124, 147,
  149, 153, 173, 174, 223,
  228, 288, 318, 355, 365,
  385, 401, 403, 427, 454,
  471, 501
Schriesheim, A., 268
Schuerch, C., 492
Schultz, E. M., 84
Schulze, S., 469
Schumann, S. C., 374
Schumann, W., 167
Schwab, F. W., 284
Schwarcz, M., 62
Schwartz, N., 523
Scott, A. D., 1, 9, 13,
  14, 20, 316
Scott, C. B., 217
Scott, F. L., 237, 406
Scott, N. D., 74
Seifert, W. K., 333, 420-
  427, 420
Semenow, D. A., 276-284,
  277, 283, 294, 303, 355,
  430, 455
Servis, K. L., 461
Setkina, V. N., 414
Sexton, M., 504
Seymour, D., 83, 237-244,
  237
Sfiras, J., 167
Shabica, Jr., A. C., 84
Shackell, L. F., 60
Shank, R. S., 373
Shatavsky, M., 153, 172-
  177, 172, 213, 288, 317,
  318, 328, 332, 333, 335,
  356, 357, 364, 385, 434,
  471, 473, 500, 501, 509,
  511
Shatkina, T. N., 412-418,
  412, 467
Shaw, T. P. G., 131
Shechter, H., 182
Sheehan, J. C., 61

Sheehan, J. J., 373
Sheehan, W. F., 126
Shiner, V. J., 454
Shoesmith, J. B., 486
Shoppee, C. W., 17-21,
  23, 127, 166, 289
Shorter, J., 37
Shortridge, R. W., 60
Shriner, R. L., 71, 168,
  221, 283, 320, 352
Sicher, J., 506
Siegel, S., 55, 70-76,
  70, 246, 276, 293, 303
Siersch, A., 118, 121
Silver, M. S., 276-284,
  281, 294, 303, 355, 395,
  421, 430, 455
Silversmith, E. F., 227,
  228, 293, 316, 365
Simmons, H. E., 283, 299,
  372, 373
Simonetta, M., 124-127,
  125, 148, 153, 173, 288,
  316, 339, 372, 385, 421
Simonsen, J. L., 51, 135
Simpson, C., 220
Skell, P. S., 38, 79, 476,
  505
Skrabal, R., 53
Sloan, M. F., 349-353,
  350, 360-367, 360, 361,
  398, 501
Slotta, K. H., 61
Smith, D. R., 120
Smith, E. L., 62
Smith, F. E., 283
Smith, G. H., 270
Smith, J. F., 38, 49-51
Smith, L. I., 53, 60, 70
Smith, P. A. S., 492
Smith, R. D., 299, 373
Smith, S., 401, 403, 512
Smith, S. G., 464
Smith, W. B., 254, 520
Smith, W. E., 266
Smyth, C. P., 220
Sneen, R., 214, 296

Sobel, P., 485
Soloway, S. B., 333, 337, 420, 422
Sommelet, M., 417
Sommer, L. H., 54, 60
Sonnenberg, J., 299, 369, 372-381, 372, 373, 379, 381-388, 381, 382, 406, 506
Sosa, A., 223
Spaeth, A., 167
Sparke, M. B., 269
Späth, E., 485
Speck, M., 210
Speer, R. J., 167, 417
Spencer, C. F., 210
Spitzer, R., 126, 181, 189, 374
Spring, F. S., 23, 26
Sprulin, H. M., 131
Spurlock, L. A., 506
Ssolonina, W., 283
Stafford, E. T., 288, 317, 319, 328, 333, 337, 351, 361, 398, 501, 528
Stanger, H., 241
Stanton, G. M., 514
Staum, M. M., 505, 520
Steacie, E. W. R., 246
Steigman, J., 61, 91
Stein, G., 31, 88, 96, 130
Stein, S., 469
Stenström, W., 481
Stephenson, J. S., 210
Stern, E. S., 481
Stevens, I. D. R., 402, 404
Stevens, P. G., 13
Stevens, R. G., 74
Stevenson, D. P., 121
Stewart, R., 485
Stiles, M., 247, 265-271, 265, 266, 269, 334
Stock, L. M., 513
Stoll, M., 195
Stoll, W., 23, 24, 26

Stork, G., 326
Story, P. R., 355, 430-436, 430, 431, 433, 468, 506
Streitwieser, Jr., A., 210, 246, 368, 380, 294, 339, 344, 349, 364, 372, 373, 382, 385, 394, 395, 415, 421, 454, 476, 480, 494, 505, 509
Strong, W. A., 60
Subba Rao, B. C., 321
Sung, W., 265, 269
Sunko, D. E., 455
Suter, C. M., 8
Suzuki, S., 382, 468, 492, 493
Swain, C. G., 69, 79, 217, 421, 454
Swan, G. A., 168
Swan, Jr., S., 409
Swern, D., 282
Symons, M. C. R., 329
Szabo, A., 5, 9

Taft, Jr., R. W., 182, 249, 422
Taher, N. A., 20, 24
Takahashi, J., 288
Tanida, H., 509-517, 509, 510, 511
Tappe, W., 454
Tarbell, D. S., 4, 10, 14
Taylor, K. J., 382
Taylor, W. I., 408, 486
Terry, E. M., 5, 8
Thomas, C. L., 321
Thompson, D., 331-332, 332, 333, 335, 372
Thompson, H. T., 195
Thorpe, R. S., 57, 121, 413
Tiers, G. V. D., 483
Tiffeneau, M., 84, 267, 520
Timmermans, J., 60, 195

Tipson, R. S., 131, 147, 179, 319, 358

Tischenko, D. V., 282

Tishler, M., 195

Tolgyesi, W. S., 527

Tori, K., 511

Traylor, T. G., 265

Traynham, J. G., 424, 506

Treppman, W., 168

Trifan, D. S., 28, 31, 46, 68, 78, 87-94, 87, 95-101, 95, 107, 114, 116, 130, 142, 149, 155, 181, 213, 227, 276, 297, 317, 328, 334, 343, 344, 356, 364, 369, 398, 421, 454, 465, 471, 492, 500, 511, 527

Trivette, Jr., C. D., 426

Trotman-Dickenson, A. F., 246

Trueblood, K. N., 177

Trumbull, Jr., E. R., 30, 56, 147

Tschesche, R., 61

Tsuji, T., 509-517, 509, 510, 511

Tsutsui, M., 180

Turner, D. W., 233

Turner, R. B., 343, 364

Tweit, R. C., 395

Uda, H., 505

Ungnade, H. E., 180

Urbanek, L., 30, 61, 130

Urech, H. J., 210

Uslar, L. V., 469

Valenta, Z., 467

Vanelli, R. E., 153

van Emster, K., 79

van Gulick, N. M., 492

van Tamelen, E. E., 356, 361

Vara, F. J., 238

Vatakencherry, P. A., 465-469, 466, 493, 505, 527

Vaughan, W. R., 349, 431

Verhoek, F. H., 218, 288

Vernon, C. A., 267

Voge, H. H., 5

Vogel, A. I., 59, 321

Vogel, E., 246

Vogel, I., 195

Vogel, M., 371

Vogelfanger, E., 86, 479, 526

von Auwers, K., 168

von Braun, J., 59, 167

Vosburgh, W. G., 173, 321

Voss, W., 60

Wadley, E. F., 431, 485

Wagner, A. F., 290

Wagner, C. D., 121

Wagner-Jauregg, T., 5, 23

Wagniere, G., 373

Waight, E. S., 233

Walbaum, H., 319

Walborsky, H. M., 78, 124, 147, 153, 173, 288, 320, 321, 326, 340, 343-348, 343, 344, 349, 352, 355, 385, 398, 427, 454, 471, 501, 505

Walia, J. S., 467, 493

Walker, E., 69

Walker, J. F., 74

Wallace, T., 416

Wallach, O., 417, 492

Wallis, E. S., 19, 23, 58, 79, 290

Walsh, A. D., 28, 46, 56, 70, 79, 135, 294

Walters, W. D., 195

Wariyar, N. S., 373

Warner, J. C., 482

Watanabe, W., 119

Waters, J. A., 514

Watson, H. B., 27, 28, 46,

51, 79, 454

Watts, W. E., 527-528, 528, 529

Way, R. L., 54

Webb, J., 340, 505

Webster, E. R., 476

Wegler, R., 13

Weinstock, T., 523

Weisgerber, C. A., 84

Weiss, A., 350

Weiss, H., 350

Weizmann, Ch., 284

Welch, R. W., 422

Welsh, L. H., 83

Werner, H., 373

Werner, L., 23

Werth, R. G., 520-525

Weston, P. E., 11, 15

Wheeler, O. H., 188, 249

Wheland, G. W., 114, 454

White, E. H., 256, 466, 495

White, R. V., 8

White, W. N., 276-284, 294, 303, 355, 430, 455

Whitmore, F. C., 17, 21, 38, 53, 57, 58, 60, 79, 81, 84, 118, 121, 269, 271, 413

Whittaker, D., 527

Wibaut, J. P., 377

Wiberg, K. B., 470, 471-473, 471

Wiberly, S. E., 382

Wichers, E., 284

Wilcox, Jr., C. F., 227, 296, 372, 386, 424, 504

Wilcox, M. F., 504

Wilder, Jr., P., 153, 420, 421, 426

Wildman, W. C., 352, 361

Wilds, A. L., 408

Wilds, R., 221

Wiley, P. F., 60

Wilhelm, M., 466

Williams, M. M., 14

Williams, R. A., 487

Williams, R. O., 501

Willner, D., 341, 493, 505

Wills, G. O., 255

Wilson, C. E., 7, 117

Wilson, C. L., 27, 28, 46, 51, 57, 68, 79, 99, 131, 255, 343

Wilson, E. B., 255

Wilson, R. A., 374

Windemuth, E., 131

Winklemann, E., 167

Winkler, R. E., 343, 364

Winstein, S., 2, 6, 7-12, 8, 9, 10, 12-15, 12, 14, 15, 20, 23-25, 23, 24, 26, 28, 31, 36, 39, 41-47, 46, 55, 61, 65, 68, 74, 78-85, 78, 79, 83, 84, 86, 87-94, 87, 90, 91, 93, 95-101, 95, 97, 98, 99, 107, 114, 115, 116, 118, 119, 124-127, 124, 125, 126, 127, 130, 142, 147, 148, 149, 153, 155, 171, 172-177, 172, 173, 174, 176, 180, 181, 182, 193, 213, 217, 222, 223-235, 223, 224, 225, 226, 227, 228, 231, 237-244, 237, 240, 241, 246, 248, 255, 265, 267, 268, 276, 285, 288-297, 288, 291, 295, 297, 298, 299, 303, 306, 316, 318, 319, 321, 328-329, 328, 331-332, 332, 333-334, 333, 334, 335-339, 335, 337, 338, 339, 343, 344, 351, 355, 356, 357, 358, 361, 363, 364, 365, 369, 372-380, 372, 373, 375, 376, 381, 381-388, 381, 384, 385, 386, 393, 394, 398-399, 398, 401-404, 401, 402, 403, 406-410, 406, 407, 408, 409, 421, 422,

423, 424, 427, 430, 431,
434, 454, 455, 461, 465,
471, 473, 479-490, 479,
480, 486, 487, 490, 492,
495, 496, 500, 501, 505,
506, 509, 511, 512, 526,
527, 528
Winstrom, L. O., 482
Winter, R., 465-469, 493,
505, 527
Wirtz, H., 420, 423
Wirz, H., 18
Wischnegradsky, A., 271
Wittekind, R. R., 523
Wittig, G., 316, 319, 509
Wittle, E. L., 18, 81
Wizinger, R., 14
Wolf, A. P., 134, 210
Wolff, N. E., 290
Wood, G. W., 210
Wood, R. E., 8, 15
Woods, W. G., 151, 280,
296, 316, 326, 339, 386,
496
Woodward, R. B., 153, 172,
175, 213, 216, 288, 317,
318, 328, 332, 333, 335,
345, 357, 385, 434, 473,
483, 500, 501, 509, 511
Wooster, C. B., 38
Wright, G. F, 168
Wrigley, T. I., 293
Wunderlich, K., 210, 433
Würsch, J., 210
Wyman, D. P., 246, 294

Yancey, J. A., 118-120,
121, 122, 155-159, 155
Yanigita, M., 486
Yates, K., 485
Yohe, G. R., 369
Yoho, C. W., 372
Yoshimira, K., 418
Youden, W. J., 221
Young, J. R., 183
Young, W. G., 8, 22, 36,

39, 46, 55, 57, 61, 74,
79, 83, 107, 115, 222,
226, 270, 293, 303, 305,
316, 362
Youngblood, G. T., 420,
426
Youssef, A. A., 326, 343-
348, 344, 398
Yu, Y. T., 349
Yuan, C., 385

Zagalo, A., 467
Zander, A., 416
Zbinden, R., 500
Zeiss, H. H., 180, 268,
352
Zelinsky, N., 62, 417
Ziegler, K., 167
Zienkowski, F., 99
Zimmerman, H. E., 353
Zincke, T., 487
Zoellner, E. A., 269
Zollinger, H., 465
Zook, H. D., 266, 434

Subject Index

Acetolysis, 24, 28, 68,
80 ff., 86, 95, 104,
114, 130, 146, 153, 175,
179, 197, 223, 237, 254,
288, 299, 316, 324, 343,
349, 355, 360, 369, 372,
381, 398, 401, 430, 447,
471, 500, 503, 505, 509
Acetoxonium ion, 42, 237
Addition compounds, 438
Addition to the double
bond, 237, 349, 420
Allyl carbinol and de-
rivatives, 53, 276, 305
Anchimeric assistance,
174 ff., 217, 223, 268,
316, 355, 360, 369, 372,
390, 471, 479, 503, 505
3-p-Anisyl-2-butyl arene-
sulfonates, 223, 401
2-p-Anisylethyl p-tolu-
enesulfonate, 485
1-p-Anisyl-2-propyl
arenesulfonates, 401
Ar₁$^{\ominus}$-3 Participation, 479
Ar₁$^{\ominus}$-5 Participation, 406

7-Benzonorbornadienyl p-
bromobenzenesulfonate,
316
2-Benzonorbornenyl p-
bromobenzenesulfonate

(exo and endo), 316
anti-7-Benzonorbornenyl
p-bromobenzenesulfo-
nates, 316, 509
Bicyclobutonium ion, 56,
276, 295, 302
puckered, 471
Bicyclo(2.2.1)heptyl,
see Norbornyl
Bicyclo(2.1.1)hexyl-5
tosylate, 471
3-Bicyclo(3.1.0)hexyl
tosylate (cis and trans),
299, 372, 381
2-Bicyclo(2.2.2)octanol
and derivatives, 343,
349, 360, 398
endo-2-Bicyclo(3.2.1)-
octanol and derivatives,
324, 360
exo-2-Bicyclo(3.2.1)-
octanol and derivatives,
343, 349, 360, 398
Bicyclo(2.2.2)octene,
349
Bicyclo(3.2.1)oct-3-en-
2-ol and derivatives,
360
endo-Bicyclo(2.2.2)oct-
5-en-2-yl tosylate, 360
Bird-cage hydrocarbon,
331
Bond angle, 151, 179,

186, 316, 500

Borohydride reduction, 186, 447 ff.

Bromide exchange, 401

α-Bromopropionate, salt and ester, 1, 20

Bromine, neighboring, 7, 12, 41

3-Bromo-2-butanols, 7, 12, 41

Bromonium ion, 4, 7, 20, 41

2-Butene, cis and trans, 10

2-Butyl-1-C^{14} p-toluene-sulfonate, 114

Cholesterol and derivatives, 17, 23, 31, 43, 124, 288

Classical carbonium ions, 155, 254, 446 ff., 465, 475, 492

Cyanohydrins, equilibrium constants, 179, 188

Cyclic ketones, 186, 447, 500, 503, 509

Cyclic mechanisms, 231

Cycloalkyl p-bromoben-zenesulfonates, 179, 188, 500

Cycloalkyl chlorides, tertiary, 188

Cyclobutanol, 311

Cyclobutyl chloride, 53, 302

Cyclocholesterol and de-rivatives, 23, 288

5-Cyclodecen-1-yl p-nitro-benzoate (cis and trans), 390

Cyclodecyl tosylate, 197, 446

Cyclododecyl tosylate, 197

Δ^4-Cycloheptenylmethyl p-

bromobenzenesulfonate, 324

cis-1,2-Cyclohexanediol, 237

cis-1,2-Cyclohexane ethyl orthoacetate, 237

2-Δ^3-Cyclohexenylethyl bromobenzenesulfonate, 398

Δ^3-Cyclohexenylmethyl p-bromobenzenesulfonate, 324

2-Δ^3-Cyclopentenylethyl p-nitrobenzenesulfonate, 369

Cyclopropylcarbinol, acid-induced rearrangement, 311

Cyclopropylcarbinols, tertiary, and their p-nitrobenzoates, 246

Cyclopropylcarbinyl de-rivatives, 53, 70, 276, 302, 451

Deamination, 118, 121, 130, 146, 254, 276, 349, 412, 465, 492

Decahydrodimethanonaph-thalene system, 333

1-Decalol (cis,cis and trans,trans), 390

trans,cis-1-Decalyl p-nitrobenzoate, 390

Dehydration, 161, 520

Dehydronorbornyl, see Norbornenyl

1,2-Di-p-anisylnorbornyl cation, 475

2,3-Dibromobutanes, 8, 12

5,7-Dibromonorbornene, 171

Dicyclopentadiene, 420

endo-Dihydrodicyclopenta-diene, 420

2,3-Dimethyl-2,3-pentane-

diol, 265
Double bond, participation, 17, 23, 124, 146, 172, 316, 328, 331, 335, 355, 369, 390, 398, 430
addition to, see Addition
Driving forces, 78, 95, 172, 267, 288, 316, 328, 369, 390, 398, 479

Elimination reactions, 372, 441
Endoxocyclohexyl, see 7-Oxa-norbornyl
Energy diagrams, 109, 114, 217, 292, 294, 443, 444
2,3-Epoxybutane, 8
Ethanolysis, 26, 72, 225, 302, 360, 479
Ethylamine-1-C^{14}, 118
exo/endo Reactivity ratios, 30, 38, 45, 95, 213, 316, 465, 471, 503, 505, 520

Formolysis, 130, 146

Ground-state energies, 288, 443

Hammett equation; ρ, σ, 509
Homoallylic systems, see also Double bond, 2-Norbornenyl, Allyl carbinyl chloride, Cholesterol, 7-Norbornadienyl, 124, 288, 355, 509
Homoaromaticity, 381
Hydride shifts, 197, 333, 520, 529

Hydrolysis, 130, 213, 246, 254, 288, 328, 349, 360, 390, 465
3-Hydroxycyclopentane carboxaldehyde, 217
4-p-Hydroxyphenyl-1-butyl p-bromobenzene-sulfonate, 406
Hyperconjugation, 30

Inductive effect, 213
Infrared, C=O stretching frequencies, 500, 503, 505
Internal return, see Ion pair return
Ion pairs, 95, 104, 223, 401
intimate and solvent-separated, 231
Ion pair return, 226, 246, 299, 302, 360, 401
Isocholesterol, see Cyclocholesterol
7-Isopropylidene-dehydro-norbornyl tosylates (exo and endo), 355
7-Isopropylidene-2-norbornyl tosylates (exo and endo), 355
Isotopic labeling, with D, 197, 299, 302, 333, 381, 465, 492
with T, 520
with C^{14}, 68, 114, 118, 130, 140, 146, 155, 161, 197, 254, 265, 276, 520
with O^{18}, 390
with Cl^{38}, 58
I-strain, 179, 186, 447

Ketene acetal, 237

α-Lactones, 2
Long-lived carbonium
  ions, 430, 475, 527,
  529

Methanolysis, 23, 246,
  420, 430, 479
2-Methylene-cis-4,5-
  tetramethylenedioxolane,
  237
Migration aptitudes, 265
Molecular orbital calcu-
  lations, 124

NMR spectra of carbonium
  ions, 430, 475, 527, 529
Norbornadiene, 420
7-Norbornadienol and de-
  rivatives, 328
7-Norbornadienyl cation,
  328, 430
anti-7-Norbornenol, 153,
  172, 506
5-Norbornenyl p-bromoben-
  zenesulfonate, 146
5-Norbornenyl cation, 30,
  146, 292
7-Norbornenyl cation,
  153, 172
5-Norbornenyl chloride,
  30
anti-7-Norbornenyl tosyl-
  ate, 153, 172
7-Norborneol, 153
2-Norbornyl m-carboxyben-
  zenesulfonate, 467
2-Norbornyl cation, 28,
  45, 68, 87, 95, 130,
  369, 452, 465, 492, 527,
  529
2-Norbornyl chloride, 30
2-Norbornyl fluoride, 527
2-Norbornyl sulfonates,
  28, 68, 87, 95, 130, 465
7-Norbornyl tosylate, 153

(+)exo-2-Norbornyl p-
  trifluoromethyl thion-
  benzoate, 464 (Ref. 1)
Nortricyclonium ion, 68,
  135
Nortricyclyl chloride,
  30

Octahydrodimethanonaph-
  thalene system, 331,
  335
7-Oxa-norbornane, chlo-
  rination, 213
7-Oxa-norbornyl chlorides,
  213

Pentamethylethanol, 155
Phenonium ion, 44, 78,
  104, 161, 223, 447 ff.,
  479, 508
3-Phenyl-2-butanol de-
  rivatives, 104, 230
  see also 3-p-Anisyl-2-
  butyl
2-Phenylcyclohexanol,
  cis and trans, 161
2-Phenyl-2,3-cis-exo-
  norbornanediol, 520
2-Phenylnorbornene, 520
3-Phenylnorcamphor, 520
π Route to bridged ions,
  see also Solvolytic ring
  closure, 398
Pinacol Rearrangement,
  265, 520
n-Propylamine-1-c14, 412
Protonated cyclopropane,
  411

Racemization, 12, 95, 465,
  492
Retention of configura-
  tion, 1, 7, 12, 17, 23,
  104, 172, 237, 254, 316,

343, 355, 360, 372, 492
Ring size, effect on re-
  activity, 179, 186, 197,
  447, 471, 500
Rotational barriers, 503

Salt effect, see Special
  salt effect
Solvolysis, see Acetoly-
  sis, Methanolysis, etc.,
  also 30, 53, 104, 130,
  175, 225, 237, 302, 331,
  333, 335, 390, 406, 420,
  500, 503, 509
Solvolytic ring closure,
  324, 331, 335, 369,
  389 (Ref. 1), 390, 398
Special salt effect, 223,
  299, 372, 401
Spiro(2,5)octa-1,4-diene-
  3-one, 479
Spiro(4,5)deca-1,4-diene-
  3-one, 406
Steric acceleration, 37,
  179, 186, 197, 288, 444,
  503, 505
Substituent effects, 479,
  509
Synartetic ions, 49

2,3,4,4-Tetramethyl-2,3-
  pentanediol, 265
Thionyl chloride, rear-
  rangement in reaction
  with, 309 f.
Transannular effects, 197,
  331, 333, 335, 390, 446
Tricyclobutonium ion, 281,
  452
Tricyclopropylcarbinol,
  245 (Ref. 1), 246
1,2,2-Triphenylethyl de-
  rivatives, 140, 254
Tris-homocyclopropenyl
  cation, 299, 372, 381

Ultraviolet spectra, 476

Wagner-Meerwein Rearrangement, 36, 44, 49, 104,
  155, 161, 254

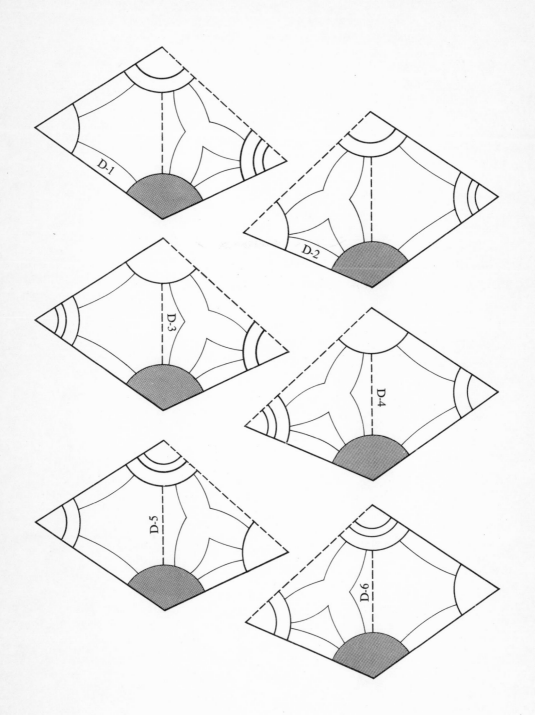